RICHARD E. JOHNSON The University of New Hampshire, Durham, New Hampshire

LONA LEE LENDSEY Oak Park and River Forest High School, Oak Park, Illinois

WILLIAM E. SLESNICK Dartmouth College, Hanover, New Hampshire

GRACE E. BATES Mount Holyoke College, South Hadley, Massachusetts

ALGEBRA

AND TRIGONOMETRY

TEACHERS' EDITION

ADDISON-WESLEY PUBLISHING COMPANY
Menlo Park, California · Reading, Massachusetts
London · Don Mills, Ontario

PREFACE

Three teaching aids have been prepared to accompany *Algebra and Trigonometry.*

Teachers' Edition

The *Teachers' Edition* contains a page-by-page commentary which is printed beside a reproduction of each page of the student text. This commentary will be of help in teaching students of all ability levels. Included in the commentary are the following: a general introduction to each chapter; suggestions, based on classroom experience, on how to teach particular topics and on how to introduce particular exercise sets; suggestions concerning the minimum number of Exercises for Discussion to be covered in class if time is limited; and quizzes for use at the end of each section in the student text.

Solution Manual

The *Solution Manual* provides step-by-step solutions of various types of problems. Teachers will not have to spend time solving the problems in order to handle classroom and homework assignments efficiently. Also, by referring to the *Solution Manual,* teachers can readily determine which problems should be assigned to particular students.

Tests

These will greatly aid teachers by saving them the time and drudgery associated with the preparation and processing of suitable tests. These tests are available in two forms, Form A and Form B, to aid the teacher who has two or more classes. Each form contains a test for each chapter, a semester test, and a final exam.

GENERAL INTRODUCTION

The mathematical features of *Algebra and Trigonometry* are as follows:

A Comprehensive Review of the Basic Concepts of Elementary Algebra

This review consists of a description of the real number system together with methods of solving equations and inequalities of the first and second degree.

An Introduction to the System of Complex Numbers

Every quadratic equation with real coefficients is shown to have a complex solution given by the quadratic formula. Whereas the real numbers serve as a set of coordinates for points on a line, complex numbers serve as a set of coordinates for points in a plane.

A Study of Functions

The logarithm function is studied in detail, and its historical role in computing is described.

An Introduction to Trigonometry

All the elementary properties of the trigonometric functions are presented. The wrapping function is used in order to motivate the modern view of trigonometric functions as having domains of real numbers rather than angles. The periodic nature of the trigonometric functions is stressed.

A Chapter on Mathematical Induction

This includes a study of arithmetic series and also of finite and infinite geometric series.

Applications of Algebra

The geometric applications include a study of conic sections. Permutations, combinations, and probability theory afford an interesting example of applied algebra. Vector algebra in a plane is introduced to show yet another type of algebraic system.

Introduction of Activities that Develop Mathematical Skills

The formalism of a mathematical proof is introduced in the final chapter on logic. Other extra sections included in the text are matrices and determinants, linear programming, and modular arithmetic.

DAILY LESSON PLAN

The following day-to-day lesson plan is intended to serve as a guide for teachers to help them adapt the text to the particular circumstances of their classes. The authors are not attempting to dictate the manner in which the material in the text should be presented, but would like to recommend that no assignments be made without prior review and study of the lesson plan.

Because the lesson plan is based on the assumption that teachers will begin each lesson by introducing the highlights of the topic and then covering the Exercises for Discussion in class, specific assignments of the Exercises for Discussion are not generally included. However, the lesson plan also includes recommendations for Exercises for Discussion to be assigned for homework after a chapter test is given. If the teacher does not have enough time to introduce all the Exercises for Discussion in class, the commentary in the *Teachers' Edition* indicates which ones are the most important.

Occasionally the authors feel that certain Exercises are especially important and should be covered in class. These Exercises will be noted in the daily lesson plan with boldface type. For example:

Section 1–3, Exercise 9

It is suggested that each day answers to the assignment for that day be displayed on the board (or on a screen) so that the students may find their mistakes quickly. Questions arising from these mistakes may then be answered carefully in order to accomplish the maximum teaching on the subject.

For shorter school years, the chapter on vectors and/or the chapter on logic may be omitted. They may also be omitted in order to spend more time on whichever of the other chapters the teacher and class prefer.

One could spend more time on the first six chapters, and postpone Chapter 7 on Logarithms until the beginning of the second semester. In this way, Section 2–12 on Matrices and Section 2–13 on Linear Programming could be included in the first semester.

Sections 2–12 on Matrices and 2–13 on Linear Programming may also be used in the second semester in the place of either Chapter 14 on Vector Algebra or Chapter 15 on Logic.

There are of course many more options in the use of the text so that the teacher can satisfy his or her own particular likes while at the same time meeting the needs of the students.

DAY	AVERAGE CLASS	BETTER THAN AVERAGE CLASS
1	Section 1–1 Exercises 1–16 Section 1–2 Exercises 1–24	Section 1–1 Exercises 1–16 Section 1–2 Exercises 1–24
2	Section 1–3 Exercises 1–8	Section 1–2 Exercises 25–28 Section 1–3 Exercises 1–11
3	**Section 1–3** **Exercise 9** Section 1–4 Exercises 1–21	Section 1–4 Exercises 1–30
4	**Section 1–4** **Exercises 22–30** Section 1–5 Exercises 1–34	Section 1–5 Exercises 1–38
5	**Section 1–5** Exercises 35–38 Section 1–6 Exercises 1, 3, 5, . . . , 23	Section 1–6 Exercises 1–25
6	Section 1–6 Exercises 2, 4, 6, . . . , 24	Section 1–7 Exercises 1, 3, 5, . . . , 39
7	**Section 1–7** **Exercises for Discussion 1–12** Section 1–7 Exercises 1–24	Section 1–7 Exercises 2, 4, 6, . . . , 40
8	**Section 1–7** **Exercises for Discussion 13–18** Section 1–7 Exercises 25–37	Section 1–8 Exercises 1–13, 19–21, 25–32, 39

DAY	AVERAGE CLASS	BETTER THAN AVERAGE CLASS
9	**Section 1–8** **Exercises for Discussion 1–7** Section 1–8 Exercises 1–18	**Class Section 1–8** **Exercises 34–37** Section 1–9 Exercises 1, 2, 5–7, 9–11, 13–18, 21, 22, 24, 25, 27, 28, 33–35
10	**Section 1–8** **Exercises for Discussion 8–15** Section 1–8 Exercises 19–34	**Section 1–10** **Exercises 11–14** Section 1–10 Exercises 1–12, 15–17
11	Section 1–9 Exercises 1, 3, 5, . . . , 37	Chapter Review Problems 1–12, 18–22, 26–28, 31–35, 38–44, 47, 50–59, 62
12	Section 1–9 Exercises 2, 4, 6, . . . , 38	Assign Chapter test Chapter Review
13	Section 1–10 Exercises 1–12	Test Section 2–1 Exercises for Discussion 1–9
14	Chapter Review Problems 1–12, 18–22, 26–28, 32–35, 42, 43, 53, 62(a), 62(d)	**Section 2–1** **Exercises 1–3, 24–26** Section 2–1 Exercises 4, 6, 8, 10–12, 14, 16, 17, 21–23
15	Assign Chapter Test	Section 2–2 Exercises 1–12
16	Test Section 2–1 Exercises for Discussion 1–5	Section 2–2 Exercises 13–17 Section 2–3 Exercises 1–4, 11
17	**Section 2–1** **Exercises for Discussion 6–9** **Exercises 1–3, 14** Section 2–1 Exercises 4–13, 15, 16	**Section 2–3** **Exercises 12–13** Section 2–3 Exercises 14, 16, 19–21 Section 2–4 Exercises for Discussion 1–4
18	Section 2–1 Exercises 17–23	**Section 2–4** **Exercises for Discussion 5–8** Section 2–4 Exercises 1, 2(a), 2(c), 3, 5, 6, 8, 10, 12, 13, 15, 16
19	Section 2–2 Exercises 1–6	Section 2–5 Exercises 1, 2, 5–9(a), 10–14, 17

DAY	AVERAGE CLASS	BETTER THAN AVERAGE CLASS
20	Section 2–3 Exercises 1–4, 7, 11, 14	**Section 2–5** **Exercises 18–23** Section 2–5 Exercises 24–32
21	Section 2–4 Exercises 1, 2(a), 2(c), 3, 4, 8–10	Section 2–6 Exercises 1–8, 13, 15, 16
22	Section 2–5 Exercises 1, 2, 5–14, 17	Section 2–7 Exercises 1, 2, 4, 5, 10, 12
23	**Section 2–5** **Exercises 18–23** Section 2–5 Exercises 24, 27, 28, 31, 32	Section 2–8 Exercises 1, 2, 4, 7, 9 Section 2–9 Exercises 1–3
24	Section 2–6 Exercises 1–8, 13, 16	Section 2–9 Exercises 4, 5 Section 2–10 Exercises 1, 5
25	Section 2–7 Exercises 1, 2, 4, 5, 10, 12	Section 2–9 Exercises 6, 7 Section 2–10 Exercises 7, 8, 13
26	Section 2–8 Exercises 1–10	Section 2–11 Exercises 1–5
27	Section 2–9 Exercises for Discussion 1–6	Section 2–11 Exercises 8–10, 12, 13, 15, 17
28	Section 2–9 Exercises 1–4 Section 2–10 Exercises 1, 2	Chapter Review Problems 1, 2(a), 3, 4(b), 5(b), 6, 7, 9, 10(a), 11–14
29	Section 2–10 Exercises 3, 4, 7, 13–15	Assign Chapter Test
30	Section 2–11 Exercises 1–5	Test Section 3–1 Exercises 2, 4, . . . , 34
31	Section 2–11 Exercises 9, 13, 17 Chapter Review Problems 1, 2(a), 3, 4(b), 5(b)	Section 3–2 Exercises 3, 6, . . . , 27, 28–32 Section 3–3 Exercises 1, 3, 5
32	**Chapter Review** **Problems 9, 10a, 11, 12, 14** Assign Chapter Test	Section 3–3 Exercises 2, 4, 6, 8 Section 3–4 Exercises 1–10

DAY	AVERAGE CLASS	BETTER THAN AVERAGE CLASS
33	Test Section 3–1 Exercises for Discussion 1–18	**Section 3–4** **Exercises 20, 21** Section 3–4 Exercises 11, 13, 18 Section 3–5 Exercises 1, 3, 7, 17, 19
34	Section 3–1 Exercises 2, 4, . . . , 34	**Section 3–5** **Exercises 18, 20, 21** Section 3–5 Exercises 2, 4, 9, 15 Section 3–6 Exercises 1–6
35	Section 3–2 Exercises 3, 6, . . . , 30	Section 3–6 Exercises 7–10 Section 3–7 Exercises 1–4
36	**Section 3–2** **Exercises 19, 28, 29, 31, 32** Section 3–3 Exercises 1–7	Section 3–7 Exercises 5, 6, 9–12
37	Section 3–4 Exercises 1–10, 13	Section 3–7 Exercises 13–17 Section 3–8 Exercises 1, 2
38	Section 3–5 Exercises 1, 6–9, 11, 16, 17	Section 3–8 Exercises 3, 5, 7, 10, 11(a), 12(a), 13
39	**Section 3–5** **Exercise 18** Section 3–6 Exercises 1–6	**Section 3–8** **Exercise 14** Chapter Review Problems 1–7, 12, 15(a), 16, 17(a), 17(b), 18, 20, 21
40	**Section 3–6** **Exercises 8, 9, 10** Section 3–7 Exercises 1, 2	**Chapter Review** **Exercise 19** Assign Chapter Test
41	Section 3–7 Exercises 3–5, 9, 10	Test Read Section 4–1
42	**Section 3–7** **Exercises 11, 12, 13** Section 3–7 Exercise 16 Section 3–8 Exercises 1–3, 7, 10, 11(a), 12(a)	Section 4–1 Exercises 1–21
43	**Section 3–8** **Exercises 13, 14** Chapter Review Problems 1–7, 12, 15(a), 16, 17(a), 18(a), 20, 21	Section 4–1 Exercises 22–38 Section 4–2 Exercises 1–8

DAY	AVERAGE CLASS	BETTER THAN AVERAGE CLASS
44	Assign Chapter Test	Section 4–2 Exercises 9–23 Section 4–3 Exercises 1–10
45	Test Read Section 4–1	**Section 4–3** **Exercises 19, 21** Section 4–3 Exercises 11–18, 22–24, 27, 28
46	Section 4–1 Exercises 1–21	Section 4–4 Exercises 1, 2, 5, 7, 9, 10, 13–15
47	Section 4–1 Exercises 22–38	Section 4–5 Exercises for Discussion 2–6, 11 Section 4–5 Exercises 1, 2, 5, 10
48	Section 4–2 Exercises 1–11	Section 4–5 Exercises for Discussion 12–16 Section 4–5 Exercises 12, 15–17, 19
49	Section 4–2 Exercises 12–22	**Section 4–5** **Exercises 18, 20–22** Section 4–6 Exercises 1–18
50	Section 4–3 Exercises 1–17	**Section 4–6** **Exercises 20, 21–25** Chapter Review Problems 1–24 Assign Chapter Test
51	Section 4–3 Exercises 21–26	Test Section 5–1 Exercises for Discussion 1–5
52	Section 4–4 Exercises 1, 2, 5, 7, 9, 10, 13, 14	Section 5–1 Exercises 1–7
53	Section 4–5 Exercises for Discussion 2–6, 11 Exercises 1, 2, 5, 10	**Section 5–1** **Exercises 8, 9** Section 5–2 Exercises 1–5
54	Section 4–5 Exercises for Discussion 12–16 Exercises 12, 15–17, 19	**Section 5–2** **Exercises 10, 11** Section 5–2 Exercises 6–8, 12, 13
55	Section 4–6 Exercises 1–16	Section 5–3 Exercises 1, 4–6, 8, 9(a)

DAY	AVERAGE CLASS	BETTER THAN AVERAGE CLASS
56	**Section 4–6** **Exercises 23, 25** Chapter Review Problems 1–12, 15, 16, 19–24	**Section 5–3** **Exercises 10(c), 12, 13** Section 5–3 Exercises 9(b), 9(c), 10(a), 10(b), 10(d), 11, 14
57	Assign Chapter Test	Section 5–4 Exercises 1–3, 9
58	Test Section 5–1 Exercises for Discussion 1–5	Section 5–4 Exercises 4–7
59	Section 5–1 Exercises 1–7	Section 5–4 Exercises 10–13
60	Section 5–2 Exercises 1–6	**Section 5–4** **Exercise 17** Section 5–4 Exercises 8, 14–16
61	**Section 5–2** **Exercise 9** Section 5–3 Exercises 1, 4–6, 8	Section 5–5 Exercise for Discussion 3 Exercises 1–3
62	**Section 5–3** **Exercises 9(a), 10(a)** Section 5–3 Exercises 2, 3, 7, 9(b), 9(c), 10(b), 10(c)	Section 5–5 Exercises 5, 7, 9, 10
63	Section 5–4 Exercises 1–3, 9	**Section 5–5** **Exercise 12** Section 5–5 Exercises 4, 8, 11, 12
64	Section 5–4 Exercises 6, 7, 10–12	Section 5–6 Exercises 1–8
65	Section 5–4 Exercises 13–15	Section 5–6 Exercises 9–15
66	**Section 5–5** **Exercises for Discussion 1–3** Section 5–5 Exercises 1, 2, 4	**Section 5–6** **Exercise 16** Section 5–6 Exercises 17–20
67	Section 5–5 Exercises 3, 5, 7, 9	Chapter Review
68	Section 5–5 Exercises 4, 8, 10	Assign Chapter Test
69	Section 5–5 Exercises 11, 12	Test Section 6–1 Exercises for Discussion 1–6

DAY	AVERAGE CLASS	BETTER THAN AVERAGE CLASS
70	Section 5–6 Exercises 1–8	Section 6–1 Exercises 1–4, 7, 9, 11–15
71	Section 5–6 Exercises 9–15	**Section 6–1** **Exercises 16, 17** Section 6–2 Exercises for Discussion 1–7 Exercises 1–6
72	Chapter Review	Section 6–2 Exercises 7–9, 11 Section 6–3 Exercises 1–3, 4(a), 5–8
73	Assign Chapter Test	Section 6–4 Exercises 1–8, 12
74	Test Section 6–1 Exercises for Discussion 1–6	**Section 6–4** **Exercises 14, 15** Section 6–5 Exercises 1–4, 7, 10–12, 17–19, 23
75	Section 6–1 Exercises 1–5, 9–11 Section 6–2 Exercises 1, 2, 4–6	**Section 6–5** **Exercises 27–29** Chapter Review Chapter Test
76	Section 6–3 Exercises 1–3 Section 6–4 Exercises 1–3	Test Section 7–1 Exercises 1–20
77	Section 6–4 Exercises 8, 12 Section 6–5 Exercises 1, 2, 8, 11, 12	Section 7–2 Exercises 2, 4, 6, . . . , 44
78	Chapter Review Chapter Test	Section 7–3 Exercises 1–10
79	Test Section 7–1 Exercises 1–20	**Section 7–3** **Exercises 11, 12** Section 7–4 Exercises 2, 4, . . . , 28
80	Section 7–2 Exercises 2, 4, . . . , 44	**Section 7–4** **Exercises 29, 30** Section 7–4 Exercises 1, 3, 5, . . . , 27
81	Section 7–3 Exercises 1–10	Section 7–5 Exercises 1–20
82	Section 7–4 Exercises 1, 3, . . . , 25	**Section 7–5** **Exercises 30, 31** Section 7–5 Exercises 21–29

DAY	AVERAGE CLASS	BETTER THAN AVERAGE CLASS
83	Section 7–5 Exercises 1–25	Section 7–6 Exercises 1–12
84	Section 7–6 Exercises 1–12	**Section 7–6** **Exercises 1–12** Section 7–7 Exercises 2, 4, . . . , 20
85	**Section 7–6** **Exercises 1–12** Section 7–7 Exercises 2, 4, . . . , 20	Section 7–7 Exercises 13, 15, 17, 19, 23, 25, 31
86	Section 7–7 Exercises 1, 3, 5, . . . , 19, 25	Section 7–8 Exercises 1–15
87	Section 7–8 Exercises 1–20	**Section 7–8** **Exercises 29, 35, 36** Section 7–8 Exercises 16–28
88	**Section 7–8** **Exercises 21–27** Section 7–8 Exercises 28–34 Section 7–7 Exercises 33, 37, 38	**Section 7–8** **Exercise 46** Section 7–7 Exercises 33, 37, 38 Section 7–8 Exercises 42, 49–51, 54
89	**Section 7–8** **Exercise 46** Section 7–9 Exercises 1, 3, 4, 7 Chapter Review	Section 7–9 Exercises 1, 3, 7–10, 13, 15, 16
90	Assign Chapter Test	Chapter Review Assign Chapter Test
91	Test	Test
92	Cumulative Review	Cumulative Review
93	Semester Examination	Semester Examination
94	Section 8–1 Exercises 1–15	Section 8–1 Exercises 1–4, 6, 8, 10, 11, 14, 15 Section 8–2 Exercises 1, 2, 4–6
95	Section 8–2 Exercises 1–13	Section 8–2 Exercises 7–10 Section 8–3 Exercises 1, 3, . . . , 11
96	Section 8–3 Exercises 1–12	**Section 8–3** **Exercises 13, 14** Section 8–4 Exercises 1, 3–7, 9(a), 9(c)

DAY	AVERAGE CLASS	BETTER THAN AVERAGE CLASS
97	Section 8–4 Exercises 1, 3–7, 9(a), 9(c)	**Section 8–4** **Exercises 10–12** Section 8–5 Exercises for Discussion 5, 6 Section 8–5 Exercises 2, 4, . . . , 16
98	**Section 8–5** **Exercises for Discussion 5, 6** Section 8–5 Exercises 2, 4, 6, . . ., 16	Section 8–6 Exercises 1–14
99	Section 8–6 Exercises 1–10	Section 8–7 Exercises 1(a), 1(c), 2(a), 2(b), 2(c), 3(a), 4, 6
100	Section 8–7 Exercises 1(a), 1(c), 2(a), 2(b), 2(c), 3(a), 4	Section 8–8 Exercises 2, 4, . . ., 18
101	Section 8–8 Exercises 1–10	Section 8–9 Exercises 2, 4, 6, 8, 10
102	Section 8–9 Exercises 2, 4, 6, 8	Section 8–10 Exercises 1–6
103	Section 8–10 Exercises 1–5	Section 8–11 Exercises 1, 2, 4, 6, 7, 10, 12, 13, 17
104	Section 8–11 Exercises 1, 2, 4, 6, 10, 12, 15	Section 8–11 Exercises 5, 14, 18, 20, 22–24
105	Chapter Review Problems 1, 2, 3(a), 4, 5(b), 6, 7(b), 8, 11, 12, 14	Chapter Review Problems 1–6, 7(a), 8, 11, 12, 14
106	Chapter Review Problems 16, 20, 22, 24, 26 Assign Chapter Test	Chapter Review Problems 15, 16, 20, 22, 24, 26, 29 Assign Chapter Test
107	Test Section 9–1 Exercises for Discussion 1–5	Test Section 9–1 Exercises for Discussion 1–5
108	Section 9–1 Exercises 1–8	Section 9–1 Exercises 1–12
109	**Section 9–1** **Exercises 9–12** Section 9–2 Exercises 1–10	Section 9–2 Exercises 1–19
110	Section 9–3 Exercises 1–7	Section 9–3 Exercises 1–8

DAY	AVERAGE CLASS	BETTER THAN AVERAGE CLASS
111	Section 9–4 Exercises 1–12	Section 9–4 Exercises 1–12
112	Section 9–5 Exercises 1–19	Section 9–5 Exercises 1–20
113	Section 9–6 Exercises 1–10	Section 9–6 Exercises 1–10
114	Section 9–6 Exercises 11–14	Section 9–6 Exercises 11–14
115	Section 9–7 Exercises 1–20	Section 9–7 Exercises 1–24
116	Section 9–8 Exercises 1–20	Section 9–8 Exercises 1–20
117	Chapter Review Problems 3, 6, 9, . . . , 45	Chapter Review Problems 2, 4, 6, . . . , 46
118	Assign Chapter Test	Assign Chapter Test
119	Test Section 10–1 Exercises for Discussion 1–3	Test Section 10–1 Exercises for Discussion 1–4
120	Section 10–1 Exercises 1–6	Section 10–1 Exercises 1–8
121	Section 10–2 Exercises 1–6, 15	Section 10–2 Exercises 1–6, 15–17, 20
122	Section 10–3 Exercises 1–4, 10–12, 16–19, 22, 23	Section 10–3 Exercises 1–4, 10–12, 16–19, 22, 23
123	Section 10–4 Exercises 1–15	Section 10–4 Exercises 1–15
124	Section 10–5 Exercises 1–10	Section 10–3 Exercises 24–26 Section 10–4 Exercises 18–23
125	Section 10–5 Exercises 11–18, 21, 23	Section 10–5 Exercises 2, 4, . . . , 24
126	Section 10–6 Exercises 1, 2	Section 10–5 Exercises 1, 3, . . . , 23
127	**Section 10–6** **Exercises for Discussion 1, 2** Section 10–6 Exercises 3–5	Section 10–6 Exercises for Discussion 1, 2 Section 10–6 Exercises 1, 2
128	Section 10–7 Exercises 1–4, 7	Section 10–6 Exercises 3–5

DAY	AVERAGE CLASS	BETTER THAN AVERAGE CLASS
129	Section 10–8 Exercises 1–10, 14–17	Section 10–7 Exercises 1–4, 7, 8, 12, 13
130	Chapter Review Assign Chapter Test	Section 10–8 Exercises 1–20
131	Test Section 11–1 Exercises for Discussion 1–4	Section 10–9 Exercises 2, 4, . . . , 30
132	Section 11–1 Exercises 1–6 Section 11–2	Chapter Review Assign Chapter Test
133	Section 11–2 Exercises 1–10	Test Section 11–1 Exercises for Discussion 1–4
134	Section 11–3 Exercises 1–6 Section 11–4	Section 11–1 Exercises 1–6 Section 11–2
135	Section 11–4 Exercises 1–6, 8, 11, 12	Section 11–2 Exercises 1–10
136	Section 11–5 Exercises 1–4 Section 11–6	Section 11–3 Exercises 1–6 Section 11–4
137	Section 11–6 Exercises 1–6	Section 11–4 Exercises 1–7, 10–13
138	Section 11–6 Exercises 7–9	Section 11–5 Exercises 1–6 Section 11–6
139	Section 11–7 Exercises 1–3	Section 11–6 Exercises 1–6, 11
140	Chapter Review Problems 1–11, 13, 21, 25, 26	Section 11–6 Exercises 7–10
141	Assign Chapter Test Chapter Review	Section 11–7 Exercises 1–5
142	Test Section 12–1 Exercises for Discussion 1–3 1–2	Chapter Review Assign Chapter Test
143	Section 12–1 Exercises 1–8 Section 12–2	Test Section 12–1 Exercises for Discussion 1–3
144	Section 12–2 Exercises 1–7 Section 12–3	Section 12–1 Exercises 1–8 Section 12–2

DAY	AVERAGE CLASS	BETTER THAN AVERAGE CLASS
145	Section 12–3 Exercises 1–4	Section 12–2 Exercises 1–9 Section 12–3
146	Section 12–4 Exercises 1–7	Section 12–3 Exercises 1–6
147	Section 12–5 Exercises 1–5	Section 12–4 Exercises 1–9
148	Chapter Review Problems 1–12	Section 12–5 Exercises 1–5
149	Assign Chapter Test	Chapter Review Assign Chapter Test
150	Test Section 13–1 Exercises for Discussion 1–3	Test Section 13–1 Exercises for Discussion 1–3
151	Section 13–1 Exercises 1–4 Section 13–2	Section 13–1 Exercises 1–6 Section 13–2
152	Section 13–2 Exercises 1, 2	Section 13–2 Exercises 1, 2, 5
153	Section 13–3 Exercises 1, 3, 5	Section 13–3 Exercises 1, 3, 5–7
154	Section 13–3 Exercises 6, 7 Section 13–4	Section 13–3 Exercises 6–9 Section 13–4
155	Section 13–4 Exercises 1–5, 9, 10, 15	Section 13–4 Exercises 1–5, 9–11, 15, 17
156	Section 13–4 Exercises 6–8, 11–13, 16, 17	Section 13–4 Exercises 6–8, 11–14, 16, 18, 21, 22
157	Section 13–5 Exercises 2, 4, . . . , 16	Section 13–5 Exercises 2, 4, . . . , 16
158	Section 13–5 Exercises 1, 3, 5, . . . , 15	Section 13–5 Exercises 1, 3, 5, . . . , 15
159	Section 13–6 Exercises 1–5, 8, 10, 11, 17	Section 13–6 Exercises 1–5, 8, 10, 11, 17–19
160	Chapter Review	Chapter Review
161	Assign Chapter Test	Assign Chapter Test
162	Test Section 14–1 Exercises for Discussion 1–4	Test Section 14–1 Exercises for Discussion 1–4

DAY	AVERAGE CLASS	BETTER THAN AVERAGE CLASS
163	Section 14–1 Exercises 1–4	Section 14–1 Exercises 1–6
164	Section 14–2 Exercises 1–8	Section 14–2 Exercises 1–14
165	Section 14–3 Exercises 1–6	Section 14–2 Exercises 15–17 Section 14–3 Exercises 1–6
166	Section 14–3 Exercises 9–14, 17–19	Section 14–3 Exercises 9–14, 17–19
167	Section 14–4 Exercises 1–6	Section 14–4 Exercises 1–7
168	Section 14–4 Exercises 7–16	Section 14–4 Exercises 8–16
169	Section 14–6 Exercises 1–10	Section 14–6 Exercises 1–11
170	Section 14–7 Exercises 1, 3, . . . , 11	Section 14–7 Exercises 1, 3, . . . , 11
171	Assign Chapter Test	Assign Chapter Test
172	Test	Test Section 15–1 Exercises 1–3
173	Use remaining days to review the course, taking problems from Cumulative Reviews. If this is more than necessary, do Section 2–12 and/or Section 2–13, or some of Chapter 15, or Section 10–9	Section 15–2 Exercises 1–9
174		Section 15–2 Exercises 10–15
175		Section 15–3 Exercises 1–8
176		Section 15–4 Exercises 1–13
177		Section 15–5 Exercises 1–7 Assign Chapter Test
178		Review
179		Review
180	Final Examination	Final Examination

READING SUGGESTIONS

Aleksandrov, A. D., Kolmogorov, A. N., and Lavrentev, M. A., eds., translated by S. H. Gould and T. Bartha; *Mathematics: Its Content, Method, and Meaning,* The M.I.T. Press.

Allendorfer, Carl B., and Oakley, Cletus O., *Principles of Mathematics* (second edition), McGraw-Hill Book Company, Inc.

Angell, Richard B., *Reasoning and Logic,* Appleton-Century-Crofts, Inc.

Banks, Houston J., *Elements of Mathematics,* Allyn and Bacon, Inc.

Beaumont, Ross A., and Pierce, Richard S., *The Algebraic Foundations of Mathematics,* Addison-Wesley Publishing Company, Inc.

Breuer, J., *Introduction to the Theory of Sets,* Prentice-Hall, Inc.

Carroll, Lewis, *The Complete Works of Lewis Carroll,* The Modern Library, Random House.

Christian, R. R., *Introduction to Logic and Sets,* Blaisdell Publishing Company.

Church, Alonzo, *Introduction to Mathematical Logic,* Vol. I, Princeton University Press.

Cohen, Morris R., *A Preface to Logic,* Meridian Books.

Commission on Mathematics, C.E.E.B., *Introductory Probability and Statistical Inference for Secondary Schools.*

Cooley, H. R., *et al., Introduction to Mathematics,* Houghton Mifflin Company.

Dantzig, T., *Numbers, The Language of Science,* The Macmillan Company.

Davis, R. L., ed., *Elementary Mathematics of Sets with Applications,* Mathematical Association of America.

Dubisch, R., *The Nature of Numbers,* The Ronald Press Company.

Evenson, A. B., *Modern Mathematics—Introductory Concepts and Their Implications,* Scott, Foresman and Company.

Exner, Robert M., and Rosskopf, Myron F., *Logic in Elementary Mathematics,* McGraw-Hill Book Company, Inc.

Freitag, H. T., and Freitag, A. H., *The Number Story,* National Council of Teachers of Mathematics.

Freund, John E., *A Modern Introduction to Mathematics,* Prentice-Hall, Inc.

Gelfond, A. O., *Transcendental and Algebraic Numbers,* Dover Publications, Inc.

Glicksman, A., *Linear Programming and the Theory of Games,* John Wiley & Sons, Inc.

Goldberg, Samuel, *Probability: An Introduction,* Prentice-Hall, Inc.

Gray, James F., *Sets, Relations, and Functions,* Holt, Rinehart and Winston, Inc.

Haag, Vincent H., *Structure of Elementary Algebra, Studies in Mathematics,* Vol. III, Yale University Press.

Hadley, G., *Linear Algebra,* Addison-Wesley Publishing Company, Inc.

Hadley, G., *Linear Programming,* Addison-Wesley Publishing Company, Inc.

Hafstrom, John E., *Basic Concepts in Modern Mathematics,* Addison-Wesley Publishing Company, Inc.

Halmos, Paul R., *Naive Set Theory,* D. Van Nostrand Company, Inc.

Henkin, Leon, *et al., Retracing Elementary Mathematics,* The Macmillan Company.

Johnson, Donovan A., *Logic and Reasoning in Mathematics,* McGraw-Hill Book Company, Inc.

Jones, Burton W., *Elementary Concepts of Mathematics,* The Macmillan Company.

Kelley, John L., *Introduction to Modern Algebra,* D. Van Nostrand Company, Inc.

Kemeny, J. G., Mirkil, H., Snell, J. L., and Thompson, G. L., *Finite Mathematical Structures,* Prentice-Hall, Inc.

Kemeny, John G., *et al., Introduction to Finite Mathematics,* Prentice-Hall, Inc.

Kline, M., *Mathematics; A Cultural Approach,* Addison-Wesley Publishing Company, Inc.

Kline, M., *Mathematics in Western Culture,* Oxford University Press.

Korner, Stephan, *The Philosophy of Mathematics: An Introduction*, Harper and Brothers.

Landin, Joseph, and Hamilton, Norman T., *Set Theory: The Structure of Arithmetic,* Allyn and Bacon, Inc.

Langer, Susanne K., *An Introduction to Symbolic Logic,* Dover Publications, Inc.

Laplace, Pierre S. de, *Oeuvres Complètes, Tome 8.*

Lung, Clarence, "Division Made Easy," *The Arithmetic Teacher,* November 1963, pp. 453–454.

May, K., *Elements of Modern Mathematics,* Addison-Wesley Publishing Company, Inc.

Meserve, Bruce E., and Sobel, Max A., *Mathematics for Secondary School Teachers,* Prentice-Hall, Inc.

Moise, Edwin E., *Elementary Geometry from an Advanced Standpoint,* Addison-Wesley Publishing Company, Inc.

Mosteller, F., and Rourke, Thomas, *Probability, a First Course,* Addison-Wesley Publishing Company, Inc.

National Council of Teachers of Mathematics, *The Mathematics Teacher,* "Linear Programming Problems for First Year Algebra," March 1960, pp. 171–176, "Linear Programming, an Aid to Decision Making," March 1960, pp. 177–179, "Mathematical Induction, i^p, and Factorial Powers," May 1960, pp. 332–334, "An Interesting Problem Involving Indeterminate Equations," November 1960, pp. 540–542, "Constructing Logic Puzzles," November 1961, pp. 524–526.

National Council of Teachers of Mathematics, *Twenty-third Yearbook: Insight into Modern Mathematics.*

National Council of Teachers of Mathematics, *Twenty-fourth Yearbook: The Growth of Mathematical Ideas, Grades K–12.*

National Council of Teachers of Mathematics, *Twenty-eighth Yearbook: Enrichment Mathematics for High School,* pp. 34–45, 46–55, and 368–378.

Newman, James R., *The World of Mathematics,* Simon and Schuster, pp. 528–543.

Neyman, J., *First Course in Probability and Statistics,* Henry Holt and Co.

Nichols, Eugene D., Heimer, Ralph T., and Garland, Henry E., *Modern Intermediate Algebra,* Holt, Rinehart and Winston, Inc., Chapter 1.

Niven, I., *Irrational Numbers,* John Wiley & Sons.

Ore, O., *Number Theory and Its History,* McGraw-Hill Book Company, Inc.

Polya, G., *Mathematics and Plausible Reasoning,* Vol. 1, Princeton University Press, Chapter 7.

Rademacher, Hans, and Toeplitz, Otto, *The Enjoyment of Mathematics,* Princeton University Press.

Rosenbloom, Paul C., *The Elements of Mathematical Logic,* Dover Publications, Inc.

Rosser, J. Barkley, *Logic for Mathematicians,* McGraw-Hill Book Company, Inc.

Sawyer, W. W., *Mathematician's Delight,* Penguin Books, Chapter 3.

Sawyer, W. W., *Prelude to Mathematics,* Pelican Books.

School Mathematics Study Group, *Concepts of Algebra,* Yale University Press, pp. 73–205.

School Mathematics Study Group, *Elementary Functions,* Yale University Press.

School Mathematics Study Group, *First Course in Algebra,* Yale University Press.

School Mathematics Study Group, *Intermediate Mathematics,* Part I, Yale University Press.

Singh, Jagjit, *Great Ideas of Modern Mathematics: Their Nature and Use,* Dover Publications, Inc.

Stebbing, L. S., *A Modern Introduction to Logic,* Harper and Brothers.

Stewart, B. M., *Theory of Numbers* (Second Edition), The Macmillan Company, Chapters 1–9.

Stoll, Robert R., *Sets, Logic, and Axiomatic Theories,* W. H. Freeman and Company.

Suppes, Patrick, *Introduction to Logic,* D. Van Nostrand Company, Inc.

Swain, Robert L., and Nichols, Eugene D., *Understanding Arithmetic,* Holt, Rinehart and Winston, Inc.

Thurston, H. A., *The Number-System,* Interscience Publishers, Inc.

Wallis, W. A., and Roberts, H. V., *Statistics: A New Approach,* The Free Press, Chapter 16.

Young, J. W., *Fundamental Concepts of Algebra and Geometry,* The Macmillan Company.

ADDITIONAL ANSWERS

Answers to Quiz, page 79

1.

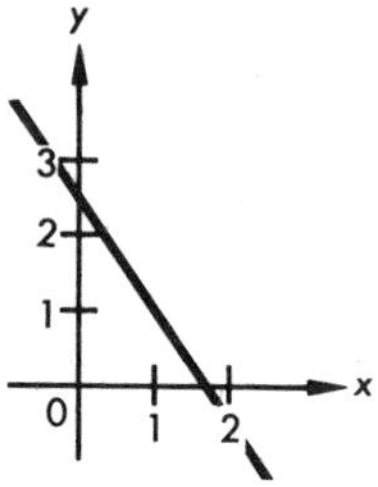

2.

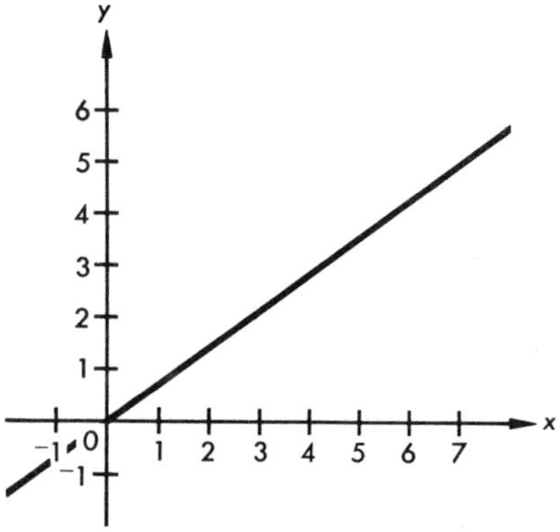

3.

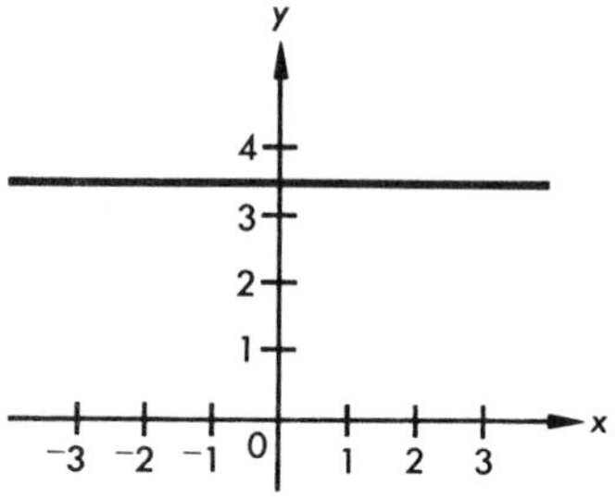

Figures, page 82

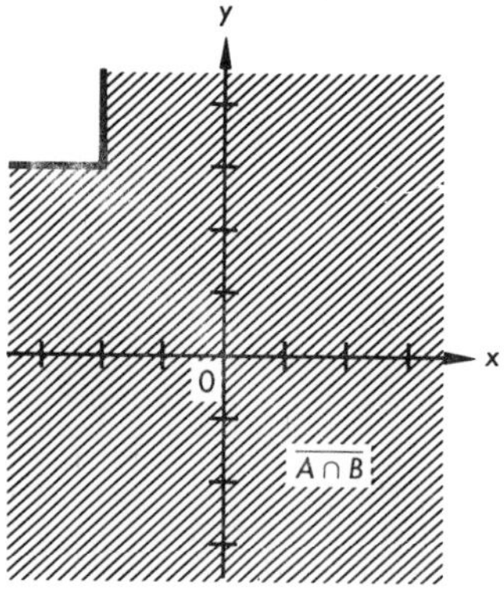

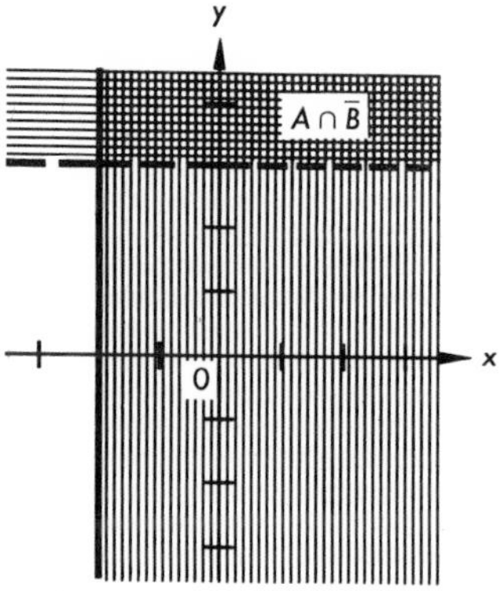

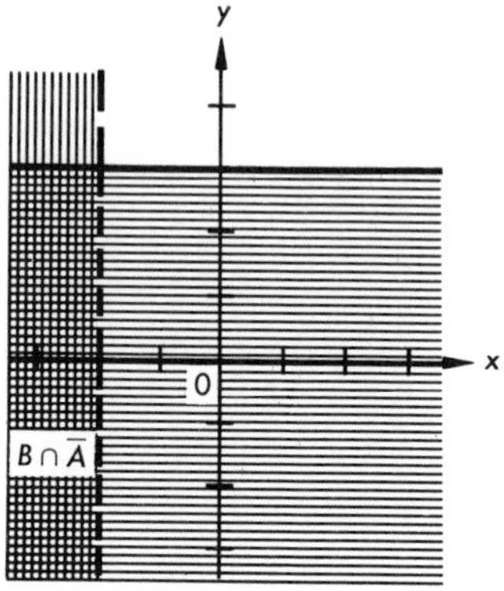

Figures, page 82 (cont'd)

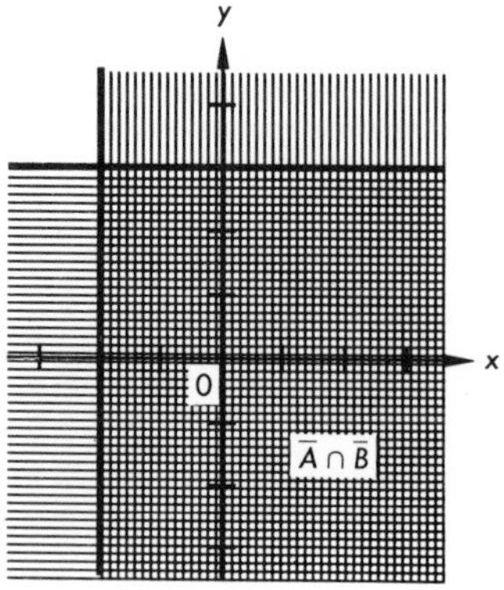

Answers to Quiz, page 83

1.

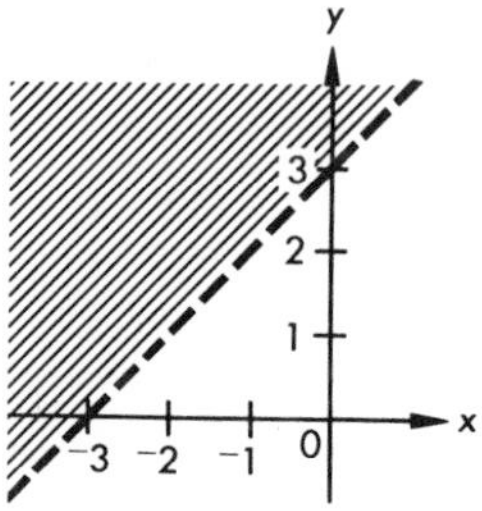

2.

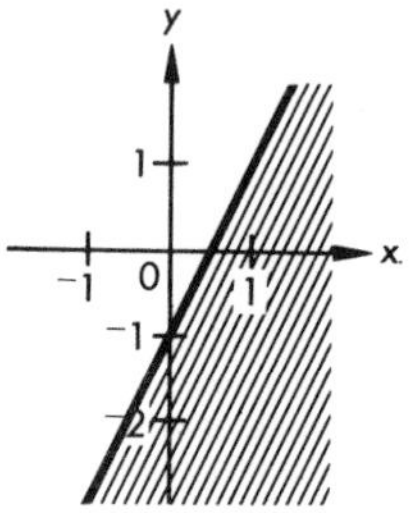

3.

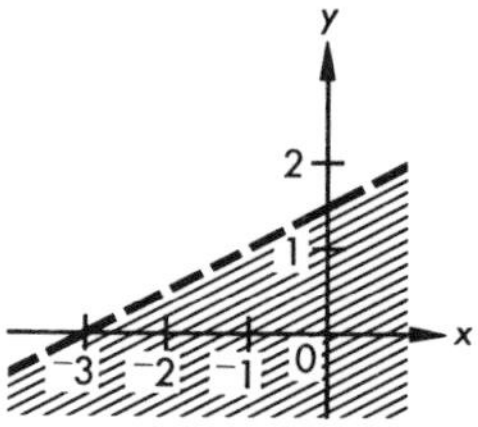

Answers to Exercises for Discussion 7–10, page 86

7.

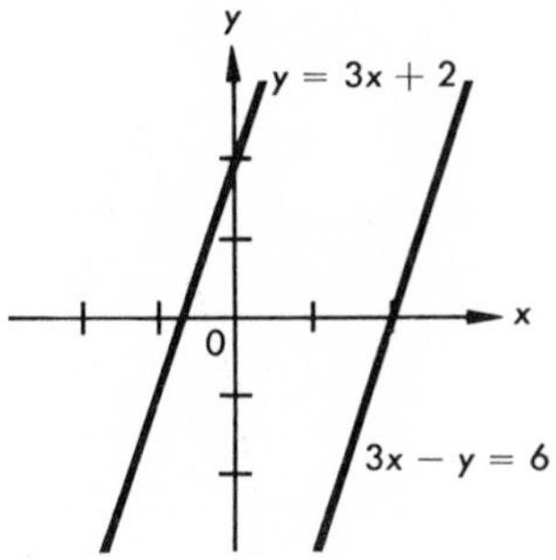

8.

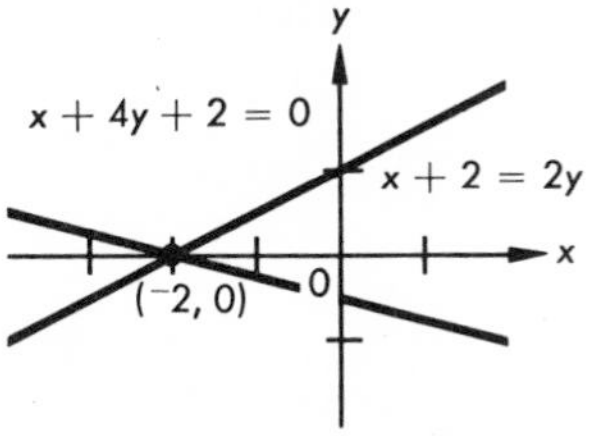

9.

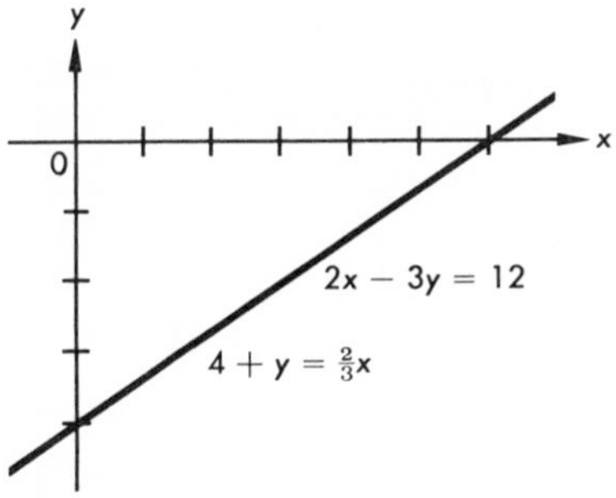

10.

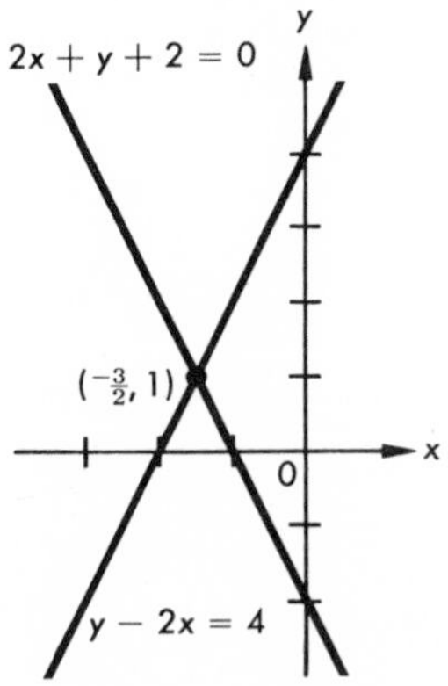

Answers to Quiz, page 99

1.

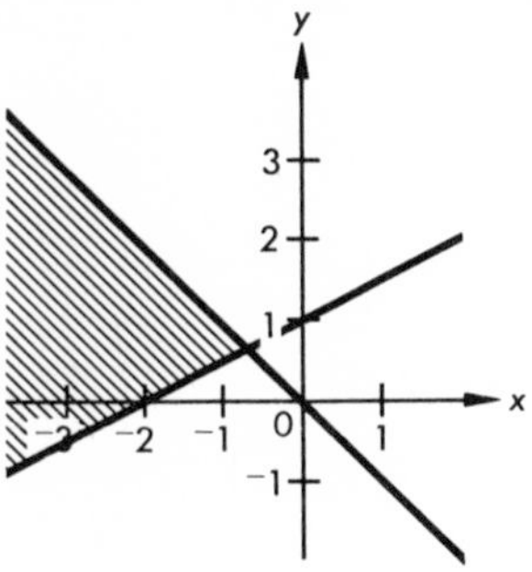

2.

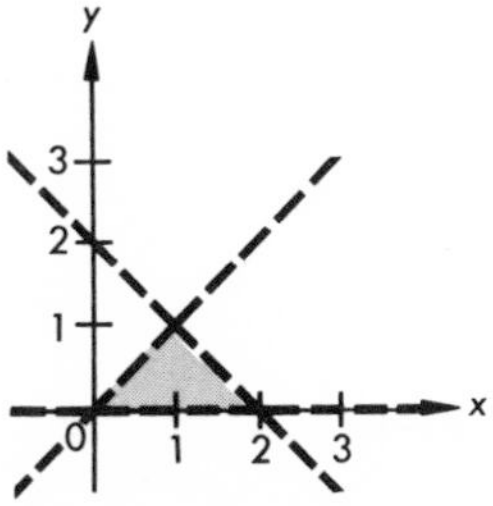

Answers to Exercises for Discussion 1, 3(a), page 144; 5(a), page 145

1.

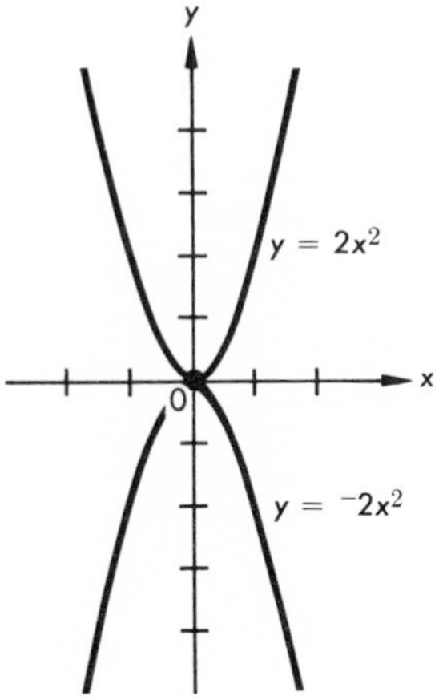

3. (a)

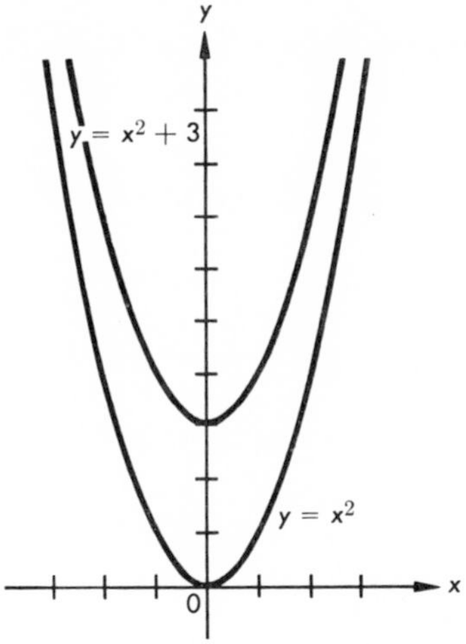

5. (a)

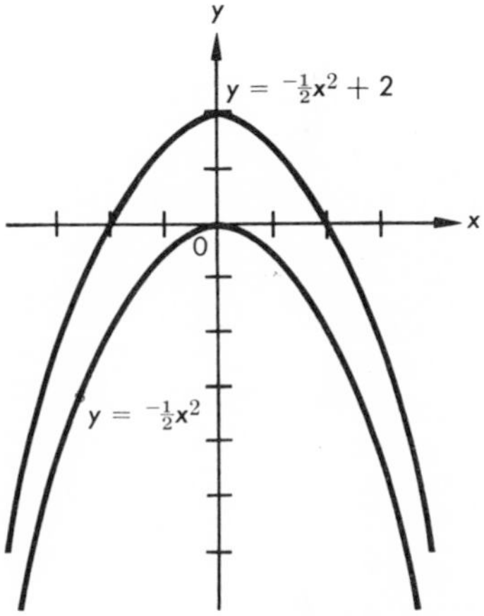

Answer to Quiz, page 145

1.

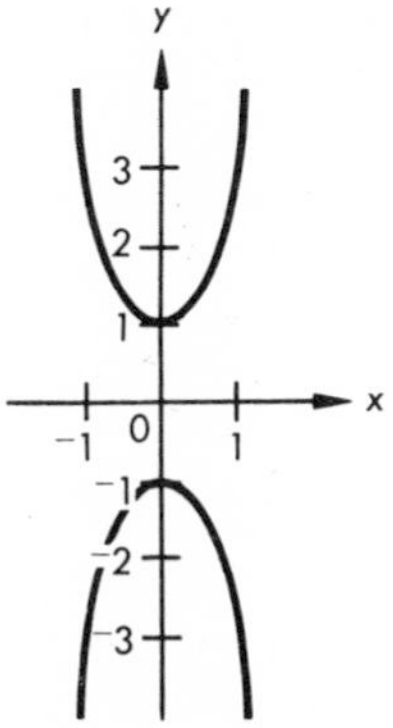

Answers to Exercises for Discussion 6, 8(d), page 151

6.

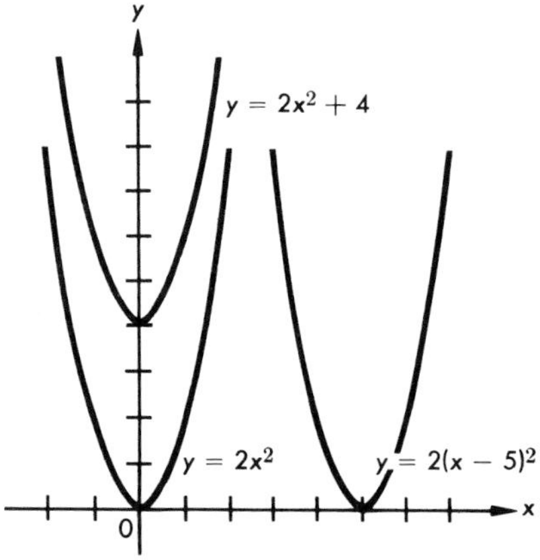

8. (d)

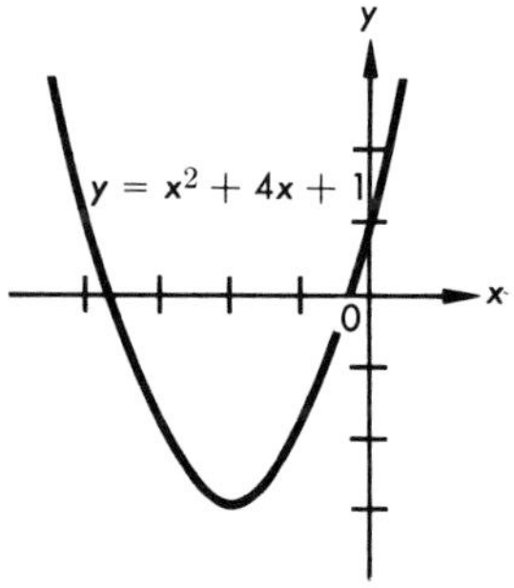

Answers to Quiz, page 154

1.

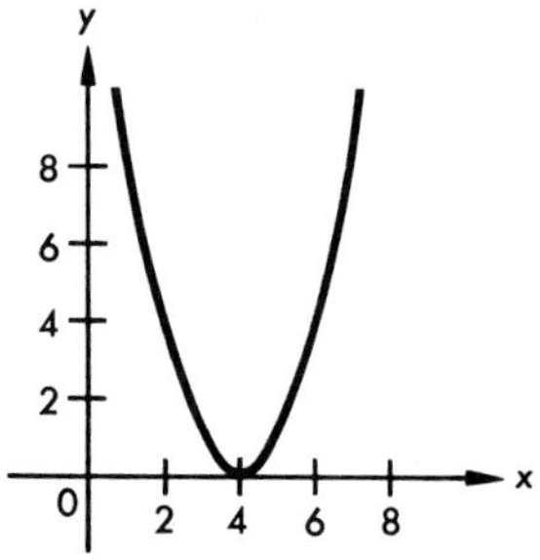

2.

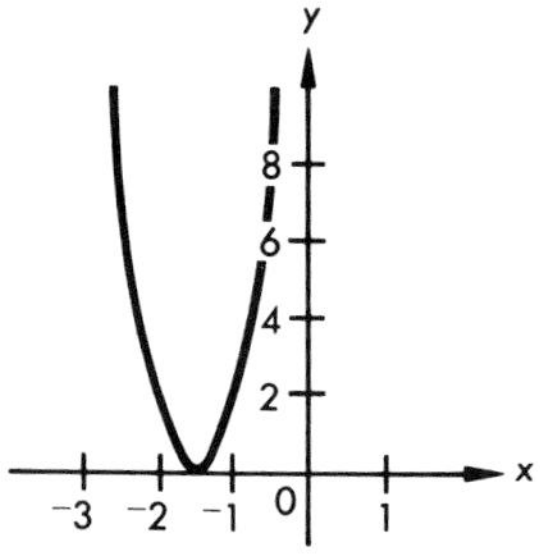

3.

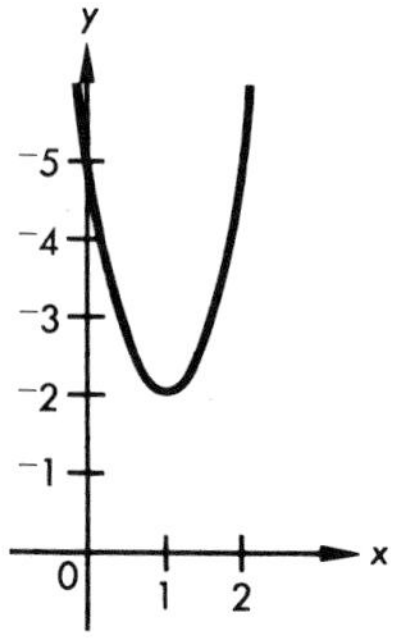

Answers to Quiz, page 158, 159

1.

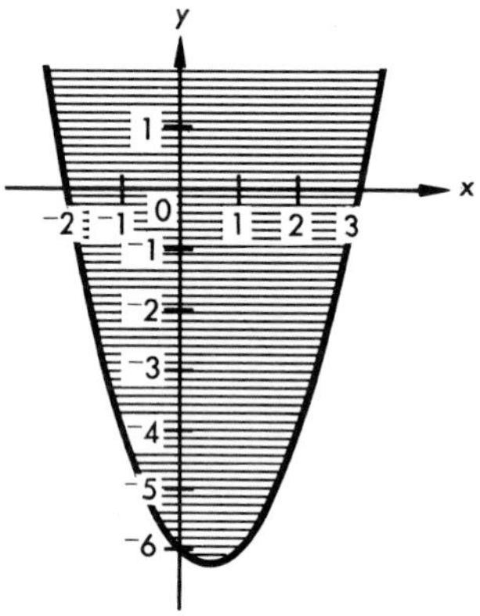

2.

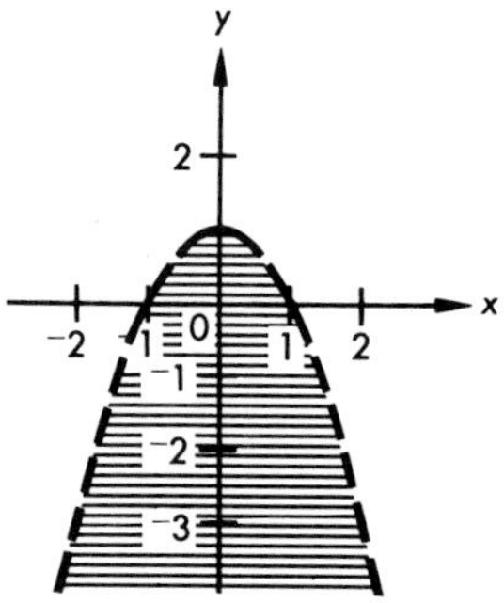

Answers to Quiz, page 209

1.

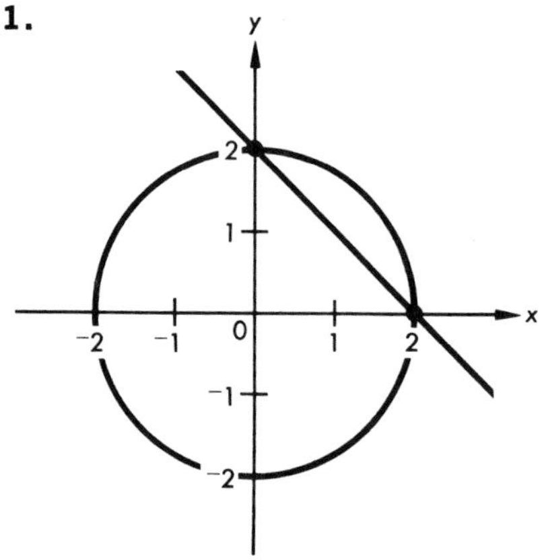

2.

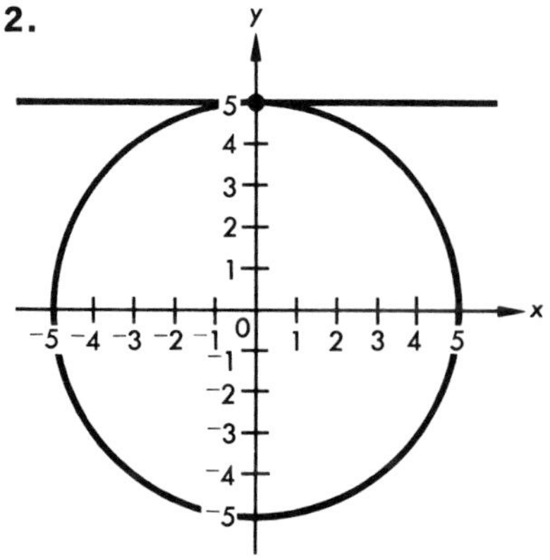

Answer to Exercise for Discussion 7(a), page 277

7. (a)

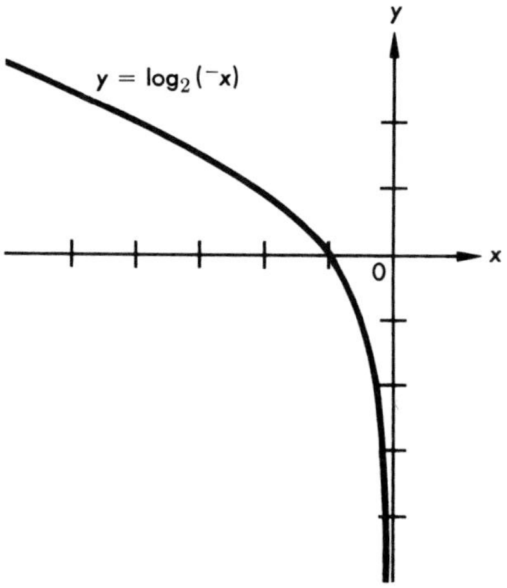

ALGEBRA

AND TRIGONOMETRY

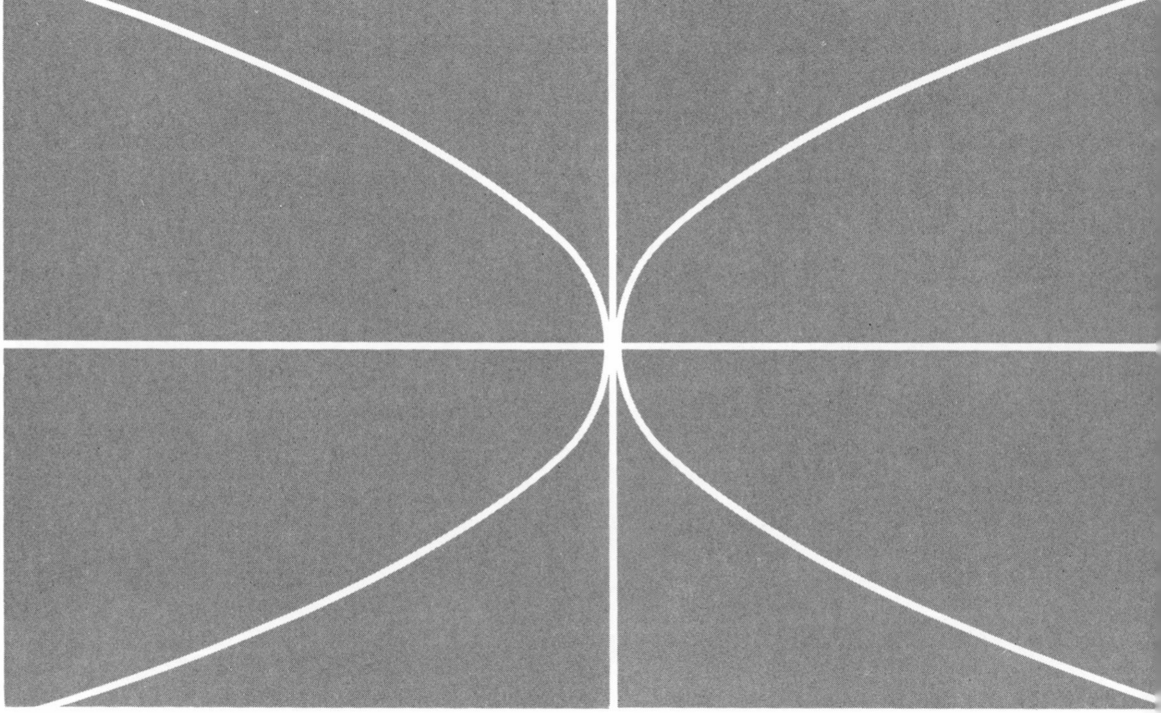

ALGEBRA

AND TRIGONOMETRY

RICHARD E. JOHNSON The University of New Hampshire,
Durham, New Hampshire

LONA LEE LENDSEY Oak Park and River Forest High School,
Oak Park, Illinois

WILLIAM E. SLESNICK Dartmouth College,
Hanover, New Hampshire

GRACE E. BATES Mount Holyoke College,
South Hadley, Massachusetts

ADDISON-WESLEY PUBLISHING COMPANY
Menlo Park, California • Reading, Massachusetts
London • Don Mills, Ontario

SECONDARY
MATHEMATICS
SERIES

THIS BOOK IS IN THE

Addison-Wesley
Secondary Mathematics Series

CONSULTING EDITORS
Richard S. Pieters Paul Rosenbloom
George B. Thomas, Jr. John Wagner

PREFACE

In this book, we assume that students are acquainted with the language of algebra, have an understanding of the structure of number systems, and have acquired some dexterity in the manipulation of algebraic expressions.

The mathematical goals of the various parts of this book can be briefly stated in the following manner. The first three chapters reintroduce students to the algebraic properties of the real number system, to equations, and to inequalities of the first and second degrees. After students have had the opportunity to observe that some second-degree equations have no solution in the real number system, we introduce (in Chapter 4) the complex number system in which every second-degree equation has a solution.

Conic sections are introduced in Chapter 5 in order to give a geometric application of quadratic equations in two variables. The discussion of conic sections is followed by Chapter 6 on functions, Chapter 7 on logarithms, and Chapter 8 on polynomials. All the elementary properties of the trigonometric functions are covered in Chapters 9 and 10. Students are thereby given the background in trigonometry that they will need in physics and more advanced mathematics courses.

Ways of counting the number of possible results of a sequence of actions are described in Chapter 11. Then in Chapter 12 these counting procedures are applied to elementary probability theory. Mathematical induction is introduced in Chapter 13, vectors in Chapter 14, and symbolic logic in Chapter 15.

The study of mathematics involves doing mathematics. Consequently, the discussion exercises are designed to lead students to a successful solution of the type of problem under analysis. The homework exercises are separated into three levels, with many discovery exercises included in the third level. Additional aids to learning may be found in several historical notes and numerous starred sections.

The content of this book has been noticeably influenced by the report of the Commission on Mathematics of the College Entrance Examination Board and by the School Mathematics Study Group.

The authors wish to express their appreciation to their colleagues for suggestions and encouragement, to the teachers who so kindly gave their impressions of the book, and to the publishers for their untiring efforts to produce a superior book.

R.E.J.
L.L.L.
W.E.S.
G.E.B.

CONTENTS

1 The Real Number System *1*

2 First-degree Equations and Inequalities *55*

3 Second-degree Equations and Inequalities *123*

CHAPTER 1

The Real Number System

The purpose of Chapter 1 is to build the framework of algebra which, in the beginning, is the real number system. Since it is not the student's first introduction to algebra, just a reminder will be sufficient for many of the properties of the real number system. As the discussion of this system progresses, the student should gain proficiency in operating with its elements. He should handle statements involving symbols such as *equal to, less than, greater than*, and *absolute value* with assurance. The elements of the real number system may be illustrated through their one-to-one correspondence with the points on a line, thus setting the stage for analytic geometry.

The following are some of the topics covered in Chapter 1:

- *Uniqueness properties*
- *Commutative and associative laws*
- *Distributive laws*
- *Identity and inverse elements*
- *Subtraction and division*
- *Cancellation laws*
- *Zero multiplication*
- *Negative multiplication*
- *Order properties*
- *Absolute value*
- *Real number system*
- *Operations of the real number system*
- *Integral exponents*
- *Laws of exponents*
- *Radicals*
- *Rational exponents*
- *Directed distance*

CHAPTER 1

Although it is doubtful that the people of the Aurignacian period could count up to ten, drawings found on the walls of caves lead us to believe that they could count up to five. (Courtesy of the Chicago Natural History Museum)

THE REAL NUMBER SYSTEM

The properties of the real number system are divided into two groups: those concerning addition and multiplication and those concerning order. In the first group, we have such familiar properties as the commutative laws, associative laws, and the distributive law. Also in this group are the properties of 0 and 1, and the properties of opposites and reciprocals.

The order properties of the real number system are concerned with the relative sizes of numbers. Given any two different real numbers, one is always greater than the other. If x is greater than y, then $x + a$ is greater than $y + a$ for every real number a, and xa is greater than ya for every positive real number a.

It is the purpose of this chapter to review the fundamental properties of the integers, rational numbers, and real numbers, and to reintroduce common mathematical notations, such as exponents and radicals.

It is suggested that one day be spent on each section of this chapter. Teachers should not allow themselves to become so bogged down in Chapter 1 that students lose their motivation for learning algebra. In other words, the presentation should be paced so that students remain interested and continue to move forward. However, it is important that enough time be spent on this chapter so that students may begin to perform proofs rather than merely reading them.

1-1 FUNDAMENTAL PROPERTIES

Real numbers consist of two mutually exclusive sets: rational and irrational numbers. Rational numbers may be expressed as the ratio of two integers; irrational numbers cannot be so expressed. Since it is possible to perform the operations of arithmetic (addition, subtraction, multiplication, and division) and stay within the set of rational numbers, this set is closed under these operations (except for division by zero). However, the set of irrational numbers is *not closed* under these operations, as may be shown by simple examples, such as

$$\sqrt{3} + (^-\sqrt{3}),\ \sqrt{6} \cdot \sqrt{54},$$

and

$$\sqrt{12} \div \sqrt{3}.$$

The significance of closure may be brought to the attention of the class by exhibiting sets that are not closed under the operations of addition and multiplication. For example, the infinite set

$$B = \{2, 4, 8, \ldots, 2^n, \ldots\}$$

is not closed under addition, but is closed under multiplication. Also, the finite set $\{^-1, 0, 1\}$ is closed under multiplication, but not under addition.

The property of uniqueness of addition may be illustrated with examples such as

$$3 + 2 = 5 \quad \text{and} \quad 9 = 1 + 8.$$

Therefore,

$$(3 + 2) + 9 = 5 + (1 + 8).$$

The property of uniqueness of multiplication may be illustrated by

$$2 + 1 = 3 \quad \text{and} \quad 5 = 4 + 1.$$

1-1 FUNDAMENTAL PROPERTIES

Chapter 1 is a review of the material studied in elementary algebra. Although your instructor may not assign this complete chapter, you should be certain that you understand all of the material covered.

The number system of elementary algebra is the *system of real numbers.* It consists of *rational numbers* and *irrational numbers.* From our previous work in algebra, we recall that quotients of integers, such as $^-\frac{1}{3}$, $\frac{2}{7}$, $\frac{3}{1}$, and $\frac{876}{29}$, are called rational numbers. Real numbers, such as $\sqrt{3}$, π, and $\sqrt[3]{2} + \sqrt{29}$, which cannot be expressed as quotients of integers are called irrational numbers.

The two basic operations of the real number system are addition and multiplication. The real number system is closed with respect to the operations of addition and multiplication. In other words, if x and y are real numbers, then so are $x + y$ and $x \cdot y$.

Addition and multiplication are unique in the following way.

UNIQUENESS OF ADDITION

If $a = b$ *and* $c = d$, *then* $a + c = b + d$. (U-A)

In other words, if a and b have the same value and c and d have the same value, then $a + c$ has the same value as $b + d$.

UNIQUENESS OF MULTIPLICATION

If $a = b$ *and* $c = d$, *then* $ac = bd$. (U-M)

Addition and multiplication have the following five fundamental properties.

COMMUTATIVE LAWS OF ADDITION AND MULTIPLICATION

The equations

$$x + y = y + x, \qquad \text{(C-A)}$$

$$x \cdot y = y \cdot x \qquad \text{(C-M)}$$

are true for all real numbers x and y.

ASSOCIATIVE LAWS OF ADDITION AND MULTIPLICATION

The equations

$$(x + y) + z = x + (y + z), \qquad (A\text{-}A)$$
$$(x \cdot y) \cdot z = x \cdot (y \cdot z) \qquad (A\text{-}M)$$

are true for all real numbers x, y, and z.

DISTRIBUTIVE LAW

The equations

$$\left.\begin{aligned} x \cdot (y + z) &= (x \cdot y) + (x \cdot z), \\ (y + z) \cdot x &= (y \cdot x) + (z \cdot x) \end{aligned}\right\} \quad (D)$$

are true for all real numbers x, y, and z.

IDENTITY ELEMENTS OF ADDITION AND MULTIPLICATION

The equations

$$x + 0 = x, \quad 0 + x = x, \qquad (Id\text{-}A)$$
$$x \cdot 1 = x, \quad 1 \cdot x = x \qquad (Id\text{-}M)$$

are true for every real number x.

INVERSE ELEMENTS OF ADDITION AND MULTIPLICATION

Each real number x has an additive inverse, ^{-}x, called the opposite of x such that

$$\left.\begin{aligned} x + {}^{-}x &= 0, \\ {}^{-}x + x &= 0. \end{aligned}\right\} \quad (Inv\text{-}A)$$

Each nonzero real number x has a multiplicative inverse, 1/x, called the reciprocal of x such that

$$\left.\begin{aligned} x \cdot \frac{1}{x} &= 1, \\ \frac{1}{x} \cdot x &= 1, \quad x \neq 0. \end{aligned}\right\} \quad (Inv\text{-}M)$$

These five properties are assumptions that we make about the real number system, and they are not to be proved.

Therefore,

$$(2 + 1) \cdot 5 = 3 \cdot (4 + 1).$$

Explanation and illustration of the use of the commutative and associative laws may be incorporated with a review of the arithmetic of signed numbers. For example, simplify

$$^{-}36 + 8 + {}^{-}14 + 12.$$

It may be shown that every time the lineup of signed numbers is changed the commutative law is used. Thus one writes

$$^{-}36 + ({}^{-}14 + 8) + 12,$$

for the given sum. When one decides on a pairing, or grouping, the associative law is used. Thus, one writes

$$({}^{-}36 + {}^{-}14) + (8 + 12),$$

and then completes the arithmetic with three simple additions.

Similarly, one commutes and associates factors to produce the easiest number combinations for getting the final product. It may help students to understand the concepts of identity elements and inverse elements of addition and multiplication if you discuss with them the following examples:

$$5 + 0 = 5,$$
$$^{-}6 + 0 = {}^{-}6,$$
$$\frac{^{-}17}{\pi} + 0 = \frac{^{-}17}{\pi}$$
$$8 \cdot 1 = 8,$$
$$^{-}19 \cdot 1 = {}^{-}19,$$
$$0 \cdot 1 = 0,$$
$$\frac{2}{3} \cdot \frac{5}{5} = \frac{2}{3}.$$

Neither zero as an addend nor one as a multiplier can change the identity of a number. However, the same cannot be said of zero as a multiplier or one as an addend, and you may wish to show this in class.

Exercises for Discussion and Exercises

The exercises may be covered quickly as part of the first class discussion of Section 1-1. With an above-average class, you might even cover the Exercises first and let the response determine the amount of discussion needed for the section. Since Exercises 13 and 16 are important, it is suggested that they be included either in class discussion or assignment.

Answer to Exercise for Discussion 5

5. To find the sum of two numbers of the same sign, add the numerical values to obtain the numerical value of their algebraic sum and prefix the common sign. To find the sum of two numbers of opposite signs, subtract the numerical value of the smaller from that of the larger number and prefix the sign of the number having the greater numerical value.

Quiz

Give the reason why each of the following statements is true.

1. $(12 + 3) + 2 = 12 + (3 + 2)$ (ans: (A-A))
2. $7(14 + 8) = 7 \cdot 14 + 7 \cdot 8$ (ans: (D))
3. $(14 \cdot 7) \cdot 3 = 3 \cdot (14 \cdot 7)$ (ans: (C-M))
4. $^-3 \cdot \frac{-1}{3} = 1$ (ans: (Inv-M))
5. $^-.5 + \frac{1}{2} = 0$ (ans: (Inv-A))

Exercises for Discussion

In Exercises 1–4, perform the addition.

1. $5 + {}^-2$ *3* **2.** $^-7 + 3$ *$^-4$* **3.** $^-6 + {}^-2$ *$^-8$* **4.** $3 + {}^-8$ *$^-5$*

5. Summarize the rules for adding signed numbers.

6. Which of the following pairs of numbers are additive inverses of each other?

(a) $2, \frac{1}{2}$ *No* (b) $^-3, \frac{27}{9}$ *Yes, since $^-3 + \frac{27}{9} = 0$* (c) $^-4, \frac{1}{4}$ *No*

7. Which of the following pairs of numbers are multiplicative inverses of each other?

(a) $5, {}^-5$ *No* (b) $\frac{1}{7}, 7$ *Yes, since $\frac{1}{7} \cdot 7 = 1$* (c) $2, .5$ *Yes, since $2 \cdot (.5) = 1$*

In Exercises 8–11, tell which of the equations are true and which are false. State the property or properties of the real number system that support each of your true answers.

8. $17 + (8 + 9) = (17 + 9) + 8$ *True; (C-A), (A-A)*

9. $(21 + 6) + 2 = 21 + (6 + 2)$ *False*

10. $(18 \cdot 23) + (18 \cdot 27) = 18(23 + 27)$ *True; (D)*

11. $20 \cdot (5 \cdot 13) = (20 \cdot 5) \cdot 13$ *True; (A-M)*

Exercises

In Exercises 1–7, tell which of the equations are true and which are false. State the property or properties of the real number system that support each of your true answers.

1. $(18 \cdot 2)3 = 18(2 \cdot 3)$ *True; (A-M)*

2. $14 + (7 + 5) = (14 + 7) + 5$ *True; (A-A)*

3. $(30 \cdot 3)5 = 5(30 \cdot 3)$ *True; (C-M)*

4. $37(15 + 22) = (15 \cdot 37) + (22 \cdot 37)$ *True; (D), (C-M)*

5. $(28 \cdot 7) \cdot 2 = 28 \cdot (7 \cdot 2)$ *True; (A-M)*

6. $19 \cdot (108 \cdot \frac{1}{19}) = (19 \cdot \frac{1}{19}) \cdot 108$ *True; (C-M), (A-M)*

7. $(36 \cdot 17) + (64 \cdot 17) = 17(36 + 64)$ *True; (C-M), (D)*

In Exercises 8–16, which of the pairs of numbers are additive inverses of each other and which are multiplicative inverses of each other?

8. $^-3, 3$ *Additive* **9.** $3, \frac{1}{3}$ *Multiplicative* **10.** $.5, \frac{1}{2}$ *Neither*

11. $7, \frac{4}{28}$ *Multiplicative* **12.** $.004, 250$ *Multiplicative* **13.** x, y if $x + y = 1$ *Neither*

14. $\frac{1}{3}, {}^-\frac{1}{3}$ *Additive* **15.** $.1, {}^-10$ *Neither* **16.** x, y if $x \cdot y = 0$ *Neither*

1–2 ADDITIONAL PROPERTIES

So far, we have discussed only the operations of addition and multiplication. The other common operations of arithmetic, subtraction and division, may be defined in terms of addition and multiplication. Hence, the properties of subtraction and division may be derived from the five properties already given. We define subtraction and division in the following way.

DEFINITION OF SUBTRACTION

The equation

$$x - y = x + {}^{-}y \qquad \textit{(Def-Sub)}$$

is true for all real numbers x and y.

DEFINITION OF DIVISION

The equation

$$x \div y = x \cdot \frac{1}{y} \qquad \textit{(Def-Div)}$$

is true for all real numbers x and y if y ≠ 0.

The notations

$$\frac{x}{y} \quad \text{and} \quad x/y$$

are also used for $x \div y$.

The following are examples of the way in which we use the definitions of subtraction and division.

$$\begin{aligned} 7 - 4 &= 7 + {}^{-}4, \quad \text{or } 3, \\ 13 - 17 &= 13 + {}^{-}17, \quad \text{or } {}^{-}4, \\ 9 \div 6 &= 9 \cdot \tfrac{1}{6}, \quad \text{or } \tfrac{3}{2}, \\ \tfrac{1}{3} \div \tfrac{7}{9} &= \tfrac{1}{3} \cdot \tfrac{9}{7}, \quad \text{or } \tfrac{3}{7}. \end{aligned}$$

The real number system is also closed with respect to the operations of subtraction and division, with the exception that division by zero is not defined. Since subtraction is defined in terms of addition and division is defined in terms of multiplication, the uniqueness properties are valid for subtraction and division.

1–2 ADDITIONAL PROPERTIES

Every subtraction problem reverts back to addition, and every division problem reverts back to multiplication, by the definitions of subtraction and division. Hence, it is especially important that the two basic operations be mastered. You may want to have your students do some rapid mental arithmetic using examples such as these:

$12 - 5$	${}^{-}9 - 13$
$12 - {}^{-}5$	${}^{-}9 - {}^{-}13$
$7 - 7$	${}^{-}7 - 7$
$7 - {}^{-}7$	${}^{-}7 - {}^{-}7$
$36 \div {}^{-}4$	${}^{-}36 \div {}^{-}4$
${}^{-}36 \div 4$	${}^{-}18 \div {}^{-}\frac{2}{3}$

The work on permutations may be anticipated by asking the class how many different arrangements are possible for the factors in a product, such as $5 \cdot 4 \cdot 2$, and then listing the six that result from using the commutative law:

$$\begin{array}{ll} 5 \cdot 4 \cdot 2, & 4 \cdot 2 \cdot 5, \\ 5 \cdot 2 \cdot 4, & 4 \cdot 5 \cdot 2, \\ 2 \cdot 4 \cdot 5, & 2 \cdot 5 \cdot 4. \end{array}$$

You could ask whether using the associative law provides twelve ways to find this product, or if there are duplicates.

The rearrangement property of addition may be illustrated with a simplification such as the following:

$$\begin{aligned} &15 - 3x - 20 \\ &= 15 + (^-3x) + (^-20) && \text{(Def-Sub)} \\ &= 15 + (^-20) + (^-3x) && \text{(C-A)} \\ &= [15 + (^-20)] + (^-3x) && \text{(A-A)} \\ &= {}^-5 - 3x. && \text{(Def-Sub)} \end{aligned}$$

You could show how the rearrangement property of multiplication is used to simplify products by using examples, such as

$$\begin{aligned} (8x)(^-3x) &= [8(^-3)] \cdot x \cdot x \quad \text{(R-M)} \\ &= {}^-24x^2. \end{aligned}$$

Because of the cancellation law of addition, we know immediately that an equation such as

$$\sqrt{x+2} + 5 = \sqrt{x+2} - 3$$

has no solution, since $5 \neq {}^-3$.

Since it is important for students to know when the cancellation law does not apply, it may be helpful to demonstrate situations, such as the following, where this law might be incorrectly used:

If $5x = 50 + 3x$, then $x \neq 10 + 3x$.
If $\frac{2}{3}x = \frac{1}{3}x + 5$, then $2x \neq x + 5$.

The student might first prove zero multiplication for a specific case, such as $5 \cdot 0 = 0$, observing that since $x \cdot 0 = 0$ for every real number x, there is a good reason for the

In the process of finding a sum of several numbers, we may make repeated use of the associative and commutative laws to move addends around in any way we wish. For example,

$$\begin{aligned} a + (b + c) &= a + (c + b) && \text{(C-A)} \\ &= (a + c) + b && \text{(A-A)} \\ &= (c + a) + b && \text{(C-A)} \\ &= c + (a + b) && \text{(A-A)} \\ &= c + (b + a). && \text{(C-A)} \end{aligned}$$

It is common practice to write

$$a + b + c$$

for either $a + (b + c)$ or $(a + b) + c$. Hence,

$$a + b + c = a + c + b = c + a + b = c + b + a,$$

and so on, by our argument above. If we continue our argument to include four or more addends, we can prove the following property.

REARRANGEMENT PROPERTY OF ADDITION

The terms of a sum may be rearranged in any way. **(R-A)**

Since the commutative and associative laws are also true for multiplication, the rearrangement property is true for multiplication.

REARRANGEMENT PROPERTY OF MULTIPLICATION

The factors of a product may be rearranged in any way. **(R-M)**

The *cancellation laws* are, in a sense, converses of uniqueness of addition and uniqueness of multiplication.

CANCELLATION LAW OF ADDITION

If $x + z = y + z$, then $x = y$. **(Can-A)**

Proof.

$$\begin{aligned} x + z &= y + z && \text{(hypothesis)} \\ x + z + {}^-z &= y + z + {}^-z && \text{(U-A)} \\ x + (z + {}^-z) &= y + (z + {}^-z) && \text{(A-A)} \\ x + 0 &= y + 0 && \text{(Inv-A)} \\ x &= y && \text{(Id-A)} \end{aligned}$$

This proves that the cancellation law of addition is valid for all real numbers x, y, and z. The *cancellation law of multiplication* can be proved in a similar manner.

CANCELLATION LAW OF MULTIPLICATION

If $x \cdot z = y \cdot z$ *and* $z \neq 0$, *then* $x = y$. *(Can-M)*

According to the following property, the product of any number and zero is always zero.

ZERO MULTIPLICATION

$x \cdot 0 = 0$ *for every real number* x *(Zero-M)*

Proof. Since $0 + 0 = 0$,

$$\begin{aligned} x \cdot (0 + 0) &= x \cdot 0, && \text{(U-M)} \\ (x \cdot 0) + (x \cdot 0) &= x \cdot 0, && \text{(D)} \\ (x \cdot 0) + (x \cdot 0) &= (x \cdot 0) + 0, && \text{(Id-A)} \\ x \cdot 0 &= 0. && \text{(Can-A)} \end{aligned}$$

From an earlier algebra course, we recall that the product of a positive number and a negative number is a negative number. This is one example of the following property.

NEGATIVE MULTIPLICATION

$x \cdot {}^-y = {}^-(x \cdot y)$ *(Neg-M)*

Proof.

$$\begin{aligned} (x \cdot {}^-y) + (x \cdot y) &= x \cdot ({}^-y + y) && \text{(D)} \\ &= x \cdot 0 && \text{(Inv-A)} \\ &= 0 && \text{(Zero-M)} \\ &= {}^-(x \cdot y) + (x \cdot y) && \text{(Inv-A)} \end{aligned}$$

Hence,

$$(x \cdot {}^-y) + (x \cdot y) = {}^-(x \cdot y) + (x \cdot y)$$

and

$$x \cdot {}^-y = {}^-(x \cdot y). \qquad \text{(Can-A)}$$

In general,

$${}^-(x \cdot y) = {}^-x \cdot y = x \cdot {}^-y.$$

statement that division by 0 is not defined.

If it is assumed that 0 has a reciprocal, 1/0, so that one can divide by 0, then $0 \cdot (1/0)$ must equal 1 by the inverse element of multiplication, but $0 \cdot (1/0)$ must equal 0 by zero multiplication. Therefore, 0 does not have a reciprocal, and division by 0 is impossible.

Negative multiplication can be introduced by using some specific cases. For example, find

$$(5 \cdot {}^-8) + (5 \cdot 8).$$

$$\begin{aligned} (5 \cdot {}^-8) + (5 \cdot 8) &= 5({}^-8 + 8) && \text{(D)} \\ &= 5 \cdot 0 && \text{(Inv-A)} \\ &= 0 && \text{(Zero-M)} \end{aligned}$$

Hence,

$$(5 \cdot {}^-8) + (5 \cdot 8) = 0.$$

Now, by the inverse elements of addition, since $(5 \cdot {}^-8)$ added to $(5 \cdot 8)$ gives 0, $(5 \cdot {}^-8)$ and $(5 \cdot 8)$ are additive inverses. Hence,

$$\begin{aligned} (5 \cdot {}^-8) &= {}^-(5 \cdot 8), \\ 5 \cdot {}^-8 &= {}^-40, \end{aligned}$$

and, by the same procedure,

$$8 \cdot {}^-5 = {}^-40.$$

This demonstration could be followed by reading the proof of negative multiplication, assuming x and y are positive numbers.

Attention should be called to the last line on page 7. If it has been shown that

$${}^-(x \cdot y) = x \cdot {}^-y,$$

then, since

$$\begin{aligned} {}^-(x \cdot y) &= {}^-(y \cdot x) && \text{(C-M)} \\ &= y \cdot {}^-x && \text{(Neg-M)} \\ &= {}^-x \cdot y, && \text{(C-M)} \end{aligned}$$

it can be said that

$$\begin{aligned} {}^-x \cdot y &= x \cdot {}^-y \\ &= {}^-(x \cdot y). \end{aligned}$$

It should be made clear to the student that the product of a positive and a negative number is negative, regardless of which factor is negative; that is, $5 \cdot {}^-8 = {}^-5 \cdot 8$. This problem may be contrasted with one in which we consider addition instead of multiplication. Then ${}^-5 + 8 = 3$ but $5 + {}^-8 = {}^-3$, and the sum definitely depends on which addend is negative. However, since 3 and ${}^-3$ are additive inverses and are, therefore, not wholly unrelated, you might ask for generalization on this point.

What is ${}^-({}^-5)$? Since the sum of any number and its opposite is zero, it is known that

$$({}^-5) + {}^-({}^-5) = 0$$

and

$$5 + ({}^-5) = 0.$$

Hence

$$({}^-5) + {}^-({}^-5) = 5 + ({}^-5)$$

and

$${}^-({}^-5) = 5. \quad \text{(Can-A)}$$

In general, if one starts with any number, takes its opposite, and then takes the opposite of this opposite, one is back to the number with which he started. This fact may be used to establish the rule that the product of two negative numbers is a positive number.

Exercises for Discussion

If time is limited, it is suggested that at least Exercises for Discussion 1–4, 8, and 9 be covered.

The signs of even and odd powers of negative numbers may be considered in connection with Exercise for Discussion 9. You may also want to use examples like $({}^-3)^{2n}$ and $({}^-3)^{2n+1}$.

Some examples of the use of negative multiplication are given below.

$$\begin{aligned} {}^-5 \cdot 4 &= {}^-(5 \cdot 4), \quad \text{or } {}^-20 \\ \tfrac{2}{3} \cdot {}^-9 &= {}^-(\tfrac{2}{3} \cdot 9), \quad \text{or } {}^-6 \end{aligned}$$

Using the inverse property of addition, we can show that ${}^-({}^-x) = x$. By this property, ${}^-x + {}^-({}^-x) = 0$. However, $x + {}^-x = 0$, also, by the inverse property of addition. Hence,

$${}^-x + {}^-({}^-x) = {}^-x + x$$

and

$${}^-({}^-x) = x. \qquad \text{(Can-A)}$$

In other words,

$${}^-({}^-x) = x \quad \text{for every real number } x.$$

For example, ${}^-({}^-8) = 8$ and ${}^-[{}^-({}^-3)] = {}^-3$.

If we use negative multiplication, we see that

$$\begin{aligned} ({}^-8) \cdot ({}^-5) &= {}^-({}^-8 \cdot 5) && \text{(Neg-M)} \\ &= {}^-(5 \cdot {}^-8) && \text{(C-M)} \\ &= {}^-[{}^-(5 \cdot 8)] && \text{(Neg-M)} \\ &= 5 \cdot 8, \quad \text{or } 40. \end{aligned}$$

Exercises for Discussion

Give the reason or reasons why each of the following statements is true.

1. If $(x + 2) + {}^-2 = 8 + {}^-2$, then $x + 2 = 8$. (Can-A)
2. If $2x - 3 = 5$, then $2x = 8$. (U-A)
3. If $5x + 10 = 30$, then $x + 2 = 6$. (U-M),(D); or (D)(Can-M)
4. If ${}^-18x = 54$, then $x = {}^-3$. (U-M), (A-M), (Inv-M): $\frac{-1}{18}({}^-18x) = \frac{-1}{18}(54)$ $(\frac{-1}{18} \cdot {}^-18)x = {}^-3$

In Exercises 5–7, complete each statement and name the property used.

5. If $x + y = 9 + y$, then $x =$ 9 ?__. (Can-A)
6. If $x/3 = 20/7$, then $7x =$ 60 ?__. (U-M)
7. If $3x - 12 = 17$, then $3x =$ 29 ?__. (U-A): $3x - 12 + 12 = 17 + 12$, or (Can-A): $3x - 12 = 29 - 12$
8. Give a reason for the key steps in the following multiplication problem.

$$\begin{aligned} ({}^-4)({}^-3) &= {}^-(4 \cdot {}^-3) && \text{\_\_?(Neg-M)} \\ &= {}^-({}^-3 \cdot 4) && \text{\_\_?(C-M)} \\ &= {}^-[{}^-(3 \cdot 4)] && \text{\_\_?(Neg-M)} \\ &= 3 \cdot 4, \quad \text{or } 12. \end{aligned}$$

9. Summarize the rules for multiplying and dividing signed numbers.

In Exercises 10–15, perform the indicated operations.

10. $(^{-}57 \div {}^{-}19) \cdot {}^{-}\frac{1}{3}$ $3 \cdot \frac{^{-}7}{3} = {}^{-}7$

11. $(17 - 63) \cdot (31 + {}^{-}31)$ 0

12. $(87 \div {}^{-}3) \cdot {}^{-}2$ $^{-}29 \cdot {}^{-}2 = 58$

13. $(^{-}7 \cdot 8) \cdot {}^{-}\frac{1}{7}$ $\frac{^{-}1}{7}(^{-}7 \cdot 8) = (\frac{^{-}1}{7} \cdot {}^{-}7) \cdot 8 = 1 \cdot 8 = 8$

14. $[(17 + 13) - 50](^{-}987)$ $(30 - 50)(^{-}987) = (^{-}20)(^{-}987) = 19{,}740$

15. $21 - {}^{-}18 - 45$ $39 - 45 = {}^{-}6$

Exercises

Give the reason or reasons why each of the following statements is true.

1. If $5 + 2 = 7$, then $(5 + 2) + 8 = 7 + 8$. (U-A)

2. If $9 = 18 \div 2$, then $2 \cdot 9 = 2(18 \div 2)$. (U-M)

3. If $12 + 9 = 21$ and $13 = 7 + 6$, then $(12 + 9) - 13 = 21 - (7 + 6)$. (U-S)

4. If $\frac{x + 2}{3} = \frac{5}{3}$, then $x + 2 = 5$. (Def-Div), (Can-M)

5. If $7(2x - 3) = 7 \cdot 81$, then $2x - 3 = 81$. (Can-M)

6. If $2x + 27 = (x + 2) + 27$, then $2x = x + 2$. (Can-A)

7. If $.04x + .05y = 23$, then $4x + 5y = 2300$. (U-M)

8. $(8 \cdot 19) \cdot 25 = (25 \cdot 8) \cdot 19$ (C-M), (A-M)

Complete each statement and name the property used.

9. If $53x = 53 \cdot \frac{9}{2}$, then $x =$ $\frac{9}{2}$? . (Can-M)

10. If $21x - 35 = 28x + 7$, then $3x - 5 =$? $4x + 1$ (D), (Can-M)

11. If $x - 2 = 0$, then $(x + 3)(x - 2) =$? 0. (U-M), (Zero-M)

In Exercises 12–22, perform the indicated operations.

12. $^{-}17 + 39 + {}^{-}83$ $^{-}61$

13. $25 \cdot 86 \cdot {}^{-}4$ $^{-}8600$

14. $^{-}93(^{-}7 + 7)$ 0

15. $^{-}76 \div {}^{-}2$ 38

16. $32 - {}^{-}21 - 67$ $^{-}14$

17. $(^{-}17)(^{-}3)$ 51

18. $^{-}20 - 15 - 7$ $^{-}42$

19. $[61(^{-}5)] \div {}^{-}61$ 5

20. $(207 \div {}^{-}23) \cdot 23$ $^{-}207$

21. $^{-}8(7 - 19)$ 96

22. $(12 - 60) \div {}^{-}3$ 16

23. If $x = 13$, what is ^{-}x? $^{-}(^{-}x)$? $^{-}13$, 13

24. If $x = {}^{-}17$, what is ^{-}x? $^{-}(^{-}x)$? 17, $^{-}17$

Answer to Exercise for Discussion 9

9. The product and the quotient of two numbers of the same sign are positive numbers, and the product and the quotient of two numbers of opposite signs are negative numbers. The numerical values, in each case, are found by taking either the products or quotients of the numerical values of the original two numbers.

It is suggested that Exercises 25–28 be done in class so all students will grasp their full import. The equation in Exercise 25,

$$^-(x + y) = {}^-x + {}^-y,$$

says that given any two numbers, they may be added and the sign of the sum changed, or the signs of the addends may be changed before the addition is completed. The result is the same either way.

Answer to Exercise 25

25. (a) $^-(5 + 3) \stackrel{?}{=} {}^-5 + {}^-3,$
$^-8 \stackrel{\checkmark}{=} {}^-8$

(b) $^-(^-7 + {}^-9) \stackrel{?}{=} {}^-(^-7) + {}^-(^-9),$
$^-(^-16) \stackrel{?}{=} 7 + 9,$
$16 \stackrel{\checkmark}{=} 16$

(c) $^-(^-12 + 6) \stackrel{?}{=} {}^-(^-12) + {}^-6,$
$^-(^-6) \stackrel{?}{=} 12 + {}^-6,$
$6 \stackrel{\checkmark}{=} 6$

(d) $^-(^-16 + 23) \stackrel{?}{=} {}^-(^-16) + {}^-23,$
$^-7 \stackrel{?}{=} 16 + {}^-23,$
$^-7 \stackrel{\checkmark}{=} {}^-7$

Quiz

Perform the indicated operations.

1. $^-37 + 12 + {}^-63$ (ans: $^-88$)
2. $160(^-13 + 13)$ (ans: 0)
3. $^-5 \cdot 23 \cdot 2$ (ans: $^-230$)
4. $(^-15)(^-5)$ (ans: 75)
5. $^-66 \div {}^-3$ (ans: 22)

1–3 ORDER PROPERTIES

The trichotomy law classifies the real numbers into three mutually exclusive sets.

Students should realize that $x > y$ is defined to mean that $x - y$ is positive, and that from this definition, we deduce the *theorem* that a positive number is greater than zero. Many students think that a positive number is *defined* to be greater than zero.

△

25. Test the equation

$$^-(x + y) = {}^-x + {}^-y$$

for the following values of x and y.

(a) 5, 3 (b) $^-7$, $^-9$ (c) $^-12$, 6 (d) $^-16$, 23

26. Do you think that the equation in Exercise 25 is true? Why? *Yes, because each expression is an additive inverse of $x+y$, and $x+y$ has only one additive inverse.*

27. Prove that the equation

$$^-x \cdot {}^-y = x \cdot y$$

is true for every pair x, y of real numbers. (Hint: Study Exercise for Discussion 8.) *See Solution Manual.*

28. If subtraction is an associative operation, then the equation

$$x - (y - z) = (x - y) - z$$

must be true for every triple x, y, z of real numbers.

(a) Describe a set of number triples for which the equation is true. *7, 2, 0*
(b) Give at least one triple of numbers for which the equation is false. *7, 2, 1*
(c) Is subtraction associative? *No*

1–3 ORDER PROPERTIES

Every nonzero real number is either a *positive number* or a *negative number*. For example, 7 and $\pi - 3$ are positive numbers, and $^-5$ and $\sqrt{15} - 4$ are negative numbers. There are three additional fundamental properties of the real number system that apply to the set of all positive real numbers. They are called the *order properties*. The order properties, like the five fundamental properties of Section 1–1, are basic assumptions which cannot be proved. If we denote the set of all positive real numbers by P, we can state these properties in the following manner.

CLOSURE OF P UNDER ADDITION

For every pair x, y of positive real numbers, $x + y$ is also a positive real number. (*Clos-A*)

CLOSURE OF P UNDER MULTIPLICATION

For every pair x, y of positive real numbers, $x \cdot y$ is also a positive real number. (*Clos-M*)

TRICHOTOMY LAW

For every real number x, one, and only one, of the following three statements is true:

$$x = 0, \quad x \textit{ is positive}, \quad {}^{-}x \textit{ is positive}. \qquad (Tri)$$

According to the trichotomy law, the system of real numbers consists of three kinds of numbers: positive numbers, negative numbers, and zero. If x is a positive number, then ^{-}x is a negative number; if x is a negative number, then ^{-}x is a positive number; if x is neither a positive number nor a negative number, then $x = 0$.

The order relations *greater than*, designated by $>$, and *less than*, designated by $<$, are defined in the following way.

DEFINITION OF GREATER THAN

$x > y$ ***if, and only if,*** $x - y$ ***is a positive number*** *(Def >)*

DEFINITION OF LESS THAN

$x < y$ ***if, and only if,*** $y > x$ *(Def <)*

For example,

$$11 > 9, \quad \text{since } 11 - 9 = 2, \text{ and 2 is positive};$$
$$^{-}7 < {}^{-}4, \text{ or } {}^{-}4 > {}^{-}7, \quad \text{since } {}^{-}4 - {}^{-}7 = 3 \text{ and 3 is positive.}$$

Since $x - 0 = x$,

$$x > 0 \quad \text{if, and only if,} \quad x \text{ is a positive number.}$$

Similarly,

$$x < 0 \quad \text{if, and only if,} \quad x \text{ is a negative number.}$$

Using the order relations, we may express closure of P under addition, closure of P under multiplication, and the trichotomy law in the following condensed form.

If $x > 0$ and $y > 0$, then $x + y > 0$. *(Clos-A)*
If $x > 0$ and $y > 0$, then $xy > 0$. *(Clos-M)*
If x is a real number, then $x = 0$, $x > 0$, or $x < 0$. *(Tri)*

You might wish to elaborate on the theorem that $x > 0$ if, and only if, x is positive, by using examples such as the following:

If $x > 0$, then x is positive.

$x > 0$ (Given)
$x - 0$ is positive (Def >)

but

$x - 0 = x$ (Id-A)

Therefore, x is positive.

If x is positive, then $x > 0$.

$x - 0 = x$ (Id-A)
$x - 0$ is positive (Given)

Therefore,

$x > 0$. (Def >)

The additive property of inequalities may be illustrated with both positive and negative values for z.

$$8 > 3 \quad \text{(True)}$$
$$8 + 6 > 3 + 6,\ 14 > 9 \quad \text{(True)}$$
$$8 + (^-5) > 3 + (^-5),\ 3 > {}^-2 \quad \text{(True)}$$

However, the two statements $x > y$ and $x \cdot z > y \cdot z$ are not equivalent if z is negative. For example,

$$7 > {}^-3, \quad \text{(True)}$$
$$7(^-2) > {}^-3(^-2),$$
$$^-14 > {}^+6. \quad \text{(False)}$$

The multiplicative properties of inequalities need to be stressed here, and the stress repeated when solving inequalities later.

We may derive other useful order properties of the real number system from the basic assumptions. The following are three such properties.

TRANSITIVE LAW OF INEQUALITIES

If $x > y$ and $y > z$, then $x > z$. $(T >)$

ADDITIVE PROPERTY OF INEQUALITIES

If $x > y$, then $x + z > y + z$ for every real number z. $(A >)$

MULTIPLICATIVE PROPERTIES OF INEQUALITIES

If $x > y$, then $xz > yz$ for every positive number z. $(^+M >)$
If $x > y$, then $xz < yz$ for every negative number z. $(^-M >)$

We shall prove some of these properties, and leave the proofs of the others as exercises.

Proof of the transitive law.

$x > y$ and $y > z$	(hypothesis)
$x - y > 0$ and $y - z > 0$	(Def >)
$(x - y) + (y - z) > 0$	(Clos-A)
$x + (^-y + y) - z > 0$	(Def-Sub), (A-A)
$x + 0 - z > 0$	(Inv-A)
$x - z > 0$	(Id-A)

Therefore,

$$x > z. \quad \text{(Def >)}$$

Proof of the multiplicative property for positive numbers.

$x > y$ and $z > 0$	(hypothesis)
$x - y > 0$ and $z > 0$	(Def >)
$(x - y)z > 0$	(Clos-M)
$xz - yz > 0$	(D)

Therefore,

$$xz > yz. \quad \text{(Def >)}$$

In a similar way, we can show that the following properties are true: *the transitive law for less than,* $(T <)$; *the additive property for less than,* $(A <)$; *multiplication of positive numbers for less than,* $(^+M <)$; *and multiplication of negative numbers for less than,* $(^-M <)$.

Exercises for Discussion

Tell which statements are true and which are false. Correct the statements that you marked false.

1. $3 > {}^{-}4$ *True, since $3 - {}^{-}4 = 7$ and $7 > 0$* **2.** ${}^{-}5 > {}^{-}6$ *True* **3.** $0 < {}^{-}10$ *False, $0 > {}^{-}10$* **4.** ${}^{-}\frac{1}{3} < {}^{-}\frac{1}{2}$ *F, since ${}^{-}\frac{1}{2} - {}^{-}\frac{1}{3} = {}^{-}\frac{1}{6}$ and ${}^{-}\frac{1}{6} \not> 0$. Therefore, ${}^{-}\frac{1}{3} > {}^{-}\frac{1}{2}$*

In Exercises 5–10, complete each of the expressions to make a true statement.

5. Since ${}^{-}12 - {}^{-}15 = 3$, ? *${}^{-}12$* > ? *${}^{-}15$*

6. Since ${}^{-}7 - {}^{-}8 = 1$, ? *${}^{-}7$* > ? *${}^{-}8$*

7. Since ${}^{-}3 - {}^{-}12 = 9$, ? *${}^{-}12$* < ? *${}^{-}3$*.

8. Since $0 - {}^{-}7 = 7$, ? *${}^{-}7$* < ? *0*.

9. Since ${}^{-}2 > {}^{-}3$ and ${}^{-}3 > {}^{-}4$, ? *${}^{-}2$* > ? *${}^{-}4$*.

10. Since ${}^{-}1 < 0$ and $0 < \frac{1}{2}$, ? *${}^{-}1$* < ? *$\frac{1}{2}$*.

11. Verify (T >) with examples in which
(a) x, y, z are all positive numbers. *$7 > 2$ and $2 > \frac{1}{2}$, hence $7 > \frac{1}{2}$*
(b) x, y, z are all negative numbers. *${}^{-}1 > {}^{-}3$ and ${}^{-}3 > {}^{-}8$, hence ${}^{-}1 > {}^{-}8$*
(c) one is positive and two are negative. *$2 > {}^{-}4$ and ${}^{-}4 > {}^{-}9$, hence $2 > {}^{-}9$*
(d) y is zero. *$2 > 0$ and $0 > {}^{-}4$, hence $2 > {}^{-}4$*

12. State the reason for each step in the proof of the following implication: If $x > y$, then $x + z > y + z$ for every real number z.

If $x > y$, then $x - y$ is positive. *(Def >)*
$(x + z) - (y + z) = x - y$ *(Def-Sub), (R-A), (Inv-A)*
Since $(x + z) - (y + z)$ is positive, $(x + z) > (y + z)$. *(Def >)*

13. Use (Tri), (Def >), and (Def <) to prove that for every pair of real numbers x and y, one, and only one, of the following three statements is true.

$$x = y, \quad x > y, \quad x < y$$

Exercises

In Exercises 1–4, tell which statements are true and which are false. Correct the statements that you marked false.

1. $0 > {}^{-}1$ *True* **2.** ${}^{-}3 < {}^{-}5$ *False, ${}^{-}3 > {}^{-}5$* **3.** ${}^{-}\frac{1}{7} < {}^{-}\frac{2}{7}$ *False, ${}^{-}\frac{1}{7} > {}^{-}\frac{2}{7}$* **4.** ${}^{-}.33 > {}^{-}.3$ *False, ${}^{-}.33 < {}^{-}.3$*

5. If $a < b$, is $a < 2b$? Give some examples, using both positive and negative numbers.

6. Verify (A >) with examples in which
(a) x and y are positive, z is negative. *$5 > 3$ and $5 + {}^{-}3 > 3 + {}^{-}3$ $(2 > 0)$*
(b) x and y are negative, z is positive. *${}^{-}6 > {}^{-}8$ and ${}^{-}6 + 4 > {}^{-}8 + 4$ $({}^{-}2 > {}^{-}4)$*
(c) x, y, z are all negative. *${}^{-}3 > {}^{-}7$ and ${}^{-}3 + {}^{-}3 > {}^{-}7 + {}^{-}3$ $({}^{-}6 > {}^{-}10)$*

Exercises for Discussion

If time is limited, it is suggested that at least Exercises for Discussion 11–13 be covered.

Answer to Exercise for Discussion 13

13. By the trichotomy law, for every real number $x - y$, one, and only one, of the following three statements is true:

$x - y = 0$,
$x - y$ is positive,
${}^{-}(x - y)$, or $y - x$, is positive.

If $x - y = 0$, then $x = y$. If $x - y$ is positive, then $x > y$ by the definition of greater than. If $y - x$ is positive, then $y > x$ by the definition of greater than, and $x < y$ by the definition of less than.

Answer to Exercise 5

5. If $a < b$ it is not always true that $a < 2b$. If $a < b$ and $b > 0$, then $a < 2b$; but if $a < b$ and $b < 0$, examples can be given illustrating each of the three possibilities, $a < 2b$, $a = 2b$, and $a > 2b$.

Exercises 11–13 might well be done in class. Exercises 9–17 should be assigned only to above-average students, and might be used for honors or extra-credit work. In an average class, you may wish to discuss the exercise and omit the proof.

7. Verify ($^{+}$M $>$) with examples in which

(a) x and y are both positive. $4 > 1$ and $4 \cdot 2 > 1 \cdot 2$ $(8 > 2)$

(b) x and y are both negative. $^{-}2 > ^{-}3$ and $^{-}2 \cdot 5 > ^{-}3 \cdot 5$ $(^{-}10 > ^{-}15)$

(c) x and y have opposite signs. $3 > ^{-}1$ and $3 \cdot 4 > ^{-}1 \cdot 4$ $(12 > ^{-}4)$

8. Verify ($^{-}$M $>$) with examples in which

(a) x and y are both positive. $4 > 1$ and $4 \cdot ^{-}2 < 1 \cdot ^{-}2$ $(^{-}8 < ^{-}2)$

(b) x and y are both negative. $^{-}2 > ^{-}3$ and $^{-}2 \cdot ^{-}5 < ^{-}3 \cdot ^{-}5$ $(10 < 15)$

(c) x and y have opposite signs. $3 > ^{-}1$ and $3 \cdot ^{-}3 < ^{-}1 \cdot ^{-}3$ $(^{-}9 < 3)$

△

9. Prove that if x and y are real numbers such that

$$x > y,$$

then

$$x \cdot z < y \cdot z$$

for every negative number z. See Solution Manual.

Before attempting to prove the statements in Exercises 10–14, use different numbers to give several examples which support each statement.

10. Prove that if x and y are real numbers such that $x > y$, then

$$x - z > y - z$$

for every real number z. See Solution Manual.

11. Prove that if z is positive, its reciprocal is positive, and if z is negative, its reciprocal is negative. See Solution Manual.

12. State and prove the relationship that exists between x/z and y/z if z is any positive number and x, y are real numbers such that $x > y$. See Solution Manual.

13. State and prove the relationship that exists between x/z and y/z if z is any negative number and x, y are real numbers such that $x > y$. See Solution Manual.

14. If x and y are both positive and $x > y$, state and prove the relationship which exists between $1/x$ and $1/y$. See Solution Manual.

▲

Before attempting to prove the statements in Exercises 15 and 16, use different numbers to give several specific examples which support each statement.

15. If x and y are both negative and $x > y$, what relationship exists between their reciprocals? Prove that your statement is true. See Solution Manual.

16. (a) Prove that if x and y are positive real numbers such that $x > y$, then $x^2 > y^2$. See Solution Manual.

(b) Prove that if x and y are positive real numbers such that $x^2 > y^2$, then $x > y$. See Solution Manual.

(c) Combine the statements in parts (a) and (b) into one statement. If x and y are positive real numbers, then $x^2 > y^2$ if and only if $x > y$.

17. Consider a number system S of ten elements, the ten digits of the real number system. Thus,

$$S = \{0, 1, 2, 3, 4, 5, 6, 7, 8, 9\}.$$

For $a \neq b$, define $a \delta b$ to be the larger of a and b. For $a = b$, define $a \delta b$ to be a. Thus, for example, $2 \delta 3 = 3$, $8 \delta 5 = 8$, $7 \delta 7 = 7$. Examine S for closure under δ, rearrangement properties of δ, identity element for δ, and inverse elements. S is closed under "δ"; this operation is commutative and associative; 0 is the identity element; no element except 0 has an inverse.

1-4 ADDITIONAL ORDER PROPERTIES

The order relation *greater than or equal to* is denoted by $\geqq$.

DEFINITION OF GREATER THAN OR EQUAL TO

$x \geqq y$, if and only if, either $x > y$ or $x = y$ (Def $\geqq$)

Similarly, the order relation *less than or equal to* is denoted by $\leqq$.

DEFINITION OF LESS THAN OR EQUAL TO

$x \leqq y$ if, and only if, $y \geqq x$ (Def $\leqq$)

For example,

$$7 \geqq 3 \quad \text{because} \quad 7 > 3,$$
$$^{-}3 \geqq {}^{-}3 \quad \text{because} \quad {}^{-}3 = {}^{-}3,$$
$$^{-}4 \leqq {}^{-}1 \quad \text{because} \quad {}^{-}4 < {}^{-}1,$$
$$\frac{1}{\sqrt{2}} \leqq \frac{\sqrt{2}}{2} \quad \text{because} \quad \frac{1}{\sqrt{2}} = \frac{\sqrt{2}}{2}.$$

If x, y, and z are three numbers such that $x < y$ and $y < z$, then we write

$$x < y < z.$$

This shows that y is a number *between* x and z. For example,

$$^{-}1 < 2 < 5 \quad \text{because} \quad {}^{-}1 < 2 \text{ and } 2 < 5.$$

Statements such as

$$x > y > z, \quad x \leqq y < z, \quad x < y \leqq z,$$

and so on, are also meaningful and are often used in mathematics.

Exercise 17 may be discussed in class and used as a review of much of the material in the first three sections. Students who cannot handle the work alone will profit from watching the teacher develop the problem with the class.

Quiz

Complete each of the expressions to make a true statement.

1. Since $^{-}6 < {}^{-}4$ and $^{-}4 < 3$, _?_ < _?_. (ans: $^{-}6 < 3$)
2. Since $^{-}7 - {}^{-}13 = 6$, _?_ > _?_. (ans: $^{-}7 > {}^{-}13$)
3. Since $^{-}2 - {}^{-}3 = 1$, _?_ < _?_. (ans: $^{-}3 < {}^{-}2$)
4. Since $7 > 2$, then $7 \cdot 3$ _?_ $2 \cdot 3$. (ans: >)
5. Since $15 > 12$, then $15 \cdot {}^{-}3$ _?_ $12 \cdot {}^{-}3$. (ans: <)
6. Since $9 > 4$, then $9 + 5$ _?_ $4 + 5$. (ans: >)

1-4 ADDITIONAL ORDER PROPERTIES

You may want to emphasize that $x \leqq y$ is both an equation and an inequality. The claim is made that x is either equal to y or less than y. Unless x is greater than y, it must be true by the trichotomy law that $x \leqq y$.

The student should understand that the nonsense statement

$$0 < 2 > {}^{-}1$$

won't fit the transitive law for less than or greater than because $0 < 2$ and $2 > {}^{-}1$ do not indicate anything about the way in which 0 is related to $^{-}1$.

Again, the introduction of the number line in Section 1-10 may be anticipated. Geometrically,

$$|3| = |{}^{-}3|$$

means that 3 and $^{-}3$ are equidistant from 0 on the number line.

Just as taking the square root of a number, $\sqrt{\ }$, is a unary operation and yields a non-negative answer (for example, $\sqrt{16} = 4$ and $\sqrt{0} = 0$), the absolute value, $|\ |$, also can be considered to be a unary operation and also yields a non-negative answer (for example, $|5| = 5$, $|{}^{-}17| = 17$, and $|0| = 0$).

It should be stressed that ^{-}x is a symbol denoting a positive number when x is negative.

Exercises for Discussion, page 17

If time is limited, it is suggested that at least Exercises for Discussion 10–15 be covered.

In Exercise for Discussion 3, the student should not approximate π to find a rational approximation to $3 - \pi$. Instead, he should decide whether π is less than or greater than 3, so that he may determine whether $3 - \pi$ is positive or negative.

In Exercise for Discussion 5, $\sqrt{3} < 2$, so $2 - \sqrt{3}$ is positive. Therefore, $|2 - \sqrt{3}| = 2 - \sqrt{3}$, and the statement given is true.

We shall never contract a statement such as $0 < 2$ and $2 > {}^{-}1$ to $0 < 2 > {}^{-}1$, or $5 > 1$ and $1 < 3$ to $5 > 1 < 3$. We contract only when two order relations are of the same type and the contraction shows us at a glance that one number is between two other numbers.

Each real number x has associated with it a non-negative number, called its *absolute value*, which is denoted by $|x|$.

DEFINITION OF ABSOLUTE VALUE

If $x \geqq 0$, then $|x| = x$.

If $x < 0$, then $|x| = {}^{-}x$. ***(Def $|x|$)***

For example,

$$|7| = 7 \text{ and } |{}^{-}7| = {}^{-}({}^{-}7), \quad \text{or } 7,$$
$$|1 - \sqrt{2}| = {}^{-}(1 - \sqrt{2}), \quad \text{or } \sqrt{2} - 1,$$
$$|0| = 0.$$

By the definition of absolute value,

$$|x| = |{}^{-}x| \quad \text{for every real number } x.$$

The rules for multiplying positive and negative numbers are summarized below for easy reference.

If $x > 0$ and $y > 0$, then $xy > 0$.
If $x > 0$ and $y < 0$, or $x < 0$ and $y > 0$, then $xy < 0$.
If $x < 0$ and $y < 0$, then $xy > 0$.

Each of the rules above may be proved by using the property for multiplication of negative numbers for greater than. For example, if $x > 0$ and $y < 0$, then

$$x \cdot y < 0 \cdot y, \qquad ({}^{-}\text{M} >)$$
$$x \cdot y < 0. \qquad (\text{Zero-M})$$

The actual product of a positive and a negative number or of two negative numbers may be found by first obtaining the product of their absolute values. For example,

$${}^{-}8 \cdot 7 = {}^{-}(8 \cdot 7) \qquad (\text{Neg-M})$$
$$= {}^{-}(|8| \cdot |7|), \quad \text{or } {}^{-}56.$$

We may also use absolute value to give the rules for multiplying positive and negative numbers.

$$x \cdot y = {}^{-}(|x| \cdot |y|) \quad \text{if } x \text{ and } y \text{ have opposite signs}$$
$$x \cdot y = |x| \cdot |y| \quad \text{if } x \text{ and } y \text{ have the same sign}$$

Exercises for Discussion

Tell which of the following statements are true and which are false. Correct the statements that you marked false.

1. $^-8 \leqq {}^-7$ True
2. $^-2 \leqq {}^-2 < 2$ True
3. $|3 - \pi| = 3 - \pi$ F; $|3-\pi| = \pi - 3$
4. $^-5 \cdot 3 = {}^-(|^-5| \cdot |3|)$ True
5. $|2 - \sqrt{3}| = {}^-(\sqrt{3} - 2)$ True
6. $|^-7| > |^-4|$ True

Express each of the following numbers without using absolute-value signs.

7. $|^-5 - {}^-6|$ $|^-5+6| = |1| = 1$
8. $|\sqrt{2} - 1.41|$ $\sqrt{2} - 1.41$
9. $|^-2| + |^-4|$ $2+4=6$

In Exercises 10–13, find all integral values of x that make each of the statements true.

10. $|x| = 4$ $\{^-4, 4\}$
11. $|x| < 5$ $^-5 < x < 5$, $\{^-4, ^-3, ^-2, ^-1, 0, 1, 2, 3, 4\}$
12. $3 < |x| < 10$
13. $|2x + 1| \leqq 21$
14. For each of the following pairs of values of x and y, compare the value of $|x| \cdot |y|$ with that of $|x \cdot y|$.
    (a) 5, 6 (b) $^-4$, 3 (c) 7, $^-8$ (d) $^-2$, $^-10$
15. In general, is $|x| \cdot |y|$ greater than, equal to, or less than $|x \cdot y|$?
    Always equal

Exercises

Tell which of the following statements are true and which are false. Correct the statements that you marked false.

1. $4 \geqq 4$ True
2. $^-5 < 5 \leqq 5$ True
3. $\frac{1}{\sqrt{3}} \geqq \frac{\sqrt{3}}{3}$ True
4. $|3 - 5| = 5 - 3$ True
5. $(6)(^-3) = |^-6| \cdot |^-3|$ F; $(^-6)(^-3) = |^-6| \cdot |^-3|$
6. $|2| \geqq |^-8|$ False, $|2| \leqq |^-8|$

Express each of the following numbers without using absolute-value signs.

7. $|^-5| - |^-6|$ $^-1$
8. $|10^{-6}|$ 10^{-6}
9. $|\sqrt{15} - 4|$ $4 - \sqrt{15}$
10. $|\frac{1}{3} - .333|$ $\frac{1}{3} - .333$
11. $\left|\frac{3}{4} - \frac{\pi}{4}\right|$ $\frac{\pi}{4} - \frac{3}{4}$
12. $|^-5 - {}^-5|$ 0
13. $|^-2 + {}^-4|$ 6
14. $|12 + {}^-9|$ 3
15. $|12| + |^-9|$ 21

For each statement below, find all integral values of x that make the statement true.

16. $|x + 1| = 3$ $\{2, ^-4\}$
17. $|x - 1| < 6$ $\{^-4, ^-3, ^-2, ^-1, 0, 1, 2, 3, 4, 5, 6\}$
18. $12 > |x + 1| > 2$ $\{^-12, ^-11, ^-10, ^-9, ^-8, ^-7, ^-6, ^-5, ^-4, 2, 3, 4, 5, 6, 7, 8, 9, 10\}$
19. $|2 - x| \leqq 7$ $\{^-5, ^-4, ^-3, ^-2, ^-1, 0, 1, 2, 3, 4, 5, 6, 7, 8, 9\}$
20. $|x - 6| = 9$ $\{^-3, 15\}$
21. $|x| + 3 = 10$ $\{^-7, 7\}$

Answers to Exercises for Discussion 12–14

12. If $3 < |x| < 10$, then
    $^-10 < x < {}^-3$ or $3 < x < 10$.
    $\{^-9, ^-8, ^-7, ^-6, ^-5, ^-4, 4, 5, 6, 7, 8, 9\}$
13. If $|2x + 1| \leqq 21$, then
    $^-21 \leqq 2x + 1 \leqq 21$,
    $^-22 \leqq 2x \leqq 20$,
    $^-11 \leqq x \leqq 10$.
    $\{^-11, ^-10, ^-9, ^-8, ^-7, ^-6, ^-5, ^-4, ^-3, ^-2, ^-1, 0, 1, 2, 3, 4, 5, 6, 7, 8, 9, 10\}$
14. (a) $|5| \cdot |6| = 5 \cdot 6 = 30$
    $|5 \cdot 6| = |30| = 30$
    (b) $|^-4| \cdot |3| = 4 \cdot 3 = 12$
    $|^-4 \cdot 3| = |^-12| = 12$
    (c) $|7| \cdot |^-8| = 7 \cdot 8 = 56$
    $|7 \cdot {}^-8| = |^-56| = 56$
    (d) $|^-2| \cdot |^-10| = 2 \cdot 10 = 20$
    $|^-2 \cdot {}^-10| = |20| = 20$

Exercises

With an above-average class, you may extend Exercise 17 to the general case $|x - a| < b$, showing that the solutions lie on a segment of the number line of length $2b$, with center at a.

For maximum insight and retention by the students, it is recommended that Exercises 22–30 should be done in class by the whole group.

Answers to Exercises 30(a), 30(b)

30. (a) If x and y are both nonnegative, or if both are nonpositive, then

$$|x| + |y| = |x + y|.$$

(b) If x and y have opposite signs, then

$$|x| + |y| > |x + y|.$$

Quiz

Tell which of the following statements are true and which are false. Correct the statements that you mark false.

1. $^-7 \leqq {}^-7 < 7$ (ans: T)
2. $|{}^-3| \cdot |7| = {}^-21$ (ans: F; $|{}^-3| \cdot |7| = 21$)
3. $|{}^-6 - {}^-6| = |6| - |{}^-6|$ (ans: T)
4. $|4 - \sqrt{17}| = 4 - \sqrt{17}$ (ans: F; $|4 - \sqrt{17}| = \sqrt{17} - 4$)

For each statement below, find all integral values of x that make the statement true.

5. $|x + 2| = 4$ (ans: $\{2, {}^-6\}$)
6. $|x + 3| \leqq 1$ (ans: $\{{}^-4, {}^-3, {}^-2\}$)

1-5 THE INTEGERS AND THE RATIONAL NUMBERS

You may emphasize in this section the density property of the rationals, a property not possessed by the integers. The class can prove, using the properties already listed, that if a and b are any two rational numbers, with $a < b$, then their arithmetic average, $(a + b)/2$, is a rational number which lies between them.

$$a < b$$
$$\frac{a}{2} < \frac{b}{2}$$
$$\frac{a}{2} + \frac{a}{2} < \frac{a}{2} + \frac{b}{2}$$
$$a < \frac{a+b}{2}$$

A similar proof may be shown for

$$\frac{a+b}{2} < b.$$

Therefore,

$$a < \frac{a+b}{2} < b.$$

In Exercises 22–29, compare the value of $|x| + |y|$ with the value of $|x + y|$ for each pair of values of x and y.

22. $(7, 10)$ $|7|+|10|=|7+10|$
23. $({}^-8, 6)$ $|{}^-8|+|6|>|{}^-8+6|$
24. $(9, {}^-4)$ $|9|+|{}^-4|>|9+{}^-4|$
25. $(0, 12)$ $|0|+|12|=|0+12|$
26. $({}^-5, {}^-4)$ $|{}^-5|+|{}^-4|=|{}^-5+{}^-4|$
27. $({}^-13, {}^-5)$ $|{}^-13|+|{}^-5|=|{}^-13+{}^-5|$
28. $(0, {}^-9)$ $|0|+|{}^-9|=|0+{}^-9|$
29. $({}^-30, {}^-12)$ $|{}^-30|+|{}^-12|=|{}^-30+{}^-12|$

30. Use the results of Exercises 22–29 to answer each of the following questions.

(a) For what values of x and y is it true that $|x| + |y| = |x + y|$?

(b) For what values of x and y is it true that $|x| + |y| > |x + y|$?

(c) Are there any values of x and y for which it is true that

$$|x| + |y| < |x + y|?$$ *No*

(d) Make a general statement that is true for all real numbers x and y, comparing the value of $|x| + |y|$ with that of $|x + y|$. *For all real numbers x and y, $|x|+|y| \geqq |x+y|$.*

1-5 THE INTEGERS AND THE RATIONAL NUMBERS

The system of integers is a subsystem of the real number system, and consists of positive integers, negative integers, and zero. If we imagine the integers arranged in a line as indicated below, they will extend endlessly in both directions.

$$\ldots, {}^-10^9, \ldots, {}^-4, {}^-3, {}^-2, {}^-1, 0, 1, 2, 3, 4, \ldots, 10^9, \ldots$$

In this line, the positive integers are to the right of 0, and the negative integers are to the left of 0.

Because the system of integers is a subsystem of the real number system, we might suppose that the eight basic properties of the real number system are also valid for the system of integers. This is almost, but not entirely, true. Clearly, the commutative, associative, and distributive laws are true. Since the sum of two integers is always an integer, *the system of integers is closed with respect to addition.* It is also *closed with respect to multiplication,* because the product of two integers is always an integer. The identity elements of the real number system, 0 and 1, are also integers. Each integer has an additive inverse which is an integer. Thus, $^-8$ is the additive inverse of 8, and 113 is the additive inverse of $^-113$. However, not every nonzero integer has a multiplicative inverse which is an integer. For example, the multiplicative inverse of the integer 8 is $\frac{1}{8}$, and $\frac{1}{8}$ is not an integer. Therefore, the *multiplicative inverse property is not valid for the system of integers.*

The order properties are valid for this system. We conclude that, with the exception of the multiplicative inverse property, the eight basic properties of the real number system are true for the system of integers.

In addition to these eight, there is one more property that applies exclusively to the system of integers. Roughly speaking, this is the property which says that every positive integer may be reached by starting with 1 and counting 2, 3, 4, and so on, in order up to the given integer. For example, we arrive at 9 by counting 1, 2, 3, 4, 5, 6, 7, 8, 9. By *counting,* we mean that after every integer n, we name its *successor,* $n + 1$. It would take a long time to count to the number 10^{100}, but we can imagine that it could be done. This new property is really a property of the set P of all positive integers. It is called the *induction property* and will be discussed later in the text.

Another important subsystem of the real number system is the rational number system. We recall that a number is called *rational* if it can be expressed as a quotient of two integers. For example, each of the numbers

$$\frac{3}{5}, \quad \frac{^-6}{8}, \quad \frac{4}{3}, \quad \frac{^-100}{^-101}, \quad 3.14159$$

is rational. Each integer n is also a rational number since $n = n/1$. Consequently, the rational number system contains the system of integers.

Each rational number can be expressed in many different ways as a quotient of two integers. For example, 2/4, 3/6, 1/2, and 13/26 are different numerals for the same rational number, and 6/14, $^-15/^-35$, 3/7, 21/49, and $^-3/^-7$ are different ways of representing the same rational number. If we are given two quotients of integers, we can tell whether they represent the same rational number by the following rule. If a, b, c, and d are integers with $b \neq 0$ and $d \neq 0$, then

$$\frac{a}{b} = \frac{c}{d} \quad \textit{if, and only if,} \quad a \cdot d = b \cdot c.$$

For example,

$$\frac{3}{7} = \frac{6}{14} \quad \text{since} \quad 3 \cdot 14 = 7 \cdot 6, \quad \text{or } 42.$$

A nonzero rational number a/b is said to be expressed in *simplest form* if $b > 0$ and the integers a and b are relatively prime, that is, if the greatest common divisor (g.c.d.) of a and b is 1. For example,

It may be instructive to show how to find as many rational numbers as you like between any two given rational numbers. For example, to find one rational number between $\frac{1}{2}$ and $\frac{1}{3}$, write them as $\frac{3}{6}$ and $\frac{2}{6}$, then multiply each by $\frac{2}{2}$, getting

$$\tfrac{6}{12} > \tfrac{5}{12} > \tfrac{4}{12};$$

to find two rationals, multiply by $\frac{3}{3}$, obtaining $\frac{9}{18} > \frac{8}{18}$ or $\frac{7}{18} > \frac{6}{18}$. To find three rationals between $\frac{3}{6}$ and $\frac{2}{6}$, multiply each by $\frac{4}{4}$, getting $\frac{12}{24}$ and $\frac{8}{24}$ and thus exhibiting $\frac{9}{24}$, $\frac{10}{24}$, and $\frac{11}{24}$ between $\frac{3}{6}$ and $\frac{2}{6}$.

It might be well to review the fact that each rational number has a decimal representation which either terminates or is infinite and repeating. You could have the student give the decimal representations of $\frac{5}{12}$ and $\frac{2}{13}$, found by division. Then have him reverse the problem and find the common fractions from decimals, such as .263 and .262626 . . .

The class could be asked to describe a method for writing an irrational number that lies between 1.2 and 1.3. (ans: Any decimal greater than 1.2 and less than 1.3 that never terminates or repeats in a pattern.)

the rational number 3/7 is expressed in simplest form, since $7 > 0$ and the g.c.d. of 3 and 7 is 1. We shall not prove it, but the simplest form of a rational number is *unique*. If a/b is the simplest form of a rational number, then any other representation has the form na/nb for some nonzero integer n.

The rational number system is *closed* with respect to the operations of addition, multiplication, subtraction, and division (except by zero). In other words, if a and b are rational numbers, then so are $a + b$, $a \cdot b$, $a - b$, and $a \div b$, if $b \neq 0$. Since the opposite of each rational number is rational and the reciprocal of each nonzero rational number is also rational, the eight basic properties of the real number system are also valid for the rational number system.

Exercises for Discussion

If time is limited, it is suggested that at least Exercises for Discussion 1–8 be covered.

Exercises for Discussion

Which, if any, of the following systems are closed?

1. The set of integers with respect to subtraction
   Yes. The difference of two integers is an integer.
2. The set of positive integers with respect to subtraction
   No. The difference of two positive integers need not be a positive integer.
3. The set of negative integers with respect to addition
   Yes. The sum of two negative integers is a negative integer.
4. The set of integers with respect to division
   No. The quotient of two integers need not be an integer.
5. The set of negative integers with respect to multiplication
   No. The product of two negative integers is not a negative integer.
6. The set of positive rational numbers with respect to division
   Yes. The quotient of two positive rational numbers is a positive rational number.
7. The set of nonpositive rational numbers with respect to multiplication
   No. The product of two nonpositive rational numbers may be positive.
8. The set of even integers with respect to addition
   Yes. The sum of two even integers is an even integer.

Write each of the following rational numbers as a quotient of integers, and express each answer in simplest form.

9. $\frac{24}{64}$ $\frac{3}{8}$ 10. $3\frac{9}{15}$ $\frac{18}{5}$ 11. 3.14 $\frac{157}{50}$ 12. $\frac{171}{711}$ $\frac{19}{79}$

In Exercises 13–16, perform the indicated operations, and express each answer in simplest form.

13. $\frac{3}{4} - \frac{2}{3}$ $\frac{9}{12} - \frac{8}{12} = \frac{1}{12}$

14. $\frac{3}{4} \cdot \frac{^-2}{3}$ $\frac{^-1}{2}$

15. $\frac{3}{4} \div \frac{^-2}{3}$ $\frac{3}{4} \cdot \frac{^-3}{2} = \frac{^-9}{8}$

16. $\frac{^-5}{12} \cdot \frac{21}{45}$ $\frac{^-1}{4} \cdot \frac{7}{9} = \frac{^-7}{36}$

17. What is the largest integer that is less than $\frac{173}{19}$? 9, since $\frac{173}{19} = 9\frac{2}{19}$
18. Between which two consecutive integers does $\frac{173}{19}$ lie? $9 < \frac{173}{19} < 10$
19. Which integer is nearest to $\frac{173}{19}$? 9
20. Is there a largest rational number which is less than $\frac{173}{19}$? No

Exercises

Write each of the following rational numbers as a quotient of integers, and express each answer in simplest form.

1. 1.414 $\frac{707}{500}$
2. $\frac{^-65}{1001}$ $\frac{^-5}{77}$
3. $\frac{98}{1008}$ $\frac{7}{72}$
4. $\frac{^-125}{500}$ $\frac{^-1}{4}$

Perform the indicated operations, and express each answer in simplest form.

5. $\frac{9}{143} - \frac{4}{77}$ $\frac{1}{91}$
6. $\frac{66}{65} \times \frac{13}{44}$ $\frac{3}{10}$
7. $\frac{4}{15} - \frac{7}{20}$ $\frac{^-1}{12}$
8. $^-\frac{3}{8} + \frac{5}{12}$ $\frac{1}{24}$
9. $^-\frac{38}{45} \div \frac{57}{70}$ $\frac{^-28}{27}$
10. $\frac{4}{39} - \frac{5}{52} + \frac{6}{65}$ $\frac{77}{780}$
11. $\frac{12}{75} - \frac{7}{60} - \frac{11}{30}$ $\frac{^-97}{300}$
12. $(\frac{4}{5} + \frac{3}{15}) \div {^-\frac{5}{9}}$ $\frac{^-9}{5}$
13. $(\frac{5}{2} - \frac{5}{3}) \times \frac{36}{15}$ 2
14. $(\frac{1}{4} + \frac{5}{12}) \div (\frac{3}{4} - \frac{2}{9})$ $\frac{24}{19}$
15. $(2\frac{1}{8} - 1\frac{5}{16}) \div 3$ $\frac{13}{48}$
16. $(\frac{4}{7} \cdot \frac{49}{40}) + (\frac{78}{15} \div \frac{91}{35})$ $\frac{27}{10}$
17. $(\frac{4}{17} \times \frac{85}{64}) + (\frac{111}{52} \times \frac{39}{74})$ $\frac{23}{16}$
18. $\frac{9}{25} - \frac{123}{75} - \frac{17}{20}$ $\frac{^-213}{100}$
19. $\frac{7}{8}(\frac{19}{57} - \frac{1}{3})$ 0
20. $(\frac{17}{68} - \frac{1}{4}) \div {^-\frac{13}{17}}$ 0

In Exercises 21–27, which, if any, of the systems are closed?

21. The set of rational numbers with respect to subtraction Yes
22. The set of positive rational numbers with respect to subtraction No
23. The set of negative rational numbers with respect to addition Yes
24. The set of rational numbers with respect to division No
25. The set of negative rational numbers with respect to multiplication No
26. The set of nonzero rational numbers with respect to division Yes
27. The set of odd integers with respect to multiplication Yes
28. Name six rational numbers between 0 and 1, between 0 and $\frac{1}{2}$, between 0 and $\frac{1}{4}$, between 0 and $\frac{1}{10}$, and between 0 and a when $a > 0$.
29. How many rational numbers are there between any two rational numbers? Infinitely many
30. What is the largest integer that is less than $\frac{137}{56}$? 2
31. What is the smallest integer that is greater than $\frac{137}{56}$? 3
32. What integer is nearest to $\frac{137}{56}$? 2
33. Can you find a largest rational number which is less than $\frac{137}{56}$? No
34. Can you find a smallest rational number which is greater than $\frac{137}{56}$? No

Answer to Exercise 28

28. $\frac{1}{7}, \frac{2}{7}, \frac{3}{7}, \frac{4}{7}, \frac{5}{7}, \frac{6}{7}$; $\frac{1}{14}, \frac{2}{14}, \frac{3}{14}, \frac{4}{14}, \frac{5}{14}, \frac{6}{14}$; $\frac{1}{28}, \frac{2}{28}, \frac{3}{28}, \frac{4}{28}, \frac{5}{28}, \frac{6}{28}$; $\frac{1}{70}, \frac{2}{70}, \frac{3}{70}, \frac{4}{70}, \frac{5}{70}, \frac{6}{70}$; $\frac{2a}{7}, \frac{3a}{7}, \frac{4a}{7}, \frac{5a}{7}, \frac{6a}{7}$.

Quiz

Perform the indicated operations, and express each answer in its simplest form.

1. $\frac{56}{33} \cdot \frac{66}{14}$ (ans: 8)
2. $^-\frac{7}{8} + \frac{3}{24}$ (ans: $^-\frac{3}{4}$)
3. $\frac{4}{25} - \frac{3}{20}$ (ans: $\frac{1}{100}$)
4. $^-\frac{46}{21} \div \frac{23}{7}$ (ans: $^-\frac{2}{3}$)

Which, if any, of the following systems are closed?

5. The set of integers with respect to multiplication (ans: yes)
6. The set of odd integers with respect to subtraction (ans: no)

1-6 IRRATIONAL NUMBERS

If you have stressed the countability of the rational numbers, you may want to go into the proof found in *A Survey of Modern Algebra*, by Birkhoff and MacLane (Macmillan Co.). This proof shows that the set of all real numbers is not countable. Therefore, since the subset of rationals is countable, the subset of irrationals must not be countable.

To help the students answer the question, "What positive rational numbers have rational square roots?" one may begin with specific cases, such as the following:

$$\frac{4}{9} = \left(\frac{2}{3}\right)^2$$

because $4 = 2^2$ and $9 = 3^2$; $\frac{4}{5}$ cannot be written as

$$\left(\frac{a}{b}\right)^2, \quad a \text{ and } b \text{ integers},$$

because 5 is not the square of an integer. Hence, $\sqrt{\frac{4}{5}}$ is an irrational number.

It may be shown that $4 + \sqrt{3}$ is irrational by assuming that $4 + \sqrt{3}$ is rational. If

$$4 + \sqrt{3} = \frac{p}{q}, \quad p \text{ and } q \text{ integers},$$

△

35. Is the set $\{^-1, 0, 1\}$ closed with respect to any of the operations of arithmetic? If so, name them. *Yes. Multiplication*

36. For which operations of arithmetic is the set of multiples of 3 closed? *Addition, subtraction, multiplication*

37. If $S = \{x \mid x = 3^n, n \text{ a positive integer}\}$, is S closed with respect to any arithmetic operations? If so, name them. *Yes. Multiplication*

38. Describe a subset of the rational numbers which is closed
(a) under $+$, $-$, and $\times$, but not $\div$. *The set of all integers*
(b) under $\times$, but not $+$. *The set of odd integers*
(c) under $+$ and $-$, but not $\times$. $\{x = \frac{p}{2} \mid p = 0, \pm 1, \pm 2, \ldots\}$

1-6 IRRATIONAL NUMBERS

There are many real numbers which cannot be expressed as a quotient of two integers. Such real numbers are called *irrational numbers.* For example, it may be shown that $\sqrt{2}$, π, $\sqrt[3]{7} - 3$, and $\sqrt{29}/4$ are irrational numbers.

We may obtain many irrational numbers by taking square roots, cube roots, and so on, of positive rational numbers. The real number y is called a *square root* of x if $y^2 = x$ and $x \geqq 0$; a *cube root* of x if $y^3 = x$; and so on. Thus, since $4^2 = 16$, 4 is a square root of 16; and since $4^3 = 64$, 4 is a cube root of 64. One of the properties of the real number system is that every positive real number has a positive square root, cube root, and so on.

There is an interesting question about rational numbers: What positive rational numbers have *rational* square roots? In other words, under what conditions is a given rational number the square of another rational number? To answer this question, let a/b be a positive rational number expressed in simplest form. If there exists another positive rational number x/y, also in simplest form, such that

$$\left(\frac{x}{y}\right)^2 = \frac{a}{b},$$

then we must have

$$\frac{x^2}{y^2} = \frac{a}{b}.$$

Now, if the integers x and y are relatively prime, then so are the integers x^2 and y^2. Hence, the rational number x^2/y^2 is expressed in simplest form. Since x^2/y^2 and a/b are simplest forms for the same rational number, and the simplest form of a rational number is unique, we must have

$$x^2 = a \quad \text{and} \quad y^2 = b.$$

Therefore, we can make the following statement.

The positive rational number a/b expressed in simplest form is the square of another rational number if, and only if, the integers a and b are squares of integers.

The squares of the positive integers, in order, are

$$1,\ 4,\ 9,\ 16,\ 25,\ 36,\ 49,\ 64,\ 81,\ 100,\ 121,\ 144, \ldots$$

Hence, only rational numbers such as

$$\tfrac{4}{9},\ \tfrac{36}{81},\ \tfrac{121}{144}$$

have rational square roots.

Knowing which rational numbers have rational square roots, we can easily give examples of irrational numbers. All we need do is select a rational number in simplest form, such as $\frac{7}{3}$ or $\frac{5}{1}$, for which the two integers involved are not both perfect squares. Then the positive square root of the number must be irrational. For example,

$$\sqrt{\tfrac{7}{3}} \quad \text{and} \quad \sqrt{5}$$

are irrational numbers. We recall that for a positive number x, $\sqrt{x}$ designates the *positive square* root of x. *Negative numbers do not have real square roots.*

If x is a rational number and y is an irrational number, then $x + y$ must be irrational. To see that this is so, let $z = x + y$. Then $y = z - x$, and y is rational if both z and x are rational, because the set of rational numbers is closed under subtraction. Since we assumed that y was irrational, z must be irrational. Similarly, if x is a nonzero rational number and y is irrational, then xy is irrational. Neither the sum nor the product of two irrational numbers need be irrational. For example, $3 - \sqrt{2}$ and $3 + \sqrt{2}$ are two irrational numbers whose sum and product are both rational:

$$(3 - \sqrt{2}) + (3 + \sqrt{2}) = 6,$$
$$(3 - \sqrt{2}) \times (3 + \sqrt{2}) = 3^2 - (\sqrt{2})^2, \quad \text{or } 7.$$

Hence, the set of irrational numbers is *not closed* under either addition or multiplication.

then

$$\sqrt{3} = \frac{p}{q} - 4,$$

which is rational. Therefore, $\sqrt{3}$ is rational, which is not true, so the assumption is false. This reveals that $4 + \sqrt{3}$ is irrational.

You may use the examples below to lead up to the generalization that if a and b are rational, and c is a rational number greater than 0, then

$$(a + b\sqrt{c}) + (a - b\sqrt{c})$$

and

$$(a + b\sqrt{c}) \cdot (a - b\sqrt{c})$$

are rational.

$$(3 + 2\sqrt{5}) + (3 - 2\sqrt{5})$$
$$(3 + 2\sqrt{5}) - (3 - 2\sqrt{5})$$
$$(3 + 2\sqrt{5}) + (3 + 2\sqrt{5})$$
$$(3 + 2\sqrt{5})(3 - 2\sqrt{5})$$
$$(3 + 2\sqrt{5})(3 + 2\sqrt{5})$$
$$(7 - \sqrt{3}) + (7 + \sqrt{3})$$
$$(7 - \sqrt{3})(7 + \sqrt{3})$$
$$(7 - \sqrt{3})^2$$

You may wish to show the students how to find a rational approximation of $\sqrt{153}$. The table on page 614 approximates the square roots of the first one hundred integers. We *simplify* $\sqrt{153}$ so that we can use the table. Thus,

$$\begin{aligned}\sqrt{153} &= \sqrt{9 \cdot 17}\\ &= \sqrt{9}\cdot\sqrt{17}\\ &= 3\sqrt{17}\end{aligned}$$

and

$$\sqrt{153} \doteq 3(4.123), \quad \text{or } 12.369.$$

Under certain circumstances the instruction "simplify" could be confusing. Here, of course, we have agreed that $\sqrt{x}$, x any positive integer, is not in its simplest form if x is divisible by a perfect square integer, so we have for the moment defined what we mean by "simplify $\sqrt{180}$." However, if at some time a student says that $\sqrt{180}$ is the answer to a question, he is not necessarily wrong for failing to mention that $\sqrt{180} = 6\sqrt{5}$, since it is not always required to reduce every answer to its simplest terms.

It is important to distinguish between "the greatest integer contained in" and "the closest integer to." For example, the closest integer to 4.98 is 5, but when the retailer marks the price "$4.98," he expects the customer to think that the largest number of whole dollars needed is 4.

Since $(\sqrt{x}\sqrt{y})^2 = (\sqrt{x})^2(\sqrt{y})^2$, or xy, for every pair x, y of positive real numbers, it follows that

$$\sqrt{xy} = \sqrt{x}\sqrt{y}$$

for every pair x, y of positive real numbers. For example,

$$\sqrt{9 \times 2} = \sqrt{9}\sqrt{2}, \quad \text{or } 3\sqrt{2}.$$

Thus, $\sqrt{18} = 3\sqrt{2}$.

This example illustrates an interesting fact about the set of positive integers: Every positive integer can be expressed as a product of two integers; the first is a *perfect square* and the second is a *square-free* integer. An integer is said to be square-free if none of its integral factors other than 1 is a perfect square. For example, 6 and 14 are square-free whereas 24 is not, since $24 = 4 \times 6$ and 4 is a perfect square.

We shall say that the square root of a positive integer is expressed in *simplest form* if it is expressed as the product of an integer and the square root of a square-free integer. For example, the simplest form of $\sqrt{18}$ is $3\sqrt{2}$.

Problem. Find the simplest form of $\sqrt{180}$.

Solution. Evidently 4 is a factor of 180 and $180 = 4 \times 45$. In turn, 9 is a factor of 45 and $180 = 4 \times 9 \times 5$. The remaining integer, 5, is square-free. Hence, $180 = 36 \times 5$ and $\sqrt{180} = 6\sqrt{5}$.

Another important property of the real number system is that *every real number other than an integer lies between two consecutive integers.* According to this property, if r is a real number that is not an integer, then there exists an integer n such that

$$n < r < n + 1.$$

The integer n is called the *greatest integer* in r. The notation $[r]$ is used in mathematics to designate the greatest integer in the real number r. Naturally, $[n] = n$ if n is an integer.

For example,

$$\begin{aligned}[\sqrt{2}] &= 1, \quad \text{since} \quad 1 < \sqrt{2} < 2;\\ [\pi] &= 3, \quad \text{since} \quad 3 < \pi < 4;\\ [3 - \sqrt{95}] &= {}^-7, \quad \text{since} \quad {}^-7 < 3 - \sqrt{95} < {}^-6.\end{aligned}$$

This new property of the real number system allows us to approximate every irrational number by a rational number with any desired degree of accuracy.

For example, either 1 or 2 is a rough approximation of $\sqrt{2}$, since $1 < \sqrt{2} < 2$. To obtain a better approximation of $\sqrt{2}$, consider the number $10\sqrt{2}$. What is $[10\sqrt{2}]$? To answer this question, we look at the integer $(10\sqrt{2})^2$, or 200. The largest perfect-square integer less than 200 is 196, which is 14^2. Hence,

$$14^2 < 200 < 15^2$$

and, taking square roots, we have

$$14 < 10\sqrt{2} < 15.$$

Finally, if we multiply each member of the inequality by $\frac{1}{10}$, we obtain

$$1.4 < \sqrt{2} < 1.5.$$

Therefore, either 1.4 or 1.5 is a one-decimal-place approximation of $\sqrt{2}$. To obtain a better approximation of $\sqrt{2}$, we find $[100\sqrt{2}]$. Obviously $(100\sqrt{2})^2 = 20{,}000$ and $140^2 < 20{,}000 < 150^2$, by our work above. It may be shown that the *largest* perfect-square integer less than 20,000 is 19,881, which is 141^2. Hence,

$$141^2 < 20{,}000 < 142^2,$$
$$141 < 100\sqrt{2} < 142,$$

and, finally,

$$1.41 < \sqrt{2} < 1.42.$$

Consequently, either 1.41 or 1.42 is a two-decimal-place approximation of $\sqrt{2}$.

Exercises for Discussion

1. Find the sum and the product of each of the following pairs of irrational numbers.

   $(5+\sqrt{3})+(5-\sqrt{3})=10$ $\quad$ $(3\sqrt{2}+\sqrt{7})+(3\sqrt{2}-\sqrt{7})=6\sqrt{2}$

   (a) $5+\sqrt{3},\ 5-\sqrt{3}$ $\quad$ (b) $3\sqrt{2}+\sqrt{7},\ 3\sqrt{2}-\sqrt{7}$

   $(5+\sqrt{3})(5-\sqrt{3})=25-3=22$ $\quad$ $(3\sqrt{2}+\sqrt{7})(3\sqrt{2}-\sqrt{7})=18-7=11$

2. Find the simplest form of each of the following expressions.

   (a) $\sqrt{98}$ $\sqrt{49\cdot 2}=7\sqrt{2}$ $\quad$ (b) $\sqrt{847}$ $\sqrt{121\cdot 7}=11\sqrt{7}$

3. Find each of the following greatest integers.

   (a) $[3+\sqrt{5}]$ 5 $\quad$ (b) $[-\sqrt{10}]$ -4

4. For which numbers in Exercise 3 is the *greatest* integer also the *nearest* integer? For (a) but not (b)

The fact that $\sqrt{2}$ is an irrational number which can be located on intervals of shorter and shorter length is very important. Even though the arithmetic involved is tedious, it is suggested that it be done in class in order to demonstrate clearly the principles involved, and to give students the opportunity of asking questions if they do not understand. Few students will subject themselves to such a mathematical procedure alone at home. It will help them if they are shown that a process is established for locating $\sqrt{2}$ in shorter and shorter intervals, each a subinterval of all the preceding ones. This may be called a chain of nested shrinking intervals. It is a fact of analysis that such a sequence contains one, and only one, common point: the point corresponding to the irrational number $\sqrt{2}$.

In Exercise for Discussion 6, a reason should be shown for changing the form of

$$\sqrt{\frac{2}{3}}$$

by first asking for a rational approximation to

$$\frac{\sqrt{2}}{\sqrt{3}}.$$

This may be done by long division.

```
               .816
1.732 )1.414 000
        1 385 6
        -------
          28 40
          17 32
          ------
          11 080
          10 392
          ------
             688
```

$$\frac{\sqrt{2}}{\sqrt{3}} \doteq .816$$

However, since

$$\frac{\sqrt{2}}{\sqrt{3}} = \frac{\sqrt{2}}{\sqrt{3}} \cdot \frac{\sqrt{3}}{\sqrt{3}}$$

$$= \frac{\sqrt{6}}{3}$$

and

$$\frac{\sqrt{6}}{3} \doteq \frac{2.449}{3}$$

(from the table on page 614) it can be seen that $\sqrt{2}/\sqrt{3} \doteq .816$ without using long division. The student should understand that he needs to rationalize the denominator only in order to approximate, and only when it will allow him to replace a tedious long division with a quick, short division.

Answers to Exercise 24(a), 24(b)

24. (a) $1 < \sqrt{3} < 2$. Therefore, either 1 or 2 is an integral approximation.

(b) $17 < 10\sqrt{3} < 18$. Therefore, either 1.7 or 1.8 is a one-decimal-place approximation.

5. (a) What is the largest integer that is less than $\sqrt{7}$? *2*
(b) What is the smallest integer that is greater than $\sqrt{7}$? *3*
(c) What integer is nearest to $\sqrt{7}$? *3*
(d) Can you find a largest rational number which is less than $\sqrt{7}$? *No*
(e) Can you find a smallest rational number which is greater than $\sqrt{7}$? *No*

6. A positive rational number can be expressed as the product of a perfect-square rational number and a square-free integer. For example,

$$\sqrt{\tfrac{2}{3}} = \sqrt{\tfrac{6}{9}} = \sqrt{\tfrac{1}{9} \cdot 6} = \tfrac{1}{3}\sqrt{6}$$

and

$$\sqrt{\tfrac{8}{5}} = \sqrt{\tfrac{40}{25}} = \sqrt{\tfrac{4}{25} \cdot 10} = \tfrac{2}{5}\sqrt{10}.$$

Write each of the following square roots of rational numbers as a rational number times the square root of a square-free integer.

(a) $\sqrt{\frac{1}{5}}$ $\sqrt{\frac{5}{25}} = \sqrt{\frac{1}{25} \cdot 5} = \frac{1}{5}\sqrt{5}$ (b) $\sqrt{\frac{3}{8}}$ $\sqrt{\frac{6}{16}} = \sqrt{\frac{1}{16} \cdot 6} = \frac{1}{4}\sqrt{6}$ (c) $\sqrt{\frac{4}{7}}$ $\sqrt{\frac{28}{49}} = \sqrt{\frac{4}{49} \cdot 7} = \frac{2}{7}\sqrt{7}$ (d) $\sqrt{\frac{2}{11}}$ $\sqrt{\frac{22}{121}} = \sqrt{\frac{1}{121} \cdot 22} = \frac{1}{11}\sqrt{22}$

Exercises

Find the simplest form of each of the following square roots.

1. $\sqrt{180}$ *$6\sqrt{5}$* **2.** $\sqrt{3872}$ *$44\sqrt{2}$* **3.** $\sqrt{529}$ *23*
4. $\sqrt{210}$ *$\sqrt{210}$* **5.** $\sqrt{3179}$ *$17\sqrt{11}$* **6.** $\sqrt{252}$ *$6\sqrt{7}$*
7. $\sqrt{2475}$ *$15\sqrt{11}$* **8.** $\sqrt{363}$ *$11\sqrt{3}$* **9.** $\sqrt{1001}$ *$\sqrt{1001}$*

We say that the square root of a positive rational number is expressed in simplest form if it is expressed as the product of a rational number and the square root of a square-free integer. Find the simplest form of each of the following square roots.

10. $\sqrt{\frac{7}{20}}$ *$\frac{1}{10}\sqrt{35}$* **11.** $\sqrt{1\frac{3}{5}}$ *$\frac{2}{5}\sqrt{10}$* **12.** $\sqrt{\frac{243}{13}}$ *$\frac{9}{13}\sqrt{39}$* **13.** $\sqrt{\frac{49}{24}}$ *$\frac{7}{12}\sqrt{6}$*
14. $\sqrt{\frac{169}{180}}$ *$\frac{13}{30}\sqrt{5}$* **15.** $\sqrt{\frac{148}{3}}$ *$\frac{2}{3}\sqrt{111}$* **16.** $\sqrt{\frac{35}{6}}$ *$\frac{1}{6}\sqrt{210}$* **17.** $\sqrt{\frac{77}{60}}$ *$\frac{1}{30}\sqrt{1155}$*

In Exercises 18–23, find each of the greatest integers.

18. $[\sqrt{19}]$ *4* **19.** $[^{-}\sqrt[3]{13}]$ *$^{-}3$* **20.** $[\sqrt[3]{^{-}13}]$ *$^{-}3$*
21. $\left[\frac{^{-}17}{5}\right]$ *$^{-}4$* **22.** $[\sqrt[7]{2}]$ *1* **23.** $[39.9995]$ *39*

24. Find approximations to $\sqrt{3}$ by determining
(a) the consecutive integers between which $\sqrt{3}$ lies.
(b) the consecutive integers between which $10\sqrt{3}$ lies (the largest integer which has a square less than 300 and the smallest integer which has a square greater than 300).
(c) the consecutive integers between which $100\sqrt{3}$ lies. *$173 < 100\sqrt{3} < 174$. Therefore, either 1.73 or 1.74 is a two-decimal-place approximation.*

△——————————————————————————

25. (a) Between which two consecutive integers does $^-\sqrt[3]{100}$ lie? $^-5 < ^-\sqrt[3]{100} < ^-4$
    (b) What is the largest integer that is less than $^-\sqrt[3]{100}$? $^-5$
    (c) Is there a largest rational number which is less than $^-\sqrt[3]{100}$? No

1-7 INTEGRAL EXPONENTS

In exponential notation, introduced into mathematics in the seventeenth century by the Frenchman René Descartes, x^6 designates the product $x \cdot x \cdot x \cdot x \cdot x \cdot x$. This notation allows the astronomer to express the approximate distance from the earth to the farthest visible star very simply as 6×10^{19} miles. Without exponential notation, the astronomer would have to indicate this distance by writing

$$60,000,000,000,000,000,000$$

(in words, 60 quintillion). Today's physicist is able to describe the diameter of an electron as

$$1 \times 10^{-13}, \quad \text{or} \quad \frac{1}{10^{13}} \text{ centimeter,}$$

instead of as .0000000000001 centimeter. Whoever reads the results of the physicist's experiments does not have to count twelve zeros in order to find out that the diameter of an electron is 1 ten-trillionth of a centimeter.

By definition,

$$x^n = \overbrace{x \cdot x \cdot \ldots \cdot x}^{n \text{ factors}}, \quad n \text{ any positive integer,}$$

for every real number x. The number n is called the *exponent* of x in x^n, and x^n is called the nth power of x. For convenience, we define

$$x^0 = 1 \quad \textit{for every nonzero real number } x.$$

Negative exponents can be defined in the following manner.

DEFINITION OF NEGATIVE EXPONENTS

The equation

$$x^{-n} = \frac{1}{x^n} \qquad \textit{(Def-Neg. Exp.)}$$

is true for every positive integer n and every nonzero real number x.

Quiz

Find the simplest form of each of the following square roots.

1. $\sqrt{112}$ (ans: $4\sqrt{7}$)

2. $\sqrt{250}$ (ans: $5\sqrt{10}$)

3. $\sqrt{127}$ (ans: $\sqrt{127}$)

4. $\sqrt{\dfrac{3}{10}}$ $\left(\text{ans: } \dfrac{\sqrt{30}}{10}\right)$

5. $\sqrt{\dfrac{12}{5}}$ $\left(\text{ans: } \dfrac{2\sqrt{15}}{5}\right)$

1-7 INTEGRAL EXPONENTS

If the material contained in Section 1-7 has been covered in the first year of algebra, it can be assigned for reading without prior explanation in class. However, not all students will have had sufficient experience with exponents, and not all who have will remember what they learned. The definition of x^n may be illustrated with specific values of x. For example, 3^4 is defined to mean $3 \cdot 3 \cdot 3 \cdot 3$ and 2^3 is defined to mean $2 \cdot 2 \cdot 2$. Show that $2^3 \cdot 2^4$ becomes 2^7 and $2^7 \div 2^3$ becomes 2^4, using the associative laws of multiplication, and that $(3 \cdot 2)^4$ becomes $3^4 \cdot 2^4$ by the commutative and associative laws of multiplication. Many students get $x^3 \cdot x^4 = x^7$ but think $2^3 \cdot 2^4$ is 4^7 instead of 2^7.

After illustrating the five laws of exponents with numerical as well as variable bases, you could extend the definition of x^n to include $n = 0$, and you may wish to use the ideas presented in Exercises for Discussion 1-3.

In other words, x^{-n} is the *reciprocal* of x^n. Since y/x is the reciprocal of x/y, it follows that

$$\left(\frac{x}{y}\right)^{-n} = \left(\frac{y}{x}\right)^{n}$$

for every integer n and all nonzero real numbers x and y. Therefore, we have defined the nth power of every nonzero real number for every integer n, whether n is positive, negative, or zero.

You are undoubtedly aware of certain basic rules for working with powers of numbers. These rules are called the *laws of exponents*, and may be stated in the following way.

LAWS OF EXPONENTS

$$x^m \cdot x^n = x^{m+n} \qquad (LE\text{-}1)$$

$$\frac{x^m}{x^n} = x^{m-n} \qquad (LE\text{-}2)$$

$$(x^m)^n = x^{mn} \qquad (LE\text{-}3)$$

$$(x \cdot y)^n = x^n \cdot y^n \qquad (LE\text{-}4)$$

$$\left(\frac{x}{y}\right)^n = \frac{x^n}{y^n} \qquad (LE\text{-}5)$$

The equations above are true for all integers m and n and all nonzero real numbers x and y.

We can sometimes use the laws of exponents to find simpler forms for algebraic expressions that have exponents. This process is illustrated in the following problem.

Problem. Simplify each of the following expressions.

(a) $\dfrac{2^6 \cdot 3^2}{2^4 \cdot 3^5}$ (b) $(a^{-3}b^2)^{-2}$ (c) $\left(\dfrac{5xy^3}{2x^5y^2}\right)^3$

Solution. We proceed in the following way.

(a)
$$\frac{2^6 \cdot 3^2}{2^4 \cdot 3^5} = \frac{2^6}{2^4} \cdot \frac{3^2}{3^5}$$

$$= 2^{6-4} \cdot 3^{2-5} \qquad \text{(LE-2)}$$

$$= 2^2 \cdot 3^{-3}$$

$$= 2^2 \cdot \frac{1}{3^3} \qquad \text{(Def-Neg. Exp.)}$$

$$= \frac{2^2}{3^3}, \quad \text{or} \quad \frac{4}{27}$$

(b) $$(a^{-3}b^{2})^{-2} = (a^{-3})^{-2}(b^{2})^{-2} \quad \text{(LE-4)}$$
$$= a^{6}b^{-4} \quad \text{(LE-3)}$$
$$= \frac{a^{6}}{b^{4}} \quad \text{(Def-Neg. Exp.)}$$

(c) $$\left(\frac{5xy^{3}}{2x^{5}y^{2}}\right)^{3} = \left(\frac{5}{2}\cdot\frac{x}{x^{5}}\cdot\frac{y^{3}}{y^{2}}\right)^{3}$$
$$= \left(\frac{5}{2}\,x^{1-5}y^{3-2}\right)^{3} \quad \text{(LE-2)}$$
$$= \left(\frac{5}{2}\,x^{-4}y^{1}\right)^{3}$$
$$= \left(\frac{5}{2}\right)^{3} x^{-12}y^{3} \quad \text{(LE-3), (LE-4)}$$
$$= \frac{125}{8}\cdot\frac{1}{x^{12}}\cdot y^{3} \quad \text{(LE-5), (Def-Neg. Exp.)}$$
$$= \frac{125y^{3}}{8x^{12}}$$

Exercises for Discussion

1. Use (LE-1) to find each of the following products.
   (a) $3^{7}\cdot 3^{0}$ $3^{7+0}=3^{7}$ (b) $(\frac{5}{6})^{0}(\frac{5}{6})^{4}$ $(\frac{5}{6})^{0+4}=(\frac{5}{6})^{4}$
2. Use (LE-2) to find each of the following quotients.
   (a) $\frac{3^{2}}{3^{2}}$ $3^{2-2}=3^{0}=1$ (b) $x^{n}\div x^{n},\quad x\neq 0$ $x^{n-n}=x^{0}=1$
3. Why is it convenient to define $x^{0} = 1$, if $x \neq 0$?

In Exercises 4–8, perform the indicated operations, and express each answer in simplest form. State the laws or definitions used.

4. $1^{0}+2^{0}+3^{0}$
   $1+1+1=3$ $(x^{0}=1)$
5. $\frac{5^{6}\cdot 2^{4}}{5^{4}\cdot 2^{3}}$ $5^{6-4}\cdot 2^{4-3}$ (LE-2) $=5^{2}\cdot 2=25\cdot 2=50$
6. $\left(\frac{3x^{2}}{2y^{3}}\right)^{4}$
7. $\left(\frac{2x^{4}\cdot x^{7}}{10y^{3}\cdot y}\right)^{3}$
8. $3+3^{-1}$
   $3+\frac{1}{3}$ (Def-Neg. Exp.) $=\frac{10}{3}$
9. If $y = \frac{1}{x}$, is $x = \frac{1}{y}$? Yes If $7^{-1} = \frac{1}{7}$, is $7 = \frac{1}{7^{-1}}$? Yes

Simplify each expression and state the laws or definitions used.

10. $(x^{-3}y^{2})^{4}$ $(x^{-3})^{4}(y^{2})^{4}$ (LE-4) $=x^{-12}y^{8}$ (LE-3) $=\frac{y^{8}}{x^{12}}$ (Def-Neg. Exp.)
11. $x^{-8}\cdot x^{-3}$ x^{-11} (LE-1) $=\frac{1}{x^{11}}$ (Def-Neg. Exp.)
12. $x^{-7}\div x^{-3}$ x^{-4} (LE-2) $=\frac{1}{x^{4}}$ (Def-Neg. Exp.)

Exercises for Discussion

If time is limited, it is recommended that at least Exercises for Discussion 3 and 10–18 be covered.

Answers to Exercises for Discussion 3, 6–7

3. As illustrated in Exercise for Discussion 1, x^{0} is the multiplicative identity, and as illustrated in Exercise for Discussion 2, the quotient of a number by itself is x^{0}. Hence, it is convenient to define x^{0} equal to 1.

6. $$\left(\frac{3x^{2}}{2y^{3}}\right)^{4} = \frac{(3x^{2})^{4}}{(2y^{3})^{4}} \quad \text{(LE-5)}$$
$$= \frac{3^{4}\cdot(x^{2})^{4}}{2^{4}\cdot(y^{3})^{4}} \quad \text{(LE-4)}$$
$$= \frac{3^{4}\cdot x^{8}}{2^{4}\cdot y^{12}} \quad \text{(LE-3)}$$
$$= \frac{81x^{8}}{16y^{12}}$$

7. $$\left(\frac{2x^{4}\cdot x^{7}}{10y^{3}\cdot y}\right)^{3} = \left(\frac{2x^{11}}{10y^{4}}\right)^{3} \quad \text{(LE-1)}$$
$$= \frac{(2x^{11})^{3}}{(10y^{4})^{3}} \quad \text{(LE-5)}$$
$$= \frac{2^{3}\cdot(x^{11})^{3}}{10^{3}\cdot(y^{4})^{3}} \quad \text{(LE-4)}$$
$$= \frac{8x^{33}}{1000y^{12}} \quad \text{(LE-3)}$$
$$= \frac{x^{33}}{125y^{12}}$$

It is suggested that Exercises for Discussion 16–18 be stressed. In Exercise for Discussion 16, the student may be asked to find

$$2+2^{-1},\quad 3+3^{-1},\quad \left(\tfrac{1}{5}\right)+\left(\tfrac{1}{5}\right)^{-1},\quad \tfrac{2}{3}+\left(\tfrac{2}{3}\right)^{-1},$$

in order to see what arithmetic is involved before simplifying $x+x^{-1}$. In Exercise for Discussion 17, the student may do the computations

$$3^{-2}-4^{-2},\quad 2^{-2}-3^{-2},\quad \left(\tfrac{3}{4}\right)^{-2}-\left(\tfrac{1}{2}\right)^{-2},$$

before finding an equivalent expression for $x^{-2}-y^{-2}$. (See Exercise 31 on the next page.)

In Exercise for Discussion 18, the student may find the value of $x^{-1}-3$, without simplifying, for $x = 1, 2, -4, \frac{1}{2}, \frac{2}{3}$, and then check to see if the values are the same in the simplified form,

$$\frac{1-3x}{x}.$$

Exercises

In Exercise 10, each fraction should be simplified, using the second law of exponents, before the two fractions are multiplied together, using the first law of exponents.

In Exercise 20, the second law of exponents should be used on each fraction before using the third and first laws of exponents.

Use (LE-3) to complete each statement.

13. $4^8 = 2^?$ $(2^2)^8 = 2^{16}$ **14.** $9^6 = 3^?$ $(3^2)^6 = 3^{12}$ **15.** $8^5 = 2^?$ $(2^3)^5 = 2^{15}$

In Exercises 16–18, write the expressions with positive exponents only, and simplify.

16. $x + x^{-1}$ $\quad x + \frac{1}{x} = \frac{x^2+1}{x}$

17. $x^{-2} - y^{-2}$ $\quad \frac{1}{x^2} - \frac{1}{y^2} = \frac{y^2-x^2}{x^2y^2}$

18. $x^{-1} - 3$ $\quad \frac{1}{x} - 3 = \frac{1-3x}{x}$

Exercises

Assume that the value of any variable that appears in a denominator is a nonzero number, and simplify each of the following algebraic expressions. Give answers without negative exponents.

1. $7^2 \cdot 7^6 \cdot 7$ $\quad 7^9$

2. $\left(\frac{1}{x}\right)^5\left(\frac{1}{x}\right)^4$ $\quad \frac{1}{x^9}$

3. $(-5xy)^3$ $\quad -125x^3y^3$

4. $\frac{x^{-2}}{x^{-5}}$ $\quad x^3$

5. $\frac{(x^{-3})^2x^5}{x^{-1}}$ $\quad 1$

6. $(-3x^{-4})^2$ $\quad \frac{9}{x^8}$

7. $-\left(\frac{2x}{y^2}\right)^5$ $\quad \frac{-32x^5}{y^{10}}$

8. $\frac{2x^6}{6x^{12}}$ $\quad \frac{1}{3x^6}$

9. $\frac{2x^{-3}}{3y^{-2}}$ $\quad \frac{2y^2}{3x^3}$

10. $\left(\frac{3xy^2}{5x^3y}\right)\left(\frac{10x^4}{21y^5}\right)$ $\quad \frac{2x^2}{7y^4}$

11. $(a^{-2}b)^4$ $\quad \frac{b^4}{a^8}$

12. $(x^5x^{-5})^5$ $\quad 1$

13. $\frac{x^0}{y^3}$ $\quad \frac{1}{y^3}$

14. $\frac{49^3 \cdot 13 \cdot 49^{-3}}{5^2+5^0}$ $\quad \frac{1}{2}$

15. $0^1 \cdot 1^0$ $\quad 0$

16. $\frac{3^6}{2^3+2^0}$ $\quad 81$

17. $(x^{-2})^{-3}$ $\quad x^6$

18. $(10^0 \cdot 10^2) + 10$ $\quad 110$

19. $\frac{(2\cdot 10^2)^3(4\cdot 10^{-2})^2}{(2\cdot 10^3)^{-1}}$ $\quad 2^8 \cdot 10^5$

20. $\left(\frac{28a^4b}{7ab^4}\right)^2\left(\frac{27ab^5}{54a^5b}\right)^3$ $\quad \frac{2b^6}{a^6}$

21. $\frac{(3\cdot 10^{-3})(4\cdot 10^5)}{2\cdot 10^4}$ $\quad \frac{3}{50}$

22. $\left(\frac{x^{-2}y}{ab^{-1}}\right)^{-2}$ $\quad \frac{a^2x^4}{b^2y^2}$

23. $\left(\frac{3x^{-2}}{2y^{-3}}\right)^{-1}$ $\quad \frac{2x^2}{3y^3}$

24. $\left(\frac{x^7y^{-2}}{y^2x^{-3}}\right)^2$ $\quad \frac{x^{20}}{y^8}$

In Exercises 25–28, use (LE-3) to complete each statement.

25. $27^6 = 3^?$ 18 **26.** $2^7 \cdot 4^3 = 2^?$ 13

27. $3^6 \cdot 81^2 = 3^?$ 14 **28.** $32^6 \div 128^3 = 2^?$ 9

29. Express each number as a power of 2 and simplify.

(a) $[(\frac{1}{4})^6 \cdot 64]^{-3}(32)^{-2}$ 256 (b) $\dfrac{16^3 - 32^4}{4^6 + 8^5}$ $\dfrac{-85}{3}$

30. Express each number as a power of 3 and simplify.

(a) $243^6 \cdot 27^8 \div 81^2$ 3^{46} (b) $\dfrac{\frac{1}{27} + \frac{1}{81}}{\frac{1}{3} - \frac{1}{9}}$ $\dfrac{2}{9}$

△

31. (a) Find the value of $x^{-2} + y^{-2}$ when $x = 3$ and $y = 4$. $\dfrac{25}{144}$

(b) What is the value of

$$\frac{1}{x^2 + y^2}$$

when $x = 3$ and $y = 4$? $\dfrac{1}{25}$

(c) Do the answers in parts (a) and (b) agree? In other words, are

$$x^{-2} + y^{-2} \quad \text{and} \quad \frac{1}{x^2 + y^2}$$

equivalent forms? No

(d) Find an equivalent form for $x^{-2} + y^{-2}$ by first obtaining an expression with positive exponents and then simplifying. $\dfrac{y^2 + x^2}{x^2y^2}$

Write the following expressions with positive exponents and then simplify.

32. $x^{-1} - x$ $\dfrac{1 - x^2}{x}$ **33.** $y^{-3} + y^3$ $\dfrac{1 + y^6}{y^3}$

34. $x^2 - y^{-2}$ $\dfrac{x^2y^2 - 1}{y^2}$ **35.** $\dfrac{x - y}{x^{-1} - y^{-1}}$ $-xy$

36. $a^{-2} + b$ $\dfrac{1 + a^2b}{a^2}$ **37.** $(x^{-2} + 3y^{-1})^{-1}$ $\dfrac{x^2y}{y + 3x^2}$

38. $\dfrac{(2x - y)^{-1}}{2x + y}$ $\dfrac{1}{4x^2 - y^2}$ **39.** $\dfrac{3a - b}{(3a - b)^{-1}}$ $(3a - b)^2$

40. $x^{-2} - y^{-2}$ $\dfrac{y^2 - x^2}{x^2y^2}$

It is important not to assign Exercises 29 and 30 without having first discussed (or assigned) Exercises 25–28 which lead up to them.

Exercise 31 could be used as part of the class discussion in connection with Exercise for Discussion 17 on page 30.

Attention should be called to the instructions for Exercises 32–40, which mean that each expression must first be written without negative exponents. This will lead to a "mixed" expression as in Exercise 32,

$$\frac{1}{x} - x,$$

or to a complex fraction as in Exercise 35,

$$\frac{x - y}{\frac{1}{x} - \frac{1}{y}},$$

which must then be changed to a single simple fraction.

Quiz

Simplify each of the following algebraic expressions. Give answers without negative exponents.

1. $x^4 \cdot x^3 \cdot x^{-2}$ (ans: x^5)
2. $(^-3xy^2)^2$ (ans: $9x^2y^4$)
3. $\dfrac{y^{-3}}{y^{-5}}$ (ans: y^2)
4. $\dfrac{4y^{-2}}{x^{-3}}$ $\left(\text{ans: } \dfrac{4x^3}{y^2}\right)$
5. $x^0 \cdot y^2$ (ans: y^2)

1–8 RADICALS

It should be emphasized that $\sqrt{x}$ is never any negative number. For example, a distinction should be made on the board between such problems as find $\sqrt{16}$, $\sqrt{25}$, $\sqrt{\frac{4}{9}}$ (ans: 4, 5, $\frac{2}{3}$), and find x if $x^2 = 16$, $x^2 = 25$, $x^2 = \frac{4}{9}$ (ans: $^\pm 4$, $^\pm 5$, $^\pm\frac{2}{3}$).

For the first law of radicals, numerical illustrations may be used, such as the following:

$$\sqrt{36\cdot 4} = \sqrt{36}\cdot\sqrt{4} = 6\cdot 2, \quad \text{or } 12,$$
$$\sqrt{36\cdot 4} = \sqrt{144} = 12,$$
$$\sqrt[3]{8\cdot 27} = \sqrt[3]{8}\cdot\sqrt[3]{27} = 2\cdot 3, \quad \text{or } 6,$$
$$\sqrt[3]{8\cdot 27} = \sqrt[3]{216} = 6.$$

1–8 RADICALS

Knowing that the area of a square is A square inches, we can find the length L, in inches, of a side of the square by the formula

$$L = \sqrt{A}.$$

Similarly, if the volume of a cube is V cubic inches, then the length E, in inches, of an edge of the cube is given by the formula

$$E = \sqrt[3]{V}.$$

We call L the positive square root of A, and E the positive cube root of V. Roots of real numbers are defined in the following way.

DEFINITION OF THE nTH ROOT OF A NUMBER

For every integer $n > 1$ and all real numbers x and y, the number y is called an nth root of x if, and only if,

$$y^n = x. \qquad \textit{(Def-nth Rt.)}$$

If $x > 0$ and $y > 0$, then we write

$$y = \sqrt[n]{x}$$

to indicate that y is the positive nth root of x. In addition, if n is an odd integer, $x < 0$, and $y < 0$, then we write

$$y = \sqrt[n]{x}$$

to indicate that y is the negative nth root of x.

One of the unusual, but quite useful, properties of the real number system is that every positive real number x has a unique positive real nth root $\sqrt[n]{x}$. If n is an odd positive integer, every negative real number x has a unique negative real nth root $\sqrt[n]{x}$.

For example,

$$\sqrt{49} = 7, \quad \sqrt[3]{27} = 3, \quad \sqrt[4]{625} = 5, \quad \sqrt[5]{^-32} = {^-2},$$

according to the definition of nth roots. Since an even power of a nonzero number is always positive, negative numbers do not have square roots, fourth roots, or, in general, nth roots if n is even.

The following two laws are useful in working with algebraic expressions involving radicals.

LAWS OF RADICALS

$$\sqrt[n]{x \cdot y} = \sqrt[n]{x} \cdot \sqrt[n]{y} \qquad (LR\text{-}1)$$

$$\sqrt[n]{\frac{x}{y}} = \frac{\sqrt[n]{x}}{\sqrt[n]{y}} \qquad (LR\text{-}2)$$

These laws are valid for all integers $n > 1$ and all positive real numbers x and y. If n is odd, then they are true for any nonzero real numbers x and y.

The laws of radicals follow directly from the laws of exponents. For example,

$$\begin{aligned}(\sqrt[n]{x} \cdot \sqrt[n]{y})^n &= (\sqrt[n]{x})^n \cdot (\sqrt[n]{y})^n && \text{(LE-4)}\\ &= x \cdot y. && \text{(Def-}n\text{th Rt.)}\end{aligned}$$

Therefore, $\sqrt[n]{x} \cdot \sqrt[n]{y}$ is the nth root of $x \cdot y$. This proves the first law of radicals.

If c/d is a rational number expressed in simplest form, then $\sqrt{c/d}$ is also a rational number if, and only if, the integers c and d are perfect squares, that is, $\sqrt{c}$ and $\sqrt{d}$ are integers. It can be shown in the same way that $\sqrt[n]{c/d}$ is a rational number if, and only if, $\sqrt[n]{c}$ and $\sqrt[n]{d}$ are integers. In this case,

$$\sqrt[n]{\frac{c}{d}} = \frac{\sqrt[n]{c}}{\sqrt[n]{d}}$$

by the second law of radicals, (LR-2). For example,

$$\sqrt[3]{\frac{125}{27}} = \frac{\sqrt[3]{125}}{\sqrt[3]{27}}, \quad \text{or } \frac{5}{3}.$$

We recall that every positive integer can be expressed as a product of a perfect-square integer and a square-free integer. In the same way, every positive integer can be expressed as a product of a perfect-cube integer and a cube-free integer, and so on. For example, $384 = 64 \times 6$, where $64 = 4^3$ and 6 has no positive perfect-cube factor other than 1. Therefore,

$$\sqrt[3]{384} = \sqrt[3]{64} \cdot \sqrt[3]{6}, \quad \text{or } 4\sqrt[3]{6}.$$

Again, we call $4\sqrt[3]{6}$ the *simplest form* for expressing the cube root of 384. The nth root of every integer can be expressed in a simplest form in this way.

The students should be able to express the law in words: "In finding the *n*th root of a product of two or more factors, one may either multiply the factors together and then take the root of their product, or first find the roots of the factors and then multiply them together. The result is the same either way."

It is expedient to take roots first in a case such as

$$\sqrt[3]{8 \cdot 17} = \sqrt[3]{8} \cdot \sqrt[3]{17} = 2\sqrt[3]{17},$$

but in a case, such as

$$\begin{aligned}\sqrt[3]{5} \cdot \sqrt[3]{75} = \sqrt[3]{5 \cdot 75} &= \sqrt[3]{125 \cdot 3}\\ &= 5\sqrt[3]{3},\end{aligned}$$

it is expedient to multiply first.

Rationalizing the denominator of a fraction may be done in different ways. One may handle

$$\frac{\sqrt{5}}{\sqrt{6}}$$

by the second law of radicals in this way:

$$\frac{\sqrt{5}}{\sqrt{6}} = \sqrt{\frac{5}{6}} = \sqrt{\frac{30}{36}} = \frac{\sqrt{30}}{\sqrt{36}} = \frac{\sqrt{30}}{6}$$

Another procedure is the following:

$$\begin{aligned}\frac{\sqrt{5}}{\sqrt{6}} &= \sqrt{\frac{5}{6}} && \text{(LR-2)}\\ &= \sqrt{\frac{5 \cdot 6}{6 \cdot 6}} && \text{(Id-M)}\\ &= \sqrt{\frac{1}{36} \cdot 30}\\ &= \sqrt{\frac{1}{36}}\sqrt{30} && \text{(LR-1)}\\ &= \tfrac{1}{6}\sqrt{30}.\end{aligned}$$

Writing

$$\sqrt{\frac{30}{36}} \quad \text{as} \quad \sqrt{\frac{1}{36} \cdot 30}$$

helps eliminate the possibility of arriving at the wrong answer $6\sqrt{30}$, instead of the correct answer, $\frac{1}{6}\sqrt{30}$.

These problems need to be explained to average classes because it may have been some time since the students have had first year algebra. It may be helpful to show them how to find the prime factors of 1152.

$$
\begin{array}{r|l}
2 & 1152 \\
2 & 576 \\
2 & 288 \\
2 & 144 \\
2 & 72 \\
2 & 36 \\
2 & 18 \\
3 & 9 \\
 & 3
\end{array}
$$

Therefore,

$$1152 = 2^7 \cdot 3^2.$$

Problem. Simplify each of the following expressions.

(a) $\sqrt[5]{1152}$

(b) $\sqrt[3]{81x^5y^{10}}$

(c) $\sqrt[3]{\dfrac{4a^5}{9b^7}}$

Solution.

(a) We can factor 1152 as follows:

$$1152 = 2^7 \times 3^2.$$

Hence,

$$\sqrt[5]{1152} = \sqrt[5]{2^5} \times \sqrt[5]{2^2 \times 3^2}$$
$$= 2\sqrt[5]{36}.$$

(b) We proceed in the following way.

$$\sqrt[3]{81x^5y^{10}} = \sqrt[3]{(3^3x^3y^9)(3x^2y)}$$
$$= \sqrt[3]{(3xy^3)^3} \cdot \sqrt[3]{3x^2y} \qquad \text{(LR-1)}$$
$$= 3xy^3\sqrt[3]{3x^2y}$$

(c) Let us rationalize the denominator while simplifying. This may be accomplished by finding an equivalent algebraic expression which has a perfect-cube denominator. Thus, we proceed as shown below.

$$\sqrt[3]{\frac{4a^5}{9b^7}} = \sqrt[3]{\frac{4a^5}{9b^7} \cdot \frac{3b^2}{3b^2}} \qquad \text{(Id-M)}$$
$$= \sqrt[3]{\frac{12a^5b^2}{27b^9}}$$
$$= \sqrt[3]{\frac{a^3}{27b^9} \cdot 12a^2b^2}$$
$$= \sqrt[3]{\frac{a^3}{27b^9}} \cdot \sqrt[3]{12a^2b^2} \qquad \text{(LR-1)}$$
$$= \frac{a}{3b^3}\sqrt[3]{12a^2b^2}, \quad \text{or} \quad \frac{a\sqrt[3]{12a^2b^2}}{3b^3}$$

Exercises for Discussion

Simplify each of the following expressions.

1. $\sqrt[3]{-27}$ -3 2. $\sqrt[5]{32}$ 2 3. $\sqrt[5]{-243}$ -3
4. $\sqrt[5]{-96x^7y^5}$ 5. $\sqrt[3]{-250x^6y^8}$ 6. $\sqrt[4]{48x^8y^{10}}$

Complete each of the following simplifications.

7. $\sqrt{\dfrac{12a^3}{5b^3}} = \sqrt{\dfrac{12a^3}{5b^3}\cdot\dfrac{5b}{5b}} = \sqrt{\dfrac{4a^2}{25b^4}\cdot ?} = ?\sqrt{?}$ $\quad 15ab$ $\quad \dfrac{2a}{5b^2}\sqrt{15ab}$

8. $\dfrac{5+\sqrt{3}}{5-\sqrt{3}} = \dfrac{5+\sqrt{3}}{5-\sqrt{3}}\cdot\dfrac{5+\sqrt{3}}{5+\sqrt{3}} = \dfrac{?}{?}$

9. $\dfrac{2\sqrt{3}-\sqrt{5}}{2\sqrt{3}+\sqrt{5}} = \dfrac{2\sqrt{3}-\sqrt{5}}{2\sqrt{3}+\sqrt{5}}\cdot\dfrac{2\sqrt{3}-\sqrt{5}}{2\sqrt{3}-\sqrt{5}} = \dfrac{?}{?}$

10. $\dfrac{\sqrt{x}-\sqrt{y}}{\sqrt{x}+\sqrt{y}} = \dfrac{\sqrt{x}-\sqrt{y}}{\sqrt{x}+\sqrt{y}}\cdot\dfrac{\sqrt{x}-\sqrt{y}}{\sqrt{x}-\sqrt{y}} = \dfrac{?}{?}$ $\quad \dfrac{x-2\sqrt{xy}+y}{x-y}$

Use (LR-1) or (LR-2) to find each product or quotient. Then simplify.

11. $\sqrt[4]{40}\cdot\sqrt[4]{14}$ $\sqrt[4]{560}$ $=\sqrt[4]{16\cdot 35} = 2\sqrt[4]{35}$ 12. $\sqrt{6}\div\sqrt{12}$ $\sqrt{\frac{6}{12}}$ $=\sqrt{\frac{1}{2}\cdot\frac{2}{2}} = \frac{1}{2}\sqrt{2}$ 13. $\sqrt{7xy}\div\sqrt{14x^2y^2}$

Simplify each radical that is not in simplest form, and find the sum or difference.

14. $6\sqrt{12x} - 5\sqrt{27x^3}$
$6\sqrt{4\cdot 3x} - 5\sqrt{9x^2\cdot 3x}$
$= 12\sqrt{3x} - 15x\sqrt{3x} = (12-15x)\sqrt{3x}$

15. $\sqrt[3]{24x^2} - 5\sqrt[3]{-81x^5}$
$\sqrt[3]{8\cdot 3x^2} - 5\sqrt[3]{-27x^3\cdot x^2}$
$= 2\sqrt[3]{3x^2} + 15x\sqrt[3]{3x^2} = (2+15x)\sqrt[3]{3x^2}$

Exercises

Simplify each of the following radicals.

1. $\sqrt{27x^4y^3}$ $3x^2y\sqrt{3y}$ 2. $\sqrt[3]{16xy^6}$ $2y^2\sqrt[3]{2x}$ 3. $\sqrt{\dfrac{2x^3}{5}}$ $\dfrac{x}{5}\sqrt{10x}$
4. $\sqrt[3]{\dfrac{2}{9x}}$ $\dfrac{1}{3x}\sqrt[3]{6x^2}$ 5. $\sqrt[5]{\dfrac{2a^6}{3b^7}}$ $\dfrac{a}{3b^2}\sqrt[5]{162ab^3}$ 6. $\sqrt[3]{\dfrac{8x^4y}{z^5}}$ $\dfrac{2x}{z^2}\sqrt[3]{xyz}$

Perform the indicated operations and give each answer in simplest form.

7. $\sqrt{3}\cdot\sqrt{6}$ $3\sqrt{2}$ 8. $\sqrt[3]{4}\cdot\sqrt[3]{10}$ $2\sqrt[3]{5}$ 9. $\dfrac{\sqrt[3]{16}}{\sqrt[3]{2}}$ 2

10. $\sqrt{\frac{3}{4}}\div\sqrt{\frac{5}{6}}$ $\frac{3}{10}\sqrt{10}$ 11. $\dfrac{\sqrt[5]{64}}{\sqrt[5]{3}}$ $\dfrac{2}{3}\sqrt[5]{162}$ 12. $(5+\sqrt{3})(5-\sqrt{3})$ 22

13. $(2\sqrt{3}+3\sqrt{2})^2$ $6(5+2\sqrt{6})$ 14. $(3-\sqrt{5})^2+\sqrt{180}$ 14

15. $\sqrt{20x^3}\cdot\sqrt{30x^7}$ $10x^5\sqrt{6}$ 16. $\sqrt[3]{-10x^7}\cdot\sqrt[3]{-4x^7}$ $2x^4\sqrt[3]{5x^2}$

17. $(\sqrt{6x}-\sqrt{3x^3})^2$ $6x-6x^2\sqrt{2}+3x^3$ 18. $\sqrt[3]{-5x^2y}\div\sqrt[3]{10xy^5}$ $\dfrac{-1}{2y^2}\sqrt[3]{4xy^2}$

Exercises for Discussion

It is suggested that all of the Exercises for Discussion be covered in class before the Exercises are assigned. The student should understand why the multiplier 1 was chosen in Exercises for Discussion 8–10.

Answers to Exercises for Discussion 4–6, 8, 9, 13

4. $\sqrt[5]{(-32x^5y^5)(3x^2)} = -2xy\sqrt[5]{3x^2}$
5. $\sqrt[3]{(-125x^6y^6)(2y^2)} = -5x^2y^2\sqrt[3]{2y^2}$
6. $\sqrt[4]{(16x^8y^8)(3y^2)} = 2x^2y^2\sqrt[4]{3y^2}$
8. $\dfrac{25+10\sqrt{3}+3}{25-3} = \dfrac{28+10\sqrt{3}}{22} = \dfrac{14+5\sqrt{3}}{11}$
9. $\dfrac{12-4\sqrt{15}+5}{12-5} = \dfrac{17-4\sqrt{15}}{7}$
13. $\sqrt{\dfrac{7xy}{14x^2y^2}} = \sqrt{\dfrac{xy}{2x^2y^2}\cdot\dfrac{2}{2}} = \dfrac{1}{2xy}\sqrt{2xy}$

Answer to Exercise 24

24. $\dfrac{x + 6\sqrt{xy} + 9y}{x - 9y}$

Exercise 34 may require special attention as it is discovery material for Section 1-9 on rational exponents which contains the algorithm for handling a problem such as this.

It is suggested that Exercises 35–37 be discussed in class so that all students, and not just the best ones, get the point.

Exercise 39 could be used as a quiz to begin the day's lesson.

Quiz

Perform the indicated operations and give each answer in its simplest form.

1. $\sqrt{5} \cdot \sqrt{15} \cdot \sqrt{25}$ (ans: $25\sqrt{3}$)
2. $\sqrt{\frac{7}{8}} \div \sqrt{\frac{21}{16}}$ (ans: $\frac{1}{3}\sqrt{6}$)
3. $\sqrt{18x^3} \cdot \sqrt{8x^{11}}$ (ans: $12x^7$)
4. $\sqrt[3]{15x^6} + \sqrt[3]{x^6}$ (ans: $x^2(\sqrt[3]{15} + 1)$)
5. $\sqrt{3x^3} \div \sqrt{27x^7}$ $\left(\text{ans: } \dfrac{1}{3x^2}\right)$
6. $\dfrac{\sqrt{2} + 1}{\sqrt{3} - \sqrt{2}}$ (ans: $\sqrt{6} + 2 + \sqrt{3} + \sqrt{2}$)

Rationalize the denominator of each fraction, and simplify.

19. $\dfrac{4}{\sqrt{3} - 1}$ $2(\sqrt{3}+1)$ **20.** $\dfrac{16}{\sqrt{7} - \sqrt{3}}$ $4(\sqrt{7}+\sqrt{3})$ **21.** $\dfrac{\sqrt{7} - \sqrt{2}}{\sqrt{7} + \sqrt{2}}$ $\dfrac{9 - 2\sqrt{14}}{5}$

22. $\dfrac{\sqrt{11} + 1}{\sqrt{11} + \sqrt{5}}$ $(11 + \sqrt{11} - \sqrt{55} - \sqrt{5})/6$ **23.** $\dfrac{\sqrt{2} + 3}{\sqrt{2} - 5}$ $\dfrac{-17 - 8\sqrt{2}}{23}$ **24.** $\dfrac{\sqrt{x} + 3\sqrt{y}}{\sqrt{x} - 3\sqrt{y}}$

In Exercises 25–33, simplify each radical that is not in simplest form, and perform the indicated operations.

25. $\sqrt{\frac{4}{15}} + 3\sqrt{15}$ $\frac{47}{15}\sqrt{15}$ **26.** $\sqrt{\frac{1}{2}} - 3\sqrt{\frac{2}{9}}$ $-\frac{1}{2}\sqrt{2}$ **27.** $\sqrt[4]{32} - \sqrt[4]{2}$ $\sqrt[4]{2}$

28. $\sqrt{32} + \dfrac{1}{\sqrt{2}} - \sqrt{\dfrac{2}{9}}$ $\frac{25}{6}\sqrt{2}$ **29.** $\sqrt{8 - \sqrt{15}} \cdot \sqrt{8 + \sqrt{15}}$ 7

30. $\sqrt{8x} + \sqrt{2x^3}$ $(2+x)\sqrt{2x}$ **31.** $\sqrt{\dfrac{x}{2}} - \sqrt{\dfrac{2}{x}}$ $\frac{x-2}{2x}\sqrt{2x}$

32. $\left(\dfrac{1}{\sqrt{x}} - \sqrt{x}\right)^2$ $\dfrac{1 - 2x + x^2}{x}$ **33.** $5\sqrt{72a} - 2\sqrt{50a} + \sqrt{288a} - \sqrt{242a}$ $21\sqrt{2a}$

34. Arrange the following numbers in order of increasing magnitude.

$$\sqrt{3}, \quad \sqrt[4]{27}, \quad \sqrt[6]{9}$$

$\sqrt[6]{9} < \sqrt{3} < \sqrt[4]{27}$

△

35. Show that the statement

$$\sqrt{x^2 + y^2} = x + y \quad \text{for every value of } x \text{ and } y$$

is not true by finding a counterexample (that is, a pair of values for x and y which makes the statement false). Let $x = 3$, $y = 4$

36. Give a counterexample to show that the following statement is false.

$$\sqrt{x - y} = \sqrt{x} - \sqrt{y} \quad \text{for every positive value of } x \text{ and } y$$

Let $x = 25$, $y = 16$

37. (a) Give a counterexample to show that the following statement is false.

Let $x = 1$, $y = {}^{-}2$

$$\sqrt{x^2 + 2xy + y^2} = x + y \quad \text{for every value of } x \text{ and } y$$

(b) Prove that for every pair x, y of real numbers, where $x > 0$ and $y > 0$, $\sqrt{x^2 + 2xy + y^2} = x + y$. $\sqrt{x^2 + 2xy + y^2} = \sqrt{(x+y)^2}$ $= x + y$ if $x > 0$, $y > 0$, and hence $x + y > 0$

▲

38. Prove the second law of radicals, (LR-2). See Solution Manual.

39. Find a fraction that has a rational denominator and is equivalent to the fraction

$$\frac{1}{\sqrt{5} - \sqrt{3} + \sqrt{2}} \cdot \quad \frac{1}{12}(\sqrt{30} - 2\sqrt{3} + 3\sqrt{2})$$

1-9 RATIONAL EXPONENTS

We have defined the exponential notation x^n for every integer n. It is natural to ask whether x^r can be defined for every rational number r. Of course, we would like to define x^r so that the laws of exponents continue to be valid for rational exponents.

For example, what is a reasonable definition of $x^{\frac{1}{3}}$? If the third law of exponents, (LE-3), is to be valid for rational exponents, then we must have

$$(x^{\frac{1}{3}})^3 = x^{\frac{1}{3}\cdot 3}, \quad \text{or } x.$$

Since $(\sqrt[3]{x})^3 = x$ for every real number x, a natural definition of $x^{\frac{1}{3}}$ is the cube root of x:

$$x^{\frac{1}{3}} = \sqrt[3]{x}.$$

With this example in mind, we define

$$x^{\frac{1}{n}} = \sqrt[n]{x}$$

for every positive integer n and for every real number x for which $\sqrt[n]{x}$ is real. Thus, for example,

$$4^{\frac{1}{2}} = \sqrt{4}, \quad \text{or } 2,$$
$$81^{\frac{1}{4}} = \sqrt[4]{81}, \quad \text{or } 3,$$
$$(^{-}32)^{\frac{1}{5}} = \sqrt[5]{^{-}32}, \quad \text{or } ^{-}2.$$

Now that we have defined the $(1/n)$-power of a real number, let us consider how we might define the (m/n)-power of a number. We first look at a special example, say $8^{\frac{2}{3}}$. If the third law of exponents, (LE-3), is to be valid, then we must have

$$\begin{aligned} 8^{\frac{2}{3}} &= (8^{\frac{1}{3}})^2 \\ &= (\sqrt[3]{8})^2 \\ &= 2^2, \quad \text{or } 4. \end{aligned}$$

With this example in mind, we give the following definition.

DEFINITION OF RATIONAL EXPONENTS

For every pair of integers m and n, with n > 1, and for every real number x for which $(\sqrt[n]{x})^m$ *is real, we define*

$$x^{\frac{m}{n}} = (\sqrt[n]{x})^m. \qquad \textit{(Def-Rat. Exp.)}$$

1-9 RATIONAL EXPONENTS

The definition of a rational exponent may also be derived using the first law of exponents. Thus,

$$\begin{aligned} x^{1/2}x^{1/2} &= x^{1/2+1/2} \\ &= x. \end{aligned}$$

Therefore,

$$x^{1/2} = \sqrt{x}.$$

Also

$$\begin{aligned} x^{1/3}x^{1/3}x^{1/3} &= x^{1/3+1/3+1/3} \\ &= x. \end{aligned}$$

Therefore,

$$x^{1/3} = \sqrt[3]{x},$$

and so on.

It should be observed that, since $2^{1/2} \cdot 2^{1/3} = 2^{5/6}$, by the first law of exponents and the definition of rational exponents, it must be that $\sqrt{2} \cdot \sqrt[3]{2} = \sqrt[6]{32}$. That is, the definition of rational exponents provides a way to multiply $\sqrt[n]{x} \cdot \sqrt[m]{x}$, which we were unable to do using the first law of exponents. For example,

$$\begin{aligned}\sqrt[3]{4} \cdot \sqrt[4]{4} &= 4^{1/3} \cdot 4^{1/4}\\ &= 4^{4/12+3/12}\\ &= 4^{7/12}\\ &= (2^2)^{7/12}\\ &= 2^{7/6}\\ &= 2\sqrt[6]{2}.\end{aligned}$$

Returning to the example on page 37, we might have computed $8^{\frac{2}{3}}$ as follows:

$$\begin{aligned}8^{\frac{2}{3}} &= (8^2)^{\frac{1}{3}}\\ &= \sqrt[3]{8^2}\\ &= \sqrt[3]{64}, \quad \text{or } 4.\end{aligned}$$

The fact that the answer is the same as before suggests that the following equation is true for all integers m and n, with $n > 0$, and all nonzero numbers x having a real number nth root.

$$(x^{\frac{1}{n}})^m = (x^m)^{\frac{1}{n}}$$

If $m > 0$, we can prove that this equation is true by proceeding as follows:

$$\begin{aligned}(\sqrt[n]{x})^m &= \underbrace{\sqrt[n]{x} \cdot \sqrt[n]{x} \cdot \ldots \cdot \sqrt[n]{x}}_{m \text{ factors}} && \text{(LE-1)}\\ &= \sqrt[n]{\underbrace{x \cdot x \cdot \ldots \cdot x}_{m \text{ factors}}} && \text{(LR-1)}\\ &= \sqrt[n]{x^m}.\end{aligned}$$

From the definition of zero and negative exponents, it follows that the equation above is also true when $m \leq 0$.

The truth of the above equation allows us to find $x^{\frac{m}{n}}$ in either one of two ways:

$$x^{\frac{m}{n}} = (x^{\frac{1}{n}})^m$$

or

$$x^{\frac{m}{n}} = (x^m)^{\frac{1}{n}}.$$

For example,

$$9^{\frac{5}{2}} = (\sqrt{9})^5 = 3^5, \quad \text{or } 243,$$

$$8^{\frac{2}{3}} = (8^2)^{\frac{1}{3}} = \sqrt[3]{64}, \quad \text{or } 4.$$

It can be proved that the five laws of exponents are valid for rational exponents as well as for integral exponents. From now on, we shall assume that these laws are true for rational exponents, and we shall use them whenever necessary.

Problem 1. Simplify each of the following expressions.

(a) $2^{\frac{2}{3}} \cdot 4^{\frac{1}{6}}$

(b) $(x^{\frac{-5}{2}} \cdot y^{\frac{7}{3}})^6$

Solution.

(a)
$$\begin{aligned} 2^{\frac{2}{3}} \cdot 4^{\frac{1}{6}} &= 2^{\frac{2}{3}} \cdot (2^2)^{\frac{1}{6}} \\ &= 2^{\frac{2}{3}} \cdot 2^{\frac{2}{6}} && \text{(LE-3)} \\ &= 2^{\frac{2}{3}} \cdot 2^{\frac{1}{3}} \\ &= 2^{\frac{2}{3}+\frac{1}{3}} && \text{(LE-1)} \\ &= 2 \end{aligned}$$

(b)
$$\begin{aligned} (x^{\frac{-5}{2}} \cdot y^{\frac{7}{3}})^6 &= (x^{\frac{-5}{2}})^6 \cdot (y^{\frac{7}{3}})^6 && \text{(LE-4)} \\ &= x^{-15} \cdot y^{14} && \text{(LE-3)} \\ &= \frac{y^{14}}{x^{15}} \end{aligned}$$

Problem 2. Simplify

$$\frac{\sqrt{ab^3}}{\sqrt[3]{a^2b}}.$$

Solution.
$$\begin{aligned} \frac{\sqrt{ab^3}}{\sqrt[3]{a^2b}} &= \frac{(ab^3)^{\frac{1}{2}}}{(a^2b)^{\frac{1}{3}}} && \text{(Def-Rat. Exp.)} \\ &= \frac{a^{\frac{1}{2}}b^{\frac{3}{2}}}{a^{\frac{2}{3}}b^{\frac{1}{3}}} && \text{(LE-4), (LE-3)} \\ &= \frac{b^{\frac{3}{2}-\frac{1}{3}}}{a^{\frac{2}{3}-\frac{1}{2}}} && \text{(LE-2)} \\ &= \frac{b^{\frac{7}{6}}}{a^{\frac{1}{6}}} \\ &= \frac{b\sqrt[6]{b}}{\sqrt[6]{a}} \\ &= \frac{b\sqrt[6]{a^5b}}{a} \end{aligned}$$

These problems need to be examined carefully in class. Then to be sure the entire class has grasped the principles involved, you might propose some similar problems, such as

$$3^{4/3} \cdot 9^{1/3} = 3^2,$$
$$(x^{3/2} \cdot y^{-2/5})^{10} = \frac{x^{15}}{y^4},$$
$$\frac{\sqrt[3]{4x}}{\sqrt{2x}} = \frac{\sqrt[6]{2}}{\sqrt[6]{x}} = \frac{\sqrt[6]{2x^5}}{x}.$$

Exercises for Discussion

If time is limited, it is suggested that at least Exercises for Discussion 17–19 be covered.

Exercises for Discussion

Simplify each of the following expressions.

1. $9^{\frac{1}{2}}$ 3 **2.** $9^{-\frac{1}{2}}$ $\frac{1}{\sqrt{9}}=\frac{1}{3}$ **3.** $27^{\frac{2}{3}}$ $3^2=9$ **4.** $27^{-\frac{2}{3}}$ $\frac{1}{9}$

5. $64^{\frac{5}{6}}$ $2^5=32$ **6.** $32^{-\frac{2}{5}}$ $\frac{1}{4}$ **7.** $3^{\frac{1}{2}}\cdot 3^{\frac{3}{2}}$ $3^2=9$ **8.** $(x^{-\frac{1}{4}}\cdot y^{\frac{5}{2}})^4$ $x^{-1}\cdot y^{10} = \frac{y^{10}}{x}$

9. $8^{\frac{3}{2}}\cdot 4^{\frac{1}{4}}$ $(2^3)^{\frac{3}{2}}(2^2)^{\frac{1}{4}} = 2^{\frac{9}{2}}\cdot 2^{\frac{1}{2}} = 2^5 = 32$ **10.** $\left(\frac{5^{\frac{1}{2}}x^{-\frac{1}{3}}}{2y^{\frac{5}{6}}}\right)^{-6}$ $\frac{5^{-3}x^2}{2^{-6}y^{-5}} = \frac{64x^2y^5}{125}$

Rewrite each expression, using fractional exponents instead of radicals.

11. $^-2\sqrt{y}$ $^-2y^{\frac{1}{2}}$ **12.** $3\sqrt[4]{4x^3y}$ $3\cdot 2^{\frac{1}{2}}x^{\frac{3}{4}}y^{\frac{1}{4}}$ **13.** $\sqrt[3]{(x-y)^2}$ $(x-y)^{\frac{2}{3}}$

In Exercises 14–16, rewrite each expression, using radicals instead of fractional exponents.

14. $(2x)^{\frac{4}{5}}$ $\sqrt[5]{(2x)^4}=\sqrt[5]{16x^4}$ **15.** $x^{\frac{1}{3}} - y^{\frac{1}{3}}$ $\sqrt[3]{x}-\sqrt[3]{y}$ **16.** $(x+y)^{\frac{1}{3}}$ $\sqrt[3]{x+y}$

17. In the following solution, radicals with different indices are multiplied. Replace each question mark by an exponent to make the equation true.

$$\begin{aligned}\sqrt{xy^3}\cdot\sqrt[3]{x^2y} &= (xy^3)^{?\,\frac{1}{2}}(x^2y)^{?\,\frac{1}{3}}\\ &= (xy^3)^{\frac{3}{6}}\cdot(x^2y)^{\frac{2}{6}}\\ &= (x^{?3}y^{?9})^{\frac{1}{6}}\cdot(x^{?4}y^{?2})^{\frac{1}{6}}\\ &= \sqrt[6]{x^{?7}y^{?11}}\\ &= ?xy\sqrt[6]{xy^5}\end{aligned}$$

18. If $x > 1$ and $m > n > 0$, how does x compare with $x^{\frac{m}{n}}$? Give some examples. $x^{\frac{m}{n}} > x$ if $x>1$ and $m>n>0$

19. If $0 < x < 1$ and $n > 0$, how does x compare with $x^{\frac{1}{n}}$?
$x > x^{\frac{1}{n}}$ if $0<x<1$ and $0<n<1$
$x = x^{\frac{1}{n}}$ if $0<x<1$ and $n=1$
$x < x^{\frac{1}{n}}$ if $0<x<1$ and $n>1$

Exercises

Rewrite each expression, using fractional exponents instead of radicals.

1. $^-x\sqrt{x}$ $^-x^{\frac{3}{2}}$ **2.** $7\sqrt{ab^5}$ $7a^{\frac{1}{2}}b^{\frac{5}{2}}$

3. $2\sqrt[3]{2x^2y}$ $2^{\frac{4}{3}}x^{\frac{2}{3}}y^{\frac{1}{3}}$ **4.** $\sqrt[4]{(x-2y)^5}$ $(x-2y)^{\frac{5}{4}}$

Rewrite each expression, using radicals instead of fractional exponents. When possible, simplify.

5. $y^{\frac{2}{3}}$ $\sqrt[3]{y^2}$ **6.** $^-3x^{\frac{4}{5}}$ $^-3\sqrt[5]{x^4}$ **7.** $(^-3x)^{\frac{4}{5}}$ $\sqrt[5]{81x^4}$ **8.** $(2xy^2)^{\frac{3}{4}}$ $y\sqrt[4]{8x^3y^2}$

9. $x^{\frac{1}{2}}y^{\frac{2}{3}}$ $\sqrt{x}\cdot\sqrt[3]{y^2}$ **10.** $x^{\frac{1}{2}} + y^{\frac{1}{2}}$ $\sqrt{x}+\sqrt{y}$ **11.** $(x+y)^{\frac{1}{2}}$ $\sqrt{x+y}$ **12.** $x^{\frac{2}{3}} - x^{-\frac{1}{3}}$ $\frac{x-1}{x}\cdot\sqrt[3]{x^2}$

Simplify each of the following expressions.

13. $16^{\frac{3}{2}}$ 64 **14.** $8^{-\frac{2}{3}}$ $\frac{1}{4}$

15. $(\frac{1}{125})^{-\frac{1}{3}}$ 5 **16.** $(80^{-2})^{\frac{1}{2}}$ $\frac{1}{80}$

17. $\dfrac{27^{\frac{2}{3}} - 27^{-\frac{2}{3}}}{9}$ $\frac{80}{81}$ **18.** $(8^{\frac{2}{3}})^{-\frac{1}{2}}$ $\frac{1}{2}$

Simplify each of the following expressions.

19. $\dfrac{(32)^{-\frac{2}{5}}}{(\frac{1}{16})^{-\frac{3}{2}}}$ $\frac{1}{256}$

20. $(10^{\frac{1}{3}})^6 + (10^{-\frac{1}{3}})^6$ 100.01

21. $(10^{\frac{1}{3}} \cdot 10^{-\frac{1}{6}})^6$ 10

22. $9^{\frac{2}{3}} \cdot 27^{\frac{2}{9}}$ 9

23. $(x^{-\frac{3}{5}}y^{\frac{5}{3}})^{15}$ $\frac{y^{25}}{x^9}$

24. $(64x^9)^{\frac{2}{3}}$ $16x^6$

25. $(36x^2)^{-\frac{3}{2}}$ $\frac{1}{(6x)^3}$

26. $\left(\dfrac{-x^{\frac{1}{2}}y^{\frac{2}{3}}}{x^{\frac{3}{4}}y^{\frac{1}{6}}}\right)^{12}$ $\frac{y^6}{x^3}$

27. $(x^{\frac{1}{2}} + y^{\frac{1}{2}})(x^{\frac{1}{2}} - y^{\frac{1}{2}})$ $x-y$

28. $(e^x - e^{-x})^2$ $e^{2x} - 2 + e^{-2x}$

29. $\dfrac{\sqrt[3]{a^2b}}{\sqrt{ab^3}}$ $\frac{1}{b^2}\sqrt[6]{ab^5}$

30. $(\sqrt{x^3y^2})(\sqrt[3]{xy})$ $xy\sqrt[6]{x^5y^2}$

31. $\sqrt[4]{a^2b^4} - b\sqrt{a}$ 0

32. $\sqrt[6]{27x^3} - \sqrt{3x}$ 0

△

33. (a) Use fractional exponents to show that $\sqrt[4]{9} = \sqrt{3}$. $\sqrt[4]{9} = (3^2)^{\frac{1}{4}} = 3^{\frac{1}{2}} = \sqrt{3}$
(b) Show that $\sqrt[6]{x^3} = \sqrt[4]{x^2}$, x non-negative. Find another way to express this number. $\sqrt[6]{x^3} = (x^3)^{\frac{1}{6}} = x^{\frac{1}{2}} = x^{\frac{2}{4}} = \sqrt[4]{x^2}$; $\sqrt{x}$

In Exercises 34–42, the *index* of the radical $\sqrt[n]{a}$ is the integer n. Use fractional exponents to express each of the following as a single radical with the smallest possible index.

34. $\sqrt[4]{49}$ $\sqrt{7}$
35. $\sqrt[8]{25}$ $\sqrt[4]{5}$
36. $\sqrt[6]{125}$ $\sqrt{5}$
37. $\sqrt[3]{16} \cdot \sqrt[6]{4}$ $2\sqrt[3]{4}$
38. $\sqrt{2}\,\sqrt[3]{3}$ $\sqrt[6]{72}$
39. $\sqrt[6]{8} \div \sqrt[4]{25}$ $\frac{1}{5}\sqrt{10}$
40. $\sqrt[3]{\sqrt{8}}$ $\sqrt{2}$
41. $\sqrt[3]{\sqrt{2\sqrt{2}}}$ $\sqrt[4]{2}$
42. $\sqrt[3]{\sqrt[5]{64}}$ $\sqrt[5]{4}$

1–10 NUMBER LINES

An interesting feature of the real number system is that it may be used as a scale on a line. Thus, if we choose a unit of length, such as an inch or a centimeter, we may represent the integers as equispaced points (the chosen unit apart) on a line. (See Fig. 1–1.) By bisecting, trisecting, and so on, each unit segment, the rational numbers may also be assigned to points on the line. For example, $\frac{1}{2}$ is assigned to the point halfway between 0 and 1; $^{-}\frac{5}{3}$ is assigned to the point two-thirds of the way from $^{-}1$ to $^{-}2$; $\frac{12}{5}$ is assigned to the point two-fifths of the way from 2 to 3; and so on. The point O, which has zero assigned to it, is called the *origin*.

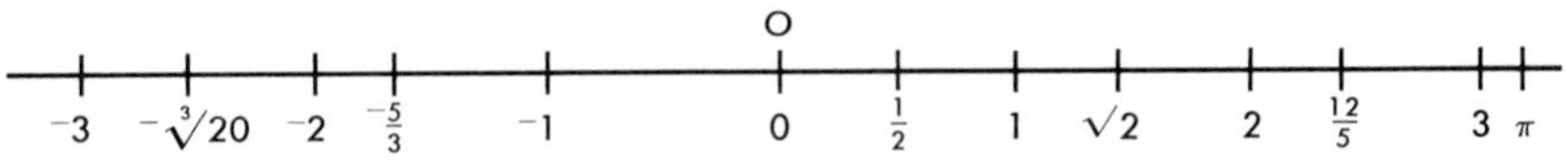

FIGURE 1–1

Quiz

Simplify each of the following expressions.

1. $25^{-1/2}$ (ans: $\frac{1}{5}$)
2. $(\frac{1}{27})^{-1/3}$ (ans: 3)
3. $36^{3/2} \cdot 6^{-2}$ (ans: 6)
4. $(x^{-2/9} \cdot y^{5/6})^{18}$ $\left(\text{ans: } \dfrac{y^{15}}{x^4}\right)$
5. $(81x^2y^2)^{-1/2}$ $\left(\text{ans: } \dfrac{1}{9xy}\right)$
6. $(11^2)^{1/2} - (11^2)^{-1/2}$ (ans: $10\frac{10}{11}$)

Exercise 33 should be taken up in class, as the students will need to understand it before proceeding to Exercises 31, 32, and 34–42.

1–10 NUMBER LINES

The analytical task of finding the directed distance from a first to a second point on a number line is important, as it clears the way for later work in the coordinate plane, each of the two axes being a number line on which it is still true that $d(AB) = b - a$.

The one-to-one correspondence between the points on a line and the members of the real number system is important enough to merit special emphasis.

Each irrational number can also be assigned to a point on the line. For example, we may find the point having $\sqrt{2}$ assigned to it in the way indicated in Fig. 1–2. In this figure, the partially drawn circle has its center at the origin and a radius of $\sqrt{2}$. Hence, it will intersect the given line at the point having $\sqrt{2}$ assigned to it.

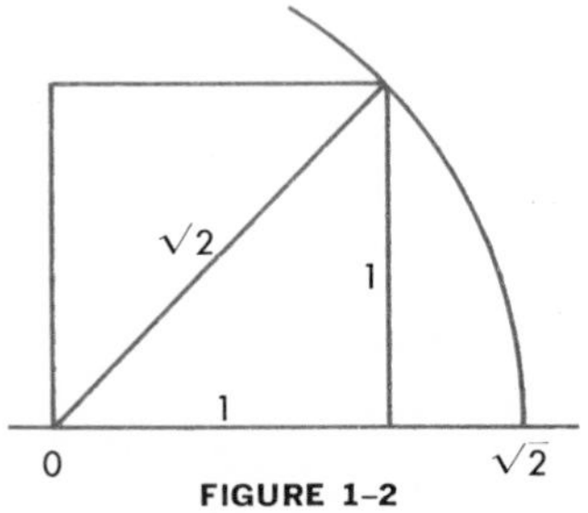

FIGURE 1–2

It is not possible to construct the point assigned to every real number by the method used for $\sqrt{2}$. For example, it is impossible (by means of straightedge and compass alone) to construct the point assigned to the irrational number π. However, we can imagine that there is a point representing π.

Each real number is assigned to a unique point on the line, and each point on the line has a unique real number assigned to it. A line having a real-number scale on it is called a *number line*. The number assigned to a point on the number line is called the *coordinate* of the point.

A number line may be assigned a *direction*. We shall always take the direction as that from the origin, O, toward the point with coordinate 1. Thus, if we imagine ourselves walking from left to right along the number line in Fig. 1–3, we are walking in the direction of the line, called the *positive direction*. We would be walking counter to the direction of the line, or in the *negative direction*, if we walked from right to left. The direction of a number line is indicated by an arrowhead as shown in Fig. 1–3. If point A on the line has coordinate a, then A is to the *right* of the origin O if, and only if, $a > 0$. Similarly, point B with coordinate b is to the *left* of O if, and only if, $b < 0$.

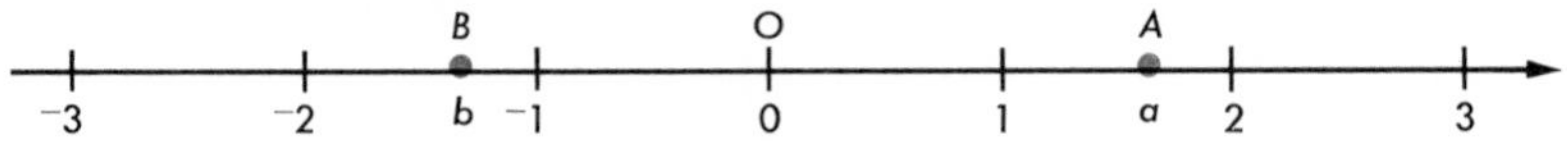

FIGURE 1–3

The distance between two points on a yardstick may be found by subtracting the coordinates of the two points. For example, the distance between points A and B on the yardstick of Fig. 1–4 is $29 - 21$,

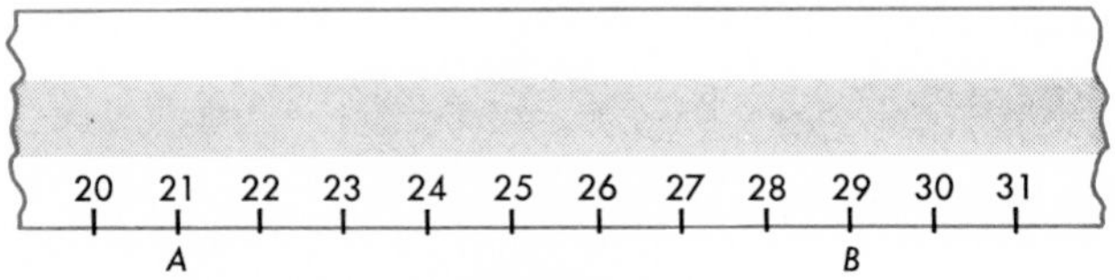

FIGURE 1–4

The terms *right* and *left* are used to indicate directions on a number line when the line is drawn in a horizontal position. If the line is drawn in a vertical position, the terms used are *above* and *below*. You could use several numerical examples to illustrate that the distance between two points is found by subtracting their coordinates. If capital letters are used for points and small letters for real numbers, the notation will be familiar when the formula is encountered on the next page.

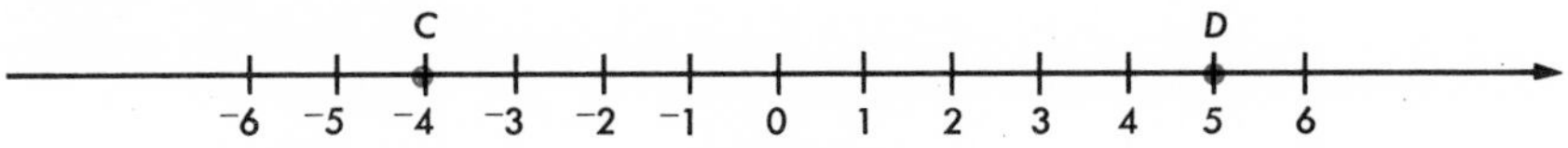

FIGURE 1-5

or 8 inches. It is possible to find the distance between any two points on a number line in the same way if the two points are on the same side of the origin. This situation is similar to our yardstick in Fig. 1–4.

If two points are on opposite sides of the origin, as are C and D in Fig. 1–5, then how do we find the distance between them? By counting unit intervals we see that the distance between C and D is 9. If we subtract the coordinate of C from that of D, we get

$$5 - {}^{-}4 = 5 + 4, \quad \text{or } 9.$$

Thus, we see that the distance between two points on opposite sides of the origin may also be found by subtracting their coordinates.

If we subtract coordinates in the opposite order in each of the cases above, we obtain 21 − 29, or $^{-}8$, for the distance between points A and B on the yardstick and $^{-}4 - 5$, or $^{-}9$, for the distance between points C and D on the number line. Each of these negative numbers is a *directed distance* as defined below.

DIRECTED DISTANCE

If points A and B on a number line have respective coordinates a and b, the directed distance from A to B is designated by d(AB) and is defined as

$$d(AB) = b - a.$$

If a number line is directed toward the right, as in Fig. 1–6, then point B is to the right of point A if, and only if, the coordinate of B is greater than the coordinate of A, that is, $b > a$. In this case, the directed distance from A to B is $b - a$, a positive number. On the other hand, point A is to the left of point B if, and only if, $a < b$. Then the directed distance from B to A is $a - b$, a negative number.

In either case, the distance or non-directed distance between points A and B, AB, is the absolute value of the difference of their coordinates, a and b.

$$AB = |a - b|$$

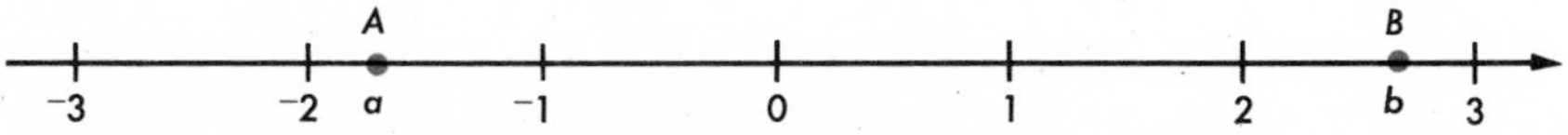

FIGURE 1-6

For a number line in a horizontal position, with the positive numbers on the right, point P with coordinate p is to the right of point Q with coordinate q if, and only if, $p > q$. If the directed distance from Q to P is $^{+}6$, this means P lies 6 units to the right of Q; if $d(QP) = {}^{-}4$, this means P lies 4 units to the left of Q.

To find the directed distance from P to Q, subtract the coordinate of the initial point from that of the terminal point.

On a vertical line, directed distance from P to Q is again the coordinate of the terminal point minus the coordinate of the initial point. Here, if the directed distance from A to B is $^{+}6$, then B lies 6 units above A. If the directed distance from A to B is $^{-}4$, then B lies 4 units below A.

Students should understand that the distance between points is found by *subtracting*, rather than adding.

One way to lead into the midpoint formula is with questions such as the following: Find the coordinate of the point midway between points *A* and *B* if *A* and *B* have coordinates as indicated in the table.

A	B	C midpoint of $\overline{AB}$
0	4	2
0	5	$2\frac{1}{2}$
0	$^-6$	$^-3$
1	3	2
1	$^-1$	0
$^-2$	4	1

Then you may want to ask for an observation about the way the coordinate of *C* is related to the coordinates of *A* and *B* before going through the proof.

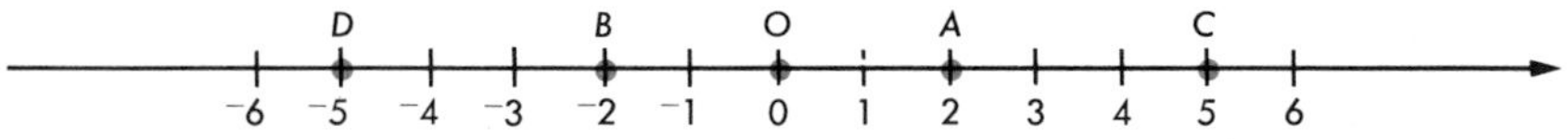

FIGURE 1–7

Knowing the directed distance between two points, we not only know the actual distance between the points, but we also know the direction from one point to the other.

To illustrate these ideas, consider the number line with points O, A, B, C, and D having the coordinates shown in Fig. 1–7. Then

$$\begin{aligned} d(OA) &= 2 - 0, \quad \text{or } 2; & d(AD) &= {}^-5 - 2, \quad \text{or } {}^-7; \\ d(OB) &= {}^-2 - 0, \quad \text{or } {}^-2; & d(DA) &= 2 - {}^-5, \quad \text{or } 7; \\ d(BC) &= 5 - {}^-2, \quad \text{or } 7; & d(DC) &= 5 - {}^-5, \quad \text{or } 10. \end{aligned}$$

Note that $d(OA) > 0$, and A is to the right of O; $d(OB) < 0$, and B is to the left of O; $d(BC) > 0$, and C is to the right of B; $d(AD) < 0$, and D is to the left of A.

For any three points A, B, and C on a number line, it is true that

$$d(AB) = {}^-d(BA)$$

and

$$d(AB) + d(BC) = d(AC).$$

If A, B, and C have respective coordinates a, b, and c, then

$$d(AB) = b - a, \quad d(BA) = a - b,$$

and the first equation is true because

$$b - a = {}^-(a - b).$$

Since $d(AB) = b - a$, $d(BC) = c - b$, and $d(AC) = c - a$, the second equation is true because

$$(b - a) + (c - b) = c - a.$$

If point C is the midpoint of the segment $\overline{AB}$, then $d(AC) = d(CB)$. Hence,

$$c - a = b - c,$$
$$2c = a + b,$$

and

$$c = \tfrac{1}{2}(a + b).$$

If we recall that one-half the sum of two numbers is called the *arithmetic mean* of the two numbers, then we have proved the following statement.

The coordinate of the midpoint of a segment of a number line is the arithmetic mean of the coordinates of the endpoints of the segment.

For example, if A has coordinate 2 and D has coordinate $^{-}5$, as shown in Fig. 1–7, the coordinate of the midpoint of segment $\overline{AD}$ is

$$\tfrac{1}{2}(2 + {}^{-}5), \quad \text{or } {}^{-}\tfrac{3}{2}.$$

Exercises for Discussion

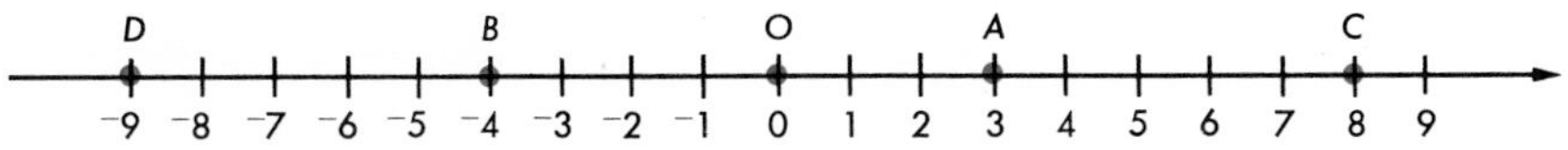

Refer to the figure to find each of the following directed distances.

1. $d(OB)$ $^{-}4-0={}^{-}4$ | **2.** $d(OA)$ $3-0=3$

3. $d(BA)$ $3-{}^{-}4=7$ | **4.** $d(AB)$ $^{-}4-3={}^{-}7$

5. $d(AB) + d(BC)$ $({}^{-}4-3)+(8-{}^{-}4)=5$ | **6.** $d(BD) + d(DO)$ $({}^{-}9-{}^{-}4)+(0-{}^{-}9)=4$

7. $d(BA) + d(AD)$ $(3-{}^{-}4)+({}^{-}9-3)={}^{-}5$ | **8.** $d(BA) + d(AC)$ $(3-{}^{-}4)+(8-3)=12$

Refer to the figure to find the coordinate of the midpoint of each of the following segments.

9. $\overline{OC}$ $\frac{1}{2}(0+8)=4$ **10.** $\overline{OB}$ $\frac{1}{2}(0+{}^{-}4)={}^{-}2$ **11.** $\overline{BC}$ $\frac{1}{2}({}^{-}4+8)=2$ **12.** $\overline{AB}$ $\frac{1}{2}(3+{}^{-}4)=\frac{{}^{-}1}{2}$

Exercises

Draw a number line, and on it, indicate points O, A, B, C, D, E, and F which have respective coordinates $0, {}^{-}\frac{1}{2}, {}^{-}4, \sqrt{2}, 2\sqrt{3}, {}^{-}6$, and 5. Find the following directed distances. See Solution Manual.

1. $d(OB)$ $^{-}4$ | **2.** $d(OC)$ $\sqrt{2}$

3. $d(AE)$ $^{-}5\frac{1}{2}$ | **4.** $d(AF)$ $5\frac{1}{2}$

5. $d(AF) - d(FA)$ 11 | **6.** $d(AB) + d(BA)$ 0

7. $d(EC) + d(CB) + d(EB)$ 4 | **8.** $d(CD) + d(DO) + d(OC)$ 0

9. $d(EC) + d(CD) + d(DF) + d(EF)$ 22

10. Refer to the number line that you drew for Exercises 1–9 to find each of the following.

(a) The coordinates of the points midway between A and B and between A and D $^{-}2\frac{1}{4}$; $\frac{{}^{-}1}{4}+\sqrt{3}$

(b) The coordinates of the points that bisect segments $\overline{BC}$, $\overline{EF}$, and $\overline{OD}$ $^{-}2+\frac{1}{2}\sqrt{2}$; $\frac{{}^{-}1}{2}$; $\sqrt{3}$

(c) The midpoint of segment $\overline{PQ}$ if P is the midpoint of segment $\overline{AF}$ and Q is the midpoint of segment $\overline{AB}$ 0

Exercises for Discussion

If time is limited, it is suggested that at least Exercises for Discussion 5–10 be covered.

Exercises 11 and 12 could be done in class, as students will need to understand them before proceeding to Exercises 13 and 14.

Answers to Exercises 11, 13, 14, 15(d)

11. (a) $(^-1 - {}^-5) + (6 - {}^-1) + (8 - 6)$
$= 4 + 7 + 2$
$= 13 = (8 - {}^-5)$

(b) $(^-10 - {}^-2) + (6 - {}^-10) + (^-5 - 6)$
$= {}^-8 + 16 + {}^-11$
$= {}^-3 = (^-5 - {}^-2)$

13. (a) $(^-1 - {}^-5)(8 - 6) + (6 - {}^-5)(^-1 - 8) + (8 - {}^-5)(6 - {}^-1)$
$= 4 \cdot 2 + 11 \cdot {}^-9 + 13 \cdot 7$
$= 8 + {}^-99 + 91 = 0$

(b) $(^-10 - {}^-2)(^-5 - 6) + (6 - {}^-2)(^-10 - {}^-5) + (^-5 - {}^-2)(6 - {}^-10)$
$= {}^-8 \cdot {}^-11 + 8 \cdot {}^-5 + {}^-3 \cdot 16$
$= 88 + {}^-40 + {}^-48 = 0$

14. $(b - a)(d - c) + (c - a)(b - d) + (d - a)(c - b)$
$= bd - bc - ad + ac + bc - cd - ab + ad + cd - bd - ac + ab = 0$

15. (d) $x = \dfrac{1}{r + s}(rb + sa)$

Before assigning Exercise 15, it might help the students to see a specific example of such a problem in class: Let $a = {}^-2$ and $b = 7$ for Exercise 15(a); for 15(b) use $a = {}^-3$, $b = 9$; and for 15(c), use $a = 1$, $b = 11$. This will help the student to understand Exercise 15 when it is assigned, and the formulas obtained in that problem can then be used to verify the answers to the problem above.

You may find it useful to discuss Exercise 17 in class, since it involves some good review of geometry.

△

11. Verify that the equation $d(AB) + d(BC) + d(CD) = d(AD)$ is true for points A, B, C, and D which have the following coordinates.

(a) $^-5$, $^-1$, 6, 8 (b) $^-2$, $^-10$, 6, $^-5$

12. Prove that the equation in Exercise 11 is true for any four points A, B, C, and D arranged in any order on a coordinate line by using a, b, c, and d to designate the coordinates of the four points.
$(b - a) + (c - b) + (d - c) = d - a$

13. Verify that the equation

$$[d(AB) \cdot d(CD)] + [d(AC) \cdot d(DB)] + [d(AD) \cdot d(BC)] = 0$$

is true for points A, B, C, and D which have the following coordinates.

(a) $^-5$, $^-1$, 6, 8 (b) $^-2$, $^-10$, 6, $^-5$

14. Prove that the equation in Exercise 13 is true for any four points A, B, C, and D arranged in any order on a coordinate line by using a, b, c, and d to designate the coordinates of the four points.

▲

15. Let A and B designate points on a number line with known coordinates a and b, respectively. For this exercise, A and B are considered fixed. Let P denote a variable point with unknown coordinate x.

(a) Given that $d(AP)/d(PB) = \frac{2}{1}$, find a formula for x in terms of a and b. $x = \frac{1}{3}(2b + a)$

(b) Find a formula for x if $d(AP)/d(PB) = \frac{3}{1}$. $x = \frac{1}{4}(3b + a)$

(c) Find a formula for x if $d(AP)/d(PB) = \frac{3}{2}$. $x = \frac{1}{5}(3b + 2a)$

(d) Find x if P divides $\overline{AB}$ into two segments in the ratio of $r : s$.

16. Find the coordinates of the trisection points of $\overline{AB}$ if A has coordinate $^-6$ and B has coordinate 5. (Hint: See Exercise 15(a).) $\frac{4}{3}$, $\frac{^-7}{3}$

17. After 0 and 1 have been located on a number line, can you suggest a ruler and compass method for locating the points corresponding to $\frac{1}{3}$ and $\frac{2}{3}$? Can you find $\frac{1}{4}$, $\frac{2}{4}$, and $\frac{3}{4}$? Can you find $\frac{1}{5}$, $\frac{2}{5}$, $\frac{3}{5}$, and $\frac{4}{5}$? Assuming this could be done, how would you find $\frac{8}{5}$? See Solution Manual.

HISTORICAL NOTE

The classic Greek scholars made a major contribution to mathematics by proving the existence of irrational numbers. Eudoxus (408–355 B.C.) developed a theory of the real number system which probably influenced Euclid to include number theory in his *Elements*. The proof of the irrationality of $\sqrt{2}$ dates back to at least the time of Pythagoras (circa 500 B.C.)

The Greek concept of real numbers was generally accepted in mathematics until the nineteenth century. After the great advances made in mathematics in the seventeenth and eighteenth centuries, mathematicians felt the need for a more precise statement of the fundamental properties of real numbers. Two German mathematicians, Cantor and Dedekind, are primarily responsible for the modern description of the system of real numbers.

In the nineteenth century, mathematicians discovered that there are two different kinds of irrational numbers: algebraic numbers and transcendental numbers. The number $\sqrt{2}$ is algebraic because it is a solution of the equation

$$x^2 - 2 = 0$$

having integral coefficients. Similarly, the number $\sqrt{5} - \sqrt{3}$ is algebraic because it is a solution of the equation

$$x^4 - 16x^2 + 4 = 0.$$

It is natural to wonder whether π is an algebraic number. In other words, does there exist an equation of the form

$$a_n x^n + a_{n-1}x^{n-1} + \cdots + a_1 x + a_0 = 0,$$

where $a_0, a_1, \ldots, a_{n-1}, a_n$ are integers and n is a positive integer, having π as a solution? This question was not answered until 1882, when the German mathematician Lindemann proved that π is not an algebraic number. Nonalgebraic real numbers, such as π, are called transcendental numbers.

KEY IDEAS AND KEY WORDS

The following are the fundamental properties of the real number system.

Commutative laws

$$x + y = y + x \qquad \text{(C-A)}$$

$$xy = yx \qquad \text{(C-M)}$$

Associative laws

$$(x + y) + z = x + (y + z) \qquad \text{(A-A)}$$

$$(xy)z = x(yz) \qquad \text{(A-M)}$$

Distributive law

$$x(y + z) = xy + xz \qquad \text{(D)}$$

Identity elements

$$x + 0 = x \qquad \text{(Id-A)}$$

$$x \cdot 1 = x \qquad \text{(Id-M)}$$

Inverse elements

$$x + {}^{-}x = 0 \qquad \text{(Inv-A)}$$

$$x \cdot \frac{1}{x} = 1, \quad \text{if } x \neq 0 \qquad \text{(Inv-M)}$$

Quiz

Draw a number line and on it, indicate points O, A, B, C, D, E, and F which have respective coordinates 0, 3, $2\sqrt{5}$, ${}^{-}\sqrt{2}$, ${}^{-}2\frac{1}{2}$, 6, and ${}^{-}1$. Find the following directed distances.

1. $d(AD)$ (ans: ${}^{-}5\frac{1}{2}$)
2. $d(CA)$ (ans: $3 + \sqrt{2}$)
3. $d(OB) - d(OA)$ (ans: $2\sqrt{5} - 3$)
4. $d(BE) + d(AB) + d(FO)$ (ans: 4)

TWISTER

One warm day, John left his school in the country to walk home. He had $3\frac{3}{4}$ miles to walk and began at exactly 3:45 P.M. At the same moment, his dog left home to meet him. John walked at a steady rate of 6 kilometers an hour; his dog raced at an average of 16 kilometers an hour. The dog met John, turned and ran back home, turned again and met John again, and then ran back home again. This went on until John reached home. How many kilometers did the dog run?

Solution: $3\frac{3}{4}$ miles = 6 kilometers. Thus, it took John one hour to walk home. Therefore, the dog was running for an hour, and thus ran 16 kilometers.

Uniqueness of addition

If $a = b$ and $c = d$, then $a + c = b + d$. (U-A)

Uniqueness of multiplication

If $a = b$ and $c = d$, then $ac = bd$. (U-M)

Order properties

If $x > 0$ and $y > 0$, then $x + y > 0$. (Clos-A)

If $x > 0$ and $y > 0$, then $xy > 0$. (Clos-M)

If x is a real number, then $x = 0$, $x > 0$, or $x < 0$. (Tri)

The following are some definitions that are valid for the real number system.

Definition of subtraction

$$x - y = x + {}^{-}y \qquad \text{(Def-Sub)}$$

Definition of division

$$x \div y = x \cdot \frac{1}{y}, \quad \text{if } y \neq 0 \qquad \text{(Def-Div)}$$

Definition of greater than

$x > y$ if, and only if, $x - y$ is positive (Def >)

Definition of less than

$x < y$ if, and only if, $y > x$ (Def <)

Definition of greater than or equal to

$x \geqq y$ if, and only if, either $x > y$ or $x = y$ (Def ≧)

Definition of less than or equal to

$x \leqq y$ if, and only if, $y \geqq x$ (Def ≦)

Definition of absolute value

$$|x| = x, \quad \text{if } x \geqq 0 \qquad \text{(Def } |x|\text{)}$$
$$|x| = {}^{-}x, \quad \text{if } x < 0$$

Operations have the following properties.

Uniqueness of subtraction

If $a = b$ and $c = d$, then $a - c = b - d$. (U-S)

Uniqueness of division

If $a = b$ and $c = d$ and $c \neq 0$, then $\frac{a}{c} = \frac{b}{d}$. (U-Div)

The following are properties which may be proved from the fundamental properties.

Rearrangement property of addition

The terms of a sum may be rearranged in any way. (R-A)

Rearrangement property of multiplication

The factors of a product may be rearranged in any way. (R-M)

Cancellation law of addition

If $x + z = y + z$, then $x = y$. (Can-A)

Cancellation law of multiplication

If $xz = yz$ and $z \neq 0$, then $x = y$. (Can-M)

Zero multiplication

$x \cdot 0 = 0$ for every real number x (Zero-M)

Negative multiplication

$$x \cdot {}^{-}y = {}^{-}(x \cdot y) \quad \text{(Neg-M)}$$

Transitive law of inequalities

If $x > y$ and $y > z$, then $x > z$. (T >)

Additive property of inequalities

If $x > y$, then $x + z > y + z$ for every real number z. (A >)

Multiplicative properties of inequalities

If $x > y$, then $xz > yz$ for every positive real number z. (${}^{+}$M >)

If $x > y$, then $xz < yz$ for every negative real number z. (${}^{-}$M >)

A nonzero rational number a/b is expressed in **simplest form** if $b > 0$ and the integers a and b are relatively prime.

We define

$$\mathbf{x^0 = 1 \quad \text{for every nonzero number } x.}$$

If n is a positive integer, then we define

$$x^n = \overbrace{x \cdot x \cdot \ldots \cdot x}^{n \text{ factors}}$$

and

$$x^{-n} = \frac{1}{x^n}, \quad \text{if } x \neq 0.$$

TWISTER

Between the Silver Lode and the Dead End mines are five others. The seven mines are an integral number of miles from each other along a straight road. The mines are so spaced that when a miner knows the number of miles a person has traveled between any two mines, he can determine which particular mines they were. What is the minimum distance between Silver Lode and Dead End for this to be possible?

Solution: The distance between the two mines must be at least 25 miles. The mines could then be located at distances 0, 1, 4, 10, 18, 23, and 25 miles from Silver Lode. There are 21 distances between mines and these are all distinct. There would be at least one duplication if the distance were any shorter.

The **laws of exponents** are as follows. They are true for all integers m and n and all nonzero real numbers x and y.

$$x^m \cdot x^n = x^{m+n} \qquad \text{(LE-1)}$$

$$\frac{x^m}{x^n} = x^{m-n} \qquad \text{(LE-2)}$$

$$(x^m)^n = x^{mn} \qquad \text{(LE-3)}$$

$$(x \cdot y)^n = x^n \cdot y^n \qquad \text{(LE-4)}$$

$$\left(\frac{x}{y}\right)^n = \frac{x^n}{y^n} \qquad \text{(LE-5)}$$

For every integer $n > 1$ and all real numbers x and y, the number y is called an ***n*th root** of x if, and only if,

$$y^n = x. \qquad \text{(Def-}n\text{th Rt.)}$$

The following are the **laws of radicals.** They are true for every integer $n > 1$ and all positive real numbers x and y and for all nonzero numbers x and y, if n is odd.

$$\sqrt[n]{x \cdot y} = \sqrt[n]{x} \cdot \sqrt[n]{y} \qquad \text{(LR-1)}$$

$$\sqrt[n]{\frac{x}{y}} = \frac{\sqrt[n]{x}}{\sqrt[n]{y}} \qquad \text{(LR-2)}$$

We define **rational exponents**

$$x^{\frac{m}{n}} = (\sqrt[n]{x})^m, \text{ or } \sqrt[n]{x^m}, \qquad \text{(Def-Rat. Exp.)}$$

for all integers m and n, with $n > 1$, and every positive real number x. If n is odd, x may also be a negative number. The laws of exponents are true for rational exponents as well as for integral exponents.

If points A and B on a number line have respectively coordinates a and b, then the **directed distance** from A to B is denoted by $d(AB)$ and defined by $d(AB) = b - a$. The **midpoint** of segment $\overline{AB}$ has coordinate $(a + b)/2$.

CHAPTER REVIEW

Give the reason or reasons why each of the following statements is true.

1. $x + (9 \cdot 5) = (5 \cdot 9) + x$ (C-A), (C-M)

2. $(x - 3) + 3 = x + (^-3 + 3)$ (Def-Sub), (A-A)

3. $x + ax = x(1 + a)$ (D)

4. If $\frac{x}{5} = \frac{3}{4} + \frac{x}{2}$, then $4x = 15 + 10x$. (U-M)

5. If $\frac{x}{5} + 19 = 3x + 19$, then $\frac{x}{5} = 3x$. (Can-A)

6. If $2x + 1 = 0$, then $x(2x + 1) = 0$. (U-M), (Zero-M)

7. If $8x + 12 = 5$, then $8x = {}^{-}7$. (U–S) or (U–A)

8. If ${}^{-}3x > 5$, then $x < {}^{-}\frac{5}{3}$. (⁻M>)

9. If $\frac{2}{3}x \geqq 10$, then $x \geqq 15$. (⁺M>)

10. If $x + 3 < 0$, then $|x + 3| = {}^{-}(x + 3)$. (Def |x|)

Perform the indicated operations.

11. $|5 - 7| - |7 - 5|$ 0

12. ${}^{-}|{}^{-}18 \cdot 19| \div |{}^{-}19 \cdot 18|$ ${}^{-}1$

13. $8 - 12 - 13$ ${}^{-}17$

14. $({}^{-}\frac{4}{5})({}^{-}\frac{20}{7})$ $\frac{16}{7}$

15. $(7 - 10) \div (20 - 26)$ $\frac{1}{2}$

16. $\sqrt{2} \cdot \sqrt{5}$ $\sqrt{10}$

17. $\sqrt[3]{{}^{-}125} \div \sqrt[3]{8}$ $\frac{{}^{-}5}{2}$

18. $16^{{}^{-}\frac{5}{4}} + 16^0$ $\frac{33}{32}$

19. $\dfrac{1}{2^{-1} + 3^{-1}}$ $\frac{6}{5}$

20. $(8^0 + 8)^{\frac{1}{2}}$ 3

In Exercises 21–30, perform the indicated operations and express each answer in simplest form.

21. $\sqrt{35} \cdot \sqrt{10}$ $5\sqrt{14}$

22. $\sqrt{\frac{8}{7}} \div \sqrt{\frac{5}{14}}$ $\frac{4}{5}\sqrt{5}$

23. $\frac{2}{3} - \frac{5}{2} - \frac{9}{5}$ $\frac{{}^{-}109}{30}$

24. $\dfrac{7^5 \cdot 6^8}{7 \cdot 6^{12}}$ $\frac{7^4}{6^4}$

25. $\left(\dfrac{4}{5}\right)^{-2}\left(\dfrac{8x^2y}{15xy^3}\right)^2$ $\frac{4x^2}{9y^4}$

26. $5^3 \cdot 125^7 \div 25^4$ 5^{16}

27. $\sqrt{12} \cdot \sqrt{50} \div \sqrt{63}$ $\frac{10}{21}\sqrt{42}$

28. $(3x^{-2}y^4)^{-3}$ $\frac{x^6}{27y^{12}}$

29. $2x^{-3} \div 5b^{-4}$ $\frac{2b^4}{5x^3}$

30. $x^{-12} \div x^{-15}$ x^3

31. Write each of the following expressions with positive exponents.
(a) $x^{-2} + y^2$ $\frac{1+x^2y^2}{x^2}$
(b) $x^{-2} - y^{-2}$ $\frac{y^2-x^2}{x^2y^2}$

For each expression, find an equivalent fraction with a rational denominator.

32. $\dfrac{6}{\sqrt{5}}$ $\frac{6}{5}\sqrt{5}$

33. $\dfrac{7}{\sqrt{14}}$ $\frac{1}{2}\sqrt{14}$

34. $\dfrac{8}{\sqrt{5} - 4}$ $\frac{{}^{-}8}{11}(\sqrt{5}+4)$

35. $\dfrac{\sqrt{5} - 2\sqrt{3}}{\sqrt{5} + 2\sqrt{3}}$ $\frac{4\sqrt{15}-17}{7}$

36. $\dfrac{1}{3\sqrt{3} - 2\sqrt{2} + \sqrt{5}}$ $\frac{1}{6}(7\sqrt{3}+8\sqrt{2}-5\sqrt{5}-2\sqrt{30})$

37. $\dfrac{4 + \sqrt{12} - \sqrt{27}}{2 + \sqrt{75}}$ $\frac{22\sqrt{3}-23}{71}$

In Exercises 38–45, perform the indicated operations and simplify.

38. $\sqrt[3]{{}^{-}16x^5y^9} - y\sqrt[3]{54x^2y^6}$ ${}^{-}(2x+3)y^3\sqrt[3]{2x^2}$

39. $\sqrt[4]{\dfrac{32p^9}{27q^2}} + \sqrt[4]{6pq^6}$ $\left(\frac{2p^2+3q}{3q}\right)\sqrt[4]{6pq^2}$

40. $\sqrt{18x} - \sqrt{50x^3}$ $(3-5x)\sqrt{2x}$

41. $\left(\dfrac{3}{\sqrt{2x}} - \dfrac{\sqrt{2x}}{3}\right)^2$ $\frac{(9-2x)^2}{18x}$

42. $5^{\frac{2}{3}} \cdot 5^{\frac{7}{3}}$ 125

43. $27^{\frac{4}{3}} \cdot 9^{\frac{3}{2}}$ 3^7

44. $\sqrt{2xy} \cdot \sqrt[3]{5x^2y^2}$ $xy\sqrt[6]{200xy}$

45. $\sqrt[3]{{}^{-}24x^4} - \sqrt[3]{81x^7}$ ${}^{-}(2x+3x^2)\sqrt[3]{3x}$

46. If x and y are real numbers such that $x > y$ and z is any real number, what relation must exist between $z - x$ and $z - y$? Prove that your statement is true. See Solution Manual.

47. If $x > y$ and $xy < 0$, state and prove the relation which exists between $1/x$ and $1/y$. See Solution Manual.

48. If x, y, z, and w are positive real numbers such that $x > y$ and $z > w$, prove that $xz > yw$. (Hint: By the multiplicative property, if $x > y$, then $x \cdot z > y \cdot z$ for z positive. Now start with $z > w$ and use the multiplier y.) See Solution Manual.

49. Prove that the equation

$$d(DA)^2 \cdot d(BC) + d(DB)^2 \cdot d(CA) + d(DC)^2 \cdot d(AB) = d(AB) \cdot d(BC) \cdot d(AC)$$

is true for any four points A, B, C, and D arranged in any order on a coordinate line. See Solution Manual.

In Exercises 50–56, draw a number line and indicate on it points O, R, S, T, P, and Q having respective coordinates 0, 5, $^-3$, 12, $^-4\frac{1}{2}$, and 20. Find each of the following directed distances. See Solution Manual.

50. $d(SR)$ 8

51. $d(PS)$ $1\frac{1}{2}$

52. $d(RO)$ $^-5$

53. $d(PR) + d(RT)$ $16\frac{1}{2}$

54. $d(SR) + d(RP)$ $^-1\frac{1}{2}$

55. $d(RT) - d(TR)$ 14

56. $d(PS) + d(SP)$ 0

57. Refer to the directions for Exercises 50–56 to find the coordinates of the midpoint of each of the following line segments.

(a) $\overline{OT}$ 6 (b) $\overline{SR}$ 1 (c) $\overline{PS}$ $\frac{^-15}{4}$ (d) $\overline{TQ}$ 16

58. Is

$$\left\{\frac{1}{x} \mid x \text{ is a nonzero integer}\right\}$$

closed with respect to multiplication? Yes

59. Is the set of multiples of 7 closed with respect to division? No

60. Is the set of positive integral powers of 2 closed with respect to subtraction? No

61. Is $\{x \mid x = r\sqrt{3}, r \text{ any rational number}\}$ closed with respect to addition? Yes

62. In each expression, find all integral values of x for which the expression is true.

(a) $|x + 7| = {}^-9$ $\emptyset$

(b) $|x - 3| \leq 7$ $\{^-4, ^-3, ^-2, ^-1, 0, 1, 2, 3, 4, 5, 6, 7, 8, 9, 10\}$

(c) $1 < |x + 2| < 8$ $\{^-9, ^-8, ^-7, ^-6, ^-5, ^-4, 0, 1, 2, 3, 4, 5\}$

(d) $|x| + 5 = 8$ $\{^-3, 3\}$

CHAPTER TEST

In Exercises 1–6, name the property of the real number system which justifies each statement.

1. $97(23 \cdot 31) = (97 \cdot 23) \cdot 31$ (A − M)
2. $(83 + 43) + (95 + 73) = (95 + 73) + (83 + 43)$ (C − A)
3. $74(6 + 4) = 74 \cdot 6 + 74 \cdot 4$ (D)
4. If $19 \cdot x = 19 \cdot (2x + 5)$, then $x = 2x + 5$. (Can − M)
5. If $17x + 3 = 5 + x$, then $17x = 2 + x$. (Can−A), or (U−S)
6. If $^-3x > 12$, then $x < {}^-4$. ($^-$M>)
7. In each expression, find all integral values of x for which the expression is true.

   (a) $|x - 4| = 10$ $\{^-6, 14\}$ (b) $|x + 4| \leqq 3$ $\{^-7, ^-6, ^-5, ^-4, ^-3, ^-2, ^-1\}$ (c) $3 \leqq |x| \leqq 6$ $\{^-6, ^-5, ^-4, ^-3, 3, 4, 5, 6\}$

Perform the indicated operations and express each answer in simplest form.

8. $\sqrt{33} \cdot \sqrt{22}$ $11\sqrt{6}$
9. $\sqrt{\frac{5x}{3y}} \div \sqrt{\frac{35x^2}{12y^6}}$ $\frac{2y^2}{7x}\sqrt{7xy}$
10. $\sqrt{50x^3y} - \sqrt{98xy^3}$ $(5x-7y)\sqrt{2xy}$
11. $\sqrt{6} \cdot \sqrt[3]{36}$ $6\sqrt[6]{6}$
12. $\left(\frac{\sqrt{x}}{5} - \frac{5}{\sqrt{x}}\right)^2$ $\frac{x}{25} - 2 + \frac{25}{x}$ or $\frac{(x-25)^2}{25x}$
13. $\sqrt[3]{^-6x^2y^5} \cdot \sqrt[3]{72x^5y}$ $^-6x^2y^2\sqrt[3]{2x}$

For each of the following expressions, find an equivalent fraction with a rational denominator.

14. $\frac{2}{\sqrt{3}}$ $\frac{2\sqrt{3}}{3}$
15. $\frac{5}{\sqrt{2} - 3}$ $\frac{^-(5\sqrt{2}+15)}{7}$
16. $\frac{4}{\sqrt{5} - \sqrt{7}}$ $^-2(\sqrt{5}+\sqrt{7})$

In Exercises 17–20, perform the indicated operations.

17. $9^{\frac{3}{2}} - 27^0 + 8^{-\frac{1}{3}}$ $26\frac{1}{2}$
18. $7^{\frac{3}{5}} \cdot 7^{\frac{2}{5}} \div 7^{-2}$ 7^3
19. $\frac{2}{3^{-1} + 5^{-1}}$ $\frac{15}{4}$
20. $\sqrt[4]{9} \cdot \sqrt{3}$ 3
21. (a) If A, B, and C are points on a number line with respective coordinates $^-10$, $^-6$, and 7, find the following directed distances.

   $$d(BC) \quad \text{and} \quad d(CB) + d(BA)$$

   13 and $^-17$

   (b) Find the midpoint of segment $\overline{AC}$. $\frac{^-3}{2}$
22. Use the properties of the real number system to prove that if $a < b$ and $c < d$, then $ac < bd$, when a, b, c, and d are positive real numbers.

   If $a<b$ and $c>0$, then $ac<bc$ ($^+$M<)
   If $c<d$ and $b>0$, then $bc<bd$ ($^+$M<)
   If $ac<bc$ and $bc<bd$, then $ac<bd$ (T<)

CHAPTER TEST

The material included in the Chapter Test was covered in the following sections:

Problems 1-3—Section 1-1
Problems 4 and 5—Section 1-2
Problem 6—Section 1-3
Problem 7—Section 1-4
Problems 8-16—Section 1-8
Problems 17-20—Section 1-9
Problem 21—Section 1-10
Problem 22—Section 1-3

CHAPTER 2

First-Degree Equations and Inequalities

The purpose of this chapter is to give the students an opportunity to review the procedures needed to solve equations and inequalities of the first degree. It is also intended as a review of the slope of the graph of a linear equation, the procedures for finding the solution set of a system of inequalities or equations of the first degree, and the procedures for solving word problems. Chapter 2 also provides an opportunity for students to study matrices and determinants for the first time.

The following are some of the topics covered in Chapter 2:

- *Linear equations*
- *Word problems involving linear equations*
- *Linear inequalities*
- *Slope*
- *Graph of a linear equation*
- *Graph of a linear inequality*
- *Systems of equations in two variables*
- *Word problems involving systems of equations in two variables*
- *Systems of inequalities in two variables*
- *Systems of equations in three or more variables*
- *Matrices and determinants*
- *Linear programming*

It is suggested that one day be spent on each section of this chapter with the exception of the starred section on matrices and determinants, which may require more time.

CHAPTER 2

Modern computers enable mathematicians and scientists to solve complex systems of equations and inequalities with speed and accuracy. (Courtesy of the General Electric Company)

FIRST-DEGREE EQUATIONS AND INEQUALITIES

The principal topic of algebra over the centuries has been solving equations. In modern times, inequalities have also been studied because of their many applications to other sciences. The simplest equations and inequalities are those of the first degree in their variables.

A linear equation in one variable usually has one solution. For example, the equation

$$2x + 3 = 13$$

has the unique solution $x = 5$. On the other hand, a linear equation in two variables usually has infinitely many solutions.

Most inequalities and systems of inequalities have infinite sets as solutions. For example, the inequality

$$2x + 3 > 13$$

has any number greater than 5 as a solution.

55

2-1 EQUATIONS IN ONE VARIABLE

The student should understand that the solution set of an equation in x is the set of values of x which makes the equation true. Thus, the solution set for the equation

$$(x + 1)(x - 4)(3x - 5) = 0$$

is $\{^{-}1, \frac{5}{3}, 4\}$.

A set of *equivalent equations* is two or more equations having the same solution set. Thus, the set of four equations listed below is a set of equivalent equations, the solution set in each case being $\{^{-}4\}$.

$$2 + \frac{3w + 1}{6} = \frac{4w - 3}{2} - \frac{5w - 9}{3}$$
$$\frac{3w + 13}{6} = \frac{2w + 9}{6}$$
$$3w + 13 = 2w + 9$$
$$w = {}^{-}4$$

An equation is solved by writing a system of equivalent equations, each simpler than the previous one, until a stage is reached where the solution set is obvious. The solution set, which is $\{^{-}4\}$ in this case, may then be checked in each equation, proceeding from the last one to the first one. However, it is customary to skip from the last equation back to the given equation for the check, assuming that no error in the first equation implies no errors in the intermediate stages of the solution.

2-1 EQUATIONS IN ONE VARIABLE

Each of the algebraic expressions

$$3x - 7, \quad 11x + 33, \quad 4x, \quad {}^{-}2, \quad 0$$

is called a linear form in the variable x. Thus, a *linear form in the variable x* is an algebraic expression of the type

$$ax + b,$$

where a and b are real numbers. Of course, there are linear forms in other variables. For example, $7y - 11$ is a linear form in the variable y.

If, in a linear form, we give the variable a value, the resulting number is called a *value* of the linear form. For example, the linear form $3x - 7$ has the value $(3 \cdot 5) - 7$, or 8, when $x = 5$.

If two linear forms in the same variable are connected by an equals sign, the resulting algebraic statement is called a *first-degree equation*, or *linear equation*, in that variable. For example,

$$3x - 7 = 11x + 33$$

is a first-degree equation in the variable x.

A number is called a *solution* of an equation in one variable if a true equation is obtained when we give the variable the value of the number. For example, 2 is a solution of the equation $3x - 1 = 7 - x$ since the equation obtained by letting $x = 2$ is true:

$$(3 \cdot 2) - 1 = 7 - 2, \quad \text{or } 5 = 5.$$

On the other hand, 3 is not a solution of this equation since the equation obtained by letting $x = 3$ is false:

$$(3 \cdot 3) - 1 = 7 - 3, \quad \text{or } 8 = 4.$$

If an equation has any solutions, then the set of all its solutions is called the *solution set of the equation*. If an equation has no solution, then its solution set is the empty set, $\emptyset$. When we *solve* an equation, we find its solution set.

Two or more equations in a variable are said to be *equivalent equations* if they have the same solution set. The process of solving an equation involves replacing the given equation by a succession of equivalent equations until we obtain an equation with an obvious solution set. For example, the given equation might be

$$2(x - 4) + 2x + 27 = 3(x + 7),$$

and the final equivalent one might be $x = 2$.

Since $\{2\}$ is the solution set of the final equation, we can show that $\{2\}$ is also the solution set of the given equation.

We can use properties, such as the uniqueness properties of addition and multiplication and the cancellation laws of addition and multiplication, to derive equivalent equations from a given equation. These properties and several others are used in the following problems.

Problem 1. Solve the equation $3x - 7 = 11x + 33$.

Solution. Each of the following equations is equivalent to the preceding one for the reason given.

$$3x - 7 = 11x + 33$$

$$(3x - 7) + (^-11x + 7) = (11x + 33) + (^-11x + 7) \qquad \text{(U-A)}$$

$$^-8x = 40 \qquad \text{(R-A)}$$

$$^-(\tfrac{1}{8})(^-8x) = {}^-(\tfrac{1}{8}) \cdot 40 \qquad \text{(U-M)}$$

$$x = {}^-5 \qquad \text{(U-M)}$$

Thus, $\{^-5\}$ is the solution set of the given equation.

Check.

$$(3 \cdot {}^-5) - 7 \stackrel{?}{=} (11 \cdot {}^-5) + 33$$

$$^-15 - 7 \stackrel{?}{=} {}^-55 + 33$$

$$^-22 \stackrel{\checkmark}{=} {}^-22$$

We check the solution to catch possible computational errors and to be certain that no errors have been made in forming each equivalent equation. If no errors have been made, the solution set of the final equation must be the solution set of the given equation.

Problem 2. Solve the equation $\frac{1}{3}y - 12 = 4 - \frac{3}{5}y$.

Solution. As before, we proceed by finding equivalent equations.

$$\tfrac{1}{3}y - 12 = 4 - \tfrac{3}{5}y$$

$$(\tfrac{1}{3}y - 12) + (\tfrac{3}{5}y + 12) = (4 - \tfrac{3}{5}y) + (\tfrac{3}{5}y + 12)$$

$$\tfrac{1}{3}y + \tfrac{3}{5}y = 4 + 12$$

$$(\tfrac{1}{3} + \tfrac{3}{5})y = 16$$

$$\tfrac{14}{15}y = 16$$

$$\tfrac{15}{14} \cdot \tfrac{14}{15}y = \tfrac{15}{14} \cdot 16$$

$$y = \tfrac{120}{7}$$

Thus, $\{17\frac{1}{7}\}$ is the solution set of the given equation.

In an average class, it may be well to do some of the sample problems in more than one way and to do some using all the steps. Then the student may progress to shorter procedures as he gains understanding and becomes more competent. For example, Problem 1 could be done in the following manner.

$$3x - 7 = 11x + 33$$

$$3x - 7 + 7 = 11x + 33 + 7 \qquad \text{(U-A)}$$

$$3x = 11x + 40 \qquad \text{(Inv-A)}$$

$$3x - 11x = 11x + 40 - 11x \qquad \text{(U-A)}$$

$$^-8x = 40 \qquad \text{(D), (R-A), (Inv-A)}$$

$$^-\tfrac{1}{8}(^-8x) = {}^-\tfrac{1}{8}(40) \qquad \text{(U-M)}$$

$$x = {}^-5 \qquad \text{(A-M), (Inv-M)}$$

Exercises for Discussion

If time is limited, it is suggested that at least Exercises for Discussion 2–7 be covered.

Exercises for Discussion 2–4 should be stressed as the concept of equivalent equations (those with the same solution set) cannot be overemphasized. Exercise for Discussion 2(b) demonstrates the common error of not multiplying the integer 5 by the l.c.m. of 2 and 3. Exercise for Discussion 3(b) demonstrates the frequent error of dividing the divisor of x into the number on the right. Performing the step

$$7 \cdot \frac{x}{7} = 7 \cdot 42$$

will help the student to avoid this mistake.

Answers to Exercises for Discussion 7–8

7. $4 - \frac{2x+1}{4} = \frac{1}{2} - \frac{9x+9}{8}$

$8\left(4 - \frac{2x+1}{4}\right)$

$= 8\left(\frac{1}{2} - \frac{9x+9}{8}\right)$

$32 - 2(2x+1) = 4 - (9x+9)$

$32 - 4x - 2 = 4 - 9x - 9$

$(30 - 4x) + (^-30 + 9x)$

$= (^-5 - 9x) + (^-30 + 9x)$

$5x = {}^-35$

$x = {}^-7$

8. $\frac{x-13}{3} = \frac{78-x}{10}$

$30\left(\frac{x-13}{3}\right) = 30\left(\frac{78-x}{10}\right)$

$10(x - 13) = 3(78 - x)$

$(10x - 130) + (3x + 130)$

$= (234 - 3x) + (3x + 130)$

$13x = 364$

$x = 28$

Check.

$$\left(\tfrac{1}{3} \cdot \tfrac{120}{7}\right) - 12 \stackrel{?}{=} 4 - \left(\tfrac{3}{5} \cdot \tfrac{120}{7}\right)$$

$$\tfrac{40}{7} - 12 \stackrel{?}{=} 4 - \tfrac{72}{7}$$

$$\frac{40 - 84}{7} \stackrel{?}{=} \frac{28 - 72}{7}$$

$$\frac{^-44}{7} \stackrel{\checkmark}{=} \frac{^-44}{7}$$

Exercises for Discussion

1. (a) Find the value of the linear form $3x + 7$ for each of the following values of x.

$^-100,\ ^-5,\ ^-2\tfrac{1}{3},\ 0,\ 2,\ \pi,\ 3\tfrac{1}{7},\ \sqrt{7}$

$^-293,\ ^-8,\ 0,\ 7,\ 13,\ 3\pi+7,\ \tfrac{115}{7},\ 3\sqrt{7}+7$

(b) Find the value of the linear form $3(x + \frac{7}{3})$ for each of the following values of x.

$^-100,\ ^-2\tfrac{1}{3},\ 0,\ 2,\ \pi$

$^-293,\ 0,\ 7,\ 13,\ 3\pi+7$

(c) For what values of x are the linear forms

$$3x + 7 \quad \text{and} \quad 3(x + \tfrac{7}{3})$$

equal? Why? *All real values; (D)*

Tell whether the two equations of each given pair are equivalent. If not, change the second equation to make them equivalent.

2. (a) $\frac{x}{2} - \frac{x}{3} = 5$ *Not equivalent, change (b) to*

(b) $3x - 2x = 5$ *$3x - 2x = 30$*

3. (a) $\frac{x}{7} = 42$ *Not equivalent, change (b) to*

(b) $x = 6$ *$x = 294$*

4. (a) $\frac{x-3}{5} + \frac{3}{2} = 4 + \frac{5-x}{10}$ *Equivalent*

(b) $2x - 6 + 15 = 40 + 5 - x$

Solve each of the following equations by writing a succession of equivalent equations, and check each solution.

5. $2(3x + 2) - 12 = 3x - 11$ *$x = {}^-1$*

6. $\frac{1}{5}(x + 1) = \frac{2}{3} + \frac{1}{9}(x - 1)$ *$x = 4$*

7. $4 - \frac{2x+1}{4} = \frac{1}{2} - \frac{9x+9}{8}$

8. $\frac{x-13}{3} = \frac{78-x}{10}$

9. $5\left(\frac{x+2}{3}\right) - x = \frac{20}{3}$

$5(x+2) - 3x = 20$

$5x + 10 - 3x = 20$

$(2x + 10) + {}^-10 = 20 + {}^-10$

$2x = 10$

$x = 5$

Exercises

Tell whether the two equations of each given pair are equivalent. If not, change the second equation to make them equivalent.

1. (a) $5x - 6 = 17$ (b) $5x = 11$ Not equivalent, change (b) to $5x = 23$
2. (a) $3x = 15$ (b) $x = 12$ Not equivalent, change (b) to $x = 5$
3. (a) $3(x - 2) - 5 = 8 - 2(x - 4)$ (b) $3x - 6 - 5 = 8 - 2x - 8$ Not equivalent, change (b) to $3x - 6 - 5 = 8 - 2x + 8$

Solve each of the following equations by writing a succession of equivalent equations, and check each solution.

4. $3x + 4 = x + 12$ 4
5. $3 - 7x = 4x - 30$ 3
6. $y = 20 - 3(y + 4)$ 2
7. $\frac{x}{5} - 1 = 6$ 35
8. $3(x - 3) = 7(2x + 1)$ $\frac{-16}{11}$
9. $5z + \frac{1}{3} = 2z - \frac{3}{2}$ $\frac{-11}{18}$
10. $\frac{1}{2}x - \frac{6}{5} = 12 - \frac{3}{2}x$ $\frac{33}{5}$
11. $0.13y + 1.17 = 1.23y - 0.04$ $\frac{11}{10}$
12. $\frac{1}{5}(x + 2) = \frac{2}{3} + \frac{1}{9}x$ 3
13. $6.1 - 5w = 4.6w + 3.22$ $\frac{3}{10}$

△

Solve each of the following equations by writing a succession of equivalent equations, and check each solution.

14. $\frac{x + 3}{5} - 2 = \frac{3x + 2}{4} - 3$ 2
15. $4 - \frac{2x - 1}{4} = \frac{1}{2} - \frac{9x}{8}$ -6
16. $\frac{6y - 1}{5} - 3y = \frac{12y - 16}{15}$ $\frac{1}{3}$
17. $2 + \frac{3w + 1}{6} = \frac{4w - 3}{2} - \frac{5w - 9}{3}$ -4
18. $5z - \frac{1}{5} = 3(z + \frac{13}{15})$ $\frac{7}{5}$
19. $\frac{x - 4}{3} = \frac{69 - x}{10}$ 19
20. $.6(1 - .8x) = .5 - .4(2 - 1.8x)$ $\frac{3}{4}$
21. $\frac{1}{3}(u + 8) - \frac{1}{4}(3 - 2u) = \frac{1}{6}$ $\frac{-21}{10}$
22. $t + 13 = 3 - 2(1 + t)$ -4
23. $\frac{w}{3} - \frac{4w + 1}{2} = w - \frac{5}{6}$ $\frac{1}{8}$

It might be useful to discuss Exercises 24–26 in class. In Exercise 25, the linear forms

$$3x + 12 \text{ and } 3(x + 4)$$

should be considered. In Exercise 26, it might be asked whether the solution for $x = 3$ is also a solution for $x^2 = 3x$ and whether any value for x other than 3 makes $x^2 = 3x$ true.

The student needs to understand that not all operations performed on both sides of an equation lead to an equation having the same solution set as the original one.

Quiz

Solve each of the following equations by writing a succession of equivalent equations.

1. $2x + 7 = 4x + 5$ (ans: 1)
2. $3 - 4x = 4x - 9$ (ans: $\frac{3}{2}$)
3. $10 - 3(x - 3) = x$ (ans: $\frac{19}{4}$)
4. $\frac{1}{5} + \frac{4}{5}x = \frac{3}{5}(x - 1)$ (ans: $^-4$)
5. $2.1y + 3.1 = 9.4$ (ans: 3)

2–2 WORD PROBLEMS

Problem 1 may be worked differently in class by letting x denote the number of miles driven in the country. Then

$$100 - x$$

denotes the number of miles driven in the city,

$$\frac{100 - x}{30}$$

is the number of hours of driving in the city, and

$$\frac{x}{60}$$

is the number of hours of driving in

24. For what value of x does the linear form $3x + 7$ have the same value as the linear form $5x - 3$? 5

25. If two linear forms in x have the same value for more than one value of x, for how many values of x do you suspect that they will have the same value? All real values of x (infinitely many)

26. Are the equations $x = 3$ and $x^2 = 3x$ equivalent?
No. The first has solution set $\{3\}$ and the second $\{0, 3\}$.

2–2 WORD PROBLEMS

As the following examples show, we can use linear equations in one variable to solve many kinds of word problems.

Problem 1. It takes a man 2 hours to drive a distance of 100 miles. If he averages 60 miles per hour in the country and 30 miles per hour in each city he passes through, how great a part of the trip does he spend in the country?

Solution. If we let t designate the number of hours he spends driving in the country, then $2 - t$ is the number of hours he spends driving in cities. The formula relating distance, d, rate, r, and time, t, is

$$d = rt.$$

Thus, the man drives a distance of $30(2 - t)$ miles in cities and $60t$ miles in the country. It is given that the sum of these distances is 100 miles:

$$60t + 30(2 - t) = 100.$$

We can solve the problem by solving the above first-degree equation in t. Let us proceed as follows:

$$\begin{aligned} 60t + 60 - 30t &= 100, \\ 30t + 60 &= 100, \\ (30t + 60) - 60 &= 100 - 60, \\ 30t &= 40, \\ t &= \tfrac{4}{3}. \end{aligned}$$

Thus, the man spends $\frac{4}{3}$ hours, or 1 hour and 20 minutes, driving in the country and $2 - \frac{4}{3}$ hours, or 40 minutes, driving in cities. He drives a distance of

$$60 \cdot \tfrac{4}{3}, \quad \text{or } 80,$$

miles in the country and $30 \cdot \frac{2}{3}$, or 20, miles in cities. Since

$$80 + 20 = 100,$$

these answers are correct.

An interesting type of problem involves the mixing of two substances in order to form a prescribed mixture. We can use first-degree equations to solve these problems also.

Problem 2. If a certain sample of sea water contains 8% salt, how much fresh water must we add to 40 pounds of the sea water so that the mixture contains only 5% salt?

Solution. In the 40 pounds of sea water, there are $.08 \times 40$, or 3.2, pounds of salt. If we add N pounds of fresh water to the 40 pounds of sea water, we can obtain $N + 40$ pounds of water. We add only fresh water to the salt water. Therefore, the amount of salt in our mixture remains the same. Since we want 5% of the mixture to be salt, we must have

$$.05(N + 40) = 3.2.$$

We may solve the above first-degree equation in N as follows:

$$\begin{aligned} .05N + 2 &= 3.2, \\ (.05N + 2) - 2 &= 3.2 - 2 \\ .05N &= 1.2, \\ N &= \frac{1.2}{.05}, \\ N &= 24. \end{aligned}$$

Thus, we must add 24 pounds of fresh water.

Check.

$$\begin{aligned} .05(24 + 40) &\overset{?}{=} 3.2 \\ .05 \times 64 &\overset{\checkmark}{=} 3.2 \end{aligned}$$

Problem 3. If a gallon of alcohol is 95% pure (that is, 95% of the gallon is pure alcohol and 5% is water), how much water must we add to obtain a mixture that will contain 60% alcohol?

Solution. If we add G gallons of water, then we obtain $G + 1$ gallons of the mixture of which

$$.60(G + 1)$$

is to be pure alcohol. Since we started with .95 gallons of pure alcohol

the country. Since the total driving time is 2 hours, we can say

$$\begin{aligned} \frac{100 - x}{30} + \frac{x}{60} &= 2, \\ 200 - 2x + x &= 120, \\ x &= 80, \\ 100 - x &= 20. \end{aligned}$$

and added no alcohol, the mixture still contains .95 gallons of pure alcohol. Thus,

$$.60(G + 1) = .95.$$

The above equation may be solved for G as follows:

$$\begin{aligned} .60G + .60 &= .95, \\ (.60G + .60) - .60 &= .95 - .60, \\ .60G &= .35, \\ G &= \frac{.35}{.60}, \quad \text{or } \frac{7}{12}. \end{aligned}$$

Thus, we must add $\frac{7}{12}$ gallons, or $2\frac{1}{3}$ quarts, of water to the alcohol.

Check.

$$\begin{aligned} .60(1 + \tfrac{7}{12}) &\stackrel{?}{=} .95 \\ .60 \times \tfrac{19}{12} &\stackrel{?}{=} .95 \\ .05 \times 19 &\stackrel{\checkmark}{=} .95 \end{aligned}$$

Exercises for Discussion

1. Let x denote an arbitrary integer, and write an algebraic expression for each of the following phrases.
   (a) The sum of four consecutive integers *e.g., $x+(x+1)+(x+2)+(x+3) = 4x+6$*
   (b) The sum of three consecutive odd integers *$(2x+1)+(2x+3)+(2x+5) = 6x+9$ or $(2y-1)+(2y+1)+(2y+3) = 6y+3$*
   (c) Three more than five times an integer *$3+5x$*
2. Consider a collection of 4¢ and 5¢ stamps. Let x denote the number of 4¢ stamps in the collection, and write an algebraic expression for each of the following phrases.
   (a) The cost of the 4¢ stamps *$4x$ (in cents), $.04x$ (in dollars)*
   (b) The number of 5¢ stamps if it is known that there are three times as many 5¢ stamps as 4¢ stamps *$3x$*
   (c) The cost of the 5¢ stamps *$15x$ (in cents), $.15x$ (in dollars)*
   (d) The number of 5¢ stamps if there are 100 stamps in the collection *$100-x$*
   (e) The cost of a collection of 50 stamps *$4x+5(50-x) = 250-x$ (in cents)*
3. Write an algebraic expression for each of the following phrases.
   (a) The distance between two trains at the end of t hours if they left the same station at the same time, were headed in the same direction, and one was traveling at a rate of 50 miles per hour and the other at 70 miles per hour *$70t - 50t = 20t$ miles*

Exercises for Discussion

You may want to cover the Exercises for Discussion in some detail in class. As the phrases are translated into mathematical expressions, questions might be formulated that could use those expressions. For Exercise for Discussion 1(a), for example, the question might be, "Are there four consecutive integers with the sum 1056?" This question can be answered by solving the equation

$$(x - 2) + (x - 1) + x + (x + 1) = 1056$$

or the equation

$$x + (x + 1) + (x + 2) + (x + 3) = 1056$$

to see if x is an integer.

(b) The distance between the trains in part (a) if they were headed in opposite directions $70t + 50t = 120t$ miles

(c) The distance separating two boys h hours after the first boy leaves camp, walking $2\frac{1}{2}$ miles per hour, if the second boy leaves camp three hours later, walking $3\frac{1}{2}$ miles per hour in the same direction $|2\frac{1}{2}h - 3\frac{1}{2}(h-3)|$ miles

4. Find two consecutive even integers whose sum is 126.

5. There are 40 coins in a collection of nickels and quarters, and the collection is worth \$5.40. How many nickels are there?

6. A pair of slacks has been marked down 15% and sells for \$12.75. What was the original price of the slacks?

Exercises

1. Let x denote Jane's present age in years, and write an algebraic expression for each of the following phrases.
   (a) Twice Jane's age next year $2(x+1)$
   (b) Four times Jane's age 3 years ago $4(x-3)$
   (c) The present age of Jane's mother if her mother is now twice as old as Jane will be 3 years from now $2(x+3)$
   (d) The present age of Jane's father if his age is now 3 years less than 4 times Jane's age 7 years ago $4(x-7)-3$

2. Write an algebraic expression for each of the following phrases, and simplify it.
   (a) The cost of 10 pounds of candy if some of it costs \$1.69 a pound and the rest costs \$1.98 a pound $169x + 198(10-x)$ (in cents)
   (b) The amount of alcohol in a mixture after x ounces of a solution which is 65% alcohol is added to 15 ounces of a solution which is 75% alcohol $.65x + .75(15)$ (in ounces)
   (c) The income from two investments totaling \$10,000 if part of it is invested at $3\frac{1}{2}\%$ and the rest is invested at $4\frac{3}{4}\%$ $.035x + .0475(10{,}000 - x)$ (in dollars)

Write an equation for each of the following problems, and solve it. In each case, tell what is denoted by the variable that you use.

3. Find three consecutive even integers whose sum is 126. 40, 42, 44

4. Find four consecutive odd integers whose sum is 136. 31, 33, 35, 37

5. If 3 times a number is added to 5 times the negative of the number, the sum is 12. Find the number. $^{-}6$

6. These early questions in algebra come from the Rhind papyrus, dated about 1600–1800 B.C. An Egyptian teacher put them to his pupil.
   (a) "Heap" and twice the "heap"; the total is 18. Tell me, my young friend, what is the "heap"? 6
   (b) "Heap" and one-fifth the "heap," take away three; the result is 21. What is the "heap"? 20

Answers to Exercises for Discussion 4–6

4. Let $2k$ be the smaller and $2k + 2$ the larger integer.

$$\begin{aligned} 2k + (2k+2) &= 126 \\ 4k &= 124 \\ k &= 31 \\ 2k &= 62 \\ 2k+2 &= 64 \end{aligned}$$

5. Let N be the number of nickels. Then $40 - N$ is the number of quarters; N nickels are worth $5N$ cents and $40 - N$ quarters are worth $25(40 - N)$ cents. Since the collection is worth 540 cents,

$$\begin{aligned} 5N + 25(40 - N) &= 540 \\ N &= 23. \end{aligned}$$

There are 23 nickels in the collection.

6. Let x be the original price (in dollars). Then

$$\begin{aligned} x - .15x &= 12.75, \\ .85x &= 12.75, \\ x &= 15. \end{aligned}$$

The original price is \$15.

Exercises

It is suggested that Exercises 1 and 2 be discussed in class.

In exercises such as 16 and 17, it may help the student to understand the problems if he draws diagrams of them. For example, in Exercise 16, the diagram might look like the one below.

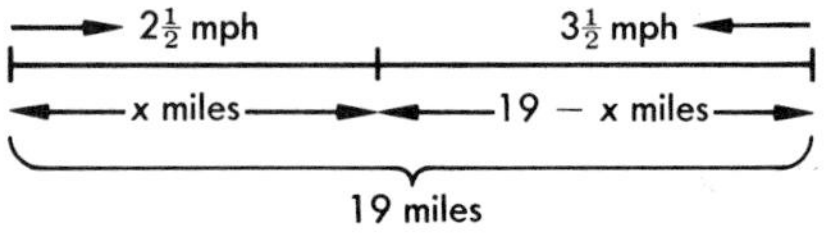

Answers to Exercises 16, 17

16. They walk 3 hr 10 min before meeting. The first man has walked $7\frac{11}{12}$ miles; the second has walked $11\frac{1}{12}$ miles.
17. It will take $3\frac{3}{4}$ hours. Each man has walked $\frac{105}{8}$, or $13\frac{1}{8}$ miles.

Quiz

1. Write an algebraic expression for each of the following phrases.
   (a) The sum of three consecutive even integers, of which x is the second one (ans: $3x$)
   (b) The product of two consecutive odd integers, of which y is the first (ans: $y(y + 2)$)
   (c) Two less than three times an integer x (ans: $3x - 2$)
   (d) The sum of two times an integer y and 4 (ans: $2y + 4$)
2. Find three consecutive integers whose sum is 27. (ans: 8, 9, 10)

△

Write an equation for each of the following problems, and solve it. In each case, tell what is denoted by the variable that you use.

7. In a local election, two-fifths of the eligible voters voted to retain Mayor Mills, three-eighths voted for his opponent, and the remaining 90 of those eligible did not vote. How many eligible voters were there in all? 400
8. Two years ago a man was 7 times as old as his son, but in 3 years he will only be 4 times as old as the boy. How old is each now? 7 years, 37 years
9. A newsboy collects \$6.30 in nickels, dimes, and quarters. He has 4 more dimes than quarters and the number of nickels is 2 more than twice the number of dimes. How many coins of each type does he have? 12 quarters, 16 dimes, 34 nickels
10. When cans of beans sell at 28¢ each, the supermarket makes a 40% profit. What should the sales price of a can be if the store is willing to make only a 10% profit? 22 cents

▲

Write an equation for each of the following problems, and solve it. In each case, tell what is denoted by the variable that you use.

11. What quantity of a solution which is to be 15% alcohol can be made from 7.5 quarts of pure alcohol? 50 quarts
12. How much pure acid should be added to 75 cubic centimeters of a 12% solution to increase the concentration to 15%? $2\frac{11}{17}$ cm^3
13. How much of the mixture in an 8-quart radiator should be drained and replaced with pure antifreeze if the mixture now consists of 75% antifreeze, and it is desired that the resultant mixture contain 90% antifreeze? 4.8 quarts
14. How much water must be evaporated from 6 gallons of a 15%-salt solution if the residual solution is to contain 25% salt? 2.4 gallons
15. How many pounds of almonds which regularly sell for \$1.10 per pound should be added to 10 pounds of peanuts which sell for 60¢ per pound if the resultant mixture should sell at 90¢ per pound? 15 pounds
16. Two men start at the same time from towns 19 miles apart and walk toward each other. One walks $2\frac{1}{2}$ miles per hour while the other covers $3\frac{1}{2}$ miles per hour. How long do they walk before meeting? How far has each man walked when they meet?
17. A man who walks $3\frac{1}{2}$ miles per hour sets out, from the same spot, to overtake a man who walks $2\frac{1}{2}$ miles per hour and who left $1\frac{1}{2}$ hours earlier. How long will it take the first walker to overtake the second one? How far has each man walked when the second one overtakes the first one?

2-3 INEQUALITIES IN ONE VARIABLE

A statement, such as

$$13x - 12 < 28 - 7x,$$

consisting of two linear forms in a variable connected by an order relation is called a *first-degree inequality,* or *linear inequality,* in the variable.

A number is called a solution of an inequality in one variable if a true statement is obtained when we give the variable the value of the number. The set of all solutions of an inequality is called the solution set of the inequality. If an inequality has no solution, its solution set is the empty set, $\emptyset$.

For example, let us determine which, if any, of the numbers $^-2$, 0, 2, and 4 are solutions of the inequality above. If we let $x = {}^-2$, we obtain

$$(13 \cdot {}^-2) - 12 < 28 - (7 \cdot {}^-2), \quad \text{or } {}^-38 < 42.$$

Since this is a true statement, $^-2$ is in the solution set of the given inequality. If we let x equal 0, 2, and 4, in turn, we obtain the following statements:

$$(13 \cdot 0) - 12 < 28 - (7 \cdot 0), \quad \text{or } {}^-12 < 28,$$

$$(13 \cdot 2) - 12 < 28 - (7 \cdot 2), \quad \text{or } 14 < 14,$$

$$(13 \cdot 4) - 12 < 28 - (7 \cdot 4), \quad \text{or } 40 < 0.$$

Since the first statement is true and the last two are false, we conclude that 0 is in the solution set and that 2 and 4 are not in the solution set of the given inequality.

We solve an inequality as we solve an equation; that is, we find its solution set. Two inequalities in a variable are said to be *equivalent* if they have the same solution set. The process of solving an inequality is the same as that of solving an equation. Thus, we try to find an equivalent inequality with an obvious solution set. For example, if the inequalities

$$\tfrac{1}{2}(5x - 6) < \tfrac{1}{6}(108 - 3x) \quad \text{and} \quad x < 7$$

are equivalent, then we can tell from the second inequality that the solution set of both inequalities is the set of all real numbers less than 7.

In the solution of the following inequalities, we shall use the additive and multiplicative properties discussed in Chapter 1.

2-3 INEQUALITIES IN ONE VARIABLE

It may be pointed out that the solution set of a first-degree equation in one variable is usually finite, whereas the solution set of a first-degree inequality in one variable is usually infinite.

The procedures used in writing a set of equivalent inequalities are similar to those for writing a set of equivalent equations. If the left and right sides of an inequality are designated by L and R, respectively, then $L > R$ means $L - R$ is positive. Since for any linear form in x having the value C, $(L + C) - (R + C)$ is just $L - R$, it follows that whenever $L - R$ is positive, so is

$$(L + C) - (R + C);$$

hence if $L > R$, then $L + C > R + C$.

Note the definition of the graph of an equation and of the graph of an inequality in one variable given on this page. You may wish to consider the graph of $x > 2$ when the domain of x is the set of integers as compared to the graph of $x > 2$ when the domain of x is the set of real numbers. This comparison is a natural way of distinguishing between the set of discrete points and the continuous line. You might also invite the class to think about the graph of $x > 2$ when the domain of x is the set of rational numbers. The problem of even indicating the graph on a number line is a touchy one—should a solid line be drawn, or should spaces be left between dots?

Exercises for Discussion, page 67

If time is limited, it is suggested that at least Exercises for Discussion 3 and 4 be covered.

Some students have difficulty with the compound statement

$$x \geqq {}^-4.$$

You can help them by always expressing this statement as, "The set of numbers which are either greater than $^-4$, or equal to $^-4$." A number is in this set if it complies with one of these restrictions; obviously, no number can comply with both. Hence, the least number in the set is $^-4$, which is the only number in the solution set of $x = {}^-4$. All other numbers in the set must obey the other qualification, $x > {}^-4$.

In Exercise for Discussion 3, the symbol $\cap$, denoting the intersection of two sets, is introduced.

Problem 1. Solve the inequality $13x - 12 < 28 - 7x$.

Solution. Each of the following inequalities is equivalent to the preceding one for the reason given.

$$13x - 12 < 28 - 7x$$

$$13x - 12 + (7x + 12) < 28 - 7x + (7x + 12) \qquad (\text{A}<)$$

$$(13x + 7x) + (12 - 12) < (28 + 12) + (7x - 7x) \qquad (\text{R-A})$$

$$20x + 0 < 40 + 0 \qquad (\text{Inv-A})$$

$$20x < 40 \qquad (\text{Id-A})$$

$$\tfrac{1}{20} \cdot 20x < \tfrac{1}{20} \cdot 40 \qquad ({}^+\text{M}<)$$

$$x < 2$$

We shall let you verify that the solution set of the given inequality is the set of all real numbers less than 2: $\{x \mid x < 2\}$.

The *graph* of an equation or inequality in one variable is the set of all points on a number line whose coordinates are solutions of the given equation or inequality. Since a first-degree equation in one variable usually has a single solution, its graph consists of a single point. On the other hand, the graph of an inequality often consists of more than one point.

For example, the graph of the inequality of Problem 1 is the set of all points on a number line having coordinates less than 2. This graph is an *open ray*, as indicated in Fig. 2–1. The hollow dot at 2 indicates that 2 is not part of the graph. The figure is incomplete, because the open ray extends infinitely far to the left.

FIGURE 2–1

Problem 2. Solve the inequality $\frac{11}{3}x + 2 \geqq \frac{7}{6}x - 8$.

Solution.

$$\tfrac{11}{3}x + 2 \geqq \tfrac{7}{6}x - 8$$

$$\tfrac{11}{3}x + 2 + ({}^-\tfrac{7}{6}x - 2) \geqq \tfrac{7}{6}x - 8 + ({}^-\tfrac{7}{6}x - 2)$$

$$\tfrac{11}{3}x + {}^-\tfrac{7}{6}x \geqq {}^-8 - 2$$

$$\tfrac{15}{6}x \geqq {}^-10$$

$$\tfrac{6}{15} \cdot \tfrac{15}{6}x \geqq \tfrac{6}{15} \cdot {}^-10$$

$$x \geqq {}^-4$$

Thus, the set of all numbers greater than or equal to $^-4$, designated by

$$\{x \mid x \geqq {}^-4\},$$

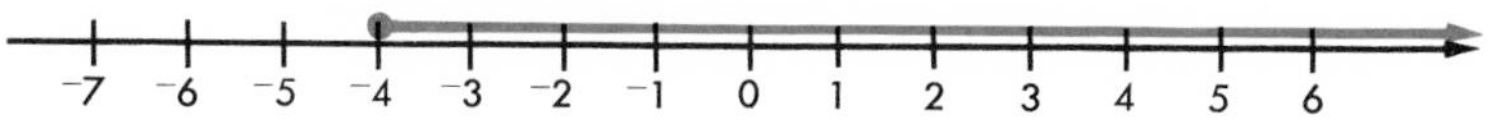

FIGURE 2-2

is the solution set of the given inequality. Its graph is the ray indicated in Fig. 2–2. The solid dot at $^-4$ shows that $^-4$ is part of the graph.

Exercises for Discussion

1. Tell which of the numbers $^-8$, 8, $^-5$, 3, 0, 1.5, $^-1.5$, 10, 1.6 are in the solution set of the inequality $2x - 5 > 7 - 6x$. $8x > 12,\ x > \frac{3}{2}$
2. Solve each of the following inequalities, and graph its solution set on a number line.
   (a) $x + 3 > 2$ (b) $x - 2 < 5$ (c) $x + 1 \geqq {}^-2$
3. The graphs of the solution sets of two different inequalities may overlap, or intersect. For example, the solution set of the inequality $x + 1 < 4$ is the set of real numbers less than 3, or $\{x \mid x < 3\}$. The solution set of the inequality $2x > {}^-4$ is the set of real numbers greater than $^-2$, or $\{x \mid x > {}^-2\}$. Those numbers which are greater than $^-2$ and also less than 3, or $\{x \mid {}^-2 < x < 3\}$, are in the solution set of both inequalities. The symbol $\cap$, called *cap*, is placed between two sets to indicate the set which is their intersection. Thus, we may write

$$\{x \mid x + 1 < 4\} \cap \{x \mid 2x > {}^-4\} = \{x \mid {}^-2 < x < 3\}.$$

The graph of the solution set of each of these two inequalities is an open ray, and the graph of the intersection of the two sets is an open interval, as shown in the figure.

$x < 3$

$x > {}^-2$

$\{x \mid x < 3\} \cap \{x \mid x > {}^-2\}$

For each pair of inequalities given below, graph the two solution sets and show their intersection.
   (a) $\{x \mid x > {}^-3\} \cap \{x \mid x < 5\}$ (b) $\{x \mid x \geqq 0\} \cap \{x \mid x \geqq 2\}$
   (c) $\{x \mid x > 3\} \cap \{x \mid x < 1\}$
4. The union of two sets R and S, designated by $R \cup S$, is the set consisting of all elements in either R or S. Graph each of the following sets.
   (a) $\{x \mid x > 1\} \cup \{x \mid x < {}^-1\}$ (b) $\{x \mid x \geqq 3\} \cup \{x \mid x \leqq 1\}$

Answers to Exercises for Discussion 2–4

2. (a) $x > {}^-1$

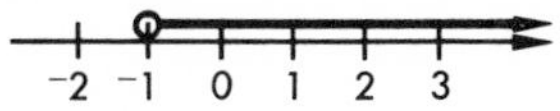

(b) $x < 7$

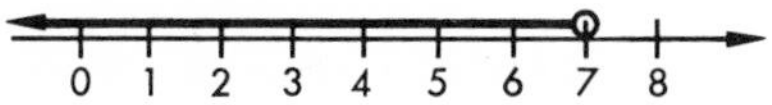

(c) $x \geqq {}^-3$

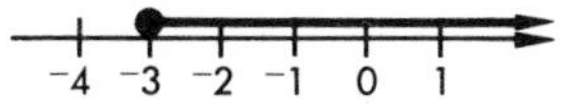

3. (a)

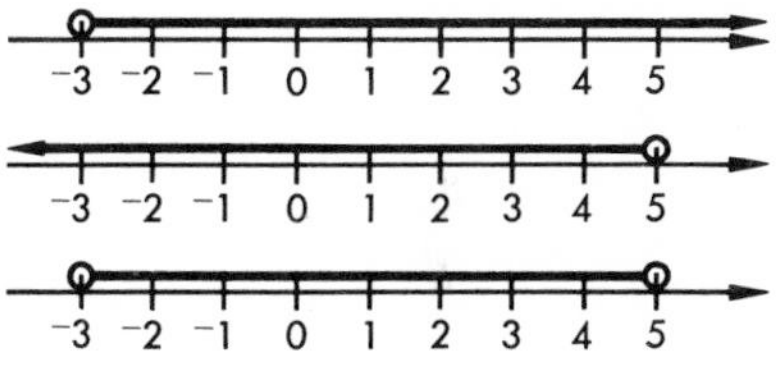

(b)

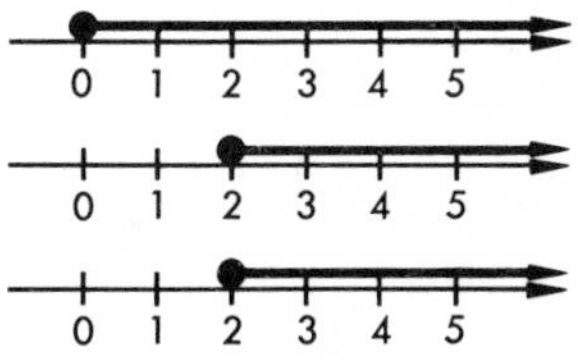

(c) The intersection is the empty set.

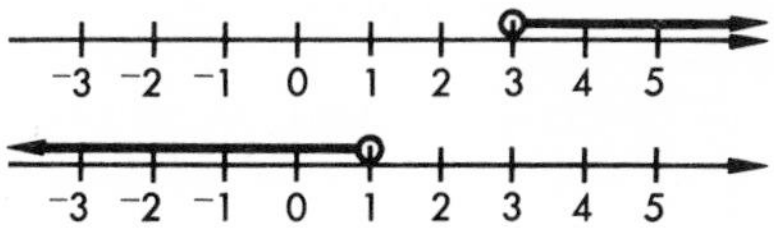

4. (a)

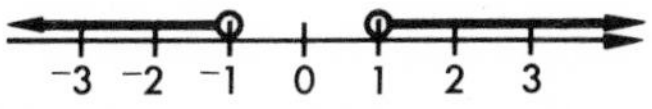

(b)

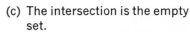

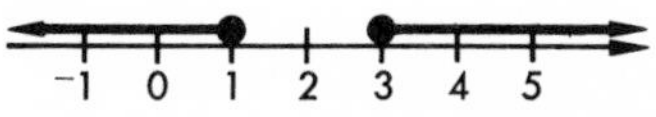

Exercises

If the class has had no experience with absolute value prior to this course, before assigning Exercise 11 you might consider the solution set and graph of each of the following:

$$|x| = 2,$$
$$|x| < 2,$$
$$|x| > 2.$$

It should become apparent that every real number belongs to the solution set of one, and only one, of these statements.

You may wish to take up the cases of

$$|x - 2| = 1,$$
$$|x - 2| < 1,$$
$$|x - 2| > 1,$$

with graphs centered at 2. In general, $|x + a| = b$ has its graph centered around ^-a. You might refer back to directed distance (Section 1-10),

$$d(AB) = b - a,$$

and observe that $x - 2$ is the directed distance from the point with coordinate 2 to the point with coordinate x. The solution set of $|x + 1| < 3$ is the set of points lying either to the left or to the right of $^-1$, but not as far as 3 units away.

In Exercises 12 and 13, you may need to review the properties of multiplication of each side by a positive number and of multiplication of each side by a negative number.

It will help students to understand Exercises 14–18 if they draw the number lines in pencil and make the graphs on them in colors.

Exercises *See Solution Manual for graphs.*

1. Tell which of the numbers

$$0, \quad {}^-4, \quad 5, \quad {}^-2, \quad {}^-3, \quad 1, \quad 3, \quad {}^-2.9, \quad {}^-3.1$$

are in the solution set of the inequality $^-7 < 2x - 1 < 5$.

2. Tell which of the numbers

$$10, \quad {}^-2, \quad 0, \quad {}^-1.5, \quad {}^-.5, \quad 1, \quad {}^-1, \quad 3$$

are in the solution set of the inequality $4 - 5x \leqq 7 - 2x$.

Solve each of the following inequalities and graph its solution set.

3. $\frac{3}{2}x - 2 < 2x + \frac{1}{3}$ *$x > \frac{^-14}{3}$*

4. $4x + 7 \geqq x - 11$ *$x \geqq {}^-6$*

5. $\frac{3}{5}x - \frac{1}{4} < \frac{49}{40} - \frac{7}{8}x$ *$x < 1$*

6. $\frac{1}{2}x + \frac{1}{3} \geqq 3 - \frac{1}{6}x$ *$x \geqq 4$*

7. $3x - \frac{1}{3} < 2x - 3$ *$x < \frac{^-8}{3}$*

8. $\frac{1}{4}(8 + x) > 1$ *$x > {}^-4$*

9. $^-3(x + 2) > {}^-9$ *$x < 1$*

10. $3(x + 1) \geqq 2(5 - x)$ *$x \geqq \frac{7}{5}$*

△

11. Graph each of the following sets.
(a) $\{x \mid x + 2 > 0\} \cup \{x \mid x + 4 < 0\}$
(b) $\{x \mid |x| < 3\}$
(c) $\{x \mid |x| \geqq 3\}$

12. (a) Graph the inequality $x > 4$.
(b) Determine which of the numbers

$$10, \quad 8, \quad 6, \quad 4, \quad 3, \quad 2, \quad 0, \quad {}^-4, \quad {}^-9, \quad {}^-10$$

are in the solution set of the inequality $^-2x > {}^-8$.
(c) Graph the inequality $^-2x > {}^-8$ on the same number line that you used in part (a). Describe $\{x \mid x > 4\} \cap \{x \mid {}^-2x > {}^-8\}$. *$\emptyset$*

13. (a) Graph each of the following inequalities below the number line used in Exercise 12. Then give four elements of each solution set.

$$x < 3, \quad 2x < {}^-6, \quad {}^-2x > {}^-6$$

(b) Find a pair of equivalent inequalities in the set of three inequalities in part (a). *$x < 3$ and $^-2x > {}^-6$ are equivalent.*

Solve each inequality of the following pairs of inequalities, and find the intersection of the solution sets of each pair. For each pair, graph both solution sets and their intersection.

14. $2x + 1 < 7$ and $3x - 1 > 2$ *$x < 3, x > 1, \{x \mid 1 < x < 3\}$*

15. $x + 1 < 2x - 4$ and $3x - 2 > 1$ *$x > 5, x > 1, \{x \mid x > 5\}$*

16. $2x + 3 \geqq 15 - 4x$ and $x - \frac{1}{3} > \frac{1}{6}x - 2$ *$x \geqq 2, x > {}^-2, \{x \mid x \geqq 2\}$*

17. $\frac{5}{4}x > 1 + x$ and $x + 2 < \frac{14}{5}$ *$x > 4, x < \frac{4}{5}, \emptyset$*

18. $\frac{1}{2}(3x - 7) > x - 5$ and $\frac{1}{2}(1 - 3x) > 1 - x$ *$x > {}^-3, x < {}^-1, \{x \mid {}^-3 < x < {}^-1\}$*

19. A football team has won 5 out of 7 games played. If there are 8 games remaining, how many more games must be won to give the team a season record of at least 60% games won out of all games played?

20. Johnny starts with the fraction $\frac{1}{2}$ and considers adding the same number x to both the numerator and the denominator. For what positive values of x will he obtain a number greater than or equal to $\frac{3}{4}$? $x \geqq 2$

21. Show that Johnny's method in Exercise 20 will always give a number greater than the original fraction $\frac{1}{2}$, as long as he adds the same positive number to both the numerator and the denominator.
See Solution Manual.

2-4 EQUATIONS IN TWO VARIABLES

An algebraic expression such as

$$3x - 2y + 4$$

is called a *linear form* in the two variables x and y. Every linear form in x and y is of the type

$$ax + by + c$$

for some real numbers a, b, and c. Note that

$$0x - 3y + 8, \quad \text{or } {}^-3y + 8,$$

may be considered to be a linear form in x and y although the variable x does not appear. Of course, ${}^-3y + 8$ is also a linear form in the one variable y.

If values are given to the variables in a linear form, the resulting number is called a *value* of the linear form. For example, the linear form $3x - 2y + 4$ has the value

$$(3 \cdot 3) - (2 \cdot {}^-5) + 4, \quad \text{or } 23,$$

when $x = 3$ and $y = {}^-5$. If we let $x = 17$ and $y = 3$ in the linear form ${}^-3y + 8$, its value is $({}^-3 \cdot 3) + 8$, or ${}^-1$. As long as we let $y = 3$, the value of this linear form is ${}^-1$ for any value given to x.

A statement consisting of two linear forms in x and y connected by an equals sign is called a *first-degree equation*, or *linear equation*, in the variables x and y.

Answer to Exercise 19

19. At least 4 of the remaining games must be won.

Quiz

Solve each of the following inequalities and graph its solution set.

1. $4x + 3 < 2x - 1$ (ans: $x < {}^-2$)

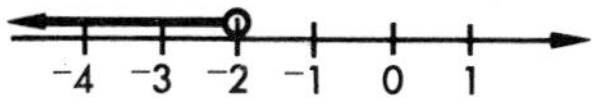

2. $5x - \frac{7}{2} \geqq 4x - \frac{5}{2}$ (ans: $x \geqq 1$)

3. $\frac{1}{3}x + 3 \leqq 3$ (ans: $x \leqq 0$)

4. ${}^-4(x - 1) > 2$ (ans: $x < \frac{1}{2}$)

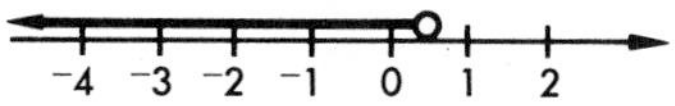

2-4 EQUATIONS IN TWO VARIABLES

It should be made clear that $x - 3$ may be considered a linear form in x and y by writing it as

$$x + (0 \cdot y) - 3.$$

Then the student will be less apt to think that the graph in two dimensions of $x - 3 = 0$ is the point (3, 0), but will recognize it to be the line $x = 3$ parallel to the y-axis. Likewise, if the student understands $y + 2$ as equivalent to $(0 \cdot x) + y + 2$, he will be ready to accept the fact that the graph of

$$y + 2 = 0$$

is a straight line parallel to the x-axis. The graph of a first-degree equation in two variables is the topic of the next section. You may wish to return and review the above concept when covering that section.

In order to help the students gain a thorough understanding of the linear equation in two variables, you might ask questions about the types of solutions. For example, "Does the equation $y = {}^{-}3x + 4$ have any solutions with x and y both negative?" "Why?" The student should see that for negative x, ${}^{-}3x$ is positive and therefore y is positive. Then you might ask, "Are there any integral solutions with x and y both positive?" The student should see that there is only one: (1, 1).

Exercises for Discussion, page 71

If time is limited, it is suggested that at least Exercises for Discussion 1–5 and 7 be covered.

In Exercise for Discussion 1, the equation could be solved for x:

$$x = \frac{y+5}{3},$$

and then you could ask for five integral values of y that lead to

Consider

$$3x - 2y + 4 = {}^{-}3y + 8$$

as an example of a first-degree equation in x and y. If we let $x = {}^{-}1$ and $y = 7$ in this equation, we obtain the *true* equation

$${}^{-}3 - 14 + 4 = {}^{-}21 + 8.$$

Therefore, the ordered pair $({}^{-}1, 7)$ is a *solution* of the given equation. On the other hand, the ordered pair (3, 6) is *not a solution* since the equation obtained by letting $x = 3$ and $y = 6$ is false.

$$9 - 12 + 4 = {}^{-}18 + 8$$

An ordered pair (a, b) is called a solution of an equation in x and y if, and only if, a true equation results when we let $x = a$ and $y = b$. The set of all solutions of an equation in x and y is called the solution set of the equation. If an equation has no solution, its solution set is the empty set, $\emptyset$.

We recall that a first-degree equation in one variable usually has only one solution. A first-degree equation in two variables, on the other hand, usually has an infinite number of solutions. A convenient method of finding solutions of a first-degree equation in two variables is to solve the given equation for one variable in terms of the other.

Problem. Solve the following equation for y in terms of x.

Solution.

$$3x - 2y + 4 = {}^{-}3y + 8$$
$$(3y - 3x - 4) + 3x - 2y + 4 = {}^{-}3y + 8 + (3y - 3x - 4)$$
$$y = {}^{-}3x + 4$$

This final equation is equivalent to the given one. Hence, the solution set of the given equation may be described as follows:

$$\{(x, y) \mid y = {}^{-}3x + 4\}.$$

By giving different values to x, we can find as many ordered pairs in the solution set of the given equation as we wish. For example, if we let $x = 3$, we obtain

$$y = ({}^{-}3 \cdot 3) + 4, \quad \text{or } {}^{-}5.$$

Thus, the ordered pair $(3, {}^{-}5)$ is in the solution set. The following elements of the solution set were found in the same way.

$$(0, 4),\quad (1, 1),\quad ({}^{-}1, 7),\quad (\tfrac{4}{3}, 0),\quad (2, {}^{-}2),\quad (100, {}^{-}296)$$

Exercises for Discussion

1. Tell which of the following ordered pairs are elements of the solution set of the equation $5x + 3y + 1 = 8x + 2y - 4$.

$$(\tfrac{1}{3}, {}^{-}4),\quad (3, 3),\quad (0, {}^{-}5),\quad (\tfrac{1}{2}, \tfrac{7}{2}),\quad (\tfrac{5}{3}, 0)$$

2. Solve the equation

$$3(2y - 1) - (x - 3) = 3x - y - 5$$

for y in terms of x.

3. Solve the equation in Exercise 2 for x in terms of y.

4. Refer to Exercises 2 and 3 when answering the following questions.
   (a) Are there solutions with $x > 0$ and $y < 0$? *Yes, e.g., $(1, \frac{-1}{7})$*
   (b) Are there solutions with $x < 0$ and $y > 0$? *No*

5. (a) Determine several elements of R when

$$R = \{(x, y) \mid 2x - y = 1\}.$$
e.g., $(1, 1), (0, {}^{-}1), (\frac{1}{2}, 0)$

   (b) Determine several elements of S when

$$S = \{(x, y) \mid {}^{-}(2x - y) = 1\}.$$
e.g., $(0, 1), (\frac{-1}{2}, 0), (\frac{1}{2}, 2)$

   (c) Determine several elements of M when

$$M = \{(x, y) \mid |2x - y| = 1\}.$$
e.g., $(0, {}^{-}1), (\frac{1}{2}, 0), (1, 1)$

   (d) Are elements of R also elements of M? Are those of S also elements of M? *Yes* *Yes*
   (e) What is the relationship of M to R and S? *$M = R \cup S$*

6. Use the results of Exercise 5 to list two linear equations in x and y where the union of their solution sets is equivalent to the solution set of the single equation $|x + y| = 3$. *$x + y = 3$ and $x + y = {}^{-}3$*

7. A bar drawn through a relation sign negates the relation. Thus,

$x \neq y$ means x is not equal to y,

$x \not< y$ means x is not less than y,

$x \not\geq y$ means x is not greater than or equal to y.

Write an inequality that has the same solution set as the inequality $x \not\geq 6$, but use a relation that is different from $x \not\geq 6$. *$x < 6$*

8. Two sets of real numbers are described below. Give several specific members of each set, and tell how the two sets are related to each other.
The sets are disjoint and their union is the set of all real numbers.

$$A = \{x \mid x > {}^{-}1\} \quad \text{and} \quad B = \{x \mid x \not\geq {}^{-}1\}$$

integral values of x. Then the equation could be solved for y:

$$y = 3x - 5,$$

to show why this form is easier to use in this particular case. Then the five number pairs that have been given could be tested to see which are solutions.

In Exercise for Discussion 2, you might ask for several integral values of x that yield integral values of y.

In Exercise for Discussion 3, you may wish to again ask for integral values of y that yield integral values of x.

In Exercise for Discussion 4, it is suggested that you also ask about solutions with $x > 0$ and $y > 0$, or with $x < 0$ and $y < 0$.

Answers to Exercises for Discussion 1–3

1. $y = 3x - 5$

${}^{-}4 = 3(\frac{1}{3}) - 5$, T; $(\frac{1}{3}, {}^{-}4)$ is in the solution set.

$3 = 3(3) - 5$, F; $(3, 3)$ is not in the solution set.

${}^{-}5 = 3(0) - 5$, T; $(0, {}^{-}5)$ is in the solution set.

$\frac{7}{2} = 3(\frac{1}{2}) - 5$, F; $(\frac{1}{2}, \frac{7}{2})$ is not in the solution set.

$0 = 3(\frac{5}{3}) - 5$, T; $(\frac{5}{3}, 0)$ is in the solution set.

2. $6y - 3 - x + 3$
$= 3x - y - 5$
$({}^{-}x + 6y) + (y + x)$
$= (3x - y - 5) + (y + x)$
$7y = 4x - 5$
$y = \frac{1}{7}(4x - 5)$

3. $({}^{-}x + 6y) + ({}^{-}3x + {}^{-}6y)$
$= (3x - y - 5)$
$+ ({}^{-}3x + {}^{-}6y)$
${}^{-}4x = {}^{-}7y - 5$
$x = \frac{1}{4}(7y + 5)$

Exercises

In Exercise 2, since there are infinitely many correct answers, you may wish to discuss the characteristics of correct answers. For example, in Exercise 2(a), could x and y both be positive? Obviously not, since the sum of three positive numbers could not be zero.

Exercises 8 and 9 may be related to the trichotomy law, that is, every number is either greater than 0, equal to 0, or less than 0. The zero can be replaced by 3, as in Exercise 8, or by 7, as in Exercise 9.

Exercises

1. Tell which of the following ordered pairs are elements of the solution set of the equation $4x + 2y + 20 = 3x + y + 15$.

   $(0, {}^{-}5)$, $(\frac{1}{2}, {}^{-}4\frac{1}{2})$, $({}^{-}3, {}^{-}2)$, $({}^{-}1, {}^{-}4)$, $(4, 1)$

2. Find five elements of the solution set of each of the following.
   (a) $x + y + 8 = 0$ e.g., $(0, {}^{-}8)$, $({}^{-}8, 0)$, $({}^{-}1, {}^{-}7)$ (b) $3x + y - 10 = 0$ e.g., $(0, 10)$, $(1, 7)$, $({}^{-}1, 13)$
   (c) $x - 2y - 8 = 0$ e.g., $(0, {}^{-}4)$, $(2, {}^{-}3)$, $(8, 0)$ (d) $\frac{1}{2}x + \frac{1}{4}y + 2 = 0$ e.g., $(0, {}^{-}8)$, $({}^{-}4, 0)$, $(1, {}^{-}10)$

In Exercises 3–6, solve each equation for y in terms of x. Find three ordered pairs that are elements of each solution set. Then check these solutions in the given equation to detect any errors that you have made.

3. $3y - 2x + 4 = 8 - 3x$ $y = \frac{1}{3}(4 - x)$
4. $5x - 6y - 9 = 2x + 4y - 3$ $y = \frac{3}{10}x - \frac{3}{5}$
5. $x - 3(x - 2y - 4) = 6 - (4x - y - 5)$ $y = \frac{{}^{-}2}{5}x - \frac{1}{5}$
6. $\frac{x}{5} - \frac{y}{6} + \frac{1}{2} = x + \frac{y}{3} - \frac{1}{10}$ $y = \frac{{}^{-}8}{5}x + \frac{6}{5}$
7. Solve each equation in Exercises 3–6 for x in terms of y. $x = {}^{-}3y + 4$; $x = \frac{10}{3}y + 2$; $x = \frac{{}^{-}5}{2}y - \frac{1}{2}$; $x = \frac{{}^{-}5}{8}y + \frac{3}{4}$
8. Compare the solution sets of $2x + 1 > 3$ and $2x + 1 \leqq 3$. Do the sets have any elements in common? No Are there any numbers which are not in either set? No
9. Compare the solution sets of $3x - 5 < 7$ and $3x - 5 \geqq 7$. Do the sets have any elements in common? No Are there any numbers which are not in either set? No

△

In Exercises 10 and 11, two sets of real numbers are described. Give several elements of each set, and tell how the two sets are related to each other. The sets have no elements in common. There are no numbers which are not in either set.

10. $A = \{x \mid 5x - 1 \nless 2\}$ and $B = \{x \mid 5x - 1 \geqq 2\}$
11. $C = \{x \mid \frac{2}{3}x - 3 \ngtr 5\}$ and $D = \{x \mid \frac{2}{3}x - 3 \leqq 5\}$ As Ex. 10
12. Write an inequality that has the same solution set as $x \nless {}^{-}\frac{13}{5}$. $x \geqq \frac{{}^{-}13}{5}$
13. List two linear equations in x and y where the union of their solution sets is equivalent to the solution set of the single equation

$$|2x - 3y| = 10.$$ $2x - 3y = 10$, $2x - 3y = {}^{-}10$

14. List a single equation in x and y whose solution set is equivalent to the union of the solution sets of the following two equations.

$$3y - 16 = 5y - x - 12$$
$$2x = 4y - 8$$ $|x - 2y| = 4$

15. (a) If $|x| + |y| = 2$, what is the largest possible value for x? for y? $x \leq 2$ $y \leq 2$

(b) Give four solutions of the equation $|x| + |y| = 2$ with $x > 0$ and $y > 0$. What linear equation also has these solutions? $x + y = 2$

(c) Give four solutions of $|x| + |y| = 2$ with $x < 0$ and $y < 0$. What linear equation also has these solutions? $^-x - y = 2$

(d) Give four solutions of $|x| + |y| = 2$ with $x < 0$ and $y > 0$ and then with $x > 0$ and $y < 0$. What two linear equations have either the first or the second four solutions? $y - x = 2$, $x - y = 2$

16. Find the linear equations that are necessary to describe the complete solution set of the equation $|2x| + |3y| = 6$. What are the restrictions in the size of x? of y?
$x > 0$ and $y > 0$: $2x + 3y = 6$
$x > 0$ and $y < 0$: $2x - 3y = 6$
$x < 0$ and $y > 0$: $^-2x + 3y = 6$
$x < 0$ and $y < 0$: $^-2x - 3y = 6$

2–5 THE GRAPH OF A FIRST-DEGREE EQUATION IN TWO VARIABLES

If we wish to construct a rectangular *cartesian coordinate system* in a plane, we select two perpendicular lines in the plane. Then we put a number scale on each line; in each case, we place the origin at the point of intersection of the lines. Unless we are given a statement to the contrary, we use the same unit of length on both lines. The two resulting number lines are customarily called the x-axis and the y-axis, and we usually place and direct them as shown in Fig. 2–3.

We assign to each point an ordered pair of real numbers; this ordered pair describes the position of the point relative to the axes. Conversely, each ordered pair is a pair of coordinates of some point in the plane. Some examples of points and their coordinates in the plane are given in Fig. 2–3. Since each ordered pair determines a point in the plane, a set of ordered pairs determines a set of points in the plane. This set of points is called the *graph of the set of ordered pairs.*

If the solution set of an equation in x and y is not the empty set, it is an example of a set of ordered pairs. The graph of the solution set is called the graph of the given equation. A first-degree equation in x and y has a straight line as

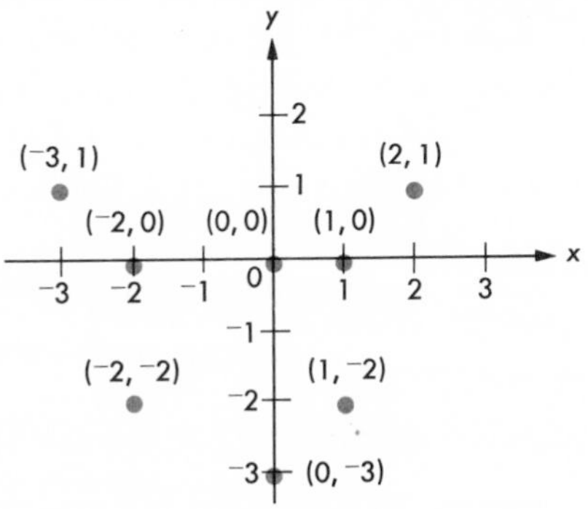

FIGURE 2–3

Exercises 15 and 16 may be used for class discussion, or assigned for honors work and then presented by a student to the class.

Quiz

In Exercises 1 and 2, first solve each equation for y in terms of x, and then for x in terms of y.

1. $4y + 3x - 5 = 3y + 2x + 5$ (ans: $y = {}^-x + 10$, $x = {}^-y + 10$)
2. $5x - 6y + 3 = 3x - 1$ (ans: $y = \frac{1}{3}x + \frac{2}{3}$, $x = 3y - 2$)
3. Tell which of the ordered pairs (0, 10), (3, −7), (−2, 12) are elements of the solution set of the equation in Exercise 1. (ans: (0, 10), (−2, 12))

2–5 THE GRAPH OF A FIRST-DEGREE EQUATION IN TWO VARIABLES

The graph of a first-degree equation in two variables is the graph of its solution set, those points, and only those points, whose coordinates are a solution of the equation. This will be a straight line in a rectangular cartesian coordinate plane.

its graph. In other words, its graph is the set of all points on a straight line. It is for this reason that a first-degree equation in x and y is called a *linear equation*. Some examples of linear equations and their graphs are given in the following problems.

Problem 1. Graph the first-degree equation $3x - 2y + 4 = 0$.

Solution. When we solve the given equation for y, we obtain the equivalent equation

$$2y = 3x + 4;$$

or

$$y = \tfrac{3}{2}x + 2.$$

Thus,

$$\{(x, y) \mid y = \tfrac{3}{2}x + 2\}$$

is the solution set of the given equation. Several elements of the solution set are given below.

$$(0, 2),\quad (2, 5),\quad (^{-}1, \tfrac{1}{2}),\quad (^{-}4, ^{-}4)$$

These ordered pairs are graphed in Fig. 2–4. The straight line containing these points is the graph of the given equation.

You might recall that each nonvertical straight line has a *slope* which we define as the ratio of the rise to the run of the line.

$$\textit{slope} = \frac{\textit{rise}}{\textit{run}}$$

From the point (0, 2) to the point (2, 5) in Fig. 2–4, the *rise*, or vertical change, is $5 - 2$, or 3 units; the *run*, or horizontal change, is $2 - 0$, or 2 units. The slope of the line is $\frac{3}{2}$.

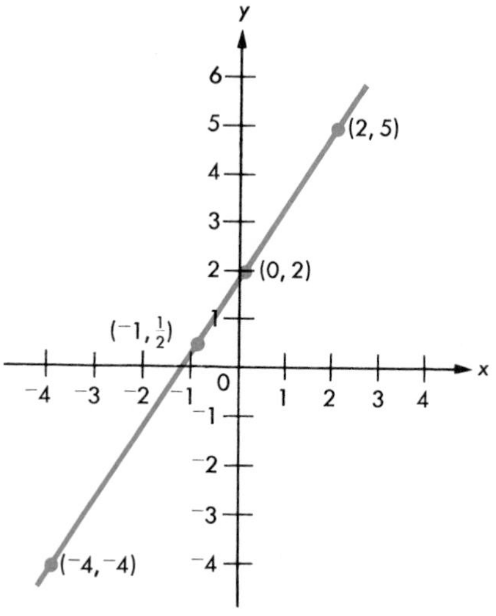

FIGURE 2–4

Problem 2. Graph the first-degree equation

$$3x - 2y + 4 = {}^{-}3y + 8.$$

Solution. In Section 2–4, we saw that this equation is equivalent to

$$y = {}^{-}3x + 4$$

and that (0, 4), (1, 1), ($^{-}$1, 7), and (2, $^{-}$2) are points on the line. The

For some students, the idea of slope will be new, as will be the so-called slope-intercept form of the equation of a straight line. Therefore, you may need to work many examples showing that for any pair of points on a line the ratio of rise to run is constant. As an aid to the less imaginative student, you might actually lead up to and state a formula for slope in terms of the coordinates of any two points. Thus, if P has coordinates (a, b) and Q has coordinates (c, d), then the slope of the line through P and Q is either

$$\frac{b - d}{a - c} \quad\text{or}\quad \frac{d - b}{c - a}.$$

It may be pointed out that in the equation $y = mx + b$ on page 75, x and y are the variables of the coordinate system or axes, while m and b are unknowns only until the position of the line has been determined. Then m and b are replaced by specific values, but x and y are still in the equation. If a point on the line is given, say (3, 4), this ordered number pair is a replacement for (x, y), not for m or b.

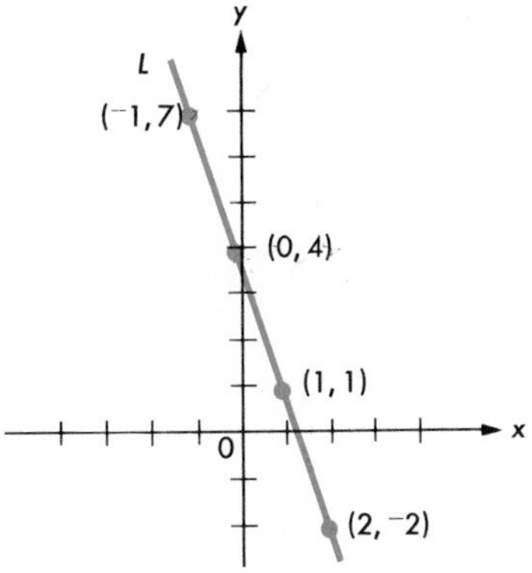

FIGURE 2-5

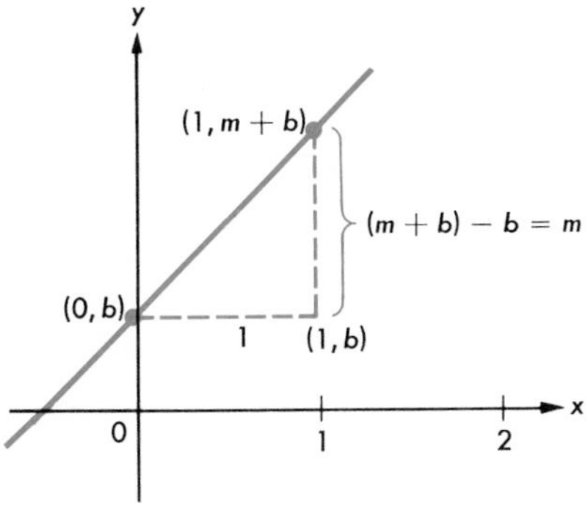

FIGURE 2-6

line L is graphed in Fig. 2–5. From the point (0, 4) to the point (2, $^-2$), the line has a rise of $^-2 - 4$, or $^-6$, and a run of $2 - 0$, or 2. Thus, its slope is $\frac{^-6}{2}$, or $^-3$. Of course, when we say that the line has a rise of $^-6$, we actually mean that the line is *falling* six units from (0, 4) to (2, $^-2$).

Whenever a first-degree equation in x and y is written in the form

$$y = mx + b,$$

where m and b are real numbers, the graph of the equation is a straight line whose slope is m. (See Fig. 2–6.) We can prove that m is the slope by noting that the points $(0, b)$ and $(1, m + b)$ are on the line, and that the rise is m and the run is 1 from $(0, b)$ to $(1, m + b)$. Since b is the y-coordinate of the point where the line crosses the y-axis, b is called the *y-intercept* of the line.

Problem 3. Consider $2x + 3 = 0$ as an equation in x and y, and draw its graph.

Solution. The given equation is equivalent to the equation $x = {^-\frac{3}{2}}$. Thus, every ordered pair of the type $(^-\frac{3}{2}, y)$ is in the solution set of the given equation. In other words, $\{(^-\frac{3}{2}, y) \mid y \text{ a real number}\}$ is the solution set of this equation. The graph of the given equation is the vertical line drawn in Fig. 2–7. Since there is no run from one point to another point on this line, the slope is not defined for this line.

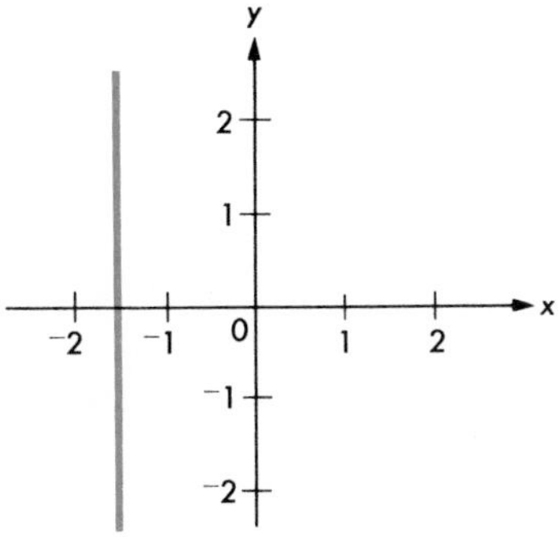

FIGURE 2-7

Exercises for Discussion, page 76

If time is limited, it is suggested that at least Exercises for Discussion 2-4 be covered.

Students have no trouble using the pattern $y = mx + b$ to produce an equation of a straight line when given the slope and the y-intercept. However, unless it has been specifically pointed out that a given equation can be written in this form and the slope of the line read immediately from the coefficient of x, many students will tackle Exercise for Discussion 5 and Exercises 10–17 (pages 76, 77) by finding two points on each line and obtaining rise and run to determine slope.

It is suggested that you stress the difference between lines with zero slope and lines whose slope is undefined.

In Exercise for Discussion 6(a), starting from the given point and using the given slope, points should be found to the right and above (1, $^-3$) and also points to the left and below (1, $^-3$).

In Exercise for Discussion 6(b), points should be found to the right and below (1, $^-3$) as well as points to the left and above (1, $^-3$), using the given slope.

In Exercise for Discussion 7, you may wish to clarify the term *family of lines* as meaning a set of lines where every member of the set has one thing in common with every other member. In the plane there are two types of families of lines. One type consists of all lines which have the same slope and hence are parallel, and the other consists of all lines going through a given point.

Answers to Exercises for Discussion 1, 2, 4(a), 5–7, 9

1. (a)

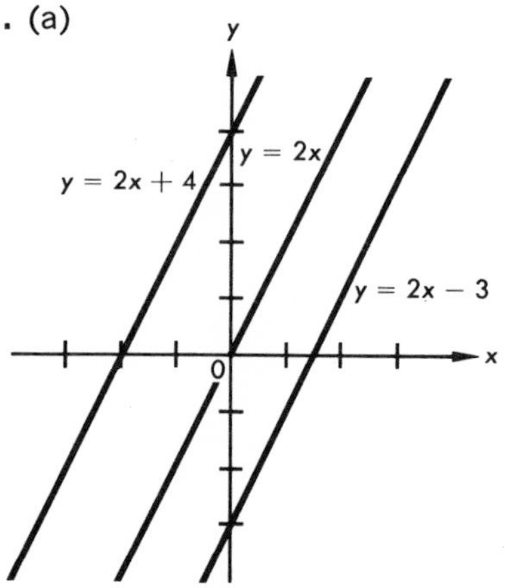

(b) They are parallel with slope 2.

(c) Each, solved for y, has a coefficient of 2 for x.

2. (a) $\frac{9-(^-3)}{7-(^-2)} = \frac{12}{9} = \frac{4}{3}$

(b) $m = \frac{y_2 - y_1}{x_2 - x_1}$

Slope is equal to difference of ordinates divided by difference of abscissas (both differences taken from same point).

4. (a) No. Use of the formula would entail division by zero.

5. (a) 1, $^-2$

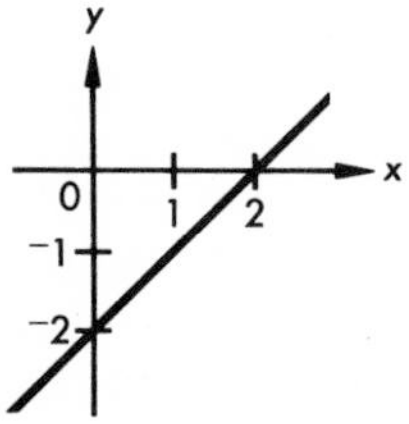

(b) $^-\frac{1}{2}$, 3

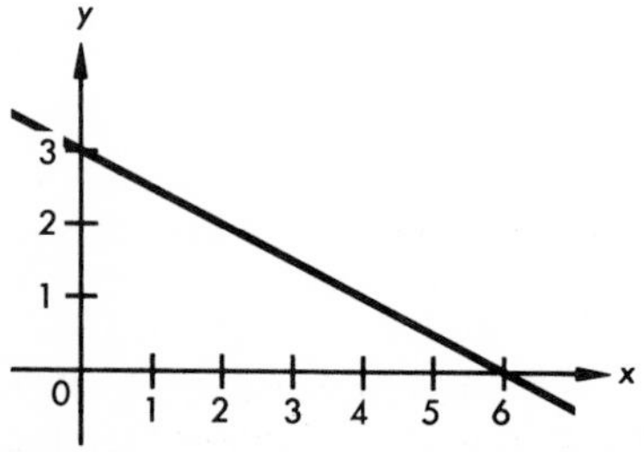

Exercises for Discussion

1. (a) Graph each of the following equations on the same coordinate system.

$$y = 2x + 4, \quad y = 2x, \quad y = 2x - 3$$

(b) What do the three graphs in part (a) have in common?
(c) What do the three equations in part (a) have in common?

2. (a) What is the slope of a line through the points $(^-2, {}^-3)$ and $(7, 9)$?
(b) Write a formula for the slope m of a line through the points (x_1, y_1) and (x_2, y_2). Express the formula in words.

3. (a) What is the slope of a line through the points $(^-1, 3)$ and $(5, 3)$? $\frac{3-3}{5-(^-1)} = 0$
(b) What is the slope of any line parallel to the x-axis? 0

4. (a) Does the line through $(^-1, 3)$ and $(^-1, 5)$ have a slope? No Why?
(b) How can you describe the set of all lines for which the slope is not defined? Vertical, parallel to the y-axis

5. Graph each of the following linear equations on a cartesian coordinate system in a plane. Give the slope and the y-intercept of each line.
(a) $x - y - 2 = 0$ (b) $\frac{1}{2}x + y = 3$

6. Through the given point, draw the line with the given slope m.
(a) $(1, {}^-3)$, $m = \frac{1}{2}$ (b) $(1, {}^-3)$, $m = {}^-2$

7. Write an equation of a family or set of lines with slope $\frac{3}{4}$. Write an equation of the line in this set that passes through the point $(^-5, 2)$.

8. Write an equation of a family or set of lines with y-intercept $^-5$. $y = mx - 5$

9. Show that the points

$$(4, 0), \quad (8, {}^-5), \quad (0, 5)$$

are collinear by showing that the slope of the line drawn between any two of them is the same as the slope of the line drawn between any other two of them.

Exercises

See Solution Manual for graphs.

Plot each pair of points, draw the straight line through them, and determine the slope of the line.

1. $(^-2, 3), (5, {}^-6)$ $\frac{-9}{7}$
2. $(^-4, {}^-1), (3, 5)$ $\frac{6}{7}$
3. $(2, {}^-1), ({}^-2, {}^-4)$ $\frac{3}{4}$
4. $(6, 2), ({}^-3, {}^-4)$ $\frac{2}{3}$

Through the given point, draw the line with the given slope m, and write an equation of the line.

5. $(0, 4)$, $m = {}^-\frac{2}{3}$ $y = \frac{-2}{3}x + 4$
6. $(^-3, {}^-2)$, $m = {}^-\frac{1}{3}$ $y + 2 = \frac{-1}{3}(x + 3)$
7. $(^-2, 3)$, $m = 0$ $y = 3$
8. $(4, 5)$, m undefined $x = 4$

9. Are the following sets of points collinear? No Why? Different slopes
(a) $(2, {}^-5), (4, 0), (7, 6)$ (b) $(0, 2), (3, 0), (1, 1)$

In Exercises 10–17, graph each of the linear equations on a cartesian coordinate system in a plane. Give first the slope and then the y-intercept of each line (if they exist).

10. $5y + 15 = 0$ *0, $^{-}3$* **11.** $3x + 6 = 0$ *No slope, no y-intercept* **12.** $2x + 5y = 10$ *$\frac{^{-}2}{5}$, 2*

13. $2x = 0$ *No slope, no y-intercept* **14.** $2x + 3y = 0$ *$\frac{^{-}2}{3}$, 0* **15.** $2x - \frac{1}{3}y = 0$ *6, 0*

16. $\frac{1}{2}x + \frac{1}{4}y = 1$ *$^{-}2$, 4* **17.** $\frac{1}{5}y = 0$ *0, 0*

18. (a) Graph each of the following equations on the same coordinate system.

$$y = 2x + 4, \quad y = 4, \quad y = {}^{-}x + 4, \quad y = \tfrac{1}{3}x + 4$$

(b) What do the four graphs in part (a) have in common? *Each has y-intercept 4, or each passes through (0, 4).*

(c) What do the four equations in part (a) have in common? *Each, solved for y, has a constant term of 4.*

19. (a) Graph each of the following equations on the same coordinate system.

$$y - 1 = x + 2, \quad y - 1 = 3(x + 2), \quad y - 1 = {}^{-}(x + 2)$$

(b) What do the three graphs in part (a) have in common? *All pass through ($^{-}2$, 1).*

(c) What do the three equations in part (a) have in common?

20. (a) Write an equation for the family of lines with a slope of $\frac{1}{2}$. *$y = \frac{1}{2}x + b$*

(b) Write an equation of the line with a slope of $\frac{1}{2}$ and a y-intercept of 3.

(c) Write an equation of the line passing through (2, 3) with a slope of $\frac{1}{2}$. *$y - 3 = \frac{1}{2}(x - 2)$*

△

21. Describe the family of lines which have the equation $y = {}^{-}x + b$. Tell in what way the members of this family differ and in what way they are alike.

22. Describe the family of lines which have the equation $y = mx - 1$.

23. Describe the family of lines which have the equation $y + 1 = m(x + 1)$.

24. (a) Write an equation for the family of lines passing through (4, $^{-}1$).

(b) Write an equation of the line passing through (4, $^{-}1$) and having a slope of $^{-}2$. *$y + 1 = {}^{-}2(x - 4)$*

(c) What is the slope of the line passing through (4, $^{-}1$) and ($^{-}3$, 6)? *$^{-}1$*

(d) Write an equation of the line passing through (4, $^{-}1$) and ($^{-}3$, 6). *$y + 1 = {}^{-}1(x - 4)$*

25. (a) Graph each of the following equations on the same set of axes.

$$\frac{x}{2} + \frac{y}{3} = 1, \quad \frac{x}{4} + \frac{y}{-6} = 1, \quad \frac{x}{-3} + \frac{y}{5} = 1$$

(b) Tell at what point each line graphed in part (a) cuts the x-axis and at what point it cuts the y-axis. Do the equations make these intercepts obvious?

(c) Give the x- and the y-intercept for the line with equation

$$\frac{x}{a} + \frac{y}{b} = 1. \quad a, b$$

(d) Write an equation of the line with x-intercept $^{-}2$ and y-intercept 2. *$\frac{x}{^{-}2} + \frac{y}{2} = 1$*

6. (a)

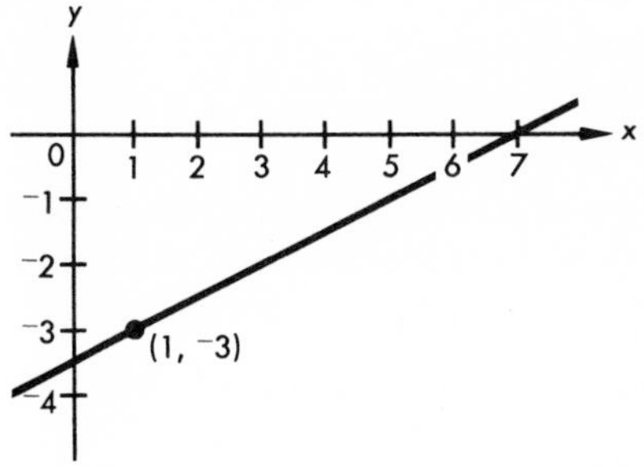

(b)

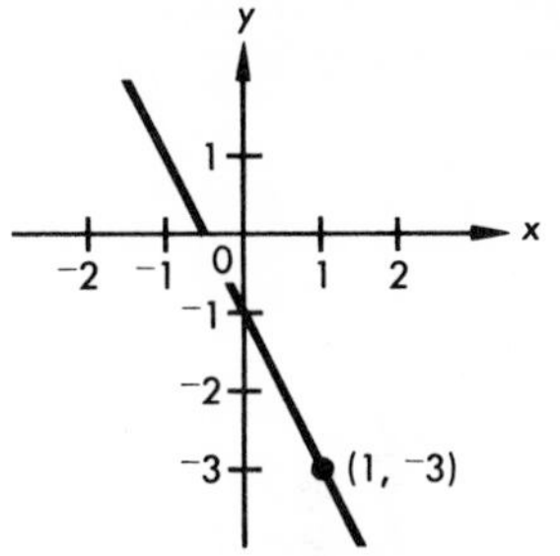

7. $y = \frac{3}{4}x + b$; $2 = \frac{3}{4}({}^{-}5) + b$;
$b = 2 + \frac{15}{4} = \frac{23}{4}$;
$y = \frac{3}{4}x + \frac{23}{4}$

9. The slope of the line passing through (4, 0) and (8, $^{-}5$) is

$$\frac{0 - ({}^{-}5)}{4 - 8} = \frac{^{-}5}{4}.$$

The slope of the line passing through (8, $^{-}5$) and (0, 5) is

$$\frac{5 - ({}^{-}5)}{0 - 8} = \frac{10}{^{-}8} = \frac{^{-}5}{4}.$$

The slope of the line passing through (0, 5) and (4, 0) is

$$\frac{0 - 5}{4 - 0} = \frac{^{-}5}{4}.$$

In Exercises 20–24, the family of lines could have been called a set of lines.

(Answers to Exercises 19(c), 20(b), 21-24(a), 25(b) on following page.)

In Exercise 26, attention should be called to the fact that

$$y = mx + b$$

is a line with slope m, y-intercept b, but $x = my + b$ is not a line with slope m, although the x-intercept is b. The slope of the graph

$$x = my + b$$

is $1/m$ and the y-intercept is $^{-}(b/m)$.

Answers to Exercises 19(c), 20(b), 21–24(a), 25(b), page 77

19. (c) Each has $y - 1$ on the left and a constant times $x + 2$ on the right; hence, each has $(^{-}2, 1)$ in its solution set.

20. (b) $y = \frac{1}{2}x + 3$

21. It is the family of lines with slope $^{-}1$ or lines parallel to the graph of $y + x = 0$; members differ in the point at which each crosses the y-axis. They are alike in slope, that is they are parallel.

22. They are the lines passing through $(0, ^{-}1)$. For different values of m, the lines have different slopes, but all have the same y-intercept.

23. They are the lines passing through $(^{-}1, ^{-}1)$. For different values of m, the lines have different slopes, but all are concurrent at $(^{-}1, ^{-}1)$.

24. (a) $y + 1 = m(x - 4)$

25. (b) In each case the x-intercept is the denominator under x, and the y-intercept is the denominator under y.

26. (a) Graph $y = 3x - 1$ and $x = 3y - 1$ on the same cartesian coordinate system. See Solution Manual.

(b) How do you think the graphs of $y = rx + s$ and $x = ry + s$ will compare? In other words, find the slope and the y-intercept of the graph of each equation. The graphs will be symmetrical about $y = x$. The first has slope r and y-intercept s. The second has slope $\frac{1}{r}$ and x-intercept s.

Write an equation for each of the lines graphed in Exercises 27–32.

27. $y = \frac{^{-}2}{3}x + 2$

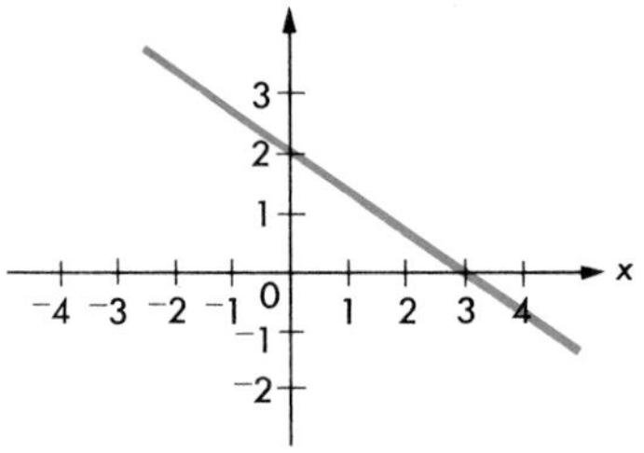

28. $x = \frac{3}{2}$

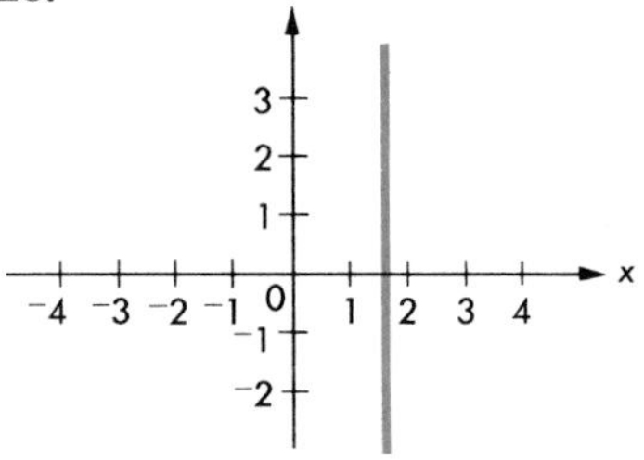

29. $y = {^{-}4}x - 4$

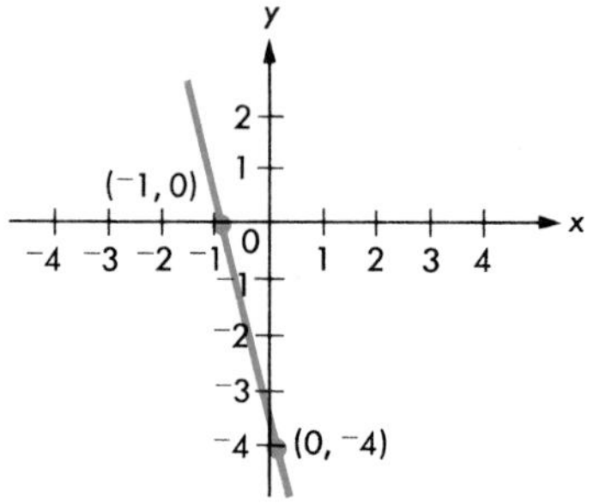

30. $y = \frac{3}{7}x + \frac{5}{7}$

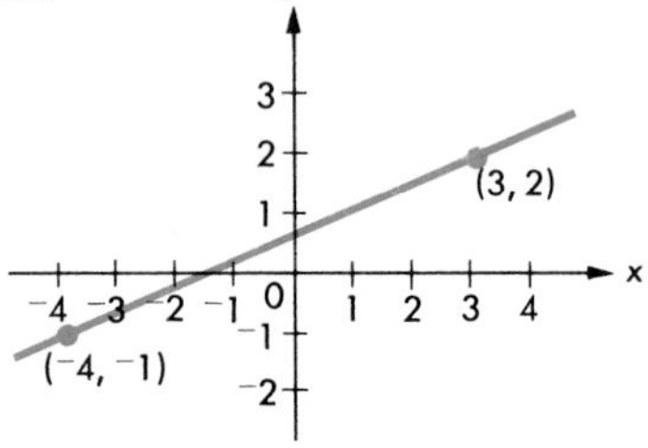

31. $y = {^{-}2}$

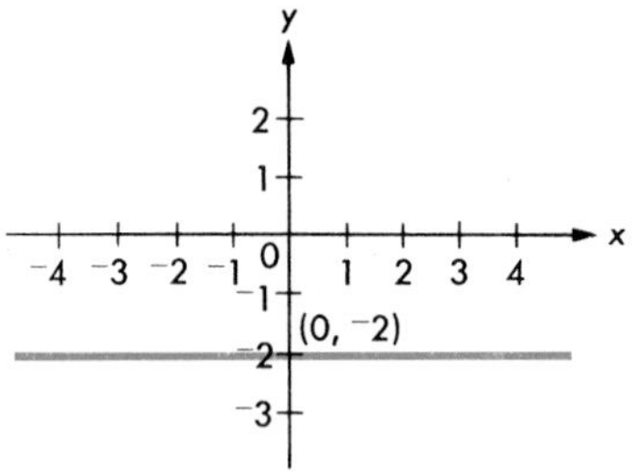

32. $y = \frac{5}{6}x - \frac{4}{3}$

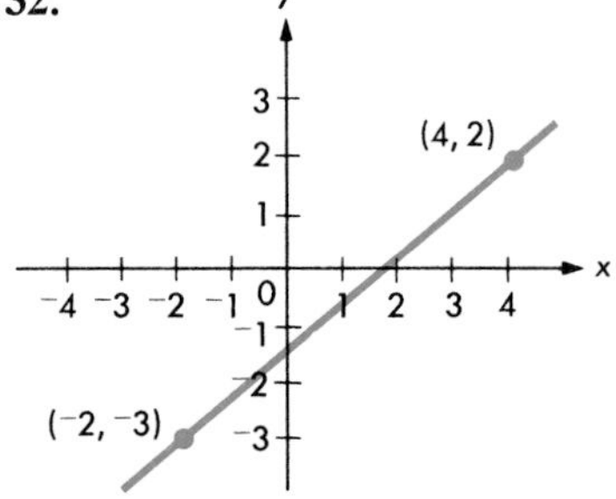

2-6 INEQUALITIES IN TWO VARIABLES

If two linear forms in x and y are connected by one of the order relations, the resulting statement is called a *first-degree inequality*, or *linear inequality*, in x and y. The solution set and graph of a linear inequality are defined in the obvious way. To solve a linear inequality, we try to find an equivalent linear inequality with an obvious solution set.

Problem 1. Discuss the solution set and draw the graph of the inequality

$$3x - 2y + 4 > {}^{-}3y + 8.$$

Solution. By adding the linear form $^{-}3x + 3y - 4$ to each side of the given inequality, we obtain the equivalent inequality

$$y > {}^{-}3x + 4.$$

Hence,

$$\{(x, y) \mid y > {}^{-}3x + 4\}$$

is the solution set of the given inequality.

Closely related to the graph of the inequality $y > {}^{-}3x + 4$ is the graph of the equation

$$y = {}^{-}3x + 4.$$

The graph of this equation is the line L discussed in Problem 2 of the preceding section and redrawn in Fig. 2–8. For each real number a, the point $(a, {}^{-}3a + 4)$ is on L. On the other hand, the point (a, b) is on the graph of the given inequality if, and only if, $b > {}^{-}3a + 4$. Geometrically, the point (a, b) is on the graph of $y > {}^{-}3x + 4$ if, and only if, it is directly *above* the point $(a, {}^{-}3a + 4)$. In the same manner, any point is on the graph of the inequality if, and only if, it is directly above a point on the line. Hence, the graph of the given inequality consists of all points *above* the line L (the shaded region in Fig. 2–9).

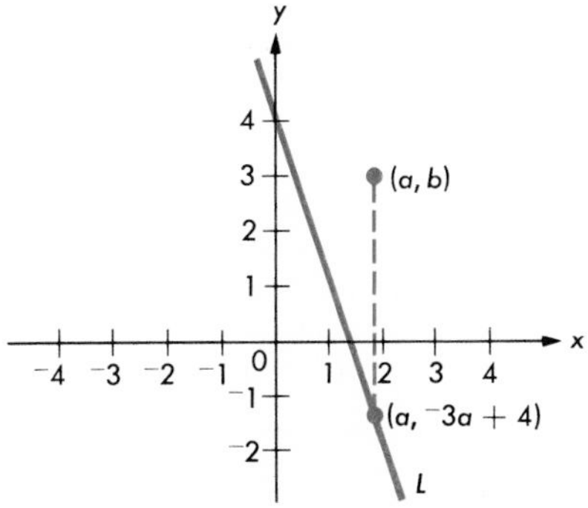

FIGURE 2–8

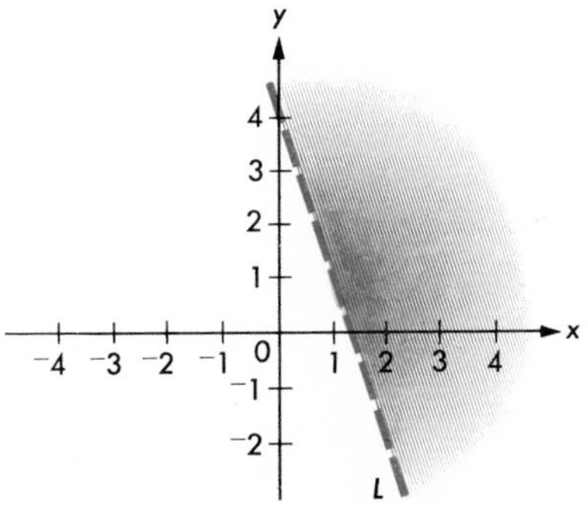

FIGURE 2–9

Quiz

(See page T12 for graphs.) Graph each of the linear equations on a cartesian coordinate system in a plane. First give the slope and then the y-intercept of each line.

1. $3x + 2y = 5$ (ans: $^{-}\frac{3}{2}, \frac{5}{2}$)
2. $5x - 7y = 0$ (ans: $\frac{5}{7}, 0$)
3. $2y - 7 = 0$ (ans: $0, \frac{7}{2}$)

2-6 INEQUALITIES IN TWO VARIABLES

In order to discuss points above or below other points, their ordinates are considered. Since the y-coordinate increases in an upward direction, the graph of $y = {}^{-}3$ divides the plane into two parts, the part above the line $y = {}^{-}3$ (which is described algebraically by the inequality $y > {}^{-}3$) and the part below the line $y = {}^{-}3$ (which is described algebraically by the inequality $y < {}^{-}3$). Similarly, points above the line

$$y = {}^{-}\tfrac{2}{3}x + 2$$

are points in the half-plane for which

$$y > {}^{-}\tfrac{2}{3}x + 2,$$

while points below the line

$$y = {}^{-}\tfrac{2}{3}x + 2$$

are points in the half-plane for which

$$y < {}^{-}\tfrac{2}{3}x + 2.$$

Students may be helped to visualize the concept of a half-plane if you consider first the half-plane of points for which $x > 0$, lying to the right of the y-axis, then the half-plane for which $x > 2$, lying to the right of the line $x = 2$, and so on. It is the x-coordinate which gives information about the right and the left, starting from the y-axis. One point lies to the right of another if it has a larger abscissa. Hence, if we have the line with equation $2x + 3y - 6 = 0$, a point is on the line if $x = {}^{-}\frac{3}{2}y + 3$; it is to the right of the line if $x > {}^{-}\frac{3}{2}y + 3$; it is to the left of the line if

$$x < {}^{-}\tfrac{3}{2}y + 3.$$

Exercises for Discussion, page 81

If time is limited, it is suggested that at least Exercises for Discussion 1–5 and 9 be covered.

In Exercise for Discussion 6, call attention to the fact that the related line $y = 2x - 3$ should be graphed before the half-plane is shaded.

Exercises for Discussion 6(c), 7, and 8 should give the student practice in both geometry and algebraic thinking.

Answers to Exercises for Discussion 1–2, 4–5, 6(b), 8, page 81

1.

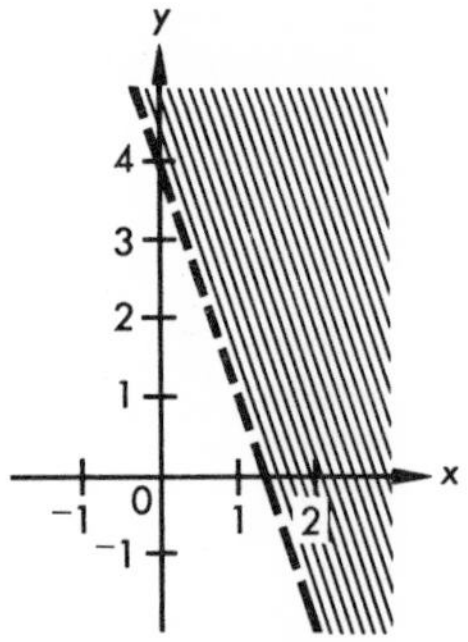

2. $\frac{1}{2} > {}^{-}3({}^{-}1) + 4$, F; no
$1 > {}^{-}3({}^{-}1) + 4$, F; no
$2 > {}^{-}3({}^{-}1) + 4$, F; no
${}^{-}1 > {}^{-}3(2) + 4$, T; yes
${}^{-}2 > {}^{-}3(2) + 4$, F; no
${}^{-}3 > {}^{-}3(2) + 4$, F; no

Such a region is called a *half-plane*. The line in the figure is broken to indicate that it is not part of the graph.

By similar reasoning, the graph of the inequality $y < {}^{-}3x + 4$ is the half-plane *below* line L of Fig. 2–9.

Problem 2. Discuss the solution set and draw the graph of the inequality

$$x - 2y - 3 < 0.$$

Solution. Upon adding $2y + 3$ to each side of the given inequality, we obtain the equivalent inequality

$$x < 2y + 3.$$

Hence,

$$\{(x, y) \mid x < 2y + 3\}$$

is the solution set of the given inequality.

The graph of the inequality $x < 2y + 3$ is closely related to the graph of the equation

$$x = 2y + 3.$$

The graph of this equation is the broken line, K, of Fig. 2–10. For each real number b, the point $(2b + 3, b)$ is on line K. On the other hand, the point (a, b) is on the graph of the inequality $x < 2y + 3$ if, and only if, $a < 2b + 3$, that is, if, and only if, the point (a, b) is directly to the *left* of the point $(2b + 3, b)$. In the same manner, any point is on the graph of the inequality if, and only if, it is directly to the left of a point on the line. Hence, the graph of the given inequality is the shaded half-plane of Fig. 2–10.

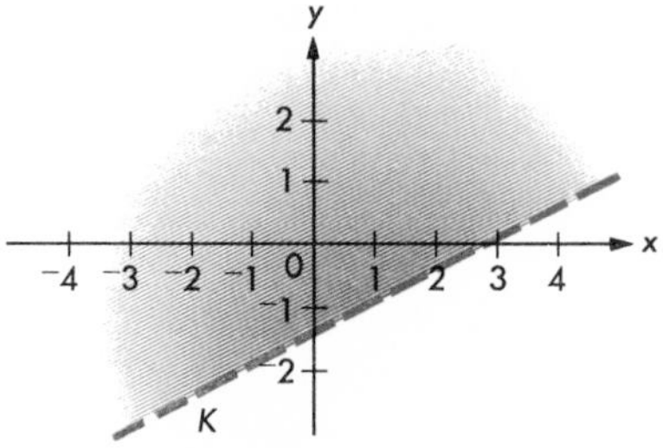

FIGURE 2–10

Problem 3. Discuss the solution set and draw the graph of the inequality

$$2x + 3 \geqq 0.$$

Solution. Since the given inequality is equivalent to the inequality

$$x \geqq {}^{-}\tfrac{3}{2},$$

the solution set is given by

$$\{(x, y) \mid x \geqq {}^{-}\tfrac{3}{2}\}.$$

Clearly, the graph of this set is the shaded *half-plane and its edge*, as shown in Fig. 2–11. The line $x = {}^{-}\frac{3}{2}$ is solid to indicate that it is part of the graph of the inequality.

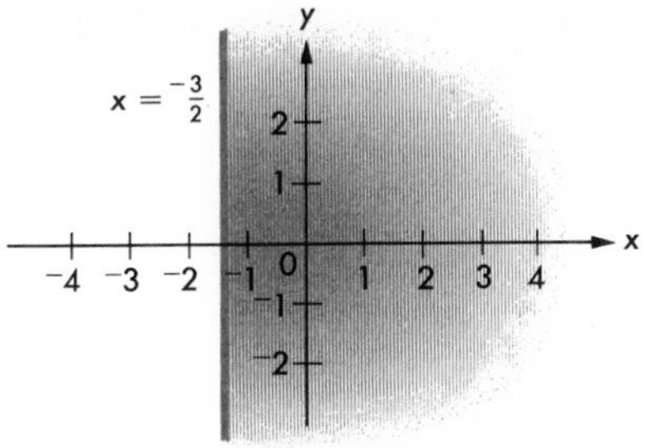

FIGURE 2–11

Exercises for Discussion

1. Graph the inequality

$$y > {}^{-}3x + 4.$$

2. Are any of the ordered pairs

$$({}^{-}1, \tfrac{1}{2}),\quad ({}^{-}1, 1),\quad ({}^{-}1, 2),\quad (2, {}^{-}1),\quad (2, {}^{-}2),\quad (2, {}^{-}3)$$

elements of the solution set of the inequality $y > {}^{-}3x + 4$?

3. In Exercise 2, which of the points are above and which are below the line $y = {}^{-}3x + 4$? Above: $(2, {}^{-}1)$ Below: $({}^{-}1, \frac{1}{2}), ({}^{-}1, 1), ({}^{-}1, 2), (2, {}^{-}3)$

4. Tell which of the points

$$(3, 0),\quad (2, 0),\quad (\tfrac{7}{2}, 0),\quad (6, 1),\quad (5, 1),$$
$$(4, 1),\quad (0, {}^{-}2),\quad ({}^{-}2, {}^{-}2),\quad ({}^{-}1, {}^{-}2)$$

lie to the left of the line $x = 2y + 3$.

5. Give the solution set and draw the graph of each inequality.
   (a) $2y + 5 \leqq 0$ (b) $x - 3 \geqq 0$

6. (a) Give the slope and y-intercept of the line bounding the graph of $y < 2x - 3$. 2, $^{-}3$
   (b) Draw the graph of $y < 2x - 3$.
   (c) Does the inequality $y < 2x - 3$, with $x > 0$ and $y < 0$, have a solution in which both variables are integers? Yes, e.g., $(2, {}^{-}1)$

7. If $({}^{-}1, b)$ is in the solution set of $x \geqq {}^{-}3y + 6$, what is the smallest integral value possible for b? ${}^{-}1 \geqq {}^{-}3b + 6$, $3b \geqq 7$ The smallest integral value of b is 3.

8. Find a pair of positive integers a and b such that (a, b) is in the solution set of $x \geqq {}^{-}3y + 6$ and $a + b$ has the smallest possible value.

4. $3 < 2(0) + 3$, F
$2 < 2(0) + 3$, T; (2, 0) lies to the left.
$\frac{7}{2} < 2(0) + 3$, F
$6 < 2(1) + 3$, F
$5 < 2(1) + 3$, F
$4 < 2(1) + 3$, T; (4, 1) lies to the left.
$0 < 2({}^{-}2) + 3$, F
${}^{-}2 < 2({}^{-}2) + 3$, T; $({}^{-}2, {}^{-}2)$ lies to the left.
${}^{-}1 < 2({}^{-}2) + 3$, F

5. (a) $\{(x, y) | y \leqq {}^{-}\frac{5}{2}\}$

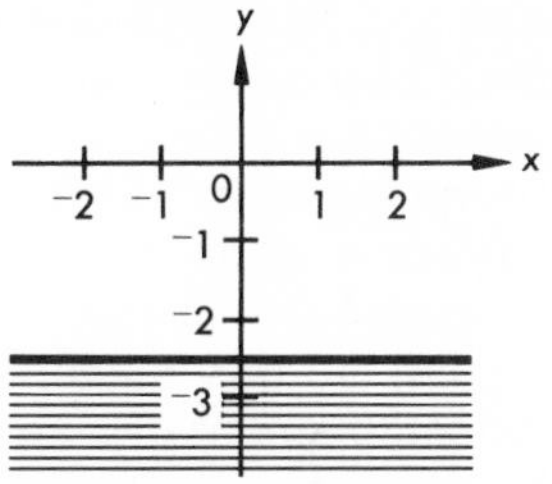

(b) $\{(x, y)\ x \geqq 3\}$

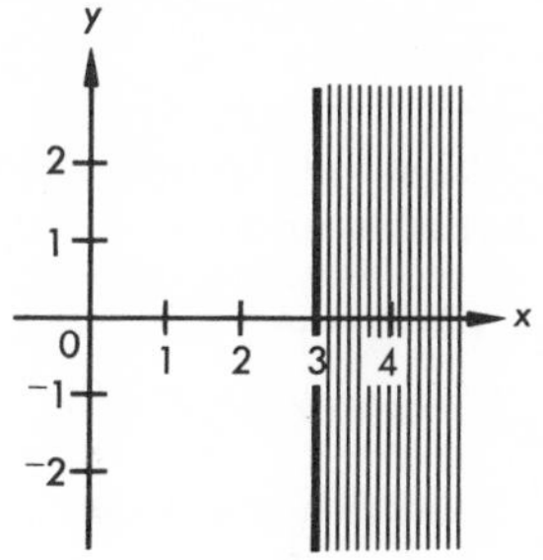

6. (b)

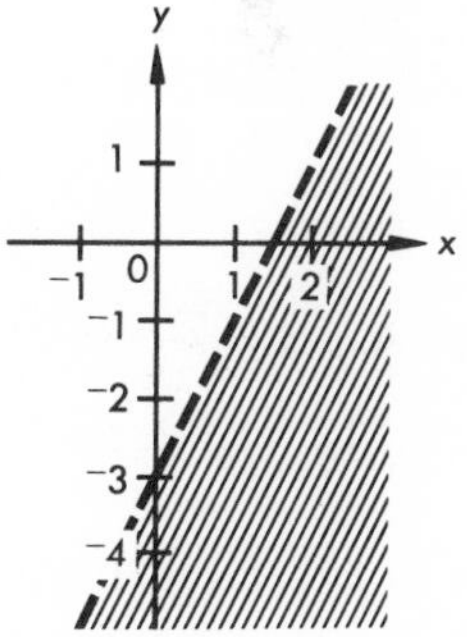

8. If $b = 1$, $a \geqq {}^{-}3(1) + 6 = 3$. Thus, $a = 3$, $b = 1$, and $a + b = 4$.
If $b = 2$, $a \geqq {}^{-}3(2) + 6 = 0$. Thus, $a = 1$, $b = 2$, and $a + b = 3$.
If $b = 3$, $a \geqq {}^{-}3(3) + 6 = {}^{-}3$. Thus, $a = 1$, $b = 3$, and $a + b = 4$.
Therefore, $a + b$ has the smallest value for $a = 1$ and $b = 2$.

It is recommended that Exercise for Discussion 9 be covered before you assign Exercises 13–16.

Exercises

Work on systems of inequalities may be anticipated by discussing the exercises on this page in sets. For example, you could ask for a description of the intersection of the graphs of Exercises 1 and 2, that is, the part of the plane where $y > 3$ and $x < {}^{-}2$. Also, ask for a description of the part of the plane where either $y > 3$ or $x < {}^{-}2$ (the union of the two sets). Exercises 2 and 3 make a good pair for an intersection infinite in extent.

You could, at this stage, introduce the complement of a set, and note the properties of the complement of the intersection of two sets as well as the complement of the union of two sets. Thus, if $\overline{A}$ designates the complement of A, that is, the points in the coordinate plane not in A, and if

$$A = \{(x, y) \mid y > 3\},$$
$$B = \{(x, y) \mid x < {}^{-}2\},$$

then

$$\overline{A} = \{(x, y) \mid y \not> 3\},$$
$$\overline{B} = \{(x, y) \mid x \not< {}^{-}2\},$$
$$\overline{A \cap B} = (A \cap \overline{B}) \cup (B \cap \overline{A}) \cup (\overline{A} \cap \overline{B}),$$

or

$$\overline{A \cap B} = \overline{A} \cup \overline{B}$$

and

$$\overline{A \cup B} = \overline{A} \cap \overline{B}.$$

(See page T12 for figures.)

Answers to Exercises 1, 2, 7–10

1. Slope 0; y-intercept 3
2. No slope; no y-intercept
7. $\{(x, y) \mid y > 3x - 2\}$
8. $\{(x, y) \mid y \leqq {}^{-}\frac{2}{3}x - 2\}$
9. $\left\{(x, y) \mid y < \dfrac{x}{3}\right\}$
10. $\{(x, y) \mid y > x + 1\}$

9. Find an inequality whose solution set has the given graph. (Hint: First obtain an equation of the bounding line.)

(a) $y < {}^{-}x + 1$

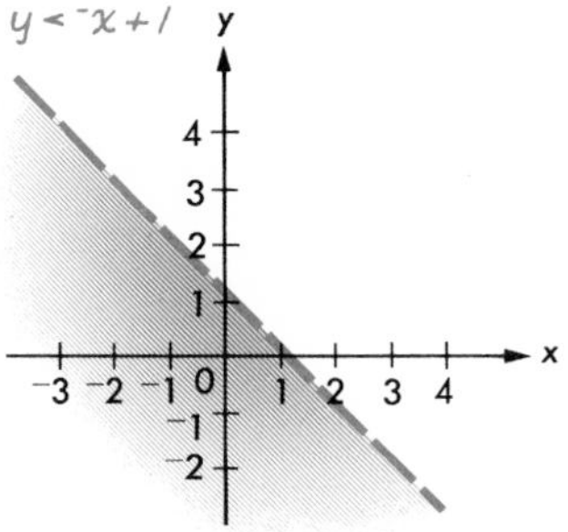

(b) $y \leqq 2$

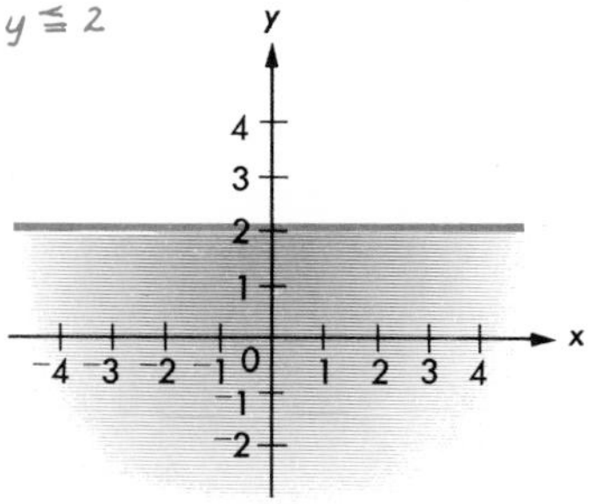

Exercises

Draw the graph of each inequality. If possible, give the slope and y-intercept of the line bounding each region. See Solution Manual for graphs.

1. $y > 3$
2. $x < {}^{-}2$
3. $y \leqq 1$ 0, 1
4. $y > {}^{-}x + 2$ ${}^{-}1$, 2
5. $x \geqq y + 2$ 1, ${}^{-}2$
6. $y < \frac{5}{2}x - 2$ $\frac{5}{2}$, ${}^{-}2$

Find the solution set of each inequality and draw the graph.

7. $2x + y - 1 < 2y - x + 1$
8. $3x + 2y - 2 \leqq x - y - 8$
9. $2x + 1 - y > x + 2y + 1$
10. $x + 1 < \frac{1}{2}(y + x + 1)$
11. $\dfrac{x}{2} - \dfrac{1}{3} \geqq \dfrac{x}{3} - y$ $\{(x,y) \mid y \geqq \frac{-1}{6}x + \frac{1}{3}\}$
12. $\dfrac{x}{2} - 1 > \dfrac{y}{4} + \dfrac{x}{5}$ $\{(x,y) \mid y < \frac{6}{5}x - 4\}$

△

Find an inequality for the solution set represented by each of the following graphs. $\{(x,y) \mid y > 2x\}$ $\{(x,y) \mid y < \frac{3}{11}x + \frac{10}{11}\}$

13.

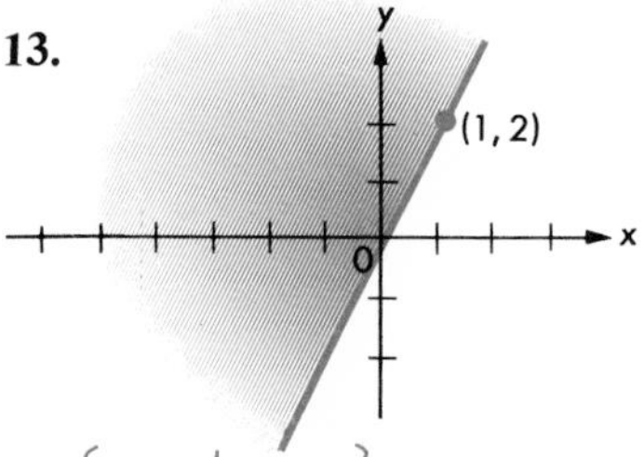

14.

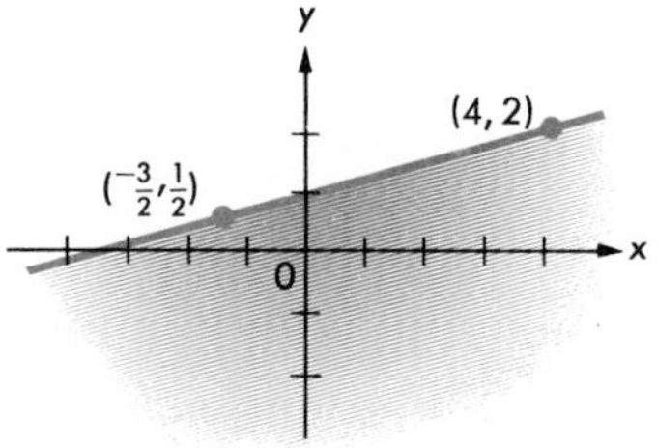

15. $\{(x,y) \mid y > {}^{-}4x\}$

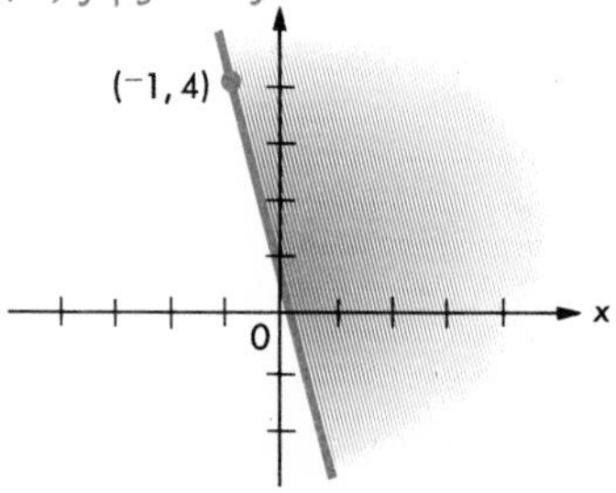

16. $\{(x,y) \mid x \geqq {}^{-}3\}$

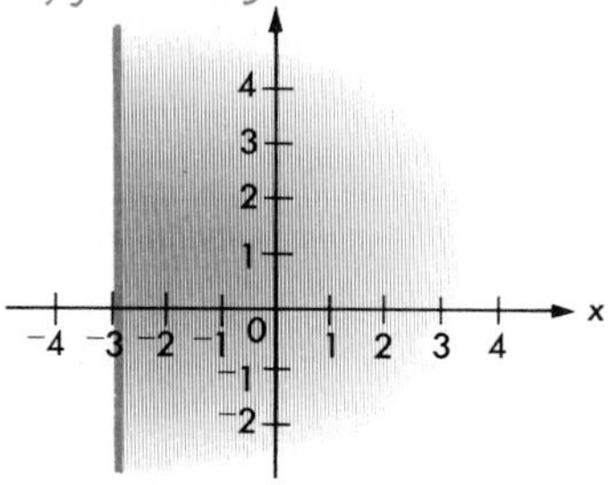

2-7 SYSTEMS OF EQUATIONS IN TWO VARIABLES

Let us suppose that we are trying to solve a physics problem that involves two variables, say x and y. Suppose also that it is physically impossible for the problem to have more than one solution. Can we solve the problem if all we know is that x and y are related by the first-degree equation

$$3x - 2y = 19?$$

Clearly not, since this equation has many solutions. For example, (7, 1) and (5, $^-2$) are solutions.

However, if we know that x and y are also related by another first-degree equation, perhaps

$$x + y = 23,$$

then we can solve the given problem. The graphs of the two first-degree equations are nonparallel lines, and their point of intersection is the graph of the unique solution of the problem.

The mathematical problem arising out of the physical problem is to solve the *system of first-degree equations*

$$\begin{cases} 3x - 2y = 19, \\ x + y = 23. \end{cases}$$

An ordered pair is a *solution* of a system of equations in x and y if it is a solution of *every* equation of the system. The set of all solutions of the system is again called the *solution set* of the system. Knowing the solution set of each equation of the system, we find the solution set of the system to be the *intersection* of the solution sets of the individual equations. Thus, if

$$S = \{(x, y) \mid 3x - 2y = 19\},$$
$$T = \{(x, y) \mid x + y = 23\},$$

then

$$S \cap T$$

is the solution set of the system above.

We shall presently find the ordered pair that is a solution of the system arising from the physical problem. However, we first want to show that systems like the following may be quickly solved.

Quiz

(See page T12 for graphs.) Find the solution set of each inequality and draw the graph.

1. $3x + y - 1 > 4x + 2$
(ans: $\{(x, y) \mid y > x + 3\}$)

2. $2y - x + 3 \leqq y + x + 2$
(ans: $\{(x, y) \mid y \leqq 2x - 1\}$)

3. $y - 1 < \frac{1}{2}(x + 1)$
(ans: $\{(x, y) \mid y < \frac{1}{2}x + \frac{3}{2}\}$)

2-7 SYSTEMS OF EQUATIONS IN TWO VARIABLES

Solving a system of equations consists of writing simpler equivalent systems until the solution becomes obvious. At each stage of the solving process, there should be as many equations as the original system contained. It is instructive to graph each system obtained in the process of solving a system of equations. For example, you could start with system (1):

$$\begin{cases} x + y = 2, \\ x - y = 3. \end{cases} \qquad (1)$$

The graph of (1) is shown in the figure below. The students should understand they are looking for the coordinates of P.

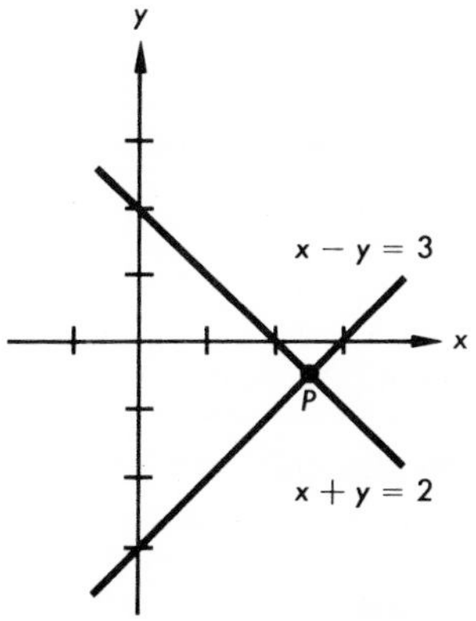

An equivalent system (2) may be written by using the first equation of (1) and a second equation obtained by adding the two equations of (1) together:

$$\begin{cases} x + y = 2, \\ \quad 2x = 5. \end{cases} \qquad (2)$$

The graph of (2) is shown in the following figure.

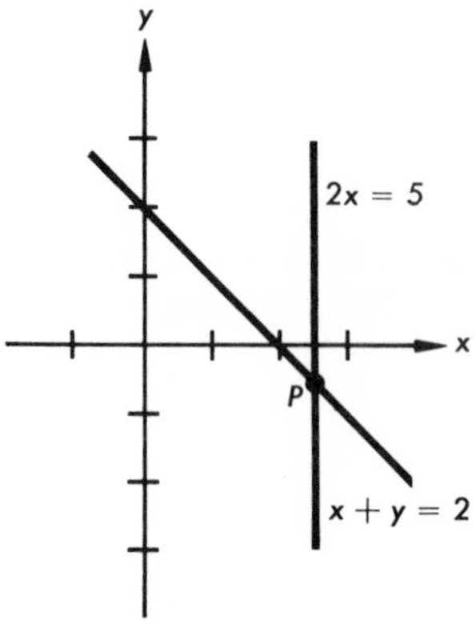

Finally, another equivalent system (3) may be written by observing that the only solution for $2x = 5$ is $x = \frac{5}{2}$. Therefore, if $x = \frac{5}{2}$ in the first equation, then

$$\begin{cases} y = {}^{-}\frac{1}{2}, \\ x = \frac{5}{2}. \end{cases} \qquad (3)$$

The graph of (3) is presented below.

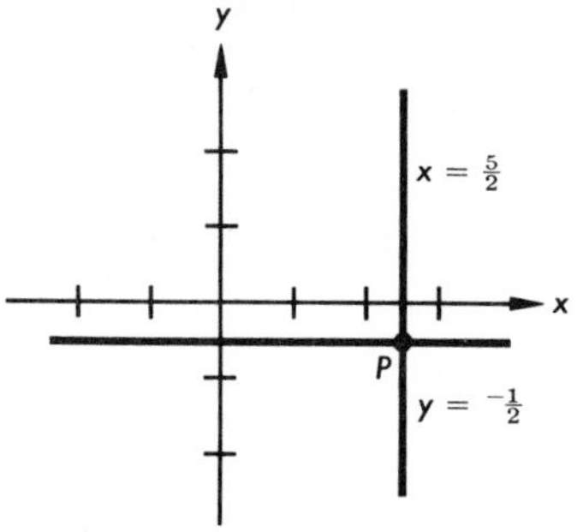

At each stage in the algebraic work we had equations of two lines through the common point of the given two lines. At last, P is seen to have coordinates $(\frac{5}{2}, {}^{-}\frac{1}{2})$.

Since the substitution method is basic for systems of equations of different degrees, it is important that it be mastered at this point,

Problem 1. Solve the system of equations

$$\begin{cases} \qquad x = 3, \\ 7x + 9y = {}^{-}15. \end{cases}$$

Solution. The solution set is given by

$$\{(x, y) \mid x = 3\} \cap \{(x, y) \mid 7x + 9y = {}^{-}15\}.$$

All elements of the first set are ordered pairs of the form $(3, y)$, and therefore, the intersection contains ordered pairs of this form. However, the ordered pair $(3, y)$ is in the second set if, and only if,

$$(7 \cdot 3) + 9y = {}^{-}15.$$

We solve this first-degree equation in one variable as follows:

$$\begin{aligned} 21 + 9y &= {}^{-}15, \\ 9y &= {}^{-}36, \\ y &= {}^{-}4. \end{aligned}$$

Hence,

$$\{(3, {}^{-}4)\}$$

is the solution set of the given system. The graphs of the equations of the system and of the solution set of the system are shown in Fig. 2–12.

Check. $\quad 3 \overset{\checkmark}{=} 3 \qquad (7 \cdot 3) + (9 \cdot {}^{-}4) \overset{?}{=} {}^{-}15$

$$21 - 36 \overset{\checkmark}{=} {}^{-}15$$

We solve a system of two first-degree equations in two variables by reducing the system to an equivalent system of the type in Problem 1. Two systems are said to be *equivalent systems* if they have the same solution set. You probably learned several methods of reducing a system of equations in your previous algebra course. A very effective way is the *substitution method,* which we shall use to solve our physics problem.

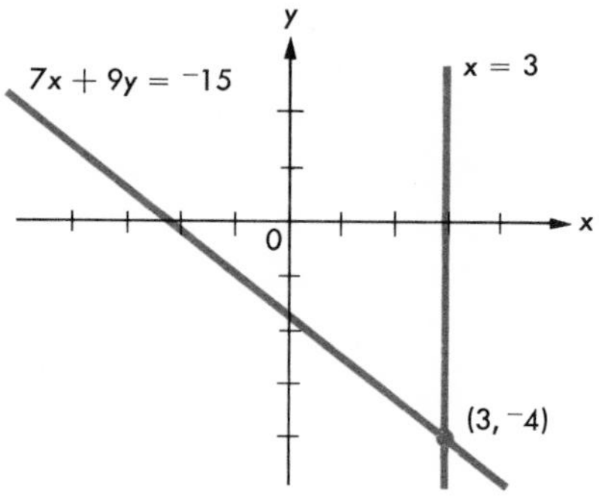

FIGURE 2–12

Problem 2. In the physics problem, we want to solve the system of equations

$$\begin{cases} 3x - 2y = 19, \\ \ x + \ y = 23. \end{cases} \qquad (1)$$

Solution. System (1) is equivalent to system (2) by uniqueness of addition.

$$\begin{cases} 3x - 2y = 19 \\ y = 23 - x \end{cases} \qquad (2)$$

Since (x, y) is a solution of the second equation of (2) if, and only if, $y = 23 - x$, then (x, y) is a solution of both equations of (2) if, and only if, $y = 23 - x$ and $3x - 2(23 - x) = 19$. In other words, (2) is equivalent to the system

$$\begin{cases} 3x - 2(23 - x) = 19, \\ y = 23 - x. \end{cases} \qquad (3)$$

The first equation of (3) is equivalent to each of the following equations:

$$3x - 46 + 2x = 19,$$
$$5x = 65,$$
$$x = 13.$$

Therefore, (3) is equivalent to the system

$$\begin{cases} x = 13, \\ y = 23 - x. \end{cases} \qquad (4)$$

The only solution of (4) is (13, 10). Hence,

$$\{(13, 10)\}$$

is the solution set of (1), the given system.

Check. $(3 \cdot 13) - (2 \cdot 10) \stackrel{?}{=} 19, \qquad 13 + 10 \stackrel{\checkmark}{=} 23$
$39 - 20 \stackrel{\checkmark}{=} 19$

Exercises for Discussion

Graph each equation in the following systems, and from your graph, find the solution set of each system.

1. $\begin{cases} x - 3 = 0 \\ y - 4 = 0 \end{cases}$ 2. $\begin{cases} y = x \\ y + 2 = 0 \end{cases}$

Solve each system of equations by the substitution method, and check each solution.

3. $\begin{cases} y + x = 3 \\ 3x - y = 1 \end{cases}$ 4. $\begin{cases} y - x = 5 \\ 4x - y = 10 \end{cases}$

5. $\begin{cases} 4x - y = 3 \\ 2x + 7y = 9 \end{cases}$ 6. $\begin{cases} x - y = 4 \\ 3x + 4y = 12 \end{cases}$

even though the addition method of Section 2-8 may be preferred for systems of linear equations.

Exercises for Discussion

If time is limited, it is suggested that at least Exercises for Discussion 1-6 be covered.

Answers to Exercises for Discussion 1-3

1. $\{(3, 4)\}$

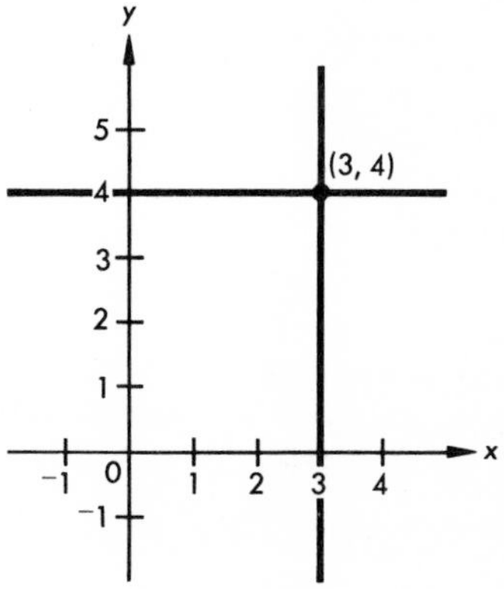

2. $\{(^-2, ^-2)\}$

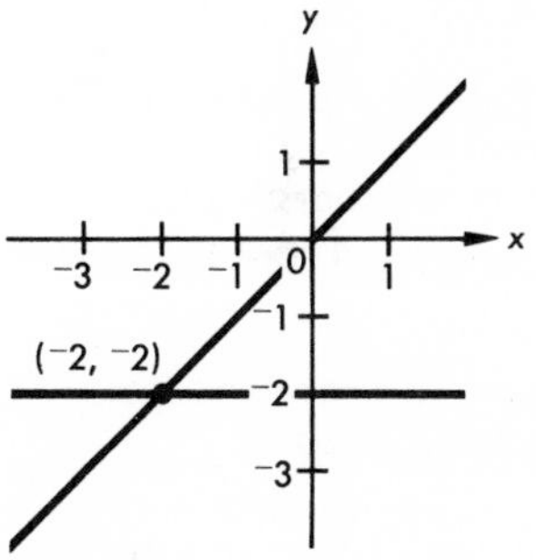

3. $\begin{cases} y + x = 3 \\ 3x - y = 1 \end{cases}$

$\begin{cases} y = 3 - x \\ 3x - (3 - x) = 1 \end{cases}$

$\begin{cases} y = 3 - x \\ 4x = 4 \end{cases}$

$\begin{cases} y = 3 - 1 \\ x = 1 \end{cases}$

$\begin{cases} x = 1 \\ y = 2 \end{cases}$

$\{(1, 2)\}$

Answers to Exercises for Discussion 4–6, page 85

4. $\begin{cases} y - x = 5 \\ 4x - y = 10 \end{cases}$
$\begin{cases} y = 5 + x \\ 4x - (5 + x) = 10 \end{cases}$
$\begin{cases} y = 5 + x \\ 3x = 15 \end{cases}$
$\begin{cases} y = 10 \\ x = 5 \end{cases}$
$\{(5, 10)\}$

5. $\begin{cases} 4x - y = 3 \\ 2x + 7y = 9 \end{cases}$
$\begin{cases} y = 4x - 3 \\ 2x + 7(4x - 3) = 9 \end{cases}$
$\begin{cases} y = 4x - 3 \\ 30x = 30 \end{cases}$
$\begin{cases} y = 1 \\ x = 1 \end{cases}$
$\{(1, 1)\}$

6. $\begin{cases} x - y = 4 \\ 3x + 4y = 12 \end{cases}$
$\begin{cases} x = 4 + y \\ 3(4 + y) + 4y = 12 \end{cases}$
$\begin{cases} x = 4 + y \\ 7y = 0 \end{cases}$
$\begin{cases} x = 4 \\ y = 0 \end{cases}$
$\{(4, 0)\}$

Note the content of the paragraph at the top of the page.

It is recommended that Exercises for Discussion 7–10 be assigned.

Answers to Exercises for Discussion 7–10

(See page T13 for graphs.)

7. Inconsistent
8. Independent
9. Dependent
10. Independent

If the graph of a system is two parallel lines, the system has an empty solution set and is said to be *inconsistent*. The two lines may coincide, in which case the system has a solution set with infinitely many elements and is said to be *dependent*. If the graphs intersect at a single point, the system is said to be *independent*. Graph the systems below, and tell if each system is dependent, independent, or inconsistent.

7. $\begin{cases} 3x - y = 6 \\ y = 3x + 2 \end{cases}$

8. $\begin{cases} x + 2 = 2y \\ x + 4y + 2 = 0 \end{cases}$

9. $\begin{cases} 2x - 3y = 12 \\ 4 + y = \frac{2}{3}x \end{cases}$

10. $\begin{cases} y - 2x = 4 \\ 2x + y + 2 = 0 \end{cases}$

Exercises

Solve graphically each of the following systems of equations, and check each solution. See Solution Manual for graphs.

1. $\begin{cases} 2x + y = 1 \\ y - x = 4 \end{cases}$ $\{(^-1, 3)\}$

2. $\begin{cases} 2x - y + 6 = 0 \\ y + 2x = 0 \end{cases}$ $\{(\frac{^-3}{2}, 3)\}$

3. $\begin{cases} 2x + 3y + 5 = 0 \\ 3x - 2y - 12 = 0 \end{cases}$ $\{(2, ^-3)\}$

Use the substitution method to solve each of the following systems.

4. $\begin{cases} x + 2y = 8 \\ x = 10 - 4y \end{cases}$ $\{(6, 1)\}$

5. $\begin{cases} u - 2v = 12 \\ v = 7u + 6 \end{cases}$ $\{(\frac{^-24}{13}, \frac{^-90}{13})\}$

6. $\begin{cases} p = 5 + 4q \\ 3p + 2q = 17 \end{cases}$ $\{(\frac{39}{7}, \frac{1}{7})\}$

7. $\begin{cases} 6m - 2n = 1 \\ 3m + 10n - 6 = 0 \end{cases}$ $\{(\frac{1}{3}, \frac{1}{2})\}$

8. $\begin{cases} 2x - 3y - 1.25 = 0 \\ 1.5y + .625x - 1 = 0 \end{cases}$ $\{(1, \frac{1}{4})\}$

9. $\begin{cases} u - (v - 2) = 2 \\ v = 2u \end{cases}$ $\{(0, 0)\}$

△

Graph the systems below, and tell whether each system is dependent, independent, or inconsistent.

10. $\begin{cases} x - y - 1 = 0 \\ x - y + 2 = 0 \end{cases}$ Inconsistent

11. $\begin{cases} x - y - 1 = 0 \\ 2x + y + 4 = 0 \end{cases}$ Independent

12. $\begin{cases} ^-2x + 2y - 2 = 0 \\ x - y + 1 = 0 \end{cases}$ Dependent

13. $\begin{cases} 2x + 2y + 10 = 0 \\ ^-4x + 3y + 7 = 0 \end{cases}$ Independent

14. $\begin{cases} 2x + 3y - 5 = 0 \\ 2x + 3y + 10 = 0 \end{cases}$ Inconsistent

15. $\begin{cases} 2x + 3y + 1 = 0 \\ 2kx + 3ky + k = 0 \end{cases}$ Dependent
$(k = 1, 2, 3, \ldots)$

2-8 MORE ON SYSTEMS OF EQUATIONS

Before solving more systems of linear equations, let us make some general observations about equivalent systems. In the first place, two systems are equivalent if each equation of one system is equivalent to the corresponding equation of the other system. For example, the two systems

$$\begin{cases} 4x + y - 7 = 0 \\ 2x + 3y = 5 \end{cases} \quad \text{and} \quad \begin{cases} y = 7 - 4x \\ 3y = 5 - 2x \end{cases}$$

are equivalent, because the first equations of each system are equivalent and the second equations are also equivalent.

Next, if a system has the form

$$\begin{cases} F_1 = G_1, \\ F_2 = G_2 \end{cases} \tag{1}$$

where F_1, G_1, F_2, and G_2 designate linear forms in x and y, then

$$\begin{cases} F_1 = G_1, \\ F_1 + F_2 = G_1 + G_2 \end{cases} \tag{2}$$

is an equivalent system. To see this, let L_1 and R_1 be the respective values of F_1 and G_1, and let L_2 and R_2 be the respective values of F_2 and G_2 when $x = a$ and $y = b$.

If (a, b) is a solution of system (1), so that

$$\begin{cases} L_1 = R_1, \\ L_2 = R_2 \end{cases}$$

are true equations, then

$$\begin{cases} L_1 = R_1, \\ L_1 + L_2 = R_1 + R_2 \end{cases}$$

are also true by uniqueness of addition. Hence, (a, b) is a solution of system (2).

Conversely, if (a, b) is a solution of system (2), so that the two equations

$$\begin{cases} L_1 = R_1, \\ L_1 + L_2 = R_1 + R_2 \end{cases}$$

Quiz

Use the substitution method to solve each of the following systems.

1. $\begin{cases} x = 2y - 3 \\ 2y + x = 1 \end{cases}$
(ans: $\{(^{-}1, 1)\}$)

2. $\begin{cases} p + q = 4 \\ 3p + 2q = 10 \end{cases}$
(ans: $\{(2, 2)\}$)

Solve graphically the following system of equations.

3. $\begin{cases} p - q = 0 \\ 2p + q = 3 \end{cases}$
(ans: $\{(1, 1)\}$)

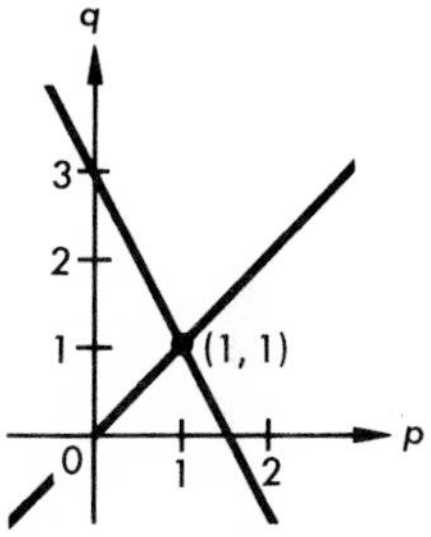

2-8 MORE ON SYSTEMS OF EQUATIONS

The student should go over this section carefully. It offers him an excellent opportunity for study of notation in abstract algebra.

are true, then

$$\begin{cases} L_1 = R_1, \\ (L_1 + L_2) - L_1 = (R_1 + R_2) - R_1, \end{cases}$$

or

$$\begin{cases} L_1 = R_1, \\ L_2 = R_2, \end{cases}$$

are also true by uniqueness of addition. Hence, (a, b) is also a solution of system (1). We conclude that systems (1) and (2) are equivalent.

The method described above for finding equivalent systems of equations is called the *addition method.* We illustrate its use in the following problems.

Problem 1. Solve the system of equations

$$\begin{cases} 9x + 4y = 19, & (L_1 = R_1) \\ 3x - 10y = {}^{-}90. & (L_2 = R_2) \end{cases} \quad (1)$$

Solution. If we multiply each side of the second equation of (1) by $^{-}3$, we obtain an equivalent system.

$$\begin{cases} 9x + 4y = 19 & (L_1 = R_1) \\ {}^{-}9x + 30y = 270 & ({}^{-}3L_2 = {}^{-}3R_2) \end{cases} \quad (2)$$

Note that the coefficients of x are opposites of each other in the two equations of (2). The first equation of system (3),

$$\begin{cases} 9x + 4y = 19, \quad (L_1 = R_1) \\ (9x + 4y) + ({}^{-}9x + 30y) = 19 + 270, \\ \qquad (L_1 + {}^{-}3L_2 = R_1 + {}^{-}3R_2), \end{cases} \quad (3)$$

is the same as the first equation of (2), while the second equation of (3) is obtained from (2) by adding the corresponding sides of the two equations of (2). Hence, (3) is equivalent to (2) by the addition method described above. On simplifying the second equation of (3), we obtain the equivalent system

$$\begin{cases} 9x + 4y = 19, \\ 34y = 289. \end{cases} \quad (4)$$

Thus, $y = \frac{17}{2}$ by the second equation, and

$$9x + (4 \cdot \tfrac{17}{2}) = 19, \quad \text{or } x = {}^{-}\tfrac{5}{3},$$

from the first equation. Hence,

$$\{({}^{-}\tfrac{5}{3}, \tfrac{17}{2})\}$$

is the solution set of the given system.

Check. $(9 \cdot {}^{-}\tfrac{5}{3}) + (4 \cdot \tfrac{17}{2}) \stackrel{?}{=} 19$ $\quad$ $(3 \cdot {}^{-}\tfrac{5}{3}) - (10 \cdot \tfrac{17}{2}) \stackrel{?}{=} {}^{-}90$

$\qquad {}^{-}15 + 34 \stackrel{\checkmark}{=} 19$ $\qquad\quad$ ${}^{-}5 - 85 \stackrel{\checkmark}{=} {}^{-}90$

Problem 2. Solve the system of equations

$$\begin{cases} 2x - 5y = {}^{-}6, & (L_1 = R_1) \\ 3x + 2y = 29. & (L_2 = R_2) \end{cases} \qquad (1)$$

Solution. If in system (1), we multiply each side of the first equation by 2 and each side of the second equation by 5, we obtain the equivalent system

$$\begin{cases} 4x - 10y = {}^{-}12, & (2L_1 = 2R_1) \\ 15x + 10y = 145. & (5L_2 = 5R_2) \end{cases} \qquad (2)$$

By the addition method, the system

$$\begin{cases} 4x - 10y = {}^{-}12, & (2L_1 = 2R_1) \\ \qquad 19x = 133 & (2L_1 + 5L_2 = 2R_1 + 5R_2) \end{cases} \qquad (3)$$

is equivalent to (2). From the second equation of (3), $x = 7$, and hence, from the first equation of (3),

$$(4 \cdot 7) - 10y = {}^{-}12,$$
$${}^{-}10y = {}^{-}40,$$
$$y = 4.$$

Therefore,

$$\{(7, 4)\}$$

is the solution set of system (1).

Check. $(2 \cdot 7) - (5 \cdot 4) \stackrel{?}{=} {}^{-}6$ $\quad$ $(3 \cdot 7) + (2 \cdot 4) \stackrel{?}{=} 29$

$\qquad 14 - 20 \stackrel{\checkmark}{=} {}^{-}6$ $\qquad\quad$ $21 + 8 \stackrel{\checkmark}{=} 29$

TWISTER

Lew and Walter were hired by the city to paint parking meters along Main Street. Lew arrived first on the job, and had painted 3 meters on the south side of the street when Walter arrived and said that Lew was supposed to be painting those on the north side. So Lew began again on the north side while Walter continued on the south. When Walter had finished his side, he went across the street and painted 6 meters for Lew, and then the job was finished. There were an equal number of meters on each side of the street. Which man painted more parking meters? How many more?

Solution: Walter painted six more meters regardless of how many there were on a side.

Exercises for Discussion

If time is limited, it is suggested that at least Exercises for Discussion 1 and 3 be covered.

Answers to Exercises for Discussion 1–2

1. (a) $\begin{cases} 6x - 15y = 27 \\ 6x + 8y = 16 \end{cases}$

   (b) $\begin{cases} 6x - 15y = 27 \\ {}^-6x - 8y = {}^-16 \end{cases}$

   (c) $\begin{cases} 8x - 20y = 36 \\ 15x + 20y = 40 \end{cases}$

   (d) $\begin{cases} {}^-8x + 20y = {}^-36 \\ 15x + 20y = 40 \end{cases}$

2. (a) $\begin{cases} {}^-4x - 8y = {}^-56 \\ 4x = 9 \end{cases}$

   $\begin{cases} {}^-8y = {}^-47 \\ 4x = 9 \end{cases}$

   $\begin{cases} x = \frac{9}{4} \\ y = \frac{47}{8} \end{cases}$

   $\{(\frac{9}{4}, \frac{47}{8})\}$

   (b) $\begin{cases} 8x - 20y = 36 \\ 15x + 20y = 125 \end{cases}$

   $\begin{cases} 8x - 20y = 36 \\ 23x = 161 \end{cases}$

   $\begin{cases} x = 7 \\ y = 1 \end{cases}$

   $\{(7, 1)\}$

Quiz

Solve each of the following systems of equations.

1. $\begin{cases} x - y = 2 \\ x + y = 2 \end{cases}$
   (ans: $\{(2, 0)\}$)
2. $\begin{cases} 3y - 2x = 4 \\ 5y + 2x = 12 \end{cases}$
   (ans: $\{(1, 2)\}$)
3. $\begin{cases} 2p - 3q = 1 \\ p + q = {}^-2 \end{cases}$
   (ans: $\{({}^-1, {}^-1)\}$)
4. $\begin{cases} y - 5x + 4 = 0 \\ y = \dfrac{{}^-5x + 1}{2} \end{cases}$
   (ans: $\{(\frac{3}{5}, {}^-1)\}$)

Exercises for Discussion

1. Start with the system of equations

$$\begin{cases} 2x - 5y = 9, \\ 3x + 4y = 8, \end{cases}$$

and write an equivalent system in which
(a) the coefficients of x are the same.
(b) the coefficients of x are opposites, or additive inverses, of each other.
(c) the coefficients of y are opposites, or additive inverses, of each other.
(d) the coefficients of y are the same.

2. Solve each system of equations by the addition method, and check each solution.

(a) $\begin{cases} x + 2y = 14 \\ 4x - 7 = 2 \end{cases}$ (b) $\begin{cases} 2x - 5y = 9 \\ 3x + 4y = 25 \end{cases}$

3. Try to solve the system of equations

$$\begin{cases} 5x + 2y = 10, \\ 3 - 5x = 2y \end{cases} \quad \begin{cases} 5x + 2y = 10 \\ {}^-5x - 2y = {}^-3 \end{cases} \quad \begin{cases} 5x + 2y = 10 \\ 0 = 7 \end{cases}$$

by the addition method. What is your conclusion about the solution set of this system? ϕ What can you say about the graphs of these two equations? The graphs are parallel lines.

Exercises

Use the addition method to solve each of the following systems of equations.

1. $\begin{cases} x + 3y = 11 \\ x - y = 17 \end{cases}$ $\{(\frac{31}{2}, \frac{{}^-3}{2})\}$
2. $\begin{cases} 8p + 4q = 3 \\ 2p - 8q = {}^-3.75 \end{cases}$ $\{(\frac{1}{8}, \frac{1}{2})\}$
3. $\begin{cases} 3m - 2n = {}^-10 \\ 4m + n = 49 \end{cases}$ $\{(8, 17)\}$
4. $\begin{cases} \frac{2}{7}x + \frac{1}{8}y = 0 \\ \frac{3}{4}x - \frac{1}{3}y = 0 \end{cases}$ $\{(0, 0)\}$
5. $\begin{cases} u = v - 1 \\ 10u + 7 = 8v \end{cases}$ $\{(\frac{1}{2}, \frac{3}{2})\}$
6. $\begin{cases} y + 2x - 4 = 0 \\ \frac{5}{2}y = 13x + 10 \end{cases}$ $\{(0, 4)\}$

Use any method to solve each of the following systems of equations.

7. $\begin{cases} p + 3(1 - q) = 0 \\ 3q - 2(6 - p) = 0 \end{cases}$ $\{(3, 2)\}$
8. $\begin{cases} 3x - y = 6 + x + 2y \\ 3(y - 2) = 2(x + 1) - 10 \end{cases}$ ϕ
9. $\begin{cases} \dfrac{x + y}{4} + \dfrac{x - y}{2} = 1 \\ \dfrac{3x - y}{4} + \dfrac{4x + 2y}{11} = 3 \end{cases}$ $\{(3, 5)\}$
10. $\begin{cases} 2p + q + 14 = 7(p - 4q + 2) \\ 3(2p - 3q + 4) = 5p + 12 \end{cases}$ $\{(0, 0)\}$
11. $\begin{cases} .07n - .04m = .01 \\ .2n - .05m = .035 \end{cases}$ $\{(\frac{1}{10}, \frac{1}{5})\}$
12. $\begin{cases} x + 2y - 1 = \dfrac{x + y}{5} \\ 2x - y = \dfrac{5 - 2x}{6} \end{cases}$ $\{(\frac{1}{2}, \frac{1}{3})\}$

2-9 APPLICATIONS

We can solve many word problems by writing and solving systems of linear equations. Consider, for example, the following problems.

Problem 1. A football game was attended by 4730 people, some paying \$1.50 each for reserved seats and the rest paying 90¢ each for general admission. If the total receipts for the game were \$5172, how many tickets of each kind were sold?

Solution. Let r designate the number of reserved-seat tickets and g the number of general-admission tickets sold. Since 4730 tickets were sold,

$$r + g = 4730.$$

The amount of money, in dollars, received from the sale of reserved-seat tickets was $1.50r$; that received from the sale of general-admission tickets was $.90g$. Since the total receipts were \$5172,

$$1.50r + .90g = 5172.$$

Thus, the solution of the given problem is the solution of the system of equations

$$\begin{cases} r + g = 4730, \\ 1.50r + .90g = 5172. \end{cases} \tag{1}$$

Let us use the substitution method to solve system (1). If we solve the first equation for g in terms of r and substitute the result in the second equation, we obtain the equivalent system

$$\begin{cases} r + g = 4730, \\ 1.50r + .90(4730 - r) = 5172. \end{cases} \tag{2}$$

The second equation of (2) may be simplified as follows:

$$\begin{aligned} 1.50r + 4257 - .90r &= 5172, \\ .60r &= 915, \\ r &= 1525. \end{aligned}$$

Thus, system (2) is equivalent to the system

$$\begin{cases} r + g = 4730, \\ r = 1525. \end{cases} \tag{3}$$

2-9 APPLICATIONS

Students may prefer to solve these problems using only one variable. Although solving an equation in one variable is generally not as involved as solving a system of equations, it may, in certain cases, be more difficult to write an equation in a single variable than to write two equations in two variables. The students must learn to judge which approach is the best for the problem at hand. They should understand that the substitution method for finding the solution of a system of equations corresponds to the solving of word problems using only one variable.

Exercises for Discussion, page 93

In Exercise or Discussion 2, it should be noted that the domain of the variable in 2(a) is the set of integers, and that in 2(b) the domain of the variable is the set of real numbers. This distinction must be borne in mind in order to be able to understand the nature of the problem in 2(c).

Answers to Exercises for Discussion 1–6, page 93

1. The total distance is

$$r \times t = (330)(10),$$

or 3300 miles. Thus, the airplane can fly 1650 miles from its base and return without refueling.

2. (a) Let l be the larger and p the smaller of the numbers. The system is

$$\begin{cases} l + p = 55, \\ l - p = 9. \end{cases}$$

Equivalent systems are

$$\begin{cases} (l + p) + (l - p) = 55 + 9, \\ l - p = 9, \end{cases}$$

$$\begin{cases} 2l = 64, \\ l - p = 9 \end{cases}$$

$$\begin{cases} l = 32, \\ p = 23. \end{cases}$$

The numbers are 32 and 23.

(b) As above, l is the larger and p the smaller of the numbers.

$$\begin{cases} l - p = 16 \\ l + p = 73 \end{cases}$$

$$\begin{cases} l - p = 16 \\ 2l = 89 \end{cases}$$

$$\begin{cases} l = 44\frac{1}{2} \\ p = 28\frac{1}{2} \end{cases}$$

The numbers are $44\frac{1}{2}$ and $28\frac{1}{2}$.

(c) Let l and p be as above.

$$\begin{cases} l - p = d \\ l + p = s \end{cases}$$

$$\begin{cases} l - p = d \\ 2l = d + s \end{cases}$$

$$\begin{cases} l = \dfrac{d + s}{2} \\ p = \dfrac{s - d}{2} \end{cases}$$

The numbers l and p will both be integers if, and only if, $d + s$ and $s - d$ are both even.

3. Let x and y be the two parts. Then $x + y = 240$. As the text

System (3) is easily solved, yielding

$$r = 1525, \quad g = 3205.$$

Check. $1525 + 3205 \overset{\checkmark}{=} 4730$ $\quad (1.50 \cdot 1525) + (.90 \cdot 3205) \overset{?}{=} 5172$

$$2287.50 + 2884.50 \overset{\checkmark}{=} 5172$$

Problem 2. An airplane carries enough gas for 10 hours of flight. Suppose that its speed in still air is 330 miles per hour. If it flies against a wind of 110 miles per hour on its outbound trip and with a wind of 110 miles per hour on the return trip, how far can it fly without refueling?

Solution. The speed of the outbound plane is 330 − 110, or 220, miles per hour, and the speed on the return flight is 330 + 110, or 440, miles per hour. Let x denote the distance, in miles, the plane travels from its base, and t the time, in hours, it takes for the outbound journey. Since the product of rate and time is distance, our first equation is

$$220t = x.$$

Our second equation relating x and t describes the return flight. Since the total time of the flight is 10 hours, and the flight out takes t hours, the flight back takes $10 - t$ hours. We have found that the speed on the return trip was 440 miles per hour and since the distance out is the same as the distance back, the equation

$$440(10 - t) = x$$

describes the flight back.

The solution of the given problem is the same as the solution of the system of equations

$$\begin{cases} 220t = x, \\ 440(10 - t) = x. \end{cases}$$

You may easily verify that the following system is equivalent to the one above.

$$\begin{cases} 220t = x \\ t = \frac{20}{3} \end{cases}$$

Hence, the solution is

$$t = \tfrac{20}{3}, \quad x = \tfrac{4400}{3}.$$

Thus, the airplane can fly approximately 1470 miles from its base and return without refueling. Does this answer check?

Exercises for Discussion

1. How far can the airplane of Problem 2 fly without refueling if there is no wind during the 10-hour flight?
2. (a) Find two integers whose sum is 55 and whose difference is 9.
   (b) Find two numbers whose difference is 16 and whose sum is 73.
   (c) State the conditions on the integers d and s, given that there are two integers whose difference is d and whose sum is s.
3. Divide 240 into two parts such that the ratio of the larger to the smaller part is 17 : 13. (Hint: The equation $x/y = 17/13$, or the equivalent linear equation $13x = 17y$, may be used to express the fact that x and y are in the ratio 17 : 13).
4. A linear form

$$ax + by$$

is known to have value 21 when $x = 3$ and $y = 2$, and to have value 65 when $x = 7$ and $y = 10$. Find the coefficients a and b of this linear form.

5. The sum of the digits of a two-digit number is one-half the number. Show that this property characterizes the number completely because there is one, and only one, number with this property. (Hint: Recall that in our decimal system an expression for the two-digit number with tens' digit, t, and units' digit, u, is $10t + u$.)
6. John's bank contains some quarters and 3 times as many dimes as nickels. If there are 26 coins totaling \$3.90 in the bank, how many of each kind of coin does the bank contain?

Exercises

1. A sum of money amounting to \$4.15 consists of dimes and quarters. If there are 19 coins in all, how many quarters are there? *15 quarters*
2. The initial investments of two partners in a business were \$50,000 and \$70,000. The partners agree to divide profits in the same ratio as their relative investments. How much does each partner receive if the first year's profits amount to \$15,000? *The heavier investor receives \$8750; his partner receives \$6250.*
3. A jet plane makes a 3000-mile trip to Europe in 5 hours, but takes 6 hours for the return trip. If the speed of the wind is constant throughout the trip, what is the speed of the wind and what is the average speed of the plane in still air? *50 mph; 550 mph*
4. The sum of the digits of a two-digit number is one-seventh the number. Find all numbers having this property. *21, 42, 63, 84*

indicates, the ratio relationship is expressed by $x/y = 17/13$, or $13x = 17y$. Equivalent to the system composed of the two equations are

$$\begin{cases} x = 240 - y, \\ 13(240 - y) = 17y, \end{cases}$$

$$\begin{cases} x = 240 - y, \\ 3120 = 30y, \end{cases}$$

$$\begin{cases} y = 104, \\ x = 136. \end{cases}$$

Thus, the two parts are 136 and 104.

4. Substituting 3 for x and 2 for y, we have $3a + 2b = 21$. Substituting 7 for x and 10 for y, we have $7a + 10b = 65$.

$$\begin{cases} 3a + 2b = 21, \\ 7a + 10b = 65, \end{cases}$$

$$\begin{cases} {}^-15a - 10b = {}^-105, \\ 7a + 10b = 65, \end{cases}$$

$$\begin{cases} ({}^-15a - 10b) + (7a + 10b) \\ \quad = {}^-105 + 65, \\ 7a + 10b = 65, \end{cases}$$

$$\begin{cases} {}^-8a = {}^-40, \\ 7a + 10b = 65, \end{cases}$$

$$\begin{cases} a = 5, \\ b = 3. \end{cases}$$

Therefore, $a = 5$ and $b = 3$. The linear form is $5x + 3y$.

5. Let t be the tens' digit and u the units' digit ($10t + u$ = number). The problem tells us that

$$t + u = \tfrac{1}{2}(10t + u).$$

Equivalent to this equation are $2t + 2u = 10t + u$ and $u = 8t$. The number t must be an integer from 1 to 9 and u must be an integer from 0 to 9. The only solution to this equation with this restriction is $t = 1$ and $u = 8$. Thus, the number is 18.

6. Let n be the number of nickels, then $3n$ is the number of dimes. Let q be the number of quarters. Since there are 26 coins,

$$n + 3n + q = 26.$$

Since the coins are worth \$3.90, $5n + 10(3n) + 25q = 390$.

$$\begin{cases} 4n + q = 26 \\ 35n + 25q = 390 \end{cases}$$

$$\begin{cases} {}^-20n - 5q = {}^-130 \\ 7n + 5q = 78 \end{cases}$$

$$\begin{cases} {}^-13n = {}^-52 \\ 7n + 5q = 78 \end{cases}$$

$$\begin{cases} n = 4 \\ q = 10 \end{cases}$$

Hence, there are 4 nickels, 12 dimes, and 10 quarters.

It is suggested that Exercise 6 be done in class and Exercises 7 and 8 be assigned. Exercise 9 is only for the better student, unless done in class.

Quiz

1. Find two integers whose sum is 105 and whose difference is 11. (ans: 58, 47)
2. Separate 64 into two parts so that the larger part is 5 less than twice the smaller part. (ans: 41, 23)
3. The sum of the digits of a two-digit number is 15. If the units' digit is 3 less than the tens' digit, find the number. (ans: 96)

△

5. Two machines A and B produce items at the constant rate of 50 and 40 items per hour, respectively. An order for 1000 items is to be filled.
   (a) If the total number of machine-hours of operation used is exactly 24, show that to fill the order, there is one, and only one, way of assigning a number of hours of operation to each machine. Machine A runs 4 hours and machine B runs 20 hours.
   (b) If it costs \$10 per hour to operate machine A and \$7 per hour to operate machine B, what is the total cost of the production that satisfies the specifications in part (a)? \$180
   (c) If the total number of machine-hours of operation used is to be *at most* 24 (instead of exactly 24), the entire order for 1000 items could be handled by machine A. Find the cost of production under such a scheme, and compare it with the cost of the production plan in part (a). \$200; more costly than plan (a)
   (d) If the hourly costs are \$10 for machine A and \$9 for machine B, compare the production costs under the plan in part (a) with that of the plan in part (c). Plan (a): \$220
   Plan (c): \$200; less costly than plan (a)

▲

6. An equation such as $2/x + 3/y = 7$ is *not* a linear equation in x and y. However, if we replace $1/x$ by X and $1/y$ by Y, we see that the resulting equation is linear in X and Y. If we had a system of such equations, we could then make these replacements and use the methods of this section to solve for X and Y. The original variables x and y would be immediately available since they are the reciprocals of X and Y. Use this method to find two numbers such that the reciprocal of the first added to 6 times the reciprocal of the second is 1, while the reciprocal of the second number added to twice the reciprocal of the first gives $\frac{5}{8}$. 4, 8
7. Machines A and B each produce items at a constant rate characteristic of the particular machine. If A produces 400 items and B produces 600 items, a total of 23 machine-hours is spent. If A produces 600 and B produces 400 items, a total of 22 machine-hours is spent. Find each machine's rate. Machine A produces 50 items per hour; Machine B produces 40 items per hour.
8. Working together, Smith and Jones can finish a job in 4 days. Smith does twice as much work in 1 day as Jones does. How long would it take Smith working alone to do the job? 6 days
9. A rifleman standing 1000 yards from his target hears the bullet strike 4 seconds after he fires. An observer 800 yards from the target and 550 yards from the rifleman hears the bullet strike 2 seconds after he hears the report of the rifle. Find the velocity of sound and the velocity of the bullet. The bullet travels 750 yd/sec and sound 375 yd/sec.

2-10 SYSTEMS OF INEQUALITIES IN TWO VARIABLES

The solution set of a system of inequalities is the *intersection* of the solution sets of the individual inequalities of the system. For example, the system

$$\begin{cases} x > 0, \\ y > 0 \end{cases}$$

has as its solution the set of all number pairs (x, y) for which $x > 0$ and $y > 0$. In set notation, the solution set is given by

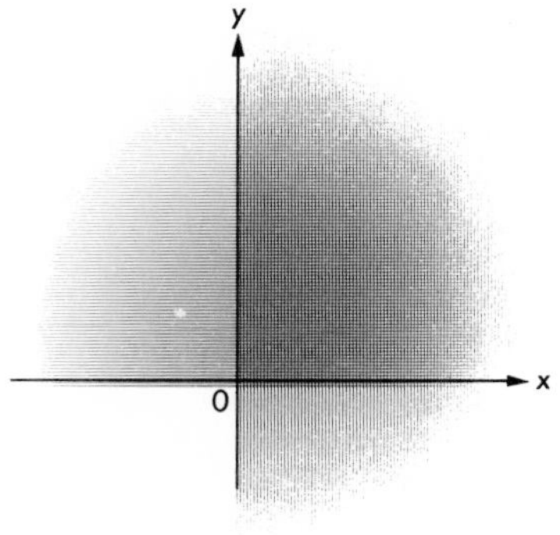

FIGURE 2-13

$$\{(x, y) \mid x > 0\} \cap \{(x, y) \mid y > 0\}.$$

The graph of this set is the set of all points in the first quadrant (the doubly shaded region of Fig. 2-13).

Problem 1. Describe the solution set and draw the graph of the system

$$\begin{cases} x - \ y - 2 < 0, \\ x + 2y - 8 > 0. \end{cases}$$

Solution. Each inequality of the system is simplified in the following way.

$$x - y - 2 < 0$$
$$(x - y - 2) + y < y$$
$$x - 2 < y, \quad \text{or } y > x - 2$$

$$x + 2y - 8 > 0$$
$$(x + 2y - 8) + {}^{-}x + 8 > {}^{-}x + 8$$
$$2y > {}^{-}x + 8$$
$$y > {}^{-}\tfrac{1}{2}x + 4$$

Thus, the given system is equivalent to the system

$$\begin{cases} y > x - 2, \\ y > {}^{-}\tfrac{1}{2}x + 4, \end{cases}$$

and its solution set S is given by

$$S = \{(x, y) \mid y > x - 2\} \cap \{(x, y) \mid y > {}^{-}\tfrac{1}{2}x + 4\}.$$

2-10 SYSTEMS OF INEQUALITIES IN TWO VARIABLES

It has already been seen that the graph of an inequality is a half-plane. Two half-planes might intersect in a quarter-plane; one half-plane might lie within the other; they might overlap in a strip if bounded by parallel lines, or fail to intersect at all. These are the possibilities, then, for the graph of a system of two inequalities. Have the class imagine and sketch all possibilities for the graph of a system of three inequalities, then for four inequalities, and so on, before they become involved with graphs of specific sets of inequalities.

The graph of a system of inequalities locates points whose coordinates form a solution for each inequality in the system. Usually the solution set for the system is infinite. One way of focusing attention on the meaning of the shaded region in Fig. 2-15, is to test the coordinates of several points outside the shaded region to show that they are not solutions of every inequality in the system. Then test the coordinates of several points inside the region of each inequality. You might ask how many integral solutions there are for the system of inequalities. The same question is good for Exercise for Discussion 1 on the next page.

Exercises for Discussion, page 97

It is suggested that you emphasize to the student the importance of neatness and of the use of separate colors in making these graphs.

Answers to Exercise for Discussion 1, page 97

1. (a)

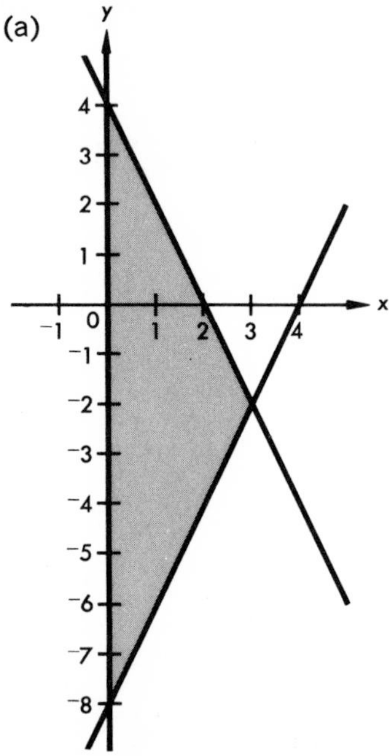

(b) Triangle with vertices (0, 4), (0, $^-8$), (3, $^-2$)

The line L of Fig. 2–14 is the graph of the equation $y = x - 2$. Therefore, the graph of the set $\{(x, y) \mid y > x - 2\}$ is the half-plane above L. In turn, the graph of the equation $y = {}^-\frac{1}{2}x + 4$ is the line K of Fig. 2–14, and the graph of the set $\{(x, y) \mid y > {}^-\frac{1}{2}x + 4\}$ is the half-plane above K. The intersection of these two half-planes is the graph of the solution set S. Thus, the graph of S is the doubly shaded region of Fig. 2–14.

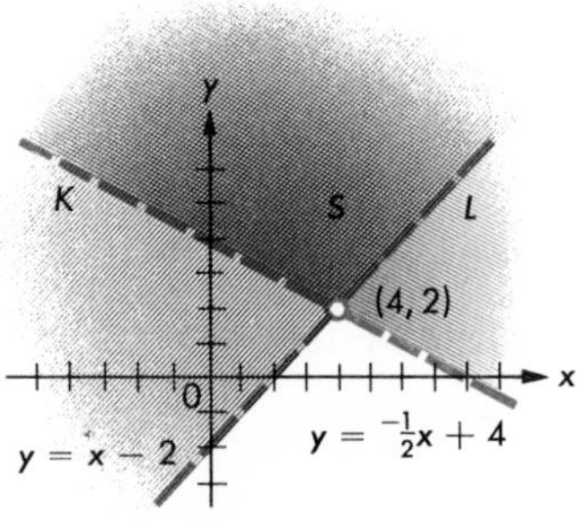

FIGURE 2–14

Problem 2. Describe the solution set and draw the graph of the system

$$\begin{cases} x - y - 2 < 0, \\ x + 2y - 8 > 0, \\ y < 7. \end{cases}$$

Solution. Evidently the solution set T consists of all points (x, y) of set S (in Problem 1) for which $y < 7$, that is,

$$T = S \cap \{(x, y) \mid y < 7\}.$$

The graph of T is the set of all points *inside* the triangle ABC (the triply shaded region of Fig. 2–15).

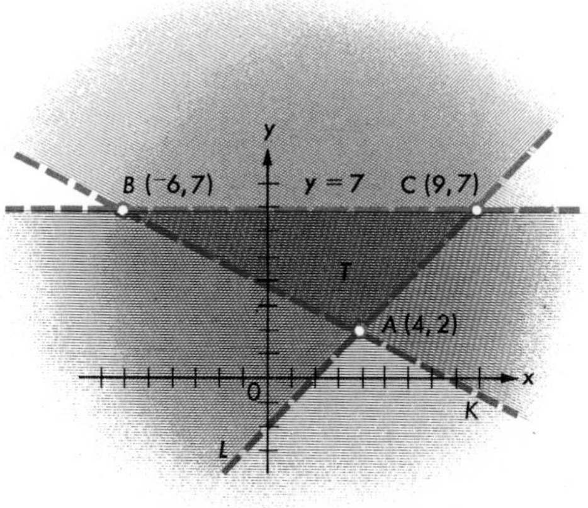

FIGURE 2–15

Problem 3. The shaded region of Fig. 2–16 lies between the two parallel lines with equations

$$x + y = 0,$$
$$x + y = 2.$$

Describe this shaded region as the graph of a system of inequalities.

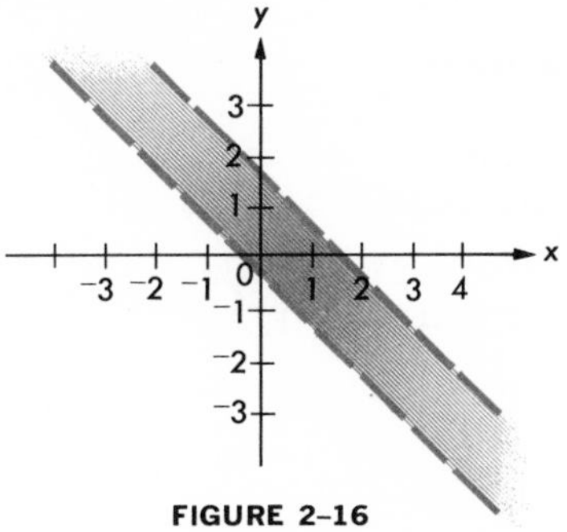

FIGURE 2–16

Solution. The shaded region is *above* the line with equation

$$x + y = 0, \quad \text{or } y = {}^{-}x,$$

and *below* the line with equation

$$x + y = 2, \quad \text{or } y = {}^{-}x + 2.$$

Thus, the shaded region is the graph of the set

$$\{(x, y) \mid y > {}^{-}x\} \cap \{(x, y) \mid y < {}^{-}x + 2\},$$

and hence of the system

$$\begin{cases} y > {}^{-}x, \\ y < {}^{-}x + 2. \end{cases}$$

Exercises for Discussion

1. (a) Draw the graph of $A \cap B \cap C$, given that

$$A = \{(x, y) \mid 2x - y \leqq 8\},$$
$$B = \{(x, y) \mid 2x + y \leqq 4\},$$
$$C = \{(x, y) \mid x \geqq 0\}.$$

   (b) Describe the region bounded by the graphs of A, B, and C by giving its shape and the coordinates of the vertices of its boundary.

   (c) Find $A \cap B$, $A \cap C$, and $B \cap C$.

2. Graph the following system of inequalities, and list the positive integral solutions of the system.

$$\begin{cases} 2x - y \leqq 8, \\ 2x + y \leqq 4, \\ x \geqq 0. \end{cases}$$

3. Describe the solution set and draw the graph of the system

$$\begin{cases} 5x - 3y - 9 < 0, \\ 2x + 3y - 12 > 0. \end{cases}$$

(c)

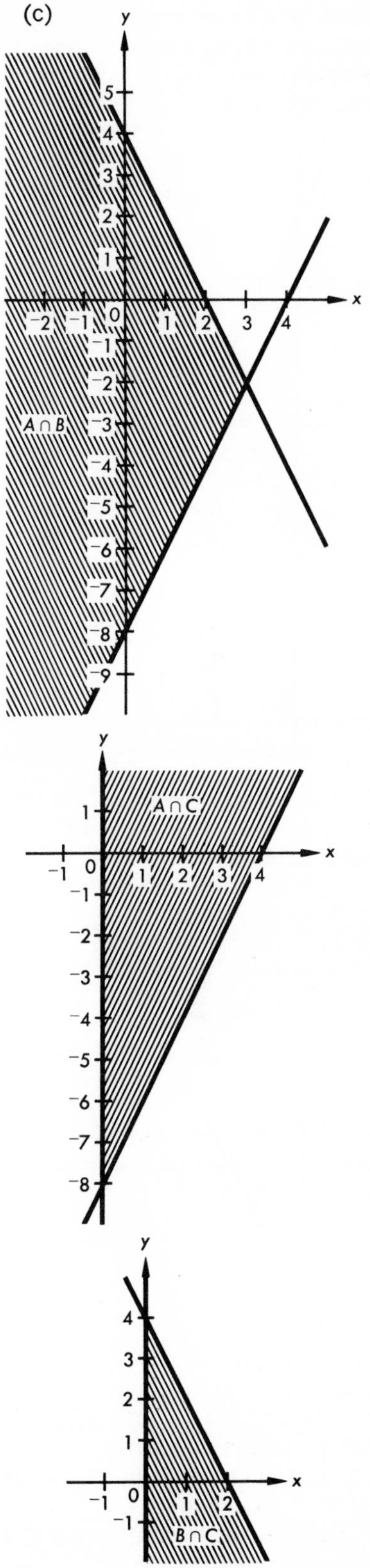

Answers to Exercises for Discussion 2, 3, page 97

2. (1, 1), (1, 2)

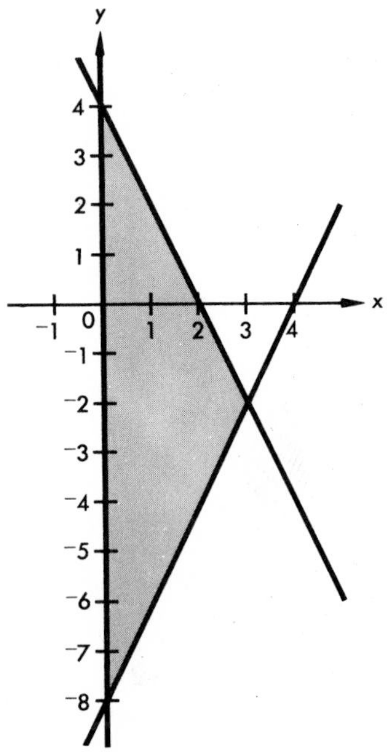

3. $S = \{(x, y) \mid 5x - 3y - 9 < 0\} \cap \{(x, y) \mid 2x + 3y - 12 > 0\}$ (Quarter-plane)

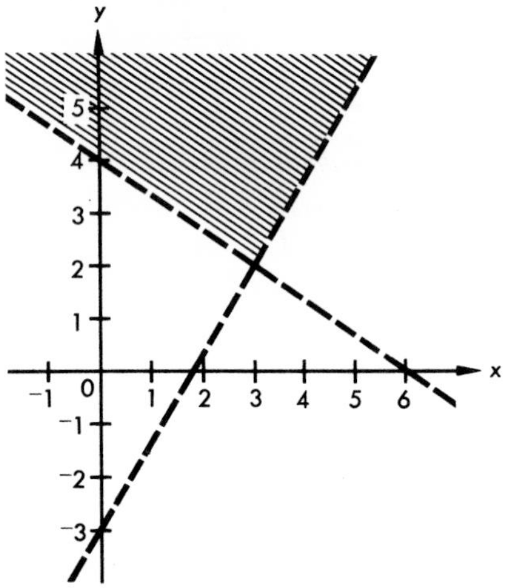

Exercises

The student should understand that corner points or vertices on the regions must be found by solving pairs of equations. For example, in Exercise 3, the following three systems must be solved:

Exercises

Describe the solution set and draw the graph of each of the following systems of inequalities. *See Solution Manual for graphs.*

1. $\begin{cases} y < 2x \\ 2x + y < 12 \end{cases}$ *Quarter-plane*

2. $\begin{cases} 2x + y > 3 \\ y < 5 - 2x \end{cases}$ *Infinite strip*

3. $\begin{cases} y < 2x \\ 2x + y < 12 \\ y > 2 \end{cases}$ *Isosceles triangle*

4. $\begin{cases} 3x + 4y \leqq 12 \\ x \leqq 4 \\ y \leqq 3 \end{cases}$ *Closed quarter-plane with corner removed*

Graph each of the following systems. In each case, list the positive integral solutions of the system.

5. $\begin{cases} 3x + 4y \leqq 12 \\ 4y \geqq 3x \\ x \geqq 0 \end{cases}$ *(1, 1), (1, 2)*

6. $\begin{cases} 50x + 40y \geqq 1000 \\ x + y \leqq 24 \\ y \geqq 0 \end{cases}$

△

In Exercises 7–12, describe the region bounded by the graphs of each of the following systems of inequalities by giving its shape (triangle, pentagon, and so on) and the coordinates of the vertices of its boundary.

7. $\begin{cases} x > 0 \\ y > 0 \\ x < 5 \\ y < 7 \\ x + y \leqq 8 \end{cases}$ *Pentagon*

8. $\begin{cases} x \geqq 3 \\ x \leqq 15 \\ y \geqq 0 \\ y \leqq 22 \\ x + y \leqq 30 \end{cases}$ *Pentagon*

9. $\begin{cases} y \geqq 0 \\ y \leqq 3 \\ 2y - x \leqq 0 \\ y \leqq 16 - 2x \end{cases}$ *Trapezoid*

10. $\begin{cases} 2x + y \geqq 8 \\ x + 3y \geqq 9 \\ 3x + 4y \geqq 22 \\ x \leqq 9 \\ y \leqq 8 \end{cases}$ *Pentagon*

11. $\begin{cases} .9x + .6y \geqq 1 \\ .1x + .4y \geqq .4 \\ x \leqq 4 \\ y \leqq \frac{5}{3} \end{cases}$ *Quadrilateral*

12. $\begin{cases} 2x + y + 9 \geqq 0 \\ {}^-x + 3y + 6 \geqq 0 \\ x + 2y - 3 \leqq 0 \\ x + y \leqq 0 \end{cases}$ *Quadrilateral*

13. Give a system of inequalities for which the graph is the intersection of the half-planes above the graph of $3x + 2y = 12$ and below the graph of $2x - 3y + 18 = 0$.

14. Give a system of inequalities for which the graph is the region which lies between the graphs of $x - 2y + 6 = 0$ and $x - 2y = 4$.

15. Give a system of inequalities for which the graph is the intersection of the half-planes below the graph of $x + y + 2 = 0$ and to the left of $2x - y = 4$. $\begin{cases} x + y + 2 < 0 \\ 2x - y < 4 \end{cases}$

16. The following table gives percentages of protein and fat contained in one gram of each of two foods.

	Protein	Fat
Bread	8%	1%
Butter	2%	80%

(a) Write a system of inequalities involving the two unknowns x and y (number of grams of bread and of butter, respectively) which expresses the fact that these two foods together are to supply daily at least 82 grams of protein and 90 grams of fat.
(b) Graph the solution set of your system in the region $x \geqq 0$ and $y \geqq 0$, and give the coordinates of the corner points.
(c) Give at least three solutions to the problem of meeting the daily minimum requirements of protein and fat. Any three points in the shaded area or on its boundary

2-11 SYSTEMS OF EQUATIONS IN THREE OR MORE VARIABLES

In modern applications of mathematics, systems of three or more first-degree equations in three or more variables are very common. It is not unusual for scientists working in economic theory to have to solve a system of fifty first-degree equations in fifty variables. Quite naturally, high-speed electronic computers are used to perform the necessary arithmetical operations. Let us look at some systems of first-degree equations in three variables.

Problem 1. Solve the system

$$\begin{cases} x - 5 = 0, \\ 3x - y - 8 = 0, \\ 7x + 4y + \frac{63}{11}z - 63 = 0. \end{cases}$$

Solution. Clearly, $x = 5$ from the first equation. Giving x the value 5 in the second equation, we see that

$$15 - y - 8 = 0,$$
$$y = 7.$$

Finally, giving x the value 5 and y the value 7 in the third equation, we get

$$35 + 28 + \tfrac{63}{11}z - 63 = 0,$$
$$\tfrac{63}{11}z = 0,$$
$$z = 0.$$

$$\begin{cases} y = 2x, \\ 2x + y = 12, \end{cases} \quad \begin{cases} y = 2x, \\ y = 2, \end{cases}$$

and $\begin{cases} 2x + y = 12, \\ y = 2. \end{cases}$

Answers to Exercises 6, 13, 14, 16(a)

6. (4, 20), (5, 19), (6, 18), (7, 16), (7, 17), (8, 15), (8, 16), (9, 14), (9, 15), (10, 13), (10, 14), (11, 12), (11, 13), (12, 10), (12, 11), (12, 12), (13, 9), (13, 10), (13, 11), (14, 8), (14, 9), (14, 10), (15, 7), (15, 8), (15, 9), (16, 5), (16, 6), (16, 7), (16, 8), (17, 4), (17, 5), (17, 6), (17, 7), (18, 3), (18, 4), (18, 5), (18, 6), (19, 2), (19, 3), (19, 4), (19, 5), (20, 1), (20, 2), (20, 3), (20, 4), (21, 1), (21, 2), (21, 3), (22, 1), ((22, 2), (23, 1)

13. $\begin{cases} 3x + 2y > 12 \\ 2x - 3y + 18 > 0 \end{cases}$

14. $\begin{cases} x - 2y + 6 > 0 \\ x - 2y < 4 \end{cases}$

16. (a) $\begin{cases} .08x + .02y \geqq 82 \\ .01x + .80y \geqq 90 \end{cases}$

Quiz

(See page T13 for graphs.)
Describe the solution set and draw the graph of each of the following systems of inequalities.

1. $\begin{cases} 2y \geqq x + 2 \\ x \leqq {}^{-}y \end{cases}$
(ans: quarter-plane)

2. $\begin{cases} y < x \\ x < 2 - y \\ y > 0 \end{cases}$
(ans: isosceles triangle)

2-11 SYSTEMS OF EQUATIONS IN THREE OR MORE VARIABLES

As the students have now graphed solution sets of first-degree equations in two variables and produced lines in a plane, you might ask the class what would be a natural extension of this idea to accommodate the solution set of a first-degree equation in three variables. Three mutually perpendicular axes are easily represented by means of yardsticks, and the discussion can proceed from the graphing of $x = 2$, first as a point on the number line, then as a straight line parallel to the y-axis in the coordinate plane, and finally as a plane parallel to the yz-plane in a representation of three-dimensional space. You can then contrast the graphs of two such different systems of three equations in three variables as are given in Exercises 4 and 12 on page 102, the first describing three planes intersecting in a point and the second describing three planes intersecting in a line. It may help students to understand the geometric significance of the solution set of three equations in three unknowns if you point out some of the various possibilities. For example the three planes may be parallel, they could intersect in a line, or they could intersect in a point.

Note that Fig. 2–17 illustrates the case where three planes intersect in a point.

Answers to Exercises for Discussion 1–4, page 101

1. $\begin{cases} x - 3y - 2z + 4 = 0 \\ (2x - 5y + 19) + {}^-2(x - 3) = 0 \\ x = 3 \end{cases}$

$\begin{cases} x - 3y - 2z + 4 = 0 \\ {}^-5y + 25 = 0 \\ x = 3 \end{cases}$

$\begin{cases} 3 - 15 - 2z + 4 = 0 \\ y = 5 \\ x = 3 \end{cases}$

From the first equation of the third system, $z = {}^-4$ and the solution is $(3, 5, {}^-4)$.

2. $\begin{cases} (2x - y - 4z) + (x + y) = 8 + 1 \\ (3x + 2y) + {}^-2(x + y) = 1 - 2 \\ x + y = 1 \end{cases}$

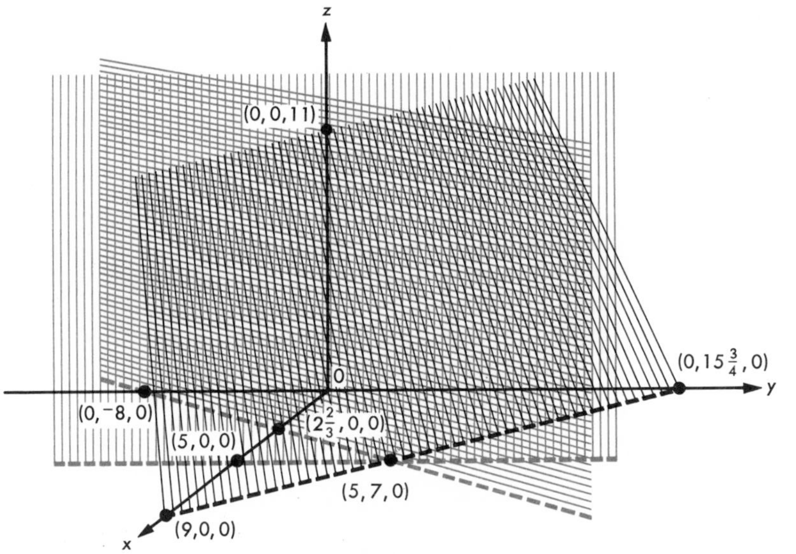

FIGURE 2–17

Thus, the ordered number triple (5, 7, 0) is the solution of the given system. (See Fig. 2–17.)

Check. $5 - 5 \overset{\checkmark}{=} 0$ $\qquad (3 \cdot 5) - 7 - 8 \overset{\checkmark}{=} 0$

$$(7 \cdot 5) + (4 \cdot 7) + (\tfrac{63}{11} \cdot 0) - 63 \overset{?}{=} 0$$
$$35 + 28 - 63 \overset{\checkmark}{=} 0$$

The system of Problem 1 is easily solved, because only the variable x occurs in the first equation and only x and y occur in the second equation. Let us try to solve the system obtained in the following problem by changing it into an equivalent system of the type of Problem 1.

Problem 2. A steel company has three blast furnaces of varying sizes. If furnaces A, B, and C are used full time, 800 tons of steel are produced per day. If A and B are used half time and C full time, 545 tons are produced. If A is not used, B is used full time, and C half time, 410 tons are produced. How many tons per day does each furnace produce?

Solution. Let a, b, and c designate the number of tons of steel produced each day by furnaces A, B, and C, respectively, when they are used full time. Then the three given conditions yield the following system of equations.

$$\begin{cases} a + b + c = 800 \\ \tfrac{1}{2}a + \tfrac{1}{2}b + c = 545 \\ b + \tfrac{1}{2}c = 410 \end{cases}$$

An equivalent system is

$$\begin{cases} a + b + c = 800, \\ {}^-a - b - 2c = {}^-1090, \\ 2b + c = 820. \end{cases}$$

By the addition method, we see that the above system is equivalent to

$$\begin{cases} a + b + c = 800, \\ (a + b + c) + ({}^-a - b - 2c) = 800 + ({}^-1090), \\ 2b + c = 820, \end{cases}$$

or

$$\begin{cases} a + b + c = 800, \\ {}^-c = {}^-290, \\ 2b + c = 820. \end{cases}$$

Thus, $c = 290$ from the second equation, and

$$\begin{aligned} 2b + 290 &= 820, \\ 2b &= 530, \\ b &= 265, \end{aligned}$$

from the third equation. Hence,

$$a + 265 + 290 = 800,$$

or

$$a = 245,$$

from the first equation.

We conclude that, working full time, furnace A produces 245 tons per day, B produces 265 tons, and C produces 290 tons.

Check.

$$245 + 265 + 290 \stackrel{\checkmark}{=} 800$$

$$\begin{aligned} (\tfrac{1}{2} \cdot 245) + (\tfrac{1}{2} \cdot 265) + 290 &\stackrel{?}{=} 545 \\ (\tfrac{1}{2} \cdot 510) + 290 &\stackrel{?}{=} 545 \\ 255 + 290 &\stackrel{\checkmark}{=} 545 \end{aligned}$$

$$\begin{aligned} 265 + (\tfrac{1}{2} \cdot 290) &\stackrel{?}{=} 410 \\ 265 + 145 &\stackrel{\checkmark}{=} 410 \end{aligned}$$

Exercises for Discussion

Solve each of the following systems of linear equations.

1. $\begin{cases} x - 3y - 2z + 4 = 0 \\ 2x - 5y + 19 = 0 \\ x - 3 = 0 \end{cases}$

2. $\begin{cases} 2x - y - 4z = 8 \\ 3x + 2y = 1 \\ x + y = 1 \end{cases}$

3. $\begin{cases} 2x - 3y + 5z = 5 \\ x + y + z = 6 \\ x - y = 1 \end{cases}$

4. $\begin{cases} 3x - 4y + 10z = {}^-7 \\ 2x - 3y - z = {}^-21 \\ x + y + z = 0 \end{cases}$

$\begin{cases} 3x - 4z = 9 \\ x = {}^-1 \\ y = 2 \end{cases}$

$\begin{cases} {}^-3 - 4z = 9 \\ x = {}^-1 \\ y = 2 \end{cases}$

From the first equation of the third system, $z = {}^-3$ and the solution is $({}^-1, 2, {}^-3)$.

3. $\begin{cases} (2x - 3y + 5z) \\ \qquad + {}^-3(x - y) = 5 - 3 \\ (x + y + z) + (x - y) = 6 + 1 \\ x - y = 1 \end{cases}$

$\begin{cases} {}^-x + 5z = 2 \\ 2x + z = 7 \\ x - y = 1 \end{cases}$

$\begin{cases} ({}^-x + 5z) - 5(2x + z) = 2 - 35 \\ 2x + z = 7 \\ x - y = 1 \end{cases}$

$\begin{cases} {}^-11x = {}^-33 \\ 2x + z = 7 \\ x - y = 1 \end{cases}$

$\begin{cases} x = 3 \\ 6 + z = 7 \\ 3 - y = 1 \end{cases}$

Solution: (3, 2, 1,)

4. $\begin{cases} (3x - 4y + 10z) \\ \qquad -10(x + y + z) = {}^-7 \\ (2x - 3y - z) \\ \qquad + (x + y + z) = {}^-21 \\ x + y + z = 0 \end{cases}$

$\begin{cases} {}^-7x - 14y = {}^-7 \\ 3x - 2y = {}^-21 \\ x + y + z = 0 \end{cases}$

$\begin{cases} x + 2y = 1 \\ (3x - 2y) \\ \qquad + (x + 2y) = {}^-21 + 1 \\ x + y + z = 0 \end{cases}$

$\begin{cases} x + 2y = 1 \\ 4x = {}^-20 \\ x + y + z = 0 \end{cases}$

$\begin{cases} {}^-5 + 2y = 1 \\ x = {}^-5 \\ {}^-5 + y + z = 0 \end{cases}$

$\begin{cases} y = 3 \\ x = {}^-5 \\ z = 2 \end{cases}$

Solution: $({}^-5, 3, 2)$

Exercises

Students may be helped by a reminder that the explanation given in Exercise 6, Section 2–9, is applicable to Exercise 8 in this section.

In relation to Exercise 17, you may wish to reiterate that a point is on the graph of an equation if, and only if, the coordinates of the point form a solution of the equation.

Exercises

Solve each of the following systems of linear equations, and check each answer.

1. $\begin{cases} 3x - 2y + 4z = 19 \\ 3y + z = {}^{-}3 \\ z = 3 \end{cases}$ $(1, {}^{-}2, 3)$

2. $\begin{cases} 2x + y - z = 5 \\ y - 2z = 7 \\ 2y + 3z = 0 \end{cases}$ $(0, 3, {}^{-}2)$

3. $\begin{cases} 5x + 3y + 2z = 1 \\ 2x - y + z = {}^{-}1 \\ {}^{-}2x + 2y - z = 2 \end{cases}$ $({}^{-}2, 1, 4)$

4. $\begin{cases} 2x + y + z = 8 \\ 4x - y + 2z = 9 \\ x + \frac{1}{2}y - z = {}^{-}2 \end{cases}$ $(\frac{5}{6}, \frac{7}{3}, 4)$

5. $\begin{cases} x + y - z = 0 \\ \frac{1}{2}x + y + z = 11 \\ 2x - y + \frac{1}{3}z = 2 \end{cases}$ $(2, 4, 6)$

6. $\begin{cases} x + y + z = 1 \\ x = y + z \\ z = .2 \end{cases}$ $(.5, .3, .2)$

7. $\begin{cases} .3x + .2y = 1 \\ .2x + .3y + .1z = .5 \\ x + y + z = 1.8 \end{cases}$ $(3.4, {}^{-}.1, {}^{-}1.5)$

8. $\begin{cases} \frac{2}{x} + \frac{3}{y} + \frac{4}{z} = 3 \\ \frac{1}{x} - \frac{2}{z} = 0 \\ \frac{6}{x} - \frac{6}{y} = 5 \end{cases}$ $(\frac{14}{11}, {}^{-}21, \frac{28}{11})$

△

9. A bank contains 24 coins which are worth \$3.00. If there are only nickels, dimes, and quarters, and the number of dimes is one-half the number of nickels and quarters combined, how many coins of each kind are there in the bank? 9 nickels, 8 dimes, 7 quarters

10. A, B, and C working together complete a job in 6 days; A and B working as a pair finish it in 7 days; B does twice as much work as C. How long would it take each of them working alone to do the job? A: $10\frac{1}{2}$ days, B: 21 days, C: 42 days

11. The sum of the angles of a triangle is 180°. The angle at B is twice as large as the angle at A, and the angle at C is 12° less than the sum of the other two angles. Find the angles. $A = 32°$, $B = 64°$, $C = 84°$

▲

12. (a) Can you find a unique solution for the following system? No

$$\begin{cases} 7a - 2b + c = 0 \\ 4a + b + 7c = 0 \\ a + b + 4c = 0 \end{cases}$$

(b) Can you find a "trivial" solution for the system in part (a)? (0, 0, 0)

(c) For what values of k is the number triple $(k, 3k, {}^{-}k)$ a solution of the system? $k = a$, $k = \frac{b}{3}$, $k = {}^{-}c$

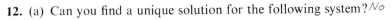

13. Find three numbers which satisfy all of the following three conditions.
   (a) The sum of the three numbers is 72.
   (b) The sum of two of the numbers is twice the third number.
   (c) One of the numbers is 22. 22, 24, 26
   (d) Is there more than one set of three numbers which satisfies all three conditions? No

14. Is there a unique set of three numbers which satisfy all of the following three conditions? If so, what is it? If not, list three such sets.
   (a) The sum of the three numbers is 72.
   (b) The sum of two of the numbers is twice the third number.
   (c) One of the numbers is 24.

15. Find all three-digit numbers, if any exist, which satisfy all of the following three conditions. 363
   (a) The sum of all three digits is 12.
   (b) The tens' digit is twice the hundreds' digit.
   (c) When the digits are reversed, the number is unchanged.

16. Find all three-digit numbers, if any exist, which satisfy all of the following three conditions. No solution
   (a) The sum of all three digits is 14.
   (b) The tens' digit is twice the hundreds' digit.
   (c) When the digits are reversed, the number is unchanged.

17. For what values of a, b, and c will the points (1, 1), (4, 4), and ($^-1$, 9) lie on the graph of the equation $y = ax^2 + bx + c$?
$a = 1,\ b = {}^-4,\ c = 4$

*2-12 MATRICES AND DETERMINANTS

Rectangular arrays of numbers, such as

$$\begin{pmatrix} 2 & ^-1 \\ 3 & 4 \end{pmatrix}, \quad \begin{pmatrix} 8 & 12 & 0 \\ 9 & -3 & -5 \end{pmatrix}, \quad \begin{pmatrix} 0 & 3 & 3 \\ -5 & 2 & 7 \\ 2 & 7 & -3 \end{pmatrix},$$

are called matrices. Matrices arise naturally in describing a system of linear equations. Thus, if S is the system

$$\begin{cases} a_1x + b_1y = d_1, \\ a_2x + b_2y = d_2 \end{cases}$$

of two linear equations in the variables x and y, then the matrix

$$\begin{pmatrix} a_1 & b_1 \\ a_2 & b_2 \end{pmatrix}$$

Answer to Exercise 14

14. The solution set is $\{(x, 48 - x, 24) \mid x \text{ any number}\}$. The three sets are

$({}^-5, 53, 24)$,
$(90, {}^-42, 24)$,
$(\sqrt{7}, 48 - \sqrt{7}, 24)$.

Quiz

Solve each of the following systems of linear equations.

1. $\begin{cases} x + y + 3z = 2 \\ 2x - y = 7 \\ y + z = 1 \end{cases}$

(ans: (5, 3, $^-2$))

2. $\begin{cases} 2x - y + z = 0 \\ x + y + 2z = {}^-6 \\ x = 2y - z \end{cases}$

(ans: (1, $^-1$, $^-3$))

*2-12 MATRICES AND DETERMINANTS

The asterisk suggests that Section 2-12 is optional. However, it is very interesting and should be seriously considered for all but the minimum courses.

It is suggested that you keep the class discussion well ahead of the assignments. The material is easy, but some students may be confused by the subscripts.

is called the *matrix of coefficients* of the variables and

$$\begin{pmatrix} a_1 & b_1 & d_1 \\ a_2 & b_2 & d_2 \end{pmatrix}$$

is called the *augmented matrix* of S. For example, the system

$$\begin{cases} 2x - y = 7 \\ 3x + 4y = {}^-2 \end{cases}$$

has matrix of coefficients

$$\begin{pmatrix} 2 & {}^-1 \\ 3 & 4 \end{pmatrix}$$

and augmented matrix

$$\begin{pmatrix} 2 & {}^-1 & 7 \\ 3 & 4 & {}^-2 \end{pmatrix}.$$

A matrix is made up of *rows* and *columns* of numbers. The matrix

$$\begin{pmatrix} 2 & {}^-1 \\ 3 & 4 \end{pmatrix}$$

has $(2, {}^-1)$ as its *first row*, $(3, 4)$ as its *second row*, and

$$\begin{pmatrix} 2 \\ 3 \end{pmatrix}, \quad \begin{pmatrix} {}^-1 \\ 4 \end{pmatrix}$$

as its *first and second columns*, respectively.

If a matrix has the same number of rows and columns, then it is called a *square matrix*. For example,

$$\begin{pmatrix} 5 & {}^-8 \\ 7 & 4 \end{pmatrix}$$

and

$$\begin{pmatrix} {}^-7 & 3 & 12 \\ 4 & 0 & 2 \\ 0 & {}^-9 & 6 \end{pmatrix}$$

are square matrices; the first is called a 2×2 *matrix*, and the second is called a 3×3 *matrix*.

Each square matrix has associated with it a number called the determinant of the matrix. The 2×2 matrix

$$A = \begin{pmatrix} a_1 & b_1 \\ a_2 & b_2 \end{pmatrix}$$

TWISTER

The sum of the ages of Mr. and Mrs. Harris and their son Peter is exactly 70 years. Mr. Harris is six times as old as Peter. When Peter is half as old as his father, the sum of their ages will be twice what it is now. How old are each of the members of the Harris family?

Solution: Letting Mr. Harris' age be a, Mrs. Harris' be b, Peter's be c, and the number of years until the sum of their ages is twice what it is now be x, one arrives at the following equations:

$$a + b + c = 70,$$
$$a = 6c,$$
$$(a + x) + (b + x) + (c + x) = 140,$$

and

$$2(c + x) = a + x.$$

Solving these, Mr. Harris is found to be 35 years old; Mrs. Harris 29 years, 2 months; and Peter 5 years, 10 months.

has a determinant denoted by $|A|$ and defined by

$$|A| = \begin{vmatrix} a_1 & b_1 \\ a_2 & b_2 \end{vmatrix} = a_1b_2 - b_1a_2.$$

For example,

$$\begin{vmatrix} 8 & 5 \\ 2 & 3 \end{vmatrix} = (8 \cdot 3) - (5 \cdot 2), \quad \text{or } 14,$$

$$\begin{vmatrix} 2 & {}^-1 \\ 3 & 4 \end{vmatrix} = (2 \cdot 4) - ({}^-1 \cdot 3), \quad \text{or } 11.$$

Determinants afford a simple notation which we can use to write solutions of systems of linear equations. For example, consider the following system of two linear equations in the variables x and y.

$$\begin{cases} a_1x + b_1y = d_1 \\ a_2x + b_2y = d_2 \end{cases} \tag{1}$$

The matrix

$$A = \begin{pmatrix} a_1 & b_1 \\ a_2 & b_2 \end{pmatrix}$$

of coefficients of the variables in system (1) has determinant

$$|A| = a_1b_2 - b_1a_2.$$

If either $b_1 = 0$ or $b_2 = 0$, then we can easily solve system (1). Thus, we shall assume that $b_1 \neq 0$ and $b_2 \neq 0$. To solve this system, we can multiply the first equation of (1) by b_2 and the second by ${}^-b_1$. Thus, the system

$$\begin{cases} b_2a_1x + b_2b_1y = b_2d_1, \\ {}^-b_1a_2x - b_1b_2y = {}^-b_1d_2 \end{cases} \tag{2}$$

is equivalent to system (1) since each equation of (2) is equivalent to the corresponding equation of (1). The second equation in (3) is the sum of the equations in (2). Thus, the system

$$\begin{cases} b_2a_1x + b_2b_1y = b_2d_1, \\ (b_2a_1 - b_1a_2)x = b_2d_1 - b_1d_2 \end{cases} \tag{3}$$

is equivalent to system (2). If $b_2a_1 - b_1a_2 \neq 0$ (that is, if $|A| \neq 0$) then from the second equation of (3), we obtain

$$x = \frac{b_2d_1 - b_1d_2}{b_2a_1 - b_1a_2}.$$

Substituting this value in the first equation, we obtain

$$b_2a_1(b_2d_1 - b_1d_2) + b_2b_1(b_2a_1 - b_1a_2)y = b_2d_1(b_2a_1 - b_1a_2).$$

We solve this equation for y and obtain

$$y = \frac{a_1d_2 - d_1a_2}{b_2a_1 - b_1a_2}.$$

Thus,

$$\left\{\left(\frac{b_2d_1 - b_1d_2}{b_2a_1 - b_1a_2}, \frac{a_1d_2 - d_1a_2}{b_2a_1 - b_1a_2}\right)\right\}$$

is the solution set of system (1) if $b_2a_1 - b_1a_2 \neq 0$.

The solution of system (1) can be expressed in terms of determinants. Thus, if we let

$$A = \begin{pmatrix} a_1 & b_1 \\ a_2 & b_2 \end{pmatrix}, \quad A_1 = \begin{pmatrix} d_1 & b_1 \\ d_2 & b_2 \end{pmatrix}, \quad A_2 = \begin{pmatrix} a_1 & d_1 \\ a_2 & d_2 \end{pmatrix},$$

then $|A| = a_1b_2 - b_1a_2$, $|A_1| = d_1b_2 - b_1d_2$, $|A_2| = a_1d_2 - d_1a_2$, and system (1) has solution set

$$\left\{\left(\frac{|A_1|}{|A|}, \frac{|A_2|}{|A|}\right)\right\}, \quad |A| \neq 0.$$

Although we assumed that $b_1 \neq 0$ and $b_2 \neq 0$ in solving system (1), it can be shown that the solution is valid even if $b_1 = 0$ or $b_2 = 0$, as long as $|A| \neq 0$. If $|A| = 0$, then system (1) has no solution when $|A_1|$ or $|A_2|$ is nonzero and many solutions when $|A_1|$ or $|A_2|$ is zero. Geometrically, these correspond to the cases in which the graphs of the two equations are parallel lines or the same straight line.

Problem 1. Use determinants to solve the following system.

$$\begin{cases} 2x - y = 7 \\ 3x + 4y = {}^-2 \end{cases}$$

Solution. The matrices A, A_1, and A_2 are given by

$$A = \begin{pmatrix} 2 & {}^-1 \\ 3 & 4 \end{pmatrix}, \quad A_1 = \begin{pmatrix} 7 & {}^-1 \\ {}^-2 & 4 \end{pmatrix}, \quad A_2 = \begin{pmatrix} 2 & 7 \\ 3 & {}^-2 \end{pmatrix}.$$

Hence,

$$|A| = 11, \quad |A_1| = 26, \quad |A_2| = {}^-25.$$

Since $|A| \neq 0$, the solutions of the system above are given by

$$x = \frac{|A_1|}{|A|}, \quad \text{or } \frac{26}{11},$$

$$y = \frac{|A_2|}{|A|}, \quad \text{or } \frac{^-25}{11}.$$

In other words, $(\frac{26}{11}, \frac{^-25}{11})$ is the unique solution of the system.

The determinant of a 3×3 matrix is defined as follows:

$$\begin{vmatrix} a_1 & b_1 & c_1 \\ a_2 & b_2 & c_2 \\ a_3 & b_3 & c_3 \end{vmatrix} = a_1b_2c_3 + b_1c_2a_3 + c_1a_2b_3 - c_1b_2a_3 - a_1c_2b_3 - b_1a_2c_3.$$

Note that each of the six terms on the right side contains three different subscripts and three different letters. In other words, each term is a product of three numbers, one from each row and one from each column of the matrix. One way to remember this is to repeat the first two columns to the right of the third column. Then the six terms are obtained in the way shown below.

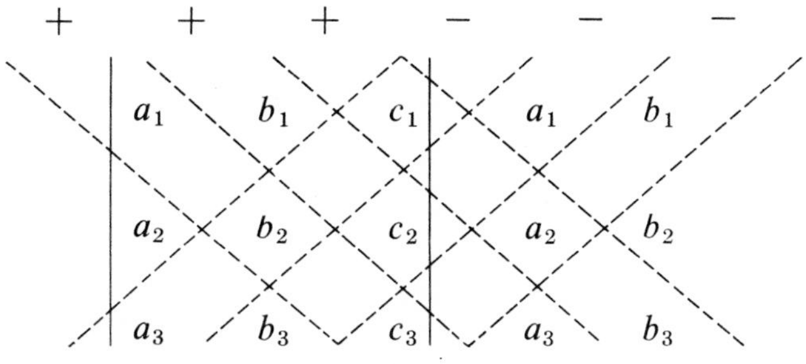

Thus, there are three terms having plus signs in front of them and three terms having minus signs. For example,

$$\begin{vmatrix} 8 & 2 & ^-1 \\ 4 & 7 & 6 \\ 2 & ^-3 & 5 \end{vmatrix} = \begin{vmatrix} 8 & 2 & ^-1 \\ 4 & 7 & 6 \\ 2 & ^-3 & 5 \end{vmatrix} \begin{matrix} 8 & 2 \\ 4 & 7 \\ 2 & ^-3 \end{matrix}$$

$$= (8 \cdot 7 \cdot 5) + (2 \cdot 6 \cdot 2) + (^-1 \cdot 4 \cdot {^-3}) - (^-1 \cdot 7 \cdot 2) - (8 \cdot 6 \cdot {^-3}) - (2 \cdot 4 \cdot 5), \quad \text{or } 434.$$

A system of three linear equations in the variables x, y, and z,

$$\begin{cases} a_1x + b_1y + c_1z = d_1, \\ a_2x + b_2y + c_2z = d_2, \\ a_3x + b_3y + c_3z = d_3, \end{cases} \tag{4}$$

can be shown to have a unique solution if the determinant, $|A|$, of its matrix of coefficients is nonzero.

$$A = \begin{pmatrix} a_1 & b_1 & c_1 \\ a_2 & b_2 & c_2 \\ a_3 & b_3 & c_3 \end{pmatrix}$$

If we let

$$A_1 = \begin{pmatrix} d_1 & b_1 & c_1 \\ d_2 & b_2 & c_2 \\ d_3 & b_3 & c_3 \end{pmatrix}, \quad A_2 = \begin{pmatrix} a_1 & d_1 & c_1 \\ a_2 & d_2 & c_2 \\ a_3 & d_3 & c_3 \end{pmatrix}, \quad A_3 = \begin{pmatrix} a_1 & b_1 & d_1 \\ a_2 & b_2 & d_2 \\ a_3 & b_3 & d_3 \end{pmatrix},$$

then the unique solution of system (4) is given by

$$x = \frac{|A_1|}{|A|}, \quad y = \frac{|A_2|}{|A|}, \quad z = \frac{|A_3|}{|A|}.$$

This proof is similar to the proof of the corresponding result for system (1), and hence, is omitted.

Problem 2. Use determinants to solve the following system.

$$\begin{cases} 2x + y - z = {}^-5 \\ {}^-5x - 3y + 2z = 7 \\ x + 4y - 3z = 0 \end{cases}$$

Solution. The matrix of coefficients is given by

$$A = \begin{pmatrix} 2 & 1 & {}^-1 \\ {}^-5 & {}^-3 & 2 \\ 1 & 4 & {}^-3 \end{pmatrix},$$

and the augmented matrix is given by

$$\begin{pmatrix} 2 & 1 & {}^-1 & {}^-5 \\ {}^-5 & {}^-3 & 2 & 7 \\ 1 & 4 & {}^-3 & 0 \end{pmatrix}.$$

The other three matrices are obtained from A by replacing each of the columns of A, in turn, by the last column of the augmented matrix.

$$A_1 = \begin{pmatrix} {}^-5 & 1 & {}^-1 \\ 7 & {}^-3 & 2 \\ 0 & 4 & {}^-3 \end{pmatrix}, \quad A_2 = \begin{pmatrix} 2 & {}^-5 & {}^-1 \\ {}^-5 & 7 & 2 \\ 1 & 0 & {}^-3 \end{pmatrix},$$

$$A_3 = \begin{pmatrix} 2 & 1 & {}^-5 \\ {}^-5 & {}^-3 & 7 \\ 1 & 4 & 0 \end{pmatrix}$$

We see that

$$|A| = (2 \cdot {}^{-}3 \cdot {}^{-}3) + (1 \cdot 2 \cdot 1) + ({}^{-}1 \cdot {}^{-}5 \cdot 4) - ({}^{-}1 \cdot {}^{-}3 \cdot 1) - (1 \cdot {}^{-}5 \cdot {}^{-}3) - (2 \cdot 2 \cdot 4), \quad \text{or } 6.$$

In a similar way, we can show that

$$|A_1| = {}^{-}12, \quad |A_2| = 30, \quad |A_3| = 36.$$

Therefore, the solution of system (5) is given by

$$x = \frac{{}^{-}12}{6}, \text{ or } {}^{-}2; \quad y = \frac{30}{6}, \text{ or } 5; \quad z = \frac{36}{6}, \text{ or } 6.$$

The following is an interesting geometrical interpretation of a determinant. If the vertices of triangle ABC have coordinates (x_1, y_1), (x_2, y_2), and (x_3, y_3) in a cartesian coordinate system, as shown in Fig. 2–18, and if matrix H is defined by

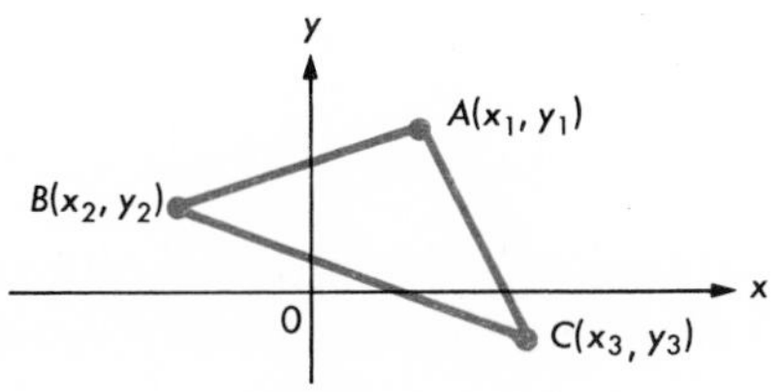

FIGURE 2–18

$$H = \begin{pmatrix} x_1 & y_1 & 1 \\ x_2 & y_2 & 1 \\ x_3 & y_3 & 1 \end{pmatrix},$$

then the *area* of triangle ABC is given by $\left|\frac{1}{2}|H|\right|$. (Here, the outer bars in the expression denote absolute value.) For example, if the vertices of a triangle are $(1, 1)$, $({}^{-}2, {}^{-}3)$, and $(4, {}^{-}2)$, then

$$H = \begin{pmatrix} 1 & 1 & 1 \\ {}^{-}2 & {}^{-}3 & 1 \\ 4 & {}^{-}2 & 1 \end{pmatrix}, \quad |H| = 21,$$

and the area of the triangle is $\frac{21}{2}$.

We can apply the formula for the area of a triangle to determine whether three points in a plane are collinear. If points A, B, and C have respective coordinates (x_1, y_1), (x_2, y_2), and (x_3, y_3), then these points are collinear if, and only if, triangle ABC has area 0. Thus, A, B, and C are collinear if, and only if,

$$\begin{vmatrix} x_1 & y_1 & 1 \\ x_2 & y_2 & 1 \\ x_3 & y_3 & 1 \end{vmatrix} = 0.$$

In order to illustrate the procedure for finding area by the use of determinants, you could take right triangle ABC, with vertices $A({}^{-}1, 2)$, $B(4, 2)$, and $C(4, 12)$. Then the area found can be checked by the formula $\frac{1}{2}$(base)(height)=area.

From this result, it follows that

$$\begin{vmatrix} x_1 & y_1 & 1 \\ x_2 & y_2 & 1 \\ x & y & 1 \end{vmatrix} = 0$$

is an equation of the line passing through the two distinct points (x_1, y_1) and (x_2, y_2). For example, the line passing through the points (2, 3) and (⁻1, 1) has equation

$$\begin{vmatrix} 2 & 3 & 1 \\ ^-1 & 1 & 1 \\ x & y & 1 \end{vmatrix} = 0,$$

or

$$2x - 3y + 5 = 0.$$

The computation of determinants of square matrices is made easier if the following theorems are used.

Theorem 1. If matrix B is obtained from a matrix A by interchanging two rows or two columns of A, then $|B| = {}^-|A|$.

Theorem 2. If matrix B is obtained from a matrix A by multiplying one row or one column of A by k and leaving the other rows or columns of A unchanged, then $|B| = k|A|$.

Theorem 3. If matrix B is obtained from a matrix A by multiplying each element of some row or column by k and adding the resulting number to the corresponding element of another row or column, then $|B| = |A|$.

Theorem 4. If an $n \times n$ matrix A has the form

$$\left(\begin{array}{c:ccc} a_1 & a_2 & a_3 \ldots & a_n \\ \hdashline 0 & & & \\ 0 & & B & \\ \vdots & & & \\ 0 & & & \end{array}\right) \text{ or } \left(\begin{array}{c:ccc} a_1 & 0 & 0 \ldots & 0 \\ \hdashline a_2 & & & \\ a_3 & & B & \\ \vdots & & & \\ a_n & & & \end{array}\right)$$

where B is an $(n - 1) \times (n - 1)$ matrix, then

$$|A| = a_1|B|.$$

Theorems 1, 2, and 3 may be illustrated by many numerical examples. A 2 × 2 matrix suffices for these. In Theorem 1, let

$$A = \begin{pmatrix} 3 & ^-5 \\ 2 & 7 \end{pmatrix},$$
$$|A| = 21 - (^-10) = 31.$$
$$B = \begin{pmatrix} ^-5 & 3 \\ 7 & 2 \end{pmatrix},$$
$$|B| = {}^-10 - 21 = {}^-31.$$

In Theorem 2, let

$$B = \begin{pmatrix} 15 & ^-25 \\ 2 & 7 \end{pmatrix},$$
$$|B| = (7 \cdot 15) + (2 \cdot 25) = 155 = 5 \cdot 31.$$

In Theorem 3, let

$$B = \begin{pmatrix} 3 + 2(^-5) & ^-5 \\ 2 + 2(7) & 7 \end{pmatrix} = \begin{pmatrix} ^-7 & ^-5 \\ 16 & 7 \end{pmatrix},$$
$$|B| = {}^-49 + 80 = 31.$$

Have students practice with columns and with rows. A 3 × 3 matrix is sufficient to illustrate Theorem 4.

Students should keep a record in the margin of each step they are doing, so they can recheck their work.

In Theorem 4, the notation 0 0 . . . 0 indicates a row or column of zeros. The following problems illustrate the ways in which these theorems can be used.

Problem 3. Find $|A|$, given that

$$A = \begin{pmatrix} 2 & 3 & ^-5 \\ 4 & ^-1 & 3 \\ 1 & 6 & ^-2 \end{pmatrix}.$$

Solution. By Theorem 1, we interchange first and third rows and obtain $|A| = {}^-|A_1|$ where

$$A_1 = \begin{pmatrix} 1 & 6 & ^-2 \\ 4 & ^-1 & 3 \\ 2 & 3 & ^-5 \end{pmatrix}.$$

By Theorem 3, we multiply the first row of A_1 by $^-4$ and add the result to the second row to obtain $|A_1| = |A_2|$ where

$$A_2 = \begin{pmatrix} 1 & 6 & ^-2 \\ 0 & ^-25 & 11 \\ 2 & 3 & ^-5 \end{pmatrix}.$$

Again by Theorem 3, multiplying the first row of A_2 by $^-2$ and adding the results to the third row, we obtain $|A_2| = |A_3|$ where

$$A_3 = \begin{pmatrix} 1 & 6 & ^-2 \\ 0 & ^-25 & 11 \\ 0 & ^-9 & ^-1 \end{pmatrix}.$$

Finally, by Theorem 4,

$$|A_3| = 1 \cdot \begin{vmatrix} ^-25 & 11 \\ ^-9 & ^-1 \end{vmatrix} = 25 + 99, \quad \text{or } 124.$$

Therefore, $|A| = {}^-124$.

Problem 4. Find $|B|$, given that

$$B = \begin{pmatrix} ^-1 & 3 & 0 & 4 \\ 2 & 5 & ^-3 & 1 \\ 4 & ^-1 & 0 & 2 \\ 3 & 13 & ^-2 & 6 \end{pmatrix}.$$

Solution. This is our first 4×4 matrix. Make two applications of Theorem 3 to the first column of B. In other words, multiply the first column of B by 3 and add the result to the second column. Then multiply the first column of B by 4 and add the result to the fourth column. Thus, $|B| = |B_1|$ where

$$B_1 = \begin{pmatrix} ^-1 & 0 & 0 & 0 \\ 2 & 11 & ^-3 & 9 \\ 4 & 11 & 0 & 18 \\ 3 & 22 & ^-2 & 18 \end{pmatrix}.$$

By Theorem 4, we obtain $|B_1| = {^-1} \cdot |B_2|$ where

$$B_2 = \begin{pmatrix} 11 & ^-3 & 9 \\ 11 & 0 & 18 \\ 22 & ^-2 & 18 \end{pmatrix}.$$

By Theorem 2, we factor 11 out of the first column of B_2 and 9 out of the third column: $|B_2| = 11 \cdot 9 \cdot |B_3|$ where

$$B_3 = \begin{pmatrix} 1 & ^-3 & 1 \\ 1 & 0 & 2 \\ 2 & ^-2 & 2 \end{pmatrix}.$$

In two applications of Theorem 3, we multiply the first row of B_3 by $^-1$ and add the result to the second row, and then multiply the first row by $^-2$ and add the result to the third row to obtain $|B_3| = |B_4|$ where

$$B_4 = \begin{pmatrix} 1 & ^-3 & 1 \\ 0 & 3 & 1 \\ 0 & 4 & 0 \end{pmatrix}.$$

Finally, by Theorem 4, we have

$$|B_4| = 1 \cdot \begin{vmatrix} 3 & 1 \\ 4 & 0 \end{vmatrix} = {^-4}.$$

Retracing our steps, we find

$$|B| = {^-1} \cdot 11 \cdot 9 \cdot {^-4}, \quad \text{or } 396.$$

Exercises

Use determinants to solve each of the following systems of linear equations.

1. $\begin{cases} 3x + 6y = 3 \\ 5x + 7y = {}^-1 \end{cases}$ $x = {}^-3,\ y = 2$

2. $\begin{cases} 7x - 9y = 8 \\ {}^-8x + 15y = 5 \end{cases}$ $x = 5,\ y = 3$

3. $\begin{cases} 2x + 3y = 1 \\ 3x + 5y = {}^-2 \end{cases}$ $x = 11,\ y = {}^-7$

4. $\begin{cases} 5x + 11y = {}^-10 \\ 9x - 2y = {}^-127 \end{cases}$ $x = {}^-13,\ y = 5$

5. $\begin{cases} 4x - 3y = 2 \\ 5x + 4y = 3 \end{cases}$ $x = \frac{17}{31},\ y = \frac{2}{31}$

6. $\begin{cases} 3x + 7y = 4 \\ 4x - 9y = 3 \end{cases}$ $x = \frac{57}{55},\ y = \frac{7}{55}$

7. $\begin{cases} 2x + 3y + 6z = 3 \\ {}^-x + 2y + 2z = {}^-1 \\ 3x - 4y - 5z = {}^-6 \end{cases}$ $x = {}^-3,\ y = {}^-7,\ z = 5$

8. $\begin{cases} 5x - 4y + 7z = {}^-4 \\ 9x - 5y + 5z = 8 \\ 4x + 3y + 3z = 2 \end{cases}$ $x = 2,\ y = 0,\ z = {}^-2$

9. $\begin{cases} {}^-3y + z = {}^-5 \\ 5x + 3z = 1 \\ 3x - 5y = {}^-6 \end{cases}$ $x = \frac{1}{2},\ y = \frac{3}{2},\ z = \frac{{}^-1}{2}$

10. $\begin{cases} 2x + 3y + 4z = 2 \\ {}^-5x + 5y + 2z = 4 \\ 3x - 4y - 6z = 2 \end{cases}$ $x = \frac{2}{3},\ y = 2,\ z = \frac{{}^-4}{3}$

11. $\begin{cases} x - y + z = 2 \\ 2x + 3y - z = {}^-1 \\ x + 2y - 3z = 3 \end{cases}$ $x = \frac{19}{11},\ y = \frac{{}^-23}{11},\ z = \frac{{}^-20}{11}$

12. $\begin{cases} 2x + y - z = 3 \\ x - 3y + 2z = {}^-2 \\ 3x + y - 3z = {}^-1 \end{cases}$ $x = \frac{18}{13},\ y = \frac{38}{13},\ z = \frac{35}{13}$

13. $\begin{cases} 2x + 3y + 4z + 5w = 4 \\ 4y + 3z - w = 1 \\ x - 2y + 3w = 2 \\ 3x + y - 2z + 7w = {}^-7 \end{cases}$ $x = {}^-3,\ y = {}^-1,\ z = 2,\ w = 1$

14. $\begin{cases} 3x - 2z + 5w = 2 \\ {}^-2x - y + 4z = 0 \\ x + 2y - 3z - 5w = 1 \\ 3y + 5z + 2w = {}^-3 \end{cases}$ $x = 3,\ y = {}^-2,\ z = 1,\ w = {}^-1$

*2–13 LINEAR PROGRAMMING

The mathematical form of certain practical problems involves a system of linear inequalities. Such a system seldom has a unique solution, but rather has many solutions, as we saw in Section 2–10. However, of all possible solutions of a system of inequalities, some one solution will prove to be the best solution of the practical problem with which we started. The branch of mathematics which solves such problems is called *linear programming.* The following example illustrates the type of problem studied in linear programming.

Consider the problem faced by a manufacturer who has two warehouses, warehouse I containing 40 units of his product and warehouse II containing 50 units. He has two orders to fill, one from town A for 30 units and the other from town B for 40 units. Should he fill the order for town A from one warehouse and that for town B from the other, or is there a more economical distribution?

Quiz

Use determinants to solve each of the following systems of linear equations.

1. $\begin{cases} 4x + 3y = 7 \\ 8x - 12y = {}^-10 \end{cases}$
(ans: $(\frac{3}{4}, \frac{4}{3})$)

2. $\begin{cases} x + y + z = 1 \\ 2x + 2y + 3z = 3 \\ x - y - z = 0 \end{cases}$
(ans: $(\frac{1}{2}, {}^-\frac{1}{2}, 1)$)

***2–13 LINEAR PROGRAMMING**

In the *New York Times*, there appeared a full-page advertisement by Batten, Barton, Durstine, and Osborn, Inc., proclaiming:

> "Linear programming showed one BBDO client how to get \$1.67 worth of effective advertising for every dollar in his budget."

Similar ads can be seen in the weekend papers of any large city. Such a newspaper clipping on your bulletin board can stimulate considerable interest in the introduction of this method, which is being applied today to solve problems of business, industry, and government. It is precisely this type of problem which has motivated the consideration of inequalities, along with equations, at the beginning of the study of algebra.

Allow a full class period for introducing the subject. You can develop the case of the manufacturer related in the text, making it a lively classroom project by asking the students to help him minimize his shipping costs. Proceed with a careful analysis of each condition of the problem, the formulating of the inequality corresponding to the condition, and the graphing of the inequality. Then go to the second graph and its intersection with the first graph. As soon as all conditions have been considered, list many solutions of the system of inequalities and describe what advice each solution gives on the problem of filling orders. Now express the shipping costs, using the two variables, and find the shipping costs for the different possible solutions you have already discussed. Be sure to list separately (1) solutions given by points inside the region and points on the boundaries which are not at the corners, and (2) all the solutions suggested by the corners. Divide the work among class members so that you get many values for the shipping costs in a short time. Only after this experience should you tell the class about the theorem which states that the maximum and minimum values of a linear form in two variables are attained at the corner points of a convex polygonal region of the plane.

If we let x designate the number of units shipped from warehouse I to town A, then $30 - x$ units must be shipped from warehouse II to town A. Similarly, if we let y denote the number of units shipped from warehouse I to town B, then $40 - y$ units must be shipped from warehouse II to town B. Each of these four numbers must be greater than or equal to zero:

$$\begin{aligned} x &\geqq 0, \\ 30 - x &\geqq 0, \quad \text{or } 30 \geqq x, \\ y &\geqq 0, \\ 40 - y &\geqq 0, \quad \text{or } 40 \geqq y. \end{aligned}$$

In addition, the number of units the manufacturer ships from each warehouse cannot exceed the number of units stored there:

$$\begin{aligned} x + y &\leqq 40, \\ (30 - x) + (40 - y) &\leqq 50, \quad \text{or } 20 \leqq x + y. \end{aligned}$$

Thus, any ordered pair of *integers* that is a solution of the following system of inequalities is a solution of the manufacturer's problem.

$$\begin{cases} x \geqq 0 \\ x \leqq 30 \\ y \geqq 0 \\ y \leqq 40 \\ x + y \leqq 40 \\ x + y \geqq 20 \end{cases}$$

The graph of this system is the shaded pentagonal region of Fig. 2–19. Of course, the boundary of this pentagon is also included in the graph.

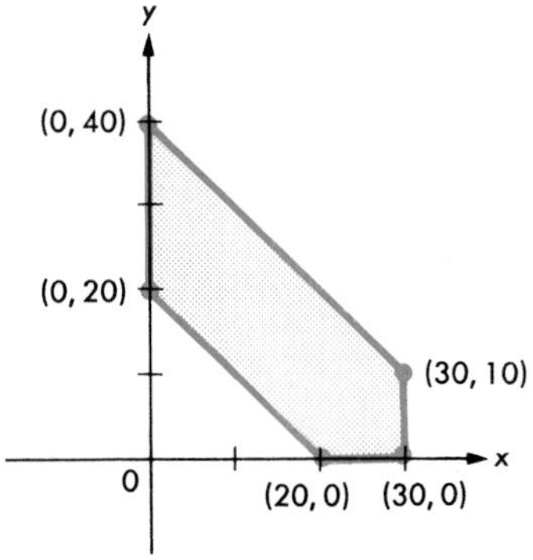

FIGURE 2–19

With what is given, there are many possible solutions of the manufacturer's problem. However, we have not yet taken into account the shipping costs from each warehouse to each town. Suppose that the shipping costs are as follows.

From warehouse	To town	Cost per unit, in dollars	Number of units shipped
I	A	10	x
I	B	14	y
II	A	12	$30 - x$
II	B	15	$40 - y$

Thus, the total shipping costs are

$$10x + 14y + 12(30 - x) + 15(40 - y)$$

dollars. This linear form in x and y reduces to

$$10x + 14y + 360 - 12x + 600 - 15y,$$

or

$$960 - 2x - y.$$

Now, our problem is to find the solution of the original problem for which the total shipping costs are smallest. Mathematically speaking, we must find the point with integral coordinates in the pentagonal region of the figure at which the linear form

$$960 - 2x - y$$

has its smallest value.

The linear form has a value for every point in the region, and it would be impossible to compute all these values to find the smallest. Even the task of computing the values at the points with integral coordinates would be tedious. However, according to a result proved in the theory of linear programming, the maximum value of the linear form occurs at a vertex of the pentagon, and the minimum value occurs at another vertex.

To find the minimum value, let us compute the value of $960 - 2x - y$ (see the table on page 116) at each of the vertices of the pentagon. According to the theory of linear programming, the maximum value of the linear form is 940, occurring at (0, 20), and the minimum value is 890, occurring at (30, 10). To see that the values are between 890 and 940, let us find the value at some points other than the vertices. At the interior point (20, 10), the value is $960 - (2 \cdot 20) - 10$, or 910; at the boundary point (15, 25), the value is $960 - (2 \cdot 15) - 25$, or 905; at the interior point (29, 9), the value is $960 - (2 \cdot 29) - 9$, or 893.

Vertex	Value of $960 - 2x - y$
(20, 0)	$960 - (2 \cdot 20) - 0$, or 920
(30, 0)	$960 - (2 \cdot 30) - 0$, or 900
(30, 10)	$960 - (2 \cdot 30) - 10$, or 890
(0, 40)	$960 - (2 \cdot 0) - 40$, or 920
(0, 20)	$960 - (2 \cdot 0) - 20$, or 940

Clearly, the lowest shipping cost is \$890, occurring when $x = 30$ and $y = 10$. Thus, the manufacturer is advised to ship all 30 units to town A from warehouse I, and to ship 10 units from warehouse I and 30 units from warehouse II to town B. By doing this, he will make the greatest profit on his two orders.

We have used a theorem from linear programming which states that a linear form defined over a convex polygonal region of the plane assumes its maximum and minimum values at vertices of the region. You can find a proof of this theorem in *Introduction to Finite Mathematics*.†

Exercises

See Solution Manual for graphs.

1. (a) If, in the problem of this section, the shipping costs are \$15 per unit from warehouse I to town A, \$12 per unit from warehouse I to town B, \$14 per unit from warehouse II to town A, and \$10 per unit from warehouse II to town B, express the shipping costs as a linear form in x and y. $C = 820 + x + 2y$

   (b) Find the value of this linear form at each corner point of the pentagon.

   (c) What shipping advice should be given to the manufacturer if he is to spend as little as possible on shipping?

2. An appliance wholesaler has 8 television sets in his warehouse in Lakeville and 8 sets in his warehouse in Alexandria. He receives orders to ship 6 sets to Central City and 4 sets to Stratford.

   (a) Let x be the number of sets to be shipped from Lakeville to Central City. What represents the number to be shipped from Alexandria to Central City? What is the lower limit of x? What is the upper limit of x? $x \leq 6$ $6 - x$ $x \geq 0$

   (b) Let y be the number of sets to be shipped from Lakeville to Stratford. What will represent the number to be shipped from Alexandria to Stratford? What is the lower limit of y? What is the upper limit of y? $4 - y$ $y \geq 0$ $y \leq 4$

Answers to Exercise 1(b), 1(c)

1. (b)

Vertex	Value
(20, 0)	840
(30, 0)	850
(30, 10)	870
(0, 40)	900
(0, 20)	860

(c) Ship 20 units from I to A, no units from I to B, 10 units from II to A, and 40 units from II to B.

† J. G. Kemeny, J. L. Snell, and G. L. Thompson, *Introduction to Finite Mathematics* (Englewood Cliffs, N. J., Prentice-Hall).

(c) Write the system of six inequalities describing the problem.
(d) Graph the system of part (c).
(e) If shipping costs per television set are \$6 from Lakeville to Central City, \$5 from Lakeville to Stratford, \$7 from Alexandria to Central City, and \$8.50 from Alexandria to Stratford, write and simplify a linear form for the total shipping cost. $C = 76 - x - 3.5y$
(f) Find the value of the linear form of part (e) at each of the six corner points of your graph.
(g) For maximum profit, what advice should be given to the wholesaler?

3. Two machines A and B produce items at the rate of 50 per hour and 40 per hour, respectively. Under a certain production plan the total number of items needed is at least 1000 items, and the total number of man-hours available for running the machines is at most 24 hours.

(a) Let x be the number of hours machine A is used and y the number of hours machine B is used, and express the two conditions above as inequalities. $50x + 40y \geqq 1000$; $x + y \leqq 24$
(b) Add to the system of inequalities in part (a) the two obvious inequalities resulting from the fact that x and y are non-negative numbers, and graph the system of these four inequalities. Find the corner points of the resulting polygon.
(c) If the hourly cost is \$10 for running machine A and \$7 for machine B, find the values of x and y which would yield the most economical production program. $(4, 20)$
(d) In part (c), if the hourly costs for A and B were \$10 and \$9, respectively, what would be the best plan? $(20, 0)$
(e) Assuming, in part (c), that the hourly costs for A and B are \$10 and \$8, respectively, show that two of the corner points give paired values of x and y which minimize the cost. (Actually any point (x, y) on the line segment between these corner points will lead to the same minimal cost.)

4. In the table below, the vitamin and mineral content of two brands of cereals, Soggies ("they sink") and Lumpies ("they clump"), is given in milligrams per ounce. The third column gives the daily minimum requirements of these vitamins and minerals. At the bottom of the first two columns, the cost per ounce of each cereal is listed. Find the number of ounces for each cereal which taken together will satisfy the daily minimum requirements of thiamine, niacin, and iron at lowest cost.
Together, 2 ounces of Soggies and 4 of Lumpies satisfy the requirements.

	Soggies	Lumpies	Daily min. requirement
Thiamine	.5	.25	2.00
Niacin	50	150	450
Iron	1.5	2.0	11.0
	$2\frac{1}{2}$¢	2¢	

Answers to Exercises 2(c), 2(f), 2(g), 3(b), 3(e)

2. (c) $\begin{cases} x \geqq 0 \\ x \leqq 6 \\ y \geqq 0 \\ y \leqq 4 \\ x + y \leqq 8 \\ x + y \geqq 2 \end{cases}$

2. (f)

Vertex	Value
(0, 2)	69
(2, 0)	74
(6, 0)	70
(6, 2)	63
(4, 4)	58
(0, 4)	62

2. (g) From Lakeville, ship four sets to Central City and four sets to Stratford. From Alexandria, ship two sets to Central City and none to Stratford.

3. (b) $\begin{cases} 50x + 40y \geqq 1000 \\ x + y \leqq 24 \\ x \geqq 0 \\ y \geqq 0 \end{cases}$

3. (e) There is a minimum value of cost at (4, 20) and at (20, 0). The line joining the two points has equations

$$50x + 40y = 1000$$

and $10x + 8y = 200$. Hence, at any point on this line, the value of $10x + 8y$ is 200.

Quiz

The following system of inequalities describes a linear programming problem:

$$\begin{cases} x \geqq 0, \\ x \leqq 5, \\ y \geqq 0, \\ y \leqq 3, \\ x + y \leqq 6 \\ x + y \geqq 2 \end{cases}$$

1. Graph the system.

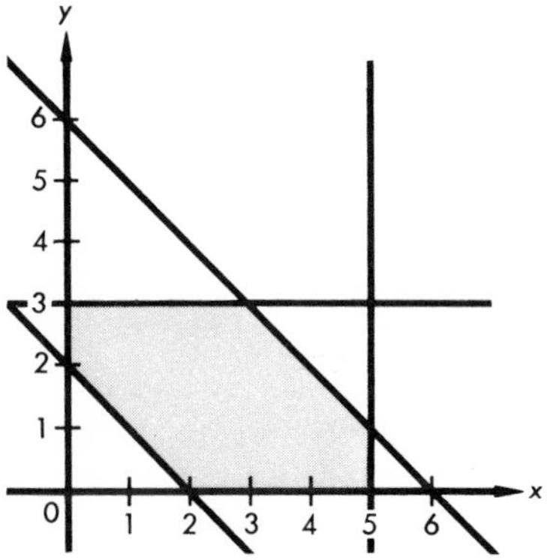

2. Find the value of the linear form $C = 43 - x - 3y$ at each of the six corner points of your graph.

(ans:

Vertex	Value
(0, 2)	37
(0, 3)	34
(3, 3)	31
(5, 1)	35
(5, 0)	38
(2, 0)	41)

3. At what point is the value of C a minimum? (ans: (3, 3))

5. A truck gardener has a plot of 50 acres and decides to plant two different vegetables, B and C. He has a maximum of 185 man-hours of labor to devote to this garden and $205 which he may spend for seed. Let your variables be the number of acres to be planted in B (b) and the number of acres to be planted in C. (c)

(a) Write an inequality which states that he has 50 acres of land available. $b + c \leqq 50$

(b) If an acre of B requires 4 man-hours for cultivation and an acre of C requires only 1 man-hour, write an inequality stating that he has 185 man-hours of labor at his disposal. $4b + c \leqq 185$

(c) If seed costs $2 an acre for B and $5 an acre for C, write an inequality stating that he has at most $205 to spend for seed. $2b + 5c \leqq 205$

(d) Write inequalities indicating the minimum number of acres which may be planted in each vegetable. $b \geqq 0, \quad c \geqq 0$

(e) Graph your system of inequalities.

(f) If labor costs $2.50 a man-hour, an acre's yield of vegetable B sells for $27, and an acre's yield of vegetable C sells for $14, find a linear form which expresses the profit of the gardener. Profit = $15b + 6.5c$

(g) How many acres should the gardener plant in each vegetable if he wishes to maximize his profit? 45 acres of B, 5 acres of C

6. A couple decides to start a record collection. They can purchase records of musical shows for $5 apiece and records of a vocalist for $2 apiece. There are only 4 records of musical shows in which they are currently interested, and 6 of their favorite vocalist. They have $25 to invest and decide that 8 records should be their limit. Let x be the number of shows and y be the number of vocals purchased.

(a) Write two inequalities which express the number of records of musical shows which they can buy. $y \geqq 0, x \leqq 4$

(b) Write two inequalities which express the number of vocalist records which they can buy. $y \geqq 0, y \leqq 6$

(c) Write an inequality which shows that they have $25 to invest. $5x + 2y \leqq 25$

(d) Write an inequality which shows that 8 records should be their limit. $x + y \leqq 8$

(e) Graph the system of inequalities which you have just written.

(f) They give a popularity rating of 3 to each record of a musical show and of 2 to each record of the vocalist. How many records of each type should they buy to give their collection the highest rating? 3 records of musical shows and 5 of a vocalist.

KEY IDEAS AND KEY WORDS

The **union** of sets A and B, $A \cup B$, consists of all elements in either A or B.

The **intersection** of A and B, $A \cap B$, consists of all elements common to A and B.

The **empty set** is denoted by $\emptyset$.

Algebraic expressions of the form

$$(\text{a number})x + (\text{a number})y + (\text{a number})$$

are called **linear forms** in the variables x and y.

A linear equation in x and y is an algebraic expression made up of two linear forms in x and y connected by an equals sign.

A **solution of an equation in x and y** is an ordered pair (a, b) such that the equation is true when $x = a$ and $y = b$.

The **solution set of an equation in x and y** is the set of all solutions of the equation.

The **graph of an equation in x and y** is the graph of its solution set.

Two equations are called **equivalent equations** if they have the same solution set.

The **graph of a linear equation** in a cartesian coordinate system is a straight line.

A line divides a plane into two pieces, each of which is called a **half-plane.**

A **linear inequality** in x and y is made up of two linear forms in x and y connected by one of the symbols $>$, $<$, $\geqq$, or $\leqq$.

The **graph of a linear inequality** in a cartesian coordinate system is a **half-plane.**

A **solution of an inequality** in one variable is a value of the variable for which the inequality is true.

The **solution set of an inequality** is the set of all its solutions.

Two **inequalities** are called **equivalent inequalities** if they have the same solution set.

The abscissa of the point at which a line crosses the x-axis is called the **x-intercept;** the ordinate of the point at which it crosses the y-axis is called the **y-intercept.**

The quotient of the **rise** by the **run** of a nonvertical line in a cartesian coordinate system is called the **slope** of the line.

A **matrix** is a rectangular array of numbers.

The horizontal lines of numbers in a matrix are called its **rows** and the vertical lines are called its **columns.**

A **determinant** is a real number associated with each square matrix. The 2×2 matrix

$$\begin{pmatrix} a_1 & b_1 \\ a_2 & b_2 \end{pmatrix}$$

has determinant

$$\begin{vmatrix} a_1 & b_1 \\ a_2 & b_2 \end{vmatrix} = a_1b_2 - b_1a_2.$$

Linear programming is that branch of mathematics which is used to maximize or minimize a linear form when the variables are in the solution set of a system of equations or inequalities.

CHAPTER REVIEW

See Solution Manual for graphs.

1. Solve each of the following equations and check each answer.

(a) $8x - 15 = 3x + 5$ 4 (b) $4 - \frac{2x + 5}{4} = \frac{1}{2} - \frac{9(x + 3)}{8}$ −9

2. Give the intersection of the solution sets of each pair of inequalities and, if possible, graph the intersection on a number line.

(a) $3x - \frac{5}{9} < 2x - 1$ and $1 + \frac{2}{3}x \leqq x + \frac{1}{4}$ ϕ

(b) $2(1 + 2x) < 3(3 + x)$ and $\frac{1}{3}(x + 2) > \frac{1}{2}x + \frac{2}{3}$ $\{x \mid x < 0\}$

(c) $4 + 3x < 5 + 4x$ and $3(2 - x) > 5 - 2x$ $\{x \mid {}^-1 < x < 1\}$

3. Graph the solution set of each of the following equations. For each graph, give the slope and both intercepts. Is there a solution in positive integers for either equation?

(a) $y = 1 - 3x$ (b) $x + \frac{1}{5}y = 2$

4. Find the solution set and draw the graph of each of the following inequalities.

(a) $x \leqq y$ (b) $x + y > 2$ (c) $2x - 3y \geqq 6$

5. Find the solution set of each of the following systems of equations.

(a) $\begin{cases} x + 2y = 9 \\ 4x - y = 0 \end{cases}$ $x = 1,\ y = 4$ (b) $\begin{cases} 2x - 5y = 6 \\ 3x + 4y = 32 \end{cases}$ $x = 8,\ y = 2$

6. Given that

$$A = \{(x, y) \mid y + 3x + 6 = 0\}, \quad B = \{(x, y) \mid y = 4 - 3x\},$$

(a) graph $A \cup B$. (b) describe $A \cap B$. ϕ

7. Tell whether the following system of equations is dependent, independent, or inconsistent. Inconsistent

$$\begin{cases} y + 3x + 6 = 0 \\ y = 4 - 3x \end{cases}$$

8. Prove that the points $({}^-1, 2)$, $(3, {}^-4)$, and $({}^-5, 8)$ are collinear. See Solution Manual.

9. Write an inequality whose solution set has for its graph the half-plane above the line with slope $\frac{2}{3}$ and y-intercept $^-4$. $y > \frac{2}{3}x - 4$

10. Describe each solution set. In (a) and (b), draw the graph of each system of inequalities, and give the coordinates of the vertices of the regions.

(a) $\begin{cases} x > {}^-2 \\ x < 2 \\ 3y \leqq x + 6 \\ x + 3y + 6 \geqq 0 \end{cases}$ Trapezoid (b) $\begin{cases} 9x + y - 14 \leqq 0 \\ 2x + 5y + 16 \geqq 0 \\ 7x - 4y + 13 \geqq 0 \end{cases}$ Triangle

(c) $\begin{cases} 2r + 3s + 4t = 3 \\ r - 2t = 0 \\ 6r + 6s = 5 \end{cases}$ $\{(\frac{1}{2}, \frac{1}{3}, \frac{1}{4})\}$

11. A newsboy has three times as many dimes as quarters. If the dimes and quarters total \$7.15, how many of each does he have? 39 dimes, 13 quarters

Answers to Chapter Review Problem 3

3. (a) Slope: $^-3$; x-intercept: $\frac{1}{3}$; y-intercept: 1; no solution in positive integers.
(b) Slope: $^-5$; x-intercept: 2; y-intercept: 10; solution in positive integers (1, 5).

12. Mr. Smith spent 4 hours driving from his home to his cabin on the lake, while he spent only 3 hours and 20 minutes returning. If his speed on the return trip was 10 miles per hour faster than his speed going, what is the distance, in miles, from his home to his cabin?

13. Joe earns \$30 a week less than twice what Jane earns. What is the minimum amount each can earn if they want to meet their combined weekly budget of \$150? What is the least each could earn to meet a budget of \$210 a week?

14. The sum of the digits of a three-digit number is 14. The tens' digit is 4 less than the sum of the hundreds' digit and the units' digit. If the tens' digit and the units' digit are interchanged, the number is increased by 18. Find the number.

15. John has a collection of nickels and dimes, with the dimes numbering three more than twice the nickels. If he has at least \$2 and at most \$3, what possible combinations of dimes and nickels could he have?

CHAPTER TEST

1. Solve the following equation.

$$\frac{3x + 10}{8} + \frac{x - 5}{2} = \frac{1}{2}$$

2. Find the solution set of the following inequality.

$$3(x + 2) - 1 > 2 - 3(x + 1)$$

3. On a number line, graph the solution set of the following inequality.

$$x + 5 > 2x + 1$$

4. Write an inequality whose solution set has for its graph the half-plane below the line which passes through the two points $(^{-}1, 6)$ and $(3, ^{-}4)$.

5. Solve the following systems of equations.

(a) $\begin{cases} 2x - 4 = y \\ x + 3y = 5 \end{cases}$ (b) $\begin{cases} x - y + z = 2 \\ x + 2z = 7 \\ y - z = 1 \end{cases}$

6. Graph the solution set of the following system of inequalities.

$$\begin{cases} y \geqq 8 - 4x \\ x \leqq 8 \end{cases}$$

7. The units' digit of a two-digit number is 5 less than twice the tens' digit. If the digits are reversed, the number is decreased by 9. What is the number?

8. Suppose that 600 tickets for the ballet were sold, some for \$1.60 each and some for \$2.25 each. If the total receipts were \$1122.50, how many tickets were sold at each price?

Answer to Chapter Review Problem 13

13. Jane must earn \$60 and Joe \$90; Jane must earn at least \$80 and Joe at least \$130.

CHAPTER TEST

The material included in the Chapter Test was covered in the following sections:

Problem 1—Section 2-1
Problems 2, 3—Section 2-3
Problem 4—Section 2-6
Problem 5(a)—Section 2-7
Problem 5(b)—Section 2-11
Problem 6—Section 2-10
Problems 7, 8—Section 2-9

Answers to Chapter Test Problems 3, 6

3.

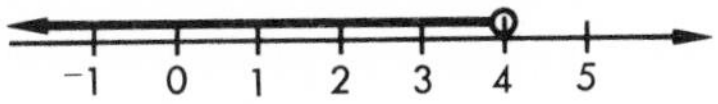

6.

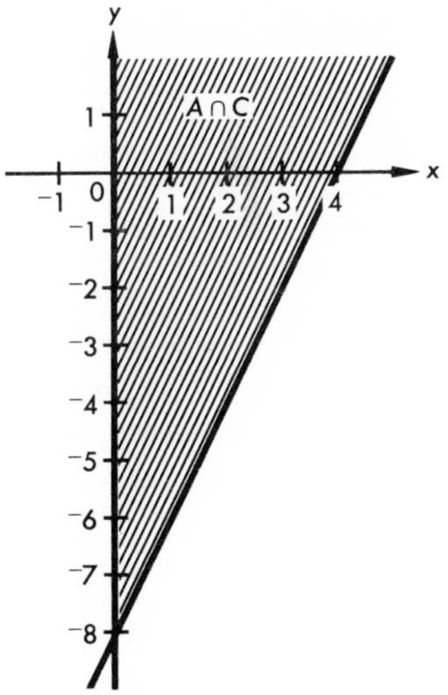

CHAPTER 3

Second-Degree Equations and Inequalities

Quadratic equations are not covered in all first-year algebra courses, and in many the work is done hurriedly at the end of the year. This chapter, therefore, contains a great deal of material for teaching, or reteaching, the skills needed to solve a quadratic by factoring or by completing the square. It should be covered carefully. The quadratic formula does not appear until Chapter 4, after the introduction of complex numbers. This should allow for proper emphasis on completing the square, a procedure which is often needed in analytics and calculus, and which is certainly equal in importance to the quadratic formula.

Finding the real-number values of x for which it is true that

$$x^2 - 5x + 6 = 0$$

focuses attention on an important property of the real number zero. The student knows that a positive real number can be written as a product in many ways; he should also realize that zero can be written as a product in almost any way, as long as at least one of the factors is zero itself. Therefore, if $x - 2 = 0$,

$$(x - 2)(x - 3) = 0,$$

no matter what $x - 3$ equals; or $(x - 2)(x - 3) = 0$ if $x - 3 = 0$, no matter what $x - 2$ equals.

The linear equation in x,

$$ax + b = 0,$$

has only one rational solution. On the other hand, the quadratic equation $ax^2 + bx + c = 0$ may have *no*

CHAPTER 3

Shown above is the reflecting surface of the 200-inch mirror of the Hale Telescope at Mount Wilson and Palomar Observatories. (Photograph from the Mount Wilson and Palomar Observatories)

SECOND-DEGREE EQUATIONS AND INEQUALITIES

A first-degree equation in one variable generally has one solution, and a second-degree equation usually has two. An easy way to solve a second-degree equation such as

$$8x^2 - 5 = 9$$

is to observe that it is equivalent to the equation

$$x^2 = \frac{7}{4}.$$

Hence, its solutions are $x = \sqrt{7}/2$ and $x = {}^{-}\sqrt{7}/2$.

The method above fails if there is a first-degree term in the equation. For example, the second-degree equation

$$8x^2 - 5x = 9$$

cannot be solved in the same simple way. However, there are systematic ways of solving such equations, as we shall see in this chapter.

Often, algebraic facts can best be described geometrically. Thus, we saw in the preceding chapter how a linear equation in two variables can be associated with a line in a plane. Solutions of the equation are then represented by points on the line. Similarly, second-degree equations in two variables, such as

$$y = x^2 - 5x + 4,$$

can be associated with curves in the plane.

rational solutions even if a, b, and c are all rational. Therefore, one must look among the irrational real numbers for possible solutions. Sometimes they are found, and sometimes not. The need is thus established for a type of number different from the real numbers, unless we are willing to permit the existence of a subset of quadratics without solutions.

The following are some of the topics covered in Chapter 3:

- *Quadratic polynomials*
- *Quadratic equations*
- *Factors of zero*
- *Completing the square*
- *The parabola*
- *The vertex of the parabola*
- *The axis of symmetry of the parabola*
- *Quadratic inequalities in two variables*
- *Modular arithmetic*

It is suggested that one day be spent on each section of this chapter, with the exception of Sections 3–6 and 3–7, on which it may be necessary to spend two days.

123

3-1 QUADRATIC POLYNOMIALS

In the best classes this review work in factoring may be done rapidly, perhaps during the first half of one class period. However, average classes will be helped by practice in writing polynomials as products before getting involved in finding their zeros.

3-1 QUADRATIC POLYNOMIALS

An expression of the form

$$ax^2 + bx + c,$$

where a, b, and c are real numbers, with $a \neq 0$, is called a *quadratic polynomial* in the variable x. The number a is called the *coefficient* of x^2. We assume that $a \neq 0$, for if $a = 0$, the expression is a linear form. The number b is the *coefficient* of x, and the number c is called the *constant term.* For example, $x^2 - 6x + 8$ and $4x^2 - 49$ are quadratic polynomials in x.

Some quadratic polynomials can be factored, that is, expressed as a product of two linear polynomials. For example, we can verify that

$$x^2 - 6x + 8 = (x - 4)(x - 2).$$

The square of a linear polynomial $Ax + B$ has the form

$$(Ax + B)^2 = A^2x^2 + 2ABx + B^2.$$

Consequently, any quadratic polynomial of the form

$$A^2x^2 + 2ABx + B^2$$

can be factored in the way shown above. We call such a quadratic polynomial a *perfect square.* The polynomial $x^2 + 10x + 25$ has the form shown above, with $A = 1$ and $B = 5$. Hence,

$$x^2 + 10x + 25 = (x + 5)^2.$$

As another example, $4x^2 - 44x + 121$ has the above form, with $A = 2$ and $B = {}^-11$: $4x^2 - 44x + 121 = (2x - 11)^2$.

Another type of quadratic polynomial which can be easily factored is one of the form $A^2x^2 - B^2$. Thus,

$$A^2x^2 - B^2 = (Ax + B)(Ax - B).$$

We call a polynomial of the form $A^2x^2 - B^2$ a *difference of two squares.* For example, $4x^2 - 49$ is a difference of two squares, with $A = 2$ and $B = 7$. Hence, $4x^2 - 49 = (2x + 7)(2x - 7)$.

If a quadratic polynomial has integral coefficients, then we can determine by trial and error whether it can be factored into two linear polynomials with integral coefficients. This is illustrated in the following problem.

Problem. If possible, factor each of the following polynomials into linear polynomials with integral coefficients.

(a) $x^2 - 3x - 10$ (b) $2x^2 - 7x + 6$ (c) $3x^2 - 8x - 12$

Solution.

(a) If $x^2 - 3x - 10$ can be factored, then

$$x^2 - 3x - 10 = (x + M)(x + N)$$

for some integers M and N. Since

$$(x + M)(x + N) = x^2 + (M + N)x + MN,$$

we must have

$$M + N = {}^-3, \quad MN = {}^-10.$$

In order for $MN = {}^-10$, M and N must be in the set

$$\{\pm 1, \pm 2, \pm 5, \pm 10\}.$$

Thus, our problem is to select M and N from this set so that their sum is $^-3$ and their product is $^-10$. By trial and error, we find that $M = {}^-5$ and $N = 2$ (or $M = 2$ and $N = {}^-5$). Hence,

$$x^2 - 3x - 10 = (x - 5)(x + 2).$$

(b) This is somewhat more difficult than (a) because the coefficient of x^2 is not 1. However, the coefficient of x^2 is 2, a prime, so that if (b) can be factored, then it has the form

$$2x^2 - 7x + 6 = (2x + M)(x + N)$$

for some integers M and N. By multiplying out the right side of the above equation, $(2x + M)(x + N) = 2x^2 + (M + 2N)x + MN$, we see that

$$M + 2N = {}^-7, \quad MN = 6.$$

Thus, our problem is to select M and N from the set $\{\pm 1, \pm 2, \pm 3, \pm 6\}$ so that $MN = 6$ and $M + 2N = {}^-7$. By trial and error, we find that $M = {}^-3$ and $N = {}^-2$. Hence,

$$2x^2 - 7x + 6 = (2x - 3)(x - 2).$$

(c) We can factor this polynomial if, and only if, we can find integers M and N such that

$$3x^2 - 8x - 12 = (3x + M)(x + N)$$
$$= 3x^2 + (M + 3N)x + MN.$$

In order that students do not lose track of what they have and have not tried in the trial-and-error process, you could encourage them to list the pairs as they use them. For example,

$$2x^2 - 7x + 6 \stackrel{?}{=} (2x - 6)(x - 1)$$

is impossible, because then

$$2x^2 - 7x + 6$$

would be divisible by 2, and

$$2x^2 - 7x + 6 \stackrel{?}{=} (2x - 2)(x - 3)$$

is impossible for the same reason.

$$2x^2 - 7x + 6 \stackrel{?}{=} (2x - 1)(x - 6) \quad \text{(No)}$$
$$\stackrel{\checkmark}{=} (2x - 3)(x - 2) \quad \text{(Yes)}$$

In relation to the material at the top of the next page, attention may be directed to number theory to explain the reasoning that M and N must both be even or both be odd. In the trial and error method, reasoning of this kind will decrease the number of useless trials.

The student should understand that polynomials may be arranged with the powers of the variable ascending as well as descending and that for purposes of factoring, one arrangement is just as effective as another.

Exercises for Discussion

In Exercise for Discussion 9,

$$25 - x^2 = (5 + x)(5 - x),$$

and the student should be reminded that

$$25 - x^2 \neq x^2 - 25,$$

and that it is not only unnecessary but undesirable to write

$$25 - x^2 = {}^{-}(x^2 - 25)$$

before factoring.

In Exercise for Discussion 10, it should be observed that the polynomial $\frac{1}{4} - x^2$ cannot be factored as a product of polynomials with integral coefficients. However, it is possible to factor the polynomial as a product of polynomials with rational coefficients in the following manner:

$$\tfrac{1}{4} - x^2 = (\tfrac{1}{2} - x)(\tfrac{1}{2} + x).$$

Exercises

It is impossible to factor the polynomial given in Exercise 21 as a product of polynomials with integral coefficients. However, it is possible to factor the polynomial as a product of polynomials with rational coefficients in the following manner:

$$.01x^2 - 49 = (.1x - 7)(.1x + 7).$$

Exercises 27–34 all involve the use of the *distributive* law *before* factoring the polynomial as the product of two binomials. In Exercise 27,

$$6x^2 - 216 = 6(x^2 - 36) = 6(x + 6)(x - 6).$$

As can be seen here, unless and until the distributive law is used, no headway can be made. However, in Exercise 29 the student may first do this:

$$30x^2 - 38x + 12 = (10x - 6) \times (3x - 2),$$

Thus, we must select M and N from the set

$$\{\pm 1, \pm 2, \pm 3, \pm 4, \pm 6, \pm 12\}$$

so that

$$M + 3N = {}^{-}8, \quad MN = {}^{-}12.$$

Since $M + 3N$ is an even integer, M and N must both be even or both be odd. However, M and N cannot both be odd and have a product of $^{-}12$, so M and N must both be even. Therefore, one must be ± 2 and the other ± 6. We find that none of these values make

$$M + 3N = {}^{-}8.$$

Hence, we conclude that the polynomial in (c) cannot be factored into linear polynomials with integral coefficients.

Exercises for Discussion

If possible, factor each of the following as a product of polynomials with integral coefficients.

1. $x^2 + 12x + 10$ Not factorable
2. $x^2 + 31x + 30$ $(x+30)(x+1)$
3. $y^2 + 62y + 61$ $(y+61)(y+1)$
4. $a^2 - 6a + 12$ Not factorable
5. $x^2 + 18x + 81$ $(x+9)(x+9)$, or $(x+9)^2$
6. $16x^2 - 8x + 1$ $(4x-1)(4x-1)$, or $(4x-1)^2$
7. $y^2 + 7y + 49$ Not factorable
8. $25y^2 - 20y + 1$ Not factorable
9. $25 - x^2$ $(5-x)(5+x)$
10. $\frac{1}{4} - x^2$ See teachers' commentary.
11. $196x^2 - 9$ $(14x-3)(14x+3)$
12. $49x^2 - 144$ $(7x-12)(7x+12)$
13. $2x^2 + 5x - 1$ Not factorable
14. $2x^2 + 5x + 2$ $(2x+1)(x+2)$
15. $2y^2 + 5y - 12$ $(2y-3)(y+4)$
16. $2y^2 - y - 6$ $(2y+3)(y-2)$
17. $3x^2 - 16x + 16$ $(3x-4)(x-4)$
18. $3y^2 + 19y - 40$ $(3y-5)(y+8)$

Exercises

If possible, factor each of the following as a product of polynomials with integral coefficients.

1. $y^2 - y - 56$ $(y-8)(y+7)$
2. $x^2 - 7x + 10$ $(x-2)(x-5)$
3. $y^2 - 26y + 48$ $(y-2)(y-24)$
4. $x^2 - 11x + 10$ $(x-1)(x-10)$
5. $b^2 + 9b + 14$ $(b+7)(b+2)$
6. $y^2 + y - 42$ $(y+7)(y-6)$
7. $a^2 - 8a + 12$ $(a-2)(a-6)$
8. $b^2 - 15b + 14$ $(b-1)(b-14)$
9. $y^2 + 8y - 15$ Not factorable
10. $x^2 - 13x + 12$ $(x-1)(x-12)$
11. $b^2 - b - 20$ $(b-5)(b+4)$
12. $y^2 + 3y - 54$ $(y+9)(y-6)$
13. $x^2 - x - 72$ $(x-9)(x+8)$
14. $a^2 - 6a - 40$ $(a-10)(a+4)$

15. $a^2 - 10a + 21$ $(a-3)(a-7)$
16. $y^2 + 9y + 5$ Not factorable
17. $x^2 + 15x + 54$ $(x+9)(x+6)$
18. $y^2 - 17y + 72$ $(y-8)(y-9)$
19. $a^2 + 12a + 35$ $(a+5)(a+7)$
20. $b^2 + 12b - 35$ Not factorable
21. $.01x^2 - 49$ See teachers' commentary.
22. $1 - 100x^2$ $(1-10x)(1+10x)$
23. $x^8 - 36$ $(x^4-6)(x^4+6)$
24. $16x^4 - 225$ $(4x^2-15)(4x^2+15)$
25. $(19x)^2 - 17^2$ $(19x-17)(19x+17)$
26. $15^2 - (4x)^2$ $(15-4x)(15+4x)$
27. $6x^2 - 216$ $6(x-6)(x+6)$
28. $x^5 - x$ $x(x+1)(x-1)(x^2+1)$
29. $30x^2 - 38x + 12$ $2(5x-3)(3x-2)$
30. $^-8x^2 - 56x + 98$ $^-2(4x^2+28x-49)$
31. $6x^3 + 15x^2 + 6x$ $3x(2x+1)(x+2)$
32. $y^3 - 16y$ $y(y-4)(y+4)$
33. $48y^3 + 147y$ $3y(16y^2+49)$
34. $6x^2 - 54x + 84$ $6(x-2)(x-7)$

3–2 EQUATIONS IN ONE VARIABLE

An equation of the form

$$ax^2 + bx + c = 0, \quad a \neq 0,$$

where a, b, and c are real numbers is called a *second-degree equation*, or *quadratic equation*, in the variable x. A number is called a *solution of a quadratic equation* if a true equation results when the variable is given the number as a value. The set of all solutions of the equation is called the *solution set of the quadratic equation*. If a quadratic equation has no solution, the solution set is the empty set.

The quadratic equation

$$2x^2 - 3x - 2 = 0$$

has 2 as a solution since

$$(2 \cdot 2^2) - (3 \cdot 2) - 2 = 0$$

is a true equation. The numbers 1 and $\frac{1}{2}$ are not solutions since

$$(2 \cdot 1^2) - (3 \cdot 1) - 2 = 0$$

and

$$[2 \cdot (\tfrac{1}{2})^2] - (3 \cdot \tfrac{1}{2}) - 2 = 0$$

are both false equations. However, $^-\frac{1}{2}$ is a solution since the equation

$$[2 \cdot (^-\tfrac{1}{2})^2] - (3 \cdot {}^-\tfrac{1}{2}) - 2 = 0$$

is true. On pages 128 and 129, we shall show that $\{2, {}^-\frac{1}{2}\}$ is the solution set of the given equation.

and then he may continue

$$(10x - 6)(3x - 2) = 2(5x - 3) \times (3x - 2).$$

It should be pointed out that

$$30x^2 - 38x + 12 = 2(15x^2 - 19x + 6).$$

If the distributive law is not used first, one of the binomials will contain the factor 2. Of course,

$$(10x - 6)(3x - 2)$$

is a correct answer according to the instructions for the exercises; the advantage of using the distributive law first is simply that it reduces the number of possibilities when factoring by trial and error.

Quiz

If possible, factor each of the following as a product of polynomials with integral coefficients.

1. $x^2 - 16$ (ans: $(x - 4)(x + 4)$)
2. $x^2 + 4x + 3$ (ans: $(x + 1)(x + 3)$)
3. $x^2 + 2x - 8$ (ans: $(x - 2)(x + 4)$)
4. $4x^2 + 4x + 1$ (ans: $(2x + 1)^2$)
5. $2x^2 - 5x - 3$ (ans: $(2x + 1)(x - 3)$)

3-2 EQUATIONS IN ONE VARIABLE

On page 7 of the text it was proved that $x \cdot 0 = 0$ for every real number x. It must now be proved that if $x \cdot y = 0$, either $x = 0$ or $y = 0$. These two theorems completely cover the question of the solution set for quadratics such as

$$3x^2 + 10x - 8 = 0,$$

which can be written in the form

$$(3x - 2)(x + 4) = 0.$$

Since the product will be zero if one of the factors is zero, it can be seen that there are two ways of making the product zero: replace x in the first factor by $\frac{2}{3}$, or replace x in the second factor by $^-4$. Furthermore, it is known that the complete solution set is $\{\frac{2}{3}, \ ^-4\}$, since any other number makes both factors different from zero and hence gives a nonzero product.

It should be pointed out that, although knowing that the product of two real numbers is zero gives us specific information about at least one of the numbers, knowing that the product of two numbers is nonzero means very little. Students should realize that the statement $x \cdot y = 6$ does not reveal very much about the individual numbers except to indicate that they agree in sign.

Students may be confused by the ambiguity resulting from the use of the word *or*. In everyday language, *or* is used most frequently as an *exclusive or*. An example of the use of the exclusive or is the statement, "We shall have roast or chicken for dinner." In other words, we shall have *either* roast *or* chicken, but not both. The *inclusive or* is used in everyday language in a statement such as, "Gravy is good with either roast or chicken," meaning it is good with *both* roast *and* chicken. In mathematics, the inclusive or is most commonly used. The inclusive or is used in the statement of the property of factors of zero, $ab = 0$ if, and only if, $b = 0$ or $a = 0$. In other words, the statement is true both when $b = 0$ and when $a = 0$, and, therefore both cases are included in the *or* statement.

128 3-23-2 | EQUATIONS IN ONE VARIABLE

If we can factor a quadratic polynomial as a product of two linear forms, we can easily solve the quadratic equation that results when the polynomial is set equal to zero. This is true because of the following property of the real number system.

FACTORS OF ZERO

$$r \cdot s = 0 \quad \textit{if, and only if,} \quad r = 0 \textit{ or } s = 0 \qquad \textit{(F-0)}$$

In other words, a product of two real numbers is zero if, and only if, at least one of the numbers is zero.

This property can be proved as follows. If $r \cdot s = 0$ and $r \neq 0$, then r has a reciprocal, and we may multiply both sides of the equation $r \cdot s = 0$ by $1/r$, obtaining

$$\frac{1}{r} \cdot (r \cdot s) = \frac{1}{r} \cdot 0, \qquad \text{(U-M)}$$

$$\left(\frac{1}{r} \cdot r\right) \cdot s = 0, \qquad \text{(A-M), (Zero-M)}$$

$$1 \cdot s = 0, \quad \text{or } s = 0. \qquad \text{(Inv-M), (Id-M)}$$

Similarly, we may prove that if $r \cdot s = 0$ and $s \neq 0$, then $r = 0$. This proves that if $r \cdot s = 0$, then $r = 0$ or $s = 0$. On the other hand, we proved in Chapter 1 that if $r = 0$ or $s = 0$, then $r \cdot s = 0$.

By multiplication, we can show that

$$(2x + 1)(x - 2) = 2x^2 - 3x - 2.$$

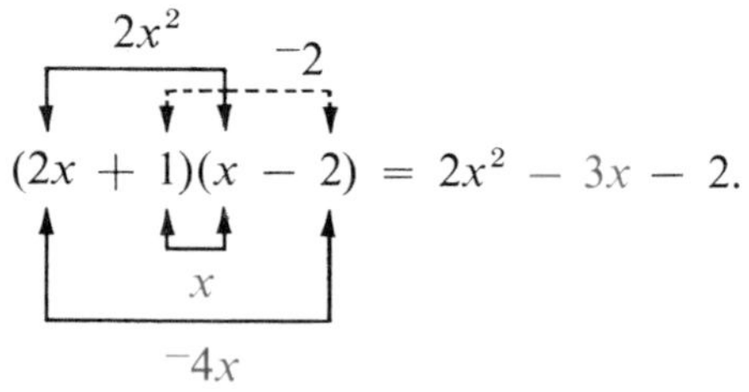

Therefore, the equation

$$2x^2 - 3x - 2 = 0$$

is equivalent to the equation

$$(2x + 1)(x - 2) = 0.$$

However, by *factors of zero,*

$$(2x + 1)(x - 2) = 0$$

if, and only if,

$$2x + 1 = 0 \quad \text{or} \quad x - 2 = 0.$$

When we solve each linear equation in the statement above, we find that

$$(2x + 1)(x - 2) = 0$$

if, and only if,

$$x = {}^{-}\tfrac{1}{2} \quad \text{or} \quad x = 2.$$

If we let x denote any number other than ${}^{-}\frac{1}{2}$ or 2, then both factors, $2x + 1$ and $x - 2$, will be nonzero. Therefore, their product will also be nonzero. Hence, no number except ${}^{-}\frac{1}{2}$ or 2 is a solution of the given equation, and we conclude that $\{{}^{-}\frac{1}{2}, 2\}$ is the solution set of this quadratic equation.

Problem. Solve the equation $3x^2 - 5x = 2x^2 - 7x + 35$.

Solution. To obtain an equivalent equation with zero on the right side, we add the additive inverse of

$$2x^2 - 7x + 35$$

to each side of the given equation. This yields

$$(3x^2 - 5x) + ({}^{-}2x^2 + 7x - 35)$$
$$= (2x^2 - 7x + 35) + ({}^{-}2x^2 + 7x - 35),$$

or

$$x^2 + 2x - 35 = 0.$$

If we can factor the quadratic polynomial $x^2 + 2x - 35$ as a product of two linear forms, the two factors should have the form $x + M$ and $x + N$. Since

$$(x + M)(x + N) = x^2 + (M + N)x + MN,$$

the product will be $x^2 + 2x - 35$ if

$$M + N = 2, \quad MN = {}^{-}35.$$

Exercises for Discussion, page 130

If time is limited it is suggested that at least Exercises for Discussion 3-9 be covered.

When solutions are proposed, as in Exercises for Discussion 1 and 2, it is hoped the student will check each one in the given equation to see which are, and which are not, in the solution set of that equation. The point of these exercises is not intended to be to emphasize the *procedure* for solving an equation. Emphasis should be placed on the *solution* and its meaning as a number value which, when it replaces the variable, converts the open sentence to a true statement.

In Exercise for Discussion 2, it should be brought out that

$$x - 1 = 40, x = 41$$

is not a solution, nor is

$$x + 2 = 40, x = 38.$$

If $x - 1 = 40$, then we would have to have $x + 2 = 1$ so that

$$(x - 1)(x + 2) = 40 \cdot 1, \text{ or } 40.$$

But obviously, if $x - 1 = 40$, then $x + 2 \neq 1$.

Students should recognize patterns well enough to handle Exercise for Discussion 9 as if it said $y^2 - 4y - 77 = 0$, and Exercise for Discussion 10(a) as if it said $y^2 - 9y - 10 = 0$. They should not have to expand and then combine terms to do any of these. They should read an exercise such as

$$4(2x + 1)^2 - 20(2x + 1) + 25 = 0$$

as "Four times the square of a number, decreased by twenty times that number, and this difference increased by twenty-five is zero." They should recognize $(2x + 1)$ as a variable denoting a number just as quickly as they do x.

Answers to Exercises for Discussion 1, 2, 4

1. The solution set of
$$6x^2 - x - 2 = 0$$
is
$$\{^-\tfrac{1}{2}, \tfrac{2}{3}\}.$$

2. The solution set of
$$(x - 1)(x + 2) = 40$$
is
$$\{^-7, 6\}.$$

4. $x^2 + 2x - 24 = 24$
$x^2 + 2x - 48 = 0$
$(x + 8)(x - 6) = 0$
$\{6, ^-8\}$

Answer to Exercise for Discussion 10(c), page 131

10. (c) $2(y - 1)^2 = 9(y - 1) + 161$
$2(y - 1)^2 - 9(y - 1) - 161 = 0$
$[2(y - 1) - 23] \times [(y - 1) + 7] = 0$
$2(y - 1) - 23 = 0$
or $(y - 1) + 7 = 0$
$2y - 25 = 0$ or $y + 6 = 0$
$\{y \mid 2(y - 1)^2 = 9(y - 1) + 161\} = \{\tfrac{25}{2}, ^-6\}$

We then find two factors of $^-35$ whose sum is 2.

$$7 \cdot {}^-5 = {}^-35 \quad \text{and} \quad 7 + {}^-5 = 2$$

Thus, $M = 7$ and $N = {}^-5$.

$$x^2 + 2x - 35 = (x + 7)(x - 5)$$

Therefore, the equation

$$(x + 7)(x - 5) = 0$$

is equivalent to the given one. Since

$$(x + 7)(x - 5) = 0$$

if, and only if,

$$x + 7 = 0 \quad \text{or} \quad x - 5 = 0,$$

the solution set of the given equation is

$$\{x \mid x + 7 = 0 \text{ or } x - 5 = 0\}, \quad \text{or } \{^-7, 5\}.$$

Check.

$$x = {}^-7$$
$$[3 \cdot ({}^-7)^2] - (5 \cdot {}^-7) \stackrel{?}{=} [2 \cdot ({}^-7)^2] - (7 \cdot {}^-7) + 35$$
$$(3 \cdot 49) + 35 \stackrel{?}{=} (2 \cdot 49) + 49 + 35$$
$$(3 \cdot 49) + 35 \stackrel{\checkmark}{=} [(2 + 1) \cdot 49] + 35$$

$$x = 5$$
$$(3 \cdot 5^2) - (5 \cdot 5) \stackrel{?}{=} (2 \cdot 5^2) - (7 \cdot 5) + 35$$
$$75 - 25 \stackrel{\checkmark}{=} 50 - 35 + 35$$

Exercises for Discussion

For each of the given quadratic equations, select from the set to the right of it those numbers which are solutions of the equation.

1. $6x^2 - x - 2 = 0$, $\{^-1, ^-\tfrac{1}{2}, 1, \tfrac{2}{3}, 3, 0\}$
2. $(x - 1)(x + 2) = 40$, $\{1, ^-2, 8, 5, 6, 10, ^-7\}$

In Exercises 3–8, solve each of the quadratic equations. Then substitute into the original equation to check each solution.

3. $x^2 - 14x - 15 = 0$ $(x-15)(x+1)=0$ $\{^-1, 15\}$
4. $(x + 6)(x - 4) = 24$
5. $7x^2 + 21x = 0$ $7x(x+3)=0$, $\{0, ^-3\}$
6. $5x^2 - 14x - 3 = 0$ $(5x+1)(x-3)=0$, $\{\tfrac{-1}{5}, 3\}$
7. $x^2 + 4x + 4 = 0$ $(x+2)^2=0$, $\{^-2\}$
8. $9x^2 + 12x + 4 = 0$ $(3x+2)^2=0$, $\{\tfrac{^-2}{3}\}$

9. We can find the solution set of $(x + 3)^2 - 4(x + 3) - 77 = 0$ in two different ways. Complete each solution below.

First solution.

$$(x + 3)^2 - 4(x + 3) - 77 = 0$$
$$x^2 + 6x + 9 - 4x - 12 - 77 = 0$$
$$x^2 + \underline{2\ ?}\ x - \underline{80\ ?} = 0$$
$$(x + \underline{10\ ?})(x - \underline{8\ ?}) = 0$$
$$x + \underline{10\ ?} = 0 \quad \text{or} \quad x - \underline{8\ ?} = 0$$
$$\{x \mid (x + 3)^2 - 4(x + 3) - 77 = 0\} = \{\underline{^-10\ ?}, \underline{8\ ?}\}$$

Second solution.

$$(x + 3)^2 - 4(x + 3) - 77 = 0$$
$$[(x + 3) - 11][(x + 3) + 7] = 0$$
$$(x + 3) - 11 = 0 \quad \text{or} \quad (x + 3) + 7 = 0$$
$$x - \underline{8\ ?} = 0 \quad \text{or} \quad x + \underline{10\ ?} = 0$$
$$\{x \mid (x + 3)^2 - 4(x + 3) - 77 = 0\} = \{\underline{8\ ?}, \underline{^-10\ ?}\}$$

10. The following equations can be solved in the two ways illustrated in Exercise 9. Use whichever method you prefer and check your solutions.

(a) $(x + 5)^2 - 9(x + 5) - 10 = 0$ $\{^-6, 5\}$
(b) $(x + 2)^2 + 4(x + 2) - 5 = 0$ $\{^-7, ^-1\}$
(c) $2(y - 1)^2 = 9(y - 1) + 161$

Exercises

For each of the given quadratic equations, select from the set to the right of it those elements which are solutions of the equation.

1. $(x + 5)(x - 9) = 0,$ $\{0, 1, 4, 9, ^-45, ^-5\}$
2. $3x^2 - 6x = 0,$ $\{^-3, ^-2, 0, 6, 1, 2, 3\}$
3. $x^2 - 5x = 2x - 6,$ $\{1, 0, 5, 3, ^-2, 6\}$

Solve each of the following equations and check each solution.

4. $x^2 - 7x + 10 = 0$ $\{2, 5\}$
5. $x^2 - 3x - 40 = 0$ $\{8, ^-5\}$
6. $2x^2 + 5x - 12 = 0$ $\{\frac{3}{2}, ^-4\}$
7. $x^2 + 2x + 1 = 0$ $\{^-1\}$
8. $x^2 + x = 6$ $\{2, ^-3\}$
9. $y^2 + 49 = {}^-14y$ $\{^-7\}$
10. $6t^2 - t - 1 = 0$ $\{\frac{^-1}{3}, \frac{1}{2}\}$
11. $x^2 - 169 = 0$ $\{13, ^-13\}$
12. $24z + 81 = z^2$ $\{^-3, 27\}$
13. $t^2 = 7(2t - 7)$ $\{7\}$
14. $3x^2 = 5x$ $\{0, \frac{5}{3}\}$
15. $51y^2 + y - 92 = 0$ $\{\frac{4}{3}, \frac{^-23}{17}\}$
16. $\frac{x^2}{9} - \frac{1}{4} = 0$ $\{\frac{3}{2}, \frac{^-3}{2}\}$
17. $10 - 2t - 15t^2 = 2$ $\{\frac{2}{3}, \frac{^-4}{5}\}$
18. $4x^2 + x = 0$ $\{0, \frac{^-1}{4}\}$
19. $(x + 9)^2 - 225 = 0$ $\{6, ^-24\}$
20. $3t^2 - \frac{7}{4}t - 3 = 0$ $\{\frac{4}{3}, \frac{^-3}{4}\}$
21. $84 - z(z + 8) = 0$ $\{6, ^-14\}$

Exercises

Students should observe the solution sets for Exercises 6, 7, 14, and 16, and note that for Exercise 6 there are two distinct solutions, for Exercise 7 only one solution, for Exercise 14 zero is one of the two solutions, and for Exercise 16 the two solutions are additive inverses. Then they should observe that the solution sets for Exercises 5, 9, 18, and 11 fall into the same four categories. The pattern for quadratics, $ax^2 + bx + c = 0$, should be studied and the class helped to formulate the following conditions:

$b = 0$ will correspond to an equation having solutions that are additive inverses;

$c = 0$ will give an equation in which zero is one of two distinct solutions (unless $b = 0$ too).

These are the short, or incomplete, quadratics. When the first assignment is brought in, before it is checked you could have the students jot down the sum and then the product of the solutions for each exercise they have done. Thus, for Exercise 6, the solution set is $\{\frac{3}{2}, ^-4\}$. Therefore, the sum is $\frac{3}{2} + (^-4)$, or $^-\frac{5}{2}$; the product is $\frac{3}{2}(^-4)$, or $^-6$. Compare these two numbers with the coefficients in the equation

$$2x^2 + 5x - 12 = 0.$$

The class may be told that, in general, if $ax^2 + bx + c = 0$, the sum of the solutions will be $^-b/a$, the product will be c/a, and that this will be proved later. In the meantime, they can use it as a check on their work. Familiarity with the above generalization will enhance interest in the proof when it is presented in Chapter 4.

Quiz

Solve each of the following equations.

1. $x^2 - x - 30$ (ans: $\{6, {}^-5\}$)
2. $3x^2 - 6x = 0$ (ans: $\{0, 2\}$)
3. $x^2 - \frac{16}{9} = 0$ (ans: $\{\frac{4}{3}, {}^-\frac{4}{3}\}$)
4. $x^2 - 8x + 16 = 0$ (ans: $\{4\}$)
5. $x^2 - x - 8 = 4$ (ans: $\{^-3, 4\}$)

3–3 MORE QUADRATIC EQUATIONS

It will be helpful to have the student formulate a sentence defining the variable used in each exercise. It is important that the sentence precede the equation, because the purpose here is to practice translating quantitative situations into equations solvable by routine methods. The actual thinking process in creating equations is more important at this point than merely solving the equation for a numerical answer.

Answers to Exercises for Discussion 1–5, page 133

1. Let x be the width of the parking strip. Then the lot will be $200 + 2x$ by $300 + 2x$. Hence,

$$(200 + 2x)(300 + 2x) = 81{,}600,$$
$$60{,}000 + 1000x + 4x^2 = 81{,}600,$$
$$4x^2 + 1000x - 21{,}600 = 0,$$
$$x^2 + 250x - 5400 = 0,$$
$$(x + 270)(x - 20) = 0,$$
$$x = {}^-270,$$
or
$$x = 20.$$

△

Solve each of the following equations and check each solution.

22. $(x - 1)(x + 2) = 10$ $\{3, {}^-4\}$
23. $2(t - 1)(t - 3) = (t - 3)(t - 2)$ $\{3, 0\}$
24. $\frac{x^2}{14} + \frac{1}{4}x = \frac{4}{28}$ $\{\frac{1}{2}, {}^-4\}$
25. $(3y + 2)^2 - (2y - 3)^2 = 4(y^2 + 5y + 18)$ $\{7, {}^-11\}$
26. $t(2t + 1) = 28$ $\{\frac{7}{2}, {}^-4\}$
27. $y(3y - 5) - 12 = 0$ $\{\frac{^-4}{3}, 3\}$

▲

Solve each of the following equations and check each solution.

28. $4(2x + 1)^2 - 20(2x + 1) + 25 = 0$ $\{\frac{3}{4}\}$
29. $2(3x + 1)^2 + 5(3x + 1) - 12 = 0$ $\{\frac{1}{6}, \frac{^-5}{3}\}$
30. $(x - 1)^2 - 81 = 0$ $\{10, {}^-8\}$
31. $(x + 4)^2 = 19(x + 4)$ $\{15, {}^-4\}$
32. $25(t + 3)^2 - 256 = 0$ $\{\frac{1}{5}, \frac{^-31}{5}\}$

3–3 MORE QUADRATIC EQUATIONS

An example of the use of quadratic equations is given in the following problem.

Problem. The flower garden shown in Fig. 3–1 is surrounded by a walk of uniform width. If the area of the walk is 1264 square feet, what is the width of the walk?

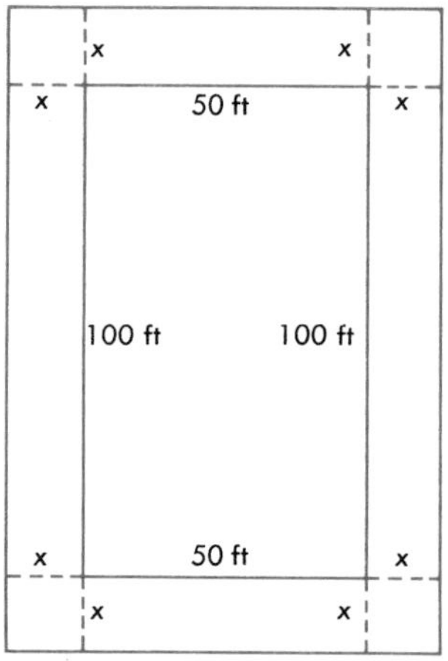

FIGURE 3–1

Solution. Let x designate the width of the walk in feet. Therefore, x must be a positive number. We may consider the walk to be composed of four rectangular pieces along the edge of the flower garden and four squares at the corners, as shown in the figure. The areas of the four rectangles along the edge are $100x$, $100x$, $50x$, and $50x$; each corner square has area x^2. Thus,

$$300x + 4x^2$$

must be the area of the walk. By what is given,

$$300x + 4x^2 = 1264.$$

We have now reduced the problem to that of finding the positive solutions of the quadratic equation above. Each of the following quadratic equations is equivalent to the preceding one.

$$75x + x^2 = 316$$
$$x^2 + 75x - 316 = 0$$
$$(x + 79)(x - 4) = 0$$

Hence, $\{^-79, 4\}$ is the solution set of the quadratic equation, and $\{4\}$ is the solution set of the problem, that is, the walk is 4 feet wide.

We may check this answer by noting that if the walk is 4 feet wide, then the flower garden, together with the walk, has dimensions 58 feet by 108 feet and area

$$58 \times 108, \quad \text{or } 6264 \text{ square feet.}$$

The area of the flower garden is 5000 square feet. Therefore, the area of the walk is

$$6264 - 5000, \quad \text{or } 1264 \text{ square feet,}$$

as given.

Exercises for Discussion

1. An apartment building 200 feet by 300 feet is built on a lot containing 81,600 square feet. If a parking strip of uniform width surrounds the building, how wide is this strip?
2. A fringed rug covering three-fifths of a floor that measures 24 feet by 30 feet is placed so that a border of uniform width surrounds the rug. What are the dimensions of the rug?
3. Find the dimensions of a rectangle which has an area that is 216 square inches and a length that is 6 inches more than its width.
4. The sum of the squares of two consecutive odd integers is 650. Find all such pairs of numbers.
5. Find three positive consecutive integers which have 509 as the sum of their squares.

The width of the parking lot must be positive. Hence, the strip is 20 feet wide.

2. Let x be the width of the border. Then the rug will be $24 - 2x$ by $30 - 2x$. Hence,

$$(24 - 2x)(30 - 2x) = \tfrac{3}{5}(24 \cdot 30).$$

Solving the equation, we obtain $x = 24$, or $x = 3$. Since the border cannot possibly be 24 feet, it must be 3 feet wide. Then the rug will be 18 by 24 feet.

3. Let w be the width. Then $w + 6$ is the length. The area is

$$w(w + 6);$$

hence, $w(w + 6) = 216$. We obtain the equivalent equations

$$w^2 + 6w - 216 = 0,$$
$$(w + 18)(w - 12) = 0.$$

If the first factor is zero, the width is a negative number of inches. If the second factor is zero, the width is 12 and the length 18 inches.

4. Let $2x - 1$ be the smaller integer. Then $2x + 1$ will be the larger. The sum of the squares is $(2x - 1)^2 + (2x + 1)^2$; hence,

$$(2x - 1)^2 + (2x + 1)^2 = 650.$$

Solving the equation, we obtain $(x - 9)(x + 9) = 0$. If the first factor is zero, the numbers are 17 and 19. If the second factor is zero, the numbers are $^-19$ and $^-17$. Both pairs satisfy the conditions of the exercise.

5. Let x be the smallest integer. Then $x + 1$ and $x + 2$ are the other two integers. Thus,

$$x^2 + (x + 1)^2 + (x + 2)^2 = 509.$$

We find the equivalent equation

$$(x + 14)(x - 12) = 0.$$

If the first factor were zero, x would be negative. If the second factor is zero, $x = 12$, $x + 1 = 13$, and $x + 2 = 14$.

Quiz

1. Find two consecutive odd integers whose product is 195. (ans: 13, 15 or $^-13$, $^-15$)
2. The sum of the square of a number and twice the number is 35. How many such numbers are there, and what are they? (ans: Two; $^-7$ or 5)
3. Find the dimensions of a rectangle if its area is 84 square inches and its width is 5 inches less than its length. (ans: 7 inches by 12 inches)

3–4 COMPLETING THE SQUARE

This section covers the important process of completing the square, which will be used to derive the quadratic formula in Chapter 4, to translate axes in Section 3–7 of this chapter and again in Chapter 5, and in later courses in mathematics such as integral calculus. This process should be emphasized in order to be sure that all students master it. All the exercises should be done, either in class or as homework.

Exercises

1. Find two numbers which differ by 4 and whose product is 96. Can you find a second set of two numbers which satisfy these conditions? 12, 8 and $^-8$, $^-12$
2. Find a pair of numbers such that their sum is 23 and the sum of their squares is 289. 8, 15 Is there more than one such pair? No
3. Find the dimensions of a rectangle if its area is 112 square inches and its length is 6 inches more than its width. 8 in. by 14 in.
4. Find two consecutive even integers whose product is 224. Find another such pair. 14, 16 and $^-14$, $^-16$
5. Find three consecutive positive integers which have 110 as the sum of their squares. 5, 6, 7
6. The sum of two positive numbers is 10. Given that one number is 2 less than the square of the other, find both numbers. 7, 3
7. What are the dimensions of a rectangle which has a perimeter of 30 inches and an area of 54 square inches? 6 in. by 9 in.

---

8. Find the lengths of the three sides of a right triangle if the hypotenuse is 1 foot longer than the longer leg and 3 feet less than 4 times as long as the shorter leg. 7 ft, 24 ft, 25 ft
9. Find the set of numbers each of which is 30 less than its own square. {6, $^-5$}
10. What two consecutive integers have cubes that differ by 217? How many such pairs are there? $^-8$, $^-9$, and 8, 9

3–4 COMPLETING THE SQUARE

Some quadratic polynomials are squares of linear forms. For example,

$$x^2 = (x)^2,$$

$$x^2 + 100x + 2500 = (x + 50)^2,$$

$$49x^2 - 70x + 25 = (7x - 5)^2,$$

are squares of linear forms. If a quadratic polynomial is the square of a linear form, it is called a *perfect square*. Some quadratic equations are easily solved because they involve perfect squares. Consider the following example.

Problem 1. Solve the quadratic equation $4x^2 - 7 = 0$.

Solution. The given equation is equivalent to the equations

$$4x^2 = 7$$

and

$$x^2 = \tfrac{7}{4}.$$

The quadratic polynomial on the left side of this equation is a perfect square; the right side is a positive number. Evidently the only values of x that make this equation true are the square roots of $\frac{7}{4}$. Since each positive number has exactly two square roots, we have

$$x^2 = \tfrac{7}{4} \text{ if, and only if, } x = \sqrt{\tfrac{7}{4}} \text{ or } x = {}^{-}\sqrt{\tfrac{7}{4}}.$$

Hence, the solution set of the given equation is

$$\{\tfrac{1}{2}\sqrt{7}, {}^{-}\tfrac{1}{2}\sqrt{7}\}.$$

A given quadratic polynomial is a perfect square if, and only if, it has the pattern

$$x^2 + 2mx + m^2, \text{ or } (x + m)^2.$$

Thus,

$$x^2 + 14x + 49$$

is a perfect square because $49 = (\frac{1}{2} \cdot 14)^2$, where $49 = m^2$ and $14 = 2m$. However,

$$x^2 + 10x + 20$$

is not a perfect square since $(\frac{1}{2} \cdot 10)^2$ is equal to 25, not 20.

If a quadratic polynomial has 1 as the coefficient of the square of the variable and zero as the constant term, then it is always possible to add a constant term to make the resulting quadratic polynomial a perfect square. For example, given the quadratic polynomial

$$x^2 + 18x,$$

we can add the square of half of the coefficient of x to it to make a perfect square:

$$x^2 + 18x + 9^2 = (x + 9)^2.$$

Before confronting the student with

$$x^2 + 2mx + m^2 = (x + m)^2,$$

you might have him consider several examples of trinomial squares, such as

$$x^2 + 6x + 9,$$
$$x^2 + 12x + 36,$$
$$x^2 - 10x + 25,$$
$$x^2 - 20x + 100,$$

and describe how the constant is related to the coefficient of x. Thus,

$$9 = (\tfrac{1}{2} \cdot 6)^2,$$
$$36 = (\tfrac{1}{2} \cdot 12)^2,$$
$$25 = (\tfrac{1}{2} \cdot 10)^2,$$
$$100 = (\tfrac{1}{2} \cdot 20)^2.$$

In general,

$$(x + a)^2 = x^2 + 2a\ \ x + a^2,$$

and the constant a^2 is the square of one-half the coefficient of x since $(\frac{1}{2} \cdot 2a)^2 = a^2$.

The student should do numerous examples containing fractions, such as

$$y^2 - \tfrac{1}{2}y + \tfrac{1}{16} \quad \text{where } \tfrac{1}{16} = (\tfrac{1}{2} \cdot \tfrac{1}{2})^2,$$
$$y^2 + \tfrac{2}{3}y + \tfrac{1}{9} \quad \text{where } \tfrac{1}{9} = (\tfrac{1}{2} \cdot \tfrac{2}{3})^2,$$
$$y^2 + 5y + \tfrac{25}{4} \quad \text{where } \tfrac{25}{4} = (\tfrac{1}{2} \cdot 5)^2.$$

Exercises for Discussion, page 137

If time is limited it is suggested that at least Exercises for Discussion 2, 3, 5, 6, and 9 be done.

In Exercise for Discussion 8(a), show that the sum of the solutions is ${}^{-}7$, and the product is 5.

The solutions in Exercise for Discussion 9 may be checked by finding the sum and the product and comparing them with the coefficients in the given equation.

Answers to Exercises for Discussion 6–9, page 137

6. Since

$$x^2 + 40x + 400 = (x + 20)^2,$$

and

$$x^2 - 40x + 400 = (x - 20)^2,$$

$$k = 40 \quad \text{or} \quad k = {}^{-}40.$$

7. Since

$$x^2 + 28x + 196 = (x + 14)^2,$$

and

$$x^2 - 28x + 196 = (x - 14)^2,$$

$$k = {}^{-}28 \quad \text{or} \quad k = 28.$$

8. (a)
$$\begin{aligned} x^2 + 7x + 5 &= 0 \\ x^2 + 7x + \tfrac{49}{4} &= {}^{-}5 + \tfrac{49}{4} \\ (x + \tfrac{7}{2})^2 &= \tfrac{29}{4} \\ x + \tfrac{7}{2} &= \sqrt{\tfrac{29}{4}}, \\ \text{or} \quad x + \tfrac{7}{2} &= {}^{-}\sqrt{\tfrac{29}{4}} \\ x &= {}^{-}\tfrac{7}{2} + \tfrac{1}{2}\sqrt{29}, \\ \text{or} \quad x &= {}^{-}\tfrac{7}{2} - \tfrac{1}{2}\sqrt{29} \end{aligned}$$

The solution set is

$$\{\tfrac{1}{2}({}^{-}7 + \sqrt{29}), \tfrac{1}{2}({}^{-}7 - \sqrt{29})\}.$$

A second example is

$$y^2 - 11y$$

which can be made into a perfect square by adding $({}^{-}\frac{11}{2})^2$, or $\frac{121}{4}$, to it:

$$y^2 - 11y + \tfrac{121}{4} = (y - \tfrac{11}{2})^2.$$

The process of adding a constant term to a quadratic polynomial to make it a perfect square is called *completing the square.* This procedure enables us to solve quadratic equations with irrational solutions, as we shall now show.

Problem 2. Solve the quadratic equation $3x^2 + 4x - 8 = 0$.

Solution. The following two equations are equivalent to the given one.

$$3x^2 + 4x = 8$$
$$x^2 + \tfrac{4}{3}x = \tfrac{8}{3}$$

The quadratic polynomial $x^2 + \frac{4}{3}x$ may be made into a perfect square by adding the constant term $(\frac{1}{2} \cdot \frac{4}{3})^2$, or $(\frac{2}{3})^2$. If we add this number to each side of the last equation above, we get the equivalent equation

$$x^2 + \tfrac{4}{3}x + \tfrac{4}{9} = \tfrac{8}{3} + \tfrac{4}{9},$$

or

$$(x + \tfrac{2}{3})^2 = \tfrac{28}{9}.$$

Again,

$$(x + \tfrac{2}{3})^2 = \tfrac{28}{9}$$

if, and only if,

$$x + \tfrac{2}{3} = \sqrt{\tfrac{28}{9}} \quad \text{or} \quad x + \tfrac{2}{3} = {}^{-}\sqrt{\tfrac{28}{9}},$$

$$x = {}^{-}\tfrac{2}{3} + \tfrac{2}{3}\sqrt{7} \quad \text{or} \quad x = {}^{-}\tfrac{2}{3} - \tfrac{2}{3}\sqrt{7}.$$

Thus,

$$\{{}^{-}\tfrac{2}{3} + \tfrac{2}{3}\sqrt{7}, {}^{-}\tfrac{2}{3} - \tfrac{2}{3}\sqrt{7}\}$$

is the solution set of the given equation. Using 2.646 as an approximation of $\sqrt{7}$, we find that the solutions are approximately 1.097 and ${}^{-}2.431$.

The method illustrated in Problem 2 is called *solving a quadratic equation by completing the square.* Every quadratic equation can be solved by this method.

Exercises for Discussion

Fill in the blanks to make each statement true.

1. $x^2 + 2 \cdot 5x + \underline{25} = (x + \underline{5})^2$
2. $x^2 - 2 \cdot 7x + \underline{49} = (x - \underline{7})^2$
3. $x^2 + 16x + \underline{64} = (x + \underline{8})^2$

In Exercises 4–7, give the value or values of k that will make each quadratic polynomial a perfect square.

4. $x^2 + 18x + k$ Since $x^2 + 18x + 81 = (x+9)^2$, $k = 81$.
5. $x^2 - 18x + k$ Since $x^2 - 18x + 81 = (x-9)^2$, $k = 81$.
6. $x^2 + kx + 400$
7. $x^2 - kx + 196$
8. (a) Use the method of completing the square to solve the quadratic equation $x^2 + 7x + 5 = 0$.
   (b) Check the larger of the two solutions in part (a).
   (c) Use the Table of Square Roots in the Appendix to find a three-decimal-place approximation of each irrational solution.
9. Use the method of completing the square to solve each of the following quadratic equations.
   (a) $x^2 - 4x = 3$ (b) $x^2 + 3 = 6x$ (c) $4x^2 + 12x + 5 = 0$

Exercises

Fill in the blanks to make each statement true.

1. $x^2 - 30x + \underline{225} = (x - \underline{15})^2$
2. $x^2 - 3x + \underline{\tfrac{9}{4}} = (x - \underline{\tfrac{3}{2}})^2$
3. $x^2 + 7x + \underline{\tfrac{49}{4}} = (x + \underline{\tfrac{7}{2}})^2$

Give the value or values of k that will make each quadratic polynomial a perfect square.

4. $x^2 + 9x + k$ $\frac{81}{4}$
5. $x^2 + kx + \frac{25}{81}$ $\frac{10}{9}$ or $\frac{-10}{9}$
6. $x^2 - 13x + k$ $\frac{169}{4}$
7. $x^2 - kx + \frac{49}{36}$ $\frac{7}{3}$ or $\frac{-7}{3}$

Use the method of completing the square to solve each of the following quadratic equations.

8. $y^2 + 4y - 2 = 0$ $\{-2+\sqrt{6}, -2-\sqrt{6}\}$
9. $z^2 - 6z - 16 = 0$ $\{8, -2\}$
10. $t^2 + 5t + 1 = 0$ $\left\{\frac{-5+\sqrt{21}}{2}, \frac{-5-\sqrt{21}}{2}\right\}$
11. $v^2 - 15v - 15 = 1$ $\{16, -1\}$

(b) $[\frac{1}{2}(^-7 + \sqrt{29})]^2 + 7[\frac{1}{2}(^-7 + \sqrt{29})] + 5 \stackrel{?}{=} 0$
$\frac{1}{4}(49 - 14\sqrt{29} + 29) + \frac{1}{2}(^-49 + 7\sqrt{29}) + 5 \stackrel{?}{=} 0$
$\frac{78}{4} - \frac{7}{2}\sqrt{29} - \frac{49}{2} + \frac{7}{2}\sqrt{29} + 5 \stackrel{?}{=} 0$
$\frac{78 - 98 + 20}{4} \stackrel{\checkmark}{=} 0$

(c) $\frac{1}{2}(^-7 + \sqrt{29}) \doteq \frac{1}{2}(^-7 + 5.385) \doteq {}^-.808$
$\frac{1}{2}(^-7 - \sqrt{29}) \doteq \frac{1}{2}(^-7 - 5.385) \doteq {}^-6.193$

9. (a)
$x^2 - 4x = 3$
$x^2 - 4x + 4 = 3 + 4$
$(x - 2)^2 = 7$
$x - 2 = \sqrt{7}$ or $x - 2 = {}^-\sqrt{7}$
$x = 2 + \sqrt{7}$ or $x = 2 - \sqrt{7}$
$\{2 + \sqrt{7}, 2 - \sqrt{7}\}$

(b)
$x^2 + 3 = 6x$
$x^2 - 6x = {}^-3$
$x^2 - 6x + 9 = {}^-3 + 9$
$(x - 3)^2 = 6$
$x - 3 = \sqrt{6}$ or $x - 3 = {}^-\sqrt{6}$
$x = 3 + \sqrt{6}$ or $x = 3 - \sqrt{6}$
$\{3 + \sqrt{6}, 3 - \sqrt{6}\}$

(c)
$4x^2 + 12x + 5 = 0$
$4x^2 + 12x = {}^-5$
$x^2 + 3x = {}^-\frac{5}{4}$
$x^2 + 3x + \frac{9}{4} = {}^-\frac{5}{4} + \frac{9}{4}$
$(x + \frac{3}{2})^2 = 1$
$x + \frac{3}{2} = 1$ or $x + \frac{3}{2} = {}^-1$
$x = {}^-\frac{1}{2}$ or $x = {}^-\frac{5}{2}$
$\{{}^-\frac{1}{2}, {}^-\frac{5}{2}\}$

Exercises 20 and 21 should be covered in class, and it should be emphasized that the answers are usable as formulas on any quadratic in x that matches the pattern used to get the formula. For example, you could have the students solve $x^2 + 8x + 3 = 0$ by the method of completing the square; then have them use the formula of Exercise 20, letting $2p = 8$, $q = 3$; and then have them use the formula of Exercise 21, letting ${}^-r = 8$, ${}^-s = 3$. The solutions should be the same all three times.

Quiz

Fill in the blanks to make each statement true.

1. $x^2 - 28x + \_?\_ = (x - \_?\_)^2$
   (ans: 196, 14)
2. $x^2 - \frac{3}{2}x + \_?\_ = (x - \_?\_)^2$
   (ans: $\frac{9}{16}$, $\frac{3}{4}$)
3. $x^2 - \_?\_\, x + \frac{9}{4} = (x - \_?\_)^2$
   (ans: $\frac{9}{2}$, $\frac{3}{2}$)

Use the method of completing the square to solve each of the following quadratic equations.

4. $y^2 + 6y + 6 = 0$
   (ans: $\{{}^-3 + \sqrt{3}, {}^-3 - \sqrt{3}\}$)
5. $m^2 - 2m + \frac{1}{2} = 0$
   (ans: $\{1 + \frac{\sqrt{2}}{2}, 1 - \frac{\sqrt{2}}{2}\}$)

3-5 MORE ON COMPLETING THE SQUARE

In a minimum course, it is suggested that Problem 1 be omitted. However, Problem 2 on the next page should be included.

Use the method of completing the square to solve each of the following quadratic equations.

12. $10x - 19 = x^2$ $\{5+\sqrt{6}, 5-\sqrt{6}\}$
13. $2y^2 + 2y - 1 = 0$ $\{\frac{{}^-1+\sqrt{3}}{2}, \frac{{}^-1-\sqrt{3}}{2}\}$
14. $6t - 1 = 2t^2$ $\{\frac{3+\sqrt{7}}{2}, \frac{3-\sqrt{7}}{2}\}$
15. $3x^2 + 5x - 1 = 0$ $\{\frac{{}^-5+\sqrt{37}}{6}, \frac{{}^-5-\sqrt{37}}{6}\}$
16. $5x^2 - 3x - 4 = 3$ $\{\frac{3+\sqrt{149}}{10}, \frac{3-\sqrt{149}}{10}\}$
17. $9x^2 + 42x + 5 = 1$ $\{\frac{{}^-7+3\sqrt{5}}{3}, \frac{{}^-7-3\sqrt{5}}{3}\}$
18. $2x^2 - 7x + 4 = 0$ $\{\frac{7+\sqrt{17}}{4}, \frac{7-\sqrt{17}}{4}\}$
19. $4x^2 + 3x = 5$ $\{\frac{{}^-3+\sqrt{89}}{8}, \frac{{}^-3-\sqrt{89}}{8}\}$

▲

Use the method of completing the square to solve each of the following equations for x.

20. $x^2 + 2px + q = 0$ when $p^2 - q > 0$ $\{{}^-p+\sqrt{p^2-q}, {}^-p-\sqrt{p^2-q}\}$
21. $x^2 - rx - s = 0$ when $r^2 + 4s > 0$ $\{\frac{1}{2}(r+\sqrt{r^2+4s}), \frac{1}{2}(r-\sqrt{r^2+4s})\}$

3-5 MORE ON COMPLETING THE SQUARE

In the following problems, we shall give some more examples of quadratic equations which are solved by completing the square.

Problem 1. Solve the quadratic equation $x^2 - 2\sqrt{3}x + 1 = 0$.

Solution. We proceed in the following manner.

$$x^2 - 2\sqrt{3}x + 1 = 0$$
$$x^2 - 2\sqrt{3}x = {}^-1$$
$$x^2 - 2\sqrt{3}x + \left(\frac{{}^-2\sqrt{3}}{2}\right)^2 = {}^-1 + \left(\frac{{}^-2\sqrt{3}}{2}\right)^2$$
$$(x - \sqrt{3})^2 = {}^-1 + 3$$
$$(x - \sqrt{3})^2 = (\sqrt{2})^2$$
$$x - \sqrt{3} = \sqrt{2} \quad \text{or} \quad x - \sqrt{3} = {}^-\sqrt{2}$$
$$x = \sqrt{3} + \sqrt{2} \quad \text{or} \quad x = \sqrt{3} - \sqrt{2}$$

Hence, the solution set is

$$\{\sqrt{3} + \sqrt{2}, \sqrt{3} - \sqrt{2}\}.$$

Check. We shall check one answer and let you check the other.

$$(\sqrt{3} + \sqrt{2})^2 - 2\sqrt{3}(\sqrt{3} + \sqrt{2}) + 1 \stackrel{?}{=} 0$$
$$3 + (2\sqrt{3} \cdot \sqrt{2}) + 2 - [(2 \cdot 3) + (2\sqrt{3} \cdot \sqrt{2})] + 1 \stackrel{?}{=} 0$$
$$5 + 2\sqrt{6} - 6 - 2\sqrt{6} + 1 \stackrel{\checkmark}{=} 0$$

Although every quadratic equation can be solved by completing the square, not every quadratic equation has a real solution. The following equation is an example.

Problem 2. Solve the quadratic equation $x^2 - 4x + 5 = 0$.

Solution. We proceed to solve this equation by completing the square:

$$x^2 - 4x = {}^-5,$$
$$x^2 - 4x + 4 = {}^-5 + 4,$$
$$(x - 2)^2 = {}^-1.$$

Because the square of a real number is non-negative, we know that there is no real-number value of x which will make the equation $(x - 2)^2 = {}^-1$ true. Thus, the equation has no real solution. Since the given equation is equivalent to $(x - 2)^2 = {}^-1$, it also has no real solution. In other words, the solution set of the given equation is the empty set, $\emptyset$.

In the next chapter, we shall see that it is possible to enlarge our number system so that every quadratic equation has a solution in the larger system. However, as long as we restrict ourselves to the real number system, we shall find that some quadratic equations have empty solution sets.

Problem 3. Is it possible to construct a rectangle with a perimeter of 36 inches and an area of 36 square inches? If so, what are its dimensions?

Solution. Some possible rectangles having areas of 36 square inches are

6 inches × 6 inches, 9 inches × 4 inches, 12 inches × 3 inches, 18 inches × 2 inches, 36 inches × 1 inch.

Their respective perimeters are 24, 26, 30, 40, and 74 inches. It seems plausible that there is some rectangle with a length between 12 inches and 18 inches and a perimeter of 36 inches.

If the desired rectangle is x inches wide, then its length is $18 - x$ inches, as shown in Fig. 3–2. We are told that the area is 36 square inches, so that

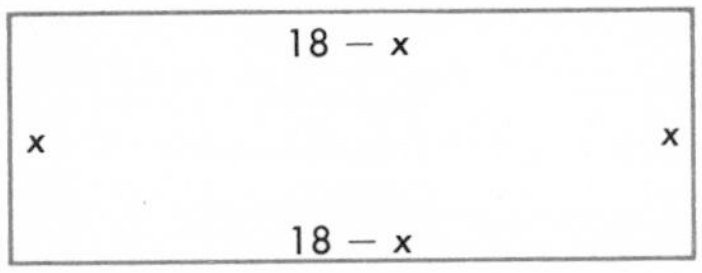

FIGURE 3–2

$$x(18 - x) = 36.$$

There does exist a rectangle with a perimeter of 36 inches and an area of 36 square inches if the equation above has a solution.

Exercises for Discussion, page 140

If time is limited, it is suggested that at least Exercises for Discussion 2 and 4–7 be covered.

Answers to Exercises for Discussion 1, 2(b), 3, 5, 8(b)

1. (a)
$$x^2 - 2\sqrt{5}x + 3 = 0$$
$$x^2 - 2\sqrt{5}x = {}^-3$$
$$x^2 - 2\sqrt{5}x + 5 = {}^-3 + 5$$
$$(x - \sqrt{5})^2 = 2$$
$$x - \sqrt{5} = \sqrt{2}$$
or
$$x - \sqrt{5} = {}^-\sqrt{2}$$
$$x = \sqrt{5} + \sqrt{2}$$
or
$$x = \sqrt{5} - \sqrt{2}$$
$$\{\sqrt{5} + \sqrt{2}, \sqrt{5} - \sqrt{2}\}$$

Check:

$$(\sqrt{5} + \sqrt{2})^2$$
$$-2\sqrt{5}(\sqrt{5} + \sqrt{2}) + 3 \stackrel{?}{=} 0$$
$$5 + 2\sqrt{10} + 2 - 10$$
$$-2\sqrt{10} + 3 \stackrel{?}{=} 0$$
$$10 - 10 \stackrel{\checkmark}{=} 0$$
$$(\sqrt{5} - \sqrt{2})^2$$
$$-2\sqrt{5}(\sqrt{5} - \sqrt{2}) + 3 \stackrel{?}{=} 0$$
$$5 - 2\sqrt{10} + 2 - 10$$
$$+2\sqrt{10} + 3 \stackrel{?}{=} 0$$
$$10 - 10 \stackrel{\checkmark}{=} 0$$

(b) The sum is

$$(\sqrt{5} + \sqrt{2})$$
$$+(\sqrt{5} - \sqrt{2}) = 2\sqrt{5},$$

which is the negative of the coefficient of x.

(c) The product is

$$(\sqrt{5} + \sqrt{2})(\sqrt{5} - \sqrt{2})$$
$$= 5 - 2 = 3,$$

which is the constant term.

2. (b)
$$x^2 - 6x + 10 = 0$$
$$x^2 - 6x = {}^-10$$
$$x^2 - 6x + 9 = {}^-10 + 9$$
$$(x - 3)^2 = {}^-1$$

Since no real number has a negative square, the solution set is $\emptyset$.

3.
$$x^2 - 6x + k = 0$$
$$x^2 - 6x = {}^-k$$
$$x^2 - 6x + 9 = {}^-k + 9$$
$$(x - 3)^2 = 9 - k$$

This will have real number solutions if $9 - k \geq 0$, or $9 \geq k$. Hence, 9 is the largest value of k.

This equation is equivalent to each of the following equations:

$$18x - x^2 = 36,$$
$$x^2 - 18x = {}^-36,$$
$$x^2 - 18x + ({}^-9)^2 = {}^-36 + ({}^-9)^2,$$
$$(x - 9)^2 = {}^-36 + 81,$$
$$(x - 9)^2 = 45.$$

Thus,

$$x - 9 = \sqrt{45} \quad \text{or} \quad x - 9 = {}^-\sqrt{45},$$

or, equivalently,

$$x = 9 + 3\sqrt{5} \quad \text{or} \quad x = 9 - 3\sqrt{5}.$$

Which of these two numbers is a solution of the given problem? If $x = 9 + 3\sqrt{5}$, then

$$18 - x = 18 - (9 + 3\sqrt{5}) = 9 - 3\sqrt{5}.$$

Hence, the two solutions of the quadratic equation are the two dimensions of the desired rectangle. Since $\sqrt{5} \doteq 2.236$ ($\doteq$ means *is approximately equal to*), $9 + 3\sqrt{5} \doteq 15.71$ and $9 - 3\sqrt{5} \doteq 2.29$. Thus, the desired rectangle is approximately 15.71 by 2.29 inches.

Exercises for Discussion

1. (a) Use the method of completing the square to solve the given equation. Then check your answer.

$$x^2 - 2\sqrt{5}\,x + 3 = 0$$

(b) Find the sum of the solutions found in part (a). Compare this sum with the coefficient of x in the quadratic equation.

(c) Find the product of the solutions found in part (a). Compare this product with the constant term in the quadratic equation.

2. Find the solution set of each of the following quadratic equations.

(a) $x^2 - 6x + 7 = 0$ $\{3+\sqrt{2}, 3-\sqrt{2}\}$ (b) $x^2 - 6x + 10 = 0$

3. What is the largest value of k that will give the quadratic equation

$$x^2 - 6x + k = 0$$

real-number solutions?

In Exercises 4–7, find the solution set of each of the quadratic equations.

4. $(x - 3)^2 = {}^-4.$ $\emptyset$

5. $x^2 - 20x = {}^-200$

6. $x^2 + x + 1 = 0$ $\emptyset$

7. $4y^2 + 4y + 5 = 0$ $\emptyset$

8. A rectangular field adjacent to a river is to be fenced in on only three sides, because the side on the river requires no fencing. A total of 100 rods of fencing are available.
   (a) Use x to denote the length of fence on each of the two sides at right angles to the river, and obtain a formula which gives the enclosed area A in terms of x. $A = x(100-2x)$
   (b) If the enclosed area is to be 1200 square rods, what are the possible dimensions of the fence?

Exercises

Solve each of the following quadratic equations. Check each solution by substitution. Compare the sum of the solutions with the coefficient of x. Compare the product of the solutions with the constant term.

1. $x^2 - 2\sqrt{6}x + 2 = 0$
2. $x^2 - 2\sqrt{6}x - 2 = 0$
3. $x^2 - \sqrt{5}x + 1 = 0$
4. $x^2 - \sqrt{5}x - 1 = 0$
5. $x^2 + \sqrt{2}x - 4 = 0$
6. $x^2 - 2\sqrt{7}x + 4 = 0$

△

In Exercises 7–14, some of the quadratic equations have real solutions and some do not. Find solutions for the equations that have them. Use the method of completing the square to show that there are no real solutions for the remaining equations.

7. $u^2 + 10u - 39 = 0$ $\{3, -13\}$
8. $3x^2 - 7x + 3 = 0$ $\left\{\frac{7+\sqrt{13}}{6}, \frac{7-\sqrt{13}}{6}\right\}$
9. $x^2 - 4x + 8 = 0$ No real solutions
10. $2t - 4 = t^2$ No real solutions
11. $2t^2 - 5t + 2 = 0$ $\{2, \frac{1}{2}\}$
12. $3x^2 + 9x + 3 = 0$ $\{\frac{1}{2}(-3+\sqrt{5}), \frac{1}{2}(-3-\sqrt{5})\}$
13. $3x^2 + 12 = 0$ No real solutions
14. $2z^2 + 16z + 7 = 0$ $\{\frac{1}{2}(-8+5\sqrt{2}), \frac{1}{2}(-8-5\sqrt{2})\}$
15. When a border of uniform width is added to a rectangular lot having dimensions 30 yards by 20 yards, the total area is double that of the original lot. Find the width of the border. 5 yd
16. The sum of two numbers is 4 and the sum of their squares is 18. Find all possible pairs of numbers which satisfy this condition. $2+\sqrt{5}$ and $2-\sqrt{5}$
17. The length of a side of a square is 4 inches shorter than its diagonal. Find all squares having this property. The length of the side of the square is $4(1+\sqrt{2})$ in.
18. If a ball is thrown from the ground upward at a speed of 100 feet per second, the height it reaches t seconds after it is thrown is given by the formula

$$h = -16t^2 + 100t.$$

   (a) How long does the ball take to rise to a height of 100 feet? $1\frac{1}{4}$ sec
   (b) Do both solutions of the quadratic equation in part (a) make sense? Yes
   (c) When does the ball return to the ground? $6\frac{1}{4}$ sec after being thrown

5.
$$\begin{aligned} x^2 - 20x &= -200 \\ x^2 - 20x + 100 &= -200 + 100 \\ (x-10)^2 &= -100 \end{aligned}$$

The solution set is the empty set, $\emptyset$.

8. (b)
$$\begin{aligned} x(100-2x) &= 1200 \\ 100x - 2x^2 &= 1200 \\ 2x^2 - 100x + 1200 &= 0 \\ x^2 - 50x + 600 &= 0 \\ (x-20)(x-30) &= 0 \\ x - 20 &= 0 \\ \text{or} \quad x - 30 &= 0 \\ x &= 20 \\ \text{or} \quad x &= 30 \end{aligned}$$

The fencing can be used in the following ways: 20 rods, 60 rods, 20 rods ($x = 20$); 30 rods, 40 rods, 30 rods ($x = 30$).

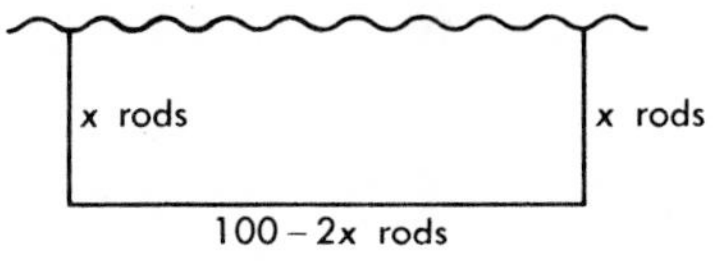

Exercises

In a minimum course it is suggested that you omit Exercises 1–6, but be sure to include some of Exercises 7–14.

Answers to Exercises 1–6

1. $\{\sqrt{6}+2, \sqrt{6}-2\}$; sum: $2\sqrt{6}$; product: 2
2. $\{\sqrt{6}+2\sqrt{2}, \sqrt{6}-2\sqrt{2}\}$; sum: $2\sqrt{6}$; product: -2
3. $\{\frac{1}{2}(\sqrt{5}+1), \frac{1}{2}(\sqrt{5}-1)\}$; sum: $\sqrt{5}$; product: 1
4. $\{\frac{1}{2}(\sqrt{5}+3), \frac{1}{2}(\sqrt{5}-3)\}$; sum: $\sqrt{5}$; product: -1
5. $\{\sqrt{2}, -2\sqrt{2}\}$; sum: $-\sqrt{2}$; product: -4
6. $\{\sqrt{7}+\sqrt{3}, \sqrt{7}-\sqrt{3}\}$; sum: $2\sqrt{7}$; product: 4

Answer to Exercise 20(b)

20. (b) 20 rods by 120 rods, the divider parallel to the shorter sides; or 30 rods by 80 rods, the divider parallel to the longer sides

Quiz

Solve the following quadratic equations.

1. $x^2 + 12x - 28 = 0$ (ans: $\{2, {}^{-}14\}$)
2. $x^2 - 6x - 3 = 0$ (ans: $\{3 \pm 2\sqrt{3}\}$)
3. $x^2 - 2\sqrt{2}x - 3 = 0$ (ans: $\{\sqrt{2} \pm \sqrt{5}\}$)
4. $x^2 - 10x + 28 = 0$ (ans: $\emptyset$)

3-6 QUADRATIC EQUATIONS OF THE FORM $y = ax^2 + c$

If $y = x^2$, then the arithmetic of signed numbers assures us that y is never negative. What is the smallest non-negative number? Since this is zero, the minimum value that y assumes is zero. How can y achieve a positive value, say 9? This can be done in two ways, by squaring ${}^{+}3$ or by squaring ${}^{-}3$. The x's that produce a value of 9 for y are opposites. Therefore, the graph of $y = x^2$ crosses the line $y = 9$ at two points, $({}^{-}3, 9)$ and $({}^{+}3, 9)$. In general, $y = x^2$ will cross the line $y = k$, $k > 0$, in two points, $({}^{-}\sqrt{k}, k)$ and $(\sqrt{k}, k)$, which are located at equal distances from the y-axis, one on the left, the other on the right.

If $y = {}^{-}x^2$, y is the negative of the square of a real number. Since the negative of a non-negative number is nonpositive, y is never positive. The maximum value that y assumes is therefore zero. The graph of $y = {}^{-}x^2$ crosses every line $y = k$, $k < 0$, at two points, $({}^{-}\sqrt{{}^{-}k}, k)$ and $(\sqrt{{}^{-}k}, k)$. Again there is symmetry about the y-axis.

19. A piece of wire 40 inches long was cut into two pieces. Each piece was then bent to form a square frame. If the sum of the areas enclosed by the two wire frames is 58 square inches, how was the wire cut? *One piece 12 in. long and one piece 18 in. long*

20. With a total of 300 rods of fencing, a rectangular field is to be completely surrounded with a fence and the enclosed area then divided in half by a fence parallel to one of the sides.

(a) Obtain a formula for the total enclosed area A in terms of one variable. *$A = \frac{1}{2}x(300 - 3x)$ or $A = \frac{1}{3}y(300 - 2y)$*

(b) Describe how the fencing can be used to make the total enclosed area 2400 square rods. Is there more than one way of doing this?

21. The length of a rectangle is 3 times its width. If the width is diminished by 1 foot and the length increased by 3 feet, the area will be 72 square feet. Find the dimensions of the original rectangle. *5 ft by 15 ft*

3-6 QUADRATIC EQUATIONS OF THE FORM $y = ax^2 + c$

If a ball is dropped from a helicopter 400 feet above the ground, then h, the height, in feet, of the ball above the ground t seconds after it is released is given by the equation

$$h = {}^{-}16t^2 + 400.$$

This equation is correct in theory only, since it neglects the friction of the ball in air. According to this formula,

$$h = 384 \text{ when } t = 1;$$
$$h = {}^{-}64 + 400, \text{ or } 336, \text{ when } t = 2;$$
$$h = {}^{-}144 + 400, \text{ or } 256, \text{ when } t = 3;$$
$$h = ({}^{-}16 \cdot 25) + 400, \text{ or } 0, \text{ when } t = 5.$$

Thus, it takes 5 seconds for the ball to reach the ground.

The equation $h = {}^{-}16t^2 + 400$ is an example of a quadratic equation in two variables, h and t. In this section, we shall study quadratic equations in two variables of the form

$$y = ax^2 + c, \qquad a \neq 0.$$

In particular, we shall study the graphs of equations of this form.

The simplest equation of this form is the one with $a = 1$ and $c = 0$:

$$y = x^2.$$

The graph of this equation is the graph of its solution set

$$S = \{(x, y) \mid y = x^2\},$$

or, equivalently,

$$S = \{(x, x^2) \mid x \text{ a real number}\}.$$

Several points on the graph of S are plotted in Fig. 3–3. The graph of S is a smooth curve, partially sketched in the figure. This curve is called a *parabola.* Some of the characteristics of this parabola are listed below.

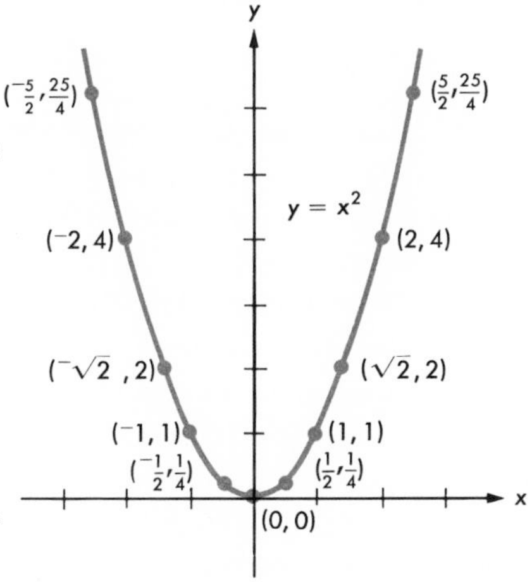

FIGURE 3–3

Symmetry. The points on the graph come in pairs:

$$(1, 1) \text{ and } (^-1, 1),$$
$$(2, 4) \text{ and } (^-2, 4),$$
$$(\sqrt{2}, 2) \text{ and } (^-\sqrt{2}, 2),$$
$$(10^3, 10^6) \text{ and } (^-10^3, 10^6),$$

and so on. In other words, if (x, y) is on the graph, then $(^-x, y)$ is also on it. This means that the two parts of the graph on opposite sides of the y-axis are *mirror images* of each other. If we were to fold our paper along the y-axis, these two parts would coincide. We say that the y-axis is an *axis of symmetry* of the parabola, or, that the parabola is *symmetric about the y-axis.*

Vertex. The point at which the axis of symmetry cuts the parabola is called the vertex of the parabola. For the parabola above, the origin (0, 0) is the vertex. In other words, the vertex is the *lowest point* on this particular parabola.

Infinite extent. The parabola extends indefinitely far from its vertex. For example, the points $(10^{10}, 10^{20})$, $(10^{100}, 10^{200})$, and $(10^{1000}, 10^{2000})$ are on the parabola. Unlike a circle, a parabola is not a closed curve. The parabola above *opens upward.*

Exercises for Discussion, page 144

If time is limited it is suggested that at least Exercises for Discussion 1–4 be covered.

Answers to Exercises for Discussion 1, 2, 3(b), 3(c), page 144, 5(c), 5(d), page 145
(See page T13 for graphs.)

1. The graph of $y = 2x^2$ is symmetric about the y-axis, opens upward, is infinite in extent, and has its vertex at (0, 0).
   The graph of $y = {}^-2x^2$ is symmetric about the y-axis, opens downward, is infinite in extent, and has its vertex at (0, 0). Both graphs have the same shape.
2. Both graphs are mirror images across the x-axis. Each is symmetric about the y-axis, infinite in extent, and has its vertex at the origin.
3. (b) For both parabolas, $x = 0$ or y — axis.
   (c) (0, 0), (0, 3). In common is the abscissa of 0.
5. (c) (0, 0), (0, 2). In common is the abscissa of 0.
   (d) Each has a highest point, its vertex.

In Exercise for Discussion 7 on page 145, the class might fill in the following table to expose the role of c.

x	x^2	$x^2 - 1$	$x^2 - 2$	$x^2 + 3$	$x^2 + 4$
0					
1					
5					
10					

In $y = x^2$, the minimum value for y is 0 because it is the minimum value for x^2, and this is attained when $x = 0$. In $y = x^2 + c$, the minimum value for y is still attained when $x = 0$ and $x^2 = 0$ is the least we ever add to c. However, the minimum value of y is now $0 + c$, or c. Hence, the low point on the graph of $y = x^2 + c$ is $(0, c)$ and lies below the x-axis for negative c, above the x-axis for positive c. The equation $y = x^2 + c$ represents a family of parabolas with the same shape and same axis of symmetry. The constant c serves to "lift" the curve vertically, or "push" it down, in both cases parallel to the curve $y = x^2$.

Answer to Exercise 1, page 145

1. The graph of $y = \frac{3}{2}x^2$ is symmetric about the y-axis, opens upward, is infinite in extent, and its vertex is at (0, 0).
   The graph of $y = {}^{-}\frac{3}{2}x^2$ is symmetric about the y-axis, opens downward, is infinite in extent, and its vertex is at (0, 0).

In Exercise 5 on page 146, a table can quickly be constructed to exhibit the role of $|a|$ in controlling how wide or how narrow the opening of the parabola is. For example, the class might fill in the following table and sketch the graphs.

x	$\frac{1}{100}x^2$	$\frac{1}{3}x^2$	$\frac{1}{2}x^2$	$2x^2$	$3x^2$	$100x^2$
0						
1						
6						
12						

It is recommended that Exercises 8, 9, and 10 be taken as a group, either assigned together or developed in class. The fact that three noncollinear points determine a unique parabola should be related to the corresponding fact concerning the geometry of a circle.

Next, let us consider the graph of the quadratic equation

$$y = {}^{-}x^2.$$

Several points on the graph are plotted in Fig. 3–4, and a smooth curve is drawn through them. This curve is also a parabola. Actually, it is the mirror image relative to the x-axis of the previous parabola. The y-axis continues to be the *axis of symmetry* of this parabola. Also, the origin (0, 0) is the *vertex*. However, the vertex of this parabola is the *highest point* on the curve. This parabola *opens downward*, extending indefinitely far from its vertex.

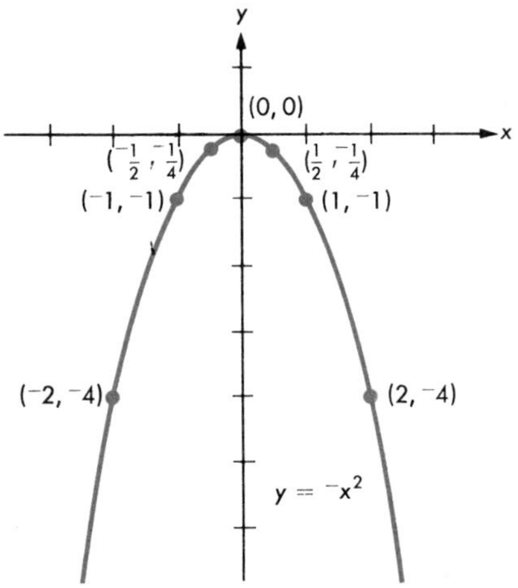

FIGURE 3–4

Exercises for Discussion

1. Graph the equations

$$y = 2x^2 \quad \text{and} \quad y = {}^{-}2x^2$$

on the same set of axes. Discuss the graphs by giving the symmetry, extent, and location of the vertices.

2. For a given value of a, how do the graphs of $y = ax^2$ and $y = {}^{-}ax^2$ change? For each graph, discuss the symmetry, extent, and location of the vertex.

3. (a) On the same set of axes draw the graphs of the equations

$$y = x^2 \quad \text{and} \quad y = x^2 + 3.$$

   (b) Write an equation of the axis of symmetry of each parabola.
   (c) Write the coordinates of the vertex of each parabola. What do the two points have in common?
   (d) In which direction does each parabola open? Both open upward.
   (e) Is the vertex the highest or the lowest point on each parabola? Shapes are the same and the vertex is the lowest point of each.

4. Write equations for the two parabolas which have a common vertex at the origin and the y-axis as the axis of symmetry of each, given that one parabola passes through the point (1, 2) and the other passes through the point (1, ⁻2). $y = 2x^2$ and $y = {}^{-}2x^2$

5. (a) Draw the graphs of the equations

$$y = {}^{-}\tfrac{1}{2}x^2 \quad \text{and} \quad y = {}^{-}\tfrac{1}{2}x^2 + 2$$

on the same set of axes.

(b) Do the curves have a common axis of symmetry? If so, give its equation. Yes $x = 0$

(c) Locate the vertices. What do they have in common?

(d) Do the parabolas have a highest point or a lowest point?

(e) Do these two graphs represent the same parabola located differently in the coordinate plane? Yes What difference in their equations accounts for this difference in location? The constant term

6. Write an equation of the parabola with vertex at (0, 4) and axis of symmetry on the y-axis when, in addition,

(a) it opens upward and has the same shape as the parabola with equation $y = 3x^2 + 8$. $y = 3x^2 + 4$

(b) it opens downward and has the same shape as the parabola with equation $y = 2x^2 - 12$. $y = {}^{-}2x^2 + 4$

7. Consider the graphs of

$$y = ax^2 \quad \text{and} \quad y = ax^2 + c,$$

with a and c nonzero real numbers.

(a) What is the axis of symmetry for each parabola? The y-axis

(b) Give the coordinates of the vertices. $(0, 0)$ and $(0, c)$

(c) How do the directions of opening compare? The directions are the same.

(d) What is a necessary condition for the parabolas to open upward? $a > 0$

Exercises

See Solution Manual for graphs.

1. On the same set of axes, draw the parabolas which are the graphs of the equations

$$y = \tfrac{3}{2}x^2 \quad \text{and} \quad y = {}^{-}\tfrac{3}{2}x^2.$$

Discuss symmetry, extent, and location of vertices.

2. (a) On the same set of axes, draw the graphs of the equations

$$y = 2x^2 \quad \text{and} \quad y = 2x^2 - 5.$$

(b) Give an equation of the axis of symmetry for each parabola. For both, $x = 0$

(c) Give the coordinates of the vertex for each parabola. $(0, 0)$ and $(0, {}^{-}5)$

(d) Could these parabolas be made to coincide with each other? Yes

Answers to Exercises 3(b), 7, 8, 10–12, page 146

3. (b) The parabolas are alike in axis of symmetry, extent, and vertices; they differ in shape.

7. The graph is parabolic with axis of symmetry at $t = 0$, vertex at (0, 400), opening downward. Do not consider negative time ($t < 0$) or the ball below the ground ($t > 5$).

8. The equation for the parabola is $y = 2x^2 + 3$.

10. In Exercise 9, the given points are symmetric with respect to the y-axis; in Exercise 8, the points are nonsymmetric.

11. Both graphs have the same shape, direction of opening, and axis of symmetry. The first has (0, 0) as its vertex, the second, (0, 3).

12. Both graphs have the same shape and vertex, (0, 0). The first opens upward and has the y-axis for its axis of symmetry; the second opens to the right and has the x-axis for its axis of symmetry.

Quiz

(See page T13 for graph.)

1. On the same set of axes, draw the graphs of the equations

$$y = {}^{-}2x^2 - 1,$$
$$y = 2x^2 + 1.$$

2. Give an equation of the axis of symmetry of each parabola. (ans: $x = 0$, $x = 0$)

3. What are the coordinates of the vertex of each parabola? (ans: (0, ⁻1), (0, 1))

4. Do the parabolas have a highest or a lowest point? Explain. (ans: Yes, the vertex of the first is its highest point and the vertex of the second is its lowest point.)

3–7 QUADRATIC EQUATIONS OF THE FORM $y = ax^2 + bx + c$

In the previous section, y was determined by a quadratic form in x which had no first-degree term in x. The study of $y = ax^2 + bx + c$ begins with the special case where $ax^2 + bx + c$ is a trinomial square. Suppose that $ax^2 + bx + c$ is

$$x^2 - 2x + 1,$$

so that $y = (x - 1)^2$. Since $(x - 1)^2$ is non-negative, y has a minimum value of zero, attained when

$$x - 1 = 0, \quad \text{or} \quad x = 1.$$

There are two alternatives for y to attain any positive value. For instance, $y = 16$ when $|x - 1| = 4$; hence, $x - 1 = 4$ and $x = 5$, or $x - 1 = {}^-4$ and $x = {}^-3$. The points $(5, 16)$ and $({}^-3, 16)$ are equally distant from the line $x - 1 = 0$, four units to the right and four units to the left, respectively.

Observe that $y = a(x - 1)^2$ is a family of parabolas with the same vertex, $(1, 0)$, and the same axis of symmetry, $x = 1$, where a controls the speed with which the curve rises or falls. Then consider

$$y = (x - 1)^2 + c,$$

which is a family of parabolas parallel to one another, all with the same axis of symmetry, $(x = 1)$, but with different vertices, the points with coordinates $(1, c)$. The minimum value for y is c, and this value is assumed when $x = 1$.

In part (a) of Problem 1, it should be emphasized that the axis of symmetry is the line $x - 3 = 0$ or $x = 3$. This can be demonstrated by computing y for pairs of x's equidistant from 3.

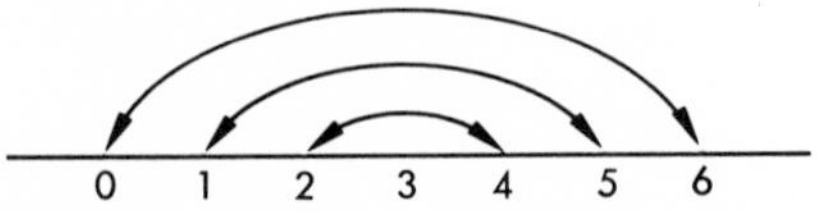

Thus, both $(2 - 3)^2$ and $(4 - 3)^2$ yield $y = 1$.

3. (a) On the same set of axes, draw the graphs of the equations

$$y = \tfrac{1}{2}x^2,$$
$$y = x^2,$$
$$y = 2x^2.$$

(b) In what respect are the parabolas alike? How do they differ?

4. On the same set of axes, draw the graphs of the equations

$$y = {}^-\tfrac{1}{3}x^2,$$
$$y = {}^-x^2,$$
$$y = {}^-3x^2.$$

5. As $|a|$ increases, what happens to the graph of $y = ax^2$? *Opening narrows*

6. In what quadrants does the graph of $y = ax^2$ lie when $a > 0$? $a < 0$?
$a > 0$: first and second quadrants
$a < 0$: third and fourth quadrants

---

7. The equation

$$h = {}^-16t^2 + 400,$$

which was discussed on page 142, may be graphed on a set of axes labeled t instead of x, and h instead of y. Draw the graph, using different scales on the two axes. Describe the graph. Why are we concerned only with those t-values which lie in the closed interval from 0 to 5?

8. The graph of a parabola described by an equation of the type

$$y = ax^2 + c$$

passes through the two points $(0, 3)$ and $(1, 5)$. What is an equation for this particular parabola? Show that the condition that the two points be on the parabola completely determines the values of a and c as the solution set of a system of two linear equations.

9. A parabola described by an equation of the type

$$y = ax^2 + c$$

is known to pass through points $(1, 4)$ and $({}^-1, 4)$.

(a) Show that this condition is *not* sufficient to determine the particular parabola. *$4 = a + c$; infinitely many solutions*

(b) Give equations of three specific parabolas of this type which satisfy the condition given. *$y = x^2 + 3$, $y = 2x^2 + 2$, $y = 3x^2 + 1$*

10. Why do the two points in Exercise 8 determine a unique parabola, although the two points in Exercise 9 do not?

11. Compare the graph of $y = {}^-4x^2$ with the graph of $y - 3 = {}^-4x^2$.

12. Compare the graph of $y = 4x^2$ with the graph of $y^2 = \tfrac{1}{4}x$.

3–7 QUADRATIC EQUATIONS OF THE FORM $y = ax^2 + bx + c$

In the preceding section, we considered dropping a ball from a helicopter. Now let us consider throwing a ball toward the ground with an initial speed of 80 feet per second. According to a law of physics, the height h of the ball above the ground t seconds after it is thrown is given by the equation $h = {}^{-}16t^2 - 80t + 400$. Thus,

$$h = {}^{-}16 - 80 + 400, \text{ or } 304, \text{ when } t = 1;$$
$$h = {}^{-}64 - 160 + 400, \text{ or } 176, \text{ when } t = 2;$$
$$h = {}^{-}144 - 240 + 400, \text{ or } 16, \text{ when } t = 3.$$

It is evident that the ball reaches the ground (that is, $h = 0$) slightly more than 3 seconds after it is thrown.

In this section, we shall study quadratic equations in two variables which have the form

$$y = ax^2 + bx + c, \qquad a \neq 0.$$

Problem 1. Discuss the graphs of the following equations.

(a) $y = (x - 3)^2$ (b) $y = (x - 3)^2 + 2$

Solution.

(a) Since $(x - 3)^2$ is nonnegative for every real number x, we must have $y \geqq 0$ in each solution (x, y) of this equation. It follows that zero is the least value of y and therefore, $(3, 0)$ is the lowest, or minimum, point on the graph. Several points are plotted in Fig. 3–5. The points appear in pairs and are equally spaced on each side of the line $x = 3$. For example, if we let $y = 4$ in this equation, then $(x - 3)^2 = 4$, and either $x - 3 = 2$ or $x - 3 = {}^{-}2$; that is, if $y = 4$, then either $x = 5$ or $x = 1$. Hence, the points $(1, 4)$ and $(5, 5)$ are on the graph. If we let

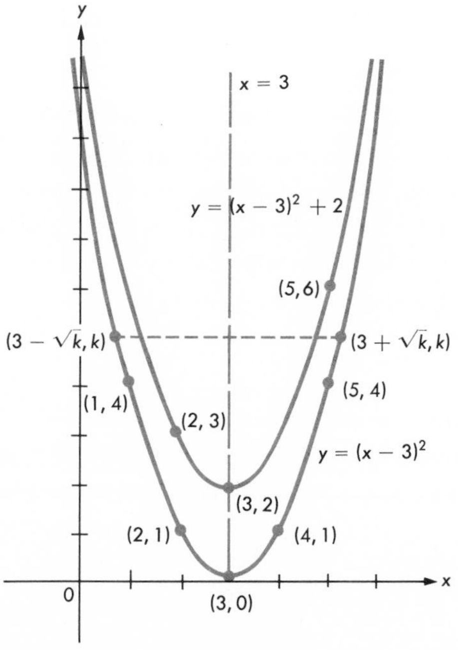

FIGURE 3–5

You could make a table like the following for both 1(a) and 1(b).

x	$y = (x-3)^2$	$y = (x-3)^2 + 2$
3	0	$0 + 2$, or 2
2, 4	1	$1 + 2$, or 3
1, 5	4	$4 + 2$, or 6

This would focus attention on the fact that the parabolas are the same except for position in the coordinate plane. In other words,

$$y = (x - 3)^2 + 2$$

is, in a sense, two units higher than $y = (x - 3)^2$.

In Problems 1 and 2, having determined the graph of all equations of the type $y = a(x + b)^2 + c$, where a, b, and c are any real numbers except that $a \neq 0$, what can be said about the graph of

$$y = dx^2 + ex + f,$$

(see Problem 3) where d, e, and f are any real numbers, $d \neq 0$? It happens that $dx^2 + ex + f$ can be cast into the pattern $a(x + b)^2 + c$ simply by using the distributive law and the property of zero that when it is added to any number, it leaves the identity of the number unchanged. First, $dx^2 + ex + f$ may be written as

$$d\left(x^2 + \frac{e}{d}x\right) + f$$

by means of the distributive law. Now zero may be added, but since there are many names for zero, the one that is particularly convenient for use here should be selected, namely,

$$d \cdot \frac{e^2}{4d^2} - d \cdot \frac{e^2}{4d^2}.$$

Thus,

$$d\left(x^2 + \frac{e}{d}x\right) + d \cdot \frac{e^2}{4d^2} + f - d \cdot \frac{e^2}{4d^2},$$

which, by the distributive law, becomes

$$d\left(x^2 + \frac{e}{d}x + \frac{e^2}{4d^2}\right) + f - \frac{e^2}{4d},$$

or

$$d\left(x + \frac{e}{2d}\right)^2 + \frac{4\,df - e^2}{4d},$$

which is the old pattern,

$$a(x + b)^2 + c,$$

with

$$a = d, \quad b = \frac{e}{2d}, \quad c = \frac{4\,df - e^2}{4d}.$$

Hence, the graph of

$$y = dx^2 + ex + f$$

is already understood. It is suggested that you go through this exercise with specific equations such as $y = 3x^2 - 5x + 9$ and

$$y = {}^-2x^2 + 5x - 4$$

before going through the problem in its full generality. In fact, in some classes the full generality might be omitted.

In relation to Problem 3, even when students know how to write $y = ax^2 + bx + c$ in the form

$$y = a(x - h)^2 + k,$$

they are apt to make many mistakes in doing it. Since this type of algebraic manipulation is very important in the study of analytic geometry and integral calculus, it should be practiced in class. Each equation may be written in standard form and just the coordinates of the vertex given, using examples such as the following:

$$\begin{aligned} y &= x^2 - 4x + 4, \\ y &= 3x^2 - 12x + 12, \\ y &= x^2 - 4x + 1, \\ y &= x^2 - 4x - 5, \\ y &= 2x^2 + 4x + 1, \\ y &= 2x^2 + 3x - 5, \\ y &= {}^-3x^2 - 6x + 2. \end{aligned}$$

$y = k$, then, by the same argument, we may show that the two points $(3 - \sqrt{k}, k)$ and $(3 + \sqrt{k}, k)$ are on the graph and are equally spaced on each side of the line $x = 3$.

The graph of $y = (x - 3)^2$ has the same shape as that of $y = x^2$, which is sketched in Fig. 3–3. Of course, the two graphs are located differently in relation to the coordinate axes. We conclude that the graph of $y = (x - 3)^2$ is a parabola with vertex (3, 0) and the line $x = 3$ as its axis of symmetry. It opens upward, extending indefinitely far above the x-axis.

(b) If (r, s) is a point on the graph of $y = (x - 3)^2$, then $(r, s + 2)$ is a point on the graph of $y = (x - 3)^2 + 2$. For example, (2, 1) is on the graph of $y = (x - 3)^2$ and (2, 3) is on the graph of $y = (x - 3)^2 + 2$; also, (5, 4) is on the graph of $y = (x - 3)^2$ and (5, 6) is on the graph of $y = (x - 3)^2 + 2$. Consequently, the graph of $y = (x - 3)^2 + 2$ is the graph of the preceding equation shifted vertically upward two units (the upper curve in Fig. 3–5). The vertex of this parabola is at (3, 2) and the axis of symmetry is the line $x = 3$.

Problem 2. Discuss the graphs of the following equations.

(a) $y = \frac{1}{2}(x + 1)^2$

(b) $y = \frac{1}{2}(x + 1)^2 - 3$

Solution.

(a) Since $\frac{1}{2}(x + 1)^2$ is non-negative for each real number x, and $\frac{1}{2}(x + 1)^2$ is zero if, and only if, $x = {}^-1$, it follows that $({}^-1, 0)$ is the minimum point on the graph. Thus, the line $x = {}^-1$ is an axis of symmetry of this graph. Several symmetrically placed pairs of points are sketched in Fig. 3–6. This graph is a parabola; its vertex is the point $({}^-1, 0)$. When we multiplied $(x + 1)^2$ by $\frac{1}{2}$, we caused this parabola to open wider than the corresponding parabola $y = (x + 1)^2$.

(b) For each real number r, $(r, \frac{1}{2}(r + 1)^2)$ is a point on graph (a) in Fig. 3–6, and $(r, \frac{1}{2}(r + 1)^2 - 3)$ is a point on graph (b). For example, (3, 8) is on graph (a) and (3, 5) is on graph (b). Thus, we conclude that the graph of this equation is the graph of the preceding equation shifted vertically downward three units (the lower curve in Fig. 3–6). The vertex of this parabola is at $({}^-1, {}^-3)$.

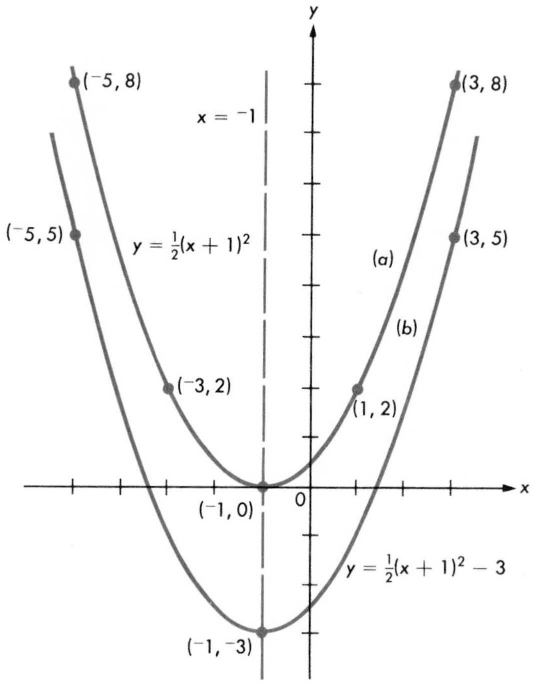

FIGURE 3-6

Problem 3. Discuss the graph of the equation $y = {}^{-}2x^2 - 4x + 3$.
Solution. We may complete the square as follows:

$$y = {}^{-}2(x^2 + 2x) + 3,$$
$$y = {}^{-}2(x^2 + 2x + 1) + 2 + 3,$$
$$y = {}^{-}2(x + 1)^2 + 5.$$

Since the last equation is equivalent to the given one, the graph of the given equation is the same as the graph of

$$y = {}^{-}2(x + 1)^2 + 5.$$

Notice that the graph of this equation is symmetric about the line $x = {}^{-}1$. Thus, for example, the pairs of points

$$({}^{-}2, 3) \text{ and } (0, 3),$$
$$({}^{-}3, {}^{-}3) \text{ and } (1, {}^{-}3),$$
$$({}^{-}11, {}^{-}195) \text{ and } (9, {}^{-}195),$$

are symmetrically located about the line $x = {}^{-}1$.

In each case, the work may be checked by substituting back into the given equation the coordinates of the vertex found from the new equation. Thus, after

$$y = 4x^2 - 4x + 3$$

has become

$$y = 4(x^2 - x + \tfrac{1}{4}) - 1 + 3,$$
$$y = 4(x - \tfrac{1}{2})^2 + 2,$$

it appears that the vertex is at $(\frac{1}{2}, 2)$. Therefore, substitute $(\frac{1}{2}, 2)$ into

$$y = 4x^2 - 4x + 3,$$
$$2 \stackrel{?}{=} 4(\tfrac{1}{2})^2 - 4(\tfrac{1}{2}) + 3,$$
$$2 \stackrel{?}{=} 4 \cdot \tfrac{1}{4} - 2 + 3,$$
$$2 \stackrel{\checkmark}{=} 1 - 2 + 3.$$

It is reasonable now to assume that the transformation on the original equation is correct.

The students should note that the graph of $y = ax^2 + bx + c$ crosses the x-axis at values of x that are solutions of

$$ax^2 + bx + c = 0.$$

You could start with *simple* specific examples. Thus, $y = x^2 - 3x - 4$ may be graphed, considering the factored form

$$y = (x - 4)(x + 1),$$

which shows immediately that (4, 0) and $({}^{-}1, 0)$ are on the graph. Thus, it can be seen that the solution set for $x^2 - 3x - 4 = 0$ is $\{4, {}^{-}1\}$. Next, $y = (x + 2)^2$ may be graphed and $x^2 + 4x + 4 = 0$ solved in order to show that when the parabola

$$y = (x + 2)^2$$

is tangent to the x-axis at $({}^{-}2, 0)$, the quadratic $x^2 + 4x + 4 = 0$ has one solution, $\{{}^{-}2\}$. Finally, graph $y = x^2 - 2$ to show that $(\sqrt{2}, 0)$ and $({}^{-}\sqrt{2}, 0)$ are on the graph and the solution set for $x^2 - 2 = 0$ is

$$\{\sqrt{2}, {}^{-}\sqrt{2}\}.$$

Exercises for Discussion and Exercises

It is suggested that Exercises for Discussion 1–5 be covered in detail during the first class session and that Exercise for Discussion 6 and Exercises 1 and 2 then be assigned.

Exercises for Discussion 7, 8, and 9 could be covered in the second class session and then Exercises 3, 4, 6, and 7 assigned.

Answers to Exercises for Discussion 1, 2, 3(a), 3(b), and 5

1. $(x - 1)^2 = 1$, $x - 1 = 1$ or $x - 1 = {}^-1$; $x = 2$ or $x = 0$

$(x - 1)^2 = 25$, $x - 1 = 5$ or $x - 1 = {}^-5$; $x = 6$ or $x = {}^-4$

$(x - 1)^2 = 36$, $x - 1 = 6$ or $x - 1 = {}^-6$; $x = 7$ or $x = {}^-5$

2. If $x = \frac{3}{2}$, then

$$(x - 1)^2 = (\tfrac{3}{2} - 1)^2 = (\tfrac{1}{2})^2.$$

If $x = \frac{1}{2}$, then

$$(x - 1)^2 = (\tfrac{1}{2} - 1)^2 = (\tfrac{1}{2})^2.$$

Hence, if

$$x = 1 + \tfrac{1}{2} \quad \text{or} \quad x = 1 - \tfrac{1}{2},$$

y will have the same value. Following the same pattern, if $x = \frac{5}{2}$, then $x = 1 + \frac{3}{2}$. If

$$x = 1 - \tfrac{3}{2}, \quad \text{or} \quad {}^-\tfrac{1}{2},$$

y will have the same value. Also, ${}^-\frac{3}{2}$ will give the same value for y as $\frac{7}{2}$.

3. (a)

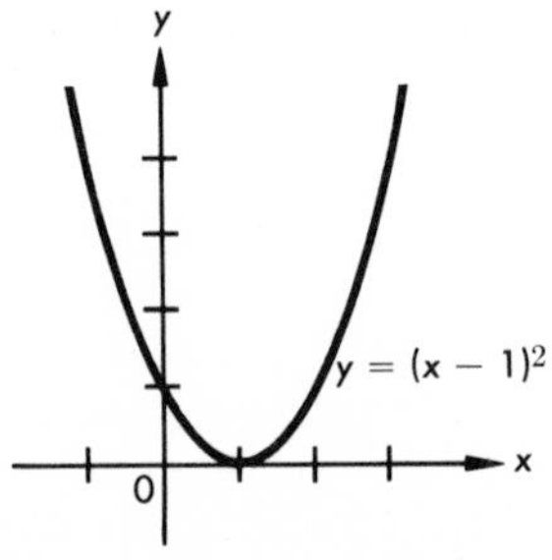

$x = 1$; $(1, 0)$

Since ${}^-2(x + 1)^2 \leqq 0$ for every real number x, the maximum value of y occurs when ${}^-2(x + 1)^2 = 0$. Hence, the point $({}^-1, 5)$ is the highest point on the graph. We conclude that the graph is a parabola with vertex $({}^-1, 5)$ and the line $x = {}^-1$ as its axis of symmetry. It opens downward and extends indefinitely far in that direction, as indicated in Fig. 3–7. By looking at the graph, we see that the parabola crosses the x-axis at approximately $({}^-2.6, 0)$ and $(.6, 0)$. Hence, ${}^-2.6$ and $.6$ are approximations of the solutions of the equation

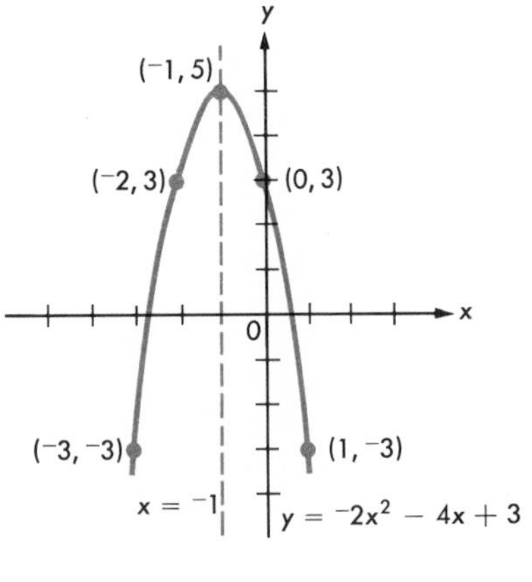

FIGURE 3–7

$$^-2x^2 - 4x + 3 = 0.$$

The exact solutions are

$$^-1 - \tfrac{1}{2}\sqrt{10} \quad \text{and} \quad {}^-1 + \tfrac{1}{2}\sqrt{10}.$$

Exercises for Discussion

1. If $y = (x - 1)^2$, for what two values of x does $y = 1$? 25? 36?
2. If $y = (x - 1)^2$, for what other value of x will y have the same value as it does when $x = \frac{3}{2}$? $\frac{5}{2}$? $\frac{7}{2}$?
3. (a) Graph the equation
$$y = (x - 1)^2.$$
Give an equation of the axis of symmetry and the coordinates of the vertex of the parabola.
(b) Graph the equation
$$y = (x - 1)^2 - 4.$$
Give an equation of the axis of symmetry and the coordinates of the vertex of the parabola.
(c) Where is the vertex of the parabola with equation $y = (x - 1)^2 + 5$? (1, 5)
4. Discuss the graph of
$$y = {}^-(x - 1)^2.$$ Opens downward
Give an equation of the axis of symmetry (Axis: $x = 1$) and the coordinates of the vertex. (1, 0) Does y have a minimum value? No If so, what is it? a maximum value? Yes If so, what is it? 0
5. Discuss the graph of
$$y = {}^-(x - 1)^2 + 3,$$
and tell how it is related to the graph of $y = {}^-(x - 1)^2$ in Exercise 4.

6. On the same set of axes, draw the graphs of the equations $y = 2x^2$, $y = 2x^2 + 4$, and $y = 2(x - 5)^2$.
   (a) In what direction do the parabolas open?
   (b) Write an equation of the axis of symmetry of each parabola.
   (c) What change in the equation $y = 2x^2$ shifts the axis of symmetry?
   (d) What are the coordinates of the vertex of each parabola?
   (e) What change in the equation $y = 2x^2$ shifts the vertex horizontally?
   (f) What change in the equation $y = 2x^2$ shifts the vertex vertically?
   (g) Write an equation of a parabola which has its vertex at (5, 4) and opens in the same direction as the graph of $y = 2x^2$.

7. Write each of the following equations in the form $y = a(x - h)^2$. Then locate the axis of symmetry and the vertex of the parabola which is the graph of each equation.
   (a) $y = 3x^2 - 30x + 75$ $= 3(x^2 - 10x + 25) = 3(x-5)^2$ Axis: $x = 5$; vertex: (5,0)
   (b) $y = {}^-2x^2 + 20x - 50$ $= {}^-2(x^2 - 10x + 25) = {}^-2(x-5)^2$ Axis: $x = 5$; vertex: (5,0)

8. (a) Find an equation of the type $y = a(x - h)^2 + k$ which is equivalent to the equation $y = x^2 + 4x + 1$. $= x^2 + 4x + (4 - 4) + 1$; $y = (x+2)^2 - 3$
   (b) Give an equation of the axis of symmetry of the graph
   $$y = x^2 + 4x + 1.$$ $x = {}^-2$
   (c) Give the coordinates of the vertex of the graph of $y = x^2 + 4x + 1$. $({}^-2, {}^-3)$
   (d) Draw the graph of $y = x^2 + 4x + 1$.
   (e) Give an approximation of the abscissas of the points at which the graph of $y = x^2 + 4x + 1$ crosses the x-axis. ${}^-3.6$ and ${}^-.4$
   (f) Find the exact solutions of the equation $x^2 + 4x + 1 = 0$, and compare them with the approximations in part (e).

9. The graph of $y = a(x - h)^2 + k$ is a parabola.
   (a) What is an equation of its axis of symmetry? $x = h$
   (b) What are the coordinates of its vertex? (h, k)
   (c) What does the sign of a determine about the parabola? Direction. If $a > 0$, it opens upward; if $a < 0$, it opens downward.
   (d) What does $|a|$ determine? Shape. If $|a|$ is smaller, curve is fatter; if $|a|$ is larger, curve is steeper.

Exercises

See Solution Manual for graphs.

1. On the same set of axes, draw the graphs of the equations $y = {}^-x^2$, $y = {}^-x^2 + 2$, and $y = {}^-(x + 2)^2$.
   (a) In what direction do the parabolas open? Downward
   (b) Write an equation of the axis of symmetry of each parabola.
   (c) What change in the equation $y = {}^-x^2$ shifts the axis of symmetry?
   (d) What are the coordinates of the vertex of each parabola?
   (e) What change in the equation $y = {}^-x^2$ shifts the vertex horizontally?
   (f) What change in the equation $y = {}^-x^2$ shifts the vertex vertically?
   (g) Sketch the graph of $y = {}^-(x + 2)^2 + 2$. Locate the vertex and give an equation of the axis of symmetry. $({}^-2, 2)$; $x = {}^-2$

(b)

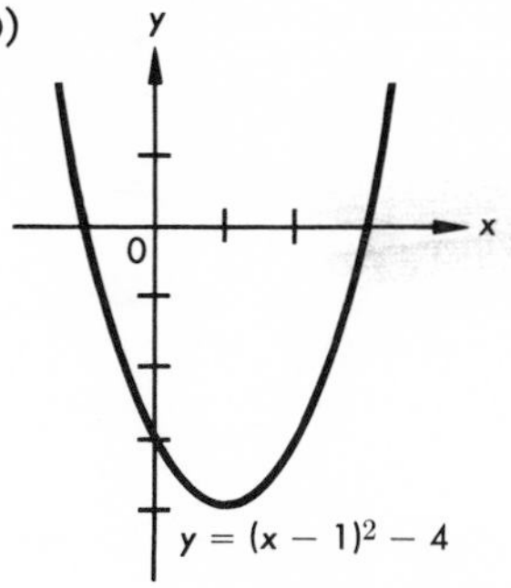

$x = 1$; $(1, {}^-4)$

5. Axis: $x = 1$; vertex: (1, 3); opens downward. Although y has no minimum value, its maximum value is 3. The graph is the same as the graph in Exercise 4, moved vertically upward 3 units.

Answers to Exercises for Discussion 6, 7, 8(f)

(See page T14 for graphs.)

6. (a) All open upward.
   (b) $x = 0$; $x = 0$; $x = 5$
   (c) A change of x^2 to $(x - a)^2$: $y = 2(x - a)^2$
   (d) (0, 0) (0, 4), (5, 0)
   (e) A change of x^2 to $(x - a)^2$: $y = 2(x - a)^2$
   (f) The addition of a constant term, $y = 2x^2 + b$
   (g) $y = 2(x - 5)^2 + 4$
7. (a) $y = 3x^2 - 30x + 75$
   $= 3(x^2 - 10x + 25)$
   $= 3(x - 5)^2$
   Axis: $x = 5$; vertex: (5, 0)
   (b) $y = {}^-2x^2 + 20x - 50$
   $= {}^-2(x^2 - 10x + 25)$
   $= {}^-2(x - 5)^2$
   Axis: $x = 5$; vertex: (5, 0)
8. (f) $x^2 + 4x + 1 = 0$
   $x^2 + 4x = {}^-1$
   $x^2 + 4x + 4 = {}^-1 + 4$
   $(x + 2)^2 = 3$
   $x = {}^-2 + \sqrt{3}$
   or $x = {}^-2 - \sqrt{3}$
   $x \doteq {}^-.3$
   or $x \doteq {}^-3.7$

(Answers to Exercises 1(b) - 1(f) on page 152)

Answers to Exercises 1(b)–1(f), page 151; 5, 6, 11(b), 11(c)

1. (b) $x = 0$, $x = 0$, $x = {}^{-}2$
   (c) x^2 to $(x - a)^2$
   (d) (0, 0), (0, 2), ($^{-}2$, 0)
   (e) x^2 to $(x - a)^2$
   (f) The addition of a constant

5. $y = {}^{-}9(x - \frac{1}{3})^2$; $(\frac{1}{3}, 0)$; $x = \frac{1}{3}$

6. $y = 3(x - 1)^2 - 1$; $(1, {}^{-}1)$; $x = 1$

11. (b) $0 < x < 35$; $(17\frac{1}{2}, 306\frac{1}{4})$
    (c) A square $17\frac{1}{2}$ by $17\frac{1}{2}$ feet

In Exercises 3–8, you may wish to refresh the student's memory about solving a quadratic equation by completing the square. It should be emphasized that the key to keeping equations equivalent lies in doing the same thing to both sides of the equations. Thus,

$$3x^2 + 6x - 5 = 0,$$
$$3x^2 + 6x = 5,$$
$$x^2 + 2x = \tfrac{5}{3},$$
$$x^2 + 2x + 1 = \tfrac{5}{3} + 1,$$
$$(x + 1)^2 = \tfrac{8}{3},$$
$$x + 1 = \pm\tfrac{2}{3}\sqrt{6},$$

and

$$x = {}^{-}1 \pm \tfrac{2}{3}\sqrt{6}.$$

In order to graph the equation

$$y = 3x^2 + 6x - 5,$$

the student must first get it into a form that will tell him instantly what the axis of symmetry is and where the vertex lies. To do this, the left side of the equation must be left alone, and thus, in a sense, nothing may be done on the right side. But zero may be added, expressed in an appropriate way. Thus,

$$y = 3x^2 + 6x - 5,$$
$$y = 3(x^2 + 2x) - 5,$$
$$y = 3(x^2 + 2x + 1) - 3 \cdot 1 - 5.$$

Adding $3 \cdot 1 - 3 \cdot 1$, or 0, to the right side, we obtain

$$y = 3(x + 1)^2 - 8.$$

2. Sketch and discuss the graphs of each of the following equations.
   (a) $y = \frac{1}{4}(x - 2)^2$ *Vertex: (2,0); axis: x = 2; opens upward*
   (b) $y = \frac{1}{4}(x - 2)^2 + 4$ *Vertex: (2,4); axis: x = 2; opens upward*

In Exercises 3–8, transform each equation into the form $y = a(x - h)^2 + k$, and draw its graph. In each case, give the coordinates of the vertex and an equation of the axis of symmetry.

3. $y = x^2 + 12x + 36$ *$y = (x+6)^2$; vertex: ($^{-}6$,0); axis: $x = {}^{-}6$*
4. $y = 3x^2 - 6x + 3$ *$y = 3(x-1)^2$; vertex: (1,0); axis: $x = 1$*
5. $y = {}^{-}9x^2 + 6x - 1$
6. $y = 3x^2 - 6x + 2$
7. $y + x^2 + 2x + 2 = 0$ *$y = {}^{-}(x+1)^2 - 1$; ($^{-}1$,$^{-}1$); $x = {}^{-}1$*
8. $y + 2x^2 + 12x + 15 = 0$ *$y = {}^{-}2(x+3)^2 + 3$; ($^{-}3$, 3); $x = {}^{-}3$*
9. Graph the equation

$$y = {}^{-}2x^2 - 12x - 15.$$

Then compare the abscissas of the crossing points on the x-axis with the exact solutions of the equation *Abscissas of crossing points are approximately $^{-}1.8$, $^{-}4.2$; exact solutions of the equation are*

$$2x^2 + 12x + 15 = 0.$$ *$\frac{{}^{-}6 + \sqrt{6}}{2}$, $\frac{{}^{-}6 - \sqrt{6}}{2}$.*

10. (a) Graph the equation

$$y = {}^{-}x^2 - 2x - 2.$$

   (b) Does the graph cross the x-axis? *No*
   (c) By looking at the graph in part (a), what can you say about the solution set of ${}^{-}x^2 - 2x - 2 = 0$? *There exist no real solutions.*

△

11. (a) Write an equation expressing the area, y square feet, of a rectangle x feet long if the perimeter is 70 feet. *$y = x(35 - x)$*
    (b) What values of x are meaningful in this problem? Sketch the graph for this set of x's. What are the coordinates of its vertex?
    (c) In this set of rectangles with perimeter 70 feet, what are the dimensions of the rectangle that encloses the maximum area?
    (d) What is the maximum area that can be enclosed by a rectangle with a perimeter of 70 feet? *$306\frac{1}{4}$ sq ft*

12. A projectile is thrown straight up from a height of 6 feet with an initial velocity of 192 feet per second. If air resistance is neglected, h, the projectile's height in feet after t seconds, is given by the equation

$$h = 6 + 192t - 16t^2.$$

Using h for the vertical axis and t for the horizontal axis, graph the equation. From the graph, determine at what time after the projectile is thrown it reaches its maximum height. What is this maximum height? *6 sec after thrown; 582 ft*

13. (a) Write a formula for the sum y of the squares of two numbers if one number is denoted by x and if it is given that the sum of the numbers is 30. $y = x^2 + (30 - x)^2$

(b) Use the graph of the formula to determine the two numbers for which the sum of their squares is a minimum. 15 and 15

(c) Are there two numbers such that the sum of their squares is a maximum? No (unless x is restricted to positive numbers)

14. A piece of wire 40 inches long is cut into two pieces, and each piece is bent to form a square frame.

(a) Write a formula for A, the sum of the areas of the two squares, in terms of x, the length of one piece of the wire. $A = \left(\frac{x}{4}\right)^2 + \left(10 - \frac{x}{4}\right)^2$

(b) Graph the formula for a meaningful x.

(c) From the graph, determine how the wire should be cut to make two squares of minimum total area. Cut in half

(d) What is the minimum total area of the two squares? 50 sq in.

(e) Is there a maximum total area of the two squares? How could you use the wire to enclose this maximum area? Yes, 100 sq ft. Do not cut wire.

(f) How does this exercise differ from Exercise 13? x must be positive.

15. Questionnaires were distributed at a Shakespearean festival in Stratford, Ontario. From them, it was learned that if tickets were sold at \$1.50, then 200 people would come. Further sampling revealed that for each 10¢ reduction in the price of admission, 25 more people would attend. For what admission price would the gross income be a maximum? \$1.15

---

16. A parabola described by an equation of the type

$$y = ax^2 + bx + c$$

is known to pass through points

$$(1, 3), \quad (^-1, 5), \quad (2, 11).$$

What is the equation for this particular parabola? $y = 3x^2 - x + 1$

17. Find the system of linear equations in a, b, and c which would have to be solvable for a parabola with an equation of the type

$$y = ax^2 + bx + c \qquad \begin{cases} a = 0 \\ b = 2 \\ c = ^-1 \end{cases}$$

to pass through points

$$(1, 1), \quad (2, 3), \quad (4, 7).$$

Does the system determine values for a, b, and c? Do these values for a, b, and c determine a parabola? Plot the three points to see what the difficulty is. No, a straight line

Hence, the axis is $x + 1 = 0$, or $x = ^-1$, and the vertex is at $(^-1, ^-8)$. The parabola may be drawn to determine y for $x = ^-3, ^-2, 0$, and 1.

A check should be made to see if the parabola drawn crosses the x-axis at

$$x = ^-1 \pm \tfrac{2}{3}\sqrt{6},$$

the solution of

$$3x^2 + 6x - 5 = 0,$$

found above.

Students should practice solving

$$ax^2 + bx + c = 0,$$

along with putting

$$y = ax^2 + bx + c$$

into the form

$$y = a(x - h)^2 + k,$$

to help them understand the basic difference between these two situations where completing the square in x is the technique to use.

It is recommended that Exercises 9 and 10 be assigned to all students.

Although Exercise 12 is too difficult for assignment to the average student, it is interesting for class work.

Exercise 14 is a good one to assign for honors work.

Although Exercise 15 is difficult, it can be interesting for class work.

Students are already familiar with the fact that a unique circle is determined by three noncollinear points; they have actually constructed such circles. In Exercises 16 and 17 they are confronting the same thing for parabolas. Algebraically, the need for three points manifests itself in the three constants a, b, c in the equation

$$y = ax^2 + bx + c,$$

where a controls steepness, b, assisted by a, locates the axis, and *c* places the vertex on the axis. A few students might be given a special library assignment to discover a construction of the parabola by means of straightedge and compass.

Quiz

(See page T14 for graphs.)

Transform each equation into the form $y = a(x - h)^2 + k$ and draw its graph. In each case, give the coordinates of the vertex and an equation of the axis of symmetry.

1. $y = x^2 - 8x + 16$ (ans: $y = (x - 4)^2$; $(4, 0)$, $x = 4$)

2. $y = 2x^2 + 12x + 18$ (ans: $y = 2(x + 3)^2$; $(^-3, 0)$, $x = {}^-3$)

3. $y = 3x^2 - 6x + 5$ (ans: $y = 3(x - 1)^2 + 2$; $(1, 2)$, $x = 1$)

3–8 QUADRATIC INEQUALITIES IN TWO VARIABLES

Students should have no difficulty with this section, since the ideas were covered in Section 6 of Chapter 2. It is worth noting that the inside of a parabola is below it or above it, depending on whether the parabola opens down or up.

Answers to Exercises for Discussion 1–3, 5, page 156

1. Since $8 = 4(^-1)^2 + 4$, the point $(^-1, 8)$ is on the graph. Since $7 > 4(0)^2 + 4$, the point $(0, 7)$ is inside the graph. Since

$$5 = 4(\tfrac{1}{2})^2 + 4,$$

the point $(\frac{1}{2}, 5)$ is on the graph. Since $21 > 4(2)^2 + 4$, the point $(2, 21)$ is inside the graph. Since $1 < 4(1)^2 + 4$, the point $(1, 1)$ is outside the graph. Since $^-10 < 4(^-5)^2 + 4$, the point $(^-5, ^-10)$ is outside the graph.

3–8 QUADRATIC INEQUALITIES IN TWO VARIABLES

Just as a line divides the plane in which it lies into two parts, a parabola divides the plane in which it lies into two parts. For example, the parabola with equation

$$y = x^2$$

divides the plane into two parts. The shaded part of Fig. 3–8 is called the *inside* of the parabola, while the rest of the plane, excluding the parabola, is called the *outside* of the parabola.

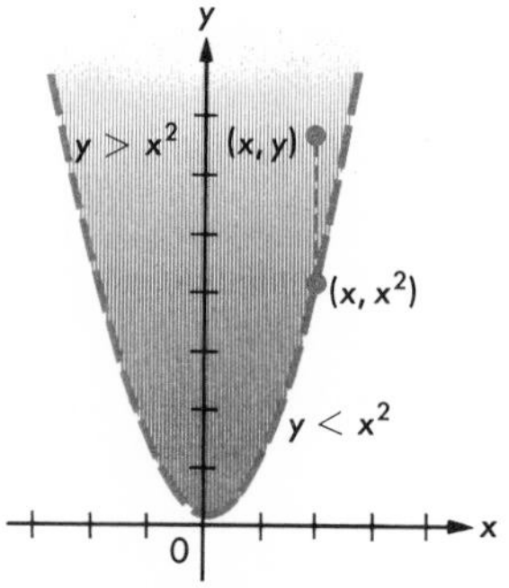

FIGURE 3–8

For each real number x, the point (x, x^2) is on the parabola $y = x^2$. The point (x, y) is inside this parabola provided it is directly above the point (x, x^2). In other words, the point (x, y) is inside the parabola if, and only if, $y > x^2$. Similarly, the point (x, y) is outside the parabola if, and only if, $y < x^2$. In the language of algebra, the inside of this parabola is the graph of the set

$$\{(x, y) \mid y > x^2\},$$

and the outside of this parabola is the graph of the set

$$\{(x, y) \mid y < x^2\}.$$

Problem 1. The parabola with equation

$$y = x^2 - 6x + 11$$

is drawn in Fig. 3–9. Describe the inside and the outside of this parabola.

Solution. For each real number x, the point $(x, x^2 - 6x + 11)$ is on the parabola. When we look at the figure, we see that a point (x, y) is inside the parabola if, and only if, it is directly above the point with coordinates $(x, x^2 - 6x + 11)$. Hence, the graph of the set

$$\{(x, y) \mid y > x^2 - 6x + 11\}$$

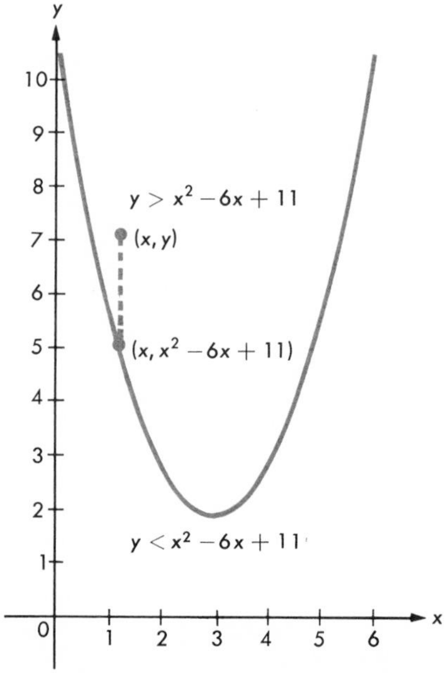

FIGURE 3–9

is the inside of the parabola, and the graph of the set

$$\{(x, y) \mid y < x^2 - 6x + 11\}$$

is the outside of the parabola.

Problem 2. The parabola with equation

$$y = {}^-2x^2 - 4x + 3$$

is drawn in Fig. 3–10. Describe the inside and the outside of this parabola.

Solution. For each real number x, the point $(x, {}^-2x^2 - 4x + 3)$ is on this parabola. Since this parabola opens downward, the inside is below the parabola. Thus, the graph of the set

$$\{(x, y) \mid y < {}^-2x^2 - 4x + 3\}$$

is the inside, and the graph of the set

$$\{(x, y) \mid y > {}^-2x^2 - 4x + 3\}$$

is the outside of this parabola.

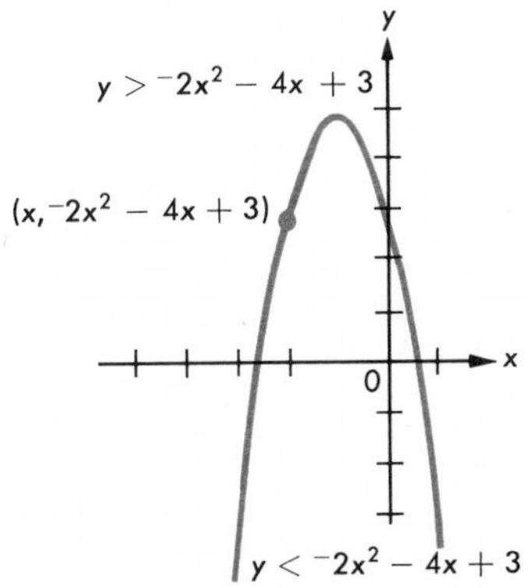

FIGURE 3–10

Problem 3. Describe the graph of the inequality $y + 3x^2 < 12x$.

Solution. By adding the quadratic polynomial ${}^-3x^2$ to each side of this inequality, we derive the equivalent inequality

$$y < {}^-3x^2 + 12x.$$

We complete the square for the quadratic polynomial ${}^-3x^2 + 12x$ as follows:

$$\begin{aligned} {}^-3x^2 + 12x &= {}^-3(x^2 - 4x), \\ {}^-3x^2 + 12x &= {}^-3(x^2 - 4x + 4) + 12, \\ {}^-3x^2 + 12x &= {}^-3(x - 2)^2 + 12. \end{aligned}$$

Thus, the given inequality is equivalent to the inequality

$$y < {}^-3(x - 2)^2 + 12.$$

2. (a) An equation of the parabola is

$$y = x^2 - 6x - 1.$$

Since the inside of the parabola lies above the parabola, it is the graph of

$$y > x^2 - 6x - 1.$$

Similarly, the outside of the parabola lies below the parabola and is the graph of

$$y < x^2 - 6x - 1.$$

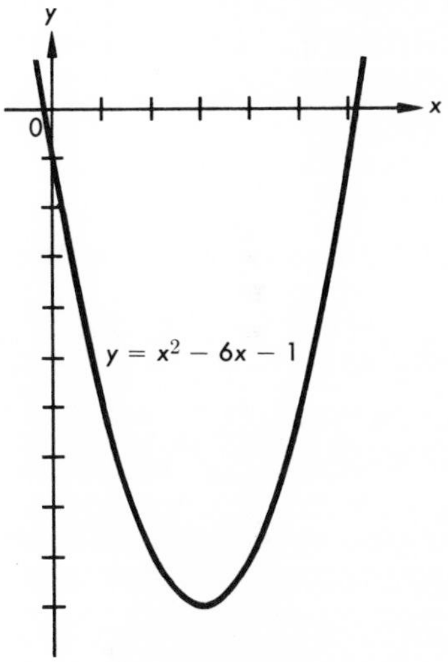

(b) An equation of the parabola is

$$y = {}^-3x^2 + 12x + 2.$$

Since the inside of the parabola lies below the parabola, it is the graph of

$$y < {}^-3x^2 + 12x + 2.$$

Also, the outside of the parabola lies above it and is the graph of

$$y > {}^-3x^2 + 12x + 2.$$

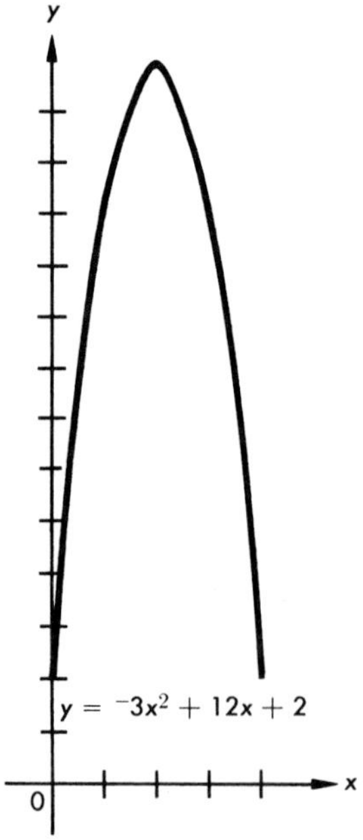

3. (a) The graph is the inside of the parabola which is the graph of $y = {}^{-}x^2 - 4x - 4$.

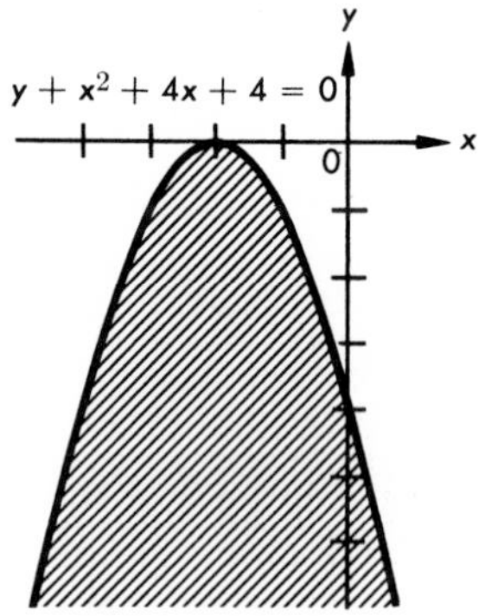

(b) The graph is the inside of the parabola which is the graph of $y = 2x^2 - 4x - 1$.

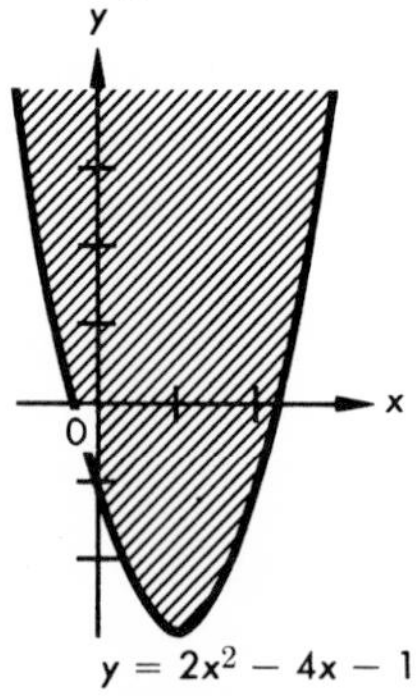

The graph of the equation

$$y = {}^{-}3(x - 2)^2 + 12$$

is a parabola with vertex (2, 12). The line $x = 2$ is the axis of symmetry, and the parabola opens downward, as shown in Fig. 3–11. A point (x, y) for which

$$y < {}^{-}3(x - 2)^2 + 12$$

is located inside the parabola. Thus, the graph of the given inequality is the inside of the parabola with equation

$$y = {}^{-}3(x - 2)^2 + 12.$$

It is the shaded region shown in Fig. 3–11.

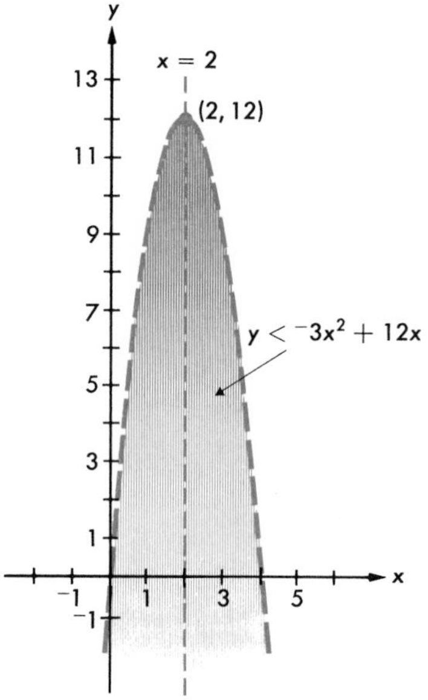

FIGURE 3–11

Exercises for Discussion

1. Tell whether each of the following points is inside, outside, or on the graph of the parabola whose equation is $y = 4x^2 + 4$.

$$({}^{-}1, 8),\quad (0, 7),\quad (\tfrac{1}{2}, 5),\quad (2, 21),\quad (1, 1),\quad ({}^{-}5, {}^{-}10)$$

2. Graph the parabola for each of the following equations. Write an inequality that describes the inside and the outside of each parabola.
   (a) $y = x^2 - 6x - 1$
   (b) $y = {}^{-}3x^2 + 12x + 2$

3. Describe the graph of each of the following inequalities by graphing a related parabola.
   (a) $y + x^2 + 4x + 4 < 0$
   (b) $y > 2x^2 - 4x - 1$ *Graph is the inside of the parabola which is the graph of $y = 2x^2 - 4x - 1$.*

4. What value of x gives the quadratic form $10 - x^2$ its maximum value? Does it have a minimum value? *Maximum value of 10 when $x = 0$; no minimum value*

.5. (a) For what values of x is the quadratic form $10 - 3x - x^2$ negative?
   (b) For what values of x is $10 - 3x - x^2$ positive?

Exercises

See Solution Manual for graphs.

1. Tell whether each of the following points is inside, outside, or on the graph of the parabola whose equation is $y = 6 - 5x^2$.

   $(0, {}^-1)$, $(5, 2)$, $(0, 8)$, $({}^-3, 3)$, $(1, 1)$, $(2, {}^-14)$, $(2, {}^-1)$
   Inside Outside Outside Outside On On Outside

2. Graph each of the following equations, and describe algebraically the inside and the outside of each parabola.
   (a) $2y = {}^-x^2 + 8x - 12$
   (b) $y = 2x^2 + 8x + 10$

Graph each of the following inequalities and describe the graph.

3. $x^2 + y \leqq 6y + 3$ The parabola and all points inside
4. $4x^2 + 4x + 1 > 8y$ Points outside parabola
5. $y + 3x^2 > 6x - 1$ Points outside parabola
6. $y + 1 \leqq {}^-5x^2$ The parabola and all points inside

△

In Exercises 7–10, find the solution set of each quadratic inequality in x.

7. $x^2 - 4x - 5 < 0$ $\{x \mid {}^-1 < x < 5\}$
8. $x^2 - 4x + 4 > 0$ $\{x \mid x \neq 2\}$
9. $x^2 - 2x + 1 < 0$ ϕ
10. $x^2 - 5x - 6 \geqq 0$ $\{x \mid x \leqq {}^-1 \text{ or } x \geqq 6\}$

11. What is the minimum value of each of the following quadratic polynomials for real values of x?
    (a) $x^2 - 6x + 8$ ${}^-1$
    (b) $x^2 - 5x - 2$ $\frac{-33}{4}$

12. What is the maximum value of each of the following quadratic polynomials for real values of x?
    (a) ${}^-x^2 + 10x + 2$ 27
    (b) $3 - x^2 + 7x$ $15\frac{1}{4}$

13. The height s, in feet, of an object above the ground at time t seconds is given by the equation $s = 64t - 16t^2$.
    (a) For what values of t is $s > 28$? $\{t \mid \frac{1}{2} < t < \frac{7}{2}\}$
    (b) For what values of t is $s < 48$? $\{t \mid 0 \leqq t < 1 \text{ or } 3 < t \leqq 4\}$
    (c) For what values of t is $s = 0$? $\{0, 4\}$

14. The volume V, in cubic inches, of water remaining in a leaking pail after t seconds is given by the equation $V = \frac{1}{5}(t - 100)^2$.
    (a) For what values of t is $V > 1000$? $\{t \mid 0 \leqq t < 100 - 50\sqrt{2}\}$
    (b) For what values of t is $V < 500$? $\{t \mid 50 < t \leqq 100\}$
    (c) When does the leaking stop? $t = 100$

5. $10 - 3x - x^2$
$= {}^-(x^2 + 3x) + 10$
$= {}^-(x^2 + 3x + \frac{9}{4}) + \frac{9}{4} + 10$
$= {}^-(x + \frac{3}{2})^2 + \frac{49}{4}$

(a) If $(x + \frac{3}{2})^2 > \frac{49}{4}$, the form is negative. Hence, $x + \frac{3}{2} < \frac{-7}{2}$ or $x + \frac{3}{2} > \frac{7}{2}$, or $x < {}^-5$ or $x > 2$. Thus, $\{x \mid x < {}^-5$ or $x > 2\}$.

(b) If $(x + \frac{3}{2})^2 < \frac{49}{4}$, the form is positive. Hence,

$${}^-\tfrac{7}{2} < x + \tfrac{3}{2} < \tfrac{7}{2}$$

or ${}^-5 < x < 2$. Thus,

$$\{x \mid {}^-5 < {}^-x < 2\}.$$

Exercises

Exercises 7–10 require classroom discussion. To determine whether a quadratic form $ax^2 + bx + c$ is positive, negative, or zero, graph the equation $y = ax^2 + bx + c$. The set of x's for which $y > 0$ is the solution set of the inequality

$$ax^2 + bx + c > 0.$$

The set of x's for which $y = 0$ is the solution set of the equation

$$ax^2 + bx + c = 0.$$

The set of x's for which $y < 0$ is the solution set of the inequality

$$ax^2 + bx + c < 0.$$

These sets should be obvious from the graphs, but it may be necessary to solve $ax^2 + bx + c = 0$ if more than an approximation to the end points of an interval is desired.

In class, you may wish to discuss determining the sign of the quadratic $x^2 - 3x + 1$ from the graph of

$$y = x^2 - 3x + 1.$$

Since $y = (x - \frac{3}{2})^2 - \frac{5}{4}$, the graph is a parabola with vertex at $(\frac{3}{2}, {}^-\frac{5}{4})$.

(Answer to Exercise 2 on page 159)

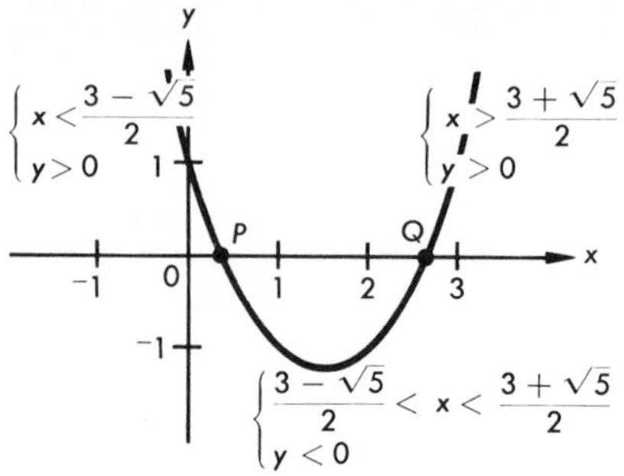

Other points on the graph are (1, $^-1$) and (2, $^-1$),(0, 1) and (3, 1). Now the points where the graph crosses the x-axis may be located exactly by solving

$$\begin{cases} y = x^2 - 3x + 1, \\ y = 0, \end{cases}$$

leading to

$$x = \frac{3+\sqrt{5}}{2}, \quad \text{or} \quad x = \frac{3-\sqrt{5}}{2},$$

$$x \doteq \frac{3+2.2}{2}, \quad \text{or} \quad \frac{3-2.2}{2},$$

$$x \doteq 2.6, \quad \text{or} \quad .4.$$

Thus, $x^2 - 3x + 1 = 0$ if

$$x = \frac{3 \pm \sqrt{5}}{2}.$$

When the parabola dips below the x-axis, $y < 0$ and so $x^2 - 3x + 1 < 0$. Hence, $x^2 - 3x + 1 < 0$ for

$$\frac{3-\sqrt{5}}{2} < x < \frac{3+\sqrt{5}}{2}.$$

When the parabola lies above the x-axis, $y > 0$ and so $x^2 - 3x + 1 > 0$. Hence, $x^2 - 3x + 1 > 0$ for

$$x > \frac{3+\sqrt{5}}{2} \quad \text{or} \quad x < \frac{3-\sqrt{5}}{2}.$$

Quiz

(See page T14 for graphs.)

Graph each of the following inequalities and describe the graph.

1. $y + 6 \geqq x^2 - x$ (ans: all points inside and on the parabola)

*3–9 MODULAR ARITHMETIC

The real number system contains infinitely many elements, but this is not true of all number systems. In fact, there is a number system, called the *integers modulo n,* where for every positive integer n, the system contains exactly n elements. Operations of addition and multiplication are defined in the system of integers modulo n, and most of the properties that apply to these operations are true for the modular system.

An example of such a modular system is the system of *integers modulo* 6, denoted by Z_6. The six elements of Z_6 are denoted by 0, 1, 2, 3, 4, and 5:

$$Z_6 = \{0, 1, 2, 3, 4, 5\}.$$

In Z_6 we add numbers by first adding them as we do in the system of integers and then "casting out," or subtracting, 6's until we obtain a number in Z_6. We perform multiplication in a similar way. For example, in each of the sums and products

$$1 + 2 = 3, \quad 0 + 4 = 4, \quad 2 + 3 = 5,$$
$$1 \times 2 = 2, \quad 2 \times 2 = 4, \quad 3 \times 0 = 0,$$

there is no need to "cast out" 6's because each sum and product is less than 6. However, $3 + 4 = 7$ in the system of integers and 7 is not in Z_6. In Z_6 we "cast out," or subtract, one 6 from 7 and obtain

$$3 + 4 = 1.$$

Also, $3 \times 5 = 15$, and 15 is not in Z_6. Therefore, we "cast out" two 6's from 15 and obtain

$$3 \times 5 = 3.$$

Similarly,

$$4 + 2 = 0, \quad 2 + 5 = 1, \quad 4 + 4 = 2,$$
$$4 \times 2 = 2, \quad 2 \times 5 = 4, \quad 4 \times 4 = 4.$$

It may be shown that in Z_6 the operations of addition and multiplication are commutative and associative and that the distributive law holds. Also, 0 is the additive identity element and 1 is the multiplicative identity element. Each number in Z_6 has an additive inverse, or opposite. Thus, $1 + 5 = 0$ and hence, 5 and 1 are opposites of each other:

$$5 = {}^-1 \quad \text{and} \quad 1 = {}^-5.$$

Also, $2 + 4 = 0$ and hence, 2 and 4 are opposites of each other:

$$4 = {}^{-}2 \quad \text{and} \quad 2 = {}^{-}4.$$

Also, $3 + 3 = 0$ and hence, 3 is its own opposite:

$$3 = {}^{-}3.$$

Not every nonzero element of Z_6 has a multiplicative inverse, or reciprocal. For example, $5 \times 5 = 1$, and therefore, 5 is its own reciprocal:

$$5 = \tfrac{1}{5}.$$

This is not too surprising, since $5 = {}^{-}1$ in Z_6 and $({}^{-}1)^2 = 1$. On the other hand, 2, 3, and 4 do not have reciprocals. For example,

$$2 \times 0 = 0, \quad 2 \times 1 = 2, \quad 2 \times 2 = 4,$$
$$2 \times 3 = 0, \quad 2 \times 4 = 2, \quad 2 \times 5 = 4,$$

so that $2x$ is never equal to 1 for any x in Z_6.

We can solve equations in Z_6 as well as we can in the system of real numbers. For example, we can solve the linear equation

$$x + 4 = 2$$

in the usual way:

$$(x + 4) + 2 = 2 + 2,$$
$$x + 0 = 4,$$
$$x = 4.$$

Some linear equations have no solution. We saw above that the equation

$$2x = 1$$

has no solution. Some linear equations have more than one solution. For example, the equation $2x = 2$ has solutions

$$x = 1 \quad \text{and} \quad x = 4.$$

Every quadratic equation can be solved, that is, its solution set can be found. We can solve an equation in x by giving x the values 0, 1, 2, 3, 4, and 5, in turn, and then determining whether the resulting equation is true. For example, to solve the quadratic equation

$$x^2 + x + 4 = 0,$$

2. $y < {}^{-}x^2 + 1$ (ans: all points inside the parabola)
3. Tell whether each of the points $(1, 1)$, $({}^{-}1, 2)$, $(0, 4)$ is inside, outside, or on the graph of the parabola whose equation is

$$y = {}^{-}2x^2 + 3.$$

(ans: on; outside; outside)

Answer to Exercise 2, page 157

2. (a) Inside:
   $\{(x, y) \mid 2y < {}^{-}x^2 + 8x - 12\}$
   Outside:
   $\{(x, y) \mid 2y > {}^{-}x^2 + 8x - 12\}$
   (b) Inside:
   $\{(x, y) \mid y > 2x^2 + 8x + 10\}$
   Outside:
   $\{(x, y) \mid y < 2x^2 + 8x + 10\}$

*3–9 MODULAR ARITHMETIC

Section 3–9 may be assigned for honors work to be reported orally either to the teacher or to the class. Reports such as this prepared by a group of from three to six students can be very exciting, and the students benefit tremendously from working on the material together. They should be encouraged to use the library in preparing this topic.

TWISTER

A 1-acre field in the shape of a right triangle has a post at the midpoint of each side. A goat is tied to the post on the hypotenuse and a sheep to each of the posts on the sides. The ropes are just long enough that each animal can reach the two adjacent vertices. What is the total area that the goat cannot reach?

Solution:

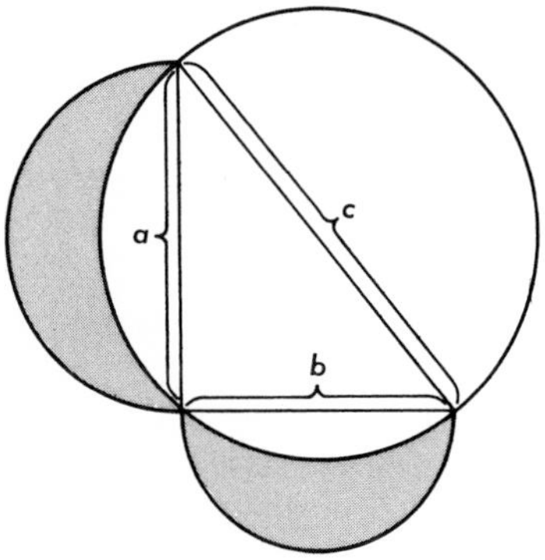

Let $r_1 = a/2, r_2 = b/2, r_3 = c/2$; the total area of the figure is

$$1 + \frac{\pi a^2}{8} + \frac{\pi b^2}{8} + \frac{\pi c^2}{8}.$$

Thus, the area the goat cannot reach is

$$1 + \frac{\pi a^2}{8} + \frac{\pi b^2}{8} + \frac{\pi c^2}{8} - \frac{2\pi c^2}{8}$$

$$= 1 + \frac{\pi}{8}(a^2 + b^2) + \frac{\pi c^2}{8} - \frac{2\pi c^2}{8}$$

$$= 1 + \frac{\pi c^2}{8} + \frac{\pi c^2}{8} - \frac{2\pi c^2}{8}$$

$= 1$ acre.

let x equal each of the following values and then determine whether the resulting equation is true.

If $x = 0$, then $0^2 + 0 + 4 = 0$, and $4 = 0$ is a false equation.
If $x = 1$, then $1^2 + 1 + 4 = 0$, and $0 = 0$ is a true equation.
If $x = 2$, then $2^2 + 2 + 4 = 0$, and $4 = 0$ is a false equation.
If $x = 3$, then $3^2 + 3 + 4 = 0$, and $4 = 0$ is a false equation.
If $x = 4$, then $4^2 + 4 + 4 = 0$, and $0 = 0$ is a true equation.
If $x = 5$, then $5^2 + 5 + 4 = 0$, and $4 = 0$ is a false equation.

Therefore, $\{1, 4\}$ is the solution set of the equation $x^2 + x + 4 = 0$ in Z_6.

As another example, we shall solve the equation $x^2 + x = 0$ in the same way that we solved the equation above.

If $x = 0$, then $0^2 + 0 = 0$, and $0 = 0$ is a true equation.
If $x = 1$, then $1^2 + 1 = 0$, and $2 = 0$ is a false equation.
If $x = 2$, then $2^2 + 2 = 0$, and $0 = 0$ is a true equation.
If $x = 3$, then $3^2 + 3 = 0$, and $0 = 0$ is a true equation.
If $x = 4$, then $4^2 + 4 = 0$, and $2 = 0$ is a false equation.
If $x = 5$, then $5^2 + 5 = 0$, and $0 = 0$ is a true equation.

Therefore, in Z_6, $\{0, 2, 3, 5\}$ is the solution set of the equation $x^2 + x = 0$. Thus, in Z_6 we have a quadratic equation which has *four* solutions, whereas every quadratic equation in the real number system has at most two solutions.

Exercises

Solve each of the following linear equations in Z_6.

1. $x + 3 = 2$ $\{5\}$
2. $5x + 1 = 4$ $\{3\}$
3. $3x = 0$ $\{0, 2, 4\}$
4. $3x = 1$ $\emptyset$
5. $4x + 5 = 1$ $\{2, 5\}$
6. $4x + 2 = 0$ $\{1, 4\}$
7. $3x = 3$ $\{1, 3, 5\}$
8. $2x + 1 = 0$ $\emptyset$

In Exercises 9–16, solve each of the quadratic equations in Z_6.

9. $x^2 + 3x + 2 = 0$ $\{1, 2, 4, 5\}$
10. $x^2 + 2 = 0$ $\{2, 4\}$
11. $x^2 + 4x + 1 = 0$ $\{1\}$
12. $2x^2 + 1 = 0$ $\emptyset$
13. $x^2 + x + 1 = 0$ $\emptyset$
14. $3x^2 + x = 0$ $\{0, 3\}$
15. $2x^2 + 4x = 0$ $\{0, 1, 3, 4\}$
16. $3x^2 + 3x = 0$ $\{0, 1, 2, 3, 4, 5\}$

17. Discuss the system of integers modulo 7:

$$Z_7 = \{0, 1, 2, 3, 4, 5, 6\}.$$

Give examples of addition and multiplication in this system. Show that each nonzero number in Z_7 has a multiplicative inverse.

18. Prove that (Can-A) is valid for Z_6. Show by example that (Can-M) is not valid for Z_6. See Solution Manual.

19. Prove that both (Can-A) and (Can-M) are valid for Z_7. See Solution Manual.

20. What numbers have square roots in Z_6? in Z_7? 0, 1, 3, 4; 0, 1, 2, 4

21. Mr. Ex, a superstitious scientist, plans to direct a 7-month expedition to Timbuctoo from May through November of some year. However, he insists that the group wait for a year in which no one of these months has a Friday the thirteenth. Explain why Mr. Ex's expedition will never take place. (Hint: Denote the days of the week by numbers from Z_7. Use 0 for Sunday, 1 for Monday, and so on. If the number x denotes May 13, what is the number for June 13? for July 13? for the thirteenth of each of the other months?) See Solution Manual.

KEY IDEAS AND KEY WORDS

An expression of the form

$$ax^2 + bx + c, \quad a \neq 0,$$

where a, b, and c are real numbers, is called a **quadratic polynomial,** or **quadratic form.** The number a is called the **coefficient** of x^2, and c is called the **constant term.**

An equation of the form

$$ax^2 + bx + c = 0, \quad a \neq 0,$$

is called a **second-degree equation,** or **quadratic equation.** A number is called a **solution** of a quadratic equation if a true statement results when the variable is given the number as a value. The set of all solutions of the equation is called the **solution set** of the equation.

If a quadratic polynomial is the square of a linear form, then it is called a **perfect square.**

The process of adding a constant term to a quadratic polynomial to make it a perfect square is called **completing the square.**

The graph of the equation

$$y = ax^2 + bx + c, \quad a \neq 0,$$

is called a **parabola.** The **vertex** of a parabola is its highest or lowest point.

Answer to Exercise 17

17. Here, 1 and 6 are their own multiplicative inverses; 2 and 4 are multiplicative inverses of each other; and 3 and 5 are multiplicative inverses of each other.

Quiz

Solve each of the following equations in Z_6.

1. $3x + 1 = 4$ (ans: $\{1, 3, 5\}$)
2. $5x + 2 = 0$ (ans: $\{2\}$)
3. $x^2 + x + 1 = 1$ (ans: $\{0, 2, 3, 5\}$)
4. $3x^2 + 1 = 4$ (ans: $\{1, 3, 5\}$)

TWISTER

A large circular table was pushed into the corner of a room, so that it touched both walls. An ink spot on the edge of the table closest to the corner was exactly 8 inches from one wall and 9 inches from the other. What was the diameter of the table?

Solution:

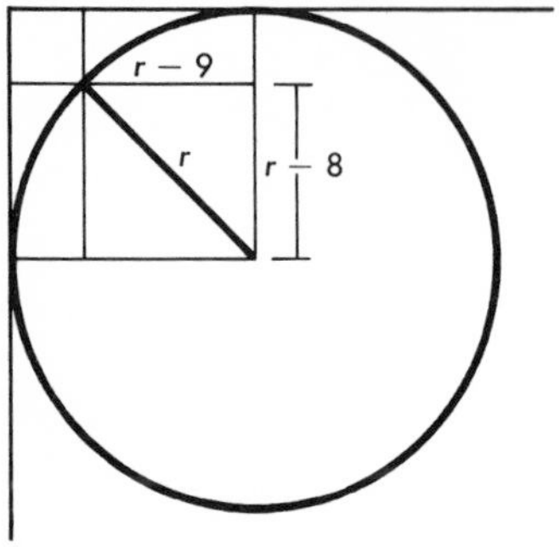

$$r^2 = (r - 8)^2 + (r - 9)^2$$
$$= 2r^2 - 34r + 145.$$

Thus,

$$r^2 - 34r + 145 = 0,$$

and

$$r = 29 \quad \text{or} \quad r = 5.$$

Since the table is said to be large, the radius must be 29 and the diameter 58 inches.

CHAPTER TEST

The material included in the Chapter Test was covered in the following sections:

Problems 1–3—Section 3-2
Problem 4—Section 3-4
Problem 5—Section 3-7
Problems 6 and 7—Section 3-8

A line is the **axis of symmetry** of a parabola if the two parts of the graph on opposite sides of the line are **mirror images** of each other.

The system of **integers modulo 6** is made up of a set of six numbers:

$$0, \quad 1, \quad 2, \quad 3, \quad 4, \quad 5.$$

Addition and multiplication are defined in the following manner. We take the sum or product and then "cast out" sixes from the answer. For example,

$$4 + 5 = 3, \quad 4 \cdot 5 = 2, \quad 3 + 5 = 2, \quad 3 \cdot 5 = 3.$$

There is a similar system of **integers modulo *n*** for every positive integer *n*.

CHAPTER REVIEW

Find the solution set of each of the equations in Exercises 1–10.

1. $2x^2 + 5x - 3 = 0$ $\{\frac{1}{2}, {}^-3\}$
2. $7x^2 = 9x$ $\{0, \frac{9}{7}\}$
3. $20x^2 - 5 = 0$ $\{\frac{1}{2}, \frac{-1}{2}\}$
4. $(3x^2 - 12)(9x^2 + 3x - 2) = 0$ $\{2, {}^-2, \frac{1}{3}, \frac{-2}{3}\}$
5. $4x^2 - 20x + 25 = 0$ $\{\frac{5}{2}\}$
6. $3x^2 + 6x + 1 = 0$ $\{{}^-1 + \frac{1}{3}\sqrt{6}, {}^-1 - \frac{1}{3}\sqrt{6}\}$
7. $(2x - 1)^2 - 7(2x - 1) + 12 = 0$ $\{2, \frac{5}{2}\}$
8. $(x - 3)^2 - 8(x - 3) + 7 = 0$ $\{4, 10\}$
9. $(x^2 - 8)(x^2 - 15) = x^2 - 8$ $\{2\sqrt{2}, {}^-2\sqrt{2}, 4, {}^-4\}$
10. $x^2(x^2 - 225) = 0$ $\{0, 15, {}^-15\}$

11. A grassy plot 25 feet by 30 feet is surrounded by a walk of uniform width. If the area of the walk is 300 square feet, how wide is it? $2\frac{1}{2}$ ft
12. One side of a right triangle is 3 inches shorter than the hypotenuse and 3 inches longer than the other side. Find the dimensions of the right triangle. 9 in., 12 in., 15 in.
13. An engineer can decrease by 2 hours the time it takes to travel 200 miles if he increases the speed of the freight train by 5 miles per hour. What is the original speed of the train? 20 mph
14. Two numbers whose sum is 57 have squares that differ by 627. Find the numbers. 23 and 34
15. Show that each of the following quadratic equations has no real solutions.
    (a) $3x^2 - 2x + 4 = 0$ (b) $x^2 + x + 1 = 0$
    See Solution Manual.
16. For what values of k will each of the following quadratic equations have real solutions?
    (a) $x^2 - kx + 6 = 0$ $\{k \mid k \leqq {}^-2\sqrt{6} \text{ or } k \geqq 2\sqrt{6}\}$
    (b) $x^2 - 6x - k = 0$ $\{k \mid k \geqq {}^-9\}$

See Solution Manual for graphs.

17. Graph each of the following equations or inequalities. Give an equation of the axis of symmetry and the coordinates of the vertex of each parabola.

(a) $y = {}^{-}2(x + 3)^2 + 1$ Axis: $x = {}^{-}3$; vertex: $({}^{-}3, 1)$
(b) $y = 2x^2 - 4x + 1$ Axis: $x = 1$; vertex: $(1, {}^{-}1)$
(c) $y \leqq 3x^2 + 6x + 1$ Axis: $x = {}^{-}1$; vertex: $({}^{-}1, {}^{-}2)$
(d) $y + x^2 \leqq 6x - 9$ Axis: $x = 3$; vertex: $(3, 0)$

18. Find the maximum or minimum value of each of the following quadratic polynomials.

(a) $5x^2 - 2x - 2$ Minimum $= \frac{{}^{-}11}{5}$ (b) $2 - 4x - 5x^2$ Maximum $= \frac{14}{5}$

19. Solve each quadratic inequality in x.

(a) $x^2 - 2x - 3 \geqq 0$ $\{x \mid x \leqq {}^{-}1 \text{ or } x \geqq 3\}$
(b) $9 + 8x - x^2 \geqq 0$ $\{x \mid {}^{-}1 \leqq x \leqq 9\}$

20. Approximate the solutions of the equation $x^2 - 2x - 4 = 0$ from the graph of $y = x^2 - 2x - 4$. ${}^{-}1.2$ and 3.2

21. Find an equation of a parabola if the graph of the parabola contains the points (1, 1), (⁻1, ⁻5), and (⁻3, 5). $y = 2x^2 + 3x - 4$

CHAPTER TEST

Solve each of the equations in Exercises 1–4.

1. $(x^2 - 1)(7x^2 + 4x - 3) = 0$ $\{1, {}^{-}1, \frac{3}{7}\}$
2. $2(x - 3)^2 - 5(x - 3) - 12 = 0$ $\{\frac{3}{2}, 7\}$
3. $(x - 2)^2(x^2 - 4) = 0$ $\{2, {}^{-}2\}$
4. $3x^2 - 6x - 2 = 0$ $\{1 + \frac{1}{3}\sqrt{15}, 1 - \frac{1}{3}\sqrt{15}\}$

5. (a) Draw the graph of the equation $y = 2x^2 - 10x - 8$.
   (b) Find the axis of symmetry and the vertex of the parabola in part (a).
6. (a) Graph the solution set of $y \geqq 10 + 12x - 3x^2$.
   (b) Find the maximum value of the quadratic form $10 + 12x - 3x^2$. 22
7. (a) Graph the solution set of $x^2 + x - 6 \leqq y$.
   (b) Find the minimum value of the quadratic form $x^2 + x - 6$. $\frac{{}^{-}25}{4}$

Answers to Chapter Test Problems 5, 6(a), 7(a)

5. (a)

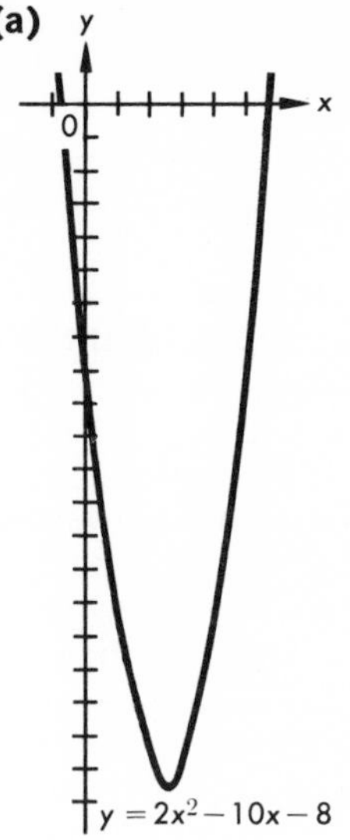

(b) Axis: $x = \frac{5}{2}$; vertex: $(\frac{5}{2}, \frac{{}^{-}41}{2})$

6. (a)

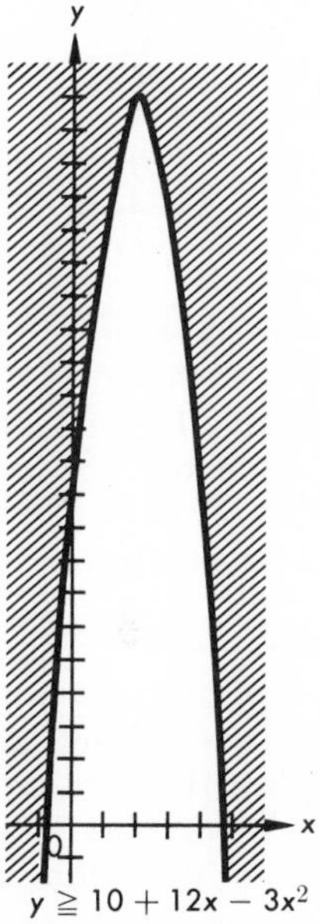

7. (a)

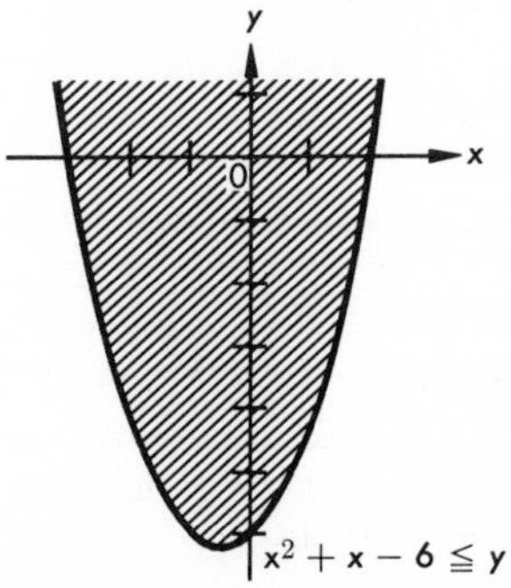

CHAPTER 4

The Complex Number System

The purpose of Chapter 4 is to investigate a new kind of number designated by the symbol i and defined to be a solution of the quadratic equation $x^2 + 1 = 0$. Hence, by definition, $i^2 + 1 = 0$, or $i = \sqrt{^-1}$.

Although i is new, half of the integral powers of i are familiar to the student (i^2, i^4, i^6, i^8, . . .). As rules of arithmetic are set up for i-numbers, real-number answers keep appearing, such as

$$(3i)^2 = {}^-9,$$
$$5i \cdot 4i = {}^-20,$$
$$5i \div 4i = \tfrac{5}{4}.$$

Therefore, it becomes apparent that the real and the imaginary numbers are part of a larger system of numbers which may be described as *complex*. They are numbers that cannot be lined up. To represent them graphically, a number plane is required which has an axis for the subset of real numbers and an axis for the subset of imaginary numbers. They are designated as $a + bi$, where a and b are real; i is $\sqrt{^-1}$; and the plus sign merely serves as a formal separation between the real and the imaginary numbers.

The following are some of the topics covered in Chapter 4:

- *Pure imaginary numbers*
- *Addition and multiplication of i-numbers*
- *Addition and multiplication of an i-number and a real number*
- *Complex numbers*

CHAPTER 4

The study of the two-dimensional flow of a stream of water involves the use of equations containing complex numbers. (Courtesy of Bureau of Reclamation, Department of the Interior)

- *Addition of complex numbers*
- *Multiplication of complex numbers*
- *Quotients of complex numbers*
- *Quadratic formula*
- *Discriminant of a quadratic equation*
- *Complex number plane*
- *Graph of a complex number*

It is suggested that one day be spent on each section of this chapter, except for Sections 4–5 and 4–6, which may require two days.

THE COMPLEX NUMBER SYSTEM

As the uses of mathematics grow, the content of mathematics necessarily expands. This process is illustrated by the number systems. In ancient times, only positive integers were used. Gradually, the need for fractions was felt, and positive rational numbers came into use. The Greek mathematicians of two thousand years ago discussed irrational numbers, such as $\sqrt{2}$. At a much later time, negative numbers were introduced into mathematics. The real number system was being used by the sixteenth century, although it was not completely understood until the nineteenth century.

As early as the sixteenth century, such strange numbers as $\sqrt{{}^{-}2}$ appeared in mathematics books. Such a number is not real because ${}^{-}2$ is not the square of a real number. However, it is natural to call $\sqrt{{}^{-}2}$ a solution of the quadratic equation

$$x^2 + 2 = 0,$$

since

$$(\sqrt{{}^{-}2})^2 + 2 = {}^{-}2 + 2, \quad \text{or } 0.$$

Numbers of the form

$$3 - 5\sqrt{{}^{-}3}$$

are used frequently in science books today. Such numbers are called complex numbers. The system of complex numbers has many of the properties of the real number system, as we shall show in this chapter.

165

4-1 PURE IMAGINARY NUMBERS

One of the goals in the teaching of high school mathematics should be to help students to be able to glean information by themselves from the printed page. This section on pure imaginary numbers with its definition of i as the solution of the quadratic equation $x^2 + 1 = 0$, and the consideration of the laws of real numbers to motivate the definitions of addition and other arithmetic operations with i-numbers, is an excellent section to assign for independent reading and study.

A comprehensive discussion and questioning period will reveal whether all details of the section have been understood. If i is defined so that $i^2 = {}^-1$ and $x^2 + 1 = 0$ has a solution, does this also provide a solution for $x^2 + 4 = 0$? The new number i seems to generate more new numbers such as $2 \cdot i$. It seems logical to try to define the arithmetic for these new numbers so that the laws of commutativity and associativity for multiplication and addition, as well as the distributive law, still hold.

A student may be asked to prove that if $ai + bi$ is defined to be $(a + b) \cdot i$, then addition of i-numbers is commutative. Another student may prove that this addition is associative. The fundamental material of Chapter 1 could be reviewed here as it may now seem more necessary to the student than it did in regard to the already familiar real number system.

4-1 PURE IMAGINARY NUMBERS

Although the quadratic equation

$$x^2 + 4 = 0$$

has no real solution, it is possible to enlarge our number system so that this equation has a solution in our new system. In this section, we shall describe how to extend the real number system to a larger system in which every quadratic equation has a solution.

We shall choose a new number which will be designated by i,† and we shall assume that it is a solution of the quadratic equation

$$x^2 + 1 = 0.$$

In other words, we shall assume that i is a new number with the property

$$i^2 = {}^-1.$$

Clearly, i is not a real number, since no real number has a negative number for its square.

Along with the new number i, we wish to consider other new numbers such as $3i$, ${}^-2i$, $7i$, $\sqrt{2}i$, and πi. Such numbers will be called *pure imaginary numbers*, or *i-numbers*. Thus, an i-number is a number of the form bi, where b is a real number.

The sum of two i-numbers is defined in a way consistent with the rules of arithmetic. If we think of bi as $b \cdot i$, and if we assume that the distributive law is valid for i-numbers, then

$$3i + 4i = (3 + 4)i, \quad \text{or } 7i;$$
$${}^-8i + 5i = ({}^-8 + 5)i, \quad \text{or } {}^-3i.$$

These examples suggest that we define the addition of i-numbers in the following way.

DEFINITION OF ADDITION OF i-NUMBERS

$$bi + di = (b + d)i \quad \textit{for all real numbers } b \textit{ and } d$$

According to this definition, the sum of two i-numbers is another i-number, that is, the set of all i-numbers is closed under addition.

---

† The symbol i was introduced into mathematics by the famous eighteenth-century Swiss mathematician Euler (pronounced "Oiler"). It is possible that he chose i because it is the first letter of the Latin word *imaginarius* (imaginary).

Is addition of i-numbers commutative? In other words, is

$$3i + 4i = 4i + 3i,$$
$$^{-}8i + 5i = 5i + {}^{-}8i,$$

and so on? By definition,

$$3i + 4i = (3 + 4)i,$$

whereas

$$4i + 3i = (4 + 3)i.$$

Since $3 + 4 = 4 + 3$ by the commutative law for addition of real numbers, it follows that $3i + 4i = 4i + 3i$. Similarly, it can be shown that

$$bi + di = di + bi$$

for any real numbers b and d. Therefore, addition of i-numbers is *commutative*.

The addition of i-numbers is also *associative*, that is,

$$bi + (di + fi) = (bi + di) + fi$$

for any real numbers b, d, and f. To prove this, observe that

$$\begin{aligned} bi + (di + fi) &= bi + (d + f)i \\ &= [b + (d + f)]i, \end{aligned}$$

whereas

$$\begin{aligned} (bi + di) + fi &= (b + d)i + fi \\ &= [(b + d) + f]i. \end{aligned}$$

Since the associative law of addition is valid for the real number system, we have

$$b + (d + f) = (b + d) + f.$$

This proves that the addition of i-numbers is an associative operation.

Let us *define*

$$0i = 0.$$

Then it follows that

$$\begin{aligned} bi + 0 &= bi + 0i \\ &= (b + 0)i \\ &= bi. \end{aligned}$$

Therefore, 0 is the *additive identity element* for i-numbers as well as for real numbers.

TWISTER

What is the fallacy in the following proof?
Since

$$\sqrt{x} \cdot \sqrt{y} = \sqrt{xy},$$

it follows that

$$\begin{aligned} \sqrt{^{-}1} \cdot \sqrt{^{-}1} &= \sqrt{(^{-}1) \cdot (^{-}1)} \\ &= \sqrt{1} \end{aligned}$$

Thus,

$$(\sqrt{^{-}1})^2 = \sqrt{1}$$

and

$$^{-}1 = 1$$

Solution: If, and only if, x and y are positive real numbers, $\sqrt{x} \cdot \sqrt{y} = \sqrt{xy}$.

Students could be asked to prove the four statements on this page and to give reasons for each step of their proof.

Each i-number has an additive inverse. For example,

$$\begin{aligned} 3i + {}^{-}3i &= (3 + {}^{-}3)i \\ &= 0i, \quad \text{or } 0, \end{aligned}$$

and ${}^{-}3i$ is the additive inverse, or opposite, of $3i$. Similarly, it can be shown that ${}^{-}bi$ is the opposite of bi for each real number b.

The product of a real number and an i-number is also defined in a way consistent with the rules of arithmetic. For example,

$$3 \cdot 4i = 12i, \quad {}^{-}5 \cdot {}^{-}7i = 35i.$$

In other words, we define the multiplication of an i-number and a real number in the following way.

DEFINITION OF MULTIPLICATION OF AN i-NUMBER AND A REAL NUMBER

$$a \cdot bi = (a \cdot b)i \quad \textit{for any real numbers } a \textit{ and } b$$

Note that the product of a real number and an i-number is an i-number. It is easily verified that the following properties are valid for this kind of multiplication.

$$\begin{aligned} (a + c)bi &= abi + cbi && \text{(D)} \\ a(bi + di) &= abi + adi && \text{(D)} \\ (a \cdot c)(bi) &= a(c \cdot bi) && \text{(A-M)} \\ 1 \cdot (bi) &= bi && \text{(Id-M)} \end{aligned}$$

For example, let us prove that $a \cdot (bi + di) = abi + adi$.

$$\begin{aligned} a \cdot (bi + di) &= a \cdot [(b + d)i] && (1) \\ &= [a \cdot (b + d)]i && (2) \\ &= (ab + ad)i && (3) \\ &= (ab)i + (ad)i && (4) \\ &= abi + adi && (5) \end{aligned}$$

Equation (1) is true by the definition of addition of i-numbers. Equation (2) follows from (1) by the definition of the product of a real number and an i-number. Equation (3) follows from (2) by the distributive law for real numbers. Equation (4) follows from (3) by the definition of addition of i-numbers. Equation (5) follows from (4) by the definition of the product of an i-number and a real number. Hence, $a \cdot (bi + di) = abi + adi$.

We have defined the sum of two *i*-numbers and the product of a real number and an *i*-number. Next, let us define the product of two *i*-numbers. If we think of $7i$ as $7 \cdot i$ and of $3i$ as $3 \cdot i$, then it is natural to define the product of $7i$ and $3i$ as follows:

$$7i \cdot 3i = (7 \cdot 3) \cdot (i \cdot i)$$
$$= 21i^2$$
$$= 21(^-1), \quad \text{or} \quad ^-21.$$

Thus, we define the multiplication of *i*-numbers in the following way.

DEFINITION OF MULTIPLICATION OF i-NUMBERS

$$bi \cdot di = {}^-bd \quad \text{for all real numbers } b \text{ and } d$$

Since $i \cdot {}^-i = {}^-i^2$, or 1, ^-i is the *multiplicative inverse*, or reciprocal, of i. Interestingly enough, ^-i also is the *additive inverse* of i since $i + {}^-i = 0$. Every nonzero *i*-number has a reciprocal. For example, since

$$3i \cdot {}^-\tfrac{1}{3}i = 3 \cdot {}^-\tfrac{1}{3} \cdot i^2, \quad \text{or } 1,$$

$^-\tfrac{1}{3}i$ is the reciprocal of $3i$. More generally,

$$\frac{^-1}{b}\,i$$

is the *reciprocal* of bi for every nonzero *i*-number bi.

Exercises for Discussion

In Exercises 1–6, use the properties discussed in this section to perform the indicated operations with *i*-numbers.

1. $(2i)^3$ $2^3 \cdot i^3 = 8i^2 \cdot i = 8(^-1)i = {}^-8i$ 2. $2(7i) - 7(3i)$ $14i - 21i = (14-21)i$ $= {}^-7i$

3. $(7i)(3i) + 21$ 4. $(^-i)^5$

5. $i + i^2 + i^3 + i^4$ 6. $i^6 + i^8$

7. Find the value of i^n when n is 4, 8, 12, 16, 20, and 100. Write a statement about the value of i^n when n is a positive integral multiple of 4. $1;\ i^{4k} = 1$

8. Find the value of i^n when n is 2, 6, 10, 14, 18, and 98. Make a statement about the value of i^n when n is 2, or 2 more than a positive integral multiple of 4. $^-1;\ i^{4k+2} = {}^-1$

9. Find the value of i^n when n is 1, 5, 9, 13, 17, and 97. Make a statement about the value of i^n when n is 1, or 1 more than a positive integral multiple of 4. $i;\ i^{4k+1} = i$

Students may be asked to prove that multiplication of *i*-numbers, defined as $(bi) \cdot (di) = {}^-bd$, is both commutative and associative, and that the distributive law holds.

Exercises for Discussion

The class could be instructed to do Exercises for Discussion 1–12 after they have read the section. (The Exercises for Discussion form a unit of thought and should all be assigned at the same time.) If time is limited, it is suggested that at least Exercises for Discussion 7–11 be covered.

Answers to Exercises for Discussion 3–6

3. $(7i)(3i) + 21$
$= (7 \cdot 3)i^2 + 21$
$= (21)\,(^-1) + 21$
$= {}^-21 + 21 = 0$

4. $(^-i)^5 = (^-1)^5 i^5$
$= {}^-1 \cdot i^4 \cdot i$
$= {}^-1(i^2)^2 \cdot i$
$= {}^-1(^-1)^2 i = {}^-i$

5. $i + i^2 + i^3 + i^4$
$= i + {}^-1 + (i \cdot i^2) + (i^2)^2$
$= i + {}^-1 + i(^-1) + (^-1)^2$
$= i - 1 - i + 1 = 0$

6. $i^6 + i^8 = (i^2)^3 + (i^2)^4$
$= (^-1)^3 + (^-1)^4$
$= {}^-1 + 1 = 0$

Answer to Exercise for Discussion 11

11. The possible values of $(i)^n$ are $i, {}^-i, 1, {}^-1$.

$$i^n = i,\ n = 4k + 1$$
$$i^n = {}^-1,\ n = 4k + 2$$
$$i^n = {}^-i,\ n = 4k + 3$$
$$i^n = 1,\ n = 4k$$

In Exercise for Discussion 12, $x^2 - 9$ is factorable over the real numbers because 9 has two square roots, 3 and $^-3$, such that

$$3 \cdot {}^-3 = {}^-9,$$

and

$$3 + {}^-3 = 0.$$

Therefore,

$$x^2 - 9 = (x - 3)(x + 3).$$

However,

$$x^2 + 9 = x^2 - {}^-9$$

cannot be factored over the real numbers because $^-9$ has no real square roots. There are no real numbers whose product is 9 and whose sum is 0. But with i-numbers, $^-9$ has two square roots, $3i$ and ^-3i, with

$$(3i)({}^-3i) = 9$$

and

$$3i + {}^-3i = 0,$$

so

$$x^2 + 9 = (x - 3i)(x + 3i).$$

Exercises

Attention should be called to the paragraph between Exercises 14 and 15. It is recommended that Exercises 15–21 be assigned.

10. Find the value of i^n when n is 3, 7, 11, 15, 19, and 99. Make a statement about the value of i^n when n is 3, or 3 more than a positive integral multiple of 4. ^-i; $i^{4k+3} = {}^-i$

11. Describe the pattern for i^n when n is a non-negative integer.

12. We can use i-numbers to write the quadratic polynomial $x^2 + 9$ as a product in the following way.

$$x^2 + 9 = x^2 - (9)({}^-1)$$
$$= x^2 - 9i^2$$
$$= (x + 3i)(x - 3i)$$

Using both i-numbers and real numbers, factor each of the following polynomials into as many linear factors as you can.

(a) $x^2 + 16$ $(x+4i)(x-4i)$ (b) $x^4 - 16$ (four linear factors) $(x^2+4)(x^2-4) = (x+2i)(x-2i)(x+2)(x-2)$

Exercises

Using the properties discussed in this section, perform the indicated operations with i-numbers.

1. $(\frac{1}{2}\sqrt{3}i)^2$ $\frac{^-3}{4}$
2. $3i(2i + \sqrt{2}i)$ $^-6 - 3\sqrt{2}$
3. $(\sqrt{3}i)[(2i)({}^-7i)]$ $14\sqrt{3}i$
4. $({}^-\sqrt{2}i)^4$ 4
5. $(3 \cdot 5i) - (8 \cdot 7i)$ ^-41i
6. ${}^-\frac{13}{2}(11i - 5i)$ ^-39i
7. $(8i)({}^-\frac{1}{8}i)$ 1
8. $({}^-7i)^2 + 49$ 0
9. $(4i)^2 - 16$ $^-32$
10. $({}^-3i)^4 - 81$ 0
11. $i + i^3$ 0
12. $i^2 + i^4$ 0
13. $i^5 + i^7$ 0
14. $i^9 + i^{10} + i^{11} + i^{12}$ 0

If we write i^{-3} as $1/i^3$ and multiply by i/i, we obtain

$$i^{-3} = \frac{1}{i^3} = \frac{1}{i^3} \cdot \frac{i}{i}, \quad \text{or } i.$$

We may simplify negative integral powers of i in a similar manner. Simplify each expression in Exercises 15–20.

15. i^{-2} $^-1$ **16.** i^{-7} i **17.** i^{-12} 1 **18.** i^{-17} ^-i **19.** i^{-38} $^-1$ **20.** i^{-19} i

21. Verify that each of the following equations is true. See Solution Manual.

(a) $i^{4k} = 1$, k any integer (b) $i^{4k+1} = i$, k any integer
(c) $i^{4k+2} = {}^-1$, k any integer (d) $i^{4k+3} = {}^-i$, k any integer

Write each of the following quotients as a real number or as an i-number.

22. $\frac{1}{i^2}$ $^-1$ **23.** $\frac{^-1}{i^3}$ ^-i **24.** $\frac{4}{i^4}$ 4 **25.** $\frac{^-1}{2i}$ $\frac{1}{2}i$ **26.** $\frac{1}{7i^5}$ $\frac{^-1}{7}i$ **27.** $\frac{^-3}{2i^{10}}$ $\frac{3}{2}$

28. Using both i-numbers and real numbers, factor each of the following polynomials into as many linear factors as you can.

(a) $9x^2 + 25$ $(3x+5i)(3x-5i)$ (b) $x^2 - 7$ $(x+\sqrt{7})(x-\sqrt{7})$

(c) $x^2 + 7$ $(x+\sqrt{7}i)(x-\sqrt{7}i)$ (d) $81x^4 - 1$ (four linear factors) $(3x+1)(3x-1)(3x-i)(3x+i)$

In Exercises 29–34, find the solution set for each equation by factoring the left side into as many linear factors as you can. Use i-numbers, if necessary.

29. $x^2 + 36 = 0$ $\{6i, {}^-6i\}$ 30. $x^2 - 36 = 0$ $\{{}^-6, 6\}$

31. $9x^2 + 25 = 0$ $\{\frac{{}^-5}{3}i, \frac{5}{3}i\}$ 32. $x^2 + 5 = 0$ $\{{}^-\sqrt{5}i, \sqrt{5}i\}$

33. $x^4 - 81 = 0$ (four solutions) $\{{}^-3, 3, {}^-3i, 3i\}$ 34. $\frac{1}{16}x^4 - 1 = 0$ $\{2, {}^-2, 2i, {}^-2i\}$

35. Find two square roots of ${}^-49$. (Hint: Let $\sqrt{{}^-49} = \sqrt{{}^-1} \cdot \sqrt{49}$.) $\{7i, {}^-7i\}$

36. Find two square roots of 18. $\{3\sqrt{2}, {}^-3\sqrt{2}\}$

37. Find two square roots of ${}^-12$. $\{2\sqrt{3}i, {}^-2\sqrt{3}i\}$

38. Find four fourth roots of 16 by finding the solution set of the equation $x^4 = 16$. $\{2, {}^-2, 2i, {}^-2i\}$

4-2 COMPLEX NUMBERS

We have worked with two number systems, the system of real numbers and the system of i-numbers. Both systems are closed with respect to addition. They have only one number in common: the additive identity 0.

Although we have defined the product of a real number and an i-number, we have not yet considered the sum of a real number and an i-number, such as ${}^-3 + 7i$ and $\sqrt{2} + 5i$. Every number of the form

$$a + bi,$$

where a and b are real numbers, is called a *complex number*. Since

$$a = a + 0i,$$

it follows that every real number is also a complex number. Furthermore,

$$bi = 0 + bi.$$

Therefore, every i-number is a complex number. Consequently, both the set of all real numbers and the set of all i-numbers are contained

It is suggested that Exercises 28–38 all be assigned and then discussed in class.

Quiz

Perform the indicated operations.

1. $\frac{8}{3}(13i - 7i)$ (ans: $16i$)
2. $3i(4i - \sqrt{3}i)$ (ans: ${}^-12 + 3\sqrt{3}$)
3. $i^2 + i^3$ (ans: ${}^-1 - i$)
4. $({}^-\sqrt{3}i)^2$ (ans: ${}^-3$)
5. $(5i)^2 + 25$ (ans: 0)
6. $\frac{{}^-4}{i^4}$ (ans: ${}^-4$)

4-2 COMPLEX NUMBERS

In the system of complex numbers, $x + yi$, we have numbers consisting of two component parts, a real part and a pure imaginary part. The subsystem composed of those complex numbers with $y = 0$ is the system of real numbers and the subsystem composed of those complex numbers with $x = 0$ is the system of pure imaginary numbers. A similar situation was met before in the subsystem of the rationals, a/b, a and b integers, where those rationals with $b = 1$ was the system of integers.

Here again is a section which may be assigned for study, followed by a question and answer period which will show whether or not the material has been understood. You could have a student demonstrate at the board that addition of complex numbers, as defined on this page, is indeed associative, as is asserted on the next page.

In relation to the definition of a complex number, it may be useful to raise the question of how such a number can be represented geometrically. The real numbers can be placed in one-to-one correspondence with points on a line. Obviously, the complex numbers cannot be so arranged. Considering $1 + i$, $1 + 2i$, $1 + 3i$, $1 - i$, $1 - 2i$, $1 - 3i$, it becomes clear that we need two number lines. Hence, the complex numbers can be assigned to the points in a plane.

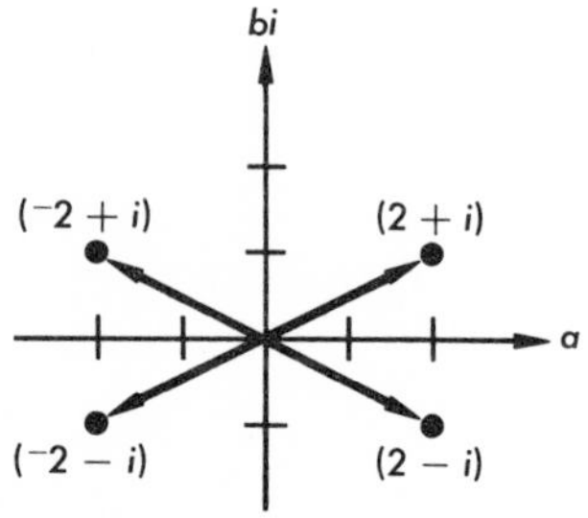

The geometric representation emphasizes that the plus sign in $3 + 2i$ does not play the same role as does the plus sign in $3 + 2$ or $3\sqrt{5} + 2\sqrt{5}$; a complex number has two distinct component parts. Hence, to say that $3 + 2i = x + yi$ is to say that $3 = x$ *and* $2 = y$. The complex number plane makes clear and plausible the statement that $a + bi = c + di$ if, and only if, $a = c$ and $b = d$.

in the set of all complex numbers. For a given complex number $a + bi$, it is customary to call a the *real part* and bi the *pure imaginary part* of $a + bi$. Two complex numbers are defined to be equal if, and only if, their real parts are equal and their pure imaginary parts are equal. It follows that

$$a + bi = c + di \quad \textit{if, and only if,} \quad a = c \textit{ and } b = d.$$

In particular,

$$a + bi = 0 \quad \text{if, and only if,} \quad a = 0 \text{ and } b = 0.$$

The adjectives *imaginary* and *complex* indicate the struggle that took place in the minds of the sixteenth-century mathematicians who first dared to use such numbers. As late as 1770, Euler apologized for the frequent use of complex numbers in his algebra book. He wrote,

> All such expressions as $\sqrt{^-1}$ (the number i), $\sqrt{^-2}$, and so on, are impossible or imaginary numbers, since they represent roots of negative quantities, and of such numbers we may truly assert that they are neither nothing, nor greater than nothing, nor less than nothing, which necessarily constitutes them imaginary or impossible.

In spite of the early suspicions toward complex numbers, they have been as useful in mathematics as negative numbers, rational numbers, and irrational numbers, and have been an indispensable tool in many applications.

How shall we add and multiply complex numbers? If we assume that the basic properties are valid, we can find the sum of two complex numbers as shown below.

$$\begin{aligned}(3 + 4i) + (^-7 + 3i) &= (3 + {^-7}) + (4i + 3i)\\ &= {^-4} + 7i\end{aligned}$$

This example suggests that we define the sum of two complex numbers in the following way.

DEFINITION OF THE SUM OF TWO COMPLEX NUMBERS

$$(a + bi) + (c + di) = (a + c) + (b + d)i$$

for all real numbers a, b, c, and d

Since

$$(c + di) + (a + bi) = (c + a) + (d + b)i$$

according to this definition, it follows from the commutative law of addition for real numbers that

$$(a + bi) + (c + di) = (c + di) + (a + bi).$$

Thus, the commutative law of addition is valid for the system of complex numbers. In a similar way, we may show that the associative law is valid for this system.

Since

$$\begin{aligned} 0 + (a + bi) &= (0 + a) + bi \\ &= a + bi, \end{aligned}$$

we conclude that *zero* is the *additive identity* element of the complex number system. The *opposite* of the complex number $a + bi$ is $^-a + {}^-bi$. Thus,

$$\begin{aligned} (a + bi) + (^-a + {}^-bi) &= (a + {}^-a) + (b + {}^-b)i \\ &= 0 + 0i, \quad \text{or } 0. \end{aligned}$$

Hence, we have

$$^-(a + bi) = {}^-a + {}^-bi.$$

If we recall how the operation of subtraction is defined in terms of addition, then we shall have no trouble in defining subtraction of complex numbers. Thus, by definition,

$$\begin{aligned} (a + bi) - (c + di) &= (a + bi) + {}^-(c + di) \\ &= (a + bi) + (^-c + {}^-di) \\ &= (a + {}^-c) + (b + {}^-d)i \\ &= (a - c) + (b - d)i. \end{aligned}$$

Just as we were able to define the sum of two complex numbers, we should be able to define their product. For example, if we assume that the distributive law and the rearrangement properties are valid for complex numbers, we can find the product of $3 + 4i$ and $^-7 + 3i$ in the following way.

$$\begin{aligned} (3 + 4i) \cdot (^-7 + 3i) &= 3(^-7 + 3i) + 4i(^-7 + 3i) \\ &= {}^-21 + 9i + {}^-28i + 12i^2 \\ &= {}^-21 + 9i - 28i + (12 \cdot {}^-1) \\ &= (^-21 - 12) + (9i - 28i) \\ &= {}^-33 + {}^-19i \end{aligned}$$

Similarly,

$$\begin{aligned}(a + bi)(c + di) &= a(c + di) + bi(c + di)\\ &= ac + adi + bci - bd\\ &= (ac - bd) + (ad + bc)i.\end{aligned}$$

Thus, if we want multiplication of complex numbers to satisfy the usual rules of arithmetic, we must define it in the following way.

DEFINITION OF MULTIPLICATION OF COMPLEX NUMBERS

$$(a + bi)(c + di) = (ac - bd) + (ad + bc)i$$

for all real numbers a, b, c, and d

Although we shall not do so, we could prove that multiplication of complex numbers, as defined above, is both commutative and associative. We could also prove that multiplication is distributive with respect to addition.

Since

$$\begin{aligned}(1 + 0i)(a + bi) &= [(1 \cdot a) - (0 \cdot b)] + [(1 \cdot b) + (0 \cdot a)]i\\ &= a + bi,\end{aligned}$$

it is clear that the real number 1 is the multiplicative identity element of the complex number system. The search for multiplicative inverses of complex numbers will be discussed in the next section.

Exercises for Discussion

In Exercises 1–10, perform the indicated operations. In each exercise, state the real part and the pure imaginary part of the complex number.

1. $(3 + 4i) + (3 - 4i)$ 6
2. $(2 + 5i) - (3 - 5i)$ $(2-3)+(5-{}^-5)i = {}^-1+10i$
3. $(\pi + 2i) - (\sqrt{2} + 3i)$
4. $(1 + i)^2$ $1+2i+i^2=1+2i+{}^-1=2i$
5. $2i(7 - 6i)$
6. $(2 + 3i)(2 - 3i)$ $4+9=13$
7. $({}^-1 + \sqrt{3}i)^3$
8. $(2 + \sqrt{5}i)^2 - 4(2 + \sqrt{5}i) + 9$
9. $(1 - i)(2 + 3i)(4 - 2i)$
10. $2(3 - i) - 5(4 + 3i)$
11. Find the value of the quadratic polynomial $x^2 - 4x + 7$ for each of the given values of x.

    (a) $x = 2 + \sqrt{3}i$ (b) $x = {}^-4 - 3i$

You may wish to ask for proofs of the assertions that the multiplication of complex numbers is commutative, associative, and distributive with respect to addition.

Answers to Exercises for Discussion 3, 5, 7–11

3. $(\pi - \sqrt{2}) + (2 - 3)i = (\pi - \sqrt{2}) - i$

5. $(2 \cdot 7)i - (2 \cdot 6)i^2 = 12 + 14i$

7. $({}^-1 + \sqrt{3}i)^3$
$= ({}^-1 + \sqrt{3}i)^2({}^-1 + \sqrt{3}i)$
$= (1 - 2\sqrt{3}i - 3)({}^-1 + \sqrt{3}i)$
$= ({}^-2 - 2\sqrt{3}i)({}^-1 + \sqrt{3}i)$
$= 2 - 6i^2 = 8$

8. $4 + 4\sqrt{5}i - 5 - 8 - 4\sqrt{5}i + 9 = 0$

9. $(1 - i)(2 + 3i)(4 - 2i)$
$= (2 - 2i + 3i + 3)(4 - 2i)$
$= (5 + i)(4 - 2i)$
$= 20 + 4i - 10i + 2$
$= 22 - 6i$

10. $(6 - 2i) - (20 + 15i) = {}^-14 - 17i$

11. (a) $(2 + \sqrt{3}i)^2 - 4(2 + \sqrt{3}i) + 7$
$= 4 + 4\sqrt{3}i - 3 - 8 - 4\sqrt{3}i + 7$
$= 0$

(b) $({}^-4 - 3i)^2 - 4({}^-4 - 3i) + 7$
$= 16 + 24i - 9 + 16 + 12i + 7$
$= 30 + 36i$

Exercises

Perform the indicated operations in the following exercises. In each exercise, state the real part and the pure imaginary part of the complex number.

1. $(^-7 + 2i) + (7 - 6i)$ ^-4i
2. $(2 + 3i) + (5 + i)$ $7 + 4i$
3. $(2 + 3i) + (2 - 3i)$ 4
4. $(3 + i) - 7$ $^-4 + i$
5. $(2 + 7i) - (3 + 4i) + (7 - 6i)$ $6 - 3i$
6. $(\sqrt{2} - i)^2$ $1 - 2\sqrt{2}\,i$
7. $(5 - 12i)(\frac{5}{169} + \frac{12}{169}i)$ 1
8. $6(2 + i) - 3(3 + 2i)$ 3
9. $(^-1 + \sqrt{3}i)^2$ $^-2 - 2\sqrt{3}\,i$
10. $(2 - \sqrt{5}i)^2 - 4(2 - \sqrt{5}i) + 9$ 0
11. $\left(\frac{\sqrt{3}}{2} + \frac{1}{2}i\right)^3$ i

△

Perform the indicated operations in the following exercises. In each exercise, state the real part and the pure imaginary part of the complex number.

12. $\left(\frac{\sqrt{3}}{2} + \frac{1}{2}i\right)^6$ (Hint: $a^6 = (a^3)^2$.) $^-1$
13. $(^-\frac{24}{625} + \frac{7}{625}i)(^-24 - 7i)$ 1
14. $(a + bi)(a - bi)$ $a^2 + b^2$
15. $(ap + bpi)(a - bi)$ $p(a^2 + b^2)$

Find the value of the quadratic polynomial $x^2 + x + 1$ for each of the given values of x.

16. $x = {}^-1 + i$ ^-i
17. $x = {}^-\frac{1}{2} + \frac{1}{2}\sqrt{3}i$ 0
18. $x = {}^-\frac{1}{2} - \frac{1}{2}\sqrt{3}i$ 0
19. $x = \frac{1}{2} - \frac{1}{2}\sqrt{3}i$ $1 - \sqrt{3}\,i$
20. $x = \frac{1}{2} + \frac{1}{2}\sqrt{3}i$ $1 + \sqrt{3}\,i$
21. $x = \frac{1}{3} + \frac{2}{3}i$ $1 + \frac{10}{9}i$
22. (a) Square and simplify

$$\left(\frac{\sqrt{2}}{2} + \frac{\sqrt{2}}{2}i\right)^2. \quad i$$

(b) Find the complex numbers that are solutions of the equation $x^2 = i$. $\left\{\frac{\sqrt{2}}{2} + \frac{\sqrt{2}}{2}i, {}^-\frac{\sqrt{2}}{2} - \frac{\sqrt{2}}{2}i\right\}$

(c) Find two solutions of the equation $x^2 = {}^-i$. $\left\{\frac{\sqrt{2}}{2} - \frac{\sqrt{2}}{2}i, {}^-\frac{\sqrt{2}}{2} + \frac{\sqrt{2}}{2}i\right\}$

Exercises

It is suggested that all the exercises in this section be covered. Exercise 13 contains discovery material for the work of the next section on reciprocals, or multiplicative inverses. Exercises 16–21 involve the arithmetic of checking a possible solution of a quadratic equation.

Exercise 22 should lead the student to discover that

$$\sqrt{i} = \frac{1}{\sqrt{2}} + \frac{1}{\sqrt{2}}i.$$

It is suggested that Exercise 23 be covered in class as it reveals the interesting fact that just as 8 has two square roots, $2\sqrt{2}$ and $^-2\sqrt{2}$, it also has three cube roots, 2, $^-1 + \sqrt{3}i$, and $^-1 - \sqrt{3}i$. On the basis of this exercise, it is possible to theorize that every real number has three cube roots. The student may be led to see that the cube roots of 1 are solutions of

$$x^3 = 1,$$
$$x^3 - 1 = 0,$$

and

$$(x - 1)(x^2 + x + 1) = 0,$$

and thus can be found by the quadratic formula

$$1, \frac{^-1 + \sqrt{3}i}{2}, \frac{^-1 - \sqrt{3}i}{2}.$$

With some direction, he should see that the cube roots of 8 are twice the cube roots of 1. Hence, to find the cube roots of 64, he need only multiply the cube roots of 1 by $\sqrt[3]{64}$, or 4. You could ask for the cube roots of 125, $^-27$, $^-1$.

Quiz

Perform the indicated operations.

1. $(6 + 5i) + (8 + 3i)$ (ans: $14 + 8i$)
2. $(^-3 + 2i) + (7 - 3i)$ (ans: $4 - i$)
3. $3(2 + 3i) + 2i$ (ans: $6 + 11i$)
4. $(3 + i)(3 - i)$ (ans: 10)
5. $(^-2 + \sqrt{2}i)^2$ (ans: $2 - 4\sqrt{2}i$)
6. $3i(7 - 6i)$ (ans: $18 + 21i$)

4-3 QUOTIENTS OF COMPLEX NUMBERS

You might find it helpful to write the following on the board: The reciprocal of 2 is $\frac{1}{2}$, and $2 \cdot \frac{1}{2} = 1$. The reciprocal of $1 + \sqrt{3}$ is

$$\frac{1}{1+\sqrt{3}}$$

and

$$(1+\sqrt{3}) \cdot \frac{1}{1+\sqrt{3}} = 1.$$

The reciprocal of $3i$ is $\frac{1}{3i}$, and

$$3i\left(\frac{1}{3i}\right) = 1.$$

The reciprocal of $2 + 5i$ is

$$\frac{1}{2+5i}$$

and so on. Now

$$\frac{1}{2+5i} = \frac{1}{2+5i} \cdot \frac{2-5i}{2-5i} \text{ (Id-M)}$$
$$= \frac{2-5i}{29}.$$

Therefore,

$$(2+5i)\left(\frac{2-5i}{29}\right) = \frac{4-25i^2}{29}$$
$$= \frac{29}{29}, \quad \text{or } 1,$$

as would be expected, since

$$(2+5i)\left(\frac{1}{2+5i}\right) = 1.$$

The student should understand that the reciprocal of an integer is a unit fraction, and the reciprocal of a real number greater than one is another real number which is less than one. The reciprocal of a complex number, $a + bi$, is another complex number of the following form:

$$\frac{a}{a^2+b^2} - \frac{b}{a^2+b^2}i.$$

▲

23. Show that $^{-}1 + \sqrt{3}i$ is a solution of the equation $x^3 = 8$. Then find two other numbers that are solutions. $\{2, {}^{-}1, -\sqrt{3}i\}$
24. Prove the associative law of addition for complex numbers. See Solution Manual.
25. Supply a reason for each step in the following proof of the commutative law of multiplication for complex numbers.

$(a + bi)(c + di) = (ac - bd) + (ad + bc)i$ __?__
Definition of multiplication of complex numbers
$= (ac - bd) + (bc + ad)i$ __?__
Commutative law of addition of real numbers
$= (ca - db) + (cb + da)i$ __?__
Commutative law of multiplication of real numbers
$= (c + di)(a + bi)$ __?__
Definition of multiplication of complex numbers

4-3 QUOTIENTS OF COMPLEX NUMBERS

The two complex numbers $3 + 4i$ and $3 - 4i$ are said to be *conjugates* of each other. We note that

$$(3 + 4i) + (3 - 4i) = 6$$
$$(3 + 4i) \cdot (3 - 4i) = (9 + 16) + ({}^{-}12 + 12)i$$
$$= 25.$$

Every complex number $a + bi$ has a *conjugate:* $a - bi$. You can easily verify that

$$(a + bi) + (a - bi) = 2a,$$
$$(a + bi) \cdot (a - bi) = a^2 + b^2.$$

Thus, the sum of a complex number and its conjugate is a real number, and the product is also a real number.

We saw that 25 is the product of $3 + 4i$ and its conjugate $3 - 4i$. Therefore, it follows that 1 is the product of $3 + 4i$ and $\frac{1}{25}(3 - 4i)$, as shown below.

$$(3 + 4i)[\tfrac{1}{25}(3 - 4i)] = \tfrac{1}{25}[(3 + 4i)(3 - 4i)]$$
$$= \tfrac{1}{25}(25), \quad \text{or } 1$$

Thus,

$$\tfrac{1}{25}(3 - 4i), \quad \text{or } \tfrac{3}{25} - \tfrac{4}{25}i,$$

is the *reciprocal of* $3 + 4i$. We indicate this in the usual way:

$$\frac{1}{3+4i} = \frac{3}{25} - \frac{4}{25}i.$$

We can find the reciprocal of every nonzero complex number in the same way. If $a + bi \neq 0$, so that either a or b is nonzero, then $a^2 + b^2 > 0$, and

$$(a + bi)\left[\frac{1}{a^2 + b^2}(a - bi)\right] = 1,$$

according to the formula for the product of a complex number and its conjugate. Hence, the reciprocal of $a + bi$ is

$$\frac{1}{a + bi} = \frac{a}{a^2 + b^2} - \frac{b}{a^2 + b^2}i.$$

For example, we may obtain the reciprocal of $^-\sqrt{2} + i$ by letting $a = {}^-\sqrt{2}$ and $b = 1$ in the equation above:

$$\frac{1}{^-\sqrt{2} + i} = \frac{^-\sqrt{2}}{3} - \frac{1}{3}i.$$

We can now find the quotient of two complex numbers. For example, let us find $(^-7 + 3i) \div (5 + 4i)$.

$$\begin{aligned}(^-7 + 3i) \div (5 + 4i) &= (^-7 + 3i)\left(\frac{1}{5 + 4i}\right) \\ &= (^-7 + 3i)(\tfrac{5}{41} - \tfrac{4}{41}i) \\ &= (\tfrac{^-35}{41} + \tfrac{12}{41}) + (\tfrac{28}{41} + \tfrac{15}{41})i \\ &= \tfrac{^-23}{41} + \tfrac{43}{41}i\end{aligned}$$

There is a shorter method for finding the quotient of two complex numbers. For example, to find $(5 - 9i) \div (1 - i)$, we might proceed as follows:

$$\begin{aligned}\frac{5 - 9i}{1 - i} &= \frac{5 - 9i}{1 - i} \cdot \frac{1 + i}{1 + i} \\ &= \frac{(5 - 9i)(1 + i)}{(1 - i)(1 + i)} \\ &= \frac{14 - 4i}{2} \\ &= 7 - 2i.\end{aligned}$$

Notice that we simply multiplied the numerator and the denominator of the given quotient by the conjugate of the denominator.

Students have learned that the multiplicative inverse of a rational number p/q is found simply by inverting the fraction and writing q/p. It should interest them, therefore, to see that a simple rule enables them to write immediately the multiplicative inverse of a complex number. Thus, $3 + 5i$ has the reciprocal

$$\frac{1}{3^2 + 5^2}(3 - 5i).$$

It can be seen that for any complex number, $a + bi$, a reciprocal,

$$\frac{1}{a^2 + b^2}(a - bi),$$

can be written unless both a and b are zero. Hence, within the system of complex numbers, as within the system of real numbers, there is one number without a reciprocal, namely $0 + (0 \cdot i)$, or simply 0. Once again, division by zero is undefined because zero has no multiplicative inverse.

The quotient of two complex numbers, $(a + bi) \div (c + di)$, can be written as a complex number by multiplying by 1, provided that 1 is written as

$$\frac{c - di}{c - di}.$$

This works because $(c + di)(c - di)$ is $c^2 + d^2$ and

$$\frac{1}{c^2 + d^2}(c - di)$$

is the reciprocal of $c + di$. Thus,

$$\begin{aligned}&\frac{a + bi}{c + di} \cdot \frac{c - di}{c - di} \\ &\quad = (a + bi)\left[\frac{1}{c^2 + d^2} \cdot (c - di)\right], \\ &\quad = \frac{ac + bd}{c^2 + d^2} + \frac{bc - ad}{c^2 + d^2}i.\end{aligned}$$

It may be shown that a real number and its reciprocal are located on the same half of the real number line.

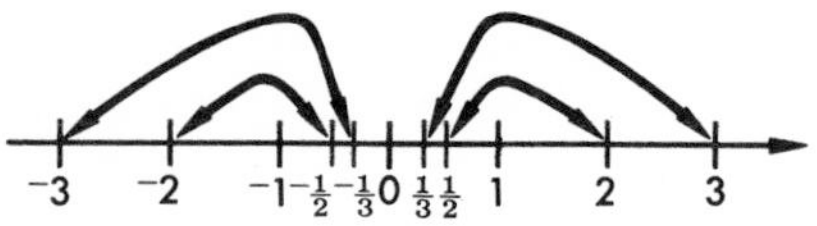

An *i*-number and its reciprocal are located on opposite halves of the *i*-number line.

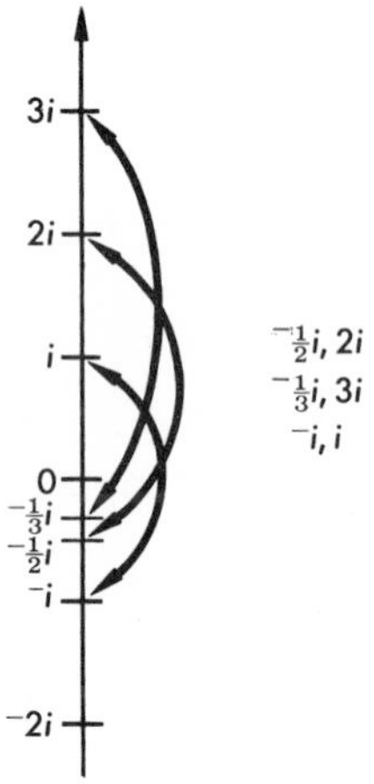

A complex number and its reciprocal locate two points out in the plane.

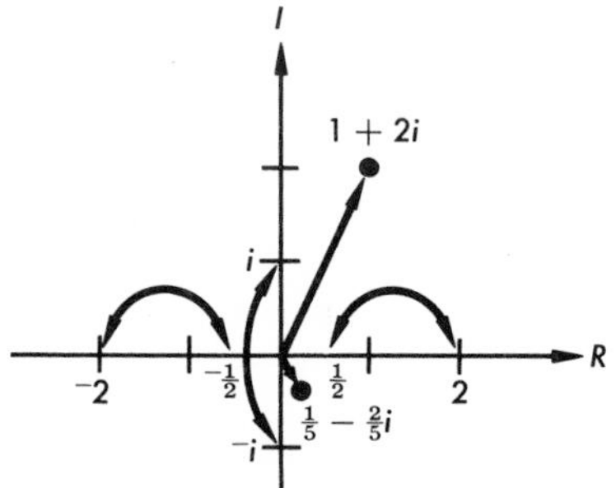

Exercises for Discussion

If time is limited, it is suggested that at least Exercises for Discussion 1–6 be covered.

Exercises for Discussion

In Exercises 1–3, give the conjugate of each of the complex numbers. Find the sum and the product of each conjugate pair of complex numbers.

1. $2 - i$ **2.** 4 *4; 4+4 = 8; 4·4 = 16* **3.** $^-5 - 2i$

4. What type of complex number is its own conjugate? Give some examples to support your answer. *Any real number is its own conjugate.*

5. What type of complex number is the opposite of its own conjugate? Give some examples to support your answer. *Any i-number is the opposite of its own conjugate.*

6. Express the reciprocal of each of the following complex numbers as a complex number.

(a) $1 + i$ $\frac{1}{1+i} = \frac{1}{1+i} \cdot \frac{1-i}{1-i} = \frac{1-i}{2} = \frac{1}{2} - \frac{1}{2}i$ (b) $5i$ $\frac{1}{5i} = \frac{1}{5i} \cdot \frac{^-5i}{^-5i} = \frac{^-5i}{25} = \frac{^-1}{5}i$

In Exercises 7–9, perform the indicated operations, and express each answer as a complex number of the form $a + bi$.

7. $\frac{1+i}{1-i}$ $\frac{1+i}{1-i} \cdot \frac{1+i}{1+i} = \frac{1+2i-1}{2} = i$ **8.** $\frac{^-3 + 2i}{7 + 4i}$

9. $\left(\frac{1 - i}{1 + 3i}\right)\left(\frac{2 + 3i}{^-1 + 4i}\right)$

10. (a) Find the conjugates of $a + bi$ and $c + di$ and add them.
(b) Add $a + bi$ and $c + di$ and find the conjugate of their sum.
(c) How is the sum of the conjugates of two complex numbers related to the conjugate of their sum? *The sum of the conjugates is equal to the conjugate of the sum.*

11. (a) Find the conjugates of $a + bi$ and $c + di$ and multiply them.
(b) Multiply $a + bi$ by $c + di$ and find the conjugate of the product.
(c) How is the product of the conjugates of two complex numbers related to the conjugate of their product? *The product of the conjugates is equal to the conjugate of the product.*

Exercises

Find the conjugate of each of the following complex numbers, and then find the sum and the product of each pair of conjugate complex numbers.

1. $4 + 2i$ *$4-2i$; 8; 20* **2.** $\sqrt{3} - \sqrt{5}i$ *$\sqrt{3}+\sqrt{5}i$; $2\sqrt{3}$; 8* **3.** $^-\sqrt{2}i$ *$\sqrt{2}i$; 0; 2*

4. $^-7$ *$^-7$; $^-14$; 49* **5.** $\frac{1}{2} - \frac{\sqrt{3}}{2}i$ *$\frac{1}{2} + \frac{\sqrt{3}}{2}i$; 1; 1*

Express the reciprocal of each of the following complex numbers as a complex number.

6. $2 + 3i$ *$\frac{2}{13} - \frac{3}{13}i$* **7.** $6 - i$ *$\frac{6}{37} + \frac{1}{37}i$* **8.** $^-2 - 5i$ *$\frac{^-2}{29} + \frac{5}{29}i$*

9. $\sqrt{3} - 3i$ *$\frac{\sqrt{3}}{12} + \frac{1}{4}i$* **10.** $c - di$ *$\frac{c}{c^2+d^2} + \frac{d}{c^2+d^2}i$*

Perform the indicated operations in the following exercises, and express each answer as a complex number of the form $a + bi$.

11. $\dfrac{6 - 3i}{2 + i}$ $\frac{9}{5} - \frac{12}{5}i$

12. $\dfrac{4 + \sqrt{3}i}{2 - \sqrt{3}i}$ $\frac{5}{7} + \frac{6}{7}\sqrt{3}i$

13. $\dfrac{1}{2 + i}$ $\frac{2}{5} - \frac{1}{5}i$

14. $\dfrac{i}{2 + i}$ $\frac{1}{5} + \frac{2}{5}i$

15. $\dfrac{6 + 3i}{2i}$ $\frac{3}{2} - 3i$

16. $\dfrac{1 - i}{1 + 3i} + \dfrac{2 + 3i}{^{-}1 + 4i}$ $\frac{33}{85} - \frac{89}{85}i$

17. $\dfrac{3}{2 - 5i} - \dfrac{2i}{^{-}2 - 5i}$ $\frac{16}{29} + \frac{19}{29}i$

18. $\left(\dfrac{2 + i}{3 - i}\right)\left(\dfrac{1 - 4i}{1 + 3i}\right)$ $\frac{-1}{5} - \frac{9}{10}i$

△

---

19. (a) Find the conjugates of $a + bi$ and $c + di$ and subtract the latter conjugate from the former. $(a - c) - i(b - d)$
    (b) Subtract $c + di$ from $a + bi$ and find the conjugate of the difference. $(a - c) - i(b - d)$
    (c) Is there a relation between the difference of the conjugates of two complex numbers and the conjugate of their difference? Equal

20. (a) Simplify $\dfrac{a - bi}{c - di}$. $\dfrac{(ac + bd)}{c^2 + d^2} - \dfrac{i(bc - ad)}{c^2 + d^2}$
    (b) Simplify $\dfrac{a + bi}{c + di}$ and find the conjugate of the quotient. $\dfrac{(ac + bd)}{c^2 + d^2} - \dfrac{i(bc - ad)}{c^2 + d^2}$
    (c) Is there a relation between the quotient of the conjugates of two complex numbers and the conjugate of their quotient? Equal

21. Since two complex numbers are defined as equal if, and only if, their real parts are equal and their pure imaginary parts are equal, the real solutions of the equation $(2x - y) + (x + y)i = 5 + 4i$ are solutions of the system

$$\begin{cases} 2x - y = 5, \\ x + y = 4. \end{cases}$$ $x = 3,\ y = 1$

Solve the system for real values of x and y.

Find the system defined by each of the following equations, and solve it for real values of x and y.

22. $x + yi = {}^{-}5 + 4i$ $x = {}^{-}5,\ y = 4$

23. $2x + 3yi - 6 + 9i = 0$ $x = 3,\ y = {}^{-}3$

24. ${}^{-}x + 4yi = (2 + 6i) - (7 - 2i)$ $x = 5,\ y = 2$

25. $x + yi = (2 - i)(2 + i)$ $x = 5,\ y = 0$

26. $(x - 3) + (y + 2)i = 7 - 6i$ $x = 10,\ y = {}^{-}8$

Answers to Exercises for Discussion 1, 3, 8, 9, 10(a), 10(b), 11(a), 11(b), page 178

1. $2 + i$;
$(2 - i) + (2 + i) = 4$
$(2 - i)(2 + i) = 4 + 1 = 5$

3. ${}^{-}5 + 2i$;
$({}^{-}5 - 2i) + ({}^{-}5 + 2i) = {}^{-}10$
$({}^{-}5 - 2i)({}^{-}5 + 2i) = 29$

8.
$$\frac{^{-}3 + 2i}{7 + 4i} = \frac{^{-}3 + 2i}{7 + 4i} \cdot \frac{7 - 4i}{7 - 4i} = \frac{^{-}21 + 14i + 12i + 8}{49 + 16} = \frac{^{-}13 + 26i}{65} = {}^{-}\tfrac{1}{5} + \tfrac{2}{5}i$$

9.
$$\left(\frac{1 - i}{1 + 3i}\right)\left(\frac{2 + 3i}{^{-}1 + 4i}\right) = \frac{5 + i}{^{-}13 + i} = \frac{5 + i}{^{-}13 + i} \cdot \frac{^{-}13 - i}{^{-}13 - i} = \frac{^{-}64 - 18i}{170} = {}^{-}\tfrac{32}{85} - \tfrac{9}{85}i$$

10. (a) $a - bi,\ c - di$;
$(a + c) - (b + d)i$
(b) $(a + c) + (b + d)i$;
$(a + c) - (b + d)i$

11. (a) $a - bi,\ c - di$;
$(ac - bd) - i(bc + ad)$
(b) $(ac - bd) + i(bc + ad)$;
$(ac - bd) - i(bc + ad)$

Exercises, page 178

It is recommended that all the exercises be covered, either as homework or in class.

In Exercises 16, 17, and 18, the student should add, subtract, or multiply (as the case may be) the two given fractions before starting to rationalize the denominator.

Exercises 21–26 are important and it is recommended that they be assigned.

Quiz

Find the conjugate of each of the following complex numbers, and then find the sum and the product of each pair of conjugate complex numbers.

1. $5 - \sqrt{3}i$ (ans: $5 + \sqrt{3}i$; 10; 28)

2. ^-3i (ans: $3i$; 0; 9)

3. 6 (ans: 6; 12; 36)

Perform the indicated operations, and express each answer as a complex number of the form $a + bi$.

4. $\dfrac{2+3i}{3-2i}$ (ans: i)

5. $\dfrac{1}{^-4 - i}$ $\left(\text{ans: } \dfrac{^-4}{17} + \dfrac{1}{17}i\right)$

4-4 QUADRATIC EQUATIONS

You may wish to refer back to page 11, where it is stated that every real number is either zero, positive, or negative. This statement allows comparison of any two real numbers, a and b, by saying

$$a = b,\ a > b, \text{ or } a < b,$$

depending on whether the difference $a - b$ is zero, positive, or negative. The situation does not carry over to complex numbers. There is no positive complex number; two complex numbers cannot be compared as to which is larger. Students sometimes think that since $x^2 = 169$ has two solutions, one positive and one negative, so does $x^2 + 169 = 0$. In the case of $x^2 - 169 = 0$, the solutions are opposites; in the case of

$$x^2 + 169 = 0,$$

the solutions are called conjugates.

27. The real number $a^2 + b^2$ which is the product of $a + bi$ and its complex conjugate is called the *norm* of $a + bi$ and is sometimes designated by $N(a + bi)$.

(a) Find and compare the norms of $a + bi$ and $a - bi$. *Equal*

(b) Find the norms of $2 + 3i$ and $1 - i$, and find the product of the norms. *13; 2; 26*

(c) Find $N(a + bi)$ and $N(c + di)$ and find their product. Find the product of $a + bi$ and $c + di$, and find $N[(a + bi)(c + di)]$. *$a^2c^2 + a^2d^2 + b^2c^2 + b^2d^2$; $a^2c^2 + a^2d^2 + b^2c^2 + b^2d^2$*

(d) How is the product of the norms of two complex numbers related to the norm of the product of the numbers? *Equal*

28. Use the results of Exercise 27 to prove that the product of two integers, each of which is the sum of the squares of two integers, is also the sum of the squares of two integers. *See Solution Manual.*

4-4 QUADRATIC EQUATIONS

In this book, we first discussed the real number system. We have now found that it is a subsystem of a larger number system, the system of complex numbers. The five basic properties of addition and multiplication stated in Chapter 1 are also valid for the complex number system. However, the order properties of the real number system (pages 10 and 11) are not valid for the system of complex numbers. In other words, it is not possible to define a set of positive complex numbers in such a way that the order properties are valid.

An important property of any number system for which the five basic properties hold is the following:

$$r \cdot s = 0 \quad \text{if, and only if,} \quad r = 0 \text{ or } s = 0. \qquad \text{(F-0)}$$

The property of factors of zero was proved for real numbers r and s in Chapter 3. The same proof holds for complex numbers r and s. We shall use this property in the work below.

We saw previously that both $2i$ and ^-2i are solutions of the quadratic equation

$$x^2 + 4 = 0.$$

Does this equation have any other solutions? To answer this question, we first observe that the quadratic polynomial $x^2 + 4$ can be factored as follows:

$$x^2 + 4 = (x + 2i)(x - 2i).$$

Hence, the given equation is equivalent to the equation

$$(x + 2i)(x - 2i) = 0.$$

Using factors of zero, we find that

$$(x + 2i)(x - 2i) = 0$$

if, and only if,

$$x + 2i = 0 \quad \text{or} \quad x - 2i = 0$$

or $(x + 2i)(x - 2i) = 0$ if, and only if,

$$x = {}^{-}2i \quad \text{or} \quad x = 2i.$$

Hence, $\{{}^{-}2i, 2i\}$ is the solution set of the equation $x^2 + 4 = 0$. Therefore, this equation has only two solutions: $2i$ and ${}^{-}2i$.

In exactly the same way, we can show that for each positive real number a, the equation

$$x^2 + a = 0 \quad \text{has solution set} \quad \{\sqrt{a}i, {}^{-}\sqrt{a}i\}.$$

A quadratic equation

$$ax^2 + bx + c = 0, \quad a \neq 0,$$

will be called *real* if the three numbers a, b, and c are real numbers. We recall from the preceding chapter that a real quadratic equation might or might not have real solutions. Does every real quadratic equation have complex solutions? Before answering this question, let us consider the following quadratic equation which, in Chapter 3, was shown to have no real solution.

Problem. Solve the real quadratic equation $x^2 - 4x + 5 = 0$.

Solution. The given equation is equivalent to each of the following equations:

$$x^2 - 4x = {}^{-}5,$$
$$x^2 - 4x + 4 = {}^{-}1.$$

The number ${}^{-}1$ has two square roots, i and ${}^{-}i$. Thus,

$$(x - 2)^2 = {}^{-}1$$

if, and only if,

$$x - 2 = i \quad \text{or} \quad x - 2 = {}^{-}i$$

or $(x - 2)^2 = {}^{-}1$ if, and only if,

$$x = 2 + i \quad \text{or} \quad x = 2 - i.$$

Thus,

$$\{2 + i, 2 - i\}$$

is the solution set of the given equation.

The student should understand that the two solutions found for the quadratic equation are the only solutions. If

$$(x + 2i)(x - 2i) = 0,$$

then either $x + 2i = 0$ or $x - 2i = 0$. Conversely, if neither $x + 2i$ nor $x - 2i$ is zero, then their product cannot be zero. Hence, there are exactly two solutions for the second-degree equation.

A real quadratic equation in x is one of the form $ax^2 + bx + c = 0$ with a, b, and c real numbers; for example, $\sqrt{2}x^2 - \frac{1}{7}x + 9 = 0$. It has already been seen that such a simple real quadratic equation as

$$x^2 + 1 = 0$$

has no real solutions. A larger number system than that of the real numbers was developed in order to find solutions for $x^2 + 1 = 0$. Does this system take care of all real quadratic equations that do not have real solutions? The answer to this question and the procedure of completing the square to derive the quadratic formula should now be easy for the student to understand.

In treating the problem of manufacturing an equation starting with its solution set, many examples should be used to show that there is an intimate connection between the solutions and the a, b, c of

$$ax^2 + bx + c = 0.$$

You could have the class obtain quadratic equations, given the following solution sets:

$\{5, {}^{-}5\}$, $\{6, \sqrt{2}\}$, $\{\sqrt{3}, \sqrt{2}\}$,
$\{1 + \sqrt{2}, 1 + 3\sqrt{2}\}$, $\{i, 2i\}$,
$\{1 - i, 1 + 2i\}$, $\{\sqrt{7}, {}^{-}\sqrt{7}\}$,
$\{2 + \sqrt{5}, 2 - \sqrt{5}\}$, $\{1\}$, $\{0, 5\}$,
$\{1 + \sqrt{3i}, 1 - \sqrt{3i}\}$, $\{i\}$, $\{0\}$.

Then you could ask for an educated guess as to the kind of solutions that would make a, b, and c real, and what kind of solutions would make a, b, and c rational.

Check.

$$x = 2 + i$$
$$(2+i)^2 - 4(2+i) + 5 \stackrel{?}{=} 0$$
$$4 + 4i + i^2 - 8 - 4i + 5 \stackrel{?}{=} 0$$
$$4 - 1 - 8 + 5 \stackrel{\checkmark}{=} 0$$

$$x = 2 - i$$
$$(2-i)^2 - 4(2-i) + 5 \stackrel{?}{=} 0$$
$$4 - 4i + i^2 - 8 + 4i + 5 \stackrel{?}{=} 0$$
$$4 - 1 - 8 + 5 \stackrel{\checkmark}{=} 0$$

This problem suggests that every real quadratic equation has complex solutions.

Exercises for Discussion

In Exercises 1–4, solve each real quadratic equation by completing the square, and check each solution.

1. $x^2 - 6x + 10 = 0$ **2.** $x^2 + 4x + 13 = 0$

3. $x^2 - 4x - 77 = 0$ **4.** $x^2 + x + 1 = 0$

5. If r and s are real numbers, we can find at least one real quadratic equation for which $\{r, s\}$ is the solution set:

$$(x - r)(x - s) = 0, \quad \text{or } x^2 - (r + s)x + rs = 0.$$

According to what property of real numbers is it true that r and s are solutions, and the only solutions, of this quadratic equation?
Factors of zero: $ab = 0$ if, and only if, $a=0$ or $b=0$.

6. (a) If r and s are complex numbers, is it still true that

$$x^2 - (r + s)x + rs = 0$$

is a quadratic equation with solution set $\{r, s\}$? *Yes*

(b) For what conditions on r and s is $x^2 - (r + s)x + rs = 0$ a real quadratic equation? *r and s must be complex conjugates of each other.*

7. Find the sum, $r + s$, and the product, rs, of each pair r, s of your solutions in Exercises 1–4. Then verify that each quadratic has the form given in Exercises 5 and 6. (This procedure is a second type of check on your solution.)

8. Each of the following is a solution set of a quadratic equation. In each case, write a quadratic equation that has the given solution set.

(a) $\{0, i\sqrt{5}\}$ (b) $\{^-1 + i, ^-1 - i\}$

Exercises for Discussion

If time is limited, it is suggested that at least Exercises for Discussion 5–8 be covered.

Answers to Exercises for Discussion 1–4, 7, 8

1. $\{x \mid x^2 - 6x + 10 = 0\}$
$= \{x \mid x^2 - 6x = {}^-10\}$
$= \{x \mid x^2 - 6x + 9 = {}^-10 + 9\}$
$= \{x \mid (x - 3)^2 = {}^-1\}$
$= \{x \mid x - 3 = i \text{ or } x - 3 = {}^-i\}$
$= \{x \mid x = 3 + i \text{ or } x = 3 - i\}$
$= \{3 + i, 3 - i\}$

2. $\{x \mid x^2 + 4x + 13 = 0\}$
$= \{x \mid x^2 + 4x = {}^-13\}$
$= \{x \mid x^2 + 4x + 4 = {}^-13 + 4\}$
$= \{x \mid (x + 2)^2 = {}^-9\}$
$= \{x \mid x + 2 = 3i \text{ or } x + 2 = {}^-3i\}$
$= \{{}^-2 + 3i, {}^-2 - 3i\}$

3. $\{x \mid x^2 - 4x - 77 = 0$
$= \{x \mid x^2 - 4x = 77\}$
$= \{x \mid x^2 - 4x + 4 = 77 + 4\}$
$= \{x \mid (x - 2)^2 = 81\}$
$= \{x \mid x - 2 = 9 \text{ or } x - 2 = {}^-9\}$
$= \{11, {}^-7\}$

4. $\{x \mid x^2 + x + 1 = 0\}$
$= \{x \mid x^2 + x = {}^-1\}$
$= \{x \mid x^2 + x + \frac{1}{4} = {}^-1 + \frac{1}{4}\}$
$= \{x \mid (x + \frac{1}{2})^2 = {}^-\frac{3}{4}\}$
$= \left\{x \mid x + \frac{1}{2} = \frac{\sqrt{3}}{2} i \text{ or } x + \frac{1}{2} = \frac{{}^-\sqrt{3}}{2} i\right\}$
$= \left\{{}^-\frac{1}{2} + \frac{\sqrt{3}}{2} i, {}^-\frac{1}{2} - \frac{\sqrt{3}}{2} i\right\}$

Exercises

Solve each equation by completing the square and check each solution.

1. $x^2 - 4x + 29 = 0$ $\{2+5i, 2-5i\}$
2. $x^2 + 8x + 25 = 0$ $\{{}^-4+3i, {}^-4-3i\}$
3. $x^2 + 2x + 4 = 0$ $\{{}^-1+\sqrt{3}i, {}^-1-\sqrt{3}i\}$
4. $x^2 + 2x - 4 = 0$ $\{{}^-1+\sqrt{5}, {}^-1-\sqrt{5}\}$
5. $x^2 - 2\sqrt{3}x + 4 = 0$ $\{\sqrt{3}+i, \sqrt{3}-i\}$
6. $x^2 - x + 1 = 0$ $\{\frac{1}{2}+\frac{\sqrt{3}}{2}i, \frac{1}{2}-\frac{\sqrt{3}}{2}i\}$

Each of the following is a solution set of a quadratic equation. In each case, write a quadratic equation that has the given solution set.

7. $\{{}^-3, 0\}$ $x^2+3x=0$
8. $\{8, {}^-4\}$ $x^2-4x-32=0$
9. $\{{}^-\frac{1}{3}, \frac{1}{2}\}$ $x^2-\frac{1}{6}x-\frac{1}{6}=0$
10. $\{2+\sqrt{3}, 2-\sqrt{3}\}$ $x^2-4x+1=0$
11. $\{{}^-2, 4\}$ $x^2-2x-8=0$
12. $\{3+\sqrt{2}, 3-\sqrt{2}\}$ $x^2-6x+7=0$
13. $\{{}^-3+4i, {}^-3-4i\}$ $x^2+6x+25=0$
14. $\left\{\frac{\sqrt{2}}{2}+\frac{\sqrt{2}}{2}i, \frac{\sqrt{2}}{2}-\frac{\sqrt{2}}{2}i\right\}$ $x^2-\sqrt{2}x+1=0$

△

Let each of the following quadratic polynomials equal zero, and solve the resulting equation by completing the square. Then write each polynomial as a product of linear factors.

15. $x^2 + 4x + 20$ $\{{}^-2+4i, {}^-2-4i\}$; $(x+2-4i)(x+2+4i)$
16. $x^2 + 4x + 1$ $\{{}^-2+\sqrt{3}, {}^-2-\sqrt{3}\}$; $(x+2-\sqrt{3})(x+2+\sqrt{3})$
17. $x^2 - 2x + 4$ $\{1+\sqrt{3}i, 1-\sqrt{3}i\}$; $(x-1-\sqrt{3}i)(x-1+\sqrt{3}i)$
18. $6y^2 - 19y + 15$ $\{\frac{5}{3}, \frac{3}{2}\}$; $(3y-5)(2y-3)$
19. $12x - 9x^2 - 5$ $\{\frac{2}{3}+\frac{1}{3}i, \frac{2}{3}-\frac{1}{3}i\}$; $(2+i-3x)(3x-2+i)$

▲

See Solution Manual.

20. Let $a + bi$ and $c + di$ be two complex numbers, with $b \neq 0$ and $d \neq 0$. Verify that each of the following statements is true.
    (a) If the sum of these two complex numbers is a real number, then $b + d = 0$, or $d = {}^-b$.
    (b) If the product of these two complex numbers is a *real* number, then $bc + ad = 0$.
    (c) If both the sum and product of these two complex numbers are real, then the numbers must be conjugate complex numbers.
    (d) If a real quadratic equation has one complex solution $a + bi$, with $b \neq 0$, then it must have $a - bi$ as its other solution.

7. (1.) Sum: $(3+i)+(3-i)=6$; Product: $(3+i)(3-i)=10$
(2.) Sum: $({}^-2+3i)+({}^-2-3i)={}^-4$; Product: $({}^-2+3i)({}^-2-3i)=13$
(3.) Sum: $(11)+({}^-7)=4$; Product: $(11)({}^-7)={}^-77$
(4.) Sum: $\left({}^-\frac{1}{2}+\frac{\sqrt{3}}{2}i\right)+\left({}^-\frac{1}{2}-\frac{\sqrt{3}}{2}i\right)={}^-1$; Product: $\left({}^-\frac{1}{2}+\frac{\sqrt{3}}{2}i\right)\left({}^-\frac{1}{2}-\frac{\sqrt{3}}{2}i\right)=1$

8. (a) $x^2-(0+i\sqrt{5})x+0\cdot i\sqrt{5}=0$, or $x^2-i\sqrt{5}x=0$
(b) $x^2-[({}^-1+i)+({}^-1-i)]x+({}^-1+i)({}^-1-i)=0$ or $x^2+2x+2=0$

Quiz

Solve each equation by completing the square.

1. $x^2+x+1=0$ (ans: $\left\{\frac{{}^-1\pm i\sqrt{3}}{2}\right\}$)
2. $x^2-3x+3=0$ (ans: $\left\{\frac{3\pm i\sqrt{3}}{2}\right\}$)
3. $x^2+2\sqrt{2}x+4=0$ (ans: $\{{}^-\sqrt{2}\pm i\sqrt{2}\}$)

Each of the following is a solution set of a quadratic equation. In each case, write a quadratic equation that has the given solution set.

4. $\{2-\sqrt{5}, 2+\sqrt{5}\}$ (ans: $x^2-4x-1=0$)
5. $\{3-i, 3+i\}$ (ans: $x^2-6x+10=0$)

4-5 THE QUADRATIC FORMULA

This derivation of the quadratic formula may be illustrated by applying it to a set of equations whose solutions have already been found. For example, if Exercises 15–19 on the previous page had already been assigned and completed, the students could check their homework by using the formula to find the solutions to the same exercises, and comparing them with those found by the method of completing the square.

The students should understand that the formula was obtained by the method of completing the square, which is still basic. The formula merely summarizes what happens to the coefficients in

$$ax^2 + bx + c = 0$$

when the method of completing the square is used to solve the equation.

To emphasize all that the discriminant, D, reveals about the solutions of a quadratic, and to provide practice on the tricky parts of the formula, you could ask the class to compute D for each of the following equations and to state the nature of the solutions.

$$
\begin{array}{ll}
3x^2 - 4x - 5 = 0 & D = 76 \\
3x^2 - 4x + 5 = 0 & D = {}^-44 \\
9x^2 - 9x - 10 = 0 & D = 441 \\
x^2 - 12x + 36 = 0 & D = 0 \\
2x^2 + x + 1 = 0 & D = {}^-7 \\
2x^2 + x - 1 = 0 & D = 9
\end{array}
$$

4-5 THE QUADRATIC FORMULA

Let us try to solve the real quadratic equation

$$ax^2 + bx + c = 0, \quad a \neq 0,$$

by completing the square. Each of the following equations is equivalent to the preceding one.

$$ax^2 + bx + c = 0$$

$$x^2 + \frac{b}{a}x + \frac{c}{a} = 0$$

$$x^2 + \frac{b}{a}x = \frac{{}^-c}{a}$$

$$x^2 + \frac{b}{a}x + \left(\frac{b}{2a}\right)^2 = \left(\frac{b}{2a}\right)^2 - \frac{c}{a}$$

$$\left(x + \frac{b}{2a}\right)^2 = \frac{b^2}{4a^2} - \frac{c}{a}$$

$$\left(x + \frac{b}{2a}\right)^2 = \frac{b^2 - 4ac}{4a^2}$$

The way in which we solve this last equation depends on whether or not the real number on the right side is negative. Since $4a^2$ is a positive number, the right side is negative if, and only if,

$$b^2 - 4ac$$

is negative. This number is called the *discriminant* of the given quadratic equation, and is designated by D:

$$D = b^2 - 4ac.$$

Case 1: $D > 0$. Since $\sqrt{D}/2a$ and ${}^-(\sqrt{D}/2a)$ are the square roots of $D/4a^2$,

$$\left(x + \frac{b}{2a}\right)^2 = \frac{D}{4a^2}$$

if, and only if,

$$x + \frac{b}{2a} = \frac{\sqrt{D}}{2a} \quad \text{or} \quad x + \frac{b}{2a} = \frac{{}^-\sqrt{D}}{2a}.$$

On solving these two linear equations, we see that

$$\left\{\frac{^-b + \sqrt{D}}{2a}, \frac{^-b - \sqrt{D}}{2a}\right\}$$

is the solution set of the given equation; the solution set consists of two real numbers.

Case 2: $D = 0$. In this instance, the right side of the last equation above is zero. Hence,

$$x + \frac{b}{2a} = 0 \quad \text{and} \quad x = {}^-\frac{b}{2a}.$$

Thus,

$$\left\{{}^-\frac{b}{2a}\right\}$$

is the solution set of the given quadratic equation; the solution set consists of one real number.

Case 3: $D < 0$. The negative number D has $\sqrt{^-D}i$ and $^-\sqrt{^-D}i$ as its complex-number square roots. *Remember that if $D < 0$, then $^-D > 0$, and $\sqrt{^-D}$ is a real number.* Now

$$\left(x + \frac{b}{2a}\right)^2 = \frac{D}{4a^2}$$

if, and only if,

$$x + \frac{b}{2a} = \frac{\sqrt{^-D}i}{2a} \quad \text{or} \quad x + \frac{b}{2a} = \frac{^-\sqrt{^-D}i}{2a}.$$

On solving these two linear equations, we obtain

$$\left\{\frac{^-b + \sqrt{^-D}i}{2a}, \frac{^-b - \sqrt{^-D}i}{2a}\right\}$$

as the solution set of the given equation, and this solution set consists of two nonreal complex numbers which are conjugates of each other.

The three cases above can be combined into one statement. Let us use the notation $\sqrt{^-2}$ for $\sqrt{2}i$, $\sqrt{^-25}$ for $\sqrt{25}i$, or $5i$, and, in general,

$$\sqrt{D} \quad \text{for} \quad \sqrt{^-D}i \quad \text{when } D \text{ is a negative real number.}$$

Using this notation, we can make the following statement which summarizes our discussion of the solutions of quadratic equations.

In Problem 1 on page 186,

$$1 + \tfrac{3}{2}\sqrt{2}$$

may be checked by substitution into $2x^2 - 4x - 7 = 0$. Then the rational approximations of

$1 + \frac{3\sqrt{2}}{2}$, namely, 3.1 and 3.12

may be checked to see how accurate the approximations are.

Exercises for Discussion, page 187

If time is limited, it is suggested that at least Exercises for Discussion 3–11 be covered.

Answers to Exercises for Discussion 2, 3, page 187

2. (a) $D = (^-4)^2 - (4 \cdot 2 \cdot 1)$
$= 16 - 8 = 8;$
real, irrational

(b) $D = (6)^2 - (4 \cdot 9 \cdot 1)$
$= 36 - 36 = 0;$
one real

(c) $D = (1)^2 - (4 \cdot 1 \cdot 1)$
$= 1 - 4 = {}^-3;$
nonreal

(d) $D = (3)^2 - (4 \cdot 2 \cdot 1)$
$= 9 - 8 = 1;$
real, rational

3. (a) Sum:

$$\frac{^-b + \sqrt{D}}{2a} + \frac{^-b - \sqrt{D}}{2a} = \frac{^-2b}{2a} = {}^-\left(\frac{b}{a}\right)$$

(b) Product:

$$\left(\frac{^-b + \sqrt{D}}{2a}\right)\left(\frac{^-b - \sqrt{D}}{2a}\right) = \frac{b^2 - D}{4a^2} = \frac{b^2 - (b^2 - 4ac)}{4a^2} = \frac{4ac}{4a^2} = \frac{c}{a}$$

Answers to Exercises for Discussion 4–10, page 187

4. $\{x \mid x^2 + 9 = 0\}$
$= \{x \mid x^2 = {}^-9\}$
$= \{x \mid x = 3i \text{ or } x = {}^-3i\}$
$= \{3i, {}^-3i\}$

5. $\{x \mid 2x^2 - 4x + 5 = 0\}$
$= \left\{x \mid x = \frac{4 + \sqrt{{}^-24}}{4}, \text{ or } x = \frac{4 - \sqrt{{}^-24}}{4}\right\}$
$= \{1 + \frac{1}{2}\sqrt{6}i, 1 - \frac{1}{2}\sqrt{6}i\}$

6. $\{x \mid 2x^2 + 9x = 0\}$
$= \{x \mid x(2x + 9) = 0\}$
$= \{x \mid x = 0, \text{ or } 2x + 9 = 0\}$
$= \{0, {}^-\frac{9}{2}\}$

7. $\{x \mid x = 1 - 3x^2\}$
$= \{x \mid 3x^2 + x - 1 = 0\}$
$= \left\{x \mid x = \frac{{}^-1 + \sqrt{13}}{6}, \text{ or } x = \frac{{}^-1 - \sqrt{13}}{6}\right\}$
$= \{{}^-\frac{1}{6} + \frac{1}{6}\sqrt{13}, {}^-\frac{1}{6} - \frac{1}{6}\sqrt{13}\}$

8. $\{y \mid y^2 - 2\sqrt{5}y + 1 = 0\}$
$= \left\{y \mid y = \frac{2\sqrt{5} + \sqrt{16}}{2}, \text{ or } y = \frac{2\sqrt{5} - \sqrt{16}}{2}\right\}$
$= \{\sqrt{5} + 2, \sqrt{5} - 2\}$

9. $\{x \mid \frac{1}{2}x^2 - \frac{2}{3}x + 1 = 0\}$
$= \{x \mid 3x^2 - 4x + 6 = 0\}$
$= \left\{x \mid x = \frac{4 + \sqrt{{}^-56}}{6}, \text{ or } x = \frac{4 - \sqrt{{}^-56}}{6}\right\}$
$= \{\frac{2}{3} + \frac{1}{3}\sqrt{14}i, \frac{2}{3} - \frac{1}{3}\sqrt{14}i\}$

10. $\{x \mid (x - 2)^2 - 5(x - 2) + 6 = 0\}$
$= \{x \mid [(x - 2) - 2][(x - 2) - 3] = 0\}$
$= \{x \mid (x - 4)(x - 5) = 0\}$
$= \{4, 5\}$

QUADRATIC FORMULA

The real quadratic equation

$$ax^2 + bx + c = 0, \quad a \neq 0,$$

has solutions

$$x = \frac{{}^-b + \sqrt{D}}{2a} \quad \textit{and} \quad x = \frac{{}^-b - \sqrt{D}}{2a}$$

where the discriminant D is

$$b^2 - 4ac.$$

Problem 1. Solve the real quadratic equation $2x^2 - 4x - 7 = 0$.

Solution. For this equation, $a = 2$, $b = {}^-4$, and $c = {}^-7$. The discriminant D of this equation is $({}^-4)^2 - (4 \cdot 2 \cdot {}^-7)$, or 72. Hence, by the quadratic formula, the solutions of this equation are

$$x = \frac{4 + \sqrt{72}}{4} \quad \text{and} \quad x = \frac{4 - \sqrt{72}}{4}.$$

Since $72 = 36 \cdot 2$, we have $\sqrt{72} = 6\sqrt{2}$, and the two solutions are

$$x = 1 + \tfrac{3}{2}\sqrt{2} \quad \text{and} \quad x = 1 - \tfrac{3}{2}\sqrt{2}.$$

As expected, the solutions are real since $D > 0$. Using $\sqrt{2} \doteq 1.414$, we find that these two irrational solutions have rational approximations

$$3.121 \quad \text{and} \quad {}^-1.121.$$

Problem 2. Solve the real quadratic equation $4x^2 - 12x + 9 = 0$.

Solution. For this equation, $a = 4$, $b = {}^-12$, and $c = 9$. Hence,

$$D = ({}^-12)^2 - (4 \cdot 4 \cdot 9), \quad \text{or } 0.$$

Since $D = 0$, the quadratic formula yields only one solution:

$$x = \frac{{}^-({}^-12)}{2 \cdot 4}, \quad \text{or } \frac{3}{2}.$$

Problem 3. Solve the real quadratic equation $3x^2 - 4x + 7 = 0$.

Solution. For this equation, $a = 3$, $b = {}^-4$, and $c = 7$. Therefore, the discriminant D is

$$({}^-4)^2 - (4 \cdot 3 \cdot 7), \quad \text{or } {}^-68.$$

Hence, by the quadratic formula, the solutions of this equation are

$$x = \frac{4 + \sqrt{^-68}}{6} \quad \text{and} \quad x = \frac{4 - \sqrt{^-68}}{6}.$$

Since $^-68 = {^-4} \cdot 17$, we have $\sqrt{^-68} = 2\sqrt{17}i$, and the solutions are

$$x = \tfrac{2}{3} + \tfrac{1}{3}\sqrt{17}i \quad \text{and} \quad x = \tfrac{2}{3} - \tfrac{1}{3}\sqrt{17}i.$$

Because $D < 0$, the two solutions are nonreal conjugate complex numbers.

Exercises for Discussion

1. Show that $(\sqrt{^-2})(\sqrt{^-8}) = {^-4}$.
   $\sqrt{^-2}\sqrt{^-8} = (i\sqrt{2})(i\sqrt{8}) = i^2\sqrt{2 \cdot 8} = (^-1)(\sqrt{16}) = {^-4}$
2. Find the discriminant of each of the following quadratic equations, and from it, determine whether the equation has nonreal solutions, one real solution, real solutions which are rational, or real solutions which are irrational.
   (a) $x^2 - 4x + 2 = 0$ (b) $y^2 + 6y + 9 = 0$
   (c) $x^2 + x + 1 = 0$ (d) $x^2 + 3x + 2 = 0$
3. Using the solutions of the quadratic formula, show that if
   $$ax^2 + bx + c = 0$$
   has two solutions, real or complex, then
   (a) the sum of the solutions is $^-(b/a)$.
   (b) the product of the solutions is c/a.

Solve each of the following quadratic equations. Check your solutions by comparing the sum and product of the solutions with $^-(b/a)$ and c/a, respectively.

4. $x^2 + 9 = 0$
5. $2x^2 - 4x + 5 = 0$
6. $2x^2 + 9x = 0$
7. $x = 1 - 3x^2$
8. $y^2 - 2\sqrt{5}y + 1 = 0$
9. $\frac{1}{2}x^2 - \frac{2}{3}x + 1 = 0$
10. $(x - 2)^2 - 5(x - 2) + 6 = 0$
11. If the formulas of Exercise 3 are applied to the solution set of a quadratic equation of the form $x^2 + bx + c = 0$, the sum of the solutions is ^-b and the product of the solutions is c. This provides an alternative method for writing a quadratic equation when its solution set is given. For example, if the solution set is $\{3 + i, 3 - i\}$, then the sum, 6, equals ^-b and the product, 10, equals c. Hence, $x^2 - 6x + 10 = 0$ is a quadratic equation with the given solution set. Use this method to write quadratic equations having the following solution sets.
    (a) $\{1 + \sqrt{3}, 1 - \sqrt{3}\}$
    Sum: 2; product: $^-2$
    $x^2 - 2x - 2 = 0$
    (b) $\{2 + i, 2 - i\}$
    Sum: 4; product: 5
    $x^2 - 4x + 5 = 0$

In relation to Exercise for Discussion 12, three simple specific graphs should be drawn, such as

$$y = x^2 - 4x + 3,$$
$$y = x^2 - 4x + 4,$$
$$y = x^2 - 4x + 5;$$

and the corresponding quadratics,

$$x^2 - 4x + 3 = 0,$$
$$x^2 - 4x + 4 = 0,$$
$$x^2 - 4x + 5 = 0,$$

should be solved before doing this exercise.

Answers to Exercises for Discussion 12–13, 16, page 188

page 188

12. If the graph intersects the x-axis at two points, the equation will have two real solutions. Hence, the discriminant is positive. If the graph is tangent to the x-axis, the equation will have one real solution. Hence, the discriminant is zero. If the graph fails to intersect the x-axis, the equation will have complex solutions. Hence, the discriminant is negative.

13. The graph of the equation $y = x^2 - 3x + m$ will intersect the x-axis at two points provided the discriminant $9 - 4m$ is positive; that is,

$$9 - 4m > 0 \quad \text{if} \quad m < \tfrac{9}{4}.$$

16. (a)

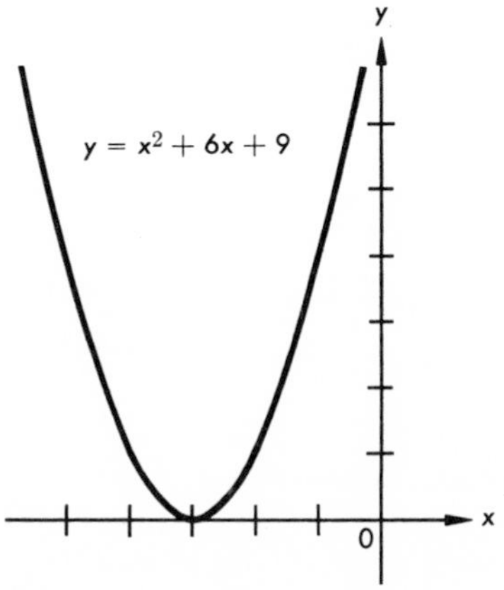

(b)

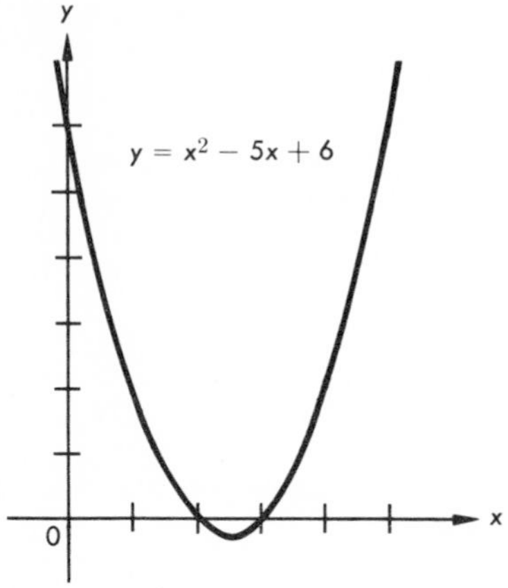

(c)

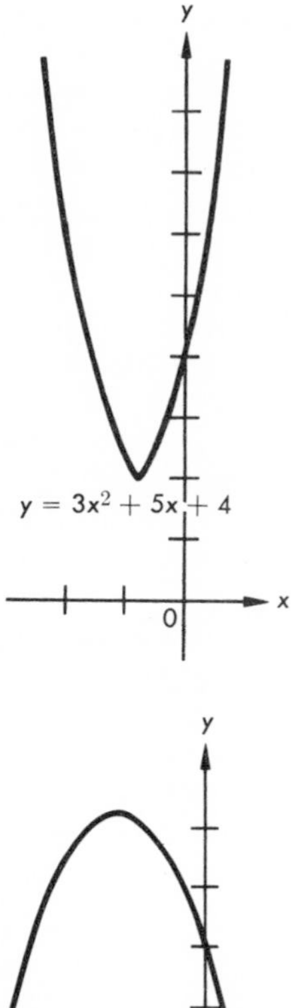

(d)

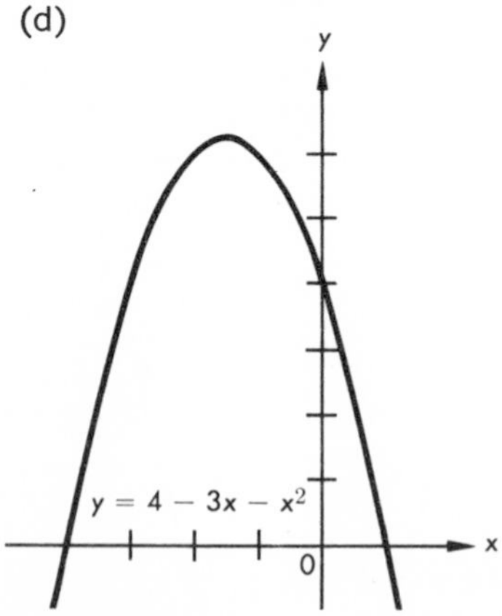

Answer to Exercise 1

1. $\{^{-}\frac{5}{6} + \frac{1}{6}\sqrt{23}i, {}^{-}\frac{5}{6} - \frac{1}{6}\sqrt{23}i\}$

12. The graph of the equation $y = ax^2 + bx + c$ can intersect the x-axis in two points, be tangent to the x-axis, or fail to intersect the x-axis. In each case, what type of solution or solutions does the quadratic equation $ax^2 + bx + c = 0$ have? In each case, what values does the discriminant have?

13. For what value or values of m does the graph of $y = x^2 - 3x + m$ cut the x-axis in two points?

14. For what value or values of m is the graph of $y = x^2 - 3x + m$ tangent to the x-axis? Tangent: $9 - 4m = 0$; $m = \frac{9}{4}$

15. For what value or values of m will the graph of $y = x^2 - 3x + m$ fail to cut the x-axis? Fail to cut: $9 - 4m < 0$; $m > \frac{9}{4}$

16. Graph each of the following equations.

(a) $y = x^2 + 6x + 9$ (b) $y = x^2 - 5x + 6$

(c) $y = 3x^2 + 5x + 4$ (d) $y = 4 - 3x - x^2$

Exercises

Solve each of the following quadratic equations. Check your solutions by comparing the sum and product of the solutions with $^{-}(b/a)$ and c/a, respectively.

1. $3x^2 + 5x + 4 = 0$

2. $x^2 - 4x + 4 = 0$ $\{2\}$

3. $x^2 + 2 = 4x$ $\{2 + \sqrt{2}, 2 - \sqrt{2}\}$

4. $5z^2 - 13z = 6$ $\{^{-}\frac{2}{5}, 3\}$

5. $x^2 + 100 = 0$ $\{10i, {}^{-}10i\}$

6. $^{-}16t^2 - 32t + 240 = 0$ $\{^{-}5, 3\}$

7. $2 - \frac{1}{2}x - \frac{3}{5}x^2 = 0$ $\{\frac{^{-}5}{12} + \frac{1}{12}\sqrt{505}, \frac{^{-}5}{12} - \frac{1}{12}\sqrt{505}\}$

8. $x^2 - (m + n)x + mn = 0,\ m \neq n$ $\{m, n\}$

9. $(2x + 1)^2 - 3(2x + 1) - 4 = 0$ $\{\frac{3}{2}, {}^{-}1\}$

△

Write a quadratic equation for each of the following solution sets.

10. $\{2, {}^{-}\frac{3}{2}\}$ $2x^2 - x - 6 = 0$

11. $\{2, {}^{-}2\}$ $x^2 - 4 = 0$

12. $\{\frac{1}{2} - \frac{1}{2}\sqrt{5}, \frac{1}{2} + \frac{1}{2}\sqrt{5}\}$ $x^2 - x - 1 = 0$

13. $\{9, {}^{-}10\}$ $x^2 + x - 90 = 0$

14. $\left\{\frac{^{-}1}{2} + \frac{\sqrt{3}}{2}i, \frac{^{-}1}{2} - \frac{\sqrt{3}}{2}i\right\}$ $x^2 + x + 1 = 0$

15. $\{i, {}^{-}i\}$ $x^2 + 1 = 0$

16. For what value or values of k is the graph of $y = x^2 - kx + k + 8$ tangent to the x-axis? $k = 8$ or $k = {}^{-}4$

17. For what value or values of k does $x^2 - 4x - k = 0$ have one real solution? $k = {}^{-}4$

18. For what value or values of p does $px^2 - 6x + p = 0$ have nonreal solutions? $p < {}^-3,\ p > 3$

19. For what value or values of p is 2 in the solution set of the quadratic equation

$$px^2 - 4x + 3 = 0? \quad p = \frac{5}{4}$$

20. For what value or values of k is one solution of $x^2 - 6x + k = 0$ twice the other solution? $k = 8$

21. (a) Is $2 - 3i$ a solution of the complex quadratic equation

$$x^2 - (3 - 2i)x + (5 - i) = 0? \quad \text{Yes}$$

(b) Is $x = 1 + i$ a solution of the equation of part (a)? Yes

(c) Factor

$$x^2 - (3 - 2i)x + (5 - i),$$

and check your factoring by multiplication. $(x - 2 + 3i)(x - 1 - i)$

22. Prove that if a and b are negative numbers, $\sqrt{a} \cdot \sqrt{b} = {}^-\sqrt{ab}$.
See Solution Manual.

4-6 THE COMPLEX NUMBER PLANE

We can assign complex numbers to points in a plane in the same way that we assign ordered pairs of real numbers. We start out with two perpendicular number lines; one line has real numbers for coordinates and the other line has i-numbers. These lines meet at their origins. Each complex number can be assigned as the coordinate of a unique point in the plane, as suggested in Fig. 4–1.

The horizontal number line in the figure is called the *real axis.* Every real number is the coordinate of a point on this axis. The vertical number line is called the *imaginary axis.* Each pure imaginary number, or i-number, is the coordinate of a

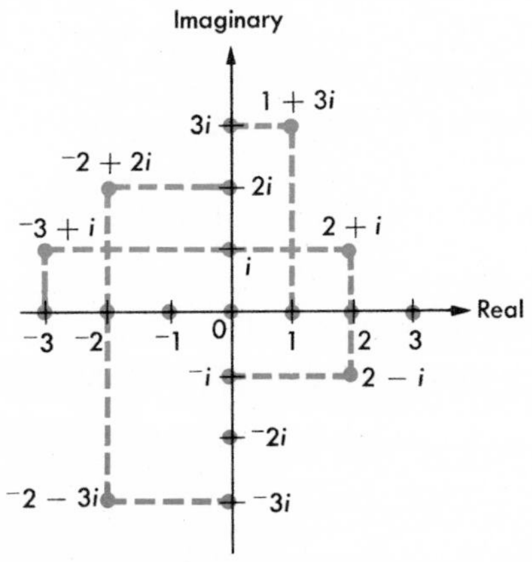

FIGURE 4–1

Quiz

Solve each of the following quadratic equations. Check your solutions by comparing the sum and product of the solutions with ${}^-\left(\frac{b}{a}\right)$ and $\frac{c}{a}$, respectively.

1. $x^2 - 3x + 5 = 0$
$\left(\text{ans: } \left\{\frac{3 \pm i\sqrt{11}}{2}\right\}\right)$

2. $3t^2 - 4t + 2 = 0$
$\left(\text{ans: } \left\{\frac{2 \pm i\sqrt{2}}{3}\right\}\right)$

3. $2y^2 + y + 7 = 0$
$\left(\text{ans: } \left\{\frac{{}^-1 \pm i\sqrt{55}}{4}\right\}\right)$

4-6 THE COMPLEX NUMBER PLANE

Note that the one-to-one correspondence between the points of the complex number plane and the numbers of the complex number system illustrates clearly two statements made earlier:

$$a + bi = 0$$

if, and only if, $a = b = 0$, and

$$x + yi = c + di$$

if, and only if, $x = c$ and $y = d$.

The problem on the next three pages should be very interesting to the class. Students may be surprised to find complex numbers involved in a motion problem and used to describe distance as adequately as real numbers.

You may wish to ask how many real numbers have absolute value 3, and how many complex numbers have absolute value 3.

You could remind the students that if x denotes any real number, $|x|$ can be thought of as the distance from the origin to the point with coordinate x on a number line. The equation $|x| = 3$ has exactly two solutions: $x = 3$ or $x = {}^-3$; $|x| < 3$ has an interval, ${}^-3 < x < 3$, for its graph; $|x| > 3$ has two open rays, $x > 3$ and $x < {}^-3$, for its graph.

If z is any complex number $(a + bi)$, $|z| = \sqrt{a^2 + b^2}$, the graph of the statement $|z| = 3$ is all points three units from the origin of the complex number plane.

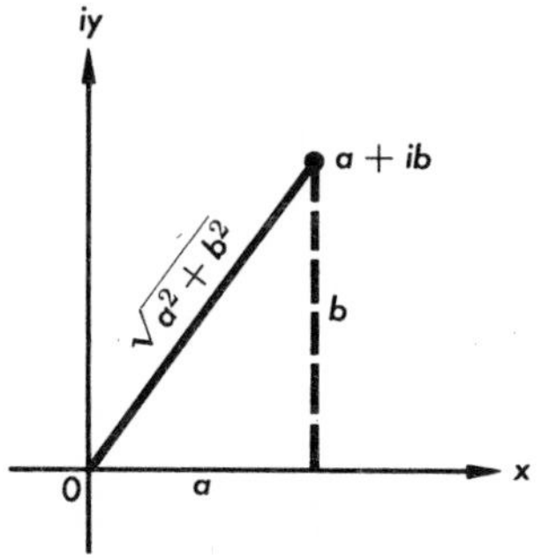

Hence, $|z| = 3$ has an infinite solution set and the graph is a circle with its center at the origin of the complex number plane and with a radius of 3. Also, $|z| < 3$ has for its graph all the points inside this circle, while $|z| > 3$ has for its graph all the points outside this circle.

point on this axis. Every point in the plane has a complex number $a + bi$ as its coordinate to describe the position of the point relative to the two axes. Thus, if lines are drawn through this point parallel to the axes, they will cross the axes at the point with coordinate a on the real axis and at the point with coordinate bi on the imaginary axis. (See Fig. 4–2.) This plane, which has a complex number assigned to each of its points, is called the *complex number plane.*†

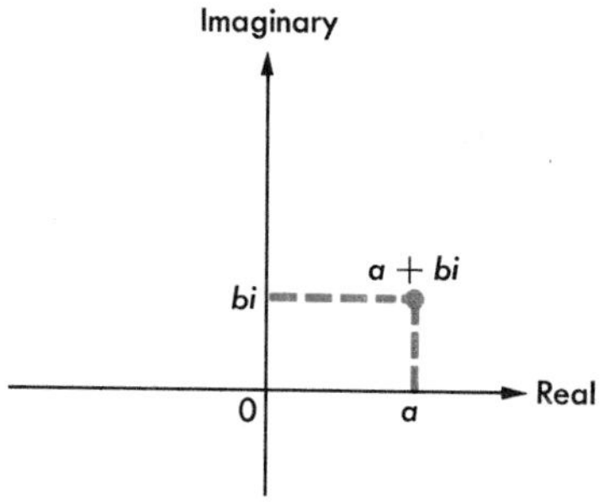

FIGURE 4–2

How does the complex number plane compare with a cartesian coordinate system in the plane? If we let the real axis be the usual x-axis and the imaginary axis be the y-axis, then the point with coordinate $a + bi$ in the complex number plane has coordinates (a, b) in the cartesian coordinate system.

The distance from the origin to the point with coordinate $a + bi$ is called the *absolute value* of the complex number $a + bi$. According to the pythagorean theorem, this distance is $\sqrt{a^2 + b^2}$. We shall use the notation $|a + bi|$ to designate the absolute value of $a + bi$. By definition,

$$|a + bi| = \sqrt{a^2 + b^2}.$$

For example,

$$|3 - 2i| = \sqrt{3^2 + ({}^-2)^2}, \quad \text{or } \sqrt{13}.$$

The following problem from a prize examination shows an unusual way of using complex numbers and the complex number plane.

Problem. Two men left a certain place and walked, each in a straight line, to their destinations which were 4 miles apart. If the distance which one of them walked was one-half the square of the distance which the other man walked, how far did each man walk?

Solution 1. Let x be the distance one man walked and y be the distance the other man walked. We might be inclined to represent what is given by the following system of equations:

$$\begin{cases} y - x = 4, \\ y = \frac{1}{2}x^2. \end{cases}$$

† Two amateur mathematicians, a Norwegian surveyor named Wessel and a Parisian bookkeeper named Argand, were the first to devise a scheme, similar to the one above, for representing the complex numbers as points in a plane.

When we solve the first equation for y and substitute it in the second, we obtain the equivalent system

$$\begin{cases} y = x + 4, \\ x + 4 = \frac{1}{2}x^2. \end{cases}$$

The second equation is equivalent to each of the following:

$$2x + 8 = x^2,$$

$$x^2 - 2x - 8 = 0,$$

$$(x - 4)(x + 2) = 0.$$

Thus, $x = 4$ or $x = {}^{-}2$. Substituting these values in the first equation, we obtain the solutions $(4, 8)$ and $({}^{-}2, 2)$ for (x, y).

These two solutions may be pictured on a number line, as shown in

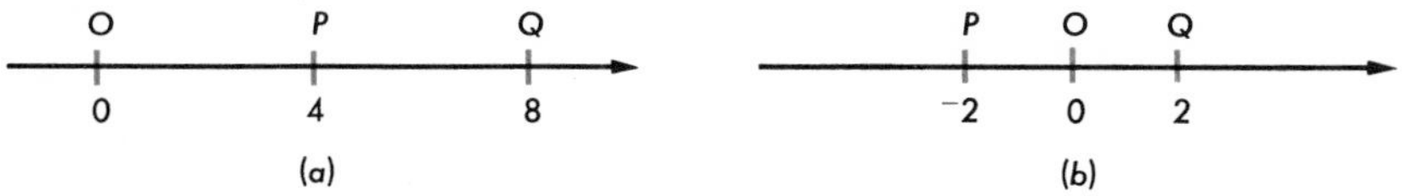

FIGURE 4–3

Fig. 4–3. In Fig. 4–3(a) one man walks from O to P and the other from O to Q.

$$8 - 4 = 4 \quad \text{and} \quad 8 = \tfrac{1}{2} \cdot 4^2$$

In Fig. 4–3(b), $OP = {}^{-}2$ and $OQ = 2$, and

$$2 - {}^{-}2 = 4, \quad 2 = \tfrac{1}{2}({}^{-}2)^2.$$

Solution 2. In the statement of the problem, it does not say which of the two distances is one-half the square of the other. Thus, our system of equations could just as well be

$$\begin{cases} y - x = 4, \\ x = \frac{1}{2}y^2. \end{cases}$$

If we solve the first equation for x and substitute it in the second, we obtain the equivalent system

$$\begin{cases} x = y - 4, \\ y - 4 = \frac{1}{2}y^2. \end{cases}$$

TWISTER

Mrs. Newcomb had rearranged her living room furniture, but was unsure about the placement of a large round table. Her husband was a bit absentminded and occasionally wandered through the house in the dark. She wanted to place the table so that he could walk from the door at one corner of the room to the diagonally opposite corner without bumping into it. She had put the table, which was 4 feet in diameter, in the corner to the left of the door. Its center was 3 feet from the 15-foot wall and 5 feet from the 9-foot wall. Could she safely leave the table there?

Solution:

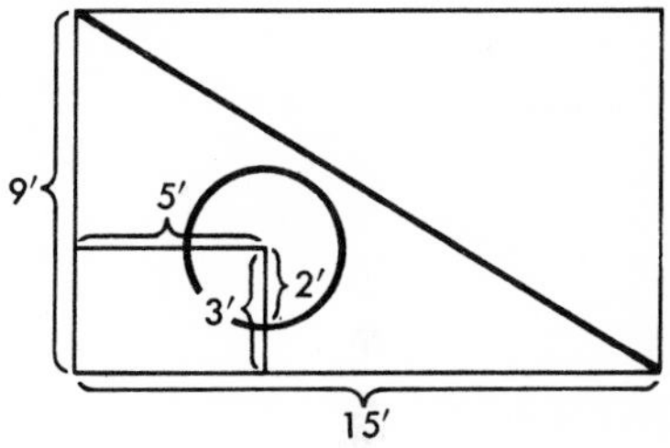

The table can be considered as a circle with equation

$$(x - 5)^2 + (y - 3)^2 = 4.$$

The path her husband would walk is a line with equation

$$y = \frac{^{-}3}{5}x + 9.$$

By solving these equations for y, the determinant is found to be negative. Thus, x and y are imaginary numbers, and the path her husband takes would not intersect the table.

The second equation of this system may be solved as follows:

$$2y - 8 = y^2,$$
$$y^2 - 2y + 8 = 0,$$
$$y = \frac{2 + \sqrt{^-28}}{2} \quad \text{or} \quad y = \frac{2 - \sqrt{^-28}}{2}.$$

Since $\sqrt{^-28} = 2\sqrt{7}i$, the two solutions of this quadratic equation are $1 + \sqrt{7}i$ and $1 - \sqrt{7}i$. Returning to the given system of equations, we have

$$x = (1 + \sqrt{7}i) - 4, \quad \text{or } x = {^-3} + \sqrt{7}i, \quad \text{when} \quad y = 1 + \sqrt{7}i.$$
$$x = (1 - \sqrt{7}i) - 4, \quad \text{or } x = {^-3} - \sqrt{7}i, \quad \text{when} \quad y = 1 - \sqrt{7}i.$$

Hence,

$$\{({^-3} + \sqrt{7}i,\ 1 + \sqrt{7}i),\ ({^-3} - \sqrt{7}i,\ 1 - \sqrt{7}i)\}$$

is the solution set of the given system.

We can interpret complex numbers as solutions of the given problem if we think of each man as starting from the origin 0 of a complex plane. One man walks to point A with coordinate x and the other to point B with coordinate y. In Fig. 4–4, this possibility is sketched for the first element of the solution set, $x = {^-3} + \sqrt{7}i$ and $y = 1 + \sqrt{7}i$. Then $y - x = 4$, in this case, and 4 is the actual distance between points A and B. According to the definition of the absolute value of a complex number, the distances walked by the two men are $|x|$ and $|y|$.

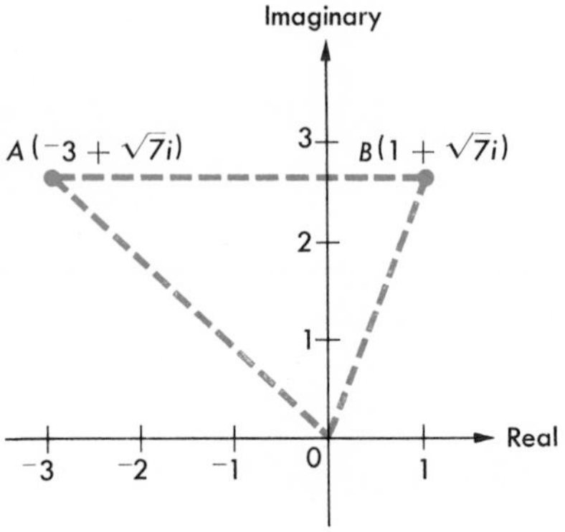

FIGURE 4–4

Since

$$|x| = \sqrt{({^-3})^2 + (\sqrt{7})^2}, \quad \text{or } 4,$$

and

$$|y| = \sqrt{1^2 + (\sqrt{7})^2}, \quad \text{or } \sqrt{8},$$

it is true that

$$|x| = \tfrac{1}{2}|y|^2, \quad \text{or } 4 = \tfrac{1}{2} \cdot 8.$$

Hence, Fig. 4–4 represents another solution of this problem. The second elements of the solution set, $x = {}^-3 - \sqrt{7}i$ and $y = 1 - \sqrt{7}i$, may be similarly interpreted.

Thus, we can assume that the men are walking in the same straight line, and we then find two solutions, one when they walk in the same direction and one when they walk in opposite directions. On the other hand, we can assume that they do not walk in the same straight line and we then find another solution in which the paths are oblique to each other.

Exercises for Discussion

In Exercises 1–8, plot each number on a complex number plane.

1. $3 + i$ **2.** $2i$ **3.** $7 - 4i$ **4.** $^-6 + 5i$

5. 5 **6.** $^-\frac{1}{2} - 3i$ **7.** $^-\frac{4}{3}i$ **8.** $^-4$

9. (a) On a complex number plane, plot the following points: A with coordinate $2 + i$, B with coordinate $1 + 5i$, and C with coordinate 0.

(b) Find point D such that $ADBC$ is a parallelogram, and give its coordinate. *D has coordinate $3 + 6i$.*

(c) Find the sum of $2 + i$ and $1 + 5i$. How does this number compare with the coordinate of D? *$(2+i)+(1+5i) = 3+6i$; same*

10. (a) On a complex number plane, plot the following points: P with coordinate $2 + 3i$, Q with coordinate $^-4 + 2i$, and R with coordinate 0.

(b) Find point S such that $PSQR$ is a parallelogram, and give its coordinate. *S has coordinate $^-2 + 5i$.*

(c) Find the sum of $2 + 3i$ and $^-4 + 2i$, and plot the point T with this sum as the coordinate. How far is T from S? *$(2+3i)+(^-4+2i) = {}^-2+5i$. T is the same point as S.*

In Exercises 11–14, find each of the absolute values.

11. $|2 - 3i|$ *$\sqrt{2^2+(^-3)^2} = \sqrt{13}$* **12.** $|4 - 3i|$ *$\sqrt{4^2+(^-3)^2} = \sqrt{25} = 5$*

13. $\left|{}^-\frac{\sqrt{3}}{2} + \frac{1}{2}i\right|$ *$\sqrt{\left(\frac{^-\sqrt{3}}{2}\right)^2+\left(\frac{1}{2}\right)^2} = \sqrt{\frac{3}{4}+\frac{1}{4}} = 1$* **14.** $|^-6i|$ *$\sqrt{0^2+(^-6)^2} = 6$*

15. In a plane with a cartesian coordinate system, consider points

$$E(0, 0),\quad F(a, b),\quad G(a + c, b + d),\quad H(c, d).$$

(a) Find the slopes of $\overline{EF}$ and $\overline{GH}$.
(b) Find the slopes of $\overline{FG}$ and $\overline{EH}$.
(c) Show that $EFGH$ is a parallelogram.

16. In the complex number plane, consider points with coordinates $0 + 0i$, $a + bi$, $c + di$, and $(a + c) + (b + d)i$. Explain how complex numbers can be added graphically by constructing a parallelogram.

Exercises for Discussion

All of the exercises on this and on the next page are important and should be covered. Exercises for Discussion 15 and 16 give the parallelogram law for the addition of complex numbers. This is the same as the parallelogram law for finding the sum of two vectors, or the resultant of two forces.

Answers to Exercises for Discussion 1–8, 9(a), 10(a)

1.–8.

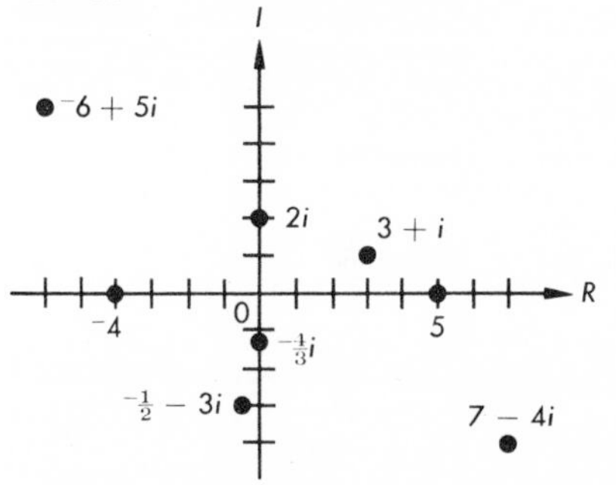

9. (a)

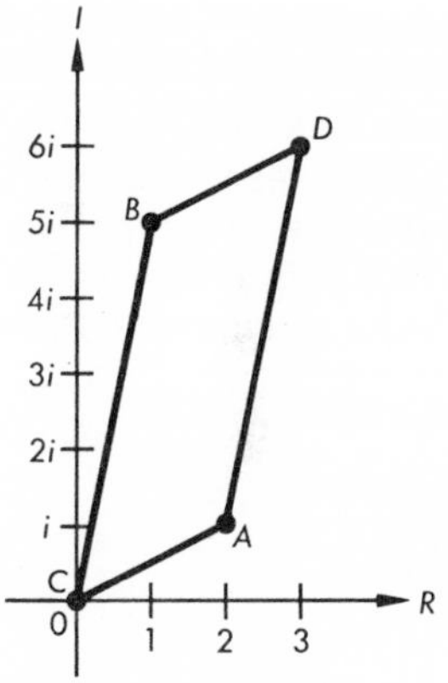

10. (a)

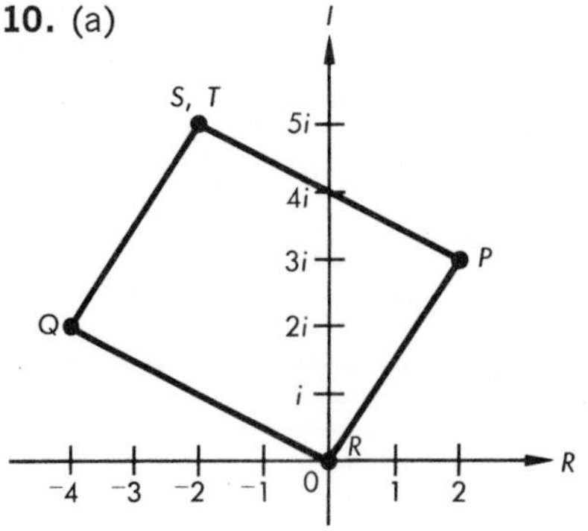

Answers to Exercises for Discussion 15–16, page 193

15. (a) Slope of

$$\overline{EF} = \frac{b-0}{a-0} = \frac{b}{a};$$

slope of

$$\overline{GH} = \frac{d-(b+d)}{c-(a+c)} = \frac{^-b}{^-a} = \frac{b}{a}$$

(b) Slope of

$$\overline{FG} = \frac{(b+d)-b}{(a+c)-a} = \frac{d}{c};$$

slope of

$$\overline{EH} = \frac{d-0}{c-0} = \frac{d}{c}$$

(c) Since both pairs of opposite sides are parallel, $EFGH$ is a parallelogram.

16. To add two complex numbers graphically, plot each on a complex number plane and draw the line segments connecting each to the origin. Complete the parallelogram which has these two line segments as sides, and the fourth vertex has for its coordinates the sum of the two complex numbers.

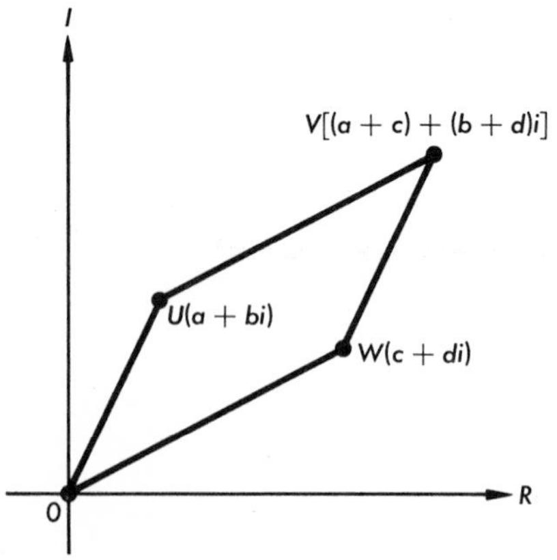

Exercises

See Solution Manual for graphs.

In Exercises 1–8, plot each number on a complex number plane.

1. $6 + 8i$	**2.** $^-8 + 6i$	**3.** $1 - i$	**4.** $2 - 3i$
5. $^-10$	**6.** $5i$	**7.** ^-2i	**8.** 5

9. Find the distance from the origin of each of the points plotted in Exercises 1–8. Which point is farthest from the origin? Which point is nearest the origin? Are any two or more points the same distance from the origin? $10, 10, \sqrt{2}, \sqrt{13}, 10, 5, 2, 5$; $6+8i, {}^-8+6i, {}^-10$; $1-i$; yes

In Exercises 10–15, find each absolute value.

10. $|3 + 4i|$ 5 **11.** $|^-3 + 4i|$ 5

12. $|^-3 - 4i|$ 5 **13.** $|3 - 4i|$ 5

14. $\left|\frac{^-\sqrt{3}}{2} - \frac{1}{2}i\right|$ 1 **15.** $\left|\frac{1}{2} - \frac{\sqrt{3}}{2}i\right|$ 1

16. On a complex number plane, plot each pair of points P, Q with the coordinates given below. Find the coordinate of the point S such that $PSQR$ is a parallelogram with one vertex at the origin R.

(a) P: $^-1 + 5i$, Q: $3 + 2i$ $2+7i$

(b) P: $2 - 3i$, Q: $^-1 + 4i$ $1+i$

(c) P: $4 + 6i$, Q: $4 - 6i$ 8

17. (a) On a complex number plane, plot the points C with coordinate $2 + 2i$ and D with coordinate $1 + 4i$.

(b) Subtract $1 + 4i$ from $2 + 2i$ and plot the point F, with the difference as its coordinate. $F = 1 - 2i$

(c) Show that the line from the origin to F is parallel to CD. See Solution Manual.

△

18. In a plane with a cartesian coordinate system, consider points $E(0, 0)$, $F(a, b)$, $G(c, d)$, and $H(a - c, b - d)$.

(a) Find the slopes of $\overline{FG}$ and $\overline{EH}$. $\frac{d-b}{c-a}$; $\frac{d-b}{c-a}$

(b) Find the slopes of $\overline{EG}$ and $\overline{HF}$. $\frac{d}{c}$; $\frac{d}{c}$

(c) Show that $EGFH$ is a parallelogram. See Solution Manual.

19. In the complex number plane, consider points with coordinates $a + bi$, $c + di$, and $(a - c) + (b - d)i$. Explain how complex numbers can be subtracted graphically by constructing a parallelogram. See Solution Manual.

20. Which, if any, of the following statements do you think is true for every pair of complex numbers x and y?

(a) $|x| + |y| > |x + y|$
(b) $|x| + |y| \geqq |x + y|$ (circled)
(c) $|x| + |y| = |x + y|$
(d) $|x| + |y| \leqq |x + y|$
(e) $|x| + |y| < |x + y|$

21. If a is real, the absolute value of a is defined by the equations

$$|a| = a \quad \text{if} \quad a \geqq 0,$$
$$|a| = {}^-a \quad \text{if} \quad a < 0.$$

However, consider a to be the complex number $a + 0i$; then refer to the definition of absolute value of a complex number, and compare these two absolute values of a. *Same*

22. The graphical addition of complex numbers is given in Exercise 16 of the Exercises for Discussion. Remember that one side of a triangle can be no longer than the sum of the other two sides, and show geometrically that your answer to Exercise 20 is correct. *See Solution Manual.*

23. (a) Solve the system

$$\begin{cases} y^2 = 6x, \\ y - x = 4\tfrac{1}{6}. \end{cases}$$

$x = \frac{^-7}{6} + 4i$, $y = 3 + 4i$ or $x = \frac{^-7}{6} - 4i$, $y = 3 - 4i$

(b) Graph your solutions on a complex number plane.
(c) Can you supply a physical interpretation of this system and its solution similar to that given for the problem of this section? *See Solution Manual.*

24. The notation $\bar{r}$ is frequently used for the conjugate of the complex number r. *See Solution Manual.*

(a) If $r = a + bi$, show that $r\bar{r} = a^2 + b^2$.
(b) Show that $\sqrt{r\bar{r}} = |r|$.
(c) Show that $|\bar{r}| = |r|$.
(d) Show that $|\overline{rs}| = |\bar{r}| \cdot |\bar{s}|$ for any two complex numbers r and s.

25. The complex number with a variable real part x and a variable pure imaginary part yi is called a *complex variable*, and z is the letter commonly used for $x + yi$. In the complex number plane, what is the graph

(a) of the equation $|z| = 4$? *Circle: center (0,0), radius 4*
(b) of the inequality $|z| < 2$? *Region inside circle: center (0,0), radius 2*
(c) of the inequality $|z| \geqq 3$? *Region outside and on circle: center (0,0), radius 3*

Quiz

In Exercises 1–3, plot each number on a complex plane.

1. $3 + 4i$
2. $^-3 + 4i$
3. ^-5i

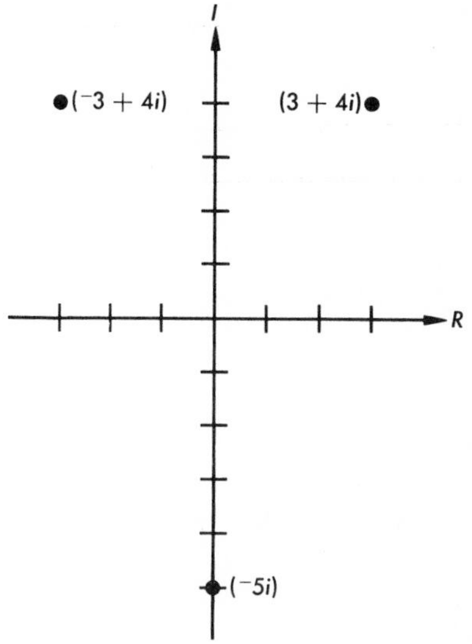

In Exercises 4–5, find each absolute value.

4. $|2 + 5i|$ (ans: $\sqrt{29}$)
5. $|^-3 + i|$ (ans: $\sqrt{10}$)

HISTORICAL NOTE

Simple quadratic equations were solved for countless centuries before a formal mathematical language was evolved. According to all the evidence we have, the completion of squares was one of the earliest methods used in solving quadratics. Therefore, it is not surprising that the quadratic formula appeared in print as soon as the appropriate symbolism was available.

Once the quadratic formula was commonly used, mathematicians tried to solve higher-degree polynomial equations by similar methods. In the sixteenth century, many mathematicians worked on solutions of cubic equations of the form

$$x^3 + ax^2 + bx + c = 0. \tag{1}$$

They soon discovered that the replacement of x by $y - a/3$ reduced Eq. (1) to the form

$$y^3 + py + q = 0. \tag{2}$$

Here p and q are simple combinations of a, b, and c. Once mathematicians found a solution r for Eq. (2), they then found that $r - a/3$ is a solution of Eq. (1).

One of the earliest solvers of Eq. (2) was the Italian mathematician Tartaglia. His solution was published in 1545 in Cardan's famous algebra book, *Ars Magna*. A somewhat more complicated solution was given by the Frenchman Vieta in 1591. The following is his solution.

First, let

$$y = z - \frac{p}{3z}$$

in Eq. (2). After simplifying the resulting equation, we obtain

$$z^6 + qz^3 - \frac{p^3}{27} = 0. \tag{3}$$

Since Eq. (3) is a quadratic equation in z^3, we can solve for z^3 by the quadratic formula:

$$z^3 = \frac{^-q}{2} \pm \sqrt{D}, \text{ where } D = \frac{p^3}{27} + \frac{q^2}{4}$$

Letting

$$A = \sqrt[3]{\frac{^-q}{2} + \sqrt{D}}, \quad B = \sqrt[3]{\frac{^-q}{2} - \sqrt{D}},$$

we can show that

$$y = A + B$$

is a solution of Eq. (2). For example, the equation

$$y^3 - 6y - 6 = 0$$

has solution

$$y = \sqrt[3]{4} + \sqrt[3]{2}.$$

Equation (2) usually has three solutions. The other two are

$$y = tA + t^2B \quad \text{and} \quad y = t^2A + tB,$$

where t is a complex cube root of 1, that is,

$$t = {}^-\tfrac{1}{2} + \tfrac{1}{2}\sqrt{3}i.$$

Quartic equations of the form

$$x^4 + ax^3 + bx^2 + cx + d = 0 \tag{4}$$

were also solved in *Ars Magna*. Supposedly, the first to solve the quartic equation was the Italian mathematician Ferrari in about 1540. He showed that the solution of Eq. (4) could be obtained from the solutions of associated cubic and quadratic equations.

KEY IDEAS AND KEY WORDS

Every number of the form $a + bi$ where a and b are real numbers, is called a **complex number.** For a given complex number $a + bi$, it is customary to call a the **real part** and bi the **pure imaginary part** of $a + bi$. **Pure imaginary numbers** are called ***i*-numbers.**

The **sum and product of two complex numbers** are defined as follows:

$$(a + bi) + (c + di) = (a + c) + (b + d)i,$$
$$(a + bi)(c + di) = (ac - bd) + (ad + bc)i.$$

The **additive inverse** of the complex number $a + bi$ is given by

$${}^-(a + bi) = {}^-a + {}^-bi.$$

The **conjugate** of $a + bi$ is, by definition, $a - bi$. The sum and product of a complex number and its conjugate are real numbers:

$$(a + bi) + (a - bi) = 2a,$$
$$(a + bi)(a - bi) = a^2 + b^2.$$

With the exception of the order properties, all the properties of addition and multiplication in the real number system are valid in the complex number system.

If a, b, and c are real numbers, with $a \neq 0$, the equation

$$ax^2 + bx + c = 0$$

is called a **real quadratic equation** and the number

$$D = b^2 - 4ac$$

is called its **discriminant.** By the **quadratic formula,** the solutions of this equation are

$$x = \frac{^-b + \sqrt{D}}{2a} \quad \text{and} \quad x = \frac{^-b - \sqrt{D}}{2a}.$$

If $D < 0$, then $\sqrt{D}$ is defined to be $\sqrt{^-D}\,i$.

The plane having a complex number assigned to each of its points is called the **complex number plane.** The distance from the origin to the point with coordinate $a + bi$ is called the **absolute value** of the complex number $a + bi$. It is given by

$$|a + bi| = \sqrt{a^2 + b^2}.$$

CHAPTER REVIEW

In Exercises 1–7, perform the indicated operations.

1. $(\sqrt{2}i)^3$ $\;{}^-2\sqrt{2}\,i$

2. $(^-7 + \sqrt{2}i) - (6 - 3\sqrt{2}i)$ $\;{}^-13 + 4\sqrt{2}\,i$

3. $(3 + 4i)(2 - 7i)$ $\;34 - 13i$

4. $\left(\frac{1}{2} - \frac{\sqrt{3}}{2}i\right) + \left(\frac{1}{2} + \frac{\sqrt{3}}{2}i\right)$ $\;1$

5. $\left(\frac{1}{2} - \frac{\sqrt{2}}{2}i\right)\left(\frac{1}{2} + \frac{\sqrt{2}}{2}i\right)$ $\;\frac{3}{4}$

6. $\frac{2 + i}{3 - i}$ $\;\frac{1}{2} + \frac{1}{2}i$

7. $\frac{3 - \sqrt{2}i}{3 + \sqrt{2}i}$ $\;\frac{7}{11} - \frac{6}{11}\sqrt{2}\,i$

8. Evaluate each of the following.

(a) $|^-3 - 4i|$ $\;5$

(b) $|(1 + \sqrt{2}\,i)(3 - \sqrt{3}i)|$ $\;6$

9. (a) Write the conjugate of the complex number $^-\sqrt{2} + 7i$, and find the sum and product of this pair of conjugate numbers. $^-\sqrt{2} - 7i$; $^-2\sqrt{2}$; 51

(b) Find the complex number which is the reciprocal of $^-3 + 4i$. $\;\frac{^-3}{25} - \frac{4}{25}i$

10. Find the real numbers x and y for which

$$(x - y) + (2x + 3y)i = (5 + 4i) - (1 - 7i).$$

$x = \frac{23}{5}$, $y = \frac{3}{5}$

Solve the following quadratic equations and check your solutions.

11. $6x^2 - 13x + 6 = 0$ $\;\{\frac{3}{2}, \frac{2}{3}\}$

12. $x^2 + 4x + 7 = 0$ $\;\{^-2 + \sqrt{3}\,i, {}^-2 - \sqrt{3}\,i\}$

13. $9 + 4x^2 = 12x$ $\;\{\frac{3}{2}\}$

14. $3x^2 + 4x + 5 = 0$ $\;\{\frac{^-2}{3} + \frac{1}{3}\sqrt{11}\,i, \frac{^-2}{3} - \frac{1}{3}\sqrt{11}\,i\}$

Write a quadratic equation for each of the following solution sets.

15. $\{2i, {}^-2i\}$ $x^2 + 4 = 0$ **16.** $\{3 - \sqrt{5}i, 3 + \sqrt{5}i\}$ $x^2 - 6x + 14 = 0$

17. $\{\frac{1}{2}, {}^-3\}$ $2x^2 + 5x - 3 = 0$ **18.** $\{{}^-2 + 3i, {}^-2 - 3i\}$ $x^2 + 4x + 13 = 0$

On a complex number plane, plot the points corresponding to each of the following numbers. See Solution Manual.

19. ${}^-2 - 3i$ **20.** ${}^-4 + 7i$ **21.** $5i$

22. ${}^-5$ **23.** ${}^-8i$ **24.** $3 - 2i$

CHAPTER TEST

1. Perform the following indicated operations in the system of complex numbers.

(a) $({}^-3 + 5i) - (2 - 3i)$ $5 + 8i$ (b) $({}^-3 + 5i)(2 - 3i)$ $9 + 19i$

(c) $\dfrac{2 + 7i}{4 - 6i}$ $-\frac{17}{26} + \frac{10}{13}i$ (d) $({}^-3i)^5$ $-243i$ (e) $\dfrac{1}{3 + 4i}$ $\frac{3}{25} - \frac{4}{25}i$

2. Solve the following quadratic equations and check each solution.

(a) $x^2 - 6x + 10 = 0$ $\{3+i, 3-i\}$ (b) $7x^2 + 4x + 1 = 0$ $\{\frac{^-2}{7} + \frac{1}{7}\sqrt{3}i, \frac{^-2}{7} - \frac{1}{7}\sqrt{3}i\}$

(c) $3x^2 + 5x - 2 = 0$ $\{\frac{1}{3}, {}^-2\}$

3. Write a quadratic equation for each of the following solution sets.

(a) $\{{}^-2, 5\}$ $x^2 - 3x - 10 = 0$ (b) $\{3 + \sqrt{3}i, 3 - \sqrt{3}i\}$ $x^2 - 6x + 12 = 0$

4. Plot the following numbers on a complex number plane. Give the absolute value of each number.

(a) $2 + 5i$ $\sqrt{29}$ (b) ${}^-3 + 4i$ 5 (c) ${}^-7i$ 7 (d) ${}^-7$ 7

5. Find real numbers x and y for which

$$(2x - y) + (x + 3y)i = 2({}^-4 + 5i).$$

$x = {}^-2, y = 4$

Cumulative Review I

Perform the indicated operations and express each answer in simplest form.

1. $(\sqrt{28})(\sqrt{45})$ $6\sqrt{35}$ **2.** $(\sqrt{3} - 1)(\sqrt{3} + 1)$ 2

3. $\sqrt{\frac{8}{3}} + \sqrt{\frac{48}{8}} - \sqrt{\frac{25}{24}}$ $\frac{5}{4}\sqrt{6}$ **4.** $(\sqrt[3]{14})(\sqrt[4]{686})$ Already in simplest form

5. $\sqrt{\frac{2}{3}} \div \sqrt{\frac{7}{15}}$ $\frac{1}{7}\sqrt{70}$ **6.** $\dfrac{3}{\sqrt{5} + \sqrt{2}}$ $\sqrt{5} - \sqrt{2}$

7. $\dfrac{1 + \sqrt{2}}{1 - \sqrt{2}}$ $-3 - 2\sqrt{2}$ **8.** $\dfrac{\sqrt{2} + \sqrt{3}}{2\sqrt{2} + \sqrt{3}}$ $\frac{1}{5} + \frac{1}{5}\sqrt{6}$

CHAPTER TEST

The material included in the Chapter Test was covered in the following sections.
Problems 1(a)–1(b)—Section 4-2
Problem 1(c)—Section 4-3
Problem 1(d)—Section 4-1
Problem 1(e)—Section 4-3
Problems 2-3—Sections 4-4 and 4-5
Problem 4—Section 4-6.
Problem 5—Section 4-3

Answers to Chapter Test Problem 4

4. (a) $\sqrt{29}$
(b) 5
(c) 7
(d) 7

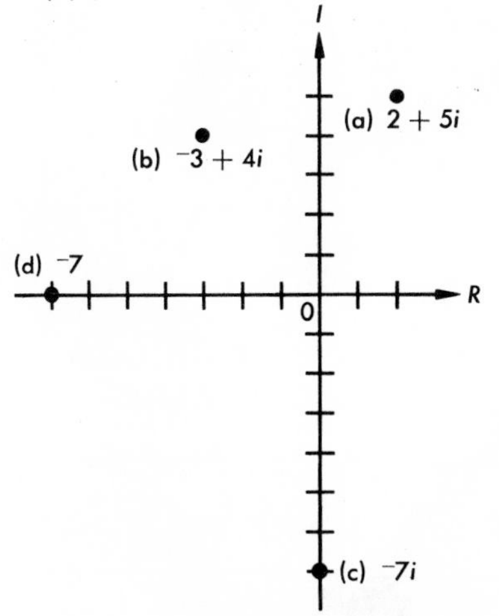

Answer to Cumulative Review Problem 17(a)

17. (a) $\{x \mid x < \frac{7}{4} - \frac{1}{4}\sqrt{577}$ or $x > \frac{7}{4} + \frac{1}{4}\sqrt{577}\}$

Write each expression with positive exponents and then simplify.

9. $\dfrac{2^0 - 2^{-2}}{2 - 2(2)^{-2}}$ $\frac{1}{2}$

10. $\dfrac{2a^{-1} + a^0}{a^{-2}}$ $2a + a^2$

11. $\left(\dfrac{2^0}{8^{\frac{1}{3}}}\right)^{-1}$ 2

12. $\dfrac{(^-3a)^3 \cdot 3a^{-\frac{2}{3}}}{(2a)^{-2} \cdot a^{\frac{1}{3}}}$ $^-324a^4$

In Exercises 13–16, find all integral values of x for which each expression is true.

13. $|x + 2| = {}^-3$ $\emptyset$

14. $|x| - 3 = 5$ $\{^-8, 8\}$

15. $|4 - x| \geq 8$ $\{x \mid x \leq {}^-4 \text{ or } x \geq 12\}$

16. $2 < |x + 1| < 5$ $\{x \mid {}^-6 < x < {}^-3 \text{ or } 1 < x < 4\}$

17. Solve the following inequalities.

(a) $(2x + 5)(x - 6) > 36$

(b) $x^3 - x^2 < 6x$ $\{x \mid x < {}^-2 \text{ or } 0 < x < 3\}$

18. If $a/b = c/d$ is a true equation and $a + b$ and $c + d$ are both different from zero, show that

$$\frac{a - b}{a + b} = \frac{c - d}{c + d}$$

is also a true equation. See Solution Manual.

19. Given the formula

$$s = \frac{a - rL}{1 - r}, \quad r = \frac{a - s}{L - s}$$

write a formula for r in terms of the other variables.

20. If the domain of x is the set of all real numbers, what is the minimum value of

$$4x^2 - 24x - 3? \quad {}^-39$$

21. Show that $\dfrac{^-2}{3} - \dfrac{\sqrt{5}}{3}i$ is a solution of the equation

$$6x^3 - x^2 - 6x - 9 = 0.$$

See Solution Manual.

22. For what value or values of k does the entire graph of the equation

$$y = x^2 + kx - x + 9$$

lie above the x-axis? $^-5 < k < 7$

23. (a) Graph the equation $y = x^2 - 2x - 8$. See Solution Manual.

(b) From your graph, find the solution set of $x^2 - 2x - 8 > {}^-5$. $\{x \mid x > 3 \text{ or } x < {}^-1\}$

(c) Solve the inequality $x^2 - 2x - 3 > 0$ by factoring. $\{x \mid x > 3 \text{ or } x < {}^-1\}$

In Exercises 24–26, solve each equation.

24. $x + 3 - \frac{10x^2 - 25}{x - 3} = 0$ $\{\frac{4}{3}, \frac{-4}{3}\}$

25. $\frac{x}{4} + \frac{1}{x} = \frac{x}{3} + \frac{2}{3x}$ $\{2, {}^-2\}$

26. $\left(2x - \frac{1}{x}\right)^2 - \left(2x - \frac{1}{x}\right) - 2 = 0$ $\{\frac{1}{2} + \frac{1}{2}\sqrt{3}, \frac{1}{2} - \frac{1}{2}\sqrt{3}, \frac{1}{2}, {}^-1\}$

27. One numeral for a number is

$$\frac{2}{1 + \sqrt{2} - i}.$$

Find another numeral for the same number of the form $a + bi$, where a and b are real numbers. $\frac{\sqrt{2}}{2} + \left(\frac{2-\sqrt{2}}{2}\right)i$

28. A picture with dimensions 8 inches by 12 inches is surrounded by a frame of uniform width. If the area of the frame is one-half the area of the picture, find a one-decimal-place approximation for the width of the frame. *1.1 in.*

29. Graph each of the following equations on a cartesian plane. *See Solution Manual.*

(a) $|x| + |y| = 8$ (b) $|x + y| = 8$

(c) $|x| - |y| = 8$ (d) $|x - y| = 8$

30. Solve each of the following inequalities.

(a) $|2x - 3| < 1$ $1 < x < 2$ (b) $|2x + 3| < x$ ϕ

31. A pet shop bought a litter of puppies for \$80. All but 3 were sold, and the total receipt from the sale was also \$80. If each puppy was sold for \$6 more than was paid for it, how many puppies were there in the litter? 8

CHAPTER 5

Conic Sections and Their Equations

The purpose of this chapter is to study the curves resulting from the intersection of a plane and a cone. These curves are most easily studied using analytic geometry. The curve may be defined geometrically so that it can actually be constructed with compass and straightedge on a piece of paper. A coordinate system may be introduced onto the plane of the paper, and knowledge of algebra and the real number system used to find an equation whose graph is the set of points just constructed.

Having manufactured the equation for a given set of geometrical facts, the graph of all similar equations can now be described with more ease and in greater detail than could be done from plotting points representing a random sampling from the solution set of the equation.

The fact that the degrees of the variable x and y determine the nature of the graph of such equations as

$$y^2 + 8x = 10$$

and

$$y^2 + 8x^2 = 10$$

is very important. The role of the parameters p, a, and b in such equations as

$$y^2 = 4px$$

and

$$\frac{x^2}{a^2} + \frac{y^2}{b^2} = 1$$

is equally important.

CHAPTER 5

Satellites follow an elliptical path, with the earth at one of the foci of the ellipse. (Courtesy of the National Aeronautics and Space Administration)

CONIC SECTIONS AND THEIR EQUATIONS

The conic sections are plane curves, so named because each of them is the curve of intersection of a plane with a right circular cone. An easy way to visualize this is to shine a flashlight on a wall. The rays of light form the cone, and the wall appears to be a plane cutting the cone. If the flashlight is pointed directly at the wall, the lighted region of the wall is circular. As the flashlight is tilted, the region first becomes elliptical, then parabolic, and finally hyperbolic in shape.

Parabolas, ellipses, and hyperbolas occur often in applications of mathematics. A parabolic mirror with a source of light at the focus will reflect the light rays parallel to the axis of the parabola. Used in reverse, it will reflect light rays from some distant galaxy to the focus. A reflecting telescope is designed on this principle. Satellites circling the earth have an elliptical path with the earth at a focus, just as planets trace an elliptical course around the sun with the sun at a focus.

Such curves can be studied algebraically as the graphs of simple second-degree equations in two variables. Circles and ellipses are similar curves, and their equations are also similar. Although the hyperbola extends indefinitely far from its center, it has many features in common with an ellipse. Consequently, its equation is similar to that of an ellipse. The parabola has quite different properties, which are reflected by an equation unlike those of the other conic sections.

Algebraic skills may also be used to solve systems of two equations where one or both are of the second degree. When one equation is linear, the system may be solved by substituting from the first-degree into the second-degree equation. If both equations have only second-degree terms in x and y, elimination of one variable by addition may be used. In this case, determinants may also be used to find x^2 and y^2, from which it is easy to find x and y.

It is apparent visually that an ellipse and a hyperbola can intersect in four, three, two, one, or no points. Correspondingly, the system of two second-degree equations has, at most, four real number solutions. Since a straight line cuts an ellipse, hyperbola, or parabola in, at most, two points, a system of equations in which one is linear and the other quadratic has, at most, two real number solutions.

The following are some of the topics covered in Chapter 5:

- *Circles*
- *Intersection of a circle and a line*
- *Distance formula*
- *Ellipses*
- *Symmetry*
- *Intercepts*
- *Hyperbolas*
- *Focus*
- *Vertices*
- *Axes*
- *Parabolas*
- *Directrix*

It is suggested that one day be spent on each section of this chapter with the exception of Sections 5–3 and 5–4 on which you may wish to spend two days.

5-1 CIRCLES

This section can be studied by the students without previous discussion in class, and then the Exercises for Discussion could be assigned.

After the circle representing the equation

$$x^2 + y^2 = 16$$

has been drawn (page 205), the fact that *every* solution (x, y) of this equation will locate a point on the circle should be made very clear. In order to do this, the circle could be drawn on a coordinate system with a fine grid, both on the board and by each student at his desk. Then you could ask questions such as the following:

Are $(0, 4)$ and $(0, {}^-4)$ solutions of $x^2 + y^2 = 16$? Are these points on the graph?

If $x = {}^\pm 1$, what must y be from the equation $x^2 + y^2 = 16$? (The table of square roots may be used to approximate y to the nearest tenth.) Are these points on the graph?

If $y = {}^\pm 2$, what must x be? Are these points on the graph?

Where does the circle intersect the x-axis? Are the coordinates of these points a solution of the equation

$$x^2 + y^2 = 16?$$

Answer to Exercise for Discussion 5(b), page 205

5. (b)

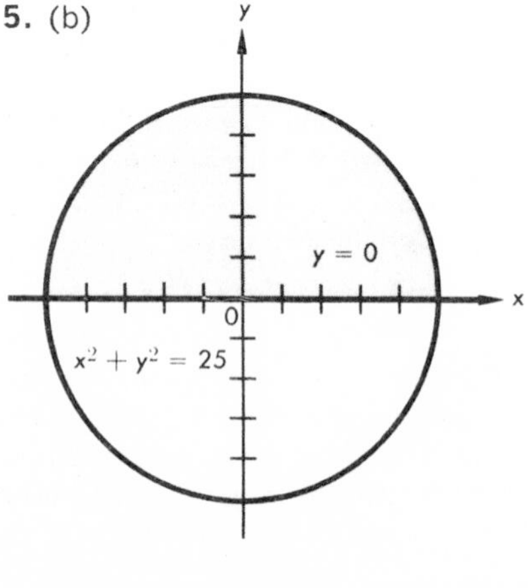

5-1 CIRCLES

The conic section which is easiest to visualize is the circle, obtained by cutting a cone with a plane perpendicular to the axis of the cone. (See Fig. 5-1.) The circle may be defined equally well as the set of all points in a plane at a given distance from a fixed point in the plane. The given distance is called the *radius* and the fixed point the *center* of the circle.

FIGURE 5-1

Consider a circle of radius r having its center at the origin of a cartesian coordinate system, as shown in Fig. 5-2. If P is a point in the plane with coordinates (x, y), then P is on this circle if, and only if, the distance from O to P is r. The distance from O to P is denoted by OP. Thus, P is on the circle if, and only if,

$$OP = r.$$

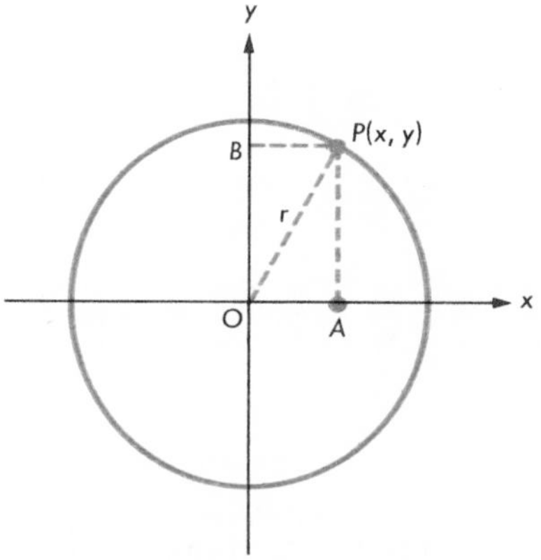

FIGURE 5-2

If we use the notation of Fig. 5-2, we have, by the pythagorean theorem,

$$(OP)^2 = (OA)^2 + (AP)^2.$$

Regardless of the quadrant in which P lies, $OA = |x|$ and $AP = OB$, or $|y|$. Hence,

$$(OP)^2 = |x|^2 + |y|^2$$
$$= x^2 + y^2.$$

We conclude that the point P with coordinates (x, y) is on the circle if, and only if,

$$x^2 + y^2 = r^2.$$

The graph of the second-degree equation

$$x^2 + y^2 = r^2,$$

in the two variables x and y, is a circle with its center at the origin and radius r.

For example, the graph of the equation

$$x^2 + y^2 = 16$$

is the circle of radius 4 sketched in Fig. 5–3.

A circle divides the plane into three sets of points: the sets of points inside the circle, on the circle, and outside the circle. We have just described the set of points on the circle of Fig. 5–3 as the graph of

$$\{(x, y) \mid x^2 + y^2 = 16\}.$$

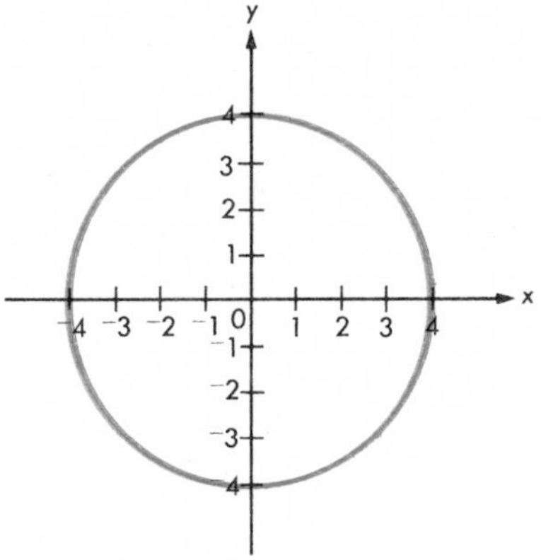

FIGURE 5–3

How do we describe the set of points inside this circle? A point $P(x, y)$ is inside this circle if, and only if, $OP < 4$, or $(OP)^2 < 16$. Since $(OP)^2 = x^2 + y^2$, the graph of

$$\{(x, y) \mid x^2 + y^2 < 16\}$$

is the set of all points inside this circle; similarly, the graph of

$$\{(x, y) \mid x^2 + y^2 > 16\}$$

is the set of all points outside this circle.

Exercises for Discussion

1. What is the radius of the circle with equation $x^2 + y^2 = 25$? 5
2. Write an equation of a circle with its center at the origin and a radius of 6. $x^2 + y^2 = 36$
3. Write a mathematical statement describing the set of all points in the plane which are at least 4 units from the origin. $x^2 + y^2 \geqq 16$
4. A circle is drawn with its center at the origin of a cartesian coordinate system. The circle passes through the point (2, 5).
   (a) What is the radius of the circle? $\sqrt{4+25} = \sqrt{29}$
   (b) Write an equation of the circle. $x^2 + y^2 = 29$
5. (a) Give three solutions, in integers, of the system of inequalities

$$\begin{cases} x^2 + y^2 \leqq 25, \\ y \geqq 0. \end{cases}$$

(3, 4), (−3, 4), (4, 3), (−4, 3), (0, 5), (1, 1), etc.

   (b) Graph the system in part (a).

Exercises

It is recommended that Exercises 4, 5, 8, and 9 be covered.

Quiz

A circle is drawn with its center at the origin of a cartesian coordinate system. The circle passes through the point (3, 4).

1. What is the radius of the circle? (ans: 5)
2. Write an equation of the circle. (ans: $x^2 + y^2 = 25$)
3. Write a mathematical statement describing the set of all points in the plane which are at least 5 units from the origin. (ans: $\{(x, y) \mid x^2 + y^2 \geqq 25\}$)
4. Graph the system

$$\begin{cases} x^2 + y^2 \leqq 25, \\ x \geqq 0. \end{cases}$$

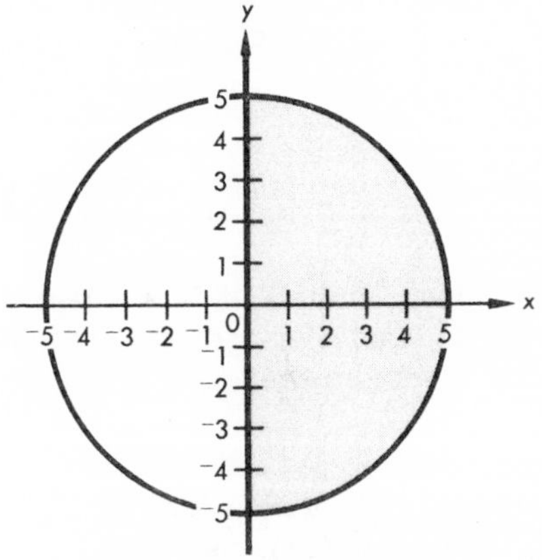

5–2 THE INTERSECTION OF A CIRCLE AND A LINE

You may wish to start by asking for all possible ways to draw two lines relative to each other in the plane of the blackboard. You could recall the types of solution sets for a pair of linear equations in the cases where the lines are parallel, are intersecting in one point, or are coincident. Then you might ask for all possible ways to draw one circle and one line relative to each other in the plane of the blackboard.

Educated guesses may be made as to what the solution set will be like for a quadratic and a linear equation such as

$$\begin{cases} x^2 + y^2 = r^2, \\ ax + by + c = 0 \end{cases}$$

in each of the three different geometric situations. The systems

$$\begin{cases} x^2 + y^2 = 25, \\ x - y + 2 = 0 \end{cases}$$

and

$$\begin{cases} x^2 + y^2 = 25, \\ x - y + 8 = 0 \end{cases}$$

may be solved in class both graphically and algebraically.

The student should not expect rational solutions for the first system, and he should also understand that even though the line and circle do not intersect in the second case, the system of equations does have a solution in the complex number field.

Exercises for Discussion, page 208

If time is limited, it is suggested that at least Exercises for Discussion 3–7 be covered.

Answers to Exercises for Discussion 1–4(a), page 208

1. (3, 0), (0, 3)

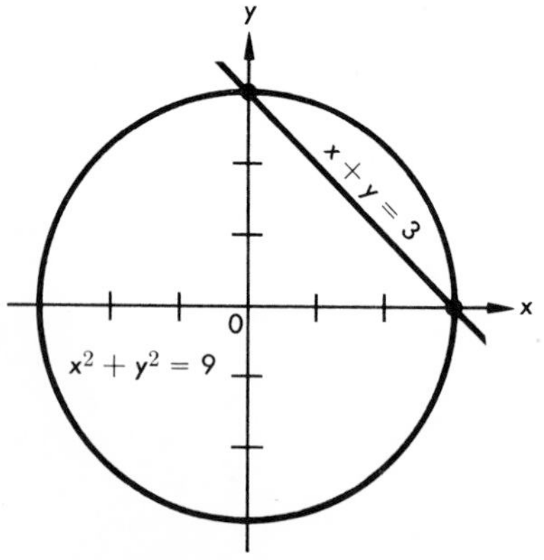

Exercises

See Solution Manual for graphs.

1. Write an equation of a circle with its center at the origin and a radius of 8. $x^2 + y^2 = 64$
2. A circle is drawn with its center at the origin of a cartesian coordinate system. The circle passes through the point ($^-1$, 3).
   (a) What is the radius of the circle? $\sqrt{10}$
   (b) Write an equation of the circle. $x^2 + y^2 = 10$
3. Write a mathematical statement describing the set of all points in the plane which are at least 9 units from the origin. $x^2 + y^2 \geqq 81$
4. (a) Give three integral solutions of the system of inequalities
   ($^-1$, 1), (0, 1), ($^-3$, 0), ($^-3$, 1), ($^-3$, $^-1$), etc.
   $$\begin{cases} x \leqq 0, \\ x^2 + y^2 \leqq 16. \end{cases}$$
   (b) Graph the system in part (a).

△

5. Find a system of inequalities whose graph is the set of all points to the right of the y-axis that are inside the circle with equation
   $$x^2 + y^2 = 49.$$ $\begin{cases} x > 0 \\ x^2 + y^2 < 49 \end{cases}$
6. Classify the points

Outside	Inside	On	Outside	Outside
(2, 3),	(1, $^-1$),	(1, $\frac{4}{3}$),	($^-\sqrt{2}$, $^-1$),	(0, 2)

   by indicating which are inside, which are outside, and which are on the circle with equation $9x^2 + 9y^2 = 25$.
7. Describe algebraically the set of all points in the plane at a distance of 4 units or less from the origin. $x^2 + y^2 \leqq 16$

▲

8. The family of concentric circles, with center at the origin, may be characterized by the equation
   $k = 10^6, 10^2, 5^2, 10, 5, 1$: circle with radius $\sqrt{k}$
   $$x^2 + y^2 = k.$$
   $k = 0$: (0, 0)
   $k = {}^-1$: an imaginary circle
   Describe the members of this family for which $k = 10^6, 10^2, 5^2, 10, 5, 1, 0,$ and $^-1$, respectively. For what real number values of k does $x^2 + y^2 = k$ represent a circle? $k > 0$
9. Find a system of inequalities whose graph is the set of all points in the region strictly between the circles with equations $x^2 + y^2 - 10 = 0$ and $9x^2 + 9y^2 - 25 = 0$. Graph the region so described.
   $\begin{cases} x^2 + y^2 < 10 \\ 9x^2 + 9y^2 > 25 \end{cases}$

5–2 THE INTERSECTION OF A CIRCLE AND A LINE

To find the point of intersection of two lines, we find the solution set of the system composed of the two equations of the lines. In the same way, we can find the points of intersection of a line and a circle by solving the system consisting of the equations of the line and the circle. A circle and a line intersect in two points at most. If the line is tangent to the circle, then they intersect in only one point. Of course, many lines and circles have no points of intersection.

Problem. Find the points of intersection, if any, of the circle with equation

$$x^2 + y^2 = 25$$

and the line with equation

$$x - y + 1 = 0.$$

Solution. One possible way of finding these points is to graph the circle and the line on the same set of axes. (See Fig. 5–4.) Then we can obtain rough approximations of the coordinates of the points of intersection of the two graphs. Stated algebraically, the problem is to solve the following system of equations.

$$\begin{cases} x^2 + y^2 = 25 \\ x - y + 1 = 0. \end{cases}$$

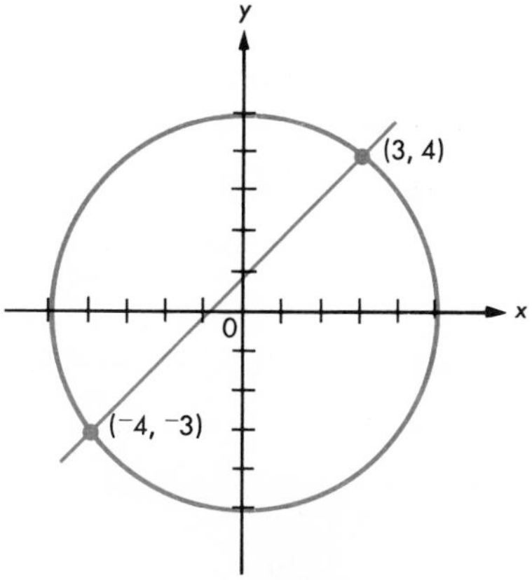

FIGURE 5–4

In other words, we are seeking those, and only those, ordered pairs which are solutions of both equations. We can solve a system consisting of one linear and one quadratic equation by essentially the same methods employed with systems of linear equations. For instance, the particular system above can be solved by using the substitution method. Thus, if we solve the linear equation for y and substitute its value in the quadratic equation, we obtain the equivalent system

$$\begin{cases} x^2 + (x + 1)^2 = 25, \\ y = x + 1. \end{cases}$$

2. (4, 0), (0, ⁻4)

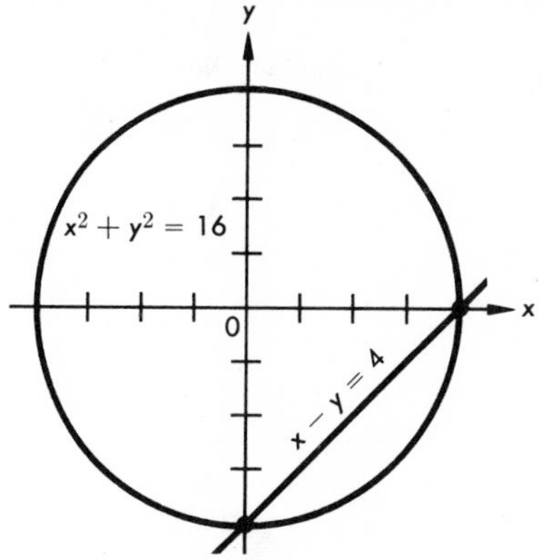

3. (3, ⁻4)

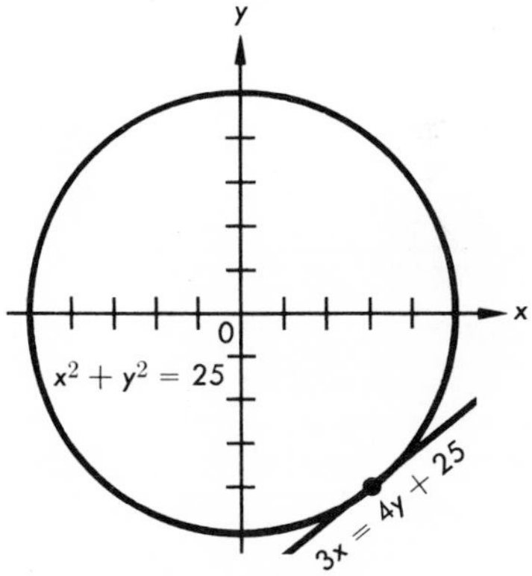

4. None

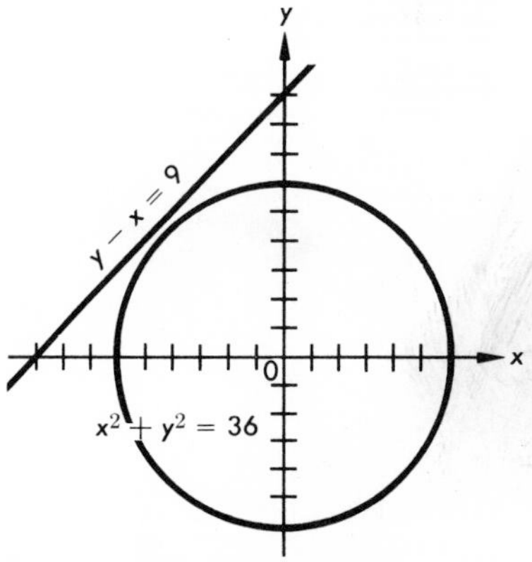

Answers to Exercises for Discussion 5, 6, 7

5. (a) 1. $\begin{cases} x^2 + y^2 = 9 \\ x + y = 3 \end{cases}$
$\begin{cases} y = 3 - x \\ x^2 + (3 - x)^2 = 9 \end{cases}$
$\begin{cases} y = 3 - x \\ 2x^2 - 6x = 0 \end{cases}$
$\begin{cases} y = 3 - x \\ 2x(x - 3) = 0 \end{cases}$
$\begin{cases} x = 0 \text{ or } x = 3 \\ y = 3 \text{ or } y = 0 \end{cases}$
$\{(0, 3), (3, 0)\}$

2. $\begin{cases} x^2 + y^2 = 16 \\ x - y = 4 \end{cases}$
$\begin{cases} x = 4 + y \\ (4 + y)^2 + y^2 = 16 \end{cases}$
$\begin{cases} x = 4 + y \\ 2y^2 + 8y = 0 \end{cases}$
$\begin{cases} x = 4 + y \\ 2y(y + 4) = 0 \end{cases}$
$\begin{cases} y = 0 \text{ or } y = {}^-4 \\ x = 4 \text{ or } x = 0 \end{cases}$
$\{(4, 0), (0, {}^-4)\}$

3. $\begin{cases} x^2 + y^2 = 25 \\ 3x = 4y + 25 \end{cases}$
$\begin{cases} x = \frac{4}{3}y + \frac{25}{3} \\ (\frac{4}{3}y + \frac{25}{3})^2 + y^2 = 25 \end{cases}$
$\begin{cases} x = \frac{4}{3}y + \frac{25}{3} \\ \frac{25}{9}y^2 + \frac{200}{9}y + \frac{400}{9} = 0 \end{cases}$
$\begin{cases} x = \frac{4}{3}y + \frac{25}{3} \\ y^2 + 8y + 16 = 0 \end{cases}$
$\begin{cases} x = \frac{4}{3}y + \frac{25}{3} \\ (y + 4)^2 = 0 \end{cases}$
$\begin{cases} y = {}^-4 \\ x = 3 \end{cases}$
$\{(3, {}^-4)\}$

4. $\begin{cases} x^2 + y^2 = 36 \\ y - x = 9 \end{cases}$
$\begin{cases} y = 9 + x \\ x^2 + (9 + x)^2 = 36 \end{cases}$
$\begin{cases} y = 9 + x \\ 2x^2 + 18x + 45 = 0 \end{cases}$
$\begin{cases} x = \frac{-9}{2} + \frac{3}{2}i \text{ or } \frac{-9}{2} - \frac{3}{2}i \\ y = \frac{9}{2} + \frac{3}{2}i \text{ or } \frac{9}{2} - \frac{3}{2}i \end{cases}$
$\{(\frac{-9}{2} + \frac{3}{2}i, \frac{9}{2} + \frac{3}{2}i), (\frac{-9}{2} - \frac{3}{2}i, \frac{9}{2} - \frac{3}{2}i)\}$

The quadratic equation of this system is equivalent to each of the following equations.

$$x^2 + x^2 + 2x + 1 = 25$$
$$2x^2 + 2x - 24 = 0$$
$$x^2 + x - 12 = 0$$
$$(x + 4)(x - 3) = 0$$

Therefore, the given system is equivalent to the system

$$\begin{cases} (x + 4)(x - 3) = 0, \\ y = x + 1. \end{cases}$$

The only values of x that make the first equation true are $x = {}^-4$ and $x = 3$. If $x = {}^-4$, then $y = {}^-4 + 1$, or ${}^-3$; if $x = 3$, $y = 3 + 1$, or 4, from the second equation. Hence,

$$\{({}^-4, {}^-3), (3, 4)\}$$

is the solution set of the given system.

Check. $({}^-4, {}^-3)$

$$({}^-4)^2 + ({}^-3)^2 \stackrel{?}{=} 25 \qquad {}^-4 - {}^-3 + 1 \stackrel{\checkmark}{=} 0$$
$$16 + 9 \stackrel{\checkmark}{=} 25$$

You can verify that the other solution also checks.

Exercises for Discussion

In Exercises 1–4, use a single set of axes on which to graph the circle and the line in each of the systems. From the graph, find the points of intersection of the circle and the line, if any.

1. $\begin{cases} x^2 + y^2 = 9 \\ x + y = 3 \end{cases}$
2. $\begin{cases} x^2 + y^2 = 16 \\ x - y = 4 \end{cases}$
3. $\begin{cases} x^2 + y^2 = 25 \\ 3x = 4y + 25 \end{cases}$
4. $\begin{cases} x^2 + y^2 = 36 \\ y - x = 9 \end{cases}$

5. (a) Solve algebraically each of the systems of equations in Exercises 1–4.
(b) What is the solution set in the system of real numbers when the graphs have no points in common? $\emptyset$ What is the solution set in the system of complex numbers? *Two ordered pairs. Corresponding elements in the pairs will be complex conjugates.*

6. In this section, we solved the following system.

$$\begin{cases} x^2 + y^2 = 25 \\ x - y + 1 = 0 \end{cases}$$

We discovered that where the line intersects the circle, x was $^-4$ or 3. Then we found the ordinates of the points of intersection by using the linear equation

$$y = x + 1.$$

What error would occur if we were to find the ordinates of the points of intersection by using the quadratic equation

$$x^2 + y^2 = 25?$$

7. A circle of radius $2\sqrt{5}$ is drawn with its center at the origin. Find the points of intersection of this circle with the line passing through the points $(^-1, 7)$ and $(3, 3)$.

Exercises

See Solution Manual for graphs.

In Exercises 1–4, solve algebraically each system of equations. Check each solution. What do you surmise about the graphs of the equations in Exercise 3? What does the solution of Exercise 4 tell you about the graphs of those equations?

1. $\begin{cases} x^2 + y^2 - 25 = 0 \\ x + y + 1 = 0 \end{cases}$ $\{(3, ^-4), (^-4, 3)\}$

2. $\begin{cases} x^2 + y^2 - 25 = 0 \\ 4x + 3y - 15 = 0 \end{cases}$ $\{(0, 5), (\frac{24}{5}, \frac{-7}{5})\}$

3. $\begin{cases} x^2 + y^2 = 20 \\ x - 2y = 10 \end{cases}$ $\{(2, ^-4)\}$; line tangent to circle

4. $\begin{cases} x^2 + y^2 - 1 = 0 \\ x + y - 2 = 0 \end{cases}$

5. Graph the equations in each system in Exercises 1–4, and check each graph against the solutions that you found algebraically.

△

6. Find a system of inequalities whose graph is the set of all points above the line $x + y = 2$, but inside the circle $x^2 + y^2 = 4$. Graph this set of points. $\begin{cases} x + y > 2 \\ x^2 + y^2 < 4 \end{cases}$

Draw the graph of each of the following systems of inequalities.

7. $\begin{cases} x^2 + y^2 \leqq 10 \\ 2y \leqq x + 5 \end{cases}$

8. $\begin{cases} x^2 + y^2 < 8 \\ y < x \\ y > 0 \end{cases}$

9. $\begin{cases} x^2 + y^2 > 4 \\ |x| < 2 \\ |y| < 2 \end{cases}$

10. $\begin{cases} x^2 + y^2 < 4 \\ |x| + |y| > 2 \end{cases}$

6. We would find the two points on the circle with a given abscissa, not just the point on the circle which has this abscissa and lies on the line.

7. The equation of the circle is

$$x^2 + y^2 = (2\sqrt{5})^2 = 20.$$

The equation of the line is

$$\frac{y - 7}{x + 1} = \frac{3 - 7}{3 + 1} \text{ or } x + y = 6.$$

The solution set for this linear-quadratic system is

$$\{(4, 2), (2, 4)\}.$$

Exercises

In Exercises 9 and 10, you could ask if there are any integral solutions.

It is recommended that Exercises 11, 12, and 13 be covered in class so that all the students may gain the information contained in them, not just those who are capable of handling such problems alone.

Answer to Exercise 4

4. $\{(1 + \frac{1}{2}\sqrt{2}i, 1 - \frac{1}{2}\sqrt{2}i), (1 - \frac{1}{2}\sqrt{2}i, 1 + \frac{1}{2}\sqrt{2}i)\}$

The line does not touch the circle.

Quiz

(See page T14 for graphs.)

In Exercises 1 and 2, use a single set of axes on which to graph the circle and the line in each of the systems. From the graph, find the points of intersection of the circle and the line, if any.

1. $\begin{cases} x^2 + y^2 = 4 \\ y + x = 2 \end{cases}$ (ans: (2, 0), (0, 2))

2. $\begin{cases} x^2 + y^2 = 25 \\ 2y = 10 \end{cases}$ (ans: (0, 5))

3. Solve algebraically each of the systems of equations in Exercises 1 and 2. (ans: {(2, 0), (0, 2)} ; {(0, 5)})

5-3 THE DISTANCE FORMULA

An equation of a circle with center not at the origin can now be written and it can be observed that in general equations of the type

$$ax^2 + ay^2 + bx + cy + d = 0$$

have graphs that are circles. Making $x^2 + bx$ a part of a trinomial square (and doing the same for $y^2 + cy$) is the only tricky algebra involved.

To find the distance between two points on a number line, one coordinate was subtracted from the other. In a number plane, if the two points are not on one of the axes (or a line parallel to one of the axes), then essentially a right triangle is constructed with its hypotenuse the line segment joining the two points, its base the difference between abscissas, and its height the difference between ordinates. Whenever the distance between two points in the number plane is found, the pythagorean theorem concerning the sides of a right triangle is used.

In relation to Problem 2 on page 212, it is essential for the class to see that geometric restrictions on the location of a set of points in the coordinate plane translate algebraically into an equation whose solution set is the set of coordinates of those points. The circle can be constructed if its center is located and its radius is specified. If it can be constructed, an equation in x and y can be found so that the points on the circle have coordinates that are solutions of the equation.

After Problem 2 has been read, you could have the class write an equation (and simplify it) for a

11. Consider the system of equations

$$\begin{cases} x^2 + y^2 = 9, \\ y = k, \end{cases}$$

which consists of a specific circle and a line which varies with k.

(a) For what values of k will the line $y = k$ fail to intersect the circle $x^2 + y^2 = 9$? Give an example. $\{k \mid k < {}^-3 \text{ or } k > 3\}$

(b) For what values of k will the line $y = k$ be tangent to the circle? How many such lines are there? $\{3, {}^-3\}$; two

(c) For what values of k will the line $y = k$ intersect the circle in exactly two points? Give an example and check it by finding the points of intersection. $\{k \mid {}^-3 < k < 3\}$

12. For what values of k will the graph of the equation $2x + y = k$ be tangent to the circle with equation $x^2 + y^2 = 4$? $k = 2\sqrt{5}$ or $k = {}^-2\sqrt{5}$

13. What is the largest possible value of the linear form $2x + y$ if (x, y) is restricted so that it is in the set $\{(x, y) \mid x^2 + y^2 \leq 4\}$? $2\sqrt{5}$

5-3 THE DISTANCE FORMULA

Before discussing other conic sections, let us derive a formula for the distance between any two points in a plane. Such a formula will be useful in finding equations of conic sections.

Let us assume that a cartesian coordinate system has been drawn on the plane. We now wish to derive a formula for the distance PQ between points P and Q in terms of the coordinates (x_1, y_1) of P and (x_2, y_2) of Q. If point R is chosen as indicated in Fig. 5–5, then $\triangle PRQ$ is a right triangle, and

$$(PQ)^2 = (PR)^2 + (RQ)^2,$$

according to the pythagorean theorem. When we look at Fig. 5–5, we see that

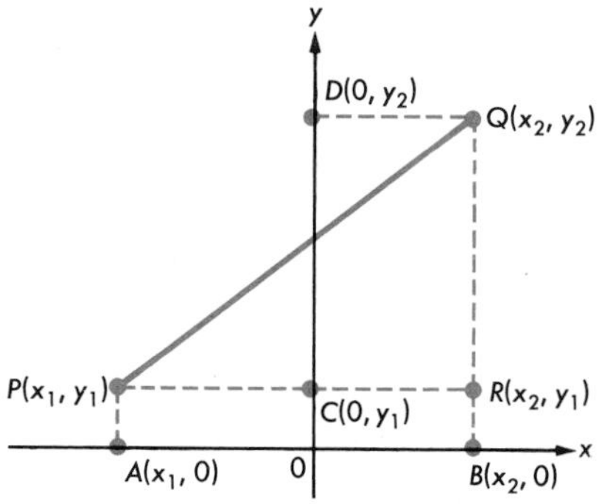

FIGURE 5–5

$$PR = AB, \quad \text{or } |x_2 - x_1|,$$
$$RQ = CD, \quad \text{or } |y_2 - y_1|.$$

Hence,

$$(PQ)^2 = |x_2 - x_1|^2 + |y_2 - y_1|^2$$
$$= (x_2 - x_1)^2 + (y_2 - y_1)^2.$$

This proves the following important formula.

DISTANCE FORMULA

The distance between the points $P(x_1, y_1)$ and $Q(x_2, y_2)$ is given by

$$PQ = \sqrt{(x_2 - x_1)^2 + (y_2 - y_1)^2}.$$

The proof of the distance formula must be modified slightly if segment $\overline{PQ}$ is parallel to a coordinate axis, but the formula continues to apply.

Problem 1. Let $\triangle ABC$ be a triangle with vertices $A(9, 6)$, $B(1, {}^-3)$, and $C({}^-1, 2)$. Find the length of each side of triangle ABC. Is $\triangle ABC$ a right triangle?

Solution. By the distance formula,

$$AB = \sqrt{(1 - 9)^2 + ({}^-3 - 6)^2}$$
$$= \sqrt{8^2 + 9^2}, \quad \text{or } \sqrt{145}.$$

$$BC = \sqrt{({}^-1 - 1)^2 + (2 - {}^-3)^2}$$
$$= \sqrt{2^2 + 5^2}, \quad \text{or } \sqrt{29}.$$

$$AC = \sqrt{({}^-1 - 9)^2 + (2 - 6)^2}$$
$$= \sqrt{10^2 + 4^2}, \quad \text{or } \sqrt{116}.$$

Thus, $\overline{AB}$ is the longest side. Hence, $\triangle ABC$ is a right triangle if, and only if,

$$(AB)^2 = (AC)^2 + (BC)^2,$$

according to the pythagorean theorem and its converse. The equation

$$(\sqrt{145})^2 = (\sqrt{116})^2 + (\sqrt{29})^2$$

or, equivalently,

$$145 = 116 + 29,$$

is true; therefore, $\triangle ABC$ is a right triangle.

circle with center at $(2, {}^-3)$ and radius 5, and for a circle with center at $(2, {}^-3)$ and radius 6. The students should observe that the coefficients of x and y do not change if the center does not change.

Then you may ask for an equation (in simplified form) of a circle with center at $({}^-3, 0)$ and radius 10, and of a circle with center at $(0, {}^-3)$ and radius 10. The students should observe the effect on the equation of the circle when the center is on one of the coordinate axes.

It is recommended that the above practice be done before taking up the pattern for all equations of circles with center located at (h, k) and radius the given constant r.

Problem 3 is the reverse of Problem 2 where the point set was given by being described geometrically and the equation in x and y was asked for. Here the equation is given, the point set (a graph or picture or description of it) is required.

To verify that the given equation

$$4x^2 + 4y^2 - 16x + 8y + 11 = 0$$

is equivalent to the transformed one,

$$(x - 2)^2 + (y + 1)^2 = \tfrac{9}{4},$$

two checks should be required: First, the x- and y-intercepts should be found from the given equation. If $x = 0$,

$$4y^2 + 8y + 11 = 0,$$
$$y = \frac{{}^-8 \pm \sqrt{64 - 176}}{8},$$

and so the circle should not cut the y-axis. If $y = 0$,

$$4x^2 - 16x + 11 = 0,$$
$$x = \frac{16 \pm \sqrt{256 - 176}}{8},$$
$$x = 2 \pm \tfrac{1}{2}\sqrt{5},$$
$$x = 3.1 \text{ or } .9,$$

and the circle should cut the positive x-axis twice.

Second, from the transformed equation, it can be seen that, since the center is at $(2, {}^{-}1)$ and the radius is $\frac{3}{2}$, the points $(2 \pm \frac{3}{2}, {}^{-}1)$ and $(2, {}^{-}1 \pm \frac{3}{2})$ should be on the graph. These may be tested in the given equation. For example, testing $(3\frac{1}{2}, {}^{-}1)$ gives

$$4(\tfrac{7}{2})^2 + 4({}^{-}1)^2 - 16(\tfrac{7}{2}) + 8({}^{-}1) + 11 \stackrel{?}{=} 0,$$
$$49 + 4 - 56 - 8 + 11 \stackrel{\checkmark}{=} 0.$$

Please note the paragraph on page 213 containing the formula for the coordinates of a point midway between two given points.

Exercises for Discussion, page 213

Exercise for Discussion 6 may be illustrated with several examples which show that the midpoint is indeed found by addition and not by subtraction, as is done in finding the distance between two points.

Answers to Exercises for Discussion 2–8, page 213

2. $(x - 2)^2 + (y - {}^{-}5)^2 = 6^2$
$x^2 - 4x + 4 + y^2 + 10y + 25 = 36$
$x^2 + y^2 - 4x + 10y = 7$

3. Yes, since $|x_2 - x_1|$ equals either $x_2 - x_1$ or $x_1 - x_2$, and two numbers which are additive inverses of each other have the same square.

4. $AB = \sqrt{({}^{-}1 - 2)^2 + (3 - 5)^2} = \sqrt{9 + 4} = \sqrt{13}$
$BC = \sqrt{(2 - \frac{3}{2})^2 + (5 - \frac{5}{2})^2} = \sqrt{\frac{1}{4} + \frac{25}{4}} = \frac{1}{2}\sqrt{26}$
$AC = \sqrt{({}^{-}1 - \frac{3}{2})^2 + (3 - \frac{5}{2})^2} = \sqrt{\frac{25}{4} + \frac{1}{4}} = \frac{1}{2}\sqrt{26}$
$p = \sqrt{13} + \frac{1}{2}\sqrt{26} + \frac{1}{2}\sqrt{26} = \sqrt{13} + \sqrt{26}$

ABC is an isosceles triangle. A and B have the same measure.

Problem 2. Find an equation of the circle with its center, C, at $({}^{-}3, 4)$ and with a radius of 7.

Solution. Point P with coordinates (x, y) is on the circle if, and only if,

$$PC = 7,$$

that is,

$$\sqrt{(x + 3)^2 + (y - 4)^2} = 7.$$

Thus,

$$(x + 3)^2 + (y - 4)^2 = 49,$$

or

$$x^2 + y^2 + 6x - 8y - 24 = 0,$$

is an equation of the circle in Fig. 5–6.

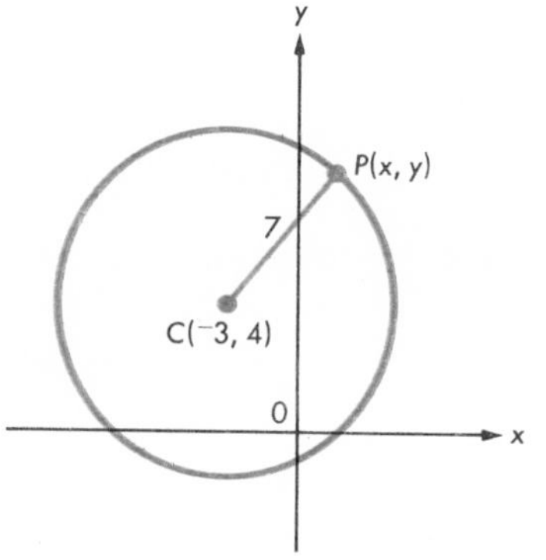

FIGURE 5–6

By the same argument as that used in Problem 2, we see that

$$(x - h)^2 + (y - k)^2 = r^2$$

is an equation of the circle having its center at (h, k) and a radius of r. An equivalent equation is

$$x^2 + y^2 - 2hx - 2ky + (h^2 + k^2 - r^2) = 0.$$

Conversely, if the graph of an equation of the form

$$Ax^2 + Ay^2 + Cx + Dy + E = 0, \quad A \neq 0,$$

consists of more than one point, then the graph is a circle. The following problem illustrates how the circle can be located in the coordinate plane.

Problem 3. Describe the graph of the equation

$$4x^2 + 4y^2 - 16x + 8y + 11 = 0.$$

Solution. We divide each side of this equation by 4, obtaining the equivalent equation

$$x^2 + y^2 - 4x + 2y + \tfrac{11}{4} = 0.$$

Then we proceed by completing the squares separately with the x-terms and the y-terms to get the equivalent equation

$$(x^2 - 4x + 4) + (y^2 + 2y + 1) = {}^{-}\tfrac{11}{4} + 4 + 1,$$

or

$$(x - 2)^2 + (y + 1)^2 = \tfrac{9}{4}.$$

We recognize this as an equation of the circle with center at $(2, ^-1)$ and radius $\frac{3}{2}$.

We recall from Chapter 1 that the midpoint of a segment of a number line has as its coordinate the arithmetic average of the coordinates of the endpoints. In a similar way, it may be shown that the midpoint of the segment having endpoints $P(x_1, y_1)$ and $Q(x_2, y_2)$ has coordinates

$$\left(\frac{x_1 + x_2}{2}, \frac{y_1 + y_2}{2}\right).$$

Exercises for Discussion

$d = \sqrt{(^-9-0)^2+(3-0)^2}$

1. How far is the point $(^-9, 3)$ from the origin? $= \sqrt{90} = 3\sqrt{10}$
2. Find an equation of the circle with center at $(2, ^-5)$ and radius 6. Simplify the equation.
3. Is $|x_2 - x_1|^2$ always equal to $(x_2 - x_1)^2$? Why?
4. Find the perimeter of triangle ABC with the following vertices.

$$A(^-1, 3), \quad B(2, 5), \quad C(\tfrac{3}{2}, \tfrac{5}{2})$$

What type of triangle is ABC? Which angles have the same measure?

5. Prove that triangle ABC with the following vertices is a right triangle.

$$A(^-7, 8), \quad B(^-1, ^-4), \quad C(15, 4)$$

6. Use the distance formula to verify that the midpoint of the segment having endpoints $A(^-1, 6)$ and $B(7, ^-10)$ has coordinates

$$\left(\frac{^-1 + 7}{2}, \frac{6 + ^-10}{2}\right), \text{ or } (3, ^-2).$$

7. Use the figure to prove that if P has coordinates (x_1, y_1), Q has coordinates (x_2, y_2), and $PM = MQ$, then M has coordinates

$$\left(\frac{x_1 + x_2}{2}, \frac{y_1 + y_2}{2}\right).$$

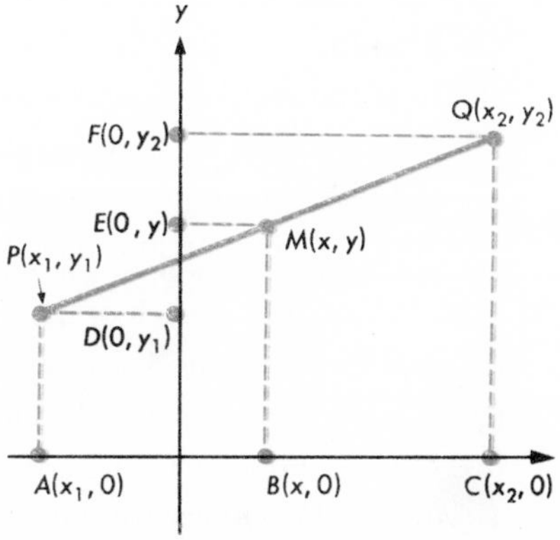

8. Find the center and radius of the circle having equation

$$x^2 + y^2 + 10x - 4y + 20 = 0.$$

---

5. $AB = \sqrt{(^-7 - ^-1)^2 + (8 - ^-4)^2}$
$= \sqrt{36 + 144}$
$= \sqrt{180}$
$BC = \sqrt{(^-1 - 15)^2 + (^-4 - 4)^2}$
$= \sqrt{256 + 64}$
$= \sqrt{320}$
$AC = \sqrt{(^-7 - 15)^2 + (8 - 4)^2}$
$= \sqrt{484 + 16}$
$= \sqrt{500}$

Since

$$(AB)^2 + (BC)^2 = 180 + 320 = 500 = (AC)^2,$$

the triangle is a right triangle by the converse of the pythagorean theorem.

6. $AM = \sqrt{(^-1 - 3)^2 + (6 - ^-2)^2}$
$= \sqrt{16 + 64}$
$= \sqrt{80}$
$BM = \sqrt{(7 - 3)^2 + (^-10 - ^-2)^2}$
$= \sqrt{16 + 64}$
$= \sqrt{80}$

Hence, $AM = BM$ and $(3, ^-2)$ is the midpoint.

7. Since AP, BM, and CQ are parallel and $PM = MQ$, then

$$AB = BC$$

and

$$\sqrt{(x_1 - x)^2} = \sqrt{(x - x_2)^2},$$
$$(x_1 - x) = (x - x_2),$$
$$2x = x_1 + x_2$$

and

$$x = \frac{x_1 + x_2}{2}.$$

Similarly,

$$y = \frac{y_1 + y_2}{2}$$

and the coordinates of M are

$$\left(\frac{x_1 + x_2}{2}, \frac{y_1 + y_2}{2}\right).$$

8. $x^2 + y^2 + 10x - 4y + 20 = 0$
$x^2 + 10x + y^2 - 4y = ^-20$
$(x^2 + 10x + 25) + (y^2 - 4y + 4) = ^-20 + 25 + 4$
$(x + 5)^2 + (y - 2)^2 = 9$

Center: $(^-5, 2)$; radius: 3

Exercises

It is recommended that all of these exercises be covered. You might do Exercises 8–10 in class to be sure that all the students understand them. The other exercises could be assigned.

Exercises

1. (a) Prove that triangle CDE with the following vertices is isosceles. See Solution Manual.

$$C(2, 3),\quad D(^{-}\tfrac{13}{2}, 3),\quad E(1, 7)$$

(b) Find the length of the altitude drawn from vertex D to base $\overline{CE}$. $2\sqrt{17}$

2. Prove that the angles at R and T are equal in the triangle with the following vertices. See Solution Manual.

$$R(^{-}1, 5),\quad S(^{-}1, ^{-}2),\quad T(6, ^{-}2)$$

3. A median of a triangle is a line joining a vertex to the midpoint of the opposite side. In triangle CDE with the following vertices, how long is the median drawn from C to the midpoint of DE? $\frac{1}{2}\sqrt{793}$

$$C(^{-}8, ^{-}5),\quad D(6, 2),\quad E(5, ^{-}4)$$

4. Use the distance formula to find RS, ST, and RT, given that R has coordinates $(^{-}1, 2)$, S has coordinates $(2, 3)$, and T has coordinates $(11, 6)$. Compare $RS + ST$ with RT to see whether points R, S, and T are collinear. $RS = \sqrt{10}$, $ST = 3\sqrt{10}$, $RT = 4\sqrt{10}$

5. If the line segment joining the points $(^{-}3, ^{-}7)$ and $(9, 2)$ is a diameter of a circle, find an equation of the circle. $x^2 + y^2 - 6x + 5y = 41$

6. (a) Find the midpoints of the three sides of a triangle with the following vertices.

$$A(4, 4),\quad B(^{-}2, 8),\quad C(2, ^{-}6)$$

$(1, 6)$, $(0, 1)$, $(3, ^{-}1)$

(b) Find the lengths of the three medians of the triangle which is defined in part (a). $\sqrt{145}$, 5, $\sqrt{106}$

7. Use the distance formula to find PQ, PR, and QR, given that P has coordinates $(^{-}3, 2)$, Q has coordinates $(1, 1)$, and R has coordinates $(5, ^{-}2)$. Is $PQ + QR = PR$? No Are points P, Q, and R collinear? No
$\sqrt{17}$, $4\sqrt{5}$, 5

8. Triangle ABC has vertices at $A(7, 8)$, $B(^{-}3, 4)$, and $C(^{-}6, ^{-}2)$.
   (a) Find the length of $\overline{BC}$. $3\sqrt{5}$
   (b) Find the midpoints of $\overline{AB}$ and $\overline{AC}$. $(2, 6)$, $(\frac{1}{2}, 3)$
   (c) Find the distance between the midpoints of $\overline{AB}$ and $\overline{AC}$. $\frac{3}{2}\sqrt{5}$
   (d) Compare the results of parts (a) and (c). What theorem in geometry does this comparison illustrate? The line joining the midpoints of two sides of a triangle is equal to half of the third side.

9. Find an equation of each of the following circles. Simplify each equation.
   (a) A circle of radius 5 with center at $(3, ^{-}4)$ $x^2 + y^2 - 6x + 8y = 0$
   (b) A circle of radius 3 with center at $(^{-}2, 1)$ $x^2 + y^2 + 4x - 2y = 4$
   (c) A circle tangent to the coordinate axes and having radius 2. (How many such circles are there?) $x^2 + y^2 \pm 4x \pm 4y + 4 = 0$; four

10. Write the equation of each of the following circles in the form

$$(x - h)^2 + (y - k)^2 = r^2.$$

In each case, locate the center and give the radius.

(a) $x^2 + y^2 - 2x - 6y + 6 = 0$ $(x-1)^2+(y-3)^2=4;\ (1,3);\ 2$
(b) $x^2 + y^2 + 4x + 2y + 4 = 0$ $(x+2)^2+(y+1)^2=1;\ (^-2,^-1);\ 1$
(c) $x^2 + y^2 - 6x + 1 = 0$ $(x-3)^2+y^2=8;\ (3,0);\ 2\sqrt{2}$
(d) $36x^2 + 36y^2 - 36y = 7$ $7x^2+(y-\frac{1}{2})^2=\frac{4}{9};\ (0,\frac{1}{2});\ \frac{2}{3}$

△

$\left(\frac{5-3\sqrt{3}}{2}, \frac{7+3\sqrt{3}}{2}\right)$ or $\left(\frac{5+3\sqrt{3}}{2}, \frac{7-3\sqrt{3}}{2}\right)$

11. Two of the vertices of an equilateral triangle are located at $P(1, 2)$ and $Q(4, 5)$. Find the third vertex. Is there more than one possibility?

12. Find the fourth vertex, D, of the parallelogram $ABCD$ if three vertices are located as follows: $(6,6)$

$$A(^-1, 5),\quad B(^-2, 3),\quad C(5, 4).$$

13. A set of points in a coordinate plane is found to have the following property: Every point of the set is twice as far from the point $A(^-5, 1)$ as it is from the point $B(3, 8)$. Find an equation for which this set is the graph. $3x^2+3y^2-34x-62y+266=0$

14. A point $P(x, y)$ is on the perpendicular bisector of the line segment joining $A(^-3, 5)$ to $B(2, ^-6)$ if, and only if,

$$PB = PA.$$

Find an equation of the perpendicular bisector of $\overline{AB}$. $5x-11y=3$

5-4 ELLIPSES

An ellipse is obtained when we cut a cone by a plane which is almost perpendicular to the axis of the cone (Fig. 5-7). Thus, if we point our flashlight not quite directly at a wall, the lighted region on the wall has an elliptical shape.

An ellipse can be constructed in the following way. Place a piece of paper on a drawing board, and put two thumb tacks into the paper at points A and B. Next, take a loop of thread which is long enough to fit over both tacks, and pull it taut with a pencil point P (Fig. 5-8).

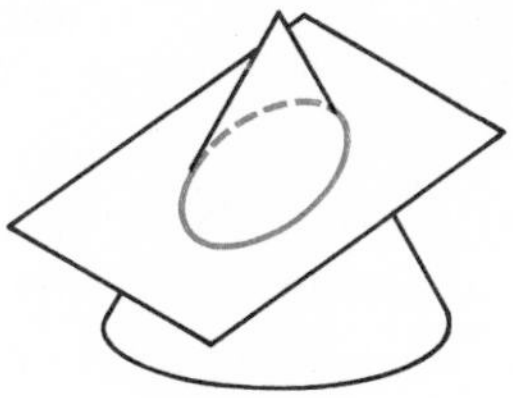

FIGURE 5-7

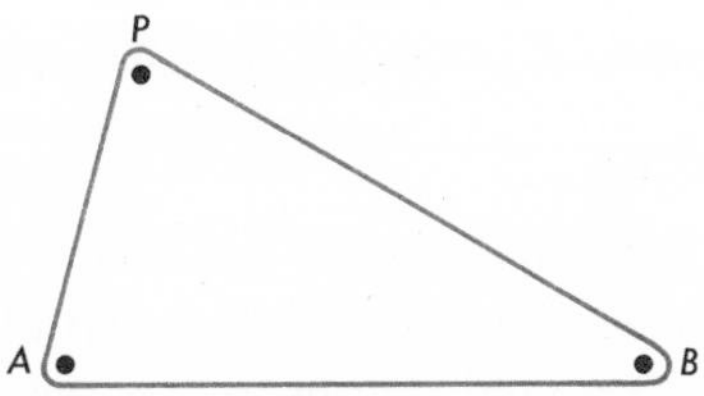

FIGURE 5-8

Exercises 11–14 could be used for honors work, or they might be deferred until you have covered the ellipse and used later in a review of the chapter.

Exercise 13 is more difficult, since it involves simplifying

$$\sqrt{(x+5)^2 + (y-1)^2} = 2\sqrt{(x-3)^2 + (y-8)^2}$$

and may be considered introductory to the radicals which will be covered in Section 5-4.

Exercise 14 is a good locus problem and it is recommended that it be thoroughly discussed in class. The role of $P(x, y)$ as any point is not always easily understood by the average student.

Quiz

1. How far is the point $(^-3, 2)$ from the point $(5, 8)$? (ans: 10 units)

2. Find an equation of the circle with center at $(1, 2)$ and radius 5. (ans: $x^2 + y^2 - 2x - 4y = 20$)

3. Find the length of the line segment with endpoints $(^-2, 3)$ and $(3, ^-2)$. (ans: $5\sqrt{2}$)

5-4 ELLIPSES

In relation to the definition of the ellipse and the explanation of the string construction of the figure, you may wish to have students draw several ellipses on the board, keeping the foci the same distance apart, say 10 inches, and using various values for k, such as 12, 14, 16, 20. Near each ellipse should be written the ratio of the distance between the foci to the value of k. The students should observe that as the denominator of the fraction increases ($\frac{10}{12}, \frac{10}{14}, \frac{10}{16}, \frac{10}{20}$), the ellipses become more and more circular. This ratio is called the *eccentricity* of the ellipse. (See Exercise 17 on page 224.)

TWISTER

Mrs. Moore always took a tape measure to the grocer's to make sure the bunch of asparagus she bought was 12 inches in circumference. One day the grocer was out of these large bunches, so Mrs. Moore bought two bunches, each 6 inches in circumference. She believed she should pay the same price for the two that she paid for the larger; however, the grocer charged her more. Who was right?

Solution: Both were wrong. The two small bunches together contained only half as much as the larger bunch.

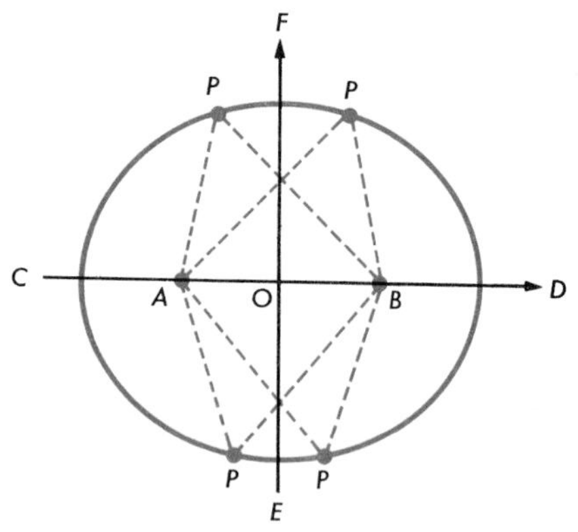

FIGURE 5-9

Keeping the thread taut, move the point P in a complete turn around points A and B. The figure drawn will be an ellipse (Fig. 5-9). As suggested by this construction, an ellipse consists of all points P such that the sum $AP + BP + AB$ is a constant. Since the distance AB does not change, the ellipse really consists of all points P such that the sum $AP + BP$ is a constant.

DEFINITION OF AN ELLIPSE

Given two points A and B in a plane and a positive number k greater than AB, the set consisting of all points P in the plane such that

$$AP + BP = k$$

is called an ellipse. Each of the points A and B is called a focus of the ellipse.

If line $\overleftrightarrow{CD}$ contains the foci A and B, and line $\overleftrightarrow{EF}$ is the perpendicular bisector of segment $\overline{AB}$, then it is reasonably clear from Fig. 5-9 that lines $\overleftrightarrow{CD}$ and $\overleftrightarrow{EF}$ are *axes of symmetry* of the ellipse. In other words, if we fold the paper along the line $\overleftrightarrow{CD}$, the upper half and the lower half of the ellipse will coincide. Similarly, if we fold the paper along the line $\overleftrightarrow{EF}$, the right half will coincide with the left half of the ellipse. The point O of intersection of the axes of symmetry is called the *center* of the ellipse.

Each ellipse has an equation which is quite similar to an equation of a circle, as we shall show. To illustrate how an equation of an ellipse can be found, let us place the foci A and B of an ellipse 2 inches apart, and let us choose the number $k = 4$ in the definition of an ellipse. Then point P in the plane is on the ellipse if, and only if,

$$AP + BP = 4. \quad (1)$$

In order to find an equation of this ellipse, we must choose a cartesian coordinate system in the plane. Although we may choose the axes as we see fit, the only choice that takes advantage of the symmetry of the ellipse is the pair of axes of symmetry. Thus, let us select the x-axis on the foci A and B, and the y-axis perpendicular to the x-axis at the center O of the ellipse (Fig. 5–10). Since the foci are 2 inches apart and equidistant from O, it follows that A has coordinates $(^-1, 0)$ and B has coordinates $(1, 0)$. Therefore, if point P has coordinates (x, y),

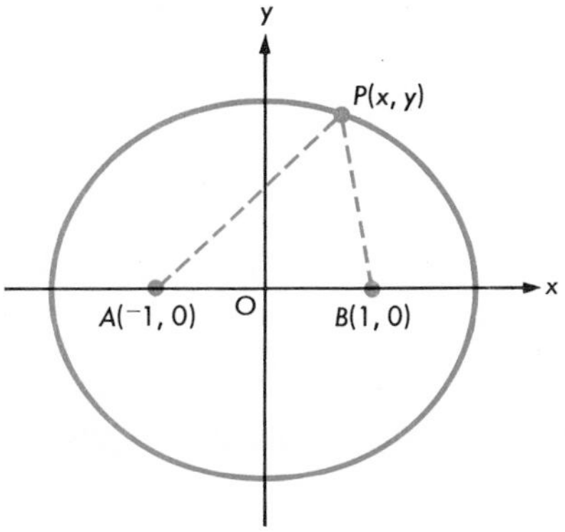

FIGURE 5–10

$$AP = \sqrt{(x+1)^2 + (y-0)^2}, \quad \text{or } \sqrt{x^2 + 2x + 1 + y^2},$$

and

$$BP = \sqrt{(x-1)^2 + (y-0)^2}, \quad \text{or } \sqrt{x^2 - 2x + 1 + y^2}.$$

In view of Eq. (1), $P(x, y)$ is on the given ellipse if, and only if,

$$\sqrt{x^2 + 2x + 1 + y^2} + \sqrt{x^2 - 2x + 1 + y^2} = 4. \quad (2)$$

This is an *equation of the ellipse.* In other words, the graph of Eq. (2) is the ellipse drawn in Fig. 5–10.

Because Eq. (2) would be awkward to use, we shall simplify it. Equation (2) is equivalent to the equation

$$\sqrt{x^2 - 2x + 1 + y^2} = 4 - \sqrt{x^2 + 2x + 1 + y^2}. \quad (3)$$

This equation is, in turn, equivalent to the equation

$$(\sqrt{x^2 - 2x + 1 + y^2})^2 = (4 - \sqrt{x^2 + 2x + 1 + y^2})^2. \quad (4)$$

In class, after discussing the derivation of the equation of the ellipse in Figure 5–10, the y-axis may be selected on the foci with A at $(0, 1)$ and B at $(0, ^-1)$ and the equation derived with the coordinate system in this position. Attention should be directed to the fact that the foci are always on the major axis, as seen in the new equation

$$\frac{x^2}{3} + \frac{y^2}{4} = 1.$$

To emphasize the wisdom of having the foci on one of the coordinate axes, you could have the class use the distance formula to find (and simplify) the equation of an ellipse whose foci are at $A(^-1, ^-2)$ and $B(3, 2)$, and in which $k = 8$. The equation

$$3x^2 - 2xy + 3y^2 - 6x + 2y - 29 = 0$$

may be missed by most students, but the point will be clear.

Students will need help at first in simplifying the equation of the ellipse. You may wish to review squaring a sum,

$$(p + q)^2 = p^2 + 2pq + q^2,$$

squaring a product,

$$(ab)^2 = a^2b^2,$$

and squaring a square root,

$$(\sqrt{x})^2 = x.$$

Although the equivalency between Eq. (3) and (4) is not as obvious as that between Eq. (1) and (2), it is clear that every solution of Eq. (2) is also a solution of this new equation. Carrying out the indicated operations in this new equation and simplifying, we obtain the following equivalent equations.

$$x^2 - 2x + 1 + y^2 = 16 - 8\sqrt{x^2 + 2x + 1 + y^2} + (x^2 + 2x + 1 + y^2)$$

$$8\sqrt{x^2 + 2x + 1 + y^2} = 16 + 4x$$

$$2\sqrt{x^2 + 2x + 1 + y^2} = 4 + x$$

Each solution of the equations above is also a solution of the equation

$$(2\sqrt{x^2 + 2x + 1 + y^2})^2 = (4 + x)^2.$$

This equation is, in turn, equivalent to each of the following equations.

$$4(x^2 + 2x + 1 + y^2) = 16 + 8x + x^2$$

$$4x^2 + 8x + 4 + 4y^2 = 16 + 8x + x^2$$

$$3x^2 + 4y^2 = 12$$

$$\frac{x^2}{4} + \frac{y^2}{3} = 1 \qquad (5)$$

As only the best students are likely to appreciate the need to prove Eq. (5) equivalent to Eq. (2), or to understand the procedure for doing it, you may wish to omit this entirely.

Our work above shows only that every solution of Eq. (2) is also a solution of Eq. (5). To show that Eq. (5) is equivalent to Eq. (2), and hence, that Eq. (5) is an equation of the given ellipse, we must show that every solution of Eq. (5) is also a solution of Eq. (2).

If (x, y) is a solution of Eq. (5), (x, y) is a solution of $3x^2 + 4y^2 = 12$. Then $3x^2 \leqq 12$, $x^2 \leqq 4$, and therefore, $^-2 \leqq x \leqq 2$. By adding 2 to each part of $^-2 \leqq x \leqq 2$, we get $0 \leqq 2 + x \leqq 4$. However, if $0 \leqq 2 + x$, then $0 \leqq 4 + x$. Similarly, by adding ^-x to each part of $^-2 \leqq x \leqq 2$, we get $0 \leqq 4 - x$. If $0 \leqq 4 + x$ and $0 \leqq 4 - x$,

$$\sqrt{(4 + x)^2} = 4 + x$$

and

$$\sqrt{(4 - x)^2} = 4 - x.$$

Consequently,

$$\sqrt{x^2 + 8x + 16} + \sqrt{x^2 - 8x + 16} = 8.$$

Recalling that $12 = 3x^2 + 4y^2$, we also have

$$\sqrt{x^2 + 8x + (4 + 3x^2 + 4y^2)} + \sqrt{x^2 - 8x + (4 + 3x^2 + 4y^2)} = 8,$$

$$\sqrt{4x^2 + 8x + 4 + 4y^2} + \sqrt{4x^2 - 8x + 4 + 4y^2} = 8,$$

$$2\sqrt{x^2 + 2x + 1 + y^2} + 2\sqrt{x^2 - 2x + 1 + y^2} = 8.$$

On dividing each side of this equation by 2, we obtain Eq. (2). Therefore, every solution of Eq. (5) is a solution of Eq. (2).

In the same way, it can be shown that every ellipse whose axes of symmetry are along the coordinate axes has an equation of the form

$$\frac{x^2}{a^2} + \frac{y^2}{b^2} = 1$$

for some positive numbers a and b. If we let $y = 0$ in this equation, we obtain

$$\frac{x^2}{a^2} = 1,$$

$$x^2 = a^2,$$

$$x = a \quad \text{or} \quad x = {}^-a.$$

Thus, the ellipse crosses the x-axis at the points $(a, 0)$ and $({}^-a, 0)$. For this reason, we call a and ${}^-a$ the *x-intercepts* of the ellipse. It may be shown in a similar way that the ellipse crosses the y-axis at the points $(0, b)$ and $(0, {}^-b)$. We call b and ${}^-b$ the *y-intercepts* of the ellipse. It is clear that the ellipse is a circle if, and only if, $a = b$.

Every ellipse has an equation of the form

$$\frac{x^2}{a^2} + \frac{y^2}{b^2} = 1,$$

and the graph of every equation of this form is an ellipse. We make use of this fact in working the following problems.

Problem 1. Describe the graph of the equation $16x^2 + 25y^2 = 400$.

Solution. If we divide each side of this equation by 400, we obtain the equivalent equation

$$\frac{x^2}{25} + \frac{y^2}{16} = 1, \quad \text{or} \quad \frac{x^2}{5^2} + \frac{y^2}{4^2} = 1.$$

TWISTER

A divided highway into the city passes under a number of bridges. The arch over each lane is in the form of a semi-ellipse, where the height is equal to the width. What is the lowest bridge under which a truck 6 feet wide and 12 feet high can pass?

Solution: The equation of the ellipse is

$$\frac{x^2}{a^2} + \frac{y^2}{4a^2} = 1$$

where $2a$ is the height of the arch; $x = 3$ and $y = 12$, so $a = 3\sqrt{5}$. Thus, the truck will be able to go under an arch $6\sqrt{5}$, or approximately 13 feet, 5 inches high.

Since the equation has the form

$$\frac{x^2}{a^2} + \frac{y^2}{b^2} = 1,$$

the graph is an ellipse with 5 and $^-5$ as its x-intercepts, and 4 and $^-4$ as its y-intercepts. The segments $\overline{CD}$ of the x-axis and $\overline{EF}$ of the y-axis, shown in Fig. 5–11, are called the *axes* of the ellipse. The longer one, $\overline{CD}$ in this case, is called the *major axis* and the shorter one, $\overline{EF}$ in our example, is called the *minor axis* of the ellipse.

The foci of this ellipse, say points A and B, are always on the major axis. If P is any point on the ellipse, then

$$AP + BP = AD + BD$$

since D is also a point on the ellipse. However, $BD = CA$ in Fig. 5–11 so that $AD + BD = AD + CA$, or CD. Hence, $AP + BP = 10$, the length of the major axis, for every point P on the ellipse. Since F is a point on the ellipse and $AF = BF$, it follows that $AF = 5$. Knowing the lengths of two sides of the right triangle AOF, we find that the length of $\overline{AO}$ is 3 by the pythagorean theorem. Hence, the foci of this ellipse are the points $A(^-3, 0)$ and $B(3, 0)$. We can now draw the ellipse by placing thumbtacks at points A and B and taking a loop of string 16 units long.

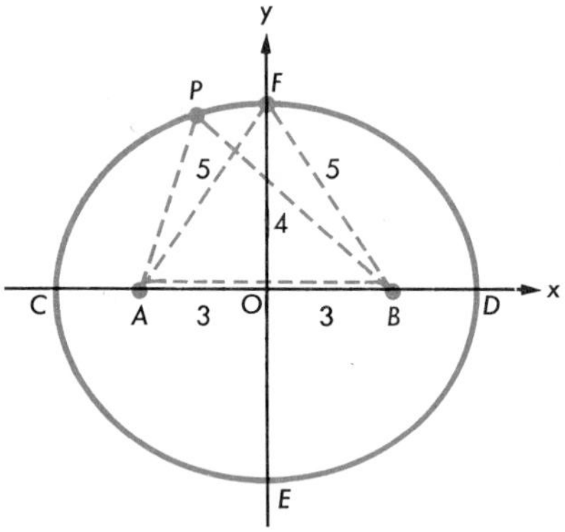

FIGURE 5–11

For the ellipse with equation

$$\frac{x^2}{a^2} + \frac{y^2}{b^2} = 1,$$

the distance, c, from the center of the ellipse to a focus may be found from either

$$c^2 = a^2 - b^2 \quad \text{if} \quad a > b$$

or

$$c^2 = b^2 - a^2 \quad \text{if} \quad b > a.$$

We can think of a circle as a special case of an ellipse when the two foci coincide at the center.

Equations of the conics derived from their definitions by use of the distance formula involve tedious arithmetic with the radicals. Thus students will be looking for a pattern that can yield the answer directly and they will therefore be apt to grasp quickly these ideas about a, b, and c.

Problem 2. Describe the graph of the equation $9x^2 + 4y^2 = 36$.

Solution. Dividing each side of this equation by 36, we obtain the equivalent equation

$$\frac{x^2}{2^2} + \frac{y^2}{3^2} = 1.$$

Since the equation has the form

$$\frac{x^2}{a^2} + \frac{y^2}{b^2} = 1,$$

the graph is an ellipse with x-intercepts 2 and $^-2$ and y-intercepts 3 and $^-3$. The axis $\overline{CD}$ is shorter than the axis $\overline{EF}$ for this ellipse (Fig. 5–12). Therefore, $\overline{CD}$ is the minor axis and $\overline{EF}$ is the major axis. Since the major axis is on the y-axis, the foci A and B are on the y-axis also. The distance c from the origin to either A or B is given by

$$c^2 = 3^2 - 2^2, \quad \text{or } c = \sqrt{5},$$

according to our statement in Problem 1. Hence, the foci have coordinates $(0, \sqrt{5})$ and $(0, {}^-\sqrt{5})$, as shown in Fig. 5–12.

Given an equation of an ellipse, we can find points on the ellipse by solving the equation either for y in terms of x or for x in terms of y. Then by assigning values to one of the variables, we can easily compute the corresponding values of the other variable.

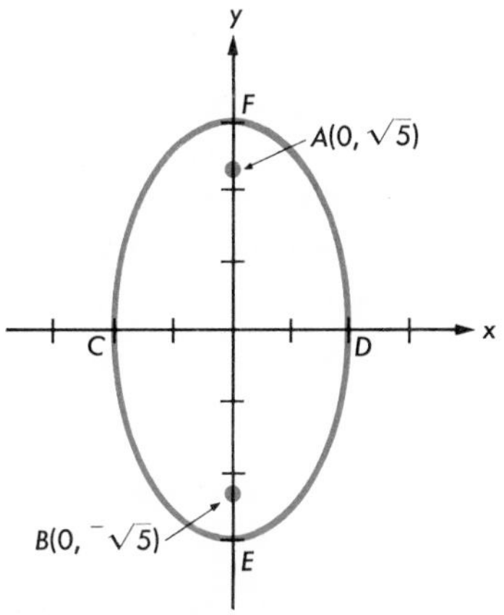

FIGURE 5–12

Exercises for Discussion

1. Consider the ellipse with equation

$$\frac{x^2}{4} + \frac{y^2}{3} = 1.$$

2 and ⁻2 √3 and ⁻√3

(a) Find the x- and y-intercepts.
(b) Show that the points $(1, \frac{3}{2})$, $(^-1, \frac{3}{2})$, $(1, {}^-\frac{3}{2})$, and $(^-1, {}^-\frac{3}{2})$ are on the ellipse.
(c) If (x, y) is any point on the ellipse, where $x \neq 0$ and $y \neq 0$, find three other related points on the ellipse.

You may wish to follow up the suggestion for finding points on the graph by assigning values to one variable and computing values for the other one.

In Problem 2, you could take

$$y = \pm\tfrac{3}{2}\sqrt{4 - x^2}$$

and find y when

$$x = \pm\tfrac{1}{2},\ \pm 1,\ \pm\tfrac{3}{2}.$$

Plotting these points should demonstrate to the student that this is an equation of a closed curve which could be drawn with a string.

Attention should be called to the fact that there are no points on the ellipse for $|x| > 2$ because $\sqrt{4 - x^2}$ is then an i-number. Also,

$$x = \pm\tfrac{2}{3}\sqrt{9 - y^2}$$

may be used to show that there are no points on the ellipse with $|y| > 3$ because $\sqrt{9 - y^2}$ is then an i-number.

Exercises for Discussion

If time is limited, it is suggested that at least Exercises for Discussion 2, 4, and 5 be covered.

Answers to Exercises for Discussion 1(b), 1(c)

1. (b) $\frac{1}{4}(1)^2 + \frac{1}{3}(\frac{3}{2})^2 = \frac{1}{4} + (\frac{1}{3} \cdot \frac{9}{4}) = 1$. Hence, $(1, \frac{3}{2})$ is on the ellipse. Similarly, $(^-1, \frac{3}{2})$, $(1, {}^-\frac{3}{2})$, and $(^-1, {}^-\frac{3}{2})$ are on the ellipse.
(c) If (x, y) is on the ellipse, then so are $(x, {}^-y)$, $(^-x, y)$, and $(^-x, {}^-y)$.

Answers to Exercises for Discussion 2(b)–5

2. (b) 12 units; 6 units
   (c) If $y = 3\sqrt{3}$ or $^-3\sqrt{3}$, then

$$\frac{x^2}{9} + \frac{27}{36} = 1,$$
$$\frac{x^2}{9} = \frac{1}{4},$$
$$x = \tfrac{3}{2} \text{ or } x = \tfrac{^-3}{2}.$$

   (d) On lines perpendicular to the major axis at the foci.

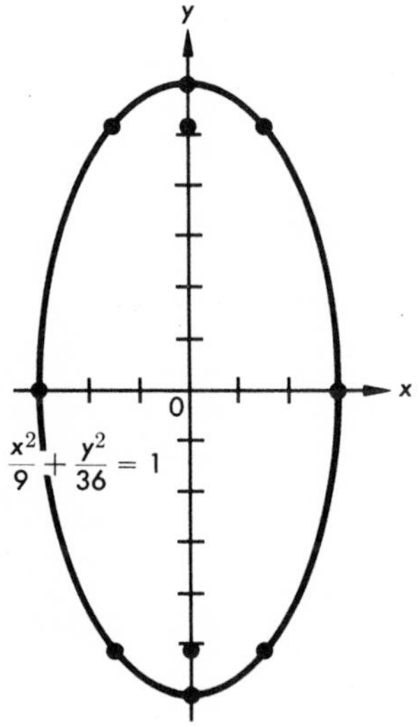

3. (a) An ellipse with the major axis horizontal; x-intercepts: 6 and $^-6$; y-intercepts: 3 and $^-3$; foci: $(^-3\sqrt{3}, 0)$ and $(3\sqrt{3}, 0)$.
   (b) $(3\sqrt{3}, \frac{3}{2})$, $(3\sqrt{3}, \frac{^-3}{2})$, $(^-3\sqrt{3}, \frac{3}{2})$, $(^-3\sqrt{3}, \frac{^-3}{2})$
   (c)

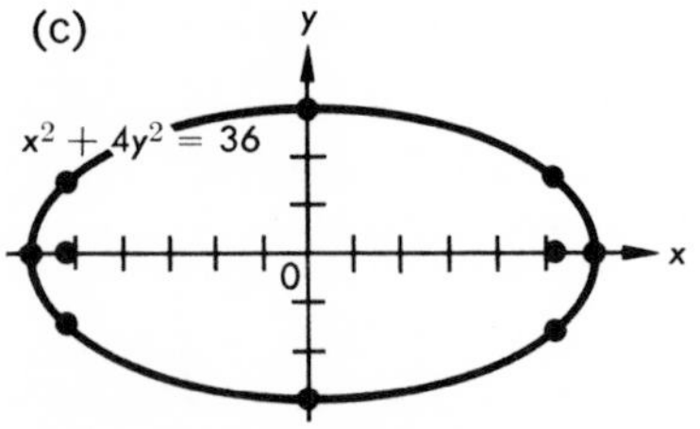

4. All points inside the ellipse which is the graph of

$$\frac{x^2}{4} + \frac{y^2}{3} = 1;$$

2. An ellipse has equation

$$\frac{x^2}{9} + \frac{y^2}{36} = 1.$$

   3, $^-3$ 6, $^-6$ $(0, 3\sqrt{3})$ and $(0, ^-3\sqrt{3})$
   (a) Find the x- and y-intercepts and the foci.
   (b) How long is the major axis? the minor axis?
   (c) Find the values of x when $y = 3\sqrt{3}$ or when $y = {}^-3\sqrt{3}$.
   (d) Sketch the graph of the ellipse. Show the points mentioned in parts (a) and (c). Where do these four points lie on the ellipse with reference to the foci?

3. (a) Describe the graph of the equation $x^2 + 4y^2 = 36$, giving the coordinates of the intercepts and of the foci.
   (b) A line through either focus perpendicular to the major axis cuts the ellipse in two points. Use the coordinates of the foci and the equation of the ellipse to find these four points.
   (c) Graph the ellipse, showing all points mentioned in parts (a) and (b).

4. Describe the graph of the inequality

$$\frac{x^2}{4} + \frac{y^2}{3} < 1.$$

   Find all integral solutions.

5. Find an equation of the ellipse with foci $A(0, ^-1)$, and $B(0, 1)$, given that point P is on the ellipse if, and only if, $AP + BP = 3$. What are the coordinates of the x- and y-intercepts?

Exercises

See Solution Manual for graphs.

1. An ellipse has equation

$$\frac{x^2}{36} + \frac{y^2}{4} = 1.$$

   $(6,0), (^-6,0); (0,2), (0,^-2);$ $(4\sqrt{2},0), (^-4\sqrt{2},0)$
   (a) Find the coordinates of the x- and y-intercepts and of the foci.
   (b) Give the lengths of the major and minor axes. 12, 4
   (c) Find y if $x = 4\sqrt{2}$ or if $x = {}^-4\sqrt{2}$. Where do these four points lie on the ellipse with reference to the foci?
   (d) Sketch the graph of the ellipse. Show the points mentioned in parts (a) and (c).

In Exercises 2–5, write an equation of the ellipses with foci at points A and B, given that P is on the ellipse. Simplify each equation.

2. $A(2, 0)$, $B(^-2, 0)$; $AP + BP = 6$ $\frac{x^2}{9} + \frac{y^2}{5} = 1$
3. $A(0, 3)$, $B(0, ^-3)$; $AP + BP = 8$ $\frac{x^2}{7} + \frac{y^2}{16} = 1$
4. $A(4, 0)$, $B(^-4, 0)$; $AP + BP = 11$ $\frac{4x^2}{121} + \frac{4y^2}{57} = 1$
5. $A(0, 5)$, $B(0, ^-5)$; $AP + BP = 13$ $\frac{4x^2}{69} + \frac{4y^2}{169} = 1$

6. Draw the graph of the equation $x^2 + 2y^2 = 18$. List the coordinates of the intercepts and of the foci. Find the coordinates of the points on the ellipse that are vertically above or below the foci. Give the lengths of the major and minor axes.

7. (a) Tell which of the following points are inside, which are outside, and which are on the ellipse with equation $4x^2 + 9y^2 = 36$.

Inside	Outside	On	Inside	Outside	Inside	Outside
$(1, 1)$,	$(1, 2)$,	$(1, \frac{4}{3}\sqrt{2})$,	$(1, \sqrt{3})$,	$(1, ^-2)$,	$(^-2, \frac{5}{4})$,	$(^-1, ^-2)$

(b) Write an algebraic expression describing the points inside the ellipse in part (a). $4x^2 + 9y^2 < 36$

(c) Write an algebraic expression describing the points outside the ellipse in part (a). $4x^2 + 9y^2 > 36$

8. (a) Draw and describe the graph of the equation $4x^2 + 18y^2 = 36$.

(b) Write a mathematical statement describing the points that are inside the ellipse of part (a). $4x^2 + 18y^2 < 36$

(c) Write a mathematical statement describing the points that are on or outside the ellipse of part (a). $4x^2 + 18y^2 \geqq 36$

9. Draw the graph of the equation $9x^2 + y^2 = 36$. List the coordinates of the intercepts and of the foci. Find the coordinates of the points on the ellipse that are horizontally to the right or to the left of the foci. Give the length of the major axis.

10. Draw the graph of the equation $64x^2 + 9y^2 = 16$. Give the coordinates and plot the intercepts, foci, and points on the ellipse that are horizontally to the right or to the left of the foci.

11. The foci of an ellipse are at points $A(4, 0)$ and $B(^-4, 0)$. A point is on the ellipse if, and only if, the sum of its distances from A and B is equal to 16. Find an equation of the ellipse and sketch it.
$3x^2 + 4y^2 = 192$

△

---

12. Find the intersections of the ellipse $3x^2 + 4y^2 = 9$ with the straight line $x = k$ for each of the following values of k.
None; $(^-\sqrt{3}, 0)$; $(1, \frac{1}{2}\sqrt{6})$, $(1, \frac{-1}{2}\sqrt{6})$; $(\sqrt{3}, 0)$; none

$$^-4, \quad ^-\sqrt{3}, \quad 1, \quad \sqrt{3}, \quad 5$$

13. Consider the system of equations

$$\begin{cases} x^2 + 3y^2 = 12, \\ x + 3y = 6. \end{cases}$$

(a) Find the solution set by graphing each member of the system and observing their points of intersection. $\{(0, 2), (3, 1)\}$

(b) Use the substitution method to find the solution set. $\{(0, 2), (3, 1)\}$

integral solutions: $(^-1, 1)$, $(^-1, 0)$, $(^-1, ^-1)$, $(0, 1)$, $(0, 0)$, $(0, ^-1)$, $(1, 1)$, $(1, 0)$, $(1, ^-1)$

5. $c = 1$, $b = \frac{3}{2}$, $a = \sqrt{b^2 - c^2} = \sqrt{\frac{9}{4} - 1} = \frac{1}{2}\sqrt{5}$

$$\frac{x^2}{\frac{5}{4}} + \frac{y^2}{\frac{9}{4}} = 1, \text{ or } \frac{4x^2}{5} + \frac{4y^2}{9} = 1$$

Exercises

It is recommended that Exercises 12 and 13 be covered as they provide practice in solving systems containing one linear and one quadratic equation.

Exercise 14 introduces a system of quadratic equations solvable by either the addition or subtraction method. It is recommended that it be assigned.

When Exercise 17 is assigned, you may wish to refer to the drawings made during the first class session on ellipses, and perhaps let the students construct these ellipses at the board.

Answers to Exercises 1(c), page 222; 6, 9, 10

1. (c) $y = \frac{2}{3}$ or $y = ^-\frac{2}{3}$; vertically above and below

6. Intercepts: $(3\sqrt{2}, 0)$, $(^-3\sqrt{2}, 0)$, $(0, 3)$, $(0, ^-3)$; foci: $(3, 0)$, $(^-3, 0)$; points above or below foci: $(3, \frac{3}{2}\sqrt{2})$, $(3, ^-\frac{3}{2}\sqrt{2})$, $(^-3, \frac{3}{2}\sqrt{2})$, $(^-3, ^-\frac{3}{2}\sqrt{2})$; major axis: $6\sqrt{2}$; minor axis: 6.

9. $(2, 0)$, $(^-2, 0)$, $(0, 6)$, $(0, ^-6)$; $(0, 4\sqrt{2})$, $(0, ^-4\sqrt{2})$; $(\frac{2}{3}, 4\sqrt{2})$, $(^-\frac{2}{3}, 4\sqrt{2})$, $(\frac{2}{3}, ^-4\sqrt{2})$, $(^-\frac{2}{3}, ^-4\sqrt{2})$; 12

10. $(\frac{1}{2}, 0)$, $(^-\frac{1}{2}, 0)$, $(0, \frac{4}{3})$, $(0, ^-\frac{4}{3})$; $(0, \frac{1}{6}\sqrt{55})$, $(0, ^-\frac{1}{6}\sqrt{55})$; $(\frac{3}{16}, \frac{1}{6}\sqrt{55})$, $(\frac{3}{16}, ^-\frac{1}{6}\sqrt{55})$, $(^-\frac{3}{16}, \frac{1}{6}\sqrt{55})$, $(^-\frac{3}{16}, ^-\frac{1}{6}\sqrt{55})$

Answers to Exercises 16(b), 16(c)

16. (b) Infinitely many

$$\frac{x^2}{64} + \frac{y^2}{b^2} = 1$$

$$\frac{x^2}{64} + \frac{y^2}{12} = 1$$

(c) Infinitely many

$$\frac{x^2}{a^2} + \frac{y^2}{16} = 1$$

$$\frac{x^2}{12} + \frac{y^2}{16} = 1$$

$(^-3, ^-2), (3, 2), (3, ^-2)$

Quiz

An ellipse has equation

$$\frac{x^2}{16} + \frac{y^2}{25} = 1.$$

1. Find the x- and y-intercepts and the foci. (ans: 4, $^-4$; 5, $^-5$; (0, 3), (0, $^-3$))
2. How long is the major axis? the minor axis? (ans: 10, 8)
3. Find the values of x when $y = 3$ or $y = {}^-3$. (ans: $\frac{16}{5}$, $^-\frac{16}{5}$)
4. Sketch the graph of the ellipse.

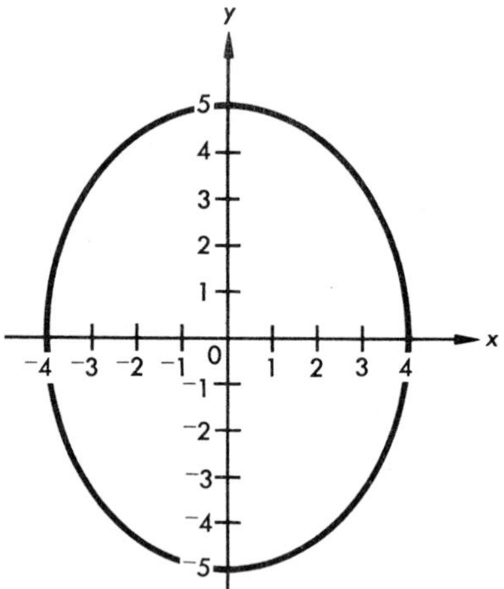

14. Consider the system of equations

$$\begin{cases} x^2 + y^2 = 13, \\ 2x^2 + 3y^2 = 35. \end{cases}$$

Circle: center (0,0), radius $\sqrt{13}$

Ellipse: center (0,0), major axis horizontal

(Hint: The *method of addition* used on a system of linear equations in x and y is applicable here.)

(a) Describe the graph of each equation of this system.

(b) Solve the system. $\{(2,3), (2,^-3), (^-2,3), (^-2,^-3)\}$

15. Graph the solution set of the system of inequalities

$$\begin{cases} x^2 + 3y^2 \geqq 3, \\ x^2 + y^2 \leqq 5. \end{cases}$$

▲

---

16. An equation of the family of ellipses with center at the origin and axes along the coordinate axes is

$$\frac{x^2}{a^2} + \frac{y^2}{b^2} = 1.$$

(a) Write an equation of the member of this family with y-intercepts 1 and $^-1$, and x-intercepts 2 and $^-2$. $\frac{x^2}{4} + \frac{y^2}{1} = 1$

(b) How many members of this family have x-intercepts 8 and $^-8$? Write an equation of this set of ellipses. Write an equation of the ellipse which has these x-intercepts and also passes through the point (4, 3).

(c) How many members of this family have y-intercepts 4 and $^-4$? Write an equation of this set of ellipses. Write an equation of the ellipse which has these y-intercepts and also passes through the point with coordinates ($^-3$, 2). Through what other three points does this ellipse automatically pass because of its two axes of symmetry?

17. (a) Graph each of the following equations on a single set of axes.

$c = 2\sqrt{6}$, $\frac{c}{a} = \frac{2\sqrt{6}}{5}$ $\quad \frac{x^2}{25} + \frac{y^2}{1} = 1, \quad \frac{x^2}{25} + \frac{y^2}{4} = 1, \quad \frac{x^2}{25} + \frac{y^2}{9} = 1,$ $c = 4$, $\frac{c}{a} = \frac{4}{5}$

$c = 3$, $\frac{c}{a} = \frac{3}{5}$ $\quad \frac{x^2}{25} + \frac{y^2}{16} = 1, \quad \frac{x^2}{25} + \frac{y^2}{25} = 1$ $\quad c = 0$, $\frac{c}{a} = 0$ $\quad c = \sqrt{21}$, $\frac{c}{a} = \frac{\sqrt{21}}{5}$

(b) Find c and c/a for each of the ellipses you just graphed, where c is half the distance between the foci and a is half the length of the major axis. Tell how the appearance of the ellipse changes as c/a changes. Is there a maximum value for c/a? No What is the minimum value for c/a? 0 As $\frac{c}{a}$ increases, the ellipse becomes flatter.

(c) The quotient c/a is called the *eccentricity* of the ellipse. Two ellipses are drawn, each with major axis 20 units long. How do their appearances compare if the eccentricity of one is $\frac{1}{20}$ and that of the other $\frac{19}{20}$? $\frac{1}{20}$ will give a rounder ellipse.

5-5 HYPERBOLAS

To visualize a hyperbola completely, we must start with a cone that has two *nappes* (see Fig. 5–13 at the bottom of the page). Then any plane which cuts both nappes without passing through the vertex intersects the cone in a hyperbola. Thus, the hyperbola has two separate parts, or branches, each extending indefinitely far. The following is a description of the hyperbola relative to its focal points.

DEFINITION OF A HYPERBOLA

Given two points A and B in a plane and a positive number k less than AB, the set consisting of every point P in the plane such that either

$$AP - BP = k \quad \text{or} \quad BP - AP = k$$

is called a hyperbola. Each of the points A and B is called a focus of the hyperbola.

In Fig. 5–14, we have sketched the hyperbola for $AB = 6$ and $k = 4$. The figure shows four symmetrically placed points of the hyperbola: P_1, P_2, P_3, and P_4. Points P_1 and P_2 are closer to B, so that

$$AP_1 - BP_1 = 4, \quad AP_2 - BP_2 = 4.$$

Points P_3 and P_4 are closer to A, so that

$$BP_3 - AP_3 = 4, \quad BP_4 - AP_4 = 4.$$

The points closer to B form the right-hand branch of the hyperbola of Fig. 5–14, and the points closer to A form the left-hand branch.

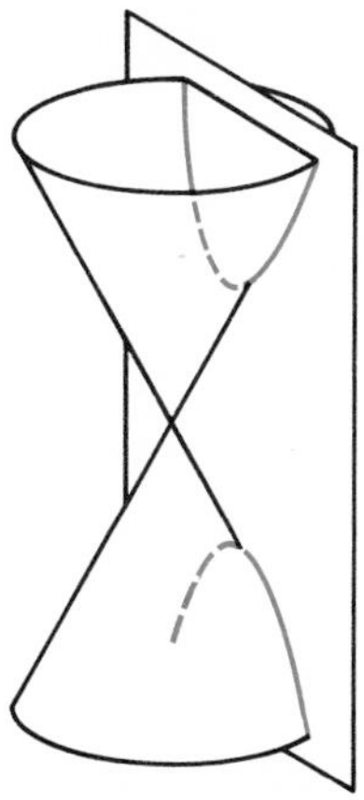

FIGURE 5–13

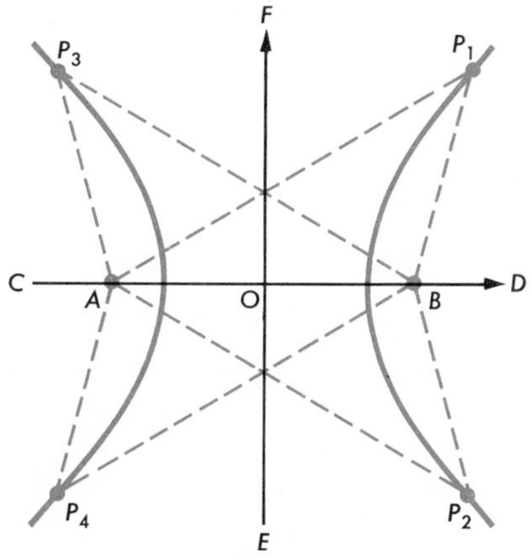

FIGURE 5–14

5-5 HYPERBOLAS

It is suggested that a specific problem be presented in class before this page is read. For example, you could mark two points, *A* and *B*, 10 inches apart on the blackboard, and instead of considering all points *P* so that the *sum* of *PA* and *PB* is constant, all points *P* could be considered so that the *difference* of *PA* and *PB* is constant. You could ask the students to propose some constant for $PA - PB$. They should note that it cannot be equal to or greater than 10 since the difference between two sides of a triangle is always less than the third side. For whatever value less than 10 that they suggest, a freehand sketch may be made of a dozen or more points satisfying the condition

$$PA - PB = k.$$

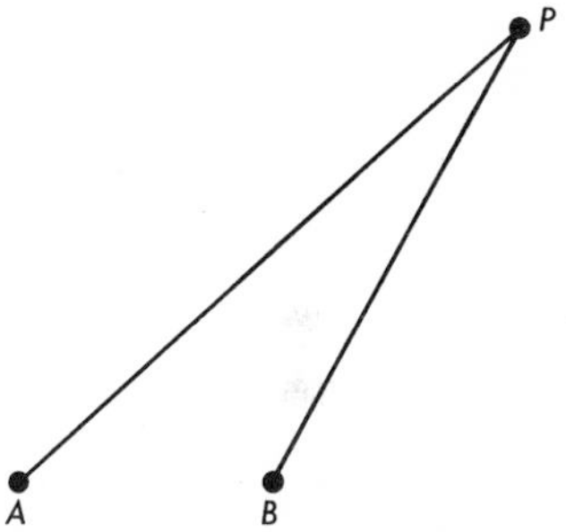

The students should observe that as *PA* increases, so does *PB*, and that this curve (unlike the ellipse where *PB* shortened as *PA* lengthened) extends indefinitely out away from *A* and *B* and is not closed.

An equation may be derived for the curve with the foci first on the *x*-axis, and then on the *y*-axis. These equations may be compared and contrasted with an equation of an ellipse.

The hyperbola, like the ellipse, has two axes of symmetry, the line $\overleftrightarrow{CD}$ through the foci and the line $\overleftrightarrow{EF}$ which is the perpendicular bisector of segment $\overline{AB}$, as shown in Fig. 5–14. The point O, in which these two axes intersect, is called the center of the hyperbola.

To find an equation of the hyperbola of Fig. 5–14, we naturally select our coordinate axes as the axes of symmetry described above. Since $AB = 6$ by assumption, A has coordinates $(^-3, 0)$ and B has coordinates $(3, 0)$. Point P of the plane (Fig. 5–15) is on the right-hand branch if, and only if,

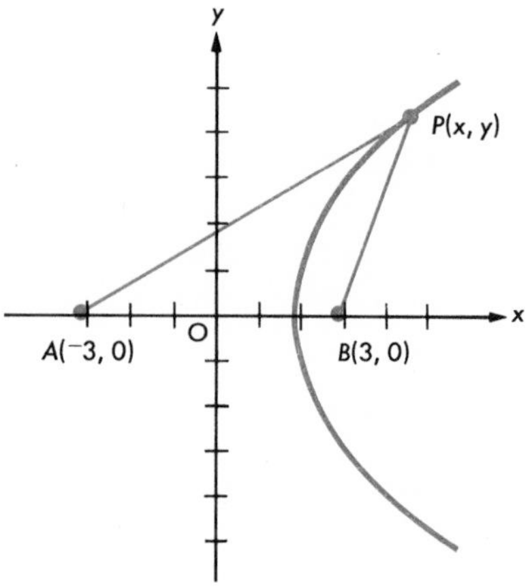

FIGURE 5–15

$$AP - BP = 4.$$

If P has coordinates (x, y) then

$$AP = \sqrt{(x + 3)^2 + (y - 0)^2}$$

and

$$BP = \sqrt{(x - 3)^2 + (y - 0)^2}$$

so that P is on the right-hand branch of the hyperbola if, and only if,

$$\sqrt{x^2 + 6x + 9 + y^2} - \sqrt{x^2 - 6x + 9 + y^2} = 4. \qquad (1)$$

Thus, Eq. (1) is an *equation of the right-hand branch* and

$$\sqrt{x^2 - 6x + 9 + y^2} - \sqrt{x^2 + 6x + 9 + y^2} = 4 \qquad (2)$$

is an *equation of the left-hand branch* of this hyperbola.

Let us simplify Eq. (1) as we did the equation of the ellipse. We proceed in the following manner.

$$\begin{aligned}
\sqrt{x^2 + 6x + 9 + y^2} &= 4 + \sqrt{x^2 - 6x + 9 + y^2} \\
x^2 + 6x + 9 + y^2 &= 16 + 8\sqrt{x^2 - 6x + 9 + y^2} \\
&\quad + (x^2 - 6x + 9 + y^2) \\
12x - 16 &= 8\sqrt{x^2 - 6x + 9 + y^2} \\
3x - 4 &= 2\sqrt{x^2 - 6x + 9 + y^2} \\
9x^2 - 24x + 16 &= 4(x^2 - 6x + 9 + y^2) \\
5x^2 - 4y^2 &= 20 \\
\frac{x^2}{4} - \frac{y^2}{5} &= 1 \qquad (3)
\end{aligned}$$

The algebra involved in simplifying the equation with two radicals should now be easy for most of the students. For those who are still not quite sure of the procedure, these equations will provide a second chance to learn it.

We leave it to you to verify that Eq. (2) also simplifies to Eq. (3). Thus, the graph of Eq. (3) contains both branches of the hyperbola.

To show that the graph of Eq. (3) is the hyperbola of Fig. 5–14, we must show that every solution of Eq. (3) is also a solution of either Eq. (1) or Eq. (2). With this in mind, let (x, y) be a solution of Eq. (3). Then $5x^2 = 20 + 4y^2$, $5x^2 \geqq 20$, and $x^2 \geqq 4$. Hence, either

$$x \geqq 2 \quad \text{or} \quad x \leqq {}^-2.$$

If (x, y) is a solution of (3) for which $x \geqq 2$, then $3x + 4 \geqq 0$ and $3x - 4 \geqq 0$. Furthermore,

$$\sqrt{(3x+4)^2} = 3x + 4, \quad \sqrt{(3x-4)^2} = 3x - 4.$$

Hence,

$$\sqrt{9x^2 + 24x + 16} - \sqrt{9x^2 - 24x + 16} = 8.$$

Now $9x^2 = 4x^2 + 5x^2$ and $5x^2 = 20 + 4y^2$, or $9x^2 = 4x^2 + 20 + 4y^2$. Therefore,

$$\sqrt{4x^2 + 20 + 4y^2 + 24x + 16}$$
$$- \sqrt{4x^2 + 20 + 4y^2 - 24x + 16} = 8,$$

or

$$\sqrt{4x^2 + 24x + 36 + 4y^2} - \sqrt{4x^2 - 24x + 36 + 4y^2} = 8,$$
$$2\sqrt{x^2 + 6x + 9 + y^2} - 2\sqrt{x^2 - 6x + 9 + y^2} = 8.$$

On dividing each side of this equation by 2, we obtain Eq. (1). Thus, every solution of Eq. (3) for which $x \geqq 2$ is also a solution of Eq. (1).

It may be shown in exactly the same way that every solution (x, y) of Eq. (3) for which $x \leqq {}^-2$ is also a solution of Eq. (2). Consequently, the graph of Eq. (3) is the hyperbola of Fig. 5–14.

Verifying that the graph of Eq. (3) is indeed the hyperbola of Fig. 5–14 may be omitted in all but the very best of classes.

In Eq. (3), what significance do the numbers 4 and 5 have in relation to the hyperbola? If we let $y = 0$, we obtain the equation

$$\frac{x^2}{4} = 1, \quad x^2 = 4,$$

and finally,

$$x = 2 \quad \text{or} \quad x = {}^-2.$$

Thus, the x-intercepts of this hyperbola are 2 and $^-2$. If we let $x = 0$ in the equation above, we obtain the equation

$$\frac{{}^-y^2}{5} = 1, \quad \text{or } y^2 = {}^-5.$$

It should be observed that in the hyperbola the foci are farther from the center than are the vertices, hence $c > a$. This may help the students to remember that

$$c^2 = a^2 + b^2$$

for the hyperbola. (In the ellipse, the foci were closer to the center than the vertices, hence, $c < a$ and $c^2 = a^2 - b^2$.)

It should be noted that $\sqrt{x^2 + 16}$ (page 229) is negative for no x, and hence, this hyperbola extends across the entire width of the x-axis. However, solving the equation for x gives

$$x = {}^{\pm}\tfrac{4}{3}\sqrt{y^2 - 9},$$

showing that if $|y| < 3$, $\sqrt{y^2 - 9}$ is an i-number. Hence, there are no points on the hyperbola in the horizontal strip bounded by the lines $y = 3$ above and $y = {}^{-}3$ below.

Problem 2 on page 230 may be done graphically in class as a check on the algebraic solution. The equation of the circle may be solved for y and permissible replacements for x, y, being supposedly real, may be discussed. From the equations

$$y = \sqrt{16 - x^2} \text{ or } y = {}^{-}\sqrt{16 - x^2},$$

the class should see that x is restricted to the set such that $|x| \leqq 4$. From the equations

$$x = \sqrt{16 - y^2} \text{ or } x = {}^{-}\sqrt{16 - y^2},$$

they should see that for x to be real y is restricted to the set such that $|y| \leqq 4$. Thus the graph of

$$x^2 + y^2 = 16$$

is bounded by a square with sides $x = 4$, $x = {}^{-}4$, $y = 4$, $y = {}^{-}4$. The curve is closed and bounded.

On the other hand, solving the equation of the hyperbola for y leads to

$$y = 2\sqrt{x^2 - 1} \quad \text{or} \quad y = {}^{-}2\sqrt{x^2 - 1}.$$

The solutions of this equation are the complex numbers $\sqrt{5}i$ and ${}^{-}\sqrt{5}i$. Since the graph consists of only the real solutions of Eq. (3), we conclude that the hyperbola has no y-intercepts. We note that the sum of 4 and 5 is the square of the distance from the center of the hyperbola to each focus. Thus, 3, the positive square root of 9, is this distance.

It can be shown that every hyperbola with the coordinate axes as its axes of symmetry has an equation either of the form

$$\frac{x^2}{a^2} - \frac{y^2}{b^2} = 1$$

or of the form

$$\frac{y^2}{a^2} - \frac{x^2}{b^2} = 1.$$

Conversely, it may be shown that every equation of either form has a hyperbola as its graph. If we let

$$c^2 = a^2 + b^2,$$

then the hyperbola

$$\frac{x^2}{a^2} - \frac{y^2}{b^2} = 1 \quad \text{has foci at } (c, 0) \text{ and } ({}^{-}c, 0).$$

$$\frac{y^2}{a^2} - \frac{x^2}{b^2} = 1 \quad \text{has foci at } (0, c) \text{ and } (0, {}^{-}c).$$

Problem 1. Discuss the graph of the equation $16y^2 = 9x^2 + 144$.

Solution. This equation is equivalent to each of the following equations.

$$16y^2 - 9x^2 = 144$$

$$\frac{16y^2}{144} - \frac{9x^2}{144} = 1$$

$$\frac{y^2}{9} - \frac{x^2}{16} = 1$$

$$\frac{y^2}{3^2} - \frac{x^2}{4^2} = 1$$

Since this equation has form

$$\frac{y^2}{a^2} - \frac{x^2}{b^2} = 1,$$

its graph is a hyperbola. The y-intercepts are 3 and $^{-}3$. There are no x-intercepts. Since

$$3^2 + 4^2 = 5^2,$$

the foci are 5 units below and above the center. Hence, (0, 5) and (0, $^{-}5$) are the foci.

We may find points on this hyperbola if we solve its equation for y in terms of x or for x in terms of y. We solve for y in terms of x as follows:

$$\frac{y^2}{3^2} = \frac{x^2}{4^2} + 1,$$

$$y^2 = \frac{3^2}{4^2}(x^2 + 4^2),$$

$$y = \tfrac{3}{4}\sqrt{x^2 + 16} \quad \text{or} \quad y = {}^{-}\tfrac{3}{4}\sqrt{x^2 + 16}.$$

Hence,

$$y = \tfrac{3}{4}\sqrt{x^2 + 16}$$

is an equation of the upper branch, and

$$y = {}^{-}\tfrac{3}{4}\sqrt{x^2 + 16}$$

is an equation of the lower branch of the hyperbola. You can verify that the following points are on the upper branch by letting x equal 0, 2, 3, and 8 in the equation of the upper branch.

$$(0, 3), \quad \left(2, \frac{3\sqrt{5}}{2}\right), \quad \left(3, \frac{15}{4}\right), \quad (8, 3\sqrt{5})$$

We used the approximation $\sqrt{5} \doteq 2.2$ to plot points in Fig. 5–16. The other points plotted in the figure were obtained by considering the symmetry of the hyperbola about the coordinate axes.

The points $C(0, {}^{-}3)$ and $D(0, 3)$ are called the *vertices* of the hyperbola, and the segment $\overline{CD}$, which joins them, is called the *transverse axis* of the hyperbola. The branches of a hyperbola extend indefinitely far from the axes. In other words, the curve is unbounded.

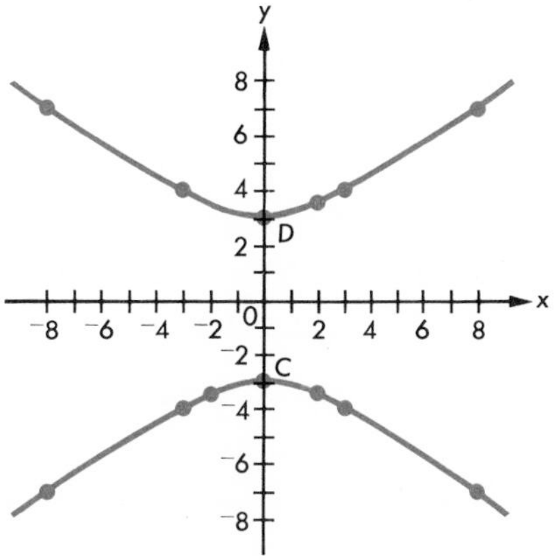

FIGURE 5–16

Thus x is restricted to the set such that $x \geqq 1$ or $x \leqq {}^{-}1$. The graph now lies to the right of $x = 1$ and to the left of $x = {}^{-}1$. Hence, it has two branches. If the equation is solved for x, it becomes

$$x = \tfrac{1}{2}\sqrt{y^2 + 4} \text{ or } x = {}^{-}\tfrac{1}{2}\sqrt{y^2 + 4}.$$

Thus there are no restrictions on y; any real number is permissible for y since $y^2 + 4$ is never negative. Considerations such as this of the extent of a graph may help the student to avoid making careless mistakes. He should not trust blindly to memory of patterns. A check on intercepts alone can often identify the conic.

Exercises for Discussion, page 231

If time is limited, it is recommended that at least Exercises for Discussion 1 and 2 be covered.

In connection with Exercise for Discussion 1(c), since this type of exercise was done in the section on the ellipse, you may wish to take the general case

$$\frac{x^2}{a^2} - \frac{y^2}{b^2} = 1$$

with foci at $(^{\pm}c, 0)$ and, letting $x = {}^{\pm}c$, solve for y, getting

$$y = \frac{^{\pm}b}{a}\sqrt{c^2 - a^2}.$$

Then, since

$$c^2 - a^2 = b^2, \; y = \frac{^{\pm}b^2}{a}.$$

Hence, we have a quick way to get four points on the hyperbola: $(^{\pm}c, {}^{\pm}b^2/a)$. (The chord through the focus perpendicular to the transverse axis has length $2b^2/a$ and is called the *latus rectum*.) The same formula applies in the case of the ellipse.

In Exercise for Discussion 3, this hyperbola should be compared as to shape with the hyperbola in Exercise for Discussion 1.

Answers to Exercises for Discussion 1(a), 1(c)–1(e), 2(a)–2(c), 3, 4, page 231

1. (a) $(5, 0)$, $(^-5, 0)$. If $x = 0$, $y^2 = {}^-16$, hence there are no y-intercepts.
   (c) $\frac{41}{25} - \frac{y^2}{16} = 1$,
   $y^2 = \frac{256}{25}$,
   $y = \frac{16}{5}$ or $^-\frac{16}{5}$
   The points are: $(\sqrt{41}, \frac{16}{5})$, $(\sqrt{41}, {}^-\frac{16}{5})$, $(^-\sqrt{41}, \frac{16}{5})$, $(^-\sqrt{41}, {}^-\frac{16}{5})$.
   (d)

x	± 6	± 7	± 10
y	$\pm\frac{4}{5}\sqrt{11}$	$\pm\frac{8}{5}\sqrt{6}$	$\pm 4\sqrt{3}$

   (e)

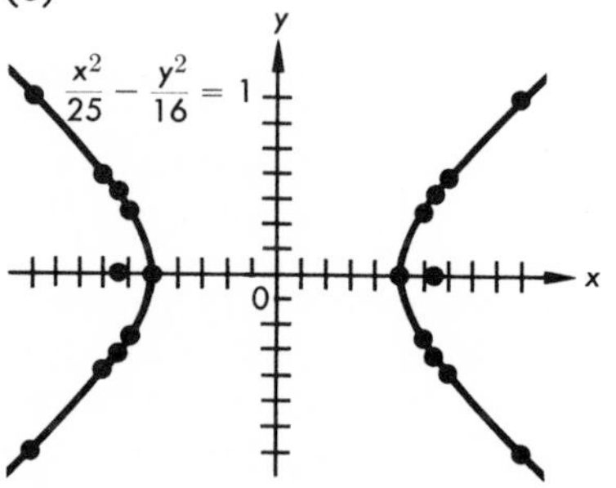

2. (a) $\sqrt{(x + 4)^2 + y^2} - \sqrt{(x - 4)^2 + y^2} = 6$ or $7x^2 - 9y^2 = 63$
   (b) $\sqrt{(x - 4)^2 + y^2} - \sqrt{(x + 4)^2 + y^2} = 6$ or $7x^2 - 9y^2 = 63$
   (c) $3, {}^-3$

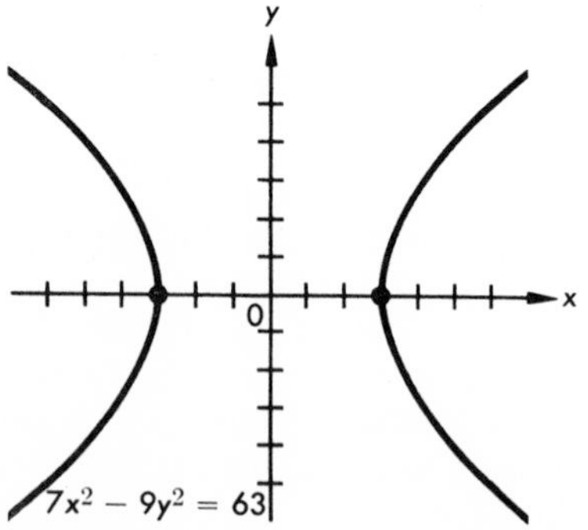

If two conic sections are drawn in the same plane, then they might have several points of intersection. It is intuitively clear that an ellipse and a hyperbola might have as many as four points of intersection. The following problem illustrates an algebraic method of finding the points of intersection of two conic sections.

Problem 2. Find the points of intersection of the circle with equation

$$x^2 + y^2 = 16$$

and the hyperbola with equation

$$4x^2 - y^2 = 4.$$

Solution. Algebraically, the problem is to find all solutions of the system of equations

$$\begin{cases} x^2 + y^2 = 16, \\ 4x^2 - y^2 = 4. \end{cases}$$

If we solve the system by the addition method, we obtain the equivalent system

$$\begin{cases} x^2 + y^2 = 16, \\ 5x^2 = 20. \end{cases}$$

The latter equation is easily solved, yielding $x = 2$ or $x = {}^-2$. Letting $x = 2$ in the first equation, we get the equation

$$y^2 = 12,$$

which is solved to yield $y = 2\sqrt{3}$ or $y = {}^-2\sqrt{3}$. Thus, $(2, 2\sqrt{3})$ and $(2, {}^-2\sqrt{3})$ are solutions of the system. If we let $x = {}^-2$ in the first equation, we again obtain $y = 2\sqrt{3}$ or $y = {}^-2\sqrt{3}$. Thus, $(^-2, 2\sqrt{3})$ and $(^-2, {}^-2\sqrt{3})$ are also solutions. Therefore, the four points of intersection of the circle and the hyperbola have coordinates

$$(2, 2\sqrt{3}), \quad (2, {}^-2\sqrt{3}),$$
$$(^-2, 2\sqrt{3}), \quad (^-2, {}^-2\sqrt{3}).$$

These four points are identified in Fig. 5–17.

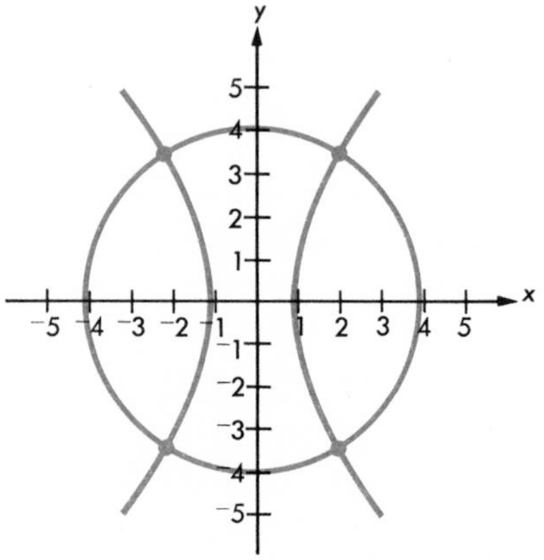

FIGURE 5–17

Exercises for Discussion

1. A hyperbola has equation $x^2/25 - y^2/16 = 1$.
   (a) Find the x-intercepts and show that there are no y-intercepts.
   (b) Find the coordinates of the foci.
   (c) Find the points of the hyperbola directly above and below the foci by substituting $x = \pm\sqrt{41}$ in the equation of the hyperbola and solving for y.
   (d) Solve the equation for y in terms of x and find y when $x = \pm 6, \pm 7$, and ± 10.
   (e) Graph the hyperbola showing all the points found in parts (a) through (d).

2. The foci of a hyperbola are at points A and B with coordinates $(^-4, 0)$ and $(4, 0)$, respectively. A point is on the hyperbola if the difference of its distances from these two points is 6.
   (a) Using the distance formula, write the equation which says that $PA - PB = 6$ where $P(x, y)$ is a point on the hyperbola.
   (b) Using the distance formula, write the equation which says that $PB - PA = 6$ where $P(x, y)$ is a point on the hyperbola.
   (c) Find the x-intercepts of this hyperbola. Sketch the hyperbola.
   (d) Show that this hyperbola does not have y-intercepts.

3. Sketch the graph of $16y^2 - 25x^2 = 400$.

4. Solve the system of equations

$$\begin{cases} 4x^2 - 5y^2 = 20, \\ 16x^2 + 25y^2 = 400, \end{cases}$$

and sketch the graph of each conic section.

Exercises

1. A hyperbola has equation $y^2/16 - x^2/9 = 1$.
   (a) Find the y-intercepts and show that there are no x-intercepts.
   (b) Find the coordinates of the foci.
   (c) Find the points horizontally directly to the right and left of the foci by substituting $y = \pm 5$ in the equation of the hyperbola and solving for x.
   (d) Solve the equation for x in terms of y and find x when $y = \pm 6, \pm 7$, and ± 10.
   (e) Graph the hyperbola, showing all the points found in parts (a) through (d).

3.

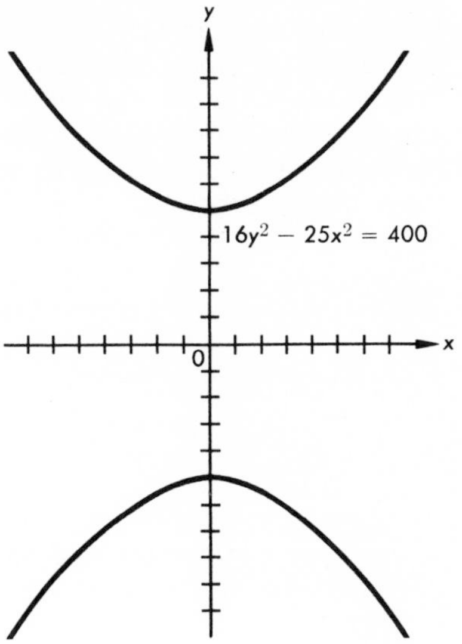

4. $\begin{cases} 4x^2 - 5y^2 = 20 \\ 16x^2 + 25y^2 = 400 \end{cases}$

$\begin{cases} 4x^2 - 5y^2 = 20 \\ 16x^2 + 25y^2 + 5(4x^2 - 5y^2) = 400 + 5 \cdot 20 \end{cases}$

$\begin{cases} 4x^2 - 5y^2 = 20 \\ 36x^2 = 500 \end{cases}$

$\begin{cases} x = \frac{5}{3}\sqrt{5} \text{ or } x = {}^-\frac{5}{3}\sqrt{5} \\ y = \frac{8}{3} \text{ or } y = \frac{^-8}{3} \end{cases}$

$\{(\frac{5}{3}\sqrt{5}, \frac{8}{3}), (\frac{5}{3}\sqrt{5}, {}^-\frac{8}{3}), ({}^-\frac{5}{3}\sqrt{5}, \frac{8}{3}), ({}^-\frac{5}{3}\sqrt{5}, {}^-\frac{8}{3})\}$

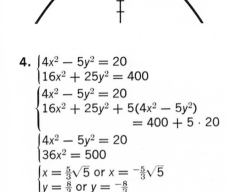

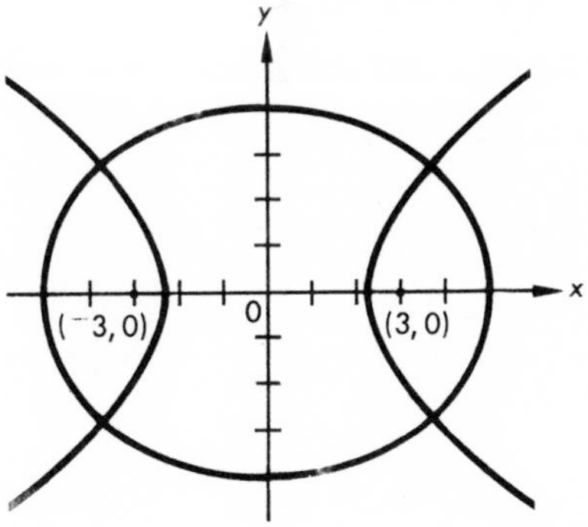

It is recommended that Exercises 2–10 all be covered.

Exercise 12 may be used for honors work. You may wish to suggest that interested students do some research on the asymptotes of a hyperbola.

Quiz

A hyperbola has equation

$$\frac{y^2}{9} - \frac{x^2}{4} = 1.$$

1. Find the y-intercepts and show that there are no x-intercepts. (ans: 3, $^-3$; if $y = 0$, $x^2 = {}^-4$)
2. Find the coordinates of the foci. (ans: $(0, \sqrt{13})$, $(0, {}^-\sqrt{13})$)
3. Find the points horizontally directly to the right and left of the foci by substituting $y = \pm\sqrt{13}$ in the equation of the hyperbola and solving for x. (ans: $(\frac{4}{3}, \sqrt{13})$, $(\frac{4}{3}, {}^-\sqrt{13})$, $({}^-\frac{4}{3}, \sqrt{13})$, $({}^-\frac{4}{3}, {}^-\sqrt{13})$)
4. Solve the equation for x in terms of y and find x when $y = {}^\pm 6$, and ${}^\pm 7$. (ans: ${}^\pm 2\sqrt{3}$, ${}^\pm\frac{4}{3}\sqrt{10}$)
5. Graph the hyperbola showing all the points found in Exercises 1 through 4.

Find an equation, in simplified form, of a hyperbola if the foci are at points A and B with coordinates as given, and if point P on the hyperbola has the given number as the difference of its distances from A and B.

2. $A(1, 0)$, $B({}^-1, 0)$; 1 $12x^2 - 4y^2 = 3$ **3.** $A(0, 2)$, $B(0, {}^-2)$; 3 $28y^2 - 36x^2 = 63$

For each of the following equations, find the intercepts of the hyperbola. Also, use the Table of Squares and Square Roots to approximate the coordinates of eight other points on the hyperbola. Sketch the graph.

4. $\frac{x^2}{4} - \frac{y^2}{9} = 1$ $(2, 0), ({}^-2, 0)$ **5.** $\frac{x^2}{9} - \frac{y^2}{9} = 1$ $(3, 0), ({}^-3, 0)$

6. $\frac{y^2}{9} - \frac{x^2}{16} = 1$ $(0, 3), (0, {}^-3)$ **7.** $25y^2 - 4x^2 = 100$ $(0, 2), (0, {}^-2)$

△

8. Use algebraic methods to find the points of intersection of the hyperbola $y^2 - 3x^2 = 6$ and each of the lines given below. In each case, sketch the graph of the hyperbola and the line.

(a) $x + y - 4 = 0$ $\{({}^-5, 9), (1, 3)\}$ (b) $x - y + 2 = 0$ $\{(1, 3)\}$ (c) $x - y - 1 = 0$ None

9. Use algebraic methods to find the solution set of the system of equations

$$\begin{cases} x^2 - 3y^2 + 12 = 0, \\ 4x^2 + 3y^2 - 192 = 0. \end{cases}$$

$\{(6, 4), (6, {}^-4), ({}^-6, 4), ({}^-6, {}^-4)\}$

Check your solutions by graphing.

10. Use algebraic methods to find the points of intersection of the two conic sections $x^2 + 4y^2 = 16$ and $x^2 - y^2 = 16$. Check your answer by sketching a graph. $\{(4, 0), ({}^-4, 0)\}$

▲

11. (a) Solve the equation $x^2/4 - y^2/5 = 1$ for y in terms of x. What values of x lead to real values for y? $y = \pm\frac{1}{2}\sqrt{5(x^2 - 4)}$; $x \leq {}^-2, x \geq 2$

(b) Solve the equation $x^2/4 - y^2/5 = 1$ for x in terms of y. Are there any values for y that lead to complex values for x? $x = \pm\frac{2}{5}\sqrt{5(y^2+5)}$ No

12. A hyperbola is drawn with focus B at $(c, 0)$ and focus A at $({}^-c, 0)$. For every point $P(x, y)$ on the hyperbola, it is true that $PA - PB = 2a$, or ${}^-2a$, depending on which branch of the hyperbola is being considered. Use the distance formula to find an equation of this hyperbola. Your equation contains the constants a and c. Show that $c^2 - a^2$ is positive and then replace it by b^2 to obtain an equation containing the constants a and b. You should see now why we said in this section that $c^2 = a^2 + b^2$. $\frac{x^2}{a^2} - \frac{y^2}{c^2 - a^2} = 1$; See Solution Manual; $\frac{x^2}{a^2} - \frac{y^2}{b^2} = 1$

5-6 PARABOLAS

The conic sections studied so far have been *central conics;* that is, each has had two axes of symmetry and a center. The final conic section to be studied, the parabola, is not a central conic. The parabola is the curve of intersection of a plane with a cone; the plane is parallel to an edge of the cone. (See Fig. 5-18.)

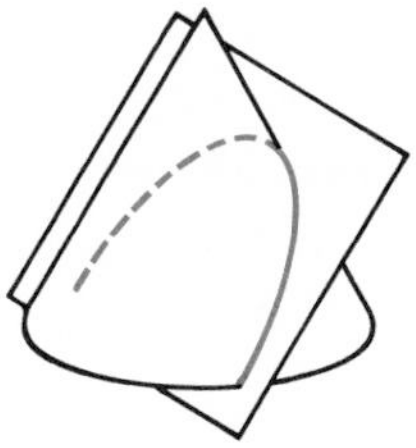

FIGURE 5-18

The parabola may be described relative to a point and a line in the following way.

DEFINITION OF A PARABOLA

Given a point F and a line L not containing F, the set consisting of every point P in the plane such that

$$PF = PQ,$$

where Q is the foot of the perpendicular drawn from P to line L (Fig. 5-19), is called a parabola. The point F is called the focus and the line L the directrix of the parabola.

With a piece of graph paper and a compass, it is easy to find as many points on a parabola as you wish. Let the directrix L be along one of the lines of the paper and let F also be on a line. In Fig. 5-19, F is two units above L. Clearly one point of the parabola is the point V halfway between F and L, that is, one unit directly under F. Incidentally, V is called the *vertex* of the parabola. Now open the compass to a radius of two units, place the point of the compass at F, and mark off points A and B on the line two units above L. Next, open the compass to a radius of three units, place the point of the compass at F, and mark off points C and D on the line three units above L, and so on.

The line through the focus of a parabola and perpendicular to the directrix is called the *axis* of the parabola. From Fig. 5-19, it can be seen that the axis is the axis of symmetry of the parabola.

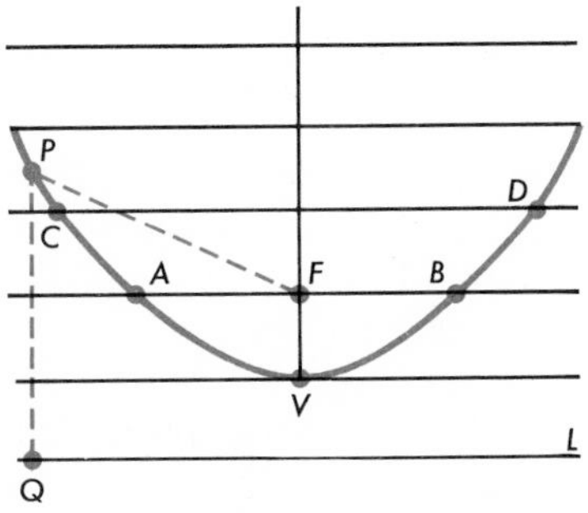

FIGURE 5-19

5-6 PARABOLAS

The graph of $y = ax^2$ was discussed fully in Chapter 3, where it was said to be a parabola with vertex at (0, 0) and the y-axis as axis of symmetry. There a set of points was named whose coordinates were in the solution set of the equation $y = ax^2$. Here a set of points is being described geometrically and an equation is being found whose solution set will be the coordinates of the points. The new equation, $x^2 = 4py$, is just the old equation with $a = 1/4p$; this is evident if $x^2 = 4py$ is solved for y, getting $y = (1/4p)x^2$. However, the nature of the derivation of the equation $x^2 = 4py$ leads to the knowledge not only that this is a parabola with vertex at (0, 0) and axis of symmetry $x = 0$, which was known before, but also that the focus is at (0, p) and the directrix is the line $y = {}^-p$. Just as a controlled the sharpness of the curve and the direction in which it opened, so does $4p$, but p gives even more basic information about the curve.

This construction may be done on the graph board while each student does it on graph paper at his desk.

Let us find an equation of a parabola. The axis of the parabola is an obvious choice for one coordinate axis, say the y-axis. While it might seem plausible to select the directrix L as the x-axis, a still better choice for the x-axis is the line through the vertex V, as indicated in Fig. 5–20.

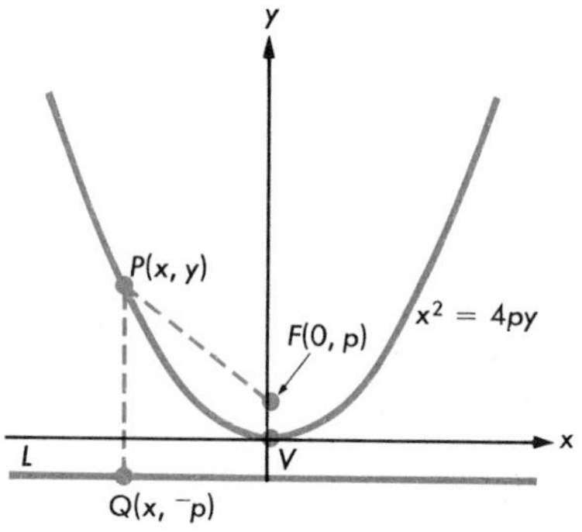

FIGURE 5–20

Let p be the distance from the vertex V to the focus F. Then F has coordinates $(0, p)$, and the directrix L has equation $y = {}^-p$. A point P in the plane is on the parabola if, and only if,

$$PF = PQ,$$

where Q is the point at the foot of the perpendicular drawn from P to line L. If P has coordinates (x, y), it follows that Q then has coordinates $(x, {}^-p)$. Since

$$PF = \sqrt{(x - 0)^2 + (y - p)^2}$$

and

$$PQ = \sqrt{(x - x)^2 + (y + p)^2},$$

$P(x, y)$ is on the parabola if, and only if,

$$\sqrt{x^2 + (y - p)^2} = \sqrt{(y + p)^2}.$$

The equation above is equivalent to the equation

$$x^2 + (y - p)^2 = (y + p)^2$$

for the reason that, if b and c are positive numbers, then $\sqrt{b} = \sqrt{c}$ if, and only if, $b = c$. In turn, this equation is equivalent to the equation

$$x^2 + y^2 - 2py + p^2 = y^2 + 2py + p^2,$$

which simplifies to

$$x^2 = 4py.$$

Thus, this simple quadratic equation is an equation of the given parabola.

Before these patterns are used freely for writing equations, it may be well to concentrate on obtaining the equation from the definition alone for several specific parabolas, such as those with focus at $(0, {}^-4)$ and directrix $y = 4$, or with focus at $({}^-\frac{2}{3}, 0)$ and directrix $x = \frac{2}{3}$. Since the patterns for which graphs appear on this and on the next page all open up or to the right, examples should be worked of specific patterns opening to the left or down.

Problem 1 on page 235 should be emphasized since it includes the pattern for an equation of a parabola when the focus is on the x-axis, and the directrix parallel to the y-axis.

Problem 1. Find an equation of the parabola with focus (0, 3) and directrix $y = {}^{-}3$.

Solution. We need only let $p = 3$ in $x^2 = 4py$ to find

$$x^2 = 12y$$

as an equation of the parabola.

If we choose the x-axis on the axis of the parabola and the y-axis through the vertex V, as shown in Fig. 5–21, then we shall obtain the same equation for the parabola except that x and y will be interchanged. Thus,

$$y^2 = 4px$$

is an equation of the parabola under consideration.

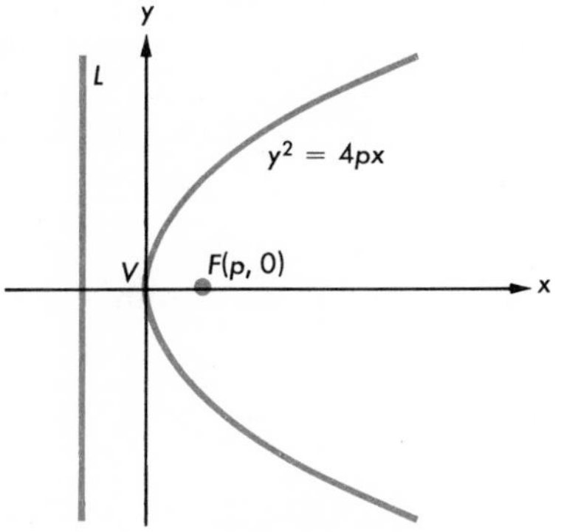

FIGURE 5–21

Problem 2. Find an equation of the parabola with focus $(\frac{1}{4}, 0)$ and directrix $x = {}^{-}\frac{1}{4}$.

Solution. We let $p = \frac{1}{4}$ in $y^2 = 4px$ obtaining

$$y^2 = 4 \cdot \tfrac{1}{4}x, \quad \text{or } y^2 = x,$$

as an equation of this parabola.

Problem 3. Find the coordinates of the points of intersection, if any, of the parabola with equation

$$x^2 = 4y$$

and the line with equation

$$x + 2y - 4 = 0.$$

Solution. We are asked to solve the system of equations

$$\begin{cases} x^2 = 4y, \\ x + 2y - 4 = 0. \end{cases}$$

If we solve the second equation for $2y$ and substitute its value in the first equation, we obtain the equivalent system

$$\begin{cases} x^2 = 2(4 - x), \\ 2y = 4 - x. \end{cases}$$

Exercises for Discussion, page 236

It is recommended that all of the Exercises for Discussion be covered. You may wish to propose the following problem in class: Find an equation of a parabola if the focus is at (2, 3) and the directrix is (a) the line

$$y + 6 = 0,$$

or (b) the line

$$x + 1 = 0.$$

The equation of (a) will be

$$18y = x^2 - 4x - 23,$$

and that of (b)

$$6x = y^2 - 6y + 12.$$

Bring out the fact that having the origin on the parabola cuts any nonzero constant from the equation. Having the axis of symmetry on a coordinate axis cuts out any first-degree term for the variable appearing to the second degree.

In Exercise for Discussion 4, the length of the *latus rectum* should be compared with the coefficient of y in part (a), and with the coefficient of x in part (c).

The students should understand that for $x^2 = 4py$, if $y = p$ then $x = {}^{\pm}2p$, and that the line joining $({}^{-}2p, p)$ and $(2p, p)$ is $4p$ units long. Hence the length of the *latus rectum* is the coefficient of the first-degree term in the equation.

Answer to Exercise for Discussion 4 page 236

4. (a) Focus: (0, 4); endpoints: (8, 4) and (⁻8, 4); length: 16
(b) Focus: $(0, \frac{5}{3})$; endpoints: $(\frac{10}{3}, \frac{5}{3})$ and $({}^{-}\frac{10}{3}, \frac{5}{3})$; length: $\frac{20}{3}$
(c) Focus: (3, 0); endpoints: (3, 6) and (3, ⁻6); length: 12

Answers to Exercises for Discussion 5–7, page 237

5. (a) Vertex: (0, 0); focus: (0, 2); endpoints: (4, 2), ($^-4$, 2); directrix: $y = {}^-2$; axis: $x = 0$

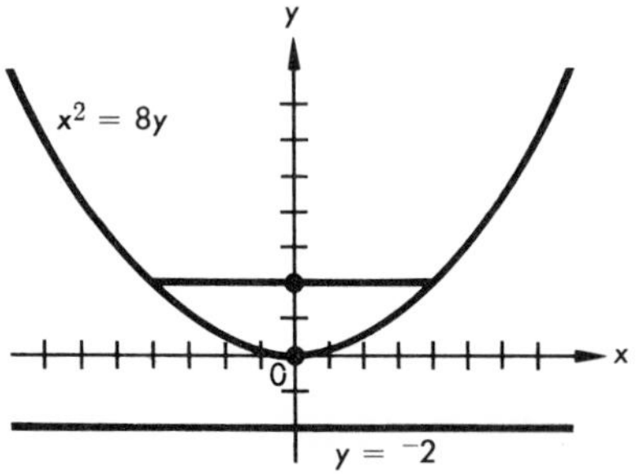

(b) Vertex: (0, 0); focus: (0, $^-2$); endpoints: (4, $^-2$), ($^-4$, $^-2$); directrix: $y = 2$; axis: $x = 0$

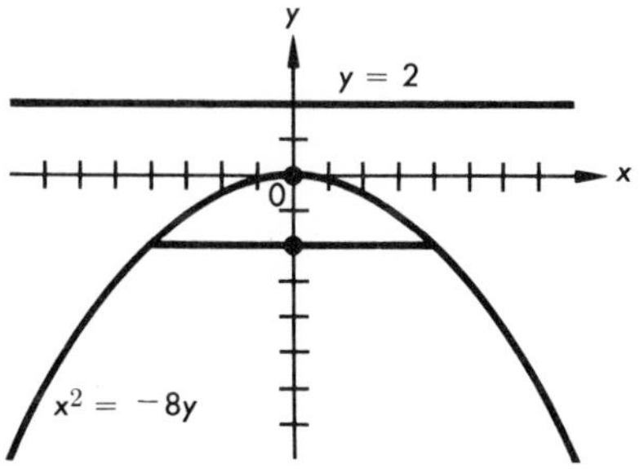

(c) Vertex: (0, 0); focus: ($\frac{5}{2}$, 0); endpoints: ($\frac{5}{2}$, 5), ($\frac{5}{2}$, $^-5$); directrix: $x = {}^-\frac{5}{2}$; axis: $y = 0$

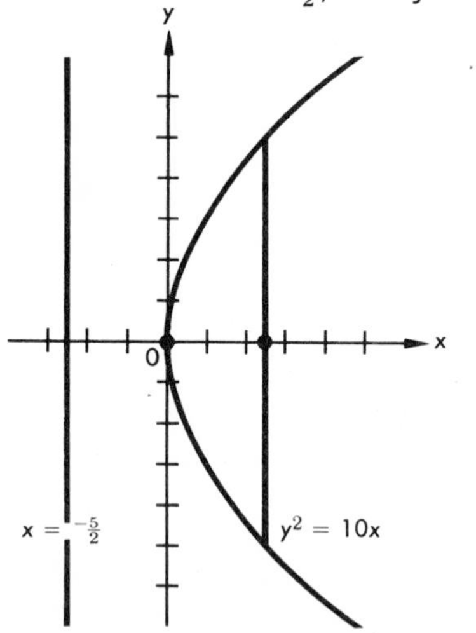

(d) Vertex: (0, 0); focus: ($^-\frac{5}{2}$, 0); endpoints: ($^-\frac{5}{2}$, 5), ($^-\frac{5}{2}$, $^-5$); directrix: $x = \frac{5}{2}$; axis: $y = 0$

The first equation of this system may be solved as follows

$$x^2 = 8 - 2x,$$
$$x^2 + 2x - 8 = 0,$$
$$(x + 4)(x - 2) = 0,$$
$$x = {}^-4 \quad \text{or} \quad x = 2.$$

If we let $x = {}^-4$ in the second equation, we obtain

$$2y = 4 - {}^-4, \quad \text{or } y = 4.$$

If we let $x = 2$, we obtain

$$2y = 4 - 2, \quad \text{or } y = 1.$$

Thus,

$$\{({}^-4,4),\ (2, 1)\}$$

is the solution set of the system that we were asked to solve.

Figure 5–22 shows the two points of intersection of the given parabola and the given line.

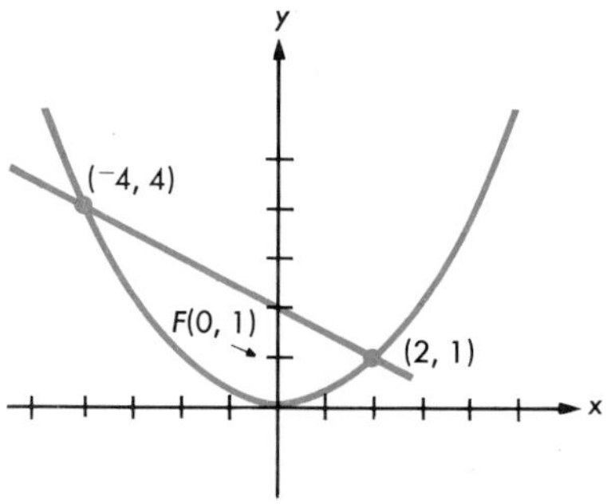

FIGURE 5–22

Exercises for Discussion

1. If the focus of a parabola is at (0, 4) and the directrix is the x-axis, does the origin lie on the parabola? *No* Is (0, 0) a solution of the equation of the parabola? *No* Could an equation of the parabola be of the form $x^2 = 4py$? *No*

2. Find an equation of the parabola with

(a) focus (0, $^-3$) and directrix $y = 3$. *$x^2 = {}^-12y$*

(b) focus ($^-\frac{1}{4}$, 0) and directrix $x = \frac{1}{4}$. *$y^2 = {}^-x$*

3. (a) Find the points on the parabola $x^2 = 12y$ for which $y = 3$. How long is the line segment joining these points? *$x^2 = 36$, $x = 6$ or $x = {}^-6$; length = 12*

(b) Find the points where the line $x = \frac{1}{4}$ intersects the parabola $y^2 = x$. How long is the line segment joining these points? *$y^2 = \frac{1}{4}$, $y = \frac{1}{2}$ or $y = \frac{-1}{2}$; length = 1*

4. The line segment through the focus perpendicular to the axis, terminating in two points on the parabola, is called the *latus rectum* of the parabola. Find the length of this line and the coordinates of its endpoints for each of the following parabolas.

(a) $x^2 = 16y$ (b) $3x^2 = 20y$ (c) $y^2 = 12x$

5. Draw the graph of each of the following parabolas, showing vertex, focus, directrix, and *latus rectum*. List the coordinates of vertex, focus, and of the endpoints of the *latus rectum*. Write the equation of the directrix and of the axis of symmetry.

   (a) $x^2 = 8y$ (b) $x^2 = {}^-8y$ (c) $y^2 = 10x$ (d) $y^2 = {}^-10x$

6. Graph the set $\{(x, y) \mid x = y^2 - 6y + 7\}$ by finding the points corresponding to $y = 0, 1, 2, 3, 4, 5,$ and 6 and drawing a smooth curve through them.

7. (a) Solve the system

$$\begin{cases} x^2 = 4y, \\ x + y = 1. \end{cases}$$

   (b) Sketch the graph of each equation of the system.

Exercises

See Solution Manual for graphs.

In each exercise, find an equation of the parabola with focus and directrix as given below.

1. $(0, \frac{1}{2})$; $y = {}^-\frac{1}{2}$ $x^2 = 2y$
2. $(5, 0)$; $x = {}^-5$ $y^2 = 20x$
3. $({}^-3, 0)$; $x = 3$ $y^2 = {}^-12x$
4. $(0, {}^-\frac{5}{2})$; $y = \frac{5}{2}$ $x^2 = {}^-10y$

Graph each of the following equations. List the coordinates of vertex, the focus, and the endpoints of *latus rectum* for each parabola. Also give the equations of the directrix and the axis of symmetry of each parabola.

5. $x^2 = 20y$ $(0,0)$; $(0,5)$; $(10,5)$, $({}^-10,5)$; $y = {}^-5$; $x = 0$
6. $y^2 = 24x$ $(0,0)$; $(6,0)$; $(6,12)$, $(6,{}^-12)$; $x = {}^-6$; $y = 0$
7. $x^2 + 6y = 0$ $(0,0)$; $(0,\frac{-3}{2})$; $(3,\frac{-3}{2})$, $({}^-3,\frac{-3}{2})$; $y = \frac{3}{2}$; $x = 0$
8. $3y^2 + 4x = 0$ $(0,0)$; $(\frac{-1}{3},0)$; $(\frac{-1}{3},\frac{2}{3})$, $(\frac{-1}{3},\frac{-2}{3})$; $x = \frac{1}{3}$; $y = 0$

△

In Exercises 9–12, find the points of intersection of the parabola and the line. Draw the appropriate graph.

9. $\begin{cases} y^2 = 4x \\ x + 2y + 3 = 0 \end{cases}$ $(1,{}^-2)$, $(9,{}^-6)$
10. $\begin{cases} x^2 + y = 0 \\ 2x - y - 3 = 0 \end{cases}$ $({}^-3,{}^-9)$, $(1,{}^-1)$
11. $\begin{cases} 2x^2 - 3y = 0 \\ 4x - y - 6 = 0 \end{cases}$ $(3,6)$
12. $\begin{cases} y^2 + x = 0 \\ x - y = 4 \end{cases}$ None

▲

In Exercises 13–15, graph the solution set of each system of inequalities.

13. $\begin{cases} y^2 \leqq 4x \\ y + 2x \leqq 4 \end{cases}$
14. $\begin{cases} y^2 - x^2 \geqq 8 \\ y^2 \leqq 9x \end{cases}$
15. $\begin{cases} y^2 \geqq 2x + 10 \\ x^2 + y^2 \leqq 25 \end{cases}$

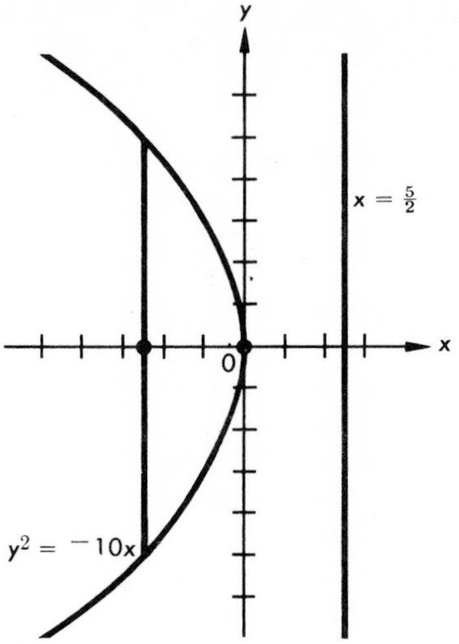

6.

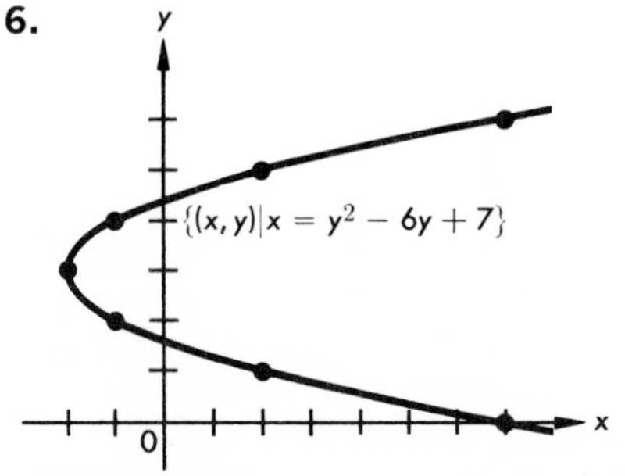

7. (a) $\begin{cases} x^2 = 4y \\ x + y = 1 \end{cases}$

$\begin{cases} x^2 = 4y \\ y = 1 - x \end{cases}$

$\begin{cases} x^2 = 4(1 - x) \\ y = 1 - x \end{cases}$

$\begin{cases} x^2 + 4x - 4 = 0 \\ y = 1 - x \end{cases}$

$\begin{cases} x = {}^-2 + 2\sqrt{2} \text{ or } {}^-2 - 2\sqrt{2} \\ y = 3 - 2\sqrt{2} \text{ or } 3 + 2\sqrt{2} \end{cases}$

(b)

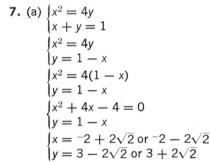

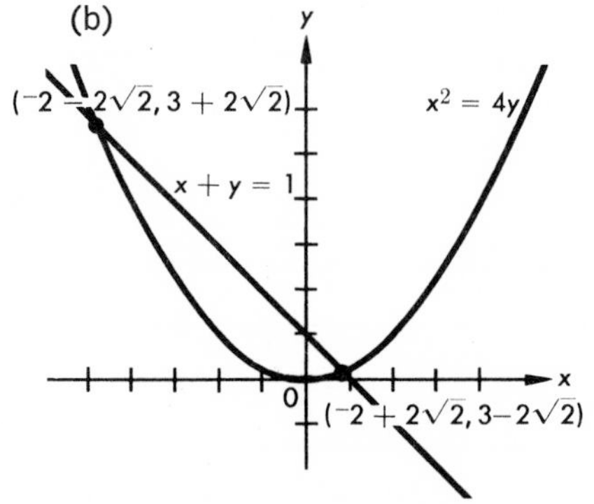

It is suggested that Exercises 16–20 be covered in class where questions can be answered as they arise.

In Exercise 17, since x^2 is never negative, $4(y - 1)$ must also never be negative. Therefore $y \geqq 1$ which immediately restricts the graph to the portion of the plane above $y = 1$, except for the point (0, 1) which would undoubtedly have to be the vertex.

In Exercise 18, $^-4(y - 1)$ must not be negative since $x^2 \geqq 0$. Hence, $y - 1 \leqq 0$ and $y \leqq 1$. This parabola then lies below the line $y = 1$, except for the point (0, 1). An approach such as this may be used by the students to check mistakes that might otherwise be made in a careless use of patterns.

Students may be interested in investigating (either in the library or through their science teachers) the property of an ellipse that is utilized in the "whispering galleries" built with ellipsoidal surfaces; or the property of a parabola utilized in the parabolic surface of a headlight; or finally, Loran navigation developed in World War II and based on a property of hyperbolas. *Analytic Geometry* by Corliss, Feinstein, and Levin (Harper & Brothers, 1949) contains a comprehensive discussion of the conic sections and their properties. So, too, do the encyclopedias.

16. Using the definition of a parabola, find an equation of the parabola with

(a) focus (0, 0) and directrix $y = {}^-4$. $x^2 = 8(y+2)$; $(0, {}^-2)$

(b) focus (0, 0) and directrix $y = 2$. $x^2 = {}^-4(y-1)$; $(0, 1)$

(c) focus (0, 3) and directrix $y = 1$. $x^2 = 4(y-2)$; $(0, 2)$

(d) focus $(0, {}^-2)$ and directrix $y + 1 = 0$. $x^2 = {}^-2(y+\frac{3}{2})$; $(0, \frac{^-3}{2})$

Study these four equations to observe the effect when the vertex is not placed at the origin, the directrix is kept parallel to the x-axis, and the focus is on the y-axis. In each case, locate the vertex, and try to put the equation in a form which shows the coordinates of the vertex.

Graph each of the following parabolas, showing its vertex, focus, and directrix.

17. $x^2 = 4(y - 1)$

18. $x^2 = {}^-4(y - 1)$

19. $x^2 = 6(y + 2)$

20. $x^2 = {}^-6(y + 2)$.

KEY IDEAS AND KEY WORDS

The distance between the points $P(x_1, y_1)$ and $Q(x_2, y_2)$ is given by the **distance formula:**

$$PQ = \sqrt{(x_2 - x_1)^2 + (y_2 - y_1)^2}.$$

A **circle** is the set of all points in a plane at a given distance, called the **radius,** from a fixed point in the plane, called the **center.** If its radius is r and its center has coordinates (h, k), then

$$(x - h)^2 + (y - k)^2 = r^2$$

is an **equation of the circle.**

If A and B are points in a plane and k is a number greater than AB, then the set of all points P in the plane such that

$$AP + PB = k$$

is called an **ellipse.** Each of the points A and B is called a **focus** of the ellipse. The midpoint O of the segment $\overline{AB}$ is called the **center** of the ellipse. The line L which passes through A and B and the line K which passes through O and is perpendicular to L, are the **axes of symmetry** of the ellipse. If the coordinate axes are axes of symmetry of the ellipse, then it has an equation of the form

$$\frac{x^2}{a^2} + \frac{y^2}{b^2} = 1$$

for some positive numbers a and b.

If A and B are points in a plane and k is a positive number less than AB, then the set of all points P in the plane such that either

$$AP - BP = k \quad \text{or} \quad BP - AP = k$$

is called a **hyperbola.** Each of the points A and B is called a **focus** of the hyperbola. A hyperbola has two **perpendicular axes of symmetry** meeting at the **center** of the hyperbola. If the coordinate axes are axes of symmetry of the hyperbola, then it has an equation of the form

$$\frac{x^2}{a^2} - \frac{y^2}{b^2} = 1 \quad \text{or} \quad \frac{y^2}{b^2} - \frac{x^2}{a^2} = 1$$

for some positive numbers a and b.

If F is a point and L is a line not containing F, then the set of all points P in the plane containing F and L such that

$$PF = PQ,$$

where Q is at the foot of the perpendicular drawn from P to L, is called a **parabola.** Point F is called the **focus,** and line L is called the **directrix** of the parabola. The point halfway between the focus and the directrix is called the **vertex** of the parabola. The line through the focus and vertex is the **axis of symmetry** of the parabola. If one coordinate axis is the axis of symmetry and the vertex is at the origin of the coordinate system, then the parabola has an equation of the form

$$x^2 = 4py \quad \text{or} \quad y^2 = 4px$$

for some nonzero number p, and the directrix of the parabola is parallel to one of the coordinate axes.

CHAPTER REVIEW

See Solution Manual for graphs.

1. (a) Show that the following points are the vertices of an equilateral triangle.

$$A(0, 0), \quad B(6, 0), \quad C(3, 3\sqrt{3})$$

See Solution Manual.

(b) Find the coordinates of the midpoints of $\overline{AC}$ and $\overline{BC}$. $(\frac{3}{2}, \frac{3}{2}\sqrt{3})$, $(\frac{9}{2}, \frac{3}{2}\sqrt{3})$

(c) Find the length of the segment joining the midpoints of part (b).

2. Write an equation of a circle having

(a) its center at the origin and radius $5\sqrt{2}$. $x^2 + y^2 = 50$

(b) its center at $(^-4, 3)$ and radius 9. $x^2 + y^2 + 8x - 6y = 56$

Discuss and sketch the graph of each of the following.

3. (a) $4x^2 + 25y^2 = 100$ (b) $4x^2 + 25y^2 > 100$
4. (a) $25x^2 - 4y^2 = 100$ (b) $25x^2 - 4y^2 > 100$
5. (a) $y^2 - 4x^2 = 4$ (b) $y^2 - 4x^2 < 4$

Quiz

In each exercise, find an equation of the parabola with focus and directrix as given below.

1. $(0, ^-2)$; $y = 2$ (ans: $x^2 = {^-8}y$)
2. $(2, 0)$; $x = {^-2}$ (ans: $y^2 = 8x$)

Graph the following equation. List the coordinates of the vertex, the focus, and the endpoints of the *latus rectum* for the parabola. Also give the equations of the directrix and the axis of symmetry.

3. $x^2 = 8y$ (ans: $(0, 0)$; $(0, 2)$; $(4, 2)$, $(^-4, 2)$; $y = {^-2}$, $x = 0$)

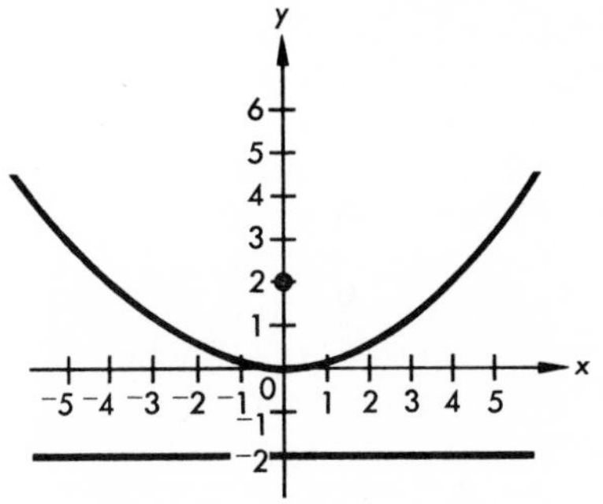

Answers to Chapter Review Problems 3–5

3. (a) Ellipse; intercepts: $(5, 0)$, $(^-5, 0)$; $(0, 2)$, $(0, ^-2)$; foci: $(\sqrt{21}, 0)$, $(^-\sqrt{21}, 0)$; major axis: x-axis
   (b) Region outside ellipse
4. (a) Hyperbola; intercepts; $(2, 0)$, $(^-2, 0)$; foci: $(\sqrt{29}, 0)$, $(^-\sqrt{29}, 0)$
   (b) Region inside hyperbola
5. (a) Hyperbola; intercepts: $(0, 2)$, $(0, ^-2)$; foci: $(0, \sqrt{5})$, $(0, ^-\sqrt{5})$
   (b) Region outside hyperbola

Answers to Chapter Review Problem 8, 12(a), 13(a), 13(b)

8. (a) $\{(^-5, 2), (^-5, ^-2), (2, 5), (2, ^-5)\}$
(b) $\{(\frac{5}{2}, ^-3), (^-\frac{5}{3}, ^-3), (0, 2)\}$

12. (a) $\{(\frac{1}{2} + \frac{1}{4}\sqrt{2}i, \frac{1}{2} - \frac{1}{4}\sqrt{2}i), (\frac{1}{2} - \frac{1}{4}\sqrt{2}i, \frac{1}{2} + \frac{1}{4}\sqrt{2}i)\}$

13. (a) Circle: center $(3, ^-4)$
(b) Parabola: vertex $(1, ^-4)$

CHAPTER TEST

The material included in the Chapter Test was covered in the following sections.
Problem 1—Section 1
Problem 2—Section 5
Problems 3, 4—Section 4
Problem 5—Section 6
Problem 6(a)—Section 2
Problem 6(b)—Section 6
Problem 6(c)—Section 1
Problems 6(d), 6(e)—Section 5
Problem 6(f)—Section 4

Answers to Chapter Test Problems 2, 4(b), 5

2.

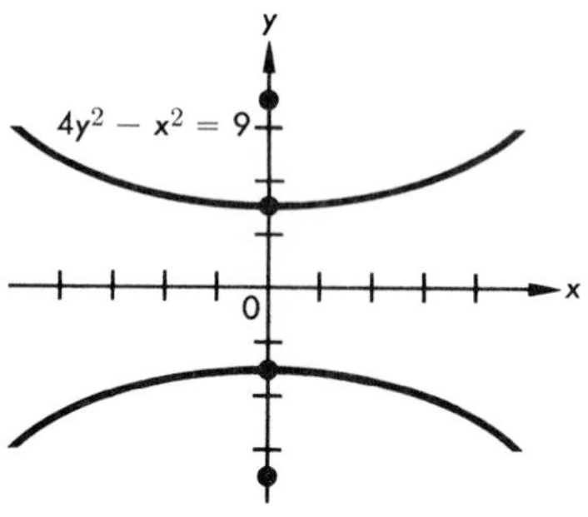

4. (b)

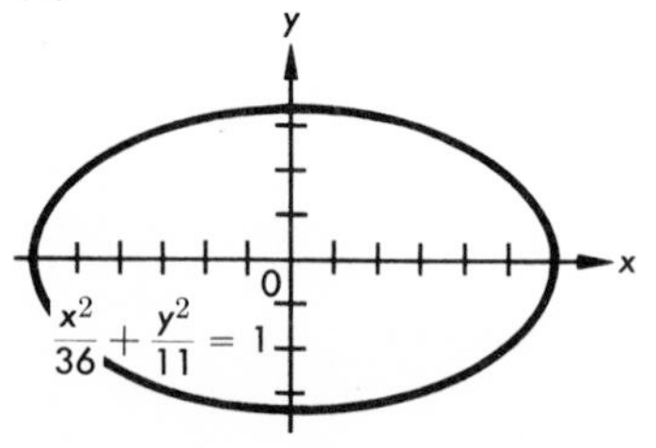

6. Discuss the graph of each of the following equations. Give the coordinates of the vertex and the focus, an equation of the directrix, and an equation of the axis of symmetry.
(a) $x^2 = 6y$ $(0,0)$; $(0, \frac{3}{2})$; $y = ^-\frac{3}{2}$; $x = 0$
(b) $y^2 + 7x = 0$ $(0,0)$; $(^-\frac{7}{4}, 0)$; $x = \frac{7}{4}$; $y = 0$

7. Solve algebraically and graphically the system of equations
$$\begin{cases} y^2 - x^2 = 1, \\ x^2 + y^2 = 1. \end{cases} \quad \{(0, 1), (0, ^-1)\}$$

8. Use algebraic methods to find the intersections of the following pairs of conic sections. Sketch graphs to check your answers.
(a) $\begin{cases} y^2 - 3x - 19 = 0 \\ x^2 + y^2 - 29 = 0 \end{cases}$
(b) $\begin{cases} 4x^2 + 5y - 10 = 0 \\ 5y^2 - 4x^2 = 20 \end{cases}$

9. Using the definition of a parabola, find an equation of the parabola with
(a) focus (0, 2) and directrix $y = ^-2$. $x^2 = 8y$
(b) focus $(^-1, 0)$ and directrix $x = 1$. $y^2 = ^-4x$

10. A square with sides parallel to the coordinate axes is inscribed in the ellipse $4x^2 + y^2 = 20$. Find its area. 16

11. Graph each of the following systems of inequalities.
(a) $\begin{cases} 3y^2 \leqq 4x \\ 4x^2 + 9y^2 \leqq 72 \end{cases}$
(b) $\begin{cases} x^2 > 4y \\ x + 2y < 4 \end{cases}$

12. Solve each of the following systems algebraically.
(a) $\begin{cases} x + y = 1 \\ 4x^2 + 4y^2 = 1 \end{cases}$
(b) $\begin{cases} 3x^2 - y^2 = 7 \\ 2x^2 + 3y^2 = 23 \end{cases}$ $\{(2, \sqrt{5}), (2, ^-\sqrt{5}), (^-2, \sqrt{5}), (^-2, ^-\sqrt{5})\}$

13. Find the center and/or vertices of each of the following conic sections.
(a) $x^2 + y^2 - 6x + 8y = 0$
(b) $y = x^2 - 2x - 3$
(c) $x = 3y^2 - 6y - 2$
Parabola: vertex $(^-5, 1)$
(d) $3x^2 + 2y^2 - 12x + 6y - 3 = 0$
Ellipse: center $(2, ^-\frac{3}{2})$

CHAPTER TEST

1. Find an equation of the circle with diameter $\overline{AB}$, given that the coordinates of A and B are $(5, ^-1)$ and $(^-1, 3)$, respectively. $x^2 + y^2 - 4x - 2y = 8$

2. Sketch the graph of $4y^2 - x^2 = 9$. Locate the center, intercepts, and foci. $(0,0)$; $(0, \frac{3}{2}), (0, ^-\frac{3}{2})$; $(0, \frac{3}{2}\sqrt{5}), (0, ^-\frac{3}{2}\sqrt{5})$

3. Solve algebraically the system
$$\begin{cases} 3x - 4y + 5 = 0, \\ 3x^2 + 8y^2 = 1. \end{cases}$$
$\{(^-1 + \frac{2}{15}\sqrt{30}i, \frac{1}{2} + \frac{1}{10}\sqrt{30}i), (^-1 - \frac{2}{15}\sqrt{30}i, \frac{1}{2} - \frac{1}{10}\sqrt{30}i)\}$

4. (a) Find an equation of an ellipse with foci at $A(^-5, 0)$ and $B(5, 0)$, given that the sum of the distances from any point $P(x, y)$ of the ellipse to points A and B is 12. $\frac{x^2}{36} + \frac{y^2}{11} = 1$
(b) Sketch the graph of the equation in part (a).

(2, 1) (2, $\frac{5}{4}$) $y = \frac{3}{4}$

5. Find the vertex and focus and give an equation of the directrix of the parabola with equation $y = x^2 - 4x + 5$. Sketch the graph.

6. Name the graph of each of the following equations.

(a) $x + y = 5$ Straight line
(b) $x^2 + 3x = y$ Parabola
(c) $5x^2 + 5y^2 = 125$ Circle
(d) $x^2 - 3y^2 = 12$ Hyperbola
(e) $y^2 - x^2 = 4$ Hyperbola
(f) $2x^2 + y^2 = 15$ Ellipse

5.

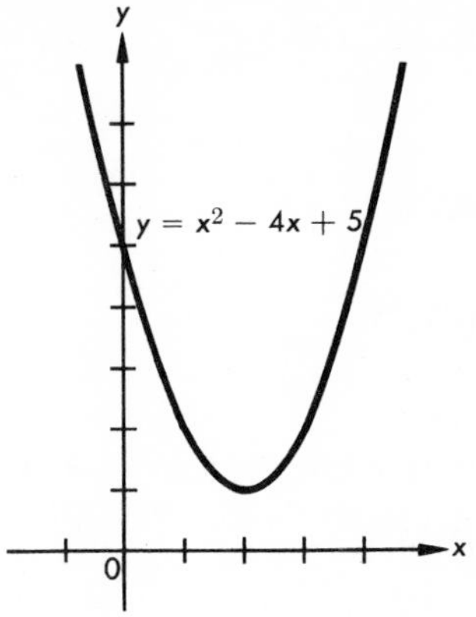

CHAPTER 6

Functions

The purpose of this chapter is to give the students an opportunity to study what is probably the most important and fundamental concept in mathematics, that is the concept of a function.

The correspondence between two sets, which is properly called a function, is already familiar to the student when it is defined by an equation. This may well be the easiest approach to use in formalizing the definition of function.

Implicit in the equation are the descriptions of the domain and range of the function. For example, if it is assumed that y denotes the number of rented units in a building containing 80 apartments and that

$$y = 80 - \frac{x - 60}{2},$$

then common sense indicates at least three things: y must be nonnegative, y cannot exceed 80, and y must be an integer. Hence,

$$80 - \frac{x - 60}{2} \geqq 0 \text{ or } x \leqq 220,$$

$$80 - \frac{x - 60}{2} \leqq 80 \text{ or } x \geqq 60,$$

and

$$\frac{x - 60}{2}$$

must be an integer or x must be even.

Thus the domain of x can be completely described as the set of even integers from 60 to 220, inclusive. The corresponding values of y (integers only) range from 80 to 0, inclusive.

CHAPTER 6

The time it takes an automobile to finish a race is a function of the speed at which the automobile is traveling. (Courtesy of the Daytona International Speedway)

FUNCTIONS

Equations may define relationships between variables. An equation of a circle such as

$$x^2 + y^2 = 100$$

can be considered to be a relationship between x and y. Thus, if $x = 6$ or $^-6$, $y = 8$ or $^-8$. In other words, the number pairs (6, 8), (6, $^-8$), ($^-6$, 8), and ($^-6$, $^-8$) are in the solution set of the equation. An equation of a parabola such as

$$y = 2x^2$$

also has a solution set consisting of number pairs: (0, 0), (1, 2), ($^-1$, 2), (5, 50), and infinitely many more. This example differs from the previous one in that for each number x, there is a unique number y such that (x, y) is in the solution set of the equation.

A function is a relationship between two variables such that to each value of one of the variables there corresponds a unique value of the other. Thus, the equation of the parabola gives y as a function of x. However, the equation of the circle does not explicitly define a function, because for certain values of either variable there are two corresponding values of the other variable.

Many common functions encountered in mathematics are not described by equations. A classical example of such a function is the prime-counting function. It associates with each positive real number x the number of primes less than or equal to x. For example, the number of primes less than or equal to 9 is 4 (the primes are 2, 3, 5, and 7), and the number of primes less than or equal to $10\sqrt{2}$ is 6 (the primes are 2, 3, 5, 7, 11, and 13).

The graph of this function thus covers the x-axis from 60 to 220, the y-axis from 0 to 80, and consists of a set of isolated points in the first quadrant.

If only real-valued functions are being considered, then the equation

$$y = \frac{1}{\sqrt{x - 2}}$$

describes a function with domain $x > 2$ and range $y > 0$. The graph consists of a smooth curve in the first quadrant to the right of the line $x = 2$.

The foregoing two functions of x could be referred to using functional notation. Thus,

$$f(x) = 80 - \frac{x - 60}{2},$$

$$g(x) = \frac{1}{\sqrt{x - 2}}.$$

Just as the operations of addition and multiplication on the set of real numbers were defined, so may these operations on the set of functions be defined. The sum function is easily graphed on a rectangular cartesian coordinate system, and the addition of ordinates could be done by counting blocks. Thus, if $f(x) = x^2$ and $g(x) = 1/x$, the trend of

$$(f + g)(x) = x^2 + \frac{1}{x}$$

quickly becomes apparent.

The following are some of the topics covered in Chapter 6:

- *Function*
- *Domain of a function*
- *Range of a function*
- *Functional notation*
- *Graph of a function*
- *Constant function*
- *Linear function*
- *Power function*
- *The sum of two functions*
- *The product of two functions*

It is suggested that one day be spent on each section of this chapter.

6-1 DEFINITION OF A FUNCTION

The Exercises for Discussion may be used to illustrate the correspondence between two sets, as well as the domain and the range of a particular function.

Since there are two variables, the idea of the graph of the function as points in a plane that correspond to the ordered number pairs (x, y) is quite natural.

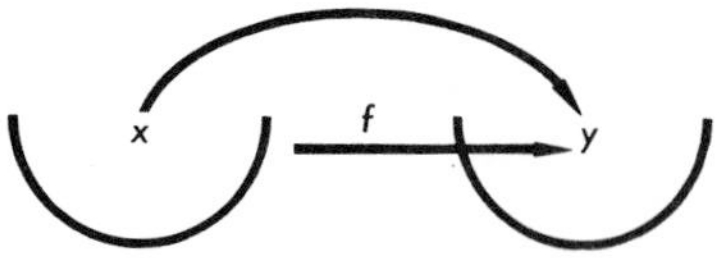

You may wish to use this concept in order to anticipate the work on the graphing of functions in Section 6-3. Then it is easy to emphasize that domain is the part of one axis which is needed for the graph (usually the axis in the horizontal position), while range is the part of the other axis needed for the graph.

Exercises for Discussion, page 245

In Exercise for Discussion 1, you may wish to do more than is asked. For example, a table of several corresponding elements could be made,

s	p
$\frac{1}{2}$	2
3	12
$\sqrt{2}$	$4\sqrt{2}$

in order to show that the graph lies entirely inside quadrant 1. The

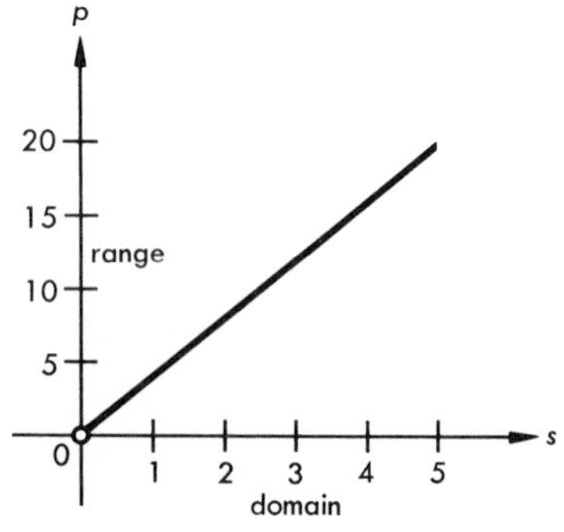

6-1 DEFINITION OF A FUNCTION

Every person in North America has a surname. If we consider one set consisting of all people in North America and a second set consisting of all of their surnames, then there is a definite correspondence between these two sets that associates with each person his or her surname. Such a correspondence between two sets is an example of a *function.* The set of people in North America is called the *domain,* and the set of surnames is called the *range* of this function.

A map of Mexico contains numerous dots, each of which is accompanied by the name of a city. Thus, on the one hand, we have a set of dots on a piece of paper and, on the other hand, a set of cities in Mexico. There is a definite correspondence between these two sets that associates with each dot in the one set a city in the other set. Again, this correspondence is an example of a function whose domain is the set of dots on the map of Mexico and whose range is the set of cities in Mexico.

The formula

$$A = s^2$$

gives the area A of a square in terms of the length s of a side. For example, if $s = 6$, then $A = 36$, and if $s = \sqrt{2}$, then $A = 2$. This formula associates a positive number A with each positive number s, and hence, defines a function whose domain and range are the set P of positive numbers.

These examples suggest the following definition.

> ***DEFINITION OF A FUNCTION***
>
> *A FUNCTION is a correspondence between two sets that associates with each element of the first set a unique element of the second set. The first set is called the DOMAIN of the function. For each element x of the domain, the corresponding element y of the second set is called the IMAGE of x under the function. The set of all images of the elements of the domain is called the RANGE of the function.*

The examples already given illustrate different ways of defining functions. Some functions are defined by equations, others by verbal statements.

The area function defined by $A = s^2$ has domain $D = \{s \mid s > 0\}$ and range $R = \{s^2 \mid s > 0\}$. Obviously, $D = R$ in this example. The distance an automobile travels at a rate of 50 miles per hour is 50 times the number of hours spent traveling. This verbal statement defines a function in which the set of positive real numbers is both the range and the domain of the function. This distance function can also be defined by the following formula.

$$d = 50t \quad \text{if } t > 0$$

A precise statement of the range of this function is not important. As long as we know the domain and have directions for finding the image of each element of the domain, we have a complete definition of the function. Often the domain of a function defined by an equation or verbal statement is not given explicitly. In such a case, the domain is assumed to be the set of all numbers for which the equation or verbal statement makes sense.

We can also consider a function as a *set of ordered pairs* in which no two pairs have the same first element. The set of all first elements is the *domain*, and the set of all second elements is the *range* of the function. Thus, there is associated with each element x in the domain a unique element y in the range.

An example of a set of ordered pairs is

$$S = \{(x, |x|) \mid x \text{ a real number}\}.$$

In this set, no two different pairs have the same first element. Set S is the *absolute-value function*, which associates with each real number x its absolute value, $|x|$.

Exercises for Discussion

Each of the formulas in Exercises 1–4 defines a function. State the domain of each function.

1. $p = 4s$; s the side and p the perimeter of a square $D = \{s \mid s > 0\}$

2. $d = s\sqrt{2}$; s the side and d the diagonal of a square $D = \{s \mid s > 0\}$

3. $s = 64 - 16t^2$; t representing the time, in seconds, elapsed after an object is dropped from a height of 64 feet, and s the distance, in feet, of the object above the ground at time t $D = \{t \mid 0 \leqq t \leqq 2\}$

4. $C = 1.25 + .045(n - 15)$; n representing the number of words in a telegram having at least 15 words, and C the cost of the telegram
$D = \{n \mid n \geqq 15 \text{ and } n \text{ is an integer}\}$

domain and the range are both the set of positive real numbers.

In Exercise for Discussion 3,

$$s = 16(2 + t)(2 - t).$$

t	s
0	64
$\frac{1}{2}$	60
$\frac{3}{4}$	55
1	48
$\frac{3}{2}$	28
$\frac{7}{4}$	15
2	0

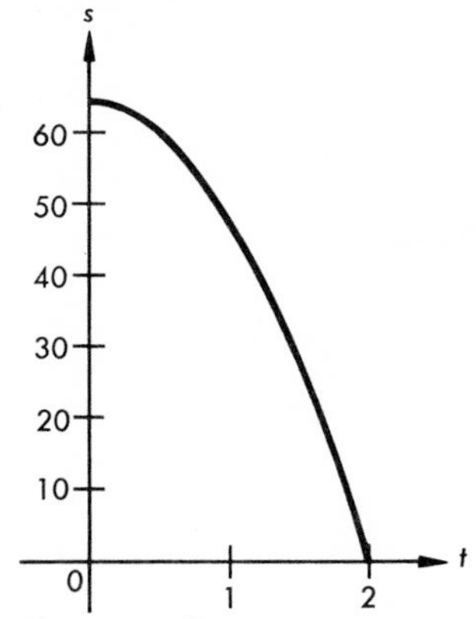

Domain: $\{0 \leqq t \leqq 2\}$
Range: $\{0 \leqq s \leqq 64\}$

The students should observe that neither negative t nor negative s makes sense in this situation.

Exercise for Discussion 4 is the first example where the domain (because of the nature of the situation) is restricted to the counting numbers (those at least as large as 15).

n	C
15	1.25
16	1.295 or 1.30
17	1.34
18	1.385 or 1.39
19	1.43

This restriction on n causes the graph to be a set of points instead of an unbroken curve.

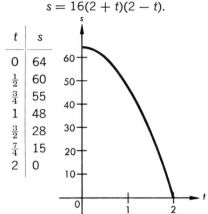

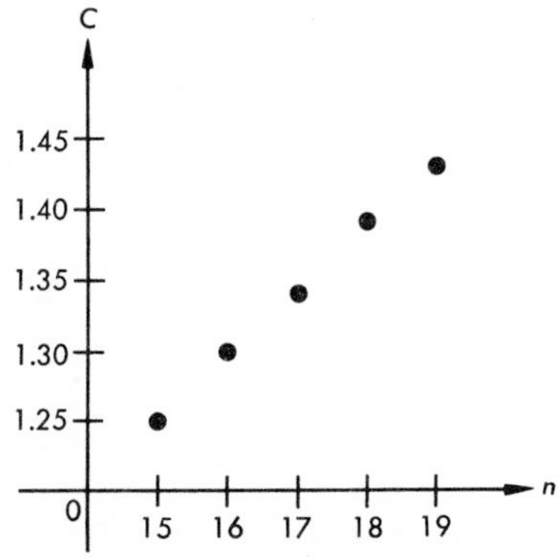

Answers to Exercise for Discussion 6(a), 6(c)

6. (a) $2y = {}^{-}5x + 10$

$y = {}^{-}\frac{5}{2}x + 5$

(c) $5x = {}^{-}2y + 10$

$x = {}^{-}\frac{2}{5}y + 2$

Exercises

These exercises are very easy, but also very important. You may wish to start Section 6–2 the same day as Section 6–1.

Exercises 1 and 2 should be contrasted with each other, particulary in reference to their graphs, which are a smooth unbroken curve for Exercise 1, and a collection of points for Exercise 2.

It is suggested that Exercise 9 be discussed in detail and that the step function be graphed.

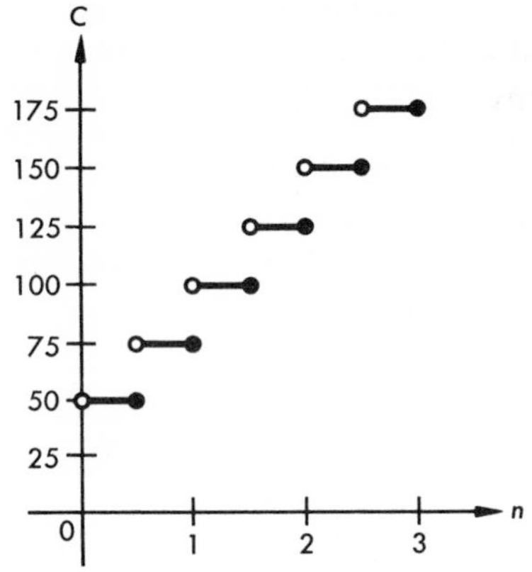

Exercises 12–18 are difficult, but basic to further work in mathematics. All of them should be done carefully by your better students. It is suggested that you require labeled diagrams for each exercise. You may wish to do the following example in class.

The volume of a right circular cone depends on two variables, base radius and height. The general formula is

$$V = \tfrac{1}{3}\pi r^2 h.$$

However, if it is known that in a

5. The following table gives for various car speeds the distance a car travels before a driver's reactions cause him to apply his brakes. (This information is based on the assumption that the average driver takes three-fourths of a second to apply his brakes.)

Speed (in mph)	20	30	40	50	60
Distance (in ft)	22	33	44	55	66

(a) Use set notation to give the domain and the range of the function defined by this set of ordered pairs. $D = \{20, 30, 40, 50, 60\}$ $R = \{22, 33, 44, 55, 66\}$

(b) Let d denote distance in feet and s the speed in miles per hour. Find a formula in which d is expressed as a function of s and for which the values in the table form a partial list of ordered pairs. $d = \frac{11}{10}s$

6. (a) Solve the linear equation $5x + 2y = 10$ for y in terms of x.

(b) Does the resulting equation in part (a) define y as a function of x? Yes

(c) Solve the linear equation in part (a) for x in terms of y.

(d) Does the resulting equation in part (c) define x as a function of y? Yes

Exercises

Each of the following formulas defines a function. State the domain of each function.

1. $d = 50t$; t representing the time, in hours, spent, and d the distance, in miles, covered by a car traveling at a constant speed of 50 miles per hour $D = \{t \mid t \geqq 0\}$

2. $C = 10n$; n representing the number of articles, and C the total cost of n articles if each costs 10¢ $D = \{n \mid n \text{ is a non-negative integer}\}$

In Exercises 3–8, each table defines a function. Using set notation, describe the domain and range of each function.

3.

x	2	3	4
y	4	9	16

$D = \{x \mid x = 2, 3, 4\}$ $R = \{y \mid y = x^2\}$

4.

x	7	8	9
y	9	10	11

$D = \{x \mid x = 7, 8, 9\}$ $R = \{y \mid y = x + 2\}$

5.

x	7	8	9
y	$^{-}3$	2	0

$D = \{x \mid x = 7, 8, 9\}$ $R = \{y \mid y = {}^{-}3, 2, 0\}$

6.

x	1	2	3	4
y	2	1	2	1

$D = \{x \mid x = 1, 2, 3, 4$ $R = \{y \mid y = 1, 2\}$

7.

x	1	2	3	4
y	1	1	1	1

$D = \{x \mid x = 1, 2, 3, 4\}$ $R = \{y \mid y = 1\}$

8.

x	2	5	7	9
y	$\frac{1}{2}$	$\frac{1}{5}$	$\frac{1}{7}$	$\frac{1}{9}$

$D = \{x \mid x = 2, 5, 7, 9$ $R = \{y \mid y = \frac{1}{x}\}$

9. For parking a car, a garage charges 50¢ for the first half-hour or any part of the half-hour and 25¢ per half-hour or any part of a half-hour thereafter. The minimum charge is 50¢, and the maximum amount of time a car may park in one day is 16 hours.

(a) Describe the domain of the function. $D = \{n \mid 0 < n \leqq 16\}$

(b) Describe the range of the function.
$R = \{25c \mid c \text{ is an integer and } 2 \leqq c \leqq 33\}$

10. (a) Solve the linear equation $4x + 3y = 12$ for y in terms of x. $y = \frac{-4}{3}x + 4$
(b) Does the resulting equation in part (a) define a function of x? Yes
(c) Solve the linear equation in part (a) for x in terms of y. $x = \frac{-3}{4}y + 3$
(d) Does the resulting equation in part (c) define a function of y? Yes

11. (a) Solve the equation $4y - 8x^2 = 12$ for y in terms of x. $y = 2x^2 + 3$
(b) Does the resulting equation in part (a) define a function of x? Yes
(c) Solve the equation in part (a) for x in terms of y. $x = \pm\sqrt{\frac{1}{2}y - \frac{3}{2}}$
(d) Does the resulting equation in part (c) define a function of y? No

△

12. Each rectangle in a set of rectangles has one side 3 units longer than the other. Write a formula which expresses the area function A of a rectangle in this set in terms of the shorter side x. Give the domain and range of A. $A = x(x+3)$; $D = \{x \mid x > 0\}$; $R = \{A \mid A > 0\}$

13. A square piece of tin is 10 inches on each side. A small square is cut from each corner and the tin folded to form an open box. (See the figure.) Find a formula which expresses the volume function V of the open box in terms of x, the side of a cut-out square. Give the domain and range of V.

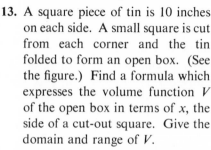

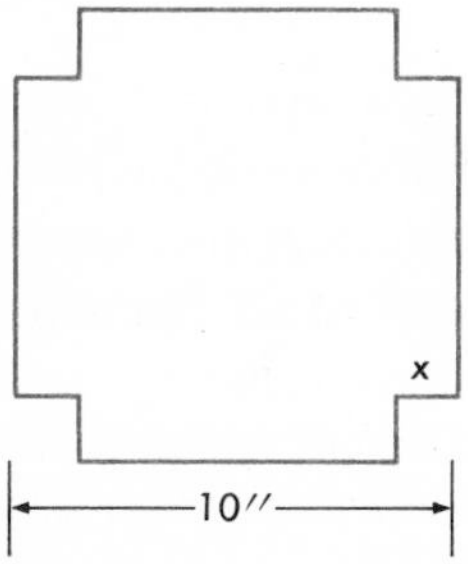

14. Each rectangle in a set of rectangles has an area of 100 square units. Write a formula expressing the base function B for a rectangle in this set in terms of the height h. Give the domain and range of B.

15. Exactly 50 yards of fencing is available for enclosing a rectangular garden. Write a formula for the area function A in terms of one of the sides of the rectangle. Give the domain and range of A.

16. A page with dimensions 12 inches by 14 inches has a border of uniform width x surrounding the printed part of the page. Write a formula for the area function A of the printed part in terms of the width of the border x. Give the domain and range of A. $A = (12 - 2x)(14 - 2x)$; $D = \{x \mid 0 < x < 6\}$; $R = \{A \mid 0 < A < 168\}$

▲

17. A closed right cylindrical can of negligible thickness has a capacity of 100π cubic inches. Express the quantity of tin as a function of the radius of the base. $Q = 2\pi r^2 + \frac{200\pi}{r}$

18. A rectangle y inches long and x inches wide has a perimeter of 10 inches.
(a) Express y as a function of x. $y = 5 - x$
(b) Express the area of the rectangle as a function of x. $A = x(5 - x)$

particular collection of right circular cones, the base radius is always one-half the height, then $r = \frac{1}{2}h$ and a formula can be written for the volume of such cones using only the height,

$$V = \tfrac{1}{3}\pi(\tfrac{1}{2}h)^2 h,$$
$$V = \frac{\pi}{12}h^3,$$

or using only the radius,

$$V = \tfrac{1}{3}\pi r^2(2r),$$
$$V = \tfrac{2}{3}\pi r^3.$$

The choice would depend upon whether one is dealing with the variable h or the variable r.

Answers to Exercises 13–15

13. $V = x(10 - 2x)^2$
$D = \{x \mid 0 < x < 5\}$
$R = \{V \mid 0 < V \leqq 74\tfrac{2}{27}\}$

14. $B = \dfrac{100}{h}$
$D = \{h \mid h > 0\}$
$R = \{B \mid B > 0\}$

15. $A = x(25 - x)$
$D = \{x \mid 0 < x < 25\}$
$R = \{A \mid 0 < x \leqq \tfrac{625}{4}\}$

Quiz

Each of the following formulas defines a function. State the domain of each function.

1. $V = e^3$, with e the edge and V the volume of a cube. (ans: $\{e \mid e > 0\}$)
2. $C = 2\pi r$, with r the radius and C the circumference of a circle. (ans: $\{r \mid r > 0\}$)
3. $y = \sqrt{x}$ (ans: $\{x \mid x$ a non-negative real number$\}$)
4. Does $y = x^2 + 1$ define a function of x? (ans: yes)
5. Solve the equation in (4) for x in terms of y. Does the resulting equation define a function of y? (ans: $x = \pm\sqrt{y - 1}$; no)

6–2 FUNCTIONAL NOTATION

The use of functional notation provides an opportunity for doing problems requiring accuracy in manipulation. It should be made clear to the students that

$$g(x) = x^2 - 8$$

and

$$g(t) = t^2 - 8$$

describe the same correspondence. One equation uses the symbol t and the other uses x, but the functional rule is the same, that is, subtract eight from the square of the chosen number.

You may wish to write on the board several functions of the same variable in order to help fix in the minds of the students the roles of the letters f, g, h in functional notation. For example,

$$f(x) = 3x - 2,$$
$$g(x) = 5 - x^2,$$
$$h(x) = x^3 - x.$$

Then you could have rapid drill, calling for $f(0)$, $g(0)$; $f(1)$, $g(1)$, $h(1)$, and so on, and continuing to define the symbol by asking the same question several ways: What is $f(0)$? What is the image of 0 under the f rule? What is the value of $f(x)$ when x is given the value 0?

Then in order to study $g(x)$ specifically, you may call for $g(2)$ and $g(^-2)$, $g(3)$ and $g(^-3)$, and so on. The students should see that $g(x)$ is equal to $g(^-x)$ and understand what this indicates concerning the graph, that is, symmetry about the y-axis.

In order to study $h(x)$ in more detail, you could ask for $h(2)$ and $h(^-2)$, $h(1)$ and $h(^-1)$, and so on. The students should observe that $h(x) = {}^-h(^-x)$ and that the graph is therefore symmetrical about the origin.

6–2 FUNCTIONAL NOTATION

An important feature of algebra is its symbolic language. For example, we can use the symbols

$$x + y = 37$$

to express the following sentence:

The sum of two numbers is thirty-seven.

Just as we use letters to designate variables, we shall use letters such as f, g, and A to designate functions. When we use the letter f to designate a function, then for each x in the domain of f,

$$f(x)$$

denotes the *image of* x under f. The symbol $f(x)$ is read "f of x." Therefore, if $x = 2$, we denote the image of 2 as $f(2)$.

Let us consider the *squaring function* f having the set P of positive real numbers as its domain D. The image $f(x)$ of each x in P is the square of x, that is,

$$f(x) = x^2 \quad \text{for each } x \text{ in } P.$$

For example, the numbers 3, $\sqrt{2}$, and 10 are in the domain of f, and their images in the range of f are as follows:

$$f(3) = 3^2, \text{ or } 9; \quad f(\sqrt{2}) = (\sqrt{2})^2, \text{ or } 2; \quad f(10) = 10^2, \text{ or } 100.$$

This function f has geometric significance: It is the *area function* of a square. Thus, if the length of a side of a square is 3 inches, the area of the square is $f(3)$, or 9 square inches. We could just as well denote this function by A and define it by the formula

$$A(s) = s^2 \quad \text{for each positive real number } s.$$

These two functions f and A are equal; that is, they have the same domain P and $f(a) = A(a)$ for each number a in P. On the other hand, the function g, defined by

$$g(x) = x^2 \quad \text{for every real number } x,$$

is not equal to f, although the equation defining g is the same as the equation defining f. They are different because the domain of g is the set of all real numbers, but the domain of f is the set of all *positive* real numbers. For example,

$$g(^-3) = (^-3)^2, \quad \text{or } 9,$$

but $f(^-3)$ is not defined since $^-3$ is not in the domain of f.

As a second example, let us consider function s and its domain D, defined in the following manner.

$$s(t) = 64 - 16t^2, \quad D = \{t \mid 0 \leqq t \leqq 2\}.$$

Some images of elements of D under s are

$$\begin{aligned} s(0) &= 64 - (16 \cdot 0^2), && \text{or } 64; \\ s(\tfrac{1}{2}) &= 64 - [16 \cdot (\tfrac{1}{2})^2], && \text{or } 60; \\ s(1) &= 64 - [16 \cdot 1^2], && \text{or } 48; \\ s(\tfrac{3}{2}) &= 64 - [16 \cdot (\tfrac{3}{2})^2], && \text{or } 28; \\ s(2) &= 64 - [16 \cdot 2^2], && \text{or } 0. \end{aligned}$$

The function s has physical significance as a *distance function.* If an object is dropped from a point 64 feet above the ground, then the distance of the object from the ground t seconds after it is dropped is $s(t)$ feet. For example, 1 second after the object is dropped, it is 48 feet above the ground. Since $s(2) = 0$, it takes the object 2 seconds to reach the ground.

As a third example, consider the function C which has the set of positive integers as its domain and is defined in the following way.

$$C(n) = \begin{cases} 1.25 \text{ if } 0 < n \leqq 15 \\ 1.25 + .045(n - 15) \text{ if } n > 15 \end{cases}$$

Note that two equations are used to define C. From the first equation, we know that each of the following is equal to 1.25.

$$C(1), C(2), \ldots, C(15)$$

From the second equation, we know that

$$\begin{aligned} C(25) &= 1.25 + .045 \cdot (25 - 15) \\ &= 1.25 + .45, \quad \text{or } 1.70. \end{aligned}$$

This function might describe the cost, in dollars, of sending a telegram having n words. Thus, a 25-word telegram would cost \$1.70.

Exercises for Discussion, page 250

If time is limited, it is suggested that at least Exercises for Discussion 2, 6 and 7 be covered.

In Exercise for Discussion 1, the students could also find $f(1 - \sqrt{2})$, $f(1/(1 - \sqrt{2}))$, $f(1/2)$, and $f(^-3)$. (ans: $8 - 9\sqrt{2}$, $^-2 - \sqrt{2}$, 0,0).

In Exercise for Discussion 2, since there is no $f(3)$, you could consider $f(2.5)$, $f(2.7)$, and $f(2.9)$ to determine the behavior of $f(x)$ close to 3 but on the left. Then $f(3.5)$, $f(3.3)$, and $f(3.1)$ may be found in order to determine the behavior of $f(x)$ close to 3 but on the right. You may wish to inject the idea that the very fact of the exclusion of 3 from the domain of $f(x)$ raises questions about the x's close to 3 and their respective images. Also, $f(13)$, $f(103)$, $f(1003)$; $f(^-7)$, $f(^-97)$, $f(^-997)$ may be considered and the students may be asked about the image of $f(x)$ as x grows in absolute value. The students should think of a function as a fluctuating quantity responding to changes in the values chosen for the variable.

In Exercise for Discussion 7, it should be stressed that

$$f(a + b) = f(a) + f(b)$$

because the function is linear, but that this will not be true in general. In other words, this is not an application of the distributive law, as is shown by the following example:

$$\begin{aligned} f(x) &= x^2 \\ f(a) &= a^2 \\ f(b) &= b^2 \\ f(a) + f(b) &= a^2 + b^2 \\ f(a + b) &= (a + b)^2 \\ &= a^2 + 2ab + b^2 \\ &\neq f(a) + f(b). \end{aligned}$$

Answers to Exercises for Discussion 2(b), 6(a), 6(b)

2. (b) $g(x) = \dfrac{4}{x^2 - 1}$

$g(2) = \dfrac{4}{2^2 - 1} = \frac{4}{3}$

$g(^-2) = \dfrac{4}{(^-2)^2 - 1} = \frac{4}{3}$

$g(3) = \dfrac{4}{3^2 - 1} = \frac{1}{2}$

$g(^-3) = \dfrac{4}{(^-3)^2 - 1} = \frac{1}{2}$

$g(4) = \dfrac{4}{4^2 - 1} = \frac{4}{15}$

$g(^-4) = \dfrac{4}{(^-4)^2 - 1} = \frac{4}{15}$

6. (a) $f(x) = \sqrt{9 - x^2}$

$f(1) = \sqrt{9 - 1^2} = 2\sqrt{2}$

$f(^-1) = \sqrt{9 - (^-1)^2} = 2\sqrt{2}$

$f(9) = \sqrt{9 - 9^2} = \sqrt{^-72}$

$= 6\sqrt{2}i$

$f(^-9) = \sqrt{9 - (^-9)^2} = 6\sqrt{2}i$

If f is a real valued function of a real variable, $f(9)$ and $f(^-9)$ are not defined.

$f(0) = \sqrt{9 - 0^2} = 3$

(b) $D = \{x \mid 9 - x^2 \geq 0\}$

$= \{x \mid 9 \geq x^2\}$

$= \{x \mid {}^-3 \leq x \leq 3\}$

Exercises for Discussion

1. Let the function f be defined as follows: The domain of f is the set of all real numbers and the image of each real number is given by the formula

$$f(x) = 2x^2 + 5x - 3.$$

Find $f(^-3)$, $f(^-\sqrt{2})$, $f(^-\frac{5}{4})$, and $f(0)$.

$f(^-3) = 2(^-3)^2 + 5(^-3) - 3 = 0$
$f(^-\sqrt{2}) = 2(^-\sqrt{2})^2 + 5(^-\sqrt{2}) - 3 = 1 - 5\sqrt{2}$
$f(\frac{^-5}{4}) = 2(\frac{^-5}{4})^2 + 5(\frac{^-5}{4}) - 3 = \frac{^-49}{8}$
$f(0) = 2(0)^2 + 5(0) - 3 = {}^-3$

2. If we want a formula such as $f(x) = 7/(x - 3)$ to give the image of each real number x in the domain of the function f, then we must exclude the value $x = 3$. In this case, it is customary to write the complete description of f as

$$f(x) = \frac{7}{x - 3}, \quad x \text{ real and } x \neq 3.$$

(a) If $g(x) = 4/(x^2 - 1)$ gives the image of a real number x under the function g, what real numbers must be excluded from the domain of g? Write a complete description of the function g. $g(x) = \frac{4}{x^2 - 1}, |x| \neq 1$ (or $x \neq 1; x \neq {}^-1$)
1 and $^-1$

(b) Find $g(2)$, $g(^-2)$, $g(3)$, $g(^-3)$, $g(4)$, and $g(^-4)$.

(c) For the real number k, $k \neq \pm 1$, how does $g(k)$ compare with $g(^-k)$?
If $k \neq \pm 1$, $g(k) = g(^-k)$.

3. The function f whose domain is the set of real numbers is defined by the equation

$$f(x) = \sqrt{x^2 + 1}.$$

$f(2\sqrt{2}) = \sqrt{(2\sqrt{2})^2 + 1} = 3$
$f(\sqrt{15}) = \sqrt{(\sqrt{15})^2 + 1} = 4$
$f(0) = \sqrt{0^2 + 1} = 1$
$f(^-1) = \sqrt{(^-1)^2 + 1} = \sqrt{2}$

(a) Find $f(2\sqrt{2})$, $f(\sqrt{15})$, $f(0)$, and $f(^-1)$.

(b) Use set notation to describe the range of f.
$R = \{y \mid y \geq 1\}$

4. If $g(x) = {}^-\sqrt{x^2 + 1}$ and the domain of g is the set of real numbers, use set notation to describe the range of the function g. $R = \{y \mid y \leq {}^-1\}$

5. A function g is defined by the equation $g(x) = 3$, and the domain of g is the set of all real numbers. This type of function is called a *constant function.*

(a) Find $g(^-7)$, $g(^-3)$, and $g(0)$. 3, 3, 3

(b) What is the range of g? $R = \{3\}$

6. A function f is defined by the equation $f(x) = \sqrt{9 - x^2}$.

(a) Find $f(1)$, $f(^-1)$, $f(9)$, $f(^-9)$, and $f(0)$.

(b) Use set notation to describe the domain of f.

(c) Use set notation to describe the range of f.
$R = \{y \mid 0 \leq y \leq 3\}$

7. Given that $f(x) = 3x$, with the domain of f the set of all real numbers,

(a) find $f(4)$, $f(5)$, $f(9)$, and compare $f(9)$ with $f(4) + f(5)$.
12, 15, 27 $f(4) + f(5) = 12 + 15 = 27 = f(9)$

(b) find $f(^-8)$, $f(3)$, $f(^-5)$, and compare $f(^-5)$ with $f(^-8) + f(3)$.
$^-24$, 9, $^-15$ $f(^-8) + f(3) = {}^-24 + 9 = {}^-15 = f(^-5)$

Exercises

In Exercises 1–4, give the restrictions, if any, on the domain of each function.

1. $f(x) = \dfrac{3}{x+2}$ $x \neq {}^-2$
2. $f(x) = x + \dfrac{1}{x}$ $x \neq 0$
3. $f(x) = 4$ None
4. $f(x) = \sqrt{16 - x^2}$ ${}^-4 \leq x \leq 4$
5. In Exercises 1–4, find $f(2)$, $f(3)$, $f(5)$, and $f({}^-1)$. $\frac{3}{4}, \frac{3}{5}, \frac{3}{7}, 3$; $2\frac{1}{2}, 3\frac{1}{3}, 5\frac{1}{5}, {}^-2$; $4, 4, 4, 4$; $2\sqrt{3}, \sqrt{7}$, undefined, $\sqrt{15}$
6. Given that $F(x) = \sqrt{x^2 - 1}$,
   (a) what real numbers must be excluded from the domain of F? Write a complete description of the function F. $\{x \mid {}^-1 < x < 1\}$; $F(x) = \sqrt{x^2-1}$, $|x| \geq 1$
   (b) find each of the following and simplify.

$$F(1),\quad F(\sqrt{2}),\quad F\left(\frac{\sqrt{13}}{2}\right),\quad F(15),\quad F({}^-10^2)$$

0, 1, $\frac{3}{2}$, $4\sqrt{14}$, $3\sqrt{1111}$

△

7. Given that $g(x) = x^2$, with the domain of g the set of all real numbers,
   (a) find $g(3)$, $g(4)$, $g(7)$, and compare $g(7)$ with $g(3) + g(4)$.
   (b) find $g({}^-2)$, $g(5)$, $g(3)$, and compare $g(3)$ with $g({}^-2) + g(5)$.
   (c) do you think that the equation $g(a) + g(b) = g(a + b)$ will be true for any pair a, b of real numbers? Explain your answer. True if $a = 0$, $b = 0$, or both.
8. Given that $g(x) = x^2$, with the domain of g the set of all real numbers,
   (a) find $g(3)$, $g(5)$, $g(15)$, and compare the number $g(15)$ with the product $g(3) \cdot g(5)$. 9, 25, 225; equal
   (b) find $g({}^-2)$, $g(6)$, $g({}^-12)$, and compare $g({}^-12)$ with $g({}^-2) \cdot g(6)$. 4, 36, 144; equal
   (c) find $\dfrac{g(28)}{g(7) \cdot g(4)}$. 1
9. The weight W of an object varies directly with its volume V, that is, $W = kV$ for some constant of proportionality k.
   (a) An object weighs 14 grams and has a volume of 10 cubic centimeters. Find the constant of proportionality. $k = \frac{7}{5}$
   (b) Use functional notation to write an expression for this weight function W. What is its domain? $W(V) = \frac{7}{5}V$; $D = \{V \mid V \geq 0\}$
   (c) Find $W(20)$ and $W(15)$. 28, 21
10. The number N of articles purchased varies inversely with the price p per article, that is, $N = k/p$ for some constant k.
    (a) If 11 articles at 12¢ per article can be bought with available money, find the constant of proportionality. $k = 132$
    (b) Using functional notation, write an expression for the function N. What is the domain of N? $N(p) = \frac{132}{p}$; $D = \{p \mid p$ an integer and $p > 0\}$
    (c) Find $N(11)$, $N(6)$, and $N(4)$. 12, 22, 33

Exercises

These exercises should be covered quickly.

In Exercise 7(c),

$$g(a) + g(b) = a^2 + b^2$$
$$g(a + b) = (a + b)^2.$$

If the students say that

$$g(a) + g(b) \neq g(a + b),$$

they should be reminded of the frequently made error of claiming that $a^2 + b^2$ is equal to $(a + b)^2$.

In Exercise 8, it may be shown again that although

$$g(ab) = g(a)g(b),$$

it is not a result of the distributive law. For example,

$$\begin{aligned} g(x) &= x^2 + x \\ g(a) &= a^2 + a \\ g(b) &= b^2 + b \\ g(ab) &= a^2b^2 + ab \\ g(a)g(b) &= (a^2 + a)(b^2 + b) \\ &= a^2b^2 + a^2b + ab^2 + ab \\ &\neq g(ab). \end{aligned}$$

In better than average classes, Exercises 11–15 may all be done.

Answers to Exercises 7(a), 7(b)

7. (a) 9, 16, 49; not equal
   (b) 4, 25, 9; not equal

Quiz

A function g is defined by the equation

$$g(x) = \frac{x}{x^2 - 4}.$$

(a) Find $f(1)$, $f(\sqrt{2})$, $f(4)$, $f(^-4)$. $\left(\text{ans: } \frac{^-1}{3}, \frac{^-\sqrt{2}}{2}, \frac{1}{3}, \frac{^-1}{3}\right)$

(b) Use set notation to describe the domain of g. (ans: $\{x \mid x \text{ a real number}, x \neq \pm 2\}$)

6-3 THE GRAPH OF A FUNCTION

The students should find themselves familiar with the material in this section. The graphs of x^n, n even, n odd, may be classified by running through the cases $n = 1, 2, 3, 4, 5, 6$, and so on, until the class understands. For n even, there is symmetry about the y-axis.

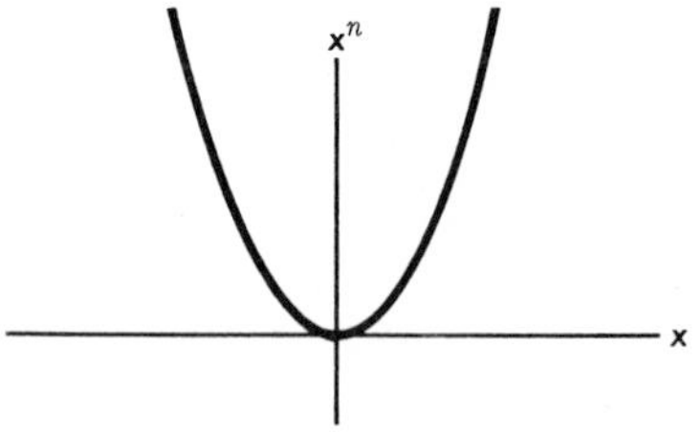

For n odd, there is symmetry about the origin.

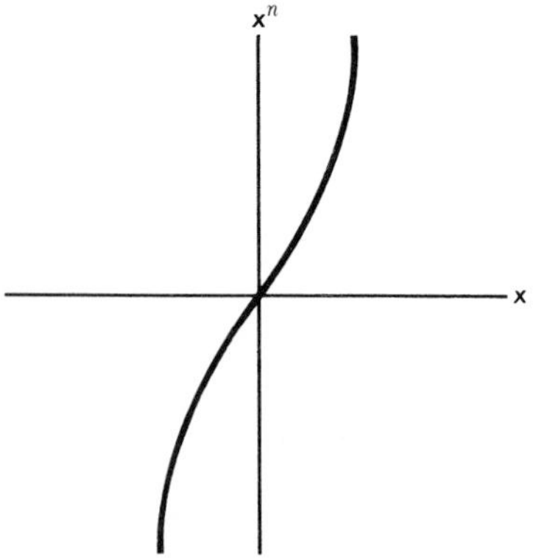

11. The function N whose domain is the set of real numbers is defined in the following way.

$$N(x) = \begin{cases} x \text{ if } x \text{ is a non-negative real number} \\ ^-x \text{ if } x \text{ is a negative real number} \end{cases}$$

(a) Find $N(2)$, $N(\sqrt{3})$, $N(1 - \sqrt{2})$, $N(^-2)$, $N(^-\sqrt{3})$, $N(\sqrt{2} - 1)$, and $N(0)$. *2, $\sqrt{3}$, $\sqrt{2}-1$, 2, $\sqrt{3}$, $\sqrt{2}-1$, 0*

(b) Describe this function and write a single equation defining $N(x)$. *$N(x) = |x|$*

12. The operation of multiplying each real number by 7 defines a certain function. If we designate this function by O, then $O(x) = 7x$ for each real number x. Similarly, each of the following operations defines a function which you may designate by O. Assume that the domain of each function O is the largest possible set of real numbers, and define each function O by an equation.

(a) Each number x is multiplied by 10. *$O(x) = 10x$*
(b) Each number x is added to 7. *$O(x) = x + 7$*
(c) Each number x is divided by $^-3$. *$O(x) = \frac{x}{-3}$*
(d) Each number x is multiplied by 1. *$O(x) = x$*
(e) Each number x is replaced by 1. *$O(x) = 1$*

13. (a) Show that the function f defined by the two equations

$$f(x) = \begin{cases} \dfrac{x - 9}{\sqrt{x} - 3}, & x \neq 9 \text{ and } x \geqq 0, \\ 6 \text{ if } x = 9 \end{cases}$$

can be defined by one equation whose domain x is the set of non-negative numbers. *See Solution Manual.*

(b) Find $f(4)$, $f(16)$, $f(25)$, and $f(100)$. *5, 7, 8, 13*

14. The function g is given by the following two equations. Find one equation which defines this function.

$$\begin{cases} g(x) = \dfrac{\sqrt{x} - 2}{x - 4}, & x \neq 4 \text{ and } x > 0, \\ g(4) = \frac{1}{4} \end{cases}$$

$g(x) = \frac{1}{\sqrt{x} + 2}$, $x > 0$

15. (a) The two functions g, h are defined below. Are they equal functions? *No*

$$g(x) = \frac{\sqrt{x^2 + 16} - 5}{x^2 - 9}, \quad x \neq \pm 3,$$

$$h(x) = \frac{1}{\sqrt{x^2 + 16} + 5}$$

(b) For what values of x does $g(x) = h(x)$? *$x \neq \pm 3$*

6–3 THE GRAPH OF A FUNCTION

If both the domain and the range of a function are sets of real numbers, then the function may be displayed by a graph in a cartesian coordinate system. The graph of a function is defined in the following way.

> *GRAPH OF A FUNCTION*
>
> ***The graph of a function f having domain D is the graph of the set***
>
> $$\{(x, f(x)) \mid x \text{ in } D\}.$$

A function L of the form

$$L(x) = mx + b,$$

where m and b are given real numbers, is called a *linear function*. Its graph is a straight line. The following problem is an example of the linear function.

Problem 1. Graph the linear function L defined by

$$L(x) = 2x - 3, \quad D = \{x \mid x \text{ real}\}.$$

Solution. We are asked to graph the set

$$\{(x, 2x - 3) \mid x \text{ in } D\},$$

which is the same as the set

$$\{(x, y) \mid y = 2x - 3\}.$$

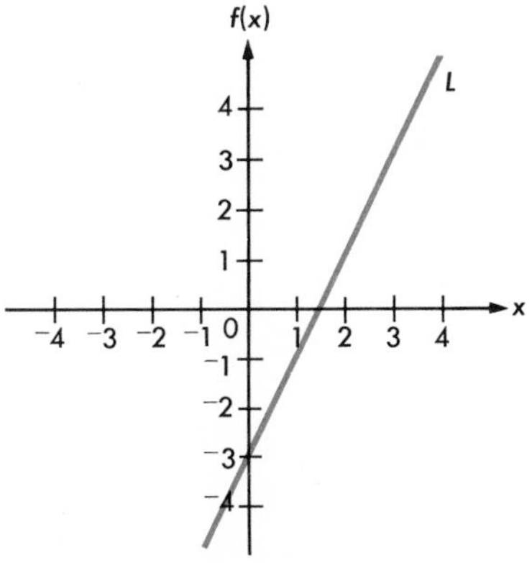

FIGURE 6–1

The graph of the latter set is the straight line of Fig. 6–1. This line has slope 2 and y-intercept $^-3$. What is its x-intercept?

A function P defined by

$$P(x) = x^n,$$

for some number n, is called the *power function with exponent n*. Its domain is the set of all real numbers having an nth power.

Exercises for Discussion, page 255

If time is limited, it is suggested that at least Exercises for Discussion 3 and 4 be covered.

In connection with Exercise for Discussion 1, the students could also graph

$$f(x) = |x - 1|,$$
$$f(x) = |x - 2|,$$
$$f(x) = |x + 2|.$$

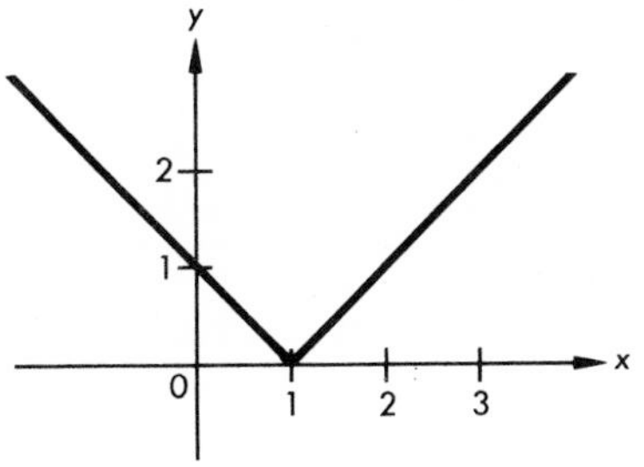

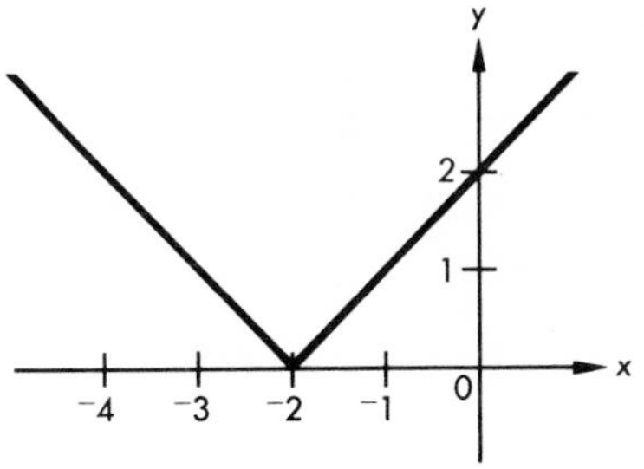

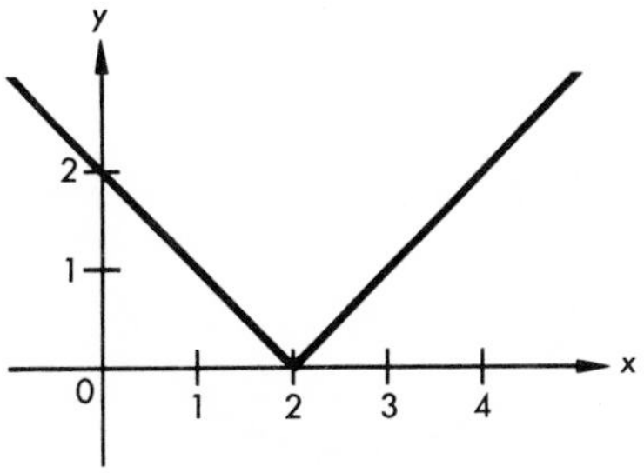

Answers to Exercises for Discussion 1, 2(a), 3(b)–3(d), 4, page 255

1.

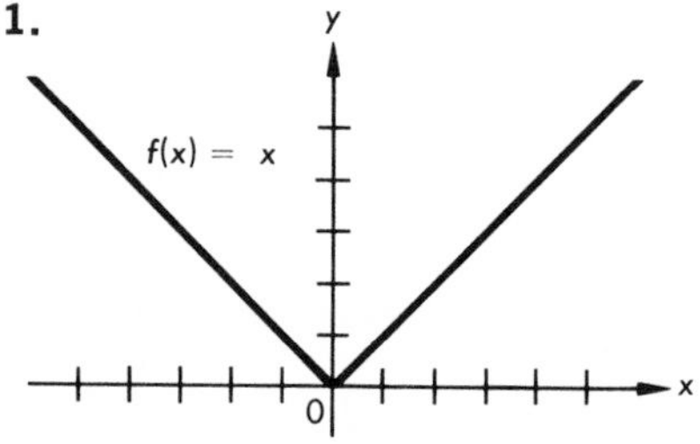

2. (a)

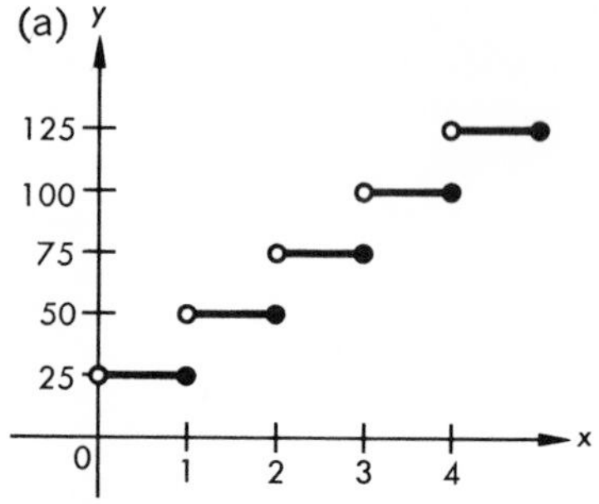

$D = \{x \mid x > 0\}$
$R = \{y \mid y = 25n,\ n \text{ a positive integer}\}$

3. (b)

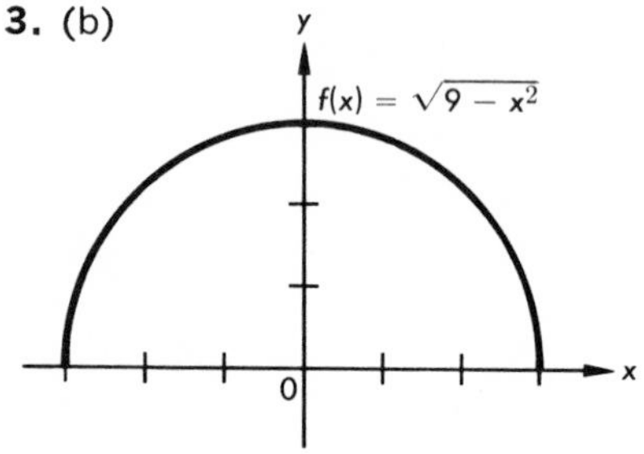

(c) The graph in (b) consists of the upper half of the graph of $x^2 + y^2 = 9$.

(d) $g(x) = {}^{-}\sqrt{9 - x^2}$

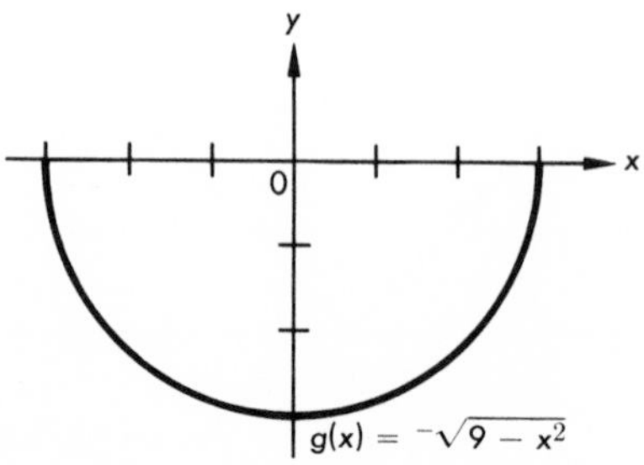

Problem 2. Graph the following power function with exponent 3.

$$P(x) = x^3, \quad D = \{x \mid x \text{ real}\}$$

Solution. The graph of P is the graph of the set

$$\{(x, y) \mid y = x^3\}.$$

The following table of values will help us to draw this graph (shown in Fig. 6–2).

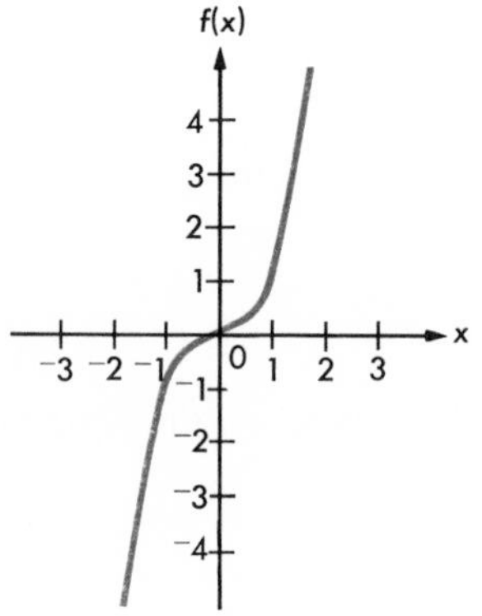

FIGURE 6–2

x	$^-3$	$^-2$	$^-1.5$	$^-1$	$^-.5$	0	.5	1	1.5	2	3
$P(x)$	$^-27$	$^-8$	$^-3.375$	$^-1$	$^-.125$	0	.125	1	3.375	8	27

The part of the graph close to the origin is very flat, but the part of the graph away from the origin is quite steep.

Problem 3. The *greatest-integer function F* is defined in the following way. For each real number x, $F(x)$ is the largest integer that is less than or equal to x. In the notation given on page 24, $F(x) = [x]$. Graph the function F.

Solution. By definition,

$$F(x) = {}^-2 \quad \text{if} \quad {}^-2 \leqq x < {}^-1,$$
$$F(x) = {}^-1 \quad \text{if} \quad {}^-1 \leqq x < 0,$$
$$F(x) = 0 \quad \text{if} \quad 0 \leqq x < 1,$$
$$F(x) = 1 \quad \text{if} \quad 1 \leqq x < 2,$$
$$F(x) = 2 \quad \text{if} \quad 2 \leqq x < 3,$$

and so on. Thus, the graph consists of an infinite number of line segments, or steps, as shown in Fig. 6–3. Each step includes its left-hand endpoint, indicated by the solid dot, and does not include its right-hand endpoint, indicated by the hollow dot.

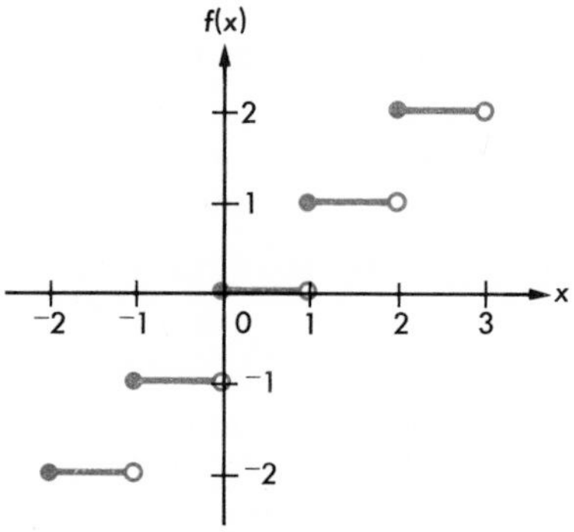

FIGURE 6–3

Exercises for Discussion

1. Graph the function defined by $f(x) = |x|$.
2. The shipping charges of a mail-order company are 25¢ for the first pound or fraction thereof, an additional 25¢ for orders weighing more than 1 pound but not more than 2 pounds, and so on, for each additional pound or fraction thereof.
   (a) Graph this shipping function, F. What is its domain? Describe the range of F.
   (b) Write a formula for $F(w)$ in terms of $[w]$. $F(w) = 25[w]$
3. (a) What is the domain of the function f defined by the equation
   $D = \{x \mid {}^{-}3 \leqq x \leqq 3\}$
   $$f(x) = \sqrt{9 - x^2}\ ?$$
   (b) Graph the function f.
   (c) How does your graph in part (b) compare with the graph of the equation $x^2 + y^2 = 9$?
   (d) Write another function g whose graph is the remaining portion of the graph defined by the equation of part (c). Graph g.
4. The figure shows the graph of a function f whose domain is the interval $\{x \mid {}^{-}2 \leqq x \leqq 3\}$ and whose range is the interval $\{y \mid {}^{-}1 \leqq y \leqq 1\}$. Sketch the graph of each of the following equations, carefully labeling your scale on each axis.

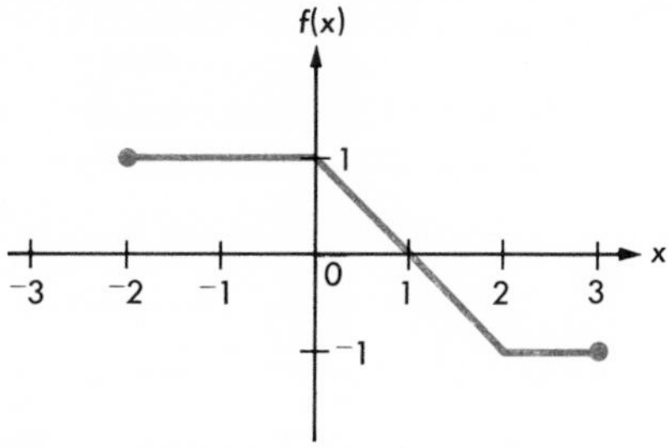

   (a) $y = f(x) + 2$ (b) $y = 2f(x)$
   (c) $y = {}^{-}f(x)$ (d) $y = |f(x)|$

Exercises

See Solution Manual for graphs.

1. Graph on the same axes the functions defined below.
$$f(x) = x,\quad g(x) = x^2,\quad h(x) = x^3,\quad k(x) = x^4$$
2. Graph the quadratic function $f(x) = x^2 + 2x + 3$.
3. Given that
$$f(x) = \begin{cases} 100 \text{ for } x = 0 \\ 105 \text{ for } x = 1 \\ 100(1.05)^x \text{ for } x = 2 \text{ and } 3, \end{cases}$$
   (a) graph the function.
   (b) state the range of the function.
   $R = \{100, 105, 110.25, 115.7625\}$

4. (a)

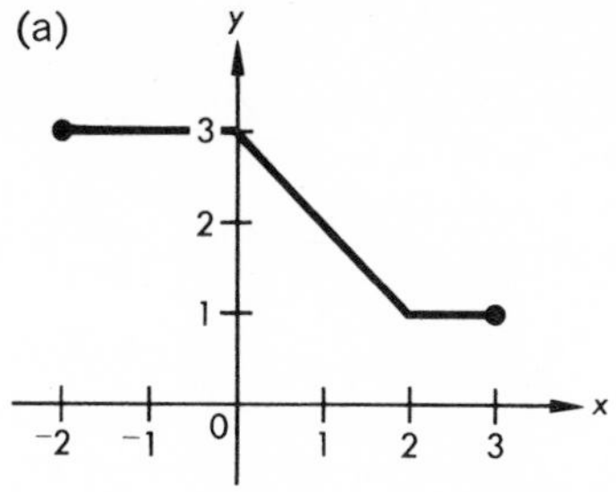

(b)

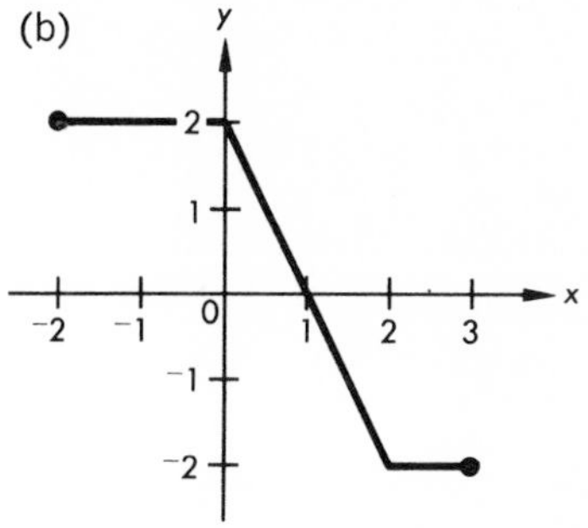

(c)

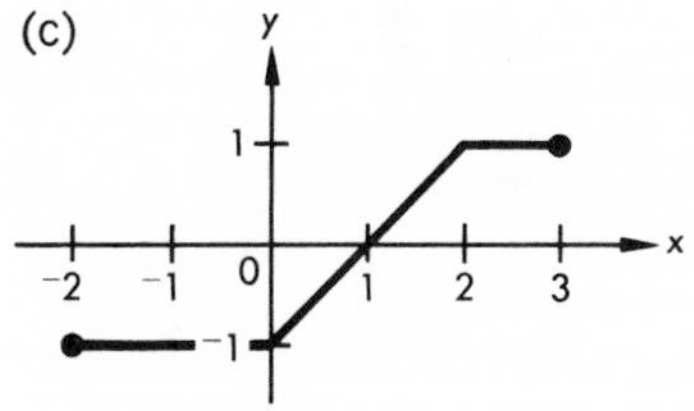

(d)

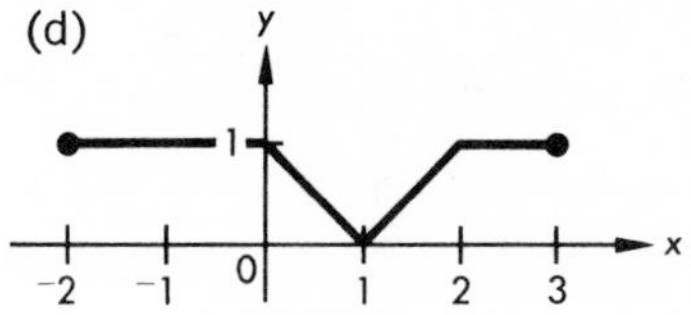

In a minimum course the exercises on the following page may be omitted, or postponed and used for review later in the year. If they are assigned, Exercise 5 should be covered in detail in class first. These exercises could also be used for independent study and extra credit.

Answers to Exercise 4

4. (a) $f(x) = \sqrt{4 - x^2}$;
$g(x) = {}^-\sqrt{4 - x^2}$;
$h(y) = \sqrt{4 - y^2}$;
$k(y) = {}^-\sqrt{4 - y^2}$

(b) $f(x) = \sqrt{x^2 - 1}$;
$g(x) = {}^-\sqrt{x^2 - 1}$;
$h(y) = \sqrt{y^2 + 1}$;
$k(y) = {}^-\sqrt{y^2 + 1}$

(c) $f(x) = \frac{3}{5}\sqrt{25 - x^2}$;
$g(x) = {}^-\frac{3}{5}\sqrt{25 - x^2}$;
$h(y) = \frac{5}{3}\sqrt{9 - y^2}$;
$k(y) = {}^-\frac{5}{3}\sqrt{9 - y^2}$

(d) $f(x) = \frac{1}{2}\sqrt{4 - x^2}$;
$g(x) = {}^-\frac{1}{2}\sqrt{4 - x^2}$;
$h(y) = 2\sqrt{1 - y^2}$;
$k(y) = {}^-2\sqrt{1 - y^2}$

Quiz

1. Graph the function defined by $f(x) = |x + 3|$ and give the domain and range of f. (ans: $\{x \mid x$ a real number$\}$, $\{y \mid y \geqq 0.\}$)

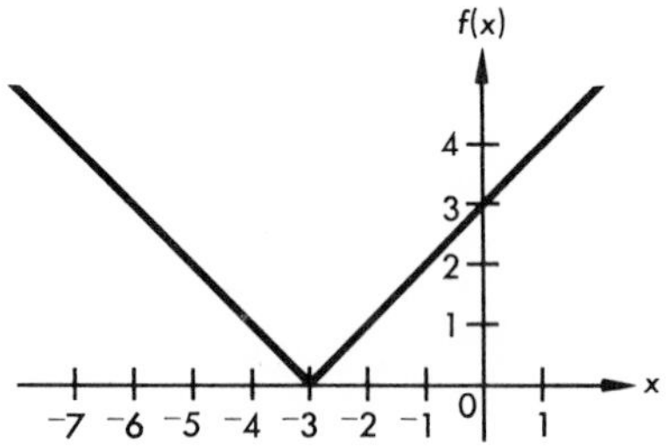

2. Graph the quadratic function $y = x^2 - 1$. Describe the domain and range of the function. (ans: $\{x \mid x$ a real number$\}$, $\{y \mid y \geqq {}^-1\}$)

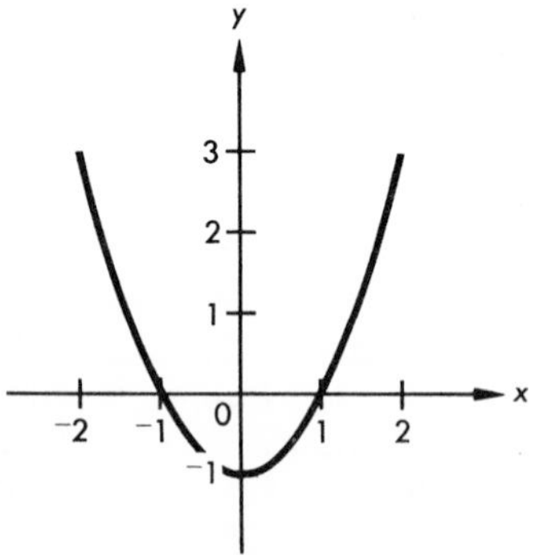

△

4. We can define four functions by solving each of the following equations first for y and then for x. In each case, give the definitions of the functions, and show how their graphs are related to the graph of the given equation. See Solution Manual.

(a) $x^2 + y^2 = 4$ (b) $x^2 - y^2 = 1$
(c) $9x^2 + 25y^2 = 225$ (d) $x^2 + 4y^2 = 4$

5. The function f, defined by the equation $f(x) = 3/(x - 2)$, has domain $D = \{x \mid x \neq 2\}$. The graph of this function is sketched below. Although we can find no points with abscissa 2, we can find points with abscissas as close to 2 as we wish. Complete the following table to see the behavior of the curve near $x = 2$ and then for $|x|$ very large.

x	1	1.5	1.75	1.9	3	2.5	2.25	2.1	12	102	1002	$^-8$	$^-98$	$^-998$
$f(x)$	?	?	?	?	?	?	?	?	?	?	?	?	?	?
	$^-3$	$^-6$	$^-12$	$^-30$	3	6	12	30	.3	.03	.003	$^-.3$	$^-.03$	$^-.003$

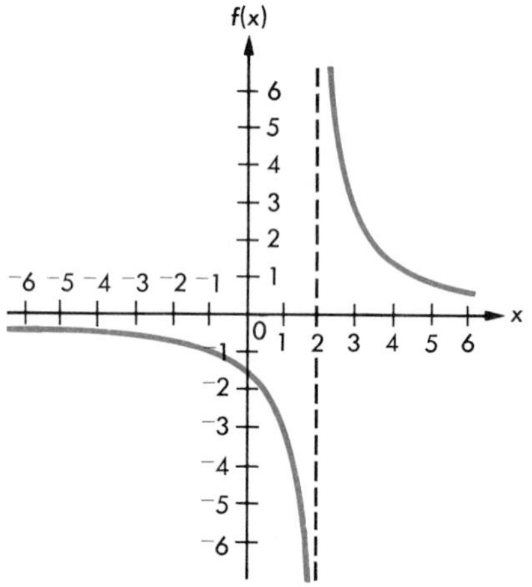

▲

Graph the following functions, paying particular attention to points whose abscissas are close to numbers excluded from the domain of the function. Draw dashed vertical lines at the excluded numbers.

6. $f(x) = x + \dfrac{1}{x}$

7. $g(x) = \dfrac{3}{(x + 2)^2}$

8. $f(x) = \dfrac{x - 2}{x - 3}$

9. $f(x) = 1 + \dfrac{1}{x - 3}$

10. $g(x) = \dfrac{4}{x^2 - 4}$

11. $h(x) = \dfrac{4x}{x^2 - 4}$

6–4 EXPONENTIAL FUNCTIONS

So far, we have defined the rth power of each positive real number a for every rational number r. Thus, for each positive real number a and each rational number r, there is defined a unique positive real number a^r. You may wonder whether it is possible to define a^r in a sensible way for an irrational exponent r. For example, can one formulate a reasonable definition of $2^{\sqrt{3}}$? Actually, it is possible to do so in a way that we shall describe in this section.

Consider, for example, the equation

$$y = 2^x.$$

We know that for every rational value of x, there is a unique real value of y which makes this equation true. We can get some idea of the shape of the graph by plotting points from the values given in the table.

x	$^-3$	$^-2.5$	$^-2$	$^-1.5$	$^-1$	$^-.5$	0	.5	1	1.5	2	2.5	3	3.5	4
y	.125	.18	.25	.35	.5	.71	1	1.41	2	2.83	4	5.66	8	11.31	16

The points we have plotted seem to lie on a smooth curve. If we were to take many more rational values of x and plot the points corresponding to them, we would obtain a better picture of this curve. In fact, we could plot so many points, say between $x = 0$ and $x = 1$, that we would not be able to distinguish between our set of points and a curve showing no breaks for irrational values of x. It would then seem reasonable to define 2^x, for x irrational, as the y-coordinate of the curve through these points. Thus, let us make the reasonable assumption that to each real number x there corresponds a unique positive number y such that the point (x, y) is on the smooth curve indicated in Fig. 6–4. Using this assumption, we can say that for each real number x, there is a unique positive number y such that the equation $y = 2^x$ is true.

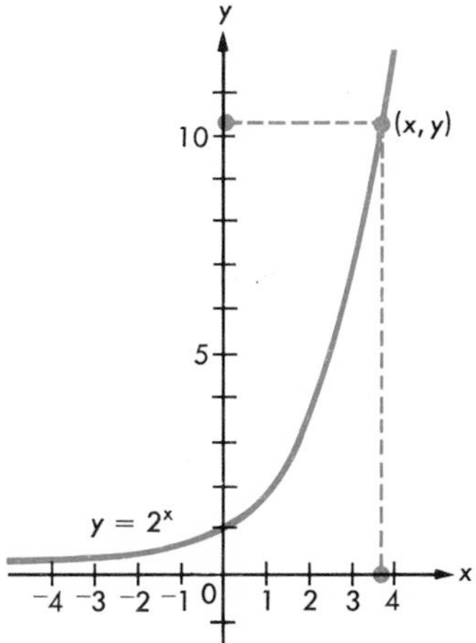

FIGURE 6–4

6–4 EXPONENTIAL FUNCTIONS

It is recommended that the definition of a^r, r irrational, be carefully considered in class. The table given on page 257 could actually be constructed in class. If $x = 1.5$,

$$\begin{aligned} y &= 2^{1.5} \\ &= 2^{3/2} \\ &= 2\sqrt{2} \doteq 2(1.414). \end{aligned}$$

If $x = 3.5$,

$$\begin{aligned} y &= 2^{3.5} \\ &= 2^3 \cdot 2^{1/2} \doteq 8(1.414). \end{aligned}$$

If $x = {}^-2.5$,

$$\begin{aligned} y &= 2^{-2.5} \\ &= 2^{-2} \cdot 2^{-1/2} \\ &= \frac{1}{4} \cdot \frac{1}{\sqrt{2}} \\ &= \frac{1}{4}\left(\frac{\sqrt{2}}{2}\right) \\ &\doteq \tfrac{1}{8}(1.414). \end{aligned}$$

All entries in the table require only $\sqrt{2} \doteq 1.414$ for approximation. Passively looking at the table is not as valuable to the student as the actual experience of doing the arithmetic.

A similar exercise could be done (or assigned) making a table for $y = 3^x$, using the same x-values that are used here, and knowing only that $\sqrt{3} \doteq 1.732$.

The information in the last paragraph on the next page may be substantiated with an actual table of values for $y = (\frac{1}{2})^x$ and a graph on the blackboard.

The pair of functions, $f(x) = 2^x$ and $g(x) = 2^{-x}$, should be considered, and the students should see that $f(1) = g({}^-1)$, $f(2) = g({}^-2)$, and, in general, $f(x) = g({}^-x)$. Hence the graph of g is doing the same thing to the *left* of the vertical axis that the graph of f did to the *right* of the vertical axis.

Exercises for Discussion, page 259

It is recommended that all four of the Exercises for Discussion be done in class, with each student doing each exercise completely at his desk. The correct solutions could finally be put on the blackboard as the class finishes each exercise.

It should be noted that the function in Exercise for Discussion 1(b) is equivalent to $E(x) = b^x$ with $b = \frac{1}{3}$, or $0 < b < 1$.

In Exercise for Discussion 2(a), if $f(x) = 2^x$ and $g(x) = 2^x + 1$, how do their graphs compare? Do they have the same shape? How is g located with reference to f? The students should note that adding a positive number to the exponential function 2^x simply lifts the graph vertically.

In Exercise for Discussion 2(b), write $2^{x/2}$ as $(2^{1/2})^x$ or $(2^x)^{1/2}$. If

$$E(x) = 2^{x/2},$$

the base $b = \sqrt{2} > 1$, and this graph is similar to the others with $b > 1$.

In Exercise for Discussion 2(c), if $f(x) = 2^x$ and $g(x) = 2^{x+1}$, how do their graphs compare? If one adds to the exponent, what happens? Does $2^{x+1} = 2^x \cdot 2$? It can be seen that $g(x) = 2 \cdot f(x)$.

What would the graph of

$$h(x) = 2^{x+3}$$

look like? Would $h(x)$ be equal to $8 \cdot f(x)$? Why?

How would the graph of

$$E(x) = 2^{x-1}$$

compare with that of $f(x) = 2^x$? You could have the students write $E(x)$ in terms of $f(x)$. ($E(x) = \frac{1}{2}f(x)$.) The graph of $E(x)$ lies below that of $f(x)$, intersecting the y-axis at $(0, \frac{1}{2})$.

A number such as $2^{\sqrt{3}}$ can be approximated in the following way. Since $1 < \sqrt{3} < 2$ and since the curve in Fig. 6–4 is rising, we must have $2^1 < 2^{\sqrt{3}} < 2^2$, that is, $2 < 2^{\sqrt{3}} < 4$. A better approximation of $2^{\sqrt{3}}$ can be obtained by taking a better approximation of $\sqrt{3}$. Thus, $1.7 < \sqrt{3} < 1.8$ and therefore,

$$2^{1.7} < 2^{\sqrt{3}} < 2^{1.8}.$$

Note that $2^{1.7}$ and $2^{1.8}$ are rational powers of 2 and hence, have been previously defined. Thus, $1.7 = \frac{17}{10}$ and $2^{1.7} = \sqrt[10]{2^{17}}$; similarly, $2^{1.8} = \sqrt[5]{2^9}$. It can be shown that $2^{1.7} \doteq 3.2$ and $2^{1.8} \doteq 3.5$ and therefore, that $3.2 < 2^{\sqrt{3}} < 3.5$.

We can now define the function E:

$$E(x) = 2^x.$$

From our discussion, we know that the domain of E is the set of all real numbers. We call E the *exponential function with base* 2. The graph of E is sketched in Fig. 6–4.

For each positive real number b unequal to 1, we may similarly define the exponential function E with base b.

DEFINITION OF THE EXPONENTIAL FUNCTION

$$E(x) = b^x, \quad \textit{domain of } E = \{x \mid x \textit{ real}\}$$

If $b > 1$, the graph of the exponential function with base b is similar to that in Fig. 6–4. We know that we cannot have $b = 1$, because the function E, defined by

$$E(x) = 1^x,$$

is simply the constant function

$$E(x) = 1.$$

If $0 < b < 1$, then b^x gets smaller and smaller as x assumes larger and larger positive values, and b^x increases as x assumes smaller and smaller negative values. For example, if E is the exponential function with base $\frac{1}{2}$,

$$E(x) = (\tfrac{1}{2})^x.$$

Then

$$E(x) = 2^{-x},$$

and the graph of E (in Fig. 6–5) is the mirror image in the y-axis of Fig. 6–4.

Exponential functions have many applications in the sciences. If ideal conditions for growth and reproduction prevail, then the growth curve of a population is exponential in nature. For example, the number, in thousands, of bacteria in a culture might be given by the exponential function

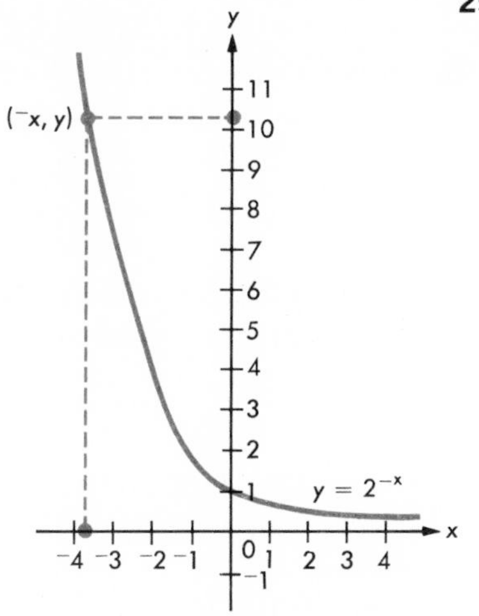

FIGURE 6–5

$$E(t) = 1000 \cdot 3^t.$$

Thus, initially, there are 1000 bacteria, that is, $E(0) = 1000$. Then

$$\begin{aligned} &\text{1 hour later, } E(1) = 3^1 \times 1000 = 3000; \\ &\text{2 hours later, } E(2) = 3^2 \times 1000 = 9000; \\ &\text{3 hours later, } E(3) = 3^3 \times 1000 = 27{,}000; \end{aligned}$$

and so on.

Exercises for Discussion

1. Graph each of the following exponential functions on the same set of axes.
   (a) $E(x) = 3^x$ (b) $E(x) = 3^{-x}$
2. Graph each of the following exponential functions.
   (a) $E(x) = 2^x + 1$ (b) $E(x) = 2^{\frac{x}{2}}$ (c) $E(x) = 2^{x+1}$
3. Let us consider the following exponential function which describes the growth of bacteria.

$$E(t) = 16^t$$

In this function, t is time measured in hours and $E(t)$ is the number, in thousands, of bacteria in a culture.

(a) What is the initial number of bacteria? $E(0) = 16^0 = 1$; number: 1000
(b) After $\frac{1}{4}$ hour, how many bacteria are there? $E(\frac{1}{4}) = 16^{\frac{1}{4}} = 2$; number: 2000
(c) After $\frac{1}{2}$ hour, how many bacteria are there? $E(\frac{1}{2}) = 16^{\frac{1}{2}} = 4$; number: 4000
(d) After 1 hour, how many bacteria are there? $E(1) = 16$; number: 16,000
(e) Verify that $E(t) = \sqrt{2}$ when $t = \frac{1}{8}$.
$E(\frac{1}{8}) = 16^{\frac{1}{8}} = (2^4)^{\frac{1}{8}} = 2^{\frac{1}{2}} = \sqrt{2}$

Answers to Exercises for Discussion 1, 2

1.

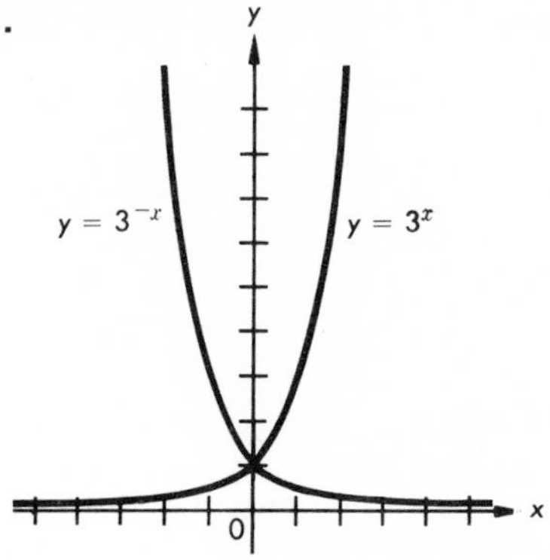

2. (a)

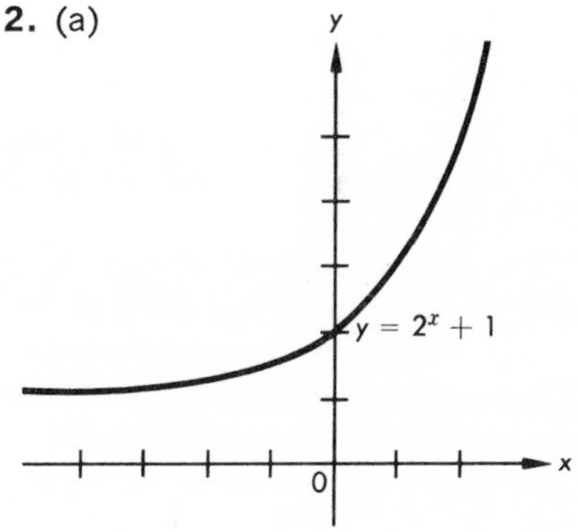

(b)

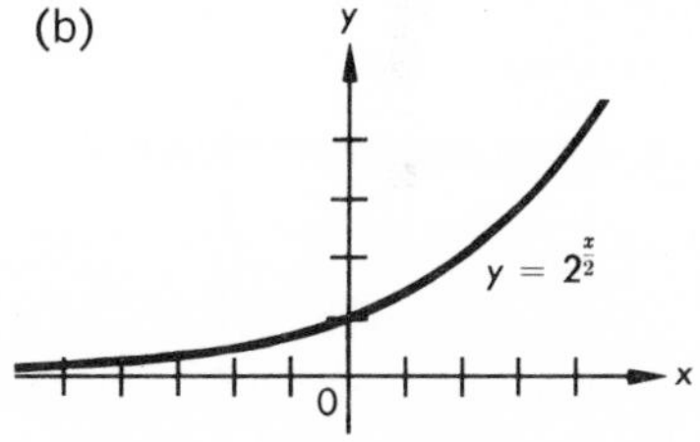

(c)

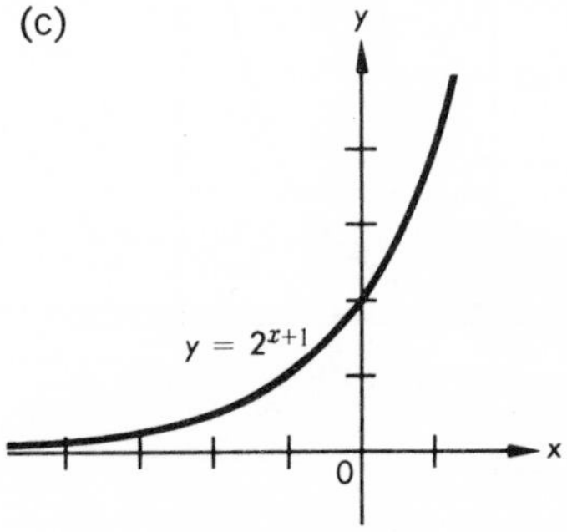

Answer to Exercise for Discussion 4(c)

4. (c) $E(t) = 150 \times 2^{-.002t}$
$E(x) = \frac{150}{8}$
$= 150 \times 2^{-3}$
$^{-}.002x = {}^{-}3$
$x = 1500$

Exercises

It is recommended that Exercises 8 and 9 be discussed in class before the exercises on the next page are assigned.

Exercises 10–13 on the opposite page are of general interest since most students will have had some of this material in their science classes.

In a minimum course, you may wish to omit Exercises 14 and 15. If they are covered, it is recommended that the algebra be related to a graph.

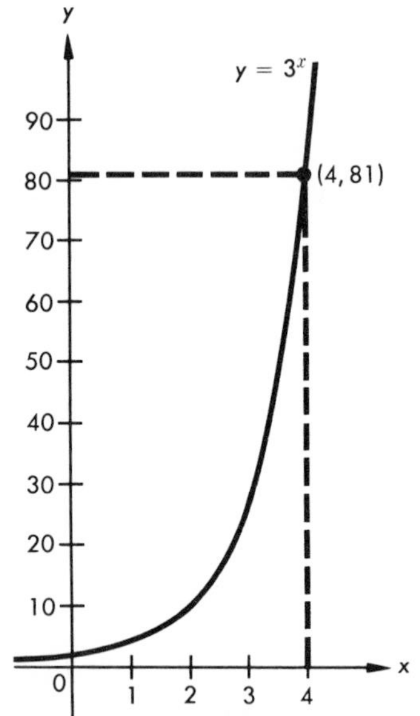

14(a)

$x < 4, 3^x < 81$
$x > 4, 3^x > 81$

4. The decay curve of a radioactive element is exponential. If the initial quantity of an element is a, then the quantity present after t units of time is given by the function

$$E(t) = a \times b^{-t}.$$

The base b will depend on the element and also on the choice of units for time. Consider the specific law of decay

$$E(t) = 150 \times 2^{-.002t},$$

where t is the time, in years, and $E(t)$ is the amount, in milligrams, of a radioactive substance present at time t.

(a) What is the initial quantity? $E(0) = 150$
(b) How much is left after 1000 years? $E(1000) = 150 \times 2^{-2} = 37.5$
(c) How long does it take for the initial quantity to decay to $\frac{1}{8}$ the original amount?
(d) Will the amount present ever vanish completely? No

Exercises

See Solution Manual for graphs.

In Exercises 1–5, graph each of the following exponential curves. In some cases, you may find it necessary to choose different scales for the two axes.

1. $y = 10^x$ 2. $y = (\frac{1}{10})^x$ 3. $y = 2^{2x}$
4. $y = (\sqrt{2})^x$ 5. $y = (\sqrt{2})^{-x}$

6. Compare the graph of $y = 2^{x-1} - 1$ with that of $y = 2^x$.
7. Graph $y = 3^{\frac{x}{2}}$ and compare it with the graph of $y = 3^x$.

△

8. The following exponential function describes the growth of bacteria.

$$E(t) = 3 \times 16^t$$

(a) What is the initial number of bacteria? 3
(b) After $\frac{1}{4}$ hour, how many bacteria are there? 6
(c) After $\frac{1}{2}$ hour, how many bacteria are there? 12
(d) After 1 hour, how many bacteria are there? 48

9. A culture of bacteria, which contains 2000 bacteria, has a count of 18,000 bacteria after 2 hours. Assuming the exponential law of growth, show that the following function fits the above conditions:
See Solution Manual.

$$E(t) = 2 \times 3^t.$$

Here $E(t)$ is the number of thousands of bacteria present after t hours. Find the number of bacteria present after 1 hour. 6000

10. A culture with an initial count of 1000 bacteria contains 8000 bacteria 3 hours later. Assuming exponential growth, find the growth formula. How long does it take this culture to double in size? $E(t) = 2^t$; one hour

11. Sometimes the population growth of a town approximately follows an exponential law for the limited period of time. Assuming this type of growth, find the estimated population in 1970 for a hypothetical town, given the following data. 10,000

1950 population	5000
1960 population	7070

12. The half-life of radium is known to be approximately 1600 years, since it takes 1600 years for a given quantity of radium to decay to one-half its initial mass. Start with 300 milligrams of radium, and verify that the law of decay is given by See Solution Manual.

$$E(t) = 300 \times 2^{-\frac{t}{1600}}.$$

Find the quantity present at the end of the first 800 years. 212.1 milligrams

13. A radioactive element has a law of decay given by

$$E(t) = 400 \times 4^{-\frac{t}{1000}}.$$

Determine its half-life by finding the time at which the amount present is one-half the original amount. 500 years

▲

14. When $b > 1$, the graph of $E(x) = b^x$ rises steadily, that is

$$b^{x_1} > b^{x_2} \quad \text{if, and only if,} \quad x_1 > x_2.$$

We may use this property of the exponential function to solve such inequalities as $2^x > 32$, since $32 = 2^5$ and $2^x > 2^5$ if, and only if, $x > 5$. In other words, the solution set of this inequality is

$$\{x \mid x > 5\}.$$

Solve each of the following inequalities.

(a) $3^x \leq 81$ $\{x \mid x \leq 4\}$ (b) $3^{2x} > 27$ $\{x \mid x > \frac{3}{2}\}$
(c) $4^x < 8$ $\{x \mid x < \frac{3}{2}\}$ (d) $2^x > 1$ $\{x \mid x > 0\}$

15. Inequalities such as $(\frac{1}{3})^x > \frac{1}{81}$ involve the exponential function with a base less than 1. Such inequalities can be solved by the use of the property stated in Exercise 14 since $(\frac{1}{3})^x = 3^{-x}$ and $\frac{1}{81} = 3^{-4}$. Thus, $3^{-x} > 3^{-4}$ if, and only if, $^-x > {}^-4$ or $x < 4$.
Solve each of the following inequalities.

(a) $(\frac{1}{32})^{2x} < \frac{1}{64}$ $\{x \mid x > \frac{3}{5}\}$ (b) $(\frac{4}{9})^{3x} < \frac{32}{243}$ $\{x \mid x > \frac{5}{6}\}$
(c) $128^{-x} \geq 16$ $\{x \mid x \leq \frac{-4}{7}\}$ (d) $(\frac{1}{2})^x > 64$ $\{x \mid x < {}^-6\}$

Quiz

1. Graph the following exponential function:

$$E(x) = 3^x - 3.$$

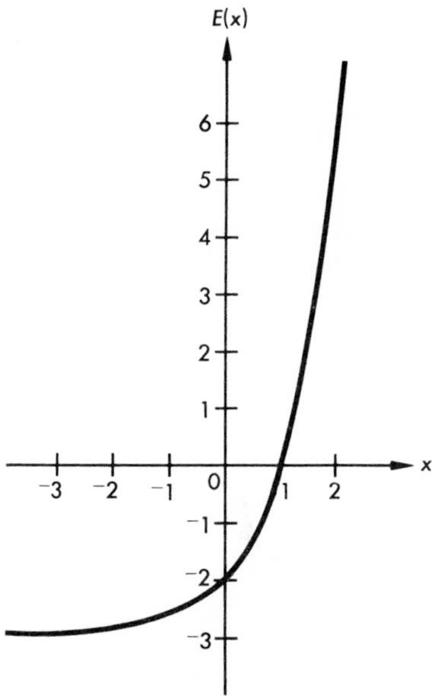

2. The following exponential function describes the growth of bacteria, where t is time measured in hours and $E(t)$ is the number, in thousands, of bacteria in a culture:

$$E(t) = 9^t.$$

(a) What is the initial number of bacteria? (ans: 1,000)
(b) After $\frac{1}{2}$ hour, how many bacteria are there? (ans: 3,000)
(c) After 1 hour, how many bacteria are there? (ans: 9,000)

*6-5 THE ALGEBRA OF FUNCTIONS

Section 6-5 is optional, not because it is difficult, but because it is not absolutely essential. Therefore, it may be omitted or postponed until after the essential topics of the chapter have been covered.

This section could also be assigned for independent study by interested, competent students.

*6-5 THE ALGEBRA OF FUNCTIONS

We shall consider only functions which have the set of real numbers as their domains and ranges. We shall show how the operations of the real number system lead to corresponding operations with functions.

If f and g are functions, then we define $f + g$, the sum of f and g, as

$$(f + g)(x) = f(x) + g(x),$$
$$\textit{domain of } (f + g) = (\textit{domain of } f) \cap (\textit{domain of } g).$$

For example, if

$$f(x) = x^2 \quad \text{and} \quad g(x) = 5x,$$

then the function $f + g$ associates with each number x the sum of x^2 and $5x$:

$$(f + g)(x) = x^2 + 5x.$$

Here the domains of f and g are assumed to be the set R of all real numbers. Thus, the domain of $f + g$ is also the set of all real numbers.

Similarly, we define fg, the product of two functions f and g, as

$$(fg)(x) = f(x)g(x),$$
$$\textit{domain of } (fg) = (\textit{domain of } f) \cap (\textit{domain of } g).$$

For example, let us consider the functions above. If

$$f(x) = x^2 \quad \text{and} \quad g(x) = 5x,$$

then the function fg associates with each number x the product of x^2 and $5x$:

$$fg(x) = x^2 \cdot 5x, \quad \text{or } 5x^3.$$

Since f and g have R as their domain, fg also has R as its domain.

As another example, let

$$f(x) = \sqrt{36 - 4x^2} \quad \text{and} \quad g(x) = x + 1.$$

The domain S of function f is the set of all numbers for which $f(x)$ is a real number:

$$S = \{x \mid 36 - 4x^2 \geqq 0\}.$$

Thus,

$$\begin{aligned} S &= \{x \mid 4x^2 \leqq 36\} \\ &= \{x \mid x^2 \leqq 9\} \\ &= \{x \mid {}^-3 \leqq x \leqq 3\}. \end{aligned}$$

The domain R of function g is the set of all real numbers. The function $f + g$ is defined by

$$(f + g)(x) = \sqrt{36 - 4x^2} + (x + 1),$$
$$\text{domain of } (f + g) = S \cap R = S.$$

The function fg is defined by

$$(fg)(x) = (x + 1)\sqrt{36 - 4x^2},$$
$$\text{domain of } (fg) = S \cap R = S.$$

We can graph the function $f + g$ by graphing f and g in the same coordinate system and then *adding ordinates.* In other words, for each x, we add the y-coordinates of the points ($(x, f(x))$ and $(x, g(x))$, and obtain the point $(x, f(x) + g(x))$ on the graph of $f + g$. This is illustrated in Fig. 6–6 for the functions considered previously:

$$f(x) = \sqrt{36 - 4x^2}$$

and

$$g(x) = x + 1.$$

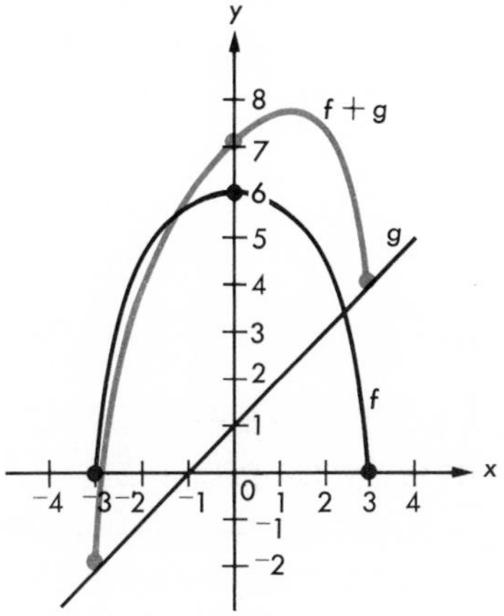

FIGURE 6–6

Exercises

See Solution Manual for graphs.

In Exercises 1–10, give the sum and product functions. Specify the domain of each sum and product function.

1. $f(x) = 3x + 2, \quad g(x) = x - 3$ $4x-1;\ 3x^2-7x-6$; both domains: all reals
2. $f(x) = x, \quad g(x) = 2^x$ $x+2^x;\ x\cdot 2^x$; both domains: all reals
3. $f(x) = x, \quad g(x) = \dfrac{1}{x^2}$ $x+\frac{1}{x^2};\ \frac{1}{x}$; both: $\{x \mid x \neq 0\}$
4. $f(x) = \sqrt{9 - x^2}, \quad g(x) = x^2$ $\sqrt{9-x^2}+x^2;\ x^2\sqrt{9-x^2}$; both: $\{x \mid {}^-3 \leqq x \leqq 3\}$
5. $f(x) = x, \quad g(x) = \dfrac{1}{x}$ $x+\frac{1}{x};\ 1$; both: $\{x \mid x \neq 0\}$
6. $f(x) = x, \quad g(x) = \sqrt{x^2 + 1}$ $x+\sqrt{x^2+1};\ x\sqrt{x^2+1}$; both: all reals
7. $f(x) = \dfrac{1}{x}, \quad g(x) = x^2 + x - 3$ $\frac{1}{x}+x^2+x-3;\ x+1-\frac{3}{x}$; both: $\{x \mid x \neq 0\}$
8. $f(x) = 3^x, \quad g(x) = 2^x$ $3^x+2^x;\ 6^x$; both: all reals
9. $f(x) = \sqrt{16 - x^2}, \quad g(x) = 4 - x$ $\sqrt{16-x^2}+4-x;\ (4-x)\sqrt{16-x^2}$; both: $\{x \mid {}^-4 \leqq x \leqq 4\}$
10. $f(x) = \sqrt{16 - x^2}, \quad g(x) = {}^-\sqrt{16 - x^2}$ $0;\ x^2-16$; both: $\{x \mid {}^-4 \leqq x \leqq 4\}$

TWISTER

An ancient Scottish rectangular castle, each of whose dimensions is an integral number of meters, is surrounded by a moat 5 meters wide. The height of the castle is twice its length and 3 times its width. Find the dimensions of the castle if the area of the castle and the area of the moat are equal.

Solution: The floor of the castle is 20 by 30 meters and the height is 60 meters.

Any of Exercises 11–17 may profitably be used in class to consider graphing the sum of two functions when each function alone is a familiar one. The work should be done on graph paper where a careful job of block counting is possible.

Quiz

In Exercises 1-4, give the sum and product functions and specify the domain of each.

1. $f(x) = x^2$, $g(x) = 2x + 1$
   (ans: $x^2 + 2x + 1$, $2x^3 + x^2$; both domains: all reals)
2. $f(x) = \frac{1}{x^3}$, $g(x) = x$
   (ans: $\frac{1}{x^3} + x$, $\frac{1}{x^2}$; both domains: $\{x \mid x \neq 0\}$)
3. $f(x) = 2^x$, $g(x) = 2^{(1/2)x}$
   (ans: $2^x + 2^{(1/2)x}$, $2^{(3/2)x}$; both domains: all reals)
4. $f(x) = \sqrt{9 - x^2}$, $g(x) = 3 + x$
   (ans: $\sqrt{9 - x^2} + 3 + x$, $(3 + x)\sqrt{9 - x^2}$; both domains: $\{x \mid {}^-3 \leqq x \leqq 3\}$)

Use the technique of *adding ordinates* to graph each function h below.

11. $f(x) = 2x, \quad g(x) = \frac{1}{x}, \quad h(x) = 2x + \frac{1}{x}$

12. $h(x) = 2^x + 2^{-x}$

13. $h(x) = x + \frac{1}{x^2}$

14. $h(x) = x + 2^x$

15. $h(x) = x - 4x^3$

16. $h(x) = x + \frac{1}{x - 1}$

17. $h(x) = x + |x|$

In Exercises 18–26, tell whether the equation $f(a + b) = f(a) + f(b)$ is true for every pair a, b of numbers in the domain of f. For example, if $f(x) = 3x$, we have $f(a + b) = 3(a + b)$ and $f(a) = 3a$, $f(b) = 3b$. Then because $3(a + b) = 3a + 3b$, the equation $f(a + b) = f(a) + f(b)$ is true for this particular f.

18. $f(x) = 3x + 2$ F
19. $f(x) = x^2$ F
20. $f(x) = {}^-6x$ T
21. $f(x) = 3^x$ F
22. $f(x) = \sqrt{x}$ F
23. $f(x) = 2^{-x}$ F
24. $f(x) = |x|$ F
25. $f(x) = 5$ F
26. $f(x) = x^3$ F

27. For which of the functions in Exercises 18–26 is the following equation true: $f(ab) = f(a) \cdot f(b)$? 19, 22, 24, 26

28. For which of the functions in Exercises 18–26 is the following equation true: $f(a + b) = f(a) \cdot f(b)$? 21, 23

29. For which of the function in Exercises 18–26 is the following equation true: $f(ab) = f(a) + f(b)$? None

KEY IDEAS AND KEY WORDS

If to each value of one variable there corresponds a unique value of a second variable, then the correspondence between these two variables is called a **function.** If to each value of a variable x there corresponds a unique value of a variable y, then we say **y is a function of x.**

The set of values of x is called the **domain of the function,** and the set of values of y is called the **range of the function.**

For each element x of the domain, the corresponding element y of the range is called the **image** of x under the function.

When we use the **functional notation** $f(x)$, the letter f designates a function and $f(x)$ denotes the image of x under the function f.

If f denotes a function, then the graph of the set of all ordered pairs $(x, f(x))$ is called the **graph of the function.**

The **linear function** f is defined by the first-degree equation

$$f(x) = mx + b.$$

The function f, defined by

$$f(x) = x^n$$

for some number n, is called the **power function with exponent n.** Its domain is the set of all real numbers having an nth power.

The function f, defined by

$$f(x) = b^x$$

where b is a positive real number that is not equal to one and x is a real number, is called the **exponential function with the base b.**

The **sum function** of two functions f and g is defined as the function $f + g$, where

$$(f + g)(x) = f(x) + g(x).$$

The **domain of the sum function** $(f + g)$ is defined as

$$(\text{domain of } f) \cap (\text{domain of } g).$$

The product function of two functions f and g is defined as the function fg, where

$$(fg)(x) = f(x)g(x).$$

The **domain of the product function** fg is defined as

$$(\text{domain of } f) \cap (\text{domain of } g).$$

The sum function, $(f + g)$, may be graphed by **adding ordinates,** if for each x, we add the y-coordinates of the points $(x, f(x))$ and $(x, g(x))$, obtaining the point $(x, f(x) + g(x))$ on the graph of $f + g$.

The function f, defined by

$$f(x) = c$$

where c is a single real number, is called a **constant function.**

CHAPTER REVIEW

See Solution Manual for graphs.

1. The number of degrees centigrade, C, is related to the number of degrees Fahrenheit, F, by the formula $C = \frac{5}{9}(F - 32)$.
   (a) Solve this equation for F and express the resulting formula in functional notation. $F(C) = \frac{9}{5}C + 32$
   (b) Find F(0), F(100), and F($^-40$). 32, 212, $^-40$
   (c) What type of function is F? Linear
2. Boyle's law states that the volume V of a gas kept at constant temperature varies inversely with the pressure P. For a particular gas kept at a certain temperature, a volume of 300 cubic inches is formed under a pressure of 15 pounds per square inch. Write an expression for the volume function V and use it to find $V(20)$. $V(P) = \frac{4500}{P}$; 225

3. Graph each of the following functions and give the domain.

(a) $f(x) = \dfrac{1}{3x+6}$ $D = \{x \mid x \neq {}^-2\}$ (b) $f(x) = \sqrt{16 - x^2}$ $D = \{x \mid {}^-4 \leqq x \leqq 4\}$

(c) $f(x) = 2^x$ $D = \{\text{all reals}\}$ (d) $f(x) = x^{\frac{1}{4}}$ $D = \{x \mid x \geqq 0\}$

4. (a) If a function f is defined by the equation

$$f(x) = \frac{3}{x^2} - 4,$$

what real numbers must be excluded from the domain of f? $x = 0$

(b) For the function f in part (a), find

$f(0)$, $f(\frac{1}{2})$, $f({}^-\frac{1}{2})$, $f(1)$, $f({}^-1)$, $f(3)$, $f({}^-3)$, $f(\frac{3}{2})$, $f(6)$.
Undefined, 8, 8, ${}^-1$, ${}^-1$, ${}^-3\frac{2}{3}$, ${}^-3\frac{2}{3}$, ${}^-2\frac{2}{3}$, ${}^-3\frac{11}{12}$

(c) Graph the function f.

5. If the domain of the function f is $\{x \mid {}^-2 \leqq x \leqq 4\}$ and $f(x) = x - 1$, graph each of the following equations.

(a) $y = f(x)$ (b) $y = f({}^-x)$

(c) $y = f(|x|)$ (d) $y = f(x + 2)$

6. Graph the function defined by the equation

$$f(x) = \left[\frac{x}{2}\right].$$

Remember that the notation for greatest integer in x is $[x]$.

7. The function g whose domain is the set of real numbers is defined as follows:

$$g(x) = \begin{cases} 0 & \text{if } x \text{ is a negative number,} \\ x & \text{if } x \text{ is a non-negative number.} \end{cases}$$

Find $g({}^-3)$, $g({}^-2)$, $g(0)$, $g(\frac{7}{4})$, $g(\sqrt{5})$, $g(6)$, and $g(\pi)$.
0, 0, 0, $\frac{7}{4}$, $\sqrt{5}$, 6, π

8. Graph each of the following functions on the same set of axes.

(a) $f(x) = x - 3$ (b) $g(x) = (x - 3)^2$

(c) $h(x) = (x - 3)^3$ (d) $k(x) = (x - 3)^4$

9. The law of decay of a radioactive element is given by

$$A = 700 \times 8^{-\frac{t}{1500}}.$$

Determine the half-life of the element by finding the time at which the amount present is one-half the original amount. 500 years

10. Find the sum and product of functions f and g, defined by the equations
$\sqrt{x^2-4} + x$; $x\sqrt{x^2-4}$

$$f(x) = \sqrt{x^2 - 4}, \quad g(x) = x.$$

Give the domains of f, g, $f + g$, and fg. $\{x \mid x \leqq {}^-2 \text{ or } x \geqq 2\}$; all reals; $\{x \mid x \leqq {}^-2 \text{ or } x \geqq 2\}$; $\{x \mid x \leqq {}^-2 \text{ or } x \geqq 2\}$

TWISTER

A rancher used 139 yards of barbed wire to enclose a rectangular grazing area and also to construct a fence along one of the diagonals, a distance of 41 yards. Later, he discovered that another rancher had used less barbed wire in enclosing a one-third larger rectangular grazing area in the same manner. If all dimensions are integral yards, what are the dimensions of the second rancher's field?

Solution: The second rancher's field is 16 by 30 yards; the diagonal is 34 yards, and the total barbed wire used is 126 yards.

CHAPTER TEST

The material included in the Chapter Test was covered in the following sections:

Problems 1-5—Section 6-2
Problem 6—Section 6-3
Problem 7(a)—Section 6-1
Problem 7(b)—Section 6-3
Problem 8—Section 6-2
Problem 9—Section 6-1
Problem 10—Section 6-5

CHAPTER TEST

1. The function f with a domain that is the set of real numbers is defined by the equation

$$f(x) = 3x^2.$$

Find each of the following.

(a) $f(0)$ 0 (b) $f(^-2)$ 12 (c) $f(5)$ 75

(d) $f(1 + \sqrt{2})$ $9+6\sqrt{2}$ (e) $f(1 - \sqrt{2})$ $9-6\sqrt{2}$

Give the domain (within the set of real numbers) of each of the functions defined in Exercises 2–5.

2. $h(x) = x - 2$ $D =$ all reals

3. $f(x) = \dfrac{1}{2x - 1}$ $D = \{x \mid x \neq \frac{1}{2}\}$

4. $g(x) = \sqrt{9 - x^2}$ $D = \{x \mid {}^-3 \leq x \leq 3\}$

5. $k(x) = x^{\frac{1}{3}}$ $D =$ all reals

6. Graph each of the following functions.

(a) $f(x) = x - 2$ (b) $f(x) = \sqrt{9 - x^2}$

7. A rectangular area is enclosed by 200 feet of fence.

(a) Express the area A as a function of the length x of one side of the rectangle. $x(100 - x)$

(b) Using an appropriate domain, graph the function. $D = \{x \mid 0 < x < 100\}$

8. If $y = 3x + 7$, solve the equation for x in terms of y, and express x as a function of y. $f(y) = \frac{1}{3}y - \frac{7}{3}$

9. Which of the following tables determine a function of x? of y? of neither?

(a) x

x	y
1	0
2	0
3	0

(b) y

x	y
0	1
0	2
0	3

(c) x and y

x	y
1	1
2	2
3	3

(d) Neither

x	y
1	1
1	2
2	2

10. Graph the following function, using the technique of *adding ordinates*.

$$h(x) = \sqrt{25 - x^2} + \tfrac{3}{4}x$$

Answers to Chapter Test Problems 6, 7(b), 10

6. (a)

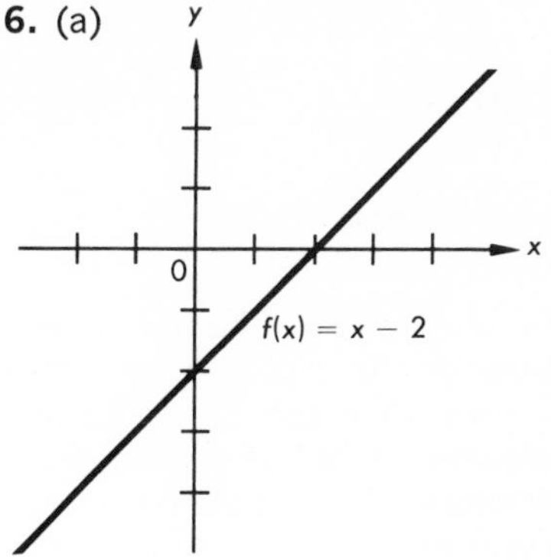

(b)

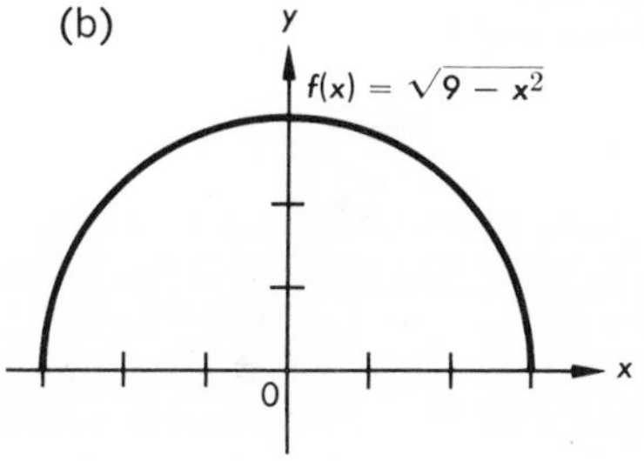

7. (b)

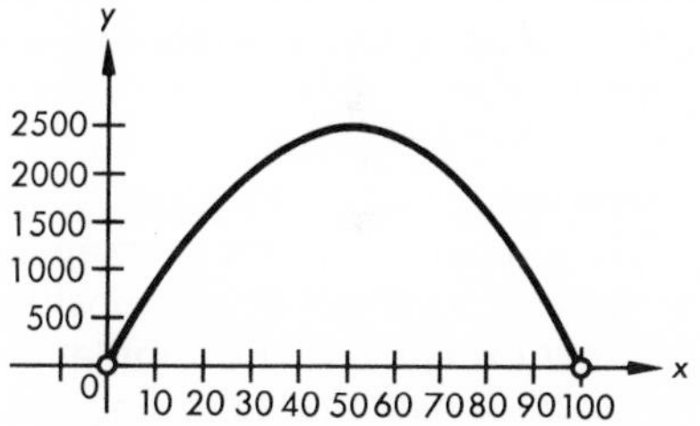

10.

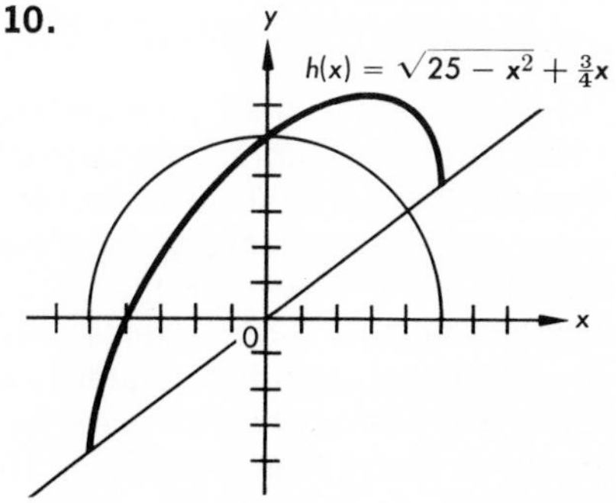

CHAPTER 7

Logarithms

The purpose of Chapter 7 is to introduce the topic of logarithms, not only as a tool to be used in computation, but as a function.

A table of the positive integral powers of 2 enables multiplication to be done easily with those numbers such as 128 and 8192 which happen to be positive integral powers of 2. In order to find

$$128 \times 8192,$$

it may be read from the table that $128 = 2^7$ and $8192 = 2^{13}$. To find the product of 128×8192, the exponential form of the factors is used and $2^7 \times 2^{13}$ is found by adding exponents. Thus,

$$128 \times 8192 \doteq 2^{7+13} \text{ or } 2^{20}.$$

If the exponential form of the product is unacceptable, a second reference to the table indicates that 2^{20} in ordinary decimal form is 1,048,576.

Every positive number may be written as a power of any positive number except 1. For example, the number 8 has the following representations in exponential form:

$$8 = 2^3,\ 4^{3/2},\ 8^1,\ 64^{1/2},\ (\tfrac{1}{16})^{-3/4}.$$

However, rather than considering many different representations of one number, it is desired to consider expressing every positive number as a power of the same positive number. Since ten is the base for our number system, a table expressing the numbers between 1 and 10 as powers of 10 makes it possible also to express as powers of 10 those positive num-

CHAPTER 7

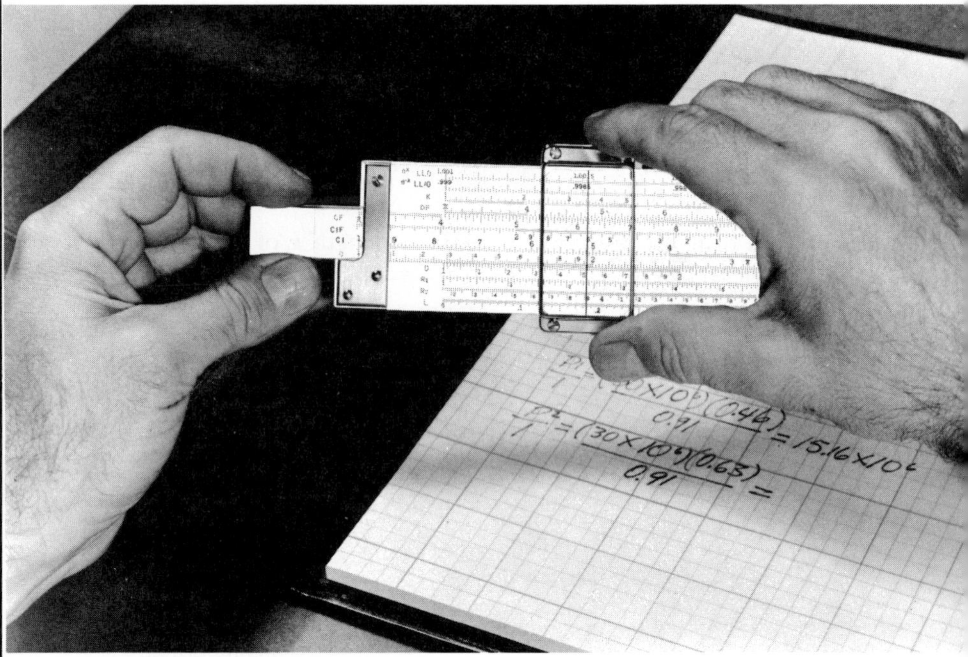

Unlike the common ruler which has a linear scale, the slide rule has a logarithmic scale. (Courtesy of Frederick Post Company)

LOGARITHMS

There are two general classes of functions, algebraic and transcendental. Included in the class of algebraic functions are polynomial functions, such as

$$f(x) = 3x^2 - 4x + 2,$$

rational functions, such as

$$g(x) = \frac{3x + 1}{3x - 1},$$

and functions involving roots, such as

$$h(x) = \sqrt{4 - x^2}.$$

Included in the class of transcendental functions are the exponential functions studied in Chapter 6, logarithmic functions to be studied in this chapter, and trigonometric functions to be studied in Chapters 9 and 10.

Exponential functions, such as

$$f(x) = 10^x,$$

are rapidly changing functions:

$$f(1) = 10, \quad f(2) = 100, \quad f(6) = 1{,}000{,}000.$$

Logarithmic functions are the opposite; they are slowly changing functions. If $g(x)$ is the logarithm of x to the base 10, then

$$g(1) = 0, \quad g(10) = 1, \quad g(1{,}000{,}000) = 6.$$

Both types of functions play an important role in mathematics and its applications in science.

bers which are less than 1 or greater than 10. Therefore, this less extensive table suffices, and is the one which appears in the appendix of the text.

Logarithms are just exponents. Every law of exponents translates into a corresponding law of logarithms. Any positive number may be written in scientific notation so that the law

$$\log_{10}(a \cdot b) = \log_{10}a + \log_{10}b$$

makes it possible to use the limited table on page 616 to find the common logarithm of the given positive number.

It is important for the students to observe the fact that a table for converting positive numbers to powers of 10, also makes it possible to convert positive numbers to powers of any positive number other than one. Thus, it is necessary to have a logarithm table for only one power and for decimal notation that table is for powers of 10.

The following are some of the topics covered in Chapter 7:

- *The logarithm function*
- *Laws of logarithms*
- *Common logarithms*
- *Characteristic of the logarithm*
- *Mantissa of the logarithm*
- *Antilogarithm*
- *Graph of the logarithm function*

It is suggested that one day be spent on each section of this chapter, except that you may wish to include some of the material in Section 7-2 with the material in Section 7-1. It is also possible that you may not wish to spend too much time on computing with logarithms.

7-1 COMPUTING WITH A TABLE OF POWERS

This material may be used as introductory classroom work after which you could go on into the next section.

7-1 COMPUTING WITH A TABLE OF POWERS

Logarithms and exponents are closely related to each other. Before defining the logarithm of a number, let us indicate how exponents can be used to work problems of arithmetic. Logarithmic computations are carried out in a very similar way, as we shall see in later sections.

The table below lists the first twenty positive integral powers of 2.

$2^1 = 2$	$2^6 = 64$	$2^{11} = 2048$	$2^{16} = 65{,}536$
$2^2 = 4$	$2^7 = 128$	$2^{12} = 4096$	$2^{17} = 131{,}072$
$2^3 = 8$	$2^8 = 256$	$2^{13} = 8192$	$2^{18} = 262{,}144$
$2^4 = 16$	$2^9 = 512$	$2^{14} = 16{,}384$	$2^{19} = 524{,}288$
$2^5 = 32$	$2^{10} = 1024$	$2^{15} = 32{,}768$	$2^{20} = 1{,}048{,}576$

We can use this table to solve the following arithmetic problems.

$$\begin{aligned} 32 \times 512 &= 2^5 \times 2^9 \\ &= 2^{5+9}, \quad \text{or } 2^{14} \\ &= 16{,}384 \end{aligned}$$

$$\begin{aligned} 131{,}072 \div 256 &= 2^{17} \div 2^8 \\ &= 2^{17-8}, \quad \text{or } 2^9 \\ &= 512 \end{aligned}$$

$$\begin{aligned} \sqrt[3]{32{,}768} &= \sqrt[3]{2^{15}} \\ &= (2^{15})^{\frac{1}{3}}, \quad \text{or } 2^5 \\ &= 32 \end{aligned}$$

$$\begin{aligned} 32^4 &= (2^5)^4 \\ &= 2^{20} \\ &= 1{,}048{,}576 \end{aligned}$$

These arithmetic problems are easily solved primarily because each number involved appears in the table. Secondly, each operation is carried out by adding, subtracting, multiplying, or dividing simple exponents according to the laws of exponents. The table would be of no use with problems not involving powers of 2. For example, it would not help us find 132×8046. However, more extensive tables can be constructed to work all such problems to yield at least approximate results.

Exercises for Discussion

Continue the table on page 270 through 2^{25}. Use the table to do the computation and to answer the questions in Exercises 1–12.

1. 8192×128 $2^{13} \times 2^{7} = 2^{20} = 1{,}048{,}576$

2. $2{,}097{,}152 \div 1024$ $2^{21} \div 2^{10} = 2^{11} = 2048$

3. $(512)^2$ $(2^9)^2 = 2^{18} = 262{,}144$

4. $\sqrt{65{,}536}$ $\sqrt{2^{16}} = 2^8 = 256$

5. $\sqrt[3]{2{,}097{,}152}$ $\sqrt[3]{2^{21}} = 2^7 = 128$

6. $\dfrac{64 \times 128}{2048}$ $\dfrac{2^6 \times 2^7}{2^{11}} = \dfrac{2^{13}}{2^{11}} = 2^2 = 4$

7. 16^5 $(2^4)^5 = 2^{20} = 1{,}048{,}576$

8. $(16{,}777{,}216)^{\frac{2}{3}}$ $(2^{24})^{\frac{2}{3}} = 2^{16} = 65{,}536$

9. Find x if $2^x = 32{,}768$. $2^x = 2^{15}$, $x = 15$

10. Find x if $2^x = (32{,}768)^{\frac{1}{2}}$. $2^x = 2^{\frac{15}{2}}$, $x = \frac{15}{2}$

11. Find x if $4^x = 8{,}388{,}608$. $2^{2x} = 2^{23}$, $2x = 23$, $x = \frac{23}{2}$

12. Is there an entry in the table representing $2^6 + 2^7$?
No, $2^6 + 2^7 = 2^6(1+2)$, which is not a positive integral power of 2.

Exercises

Use the table of positive integral powers of 2 to compute the following.

1. $16 \cdot 512$ 8192

2. $131{,}072 \div 32{,}768$ 4

3. $(256)^3$ 16,777,216

4. $(8{,}388{,}608) \div (4096 \times 32)$ 64

5. $(1{,}048{,}576)^{-\frac{3}{4}}$ $\frac{1}{32{,}768}$

6. $\left(\dfrac{262{,}144}{512 \times 16{,}384}\right)^2$ $\frac{1}{1024}$

7. $\sqrt{\dfrac{524{,}288 \times 8192}{4{,}194{,}304}}$ 32

8. $\sqrt{2^3 + 2^3}$ 4

9. $\sqrt{\frac{1}{8} \times 2048}$ 16

10. $\dfrac{32{,}768 \times \sqrt{4096}}{(256)^{\frac{3}{4}} \times \sqrt[3]{512}}$ 4096

△

Make a table of positive integral powers of 3 through 3^{15}. Use the table to do the following exercises.

11. 243×6561 1,594,323

12. $1{,}594{,}323 \div 2187$ 729

13. $\sqrt[3]{14{,}348{,}907}$ 243

14. $(2187)^2$ 4,782,969

15. $(4{,}782{,}969)^{\frac{2}{7}}$ 81

16. $(531{,}441)^{-\frac{5}{6}}$ $\frac{1}{59{,}049}$

17. Find x if $3^x = 6561$. $x = 8$

18. Find x if $3^x = \frac{1}{6561}$. $x = -8$

19. Find x if $9^x = 2187$. $x = \frac{7}{2}$

20. Find x if $3^{2x+1} = 243$. $x = 2$

21. Find x if $9^{2x} = 19{,}683$. $x = \frac{9}{4}$

▲

22. Find x and y if $2^{x+y} = 16{,}384$ and $3^{x-y} = 729$. $x = 10$, $y = 4$

23. Use the tables of powers of 2 and of 3 to find the following.

(a) 6^5 7776 (b) 12^4 20,736 (c) 18^4 104,976

Exercises for Discussion

If time is limited, it is suggested that the table on the preceding page be used, and that at least Exercises for Discussion 4, 6, 9, 10, and 12 be covered.

Table Required in Exercises for Discussion

$2^{21} = 2{,}097{,}152$
$2^{22} = 4{,}194{,}304$
$2^{23} = 8{,}388{,}608$
$2^{24} = 16{,}777{,}216$
$2^{25} = 33{,}554{,}432$

Exercises

It is recommended that Exercises 11–23 be assigned.

Table Required in Exercises 11–23

$3^1 = 3$
$3^2 = 9$
$3^3 = 27$
$3^4 = 81$
$3^5 = 243$
$3^6 = 729$
$3^7 = 2{,}187$
$3^8 = 6{,}561$
$3^9 = 19{,}683$
$3^{10} = 59{,}049$
$3^{11} = 177{,}147$
$3^{12} = 531{,}441$
$3^{13} = 1{,}594{,}323$
$3^{14} = 4{,}782{,}969$
$3^{15} = 14{,}348{,}907$

Quiz

Use the table of positive integral powers of 2 to compute the following.

1. $1024 \cdot 512$ (ans: 524,288)

2. $(32)^4$ (ans: 1,048,576)

3. $16{,}384 \div 256$ (ans: 64)

4. $\sqrt{4096}$ (ans: 64)

5. $\dfrac{128 \cdot 512}{65536}$ (ans: 1)

6. $\sqrt{\frac{1}{4} \cdot 1024}$ (ans: 16)

7-2 LOGARITHMS

The exponential and logarithmic equations may be used in pairs until the idea becomes established in the minds of the students that the statements are inverses.

Several questions may be asked concerning logarithms. What is a logarithm? Is it an exponent? How many logarithms does 8 have? Does the logarithm of 8 depend on the base? The logarithm of 8 is defined thus:

If $b^x = 8$, then $x = \log_b 8$.

To show that logarithms, like exponents, may be negative or positive, integral or fractional, and that a number has many logarithms, depending on what the base is, a set of statements may be built up such as the following:

Since $2^6 = 64$, 6 is the logarithm of 64 when the base is 2.
Since $4^3 = 64$, 3 is the logarithm of 64 when the base is 4.
Since $8^2 = 64$, 2 is the logarithm of 64 when the base is 8.
Since $(\frac{1}{4})^{-3} = 64$, $^-3$ is the logarithm of 64 when the base is $\frac{1}{4}$.
Since $32^{6/5} = 64$, $\frac{6}{5}$ is the logarithm of 64 when the base is 32.

Sentences such as the above may be written on the board before using the abbreviated form:

If $(\frac{1}{8})^{-2} = 64$, then $^-2 = \log_{1/8} 64$.

7-2 LOGARITHMS

Let us consider an exponential function E, defined by

$$E(x) = b^x,$$

where $b > 0$ and $b \neq 1$.

The domain of E is the set of all real numbers, and the range of E is the set of *positive* real numbers. Thus, for each real number r, there exists a unique positive real number s such that $s = b^r$.

If we draw the graph of E, as shown in Fig. 7–1, then another property of the function can be seen: For each positive number s, the line $y = s$ intersects the graph of E in one, and only one, point, (r, s). This means that the range of E is the set of all positive real numbers, and that for each positive real number s, there exists a *unique* real number r such that $b^r = s$.

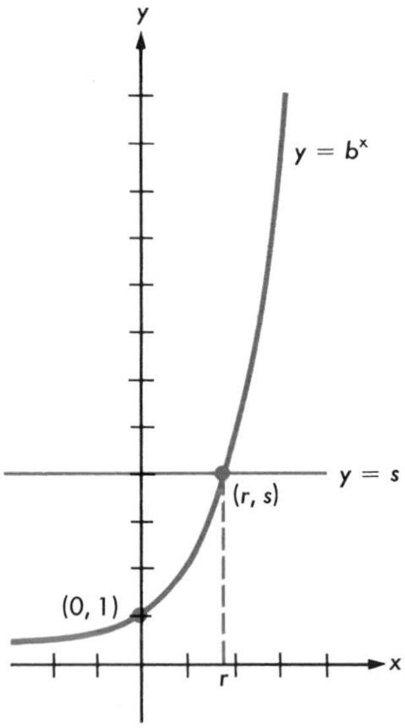

FIGURE 7–1

The remarks above lead us to define the logarithm function to the base b, denoted by $\log_b$, in the following manner.

DEFINITION OF THE LOGARITHM FUNCTION

For every positive number s,

$$\log_b s = r,$$

where r is the number such that $b^r = s$ (assuming $b > 0$ and $b \neq 1$).

According to this definition, the function $\log_b$ has the set of all pos tive real numbers as its domain. Also,

$\log_b s$ is the power to which b must be raised to give s.

To illustrate the definition, let us find each of the following logarithms.

$\log_2 16$. If we let $r = \log_2 16$, then $2^r = 16$. Since $16 = 2^4$, we conclude that $r = 4$. Thus,

$$\log_2 16 = 4.$$

$\log_2 \sqrt[3]{2}$. If we let $r = \log_2 \sqrt[3]{2}$, then $2^r = \sqrt[3]{2}$. Since $\sqrt[3]{2} = 2^{\frac{1}{3}}$, we conclude that $2^r = 2^{\frac{1}{3}}$ and $r = \frac{1}{3}$. Thus,

$$\log_2 \sqrt[3]{2} = \tfrac{1}{3}.$$

$\log_2 \frac{1}{4}$. If we let $r = \log_2 \frac{1}{4}$, then $2^r = \frac{1}{4}$. Since $\frac{1}{4} = 2^{-2}$, we conclude that $r = {}^{-}2$. Thus,

$$\log_2 \tfrac{1}{4} = {}^{-}2.$$

$\log_5 5$. If we let $r = \log_5 5$, then $5^r = 5$. Since $5^1 = 5$, we conclude that $r = 1$ and

$$\log_5 5 = 1.$$

$\log_8 16$. If we let $r = \log_8 16$, then $8^r = 16$. To find the power of 8 that is equal to 16, we replace 8 by 2^3, obtaining the equation $(2^3)^r = 16$ or, equivalently, $2^{3r} = 16$. Since $16 = 2^4$, we conclude that $2^{3r} = 2^4$ and $3r = 4$. Thus, $r = \frac{4}{3}$ and

$$\log_8 16 = \tfrac{4}{3}.$$

$\log_{\frac{1}{10}} 1000$. If we let $r = \log_{\frac{1}{10}} 1000$, then $(\frac{1}{10})^r = 1000$. Since $\frac{1}{10} = 10^{-1}$, we conclude that $(10^{-1})^r = 1000$, or

$$10^{-r} = 1000.$$

Now $1000 = 10^3$, and, therefore, ${}^{-}r = 3$ or $r = {}^{-}3$. Thus,

$$\log_{\frac{1}{10}} 1000 = {}^{-}3.$$

Each problem above is solved by making use of the fact that the two equations

$$y = \log_b x \quad \textit{and} \quad b^y = x$$

are equivalent, that is, that they have the same solution set.

The key information here is twofold:
$y = \log_b x$ and $b^y = x$ are equivalent equations; $b^r = b^x$ if, and only if, $r = x$.

Problem. Solve each of the following equations.

(a) $4 = \log_5 x$ (b) $y = \log_4 32$ (c) $\frac{2}{3} = \log_b 9$

Solution.

(a) The equation $4 = \log_5 x$ is equivalent to the equation $5^4 = x$. Hence, $x = 625$ is the solution.

(b) The equation $y = \log_4 32$ is equivalent to the equation $4^y = 32$. Since $4 = 2^2$ and $32 = 2^5$, another equivalent equation is $(2^2)^y = 2^5$, or $2^{2y} = 2^5$. Hence, $2y = 5$ and $y = \frac{5}{2}$.

(c) The equation $\frac{2}{3} = \log_b 9$ is equivalent to the equation $b^{\frac{2}{3}} = 9$. In turn, this latter equation is equivalent to the equation $(b^{\frac{2}{3}})^{\frac{3}{2}} = 9^{\frac{3}{2}}$, or $b = 9^{\frac{3}{2}}$. Hence, $b = 27$ is the solution. Although it is true that $(^-27)^{\frac{2}{3}} = (\sqrt[3]{^-27})^2$, or 9, so that $b = {}^-27$ is a solution of the equation $b^{\frac{2}{3}} = 9$, no negative number can be a base for logarithms. Thus, $b = 27$ is the only solution of the given equation.

The following properties of logarithms follow from the definition of a logarithm.

$$\log_b 1 = 0 \quad \text{since} \quad b^0 = 1$$
$$\log_b b = 1 \quad \text{since} \quad b^1 = b$$
$$\log_b b^r = r \quad \text{since} \quad b^r = b^r$$
$$\log_{\frac{1}{b}} x = {}^-\log_b x \quad \text{since} \quad \left(\frac{1}{b}\right)^r = b^{-r}$$

In view of the last property, we might as well restrict the base b to be greater than 1, for if $0 < b < 1$, then $1/b > 1$, and each logarithm to the base b is easily expressed in terms of a logarithm to the base $1/b$. For example,

$$\log_{\frac{1}{2}} 4 = {}^-\log_2 4, \quad \text{or } {}^-2,$$
$$\log_{\frac{1}{10}} .001 = {}^-\log_{10} .001, \quad \text{or } {}^-({}^-3), \quad \text{or } 3.$$

Exercises for Discussion

If time is limited, it is suggested that at least the even numbered Exercises for Discussion be covered.

Exercises for Discussion

Write the logarithmic equation that corresponds to each of the following exponential equations.

1. $3^5 = 243$ $\log_3 243 = 5$
2. $10^{-3} = .001$ $\log_{10} .001 = {}^-3$
3. $81^{\frac{3}{4}} = 27$ $\log_{81} 27 = \frac{3}{4}$
4. $N = p^q$ $\log_p N = q$

Write the exponential equation that corresponds to each of the following logarithmic equations.

5. $\log_5 125 = 3$ $5^3 = 125$
6. $\log_{10} .01 = {}^-2$ $10^{-2} = .01$
7. $\log_r N = s$ $r^s = N$

Solve each of the following equations for n.

8. $\log_2 (\frac{1}{64}) = n$ $2^n = \frac{1}{64}, 2^n = 2^{-6}, n = -6$
9. $\log_{32} n = .8$ $32^{.8} = n, (2^5)^{.8} = n, n = 2^4 = 16$
10. $\log_9 243 = n$ $9^n = 243, 3^{2n} = 3^5, 2n = 5, n = \frac{5}{2}$
11. $\log_{10} n = 6$ $10^6 = n, n = 1,000,000$

Find the value of each of the following logarithms.

12. $\log_5 \frac{1}{25}$
13. $\log_{12} 12$
14. $\log_2 \sqrt[3]{128}$
15. $\log_{10} 10{,}000$

Exercises

Write the logarithmic equation that corresponds to each of the following exponential equations.

1. $2^5 = 32$ $\log_2 32 = 5$
2. $3^{-2} = \frac{1}{9}$ $\log_3 \frac{1}{9} = -2$
3. $25^{\frac{3}{2}} = 125$ $\log_{25} 125 = \frac{3}{2}$
4. $7^0 = 1$ $\log_7 1 = 0$
5. $16^{-\frac{3}{2}} = \frac{1}{64}$ $\log_{16} \frac{1}{64} = -\frac{3}{2}$
6. $10^0 = 1$ $\log_{10} 1 = 0$
7. $16^{-\frac{3}{4}} = .125$ $\log_{16} .125 = -\frac{3}{4}$
8. $(\frac{1}{3})^{-2} = 9$ $\log_{\frac{1}{3}} 9 = -2$

Write the exponential equation that corresponds to each of the following logarithmic equations.

9. $\log_{10} 100 = 2$ $10^2 = 100$
10. $\log_8 4 = \frac{2}{3}$ $8^{\frac{2}{3}} = 4$
11. $\log_{\frac{1}{3}} 81 = -4$ $(\frac{1}{3})^{-4} = 81$
12. $\log_{25} \frac{1}{125} = -\frac{3}{2}$ $25^{-\frac{3}{2}} = \frac{1}{125}$
13. $\log_8 1 = 0$ $8^0 = 1$
14. $\log_a y = x$ $a^x = y$
15. $\log_n 256 = 2$ $n^2 = 256$
16. $\log_{16} 8 = \frac{3}{4}$ $16^{\frac{3}{4}} = 8$
17. $\log_n 9 = .4$ $n^{.4} = 9$
18. $\log_{\frac{1}{8}} 4 = -\frac{2}{3}$ $(\frac{1}{8})^{-\frac{2}{3}} = 4$

Find the value of each of the following logarithms.

19. $\log_{10} 10^2$ 2
20. $\log_2 2^{10}$ 10
21. $\log_b b^4$ 4
22. $\log_b b$ 1
23. $\log_7 \sqrt[3]{7}$ $\frac{1}{3}$
24. $\log_2 8\sqrt{32}$ $\frac{11}{2}$
25. $\log_7 \frac{1}{49}$ -2
26. $\log_3 \sqrt[5]{81}$ $\frac{4}{5}$
27. $\log_{10} \sqrt[3]{100}$ $\frac{2}{3}$
28. $\log_{27} 81$ $\frac{4}{3}$
29. $\log_{\frac{1}{10}} 100$ -2
30. $\log_{100} .001$ $-\frac{3}{2}$

△

Solve each of the following equations for n.

31. $\log_{10} .0001 = n$ -4
32. $\log_{36} n = -\frac{3}{2}$ $\frac{1}{216}$
33. $\log_n 125 = -\frac{3}{4}$ $\frac{1}{625}$
34. $\log_7 7^{-3} = n$ -3
35. $\log_{49} n = \frac{3}{2}$ 343
36. $\log_n 1000 = 1.5$ 100
37. $\log_{16} 8 = n$ $\frac{3}{4}$
38. $\log_{64} n = \frac{7}{6}$ 128
39. $\log_n (\frac{1}{81}) = -2$ 9

▲

In Exercises 40–45, solve each of the equations for x.

40. $\log_{10} 1 = x$ 0
41. $\log_x 1 = 0$ x = any positive number
42. $\log_4 x = -3$ $\frac{1}{64}$
43. $\log_x 3 = \frac{1}{4}$ 81
44. $x = \log_{36} 216$ $\frac{3}{2}$
45. $x = \log_2 2$ 1

Answers to Exercises for Discussion 12–15

12. $\log_5 \frac{1}{25} = n$, $5^n = \frac{1}{25}$, $5^n = 5^{-2}$, $n = -2$
13. $\log_{12} 12 = n$, $12^n = 12$, $n = 1$
14. $\log_2 \sqrt[3]{128} = n$, $2^n = \sqrt[3]{2^7}$, $2^n = 2^{7/3}$, $n = \frac{7}{3}$
15. $\log_{10} 10{,}000 = n$, $10^n = 10{,}000$, $10^n = 10^4$, $n = 4$

Quiz

Write the logarithmic equation that corresponds to each of the following exponential equations.

1. $16^{3/2} = 64$ (ans: $\log_{16} 64 = \frac{3}{2}$)
2. $25^{-3/2} = \frac{1}{125}$ (ans: $\log_{25} \frac{1}{125} = -\frac{3}{2}$)

Write the exponential equation that corresponds to each of the following logarithmic equations.

3. $\log_{14} 1 = 0$ (ans: $14^0 = 1$)
4. $\log_3 \frac{1}{9} = -2$ (ans: $3^{-2} = \frac{1}{9}$)

Find the value of each of the following logarithms.

5. $\log_{10} 10^4$ (ans: 4)
6. $\log_x x$ (ans: 1)

Solve each of the following equations for n.

7. $\log_8 4 = n$ (ans: 2/3)
8. $\log_n 81 = -4$ (ans: 1/3)

7-3 LOGARITHMIC GRAPHS

In making the graph of any logarithmic equation, the student should first write an equivalent exponential equation for use in constructing the table of values.

The domain of $y = \log_b x$ is the set of positive real numbers. The range is the entire set of real numbers. The students should note that this is the reverse of the situation for $y = 2^x$. They should observe that if $b > 1$, both the exponential and the logarithmic functions increase as x increases.

Exercises for Discussion, page 277

In Exercise for Discussion 1(a), $y = \log_5 x$ is equivalent to $5^y = x$. This exponential equation may be used to construct a table of values from which to graph.

x	y	
$\frac{1}{25}$	-2	$5^y = x$
$\frac{1}{5}$	-1	Select y,
1	0	compute x.
5	1	
25	2	

In relation to Exercise for Discussion 1(b), many students will observe that to obtain a table of values for $y = 5^x$, all they need do is reverse the table in 1(a):

x	y
-2	$\frac{1}{25}$
-1	$\frac{1}{5}$
0	1
1	5
2	25

Interchanging x and y in an equation reflects the graph about the 45° line through quadrants I and III, since this is the line $y = x$.

7-3 LOGARITHMIC GRAPHS

The graph of the function $\log_b$ is simply the graph of the equation

$$y = \log_b x.$$

The particular graph of $\log_2$ is sketched in Fig. 7-2 from the following table of values.

x	$\frac{1}{8}$	$\frac{1}{4}$	$\frac{1}{2}$	1	2	4	8	16
y	-3	-2	-1	0	1	2	3	4

This graph is very similar to the exponential graph with base 2 sketched in Fig. 7-1. In fact, the two graphs can be made to coincide by turning over the piece of paper on which one is drawn and placing the positive x-axis of the logarithmic graph along the positive y-axis of the exponential graph. This is so because the two equations $y = \log_2 x$ and $2^y = x$ are equivalent.

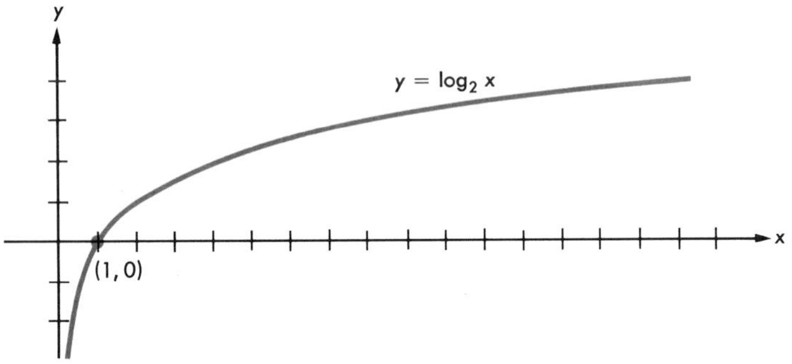

FIGURE 7-2

The logarithmic graph with base $b > 1$ has the following important properties, which are illustrated in Fig. 7-2.

1. *The entire graph is to the right of the y-axis.*
2. *The graph has x-intercept* 1.
3. *The graph is rising as we traverse it from left to right. In other words,*

$$\log_b x_1 > \log_b x_2 \quad \textit{if, and only if,} \quad x_1 > x_2.$$

The first property is true because $\log_b x$ is defined only if $x > 0$, and the second property is true because $\log_b x = 0$, if and only if, $x = 1$. The proof of the third property is too difficult to be included in this text.

Exercises for Discussion

1. Graph each of the following equations on the same set of axes.

   (a) $y = \log_5 x$ (b) $y = 5^x$

   Is there a line of folding so that the two graphs would coincide? *$y = x$* By what transformation could one equation be obtained from the other? *By interchanging x and y*

2. Graph each of the following equations on the same set of axes.

   (a) $y = \log_2 x$ (b) $y = \log_3 x$
   (c) $y = \log_5 x$ (d) $y = \log_{10} x$

   What point does the following family of logarithmic curves have in common? *(1, 0)*

   $$\{y = \log_b x \mid b \text{ a real number, } b > 1\}$$

3. Using Property 3 of the logarithmic curve with base $b > 1$, give two consecutive integers between which each of the following numbers lies.

   (a) $\log_2 6.45$ (b) $\log_{10} 36.125$ (c) $\log_{10} .375$

4. If $0 < N < 1$, what can be said about $\log_{10} N$? *If $0 < N < 1$, then $\log_{10} N < \log_{10} 1$ or $\log_{10} N < 0$.*
5. If $N > 1$, what can be said about $\log_{10} N$? *If $N > 1$, $\log_{10} N > 0$.*
6. If M is a number greater than the positive number N, how do the numbers $\log_{10} M$ and $\log_{10} N$ compare? *If $M > N$, $\log_{10} M > \log_{10} N$.*
7. (a) Graph $y = \log_2 (^-x)$.
   (b) For what set of values of x is $\log_2 (^-x)$ defined? *For $x < 0$*

Exercises

See Solution Manual for graphs.

Graph each of the following equations.

1. $y = \log_3 x$ 2. $y = \log_3 2x$ 3. $y = 2 + \log_3 x$
4. $y = \log_3 (x + 2)$ 5. $y = 2 \log_3 x$ 6. $y = \log_3 x^2$
7. $y = \frac{1}{2} \log_3 x$ 8. $y = \log_3 \sqrt{x}$

9. Refer to Exercises 1–8 to answer the following questions.
   (a) Which of the graphs are identical? *$y = \frac{1}{2} \log_3 x$ and $y = \log_3 \sqrt{x}$*
   (b) Which of the graphs have the same x-intercept? *1, 5, 6, 7, 8*
   (c) For what set of values of x is the equation defined? *For 1, 2, 3, 5, 7, 8: $\{x \mid x > 0\}$; For 4: $\{x \mid x > ^-2\}$; For 6: $\{x \mid x \neq 0\}$*

△

10. Graph $y = \log_3 (^-x)$ and $y = {^-\log_3} x$ on the same set of axes.
11. For what set of values of x is $\log_2 (x + 1)$ defined? *$x > ^-1$* Graph the equation $y = \log_2 (x + 1)$. Compare the graph with that of $y = \log_2 x$. *$y = \log_2 x$ is one unit to the right.*
12. (a) Sketch the graph of the equation $y = \log_5 1/x$.
    (b) Graph the equation $y = {^-\log_5} x$.

Answers to Exercise for Discussion 1–3, 7(a)

1.

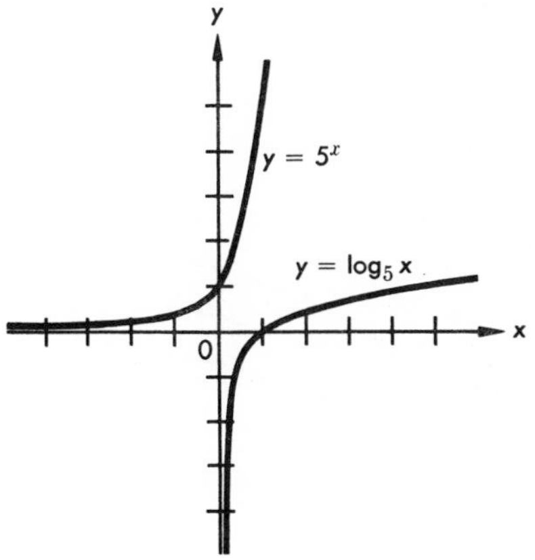

2.

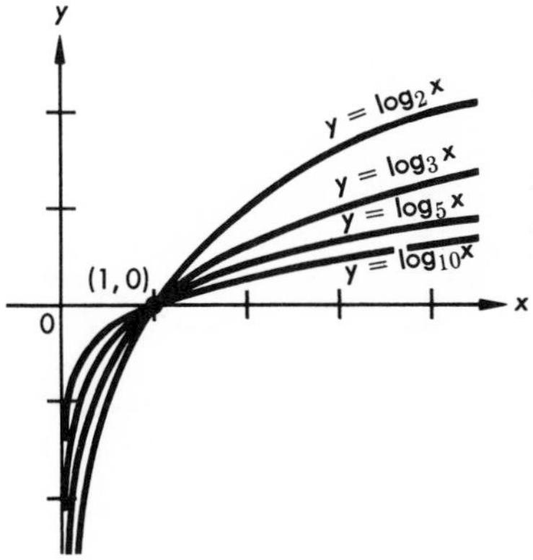

3. (a) Since $2^2 < 6.45 < 2^3$, $2 < \log_2 6.45 < 3$
   (b) Since $10^1 < 36.125 < 10^2$, $1 < \log_{10} 36.125 < 2$
   (c) Since $10^{-1} < .375 < 10^0$, $^-1 < \log_{10} .375 < 0$
7. (a) (See page T13 for graph.)

Exercises

Exercises 10–12 may be used later in a review of the chapter, or still later in a review of the course. It is recommended that you keep proceeding further to new ideas rather than spending too much time on any one set of exercises.

Quiz

Graph each of the following equations.

1. $y = \log_2 x$
2. $y = \log_2 2x$
3. $y = \log_2 x + 2$

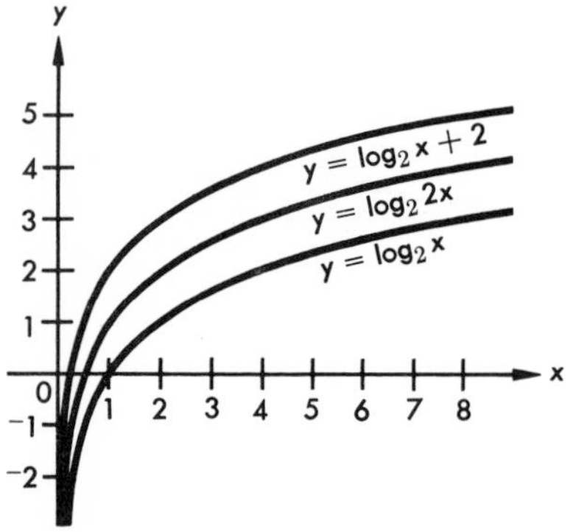

4. $y = 2 \log_2 x$
5. $y = \log_2 (x + 2)$

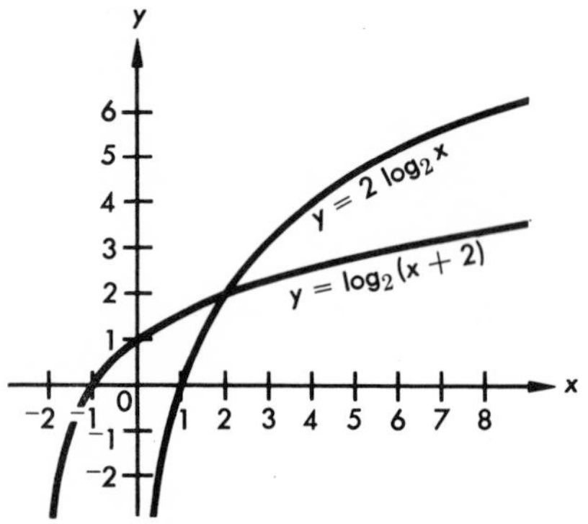

7–4 THE LAWS OF LOGARITHMS

The first law of logarithms may be illustrated specifically before producing the proof by posing the following questions:

$\log_3 729 = ?$ (ans: 6)
$\log_3 9 = ?$ (ans: 2)
$\log_3 81 = ?$ (ans: 4).

7–4 THE LAWS OF LOGARITHMS

The laws of exponents, which we verified first for use with positive integers and later for use with rational numbers, will now be assumed to be valid for real numbers. Since $\log_b x = y$ if, and only if, $x = b^y$, we might expect that the laws of exponents could be translated into the language of logarithms. This is the case, as we shall show below. In our development, the base b is always assumed to be a real number greater than 1.

According to the first law of exponents, the equation

$$b^{r+s} = b^r \cdot b^s$$

is true for every pair r, s of real numbers. Let us try to convert this equation into one relating logarithms by letting

$$z = b^{r+s}, \quad x = b^r, \quad y = b^s.$$

By the first law of exponents, $z = xy$. Each of the above equations can be translated into the language of logarithms, yielding the three equivalent equations

$$r + s = \log_b z, \quad r = \log_b x, \quad s = \log_b y.$$

Since $r + s$ is the sum of r and s, it follows that

$$\log_b z = \log_b x + \log_b y.$$

If we recall that $z = xy$, then we have proved the following law.

FIRST LAW OF LOGARITHMS

$$\log_b xy = \log_b x + \log_b y \qquad \textbf{(LL-1)}$$

This equation is true for every pair x, y of positive real numbers. The first law of logarithms can be stated in words in the following way.

The logarithm of the product of two positive numbers is the sum of the logarithms of the two numbers.

If we start with the second law of exponents and reason as we did above, then we can derive the following law.

SECOND LAW OF LOGARITHMS

$$\log_b \frac{x}{y} = \log_b x - \log_b y \qquad \text{(LL-2)}$$

This equation is also true for every pair x, y of positive real numbers. The second law of logarithms can be stated in words in the following way.

The logarithm of the quotient of two positive numbers is the logarithm of the dividend minus the logarithm of the divisor.

According to the third law of exponents, the equation

$$b^{ar} = (b^a)^r$$

is true for every pair a, r of real numbers. To convert this equation to one relating logarithms, let

$$y = b^{ar} \quad \text{and} \quad x = b^a.$$

By the third law of exponents, $y = x^r$. The two equations above are equivalent to the two logarithmic equations

$$ar = \log_b y, \quad a = \log_b x.$$

Since ar equals r times a, we have

$$\log_b y = r \cdot \log_b x.$$

Replacing y by x^r, we obtain the following law.

THIRD LAW OF LOGARITHMS

$$\log_b x^r = r \cdot \log_b x \qquad \text{(LL-3)}$$

This equation is true for every real number r and every positive real number x. The third law of logarithms can be stated in words in the following way.

The logarithm of the rth power of a positive number is r times the logarithm of the number.

Now it can be seen that $729 = 9 \cdot 81$ and that

$$\log_3 729 = \log_3 9 + \log_3 81.$$

It is also true that

$$\log_3 (243 \cdot 729) = \log_3 243 + \log_3 729.$$

In general,

$$\log_3 (m \cdot n) = \log_3 m + \log_3 n,$$

and even more generally,

$$\log_b (m \cdot n) = \log_b m + \log_b n,$$

provided m and n are positive real numbers.

All three of these laws should be related to the work with the table of powers of 2 at the beginning of Section 7-1, where multiplication involved addition of exponents, and division involved subtraction of exponents, and so on.

Problem 2 will require special attention in class. You may wish to start with simpler examples:

$\log_2 7 + \log_2 9 = \log_2 ?$ (ans: 63)

$\log_2 20 - \log_2 4 = \log_2 ?$ (ans: 5)

$2 \log_2 5 = \log_2 5^?$ (ans: 2)

$\log_2 20 - 2 \log_2 5 = \log_2 ?$ (ans: $\frac{4}{5}$)

Problem 1. Find each of the following.

(a) $\log_2 16\sqrt{8}$ (b) $\log_3 \frac{\sqrt[4]{27}}{9}$

Solution.

$$\begin{aligned}\text{(a) } \log_2 16\sqrt{8} &= \log_2 16 + \log_2 \sqrt{8} && \text{(LL-1)}\\ &= \log_2 16 + \log_2 8^{\frac{1}{2}}\\ &= \log_2 16 + \tfrac{1}{2}\log_2 8 && \text{(LL-3)}\\ &= \log_2 2^4 + \tfrac{1}{2}\log_2 2^3\\ &= 4 + (\tfrac{1}{2}\cdot 3), \quad \text{or } \tfrac{11}{2}\end{aligned}$$

In other words, $\log_2 16\sqrt{8} = \frac{11}{2}$.

$$\begin{aligned}\text{(b) } \log_3 \frac{\sqrt[4]{27}}{9} &= \log_3 \sqrt[4]{27} - \log_3 9 && \text{(LL-2)}\\ &= \log_3 27^{\frac{1}{4}} - \log_3 9\\ &= \tfrac{1}{4}\log_3 27 - \log_3 9 && \text{(LL-3)}\\ &= \tfrac{1}{4}\log_3 3^3 - \log_3 3^2\\ &= (\tfrac{1}{4}\cdot 3) - 2, \quad \text{or } \tfrac{^-5}{4}\end{aligned}$$

In other words,

$$\log_3 \frac{\sqrt[4]{27}}{9} = \frac{^-5}{4}.$$

Problem 2. Express the following number as the logarithm of a single number.

$$3\log_5 4 - 2\log_5 6 + \tfrac{3}{2}\log_5 18$$

Solution. We proceed as follows:

$$\begin{aligned}&3\log_5 4 - 2\log_5 6 + \tfrac{3}{2}\log_5 18\\ &\quad = \log_5 4^3 - \log_5 6^2 + \log_5 18^{\frac{3}{2}} && \text{(LL-3)}\\ &\quad = \log_5 64 - \log_5 36 + \log_5 (\sqrt{18})^3\\ &\quad = \log_5 \tfrac{64}{36} + \log_5 (3\sqrt{2})^3 && \text{(LL-2)}\\ &\quad = \log_5 \tfrac{16}{9} + \log_5 54\sqrt{2}\\ &\quad = \log_5 (\tfrac{16}{9}\cdot 54\sqrt{2}) && \text{(LL-1)}\\ &\quad = \log_5 (96\sqrt{2}).\end{aligned}$$

Problem 3. Solve the equation $\log_4 3 + \log_4 (x + 2) = 2$.

Solution. Using the first law of logarithms, we have

$$\log_4 3 + \log_4 (x + 2) = \log_4 3(x + 2).$$

Hence, the given equation is equivalent to the equation

$$\log_4 3(x + 2) = 2.$$

This logarithmic equation is equivalent to the exponential equation

$$3(x + 2) = 4^2.$$

Hence,

$$3x + 6 = 16 \quad \text{and} \quad x = \tfrac{10}{3}.$$

Exercises for Discussion

1. Prove the second law of logarithms, (LL-2).

Find the value of each of the following by using the laws of logarithms.

2. $\log_2 \sqrt[3]{32}$ $\log_2 2^{\frac{5}{3}} = \frac{5}{3}\log_2 2 = \frac{5}{3}$

3. $\log_3 \left(\frac{\sqrt[5]{9}}{3}\right)$ $\log_3 \frac{3^{\frac{2}{5}}}{3} = \log_3 3^{\frac{-3}{5}} = \frac{-3}{5}\log_3 3 = \frac{-3}{5}$

4. $\log_5 \left(\frac{\sqrt[3]{25}}{\sqrt{5}}\right)$ $\log_5 \left(\frac{5^{\frac{2}{3}}}{5^{\frac{1}{2}}}\right) = \log_5 5^{\frac{1}{6}} = \frac{1}{6}\log_5 5 = \frac{1}{6}$

5. $\log_{10} (10\sqrt[3]{100})$ $\log_{10}(10 \cdot 10^{\frac{2}{3}}) = \log_{10} 10^{\frac{5}{3}} = \frac{5}{3}\log_{10} 10 = \frac{5}{3}$

Express each of the following numbers as the logarithm of a single number.

6. $\log_4 3 + \log_4 7$ $\log_4 3 \cdot 7 = \log_4 21$
7. $2 \log_5 27 - \frac{1}{3} \log_5 9$
8. $3 \log_5 2 - \frac{1}{2} \log_5 3$
9. $\frac{3}{2} \log_5 6 + 2 \log_5 3$ $\log_5 6^{\frac{3}{2}} + \log_5 3^2 = \log_5 (6\sqrt{6} \cdot 9) = \log_5 54\sqrt{6}$

If $\log_{10} 2 = p$ and $\log_{10} 3 = q$, find an expression in terms of p and q for each logarithm in Exercises 10–15.

10. $\log_{10} 4$ $\log_{10} 2^2 = 2\log_{10} 2 = 2p$
11. $\log_{10} (\frac{2}{3})$ $\log_{10} 2 - \log_{10} 3 = p - q$
12. $\log_{10} \sqrt{2}$ $\log_{10} 2^{\frac{1}{2}} = \frac{1}{2}\log_{10} 2 = \frac{1}{2}p$
13. $\log_{10} .5$ $\log_{10} \frac{1}{2} = \log_{10} 1 - \log_{10} 2 = 0 - p = {}^-p$
14. $\log_{10} 30$ $\log_{10} (10 \cdot 3) = \log_{10} 10 + \log_{10} 3 = 1 + q$
15. $\log_{10} \frac{1}{3}$ $\log_{10} 1 - \log_{10} 3 = 0 - q = {}^-q$

16. Solve the following equation.

$$\log_{32} \tfrac{4}{3} + \log_{32} 48 = N$$

$\log_{32} \frac{4}{3} \cdot 48 = N,\ \log_{32} 64 = N,\ 32^N = 64,\ 2^{5N} = 2^6,\ 5N = 6,\ N = \frac{6}{5}$

Problem 3 requires explanation. After following the procedure of the text, which depends on writing an exponential equation equivalent to the given logarithmic one, the problem may be done in a slightly different way:

$$\log_4 3 + \log_4 (x + 2) = \log_4 4^2$$
$$\log_4 3(x + 2) = \log_4 4^2$$

Now the fact may be used that if two numbers have equal logarithms relative to the same base, the numbers must be equal. Therefore,

$$3(x + 2) = 4^2.$$

Exercises for Discussion

If time is limited, it is recommended that at least Exercises for Discussion 4–7 and 11 be covered.

Answers to Exercises for Discussion 1, 7, 8.

1. $\log_b \frac{x}{y} = \log_b x - \log_b y$ (LL-2)

Proof: Let $x = b^r$, $y = b^s$, then

$$\frac{x}{y} = \frac{b^r}{b^s} = b^{r-s},$$

so,

$$\log_b \frac{x}{y} = r - s \qquad \text{(Def-Log)}$$
$$= \log_b x - \log_b y.$$

7. $2 \log_5 27 - \frac{1}{3} \log_5 9$
$= \log_5 (3^3)^2 - \log_5 (3^2)^{1/3}$
$= \log_5 \frac{3^6}{3^{2/3}}$
$= \log_5 3^{16/3}$
$= \log_5 243\sqrt[3]{3}$

8. $3 \log_5 2 - \frac{1}{2} \log_5 3$
$= \log_5 2^3 - \log_5 3^{1/2}$
$= \log_5 \frac{8}{\sqrt{3}}$
$= \log_5 \frac{8}{3}\sqrt{3}$

Exercises

Exercise 20 involves equating two numbers whose logs to the same base are equal if handled this way:

$$\log_5 6 = \log_5 x - \log_5 7$$

$$\log_5 6 = \log_5 \frac{x}{7}.$$

Therefore,

$$6 = \frac{x}{7}.$$

On the other hand, it may be said that

$$\log_5 x - \log_5 7 - \log_5 6 = 0$$

$$\log_5 \frac{x}{7 \cdot 6} = 0$$

$$\frac{x}{7 \cdot 6} = 5^0, \text{ or } 1.$$

Quiz

Find each of the following logarithms.

1. $\log_4 (64 \cdot 256)$ (ans: 7)
2. $\log_5 (125 \div \frac{1}{5})$ (ans: 4)
3. $\log_6 (36 \cdot \sqrt{6^6})$ (ans: 5)

Express each of the following numbers as the logarithm of a single number.

4. $\log_3 20 + \log_3 2$ (ans: $\log_3 40$)
5. $\log_7 9 - \log_7 3$ (ans: $\log_7 3$)
6. $2 \log_4 3 + 3 \log_4 3$ (ans: $\log_4 243$)

Exercises

Find each of the following logarithms.

1. $\log_5 (25 \cdot 125)$ 5
2. $\log_6 \sqrt{216}$ $\frac{3}{2}$
3. $\log_3 \sqrt[4]{9^5}$ $\frac{5}{2}$
4. $\log_7 (49 \div 7^5)$ $^-3$
5. $\log_3 81\sqrt{27}$ $\frac{11}{2}$
6. $\log_2 \frac{\sqrt[4]{8}}{4}$ $\frac{-5}{4}$

Express each of the following numbers as the logarithm of a single number.

7. $\log_5 6 - \log_5 2$ $\log_5 3$
8. $\log_5 80 + \log_5 \frac{1}{4}$ $\log_5 20$
9. $4 \log_3 10 - 2 \log_3 5$ $\log_3 400$
10. $5 \log_7 9 - 4 \log_7 15 + \frac{3}{2} \log_7 12$ $\log_7 \frac{17496}{625}\sqrt{3}$

△

If $\log_{10} 5 = r$ and $\log_{10} 7 = s$, find an expression for each of the following in terms of r and s.

11. $\log_{10} 35$ $r+s$
12. $\log_{10} \frac{7}{5}$ $s-r$
13. $\log_{10} 49$ $2s$
14. $\log_{10} \frac{343}{25}$ $3s-2r$
15. $\log_{10} (\sqrt{7} \cdot \sqrt[3]{5})$ $\frac{1}{2}s + \frac{1}{3}r$
16. $\log_{10} \frac{7}{10} \cdot \log_{10} 125$ $3rs - 3r$
17. $\log_{10} 50 - \log_{10} 700$ $r-s-1$
18. $\log_{10} \sqrt{\frac{7}{5}}$ $\frac{1}{2}(s-r)$

Solve each of the following equations.

19. $\log_4 72 - \log_4 9 = N$ $N = \frac{3}{2}$
20. $\log_5 6 = \log_5 x - \log_5 7$ $x = 42$
21. $\log_7 98 + \log_7 3.5 = N$ $N = 3$
22. $\log_3 63 - \log_3 7x = \log_3 2$ $x = \frac{9}{2}$
23. $\log_8 \sqrt{.125} = x$ $x = \frac{-1}{2}$
24. $\log_5 4 + \log_5 (2x - 3) = 20$ $x = \frac{12 + 5^{20}}{8}$

▲

In Exercises 25–27, use the laws of logarithms to prove that each of the equations is true. See Solution Manual.

25. $\log_b 16 - \log_b 8 + \log_b 5 = \log_b 10$
26. $2 \log_x a - 2 \log_x b + 3 \log_x \sqrt{b} - \frac{1}{3} \log_x a = \frac{1}{6} \log_x \frac{a^{10}}{b^3}$
27. $\log_3 \frac{x^2 3^x}{3^{x^2}} = x - x^2 + 2 \log_3 x$
28. Solve the following equation for x.

$$\log_2 2 + \log_2 (x + 2) - \log_2 (3x - 5) = 3$$ $x = 2$

29. Prove that See Solution Manual.

$$\log_{10} \frac{3x - \sqrt{9x^2 - 1}}{3x + \sqrt{9x^2 - 1}} = 2 \log_{10} (3x - \sqrt{9x^2 - 1}).$$

30. Solve each of the following equations.

(a) $y = 2 \log_2 8$ 6 (b) $y = 3 \log_3 81$ 12

(c) $y = 10 \log_2 4$ 20 (d) $^-y = b \log_b b^5$ −56

7-5 COMMON LOGARITHMS

There are two bases for logarithms that are extensively used today. One is the base e ($e \doteq 2.71828$) widely used in higher mathematics. Logarithms to the base e are called *natural logarithms.* The other is the base 10, chosen because of our decimal system of notation. Logarithms to the base 10 are called *common logarithms.* We shall discuss only common logarithms in this section. Whenever we write $\log N$ without indicating the base, it is always understood that the base is 10; that is,

$$\log N \quad \text{means} \quad \log_{10} N.$$

By the very definition of logarithms,

$$\log 10^n = n$$

for every real number n. Thus, for example,

$$\log .01 = {}^-2 \quad \text{because} \quad .01 = 10^{-2},$$

$$\log .1 = {}^-1 \quad \text{because} \quad .1 = 10^{-1},$$

$$\log 1 = 0 \quad \text{because} \quad 1 = 10^0,$$

$$\log 10 = 1 \quad \text{because} \quad 10 = 10^1,$$

$$\log 100 = 2 \quad \text{because} \quad 100 = 10^2,$$

and so on.

We do not know, offhand, the logarithm of any positive rational number other than an integral power of 10. For example, we do not know what log 7 is. Since 7 is between 1 and 10, and since $\log 1 = 0$ and $\log 10 = 1$, we have by the third property on page 276 that log 7 is between 0 and 1:

$$0 < \log 7 < 1.$$

7-5 COMMON LOGARITHMS

The emphasis now should be on using the laws of logarithms which have just been studied, with the base restricted to 10. The scientific notation should be carefully explained and then a list of numbers such as the following could be written in scientific notation:

15.8	(ans: 1.58×10^1)
1580	(ans: 1.580×10^3)
.0158	(ans: 1.58×10^{-2})
9.67	(ans: 9.67×10^0)
.00967	(ans: 9.67×10^{-3})
96,700	(ans: 9.67×10^4)

Then you could turn to the table of common logarithms on page 616 and explain that the table indicates that

$$\log_{10} 2.34 = .3692$$

or

$$2.34 = 10^{.3692},$$

$$\log_{10} 7.90 = .8976$$

or

$$7.90 = 10^{.8976},$$

and so on. It is already known from the first law of logarithms that, since $15.8 = 1.58 \times 10$,

$$\log 15.8 = \log 1.58 + \log 10$$
$$= .1987 + 1, \text{ or } 1.1987$$

and this tells us that

$$15.8 = 10^{1.1987}.$$

Many examples of this kind should be done before introducing the greatest integer, or characteristic, of a logarithm. The logarithmic and exponential equations should be displayed in pairs.

It is recommended that much practice be done in class writing $\log_{10} N$ as an integer plus a fraction and leaving the answer that way. For example, if $\log_{10} 2 \doteq .3010$, then

$$\begin{aligned} \log 20 &= \log (2 \times 10) \\ &= \log 2 + \log 10 \\ &\doteq .3010 + 1; \\ \log 2000 &= \log (2 \times 1000) \\ &= \log 2 + \log 10^3 \\ &\doteq .3010 + 3; \\ \log .2 &= \log (2 \div 10) \\ &= \log 2 - \log 10 \\ &\doteq .3010 - 1, \\ &\quad \text{or } .3010 + {}^{-}1; \\ \log .02 &= \log (2/100) \\ &= \log 2 - \log 100 \\ &= \log 2 - \log 10^2 \\ &\doteq .3010 - 2, \\ &\quad \text{or } .3010 + {}^{-}2. \end{aligned}$$

From these four statements it can be seen that

$$\begin{aligned} 20 &\doteq 10^{.3010} \times 10^1 \\ 2000 &\doteq 10^{.3010} \times 10^3 \\ .2 &\doteq 10^{.3010} \times 10^{-1} \\ .02 &\doteq 10^{.3010} \times 10^{-2}. \end{aligned}$$

Actually, it is shown in more advanced mathematics that log 7 is an irrational number, so that it cannot possibly be represented as a quotient of two integers. However, as is the case with any irrational number, we can *approximate* log 7 by a rational number. It can be shown that

$$\log 7 \doteq .8451$$

to four-decimal-place accuracy.

If we know a four-decimal-place approximation of log 7, we can easily find four-decimal-place approximations of log 70, log 700, log .7, and so on. Thus, since $70 = 10 \times 7$,

$$\begin{aligned} \log 70 &= \log (10 \times 7) \\ &= \log 10 + \log 7 \\ &= 1 + \log 7 \\ &\doteq 1 + .8451 \\ &\doteq 1.8451. \end{aligned}$$

Similarly,

$$\begin{aligned} \log 700 &= \log (100 \times 7) \\ &= \log 100 + \log 7 \\ &= 2 + \log 7 \\ &\doteq 2 + .8451 \\ &\doteq 2.8451. \end{aligned}$$

Also,

$$\begin{aligned} \log .7 &= \log (7 \div 10) \\ &= \log 7 - \log 10 \\ &\doteq .8451 - 1 \\ &\doteq {}^{-}.1549. \end{aligned}$$

Furthermore, we can approximate log 49, since $49 = 7^2$, and

$$\begin{aligned} \log 49 &= \log 7^2 \\ &= 2 \log 7 \\ &\doteq 2 \times .8451 \\ &\doteq 1.6902. \end{aligned}$$

In computing with logarithms, it is usually helpful to think of each positive real number as a number expressed in *scientific notation*. The positive number N is represented in scientific notation if it is expressed as the product of a number between 1 and 10 and an integral power of 10, that is, if

$$N = B \times 10^k, \quad \text{where } 1 \leqq B < 10 \text{ and } k \text{ is an integer.}$$

For example, each of the following positive numbers is expressed in scientific notation.

Number	Scientific notation
123	1.23×10^2
.0123	$1.23 \times 10^{^-2}$
98,752	9.8752×10^4
.1961	$1.961 \times 10^{^-1}$
1,000,000	1×10^6

If the positive integer N is expressed in scientific notation,

$$N = B \times 10^k, \quad \text{where } 1 \leqq B < 10 \text{ and } k \text{ is an integer,}$$

then

$$\log N = \log(B \times 10^k)$$
$$= \log B + \log 10^k. \qquad \text{(LL-1)}$$

Since $\log 10^k = k$, we have

$$\log N = \log B + k.$$

Note that

$$0 \leqq \log B < 1 \quad \text{since} \quad 1 \leqq B < 10.$$

Thus, $\log N$ is expressed as a sum of an integer and a non-negative real number less than 1. Clearly,

$$k \leqq \log N < k + 1$$

so that k is the *greatest integer* contained in $\log N$ and $\log B$ is the *fractional part* of $\log N$. The non-negative number $\log B$ is often called the *mantissa* of $\log N$ and the integer k the *characteristic* of $\log N$.

To summarize, if we express N in scientific notation,

$$N = B \times 10^k, \quad \text{where } 1 \leqq B < 10,\ k \text{ an integer,}$$

then

$$\log N = \underbrace{\overbrace{k}^{\text{greatest integer}}}_{\text{characteristic}} + \underbrace{\overbrace{\log B,}^{\text{fractional part}}}_{\text{mantissa}} \quad 0 \leqq \log B < 1.$$

TWISTER

Not knowing much about logarithms, a student evaluating an expression of the form

$$\frac{\log A}{\log B}$$

decided to cancel common factors in both the numerator and the denominator. He thus cancelled the "factor" log and arrived at the result $\frac{2}{3}$. This answer proved to be correct. What were the values of A and B?

Solution: Since

$$\frac{\log A}{\log B} = \frac{A}{B} = \frac{2}{3},$$

$$3 \log A = 2 \log \frac{3A}{2},$$

and

$$A = \tfrac{9}{4},\ B = \tfrac{27}{8}.$$

The original expression was therefore

$$\frac{\log \frac{9}{4}}{\log \frac{27}{8}}.$$

A detailed graph of $y = \log_{10} x$ may be used (preferably on a graph board) to explain the table. The table makes it possible to express the numbers between 1 and 10 as powers of 10.

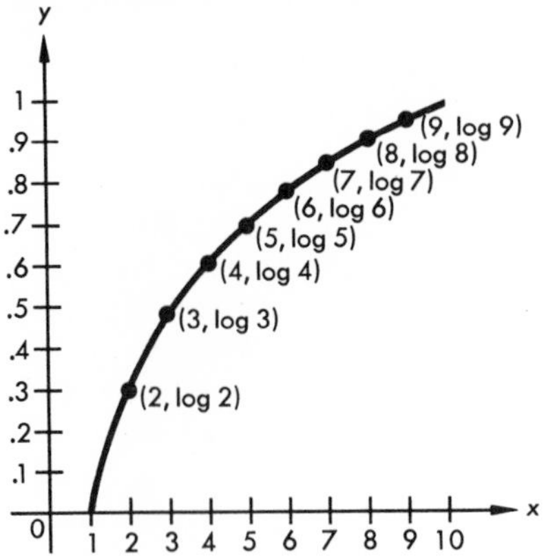

Thus, $2 \doteq 10^{.3010}$, because the table says

$$\log_{10} 2.00 \doteq .3010.$$

Because the logs of numbers between 1 and 10 range from 0 to 1, the entries in the table are all numbers between 0 and 1. The table indicates $\log_{10} 4.98 \doteq .6972$, and this checks with the graph. Likewise, $\log_{10} 7.34 \doteq .8657$, and this also checks with the graph.

The Table of Common Logarithms in the Appendix lists four-decimal-place approximations of the mantissas of the common logarithms of all integers from 100 to 999. The characteristic of $\log N$ if $100 \leqq N < 1000$ is 2, since $10^2 \leqq N < 10^3$ means that

$$2 \leqq \log N < 3.$$

A portion of this table is reproduced below.

N	0	1	2	3	4	5	6	7	8	9
38	.5798	.5809	.5821	.5832	.5843	.5855	.5866	.5877	.5888	.5899
39	.5911	.5922	.5933	.5944	.5955	.5966	.5977	.5988	.5999	.6010

This part of the table lists the mantissa of the logarithm of each integer from 380 through 399. The characteristic of the logarithm of each of these integers is obviously 2. Thus, from the table,

$$\log 380 \doteq 2 + .5798, \quad \log 381 \doteq 2 + .5809, \quad \log 387 \doteq 2 + .5877,$$
$$\log 390 \doteq 2 + .5911, \quad \log 394 \doteq 2 + .5955, \quad \log 399 \doteq 2 + .6010.$$

We should keep in mind the definition of the logarithm. Thus, since

$$\log 381 \doteq 2.5809,$$

we have

$$10^{2.5809} \doteq 381,$$

and so on.

In using this table, we can think of it as a table of logarithms of numbers from 1.00 to 9.99. Hence, if we express a given number in scientific notation, the mantissa of the logarithm of the number may be read directly from the table. For example, $39{,}600 = 3.96 \times 10^4$ in scientific notation. Hence,

$$\begin{aligned} \log 39{,}600 &= \log 3.96 + \log 10^4, \\ &\doteq .5977 + 4, \quad \text{or } 4.5977. \end{aligned}$$

Also,

$$\begin{aligned} .0388 &= 3.88 \times 10^{^-2}, \\ \log .0388 &= \log 3.88 + \log 10^{^-2} \\ &\doteq .5888 - 2. \end{aligned}$$

We could express the final answer in the form $^-1.4112$, but we usually want it in the first form, $.5888 - 2$.

Exercises for Discussion

1. Express the numbers in each of the following statements in scientific notation.

   (a) The distance that light travels in one year is called a *light-year*, which is approximately 5,870,000,000,000 miles. 5.87×10^{12} mi

   (b) The diameter of the Einstein universe, according to the theory of relativity, is 2,000,000,000 light-years, or

   2×10^{9} light-years, 1.1740×10^{22} mi

   11,740,000,000,000,000,000,000 miles.

   (c) The thickness of an oil film is about .0000005 centimeters. 5×10^{-7} cm

   (d) The diameter of the orbit of an electron of a hydrogen atom is about .000 000 000 53 millimeters. 5.3×10^{-10} mm

   (e) The mass of a molecule of water is about

   .000 000 000 000 000 000 000 03 grams.

   3×10^{-23} gm

2. If log 5 = .6990, find each of the following logarithms.

   (a) log 500 (b) log .005 (c) log 125

3. Complete each of the following statements.

   (a) $10^2 < 123 <$ 10^3; 2 $< \log 123 < 3$

   (b) 10^3 $< 1230 < 10^4$; $3 < \log 1230 <$ 4

4. For each number given, first find the successive integral powers of 10 between which the number lies. Then find the successive integers between which the logarithm of the number lies.

   (a) 15.6 (b) 15,600 (c) 1.56

5. Give the integral part, or characteristic, of the common logarithm of each of the following numbers.

   (a) 1.23×10^2 2 (b) 1.23×10^{-1} $^-1$ (c) 1.23×10^4 4

6. Write each number in scientific notation and give the integral part, or characteristic, of its logarithm to the base 10.

   (a) 32.5 3.25×10^1; 1 (b) 3250 3.25×10^3; 3 (c) .00325 3.25×10^{-3}; $^-3$

7. Use the Table of Common Logarithms to find the common logarithm of each of the following numbers. Then express each number as a power of 10.

   (a) 245 (b) 34.6 (c) 52,000

   (d) .123 (e) .0478 (f) .00678

Exercises for Discussion

Each exercise should be gone over carefully. The students should be reminded repeatedly that a logarithm is an exponent, that every positive real number n may be expressed exponentially as a power of 10, and that this exponent is called the common logarithm of the number. Thus, if $n = 10^x$, $x = \log_{10} n$. The table of common logarithms and scientific notation are the tools for finding x when n is given. (You might even comment that the table can also be read backwards to find n when x is given.)

Answers to Exercises for Discussion 2, 4, 7

2. (a) $\log 500 = \log 100 \cdot 5 = \log 100 + \log 5 = 2 + .6990 = 2.6990$

(b) $\log .005 = \log .001 \cdot 5 = \log .001 + \log 5 = {}^-3 + .6990 = {}^-2.3010$

(c) $\log 125 = \log 5^3 = 3 \log 5 = 3 \cdot .6990 = 2.0970$

4. (a) $10^1 < 15.6 < 10^2$; $1 < \log 15.6 < 2$

(b) $10^4 < 15{,}600 < 10^5$; $4 < \log 15600 < 5$

(c) $10^0 < 1.56 < 10^1$; $0 < \log 1.56 < 1$

7. (a) $\log 245 = 2.3892$; $245 = 10^{2.3892}$

(b) $\log 34.6 = 1.5391$; $34.6 = 10^{1.5391}$

(c) $\log 52{,}000 = 4.7160$; $52{,}000 = 10^{4.7160}$

(d) $\log .123 = {}^-1 + .0899 = {}^-.9101$; $.123 = 10^{-.9101}$

(e) $\log .0478 = {}^-2 + .6794 = {}^-1.3206$; $.0478 = 10^{-1.3206}$

(f) $\log .00678 = {}^-3 + .8312 = {}^-2.1688$; $.00678 = 10^{-2.1688}$

Exercises

Exercises 30 and 31 should be discussed carefully and the graph of $y = \log_{10} x$ used along with them.

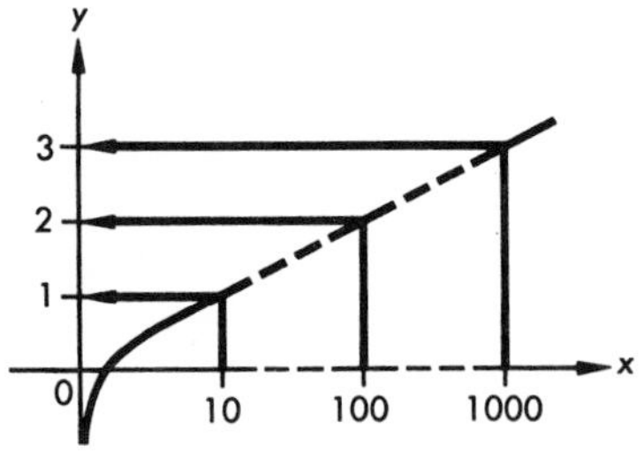

Quiz

If N equals each of the following numbers, find $\log N$.

1. 1230 (ans: 3.0899)
2. 12.3 (ans: 1.0899)
3. .00123 (ans: $^{-}2.9101$)
4. .394 (ans: $^{-}0.4045$)
5. 39400 (ans: 4.5955)
6. .000394 (ans: $^{-}3.4045$)

Exercises

Write each number in scientific notation and give the integral part, or characteristic, of its logarithm to the base 10.

1. 342.1 3.421×10^2; 2 **2.** .4762 4.762×10^{-1}; $^{-}1$ **3.** 20.51 2.051×10^1; 1

4. .003021 3.021×10^{-3}; $^{-}3$ **5.** 56,500 5.65×10^4; 4 **6.** .00006789 6.789×10^{-5}; $^{-}5$

Use the Table of Common Logarithms to find the common logarithm of each of the following numbers. Then express each number as a power of 10.

7. 1540 3.1875; $10^{3.1875}$ **8.** .0764 $^{-}1.1169$; $10^{^{-}1.1169}$ **9.** 7.08 .8500; $10^{.8500}$ **10.** 650,000 5.8129; $10^{5.8129}$

11. .000403 $^{-}3.3947$; $10^{^{-}3.3947}$ **12.** .000008 $^{-}5.0969$; $10^{^{-}5.0969}$ **13.** 923 2.9652; $10^{2.9652}$ **14.** 32,500 4.5119; $10^{4.5119}$

Given that N equals each of the numbers in Exercises 15–29, find $\log N$.

15. .256 $^{-}.5918$ **16.** 256 2.4082 **17.** .0256 $^{-}1.5918$ **18.** 2560 3.4082

19. .000256 $^{-}3.5918$ **20.** 256,000 5.4082 **21.** 32.4 1.5105 **22.** 32,400 4.5105

23. 3,240,000 6.5105 **24.** .00852 $^{-}2.0696$ **25.** 8.52 .9304 **26.** .0000852 $^{-}4.0696$

27. 2060 3.3139 **28.** .0206 $^{-}1.6861$ **29.** 20,600 4.3139

30. (a) Consider the set of all numbers with a single digit to the left of the decimal, such as 1, 2.435, and 9.7468. Between which consecutive integral powers of 10 does N lie if $1 \leqq N < 10$? What is the characteristic, or integral part, of $\log N$? 0 and 1; 0

(b) Consider the set of all numbers with two digits to the left of the decimal, such as 10, 21.5, and 99.06. If $10 \leqq N < 100$, between which consecutive integral powers of 10 does N lie? What is the characteristic of $\log N$? 1 and 2; 1

(c) If $100 \leqq N < 1000$, what is the integral part of $\log N$? 2

(d) If N is a positive number with k digits to the left of the decimal, between which consecutive integral powers of 10 does N lie? What is the characteristic of $\log N$? $k-1$ and k; $k-1$

(e) State a rule for finding the characteristic of $\log N$ when N is any positive number greater than or equal to 1. See Solution Manual.

31. (a) Consider the set of all numbers less than 1, but not less than .1, such as .1, .1012, .234, and .9999. If $.1 \leqq N < 1$, between which consecutive integral powers of 10 does N lie? What is the characteristic of $\log N$? $^{-}1$ and 0; $^{-}1$

(b) If $.01 \leqq N < .1$, between which consecutive integral powers of 10 does N lie? What is the characteristic of $\log N$? $^{-}2$ and $^{-}1$; $^{-}2$

(c) List six members of the set

$$\{N \mid .001 \leqq N < .01\}.$$

For each such N, what is the greatest integer contained in $\log N$? $^{-}3$

(d) If N is a positive number less than 1, having its first nonzero digit in the kth place to the right of the decimal, what is the characteristic of $\log N$?

7-6 LOGARITHMS OF PRODUCTS, QUOTIENTS, AND POWERS

With the aid of the Table of Common Logarithms in the Appendix and the laws of logarithms, we can find logarithms of products, quotients, and powers of numbers. The following problems illustrate how we might do this.

Problem 1. Find log (56.4 × .0709).

Solution. We approximate this logarithm as follows:

$$\log(56.4 \times .0709) = \log 56.4 + \log .0709. \qquad \text{(LL-1)}$$

Now

$$\begin{aligned} \log 56.4 &= \log(5.64 \times 10^1) \doteq .7513 + 1 \\ + \log .0709 &= \log(7.09 \times 10^{-2}) \doteq .8506 - 2 \\ & \qquad 1.6019 - 1 \end{aligned}$$

Hence,

$$\log(56.4 \times .0709) \doteq .6019.$$

Our final answer is reasonable, since $56.4 \times .0709 \doteq 60 \times .07$, or 4.2, and log 4.2 is between 0 and 1.

Problem 2. Find log (56.4 ÷ .0709).

Solution. We use logarithms from Problem 1 in our work below.

$$\log(56.4 \div .0709) = \log 56.4 - \log .0709 \qquad \text{(LL-2)}$$

Now

$$\begin{aligned} \log 56.4 &\doteq .7513 + 1 = 1.7513 \\ - \log .0709 &\doteq .8506 - 2 = .8506 - 2 \\ & \qquad .9007 + 2 \end{aligned}$$

We rewrote .7513 + 1 in the form 1.7513 in order to keep the decimal part of the difference of the two logarithms positive. Thus,

$$\log(56.4 \div .0709) = 2.9007.$$

Our final answer is reasonable, since $56.4 \div .0709 \doteq 56 \div .07$, or 800, and log 800 is less than, but close to, 3.

7-6 LOGARITHMS OF PRODUCTS, QUOTIENTS, AND POWERS

These laws of logarithms should be related once again to the laws of exponents. If

$$56.4 = 10^{.7513+1}$$

and

$$.0709 = 10^{.8506-2}$$

then

$$56.4 \times .0709 = 10^{(.7513+1)+(.8506-2)} = 10^{.6019}.$$

Therefore,

$$\log(56.4 \times .0709) = .6019.$$

The checks using estimation presented in the text in Problems 1 and 2 should be brought to the notice of the students. It is important for the student to understand that he should never consider an outlandish answer which common sense would repudiate.

Problem 3. Find log $\sqrt[3]{942}$.

Solution. We proceed as follows:

$$\begin{aligned}\log \sqrt[3]{942} &= \log 942^{\frac{1}{3}}\\ &= \tfrac{1}{3}\log 942\\ &= \tfrac{1}{3}\log (9.42 \times 10^2)\\ &\doteq \tfrac{1}{3}(.9741 + 2),\\ &= \tfrac{1}{3}(2.9741), \quad \text{or } .9914.\end{aligned}$$

Our answer is reasonable, since $\sqrt[3]{942} < \sqrt[3]{1000}$, or 10, and, therefore, $\log \sqrt[3]{942} < 1$.

Problem 4. Find log $\sqrt[3]{.942}$.

Solution. Since $.942 = 9.42 \times 10^{-1}$, we have, as in Problem 3,

$$\log \sqrt[3]{.942} \doteq \tfrac{1}{3}(.9741 - 1).$$

Before dividing by 3, we change $.9741 - 1$ into a form so that the negative part of log .942 is exactly divisible by 3. Thus, we express

$$.9741 - 1 \quad \text{in the form} \quad 2.9741 - 3.$$

Then

$$\tfrac{1}{3}(2.9741 - 3) = .9914 - 1.$$

Hence,

$$\log \sqrt[3]{.942} \doteq .9914 - 1.$$

Problem 5. Find $\log \dfrac{3}{\sqrt[5]{.008}}$.

Solution. We proceed as follows:

$$\log \frac{3}{\sqrt[5]{.008}} = \log 3 - \log \sqrt[5]{.008} \qquad \text{(LL-2)}$$

$$= \log 3 - \tfrac{1}{5}\log .008. \qquad \text{(LL-3)}$$

Since $\log .008 = \log (8 \times 10^{-3}) \doteq .9031 - 3$, then

$$\begin{aligned}\tfrac{1}{5}\log .008 &\doteq \tfrac{1}{5}(.9031 - 3)\\ &\doteq \tfrac{1}{5}(2.9031 - 5)\\ &\doteq .5806 - 1.\end{aligned}$$

The log 3 ≐ .4771, but before subtracting, we change the form of log 3 and proceed as below.

$$\begin{array}{rcl} \log 3 & \doteq & 1.4771 - 1 \\ -\ \log \sqrt[5]{.008} & \doteq & .5806 - 1 \\ \hline & & .8965 \end{array}$$

Thus,

$$\log \frac{3}{\sqrt[5]{.008}} \doteq .8965.$$

Exercises for Discussion

1. Find log (863 × .145 × 20.7) by completing the solution.

Partial solution.

$$\log (863 \times .145 \times 20.7) = \log 863 + \log .145 + \log 20.7$$

$$\begin{array}{rcccl} \log 863 & = & \log (8.63 \times 10^2) & \doteq & \underline{\ ?\ } + 2 \\ \log .145 & = & \log (1.45 \times 10^{-1}) & \doteq & \underline{\ ?\ } - 1 \\ +\ \log 20.7 & = & \log (2.07 \times 10) & \doteq & \underline{\ ?\ } + 1 \\ \hline & & & & \underline{\ ?\ } \end{array}$$

2. Find log (79,200 ÷ 345) by completing the solution.

Partial solution.

$$\log (79{,}200 \div 345) = \log 79{,}200 - \log 345$$

$$\begin{array}{rcl} \log (7.92 \times 10^4) & \doteq & \underline{\ ?\ } \\ -\ \log (3.45 \times 10^2) & \doteq & \underline{\ ?\ } \\ \hline & & \underline{\ ?\ } \end{array}$$

3. Find $\log \sqrt[4]{.163}$ by completing the solution.

Partial solution.

$$\log .163 = \log (1.63 \times 10^{-1}) \doteq .2122 - 1$$

$$\log \sqrt[4]{.163} \doteq \tfrac{1}{4}(.2122 - 1) = \tfrac{1}{4}(3.2122 - 4) = \underline{\ ?\ }$$

4. Find log (3.16 ÷ 405) by completing the solution.

Partial solution.

$$\log 3.16 \doteq .4997 = \underline{\ ?\ }$$

$$\log (4.05 \times 10^2) \doteq .6075 + 2 = \underline{\ ?\ }$$

5. Find

$$\log \sqrt{\frac{13.5}{.0472}}.$$

Exercises for Discussion

Exercises for Discussion 1–4 may be used to help the student learn how to arrange the work on his paper for logarithmic computation. If time is limited, it is suggested that at least Exercises for Discussion 1 and 5 be covered.

Answer to Exercise for Discussion 5

5. $\log \sqrt{\dfrac{13.5}{.0472}} = \tfrac{1}{2}(\log 13.5 - \log .0472)$

$$\begin{array}{rcl} \log 13.5 & \doteq & 1.1303 \\ \log .0472 & \doteq & .6739 - 2 \\ \hline & & .4564 + 2 \end{array}$$

$$\log \sqrt{\frac{13.5}{.0472}} = \tfrac{1}{2}(2.4564) = 1.2282$$

Quiz

If N equals each of the following numbers, find log N.

1. $3.71 \times .543$ (ans: 0.3042)

2. $53.7 \div .0231$ (ans: 3.3664)

3. $\sqrt[3]{294}$ (ans: .8228)

4. $\dfrac{521}{7.2 \times .32}$ (ans: 2.3544)

5. $(8.63)^{5/4}$ (ans: 1.17)

*7-7 COMPUTING WITH LOGARITHMS

The emphasis is still on the connection between the two equations $\log_{10} N = x$ and $10^x = N$, and the use of the properties of logarithms. The exercises involve numbers with three significant digits. It is sufficient to read the results to three significant digits. Interpolation is not introduced until the next section.

The students should practice obtaining N from log N on many examples such as the following:

$\log N = .5378,$
$N = 10^{.5378},$
$N = 3.45;$

$\log N = .5378 + 1,$
$N = 10^{.5378} \times 10^1,$
$N = 3.45 \times 10^1,$ or 34.5;

$\log N = .5378 - 1,$
$N = 10^{.5378} \times 10^{-1},$
$N = 3.45 \times 10^{-1},$ or .345;

$\log N = 8.5378 - 10,$
$N = 10^{8.5378-10},$
$N = 10^{.5378-2},$
$N = 10^{.5378} \times 10^{-2},$
$N = 3.45 \times 10^{-2},$ or .0345;

$\log N = {}^{-}2.4622,$
$\log N = .5378 - 3,$
$N = 10^{.5378} \times 10^{-3},$
$N = 3.45 \times 10^{-3},$ or .00345.

The students should note that N is first expressed in exponential form, base 10, then in scientific notation, and finally in decimal form.

Exercises

Given that x equals each of the following numbers, find log x.

1. $4.96 \times .0175$ $\bar{1}.0615$

2. $49.6 \div .175$ 2.4525

3. $\sqrt[4]{496}$ .6739

4. $(.00504)^3$ $\bar{6}.8928$

5. $\frac{563}{392}$ .1572

6. $\sqrt{.824}$ $\bar{}.0421$

7. $\sqrt[3]{.0875}$ $\bar{}.3527$

8. $\dfrac{1}{\sqrt[5]{.002}}$ .5398

9. $\dfrac{30.4}{726}$ $\bar{1}.3780$

10. $36.5 \times 89{,}700 \times .475$ 6.1918

11. $\dfrac{89{,}700}{36.5 \times .475}$ 3.7138

12. $(37.8)^{\frac{3}{2}}$ 2.3662

*7-7 COMPUTING WITH LOGARITHMS

Before computing with logarithms, we must learn how to approximate N if we know log N. In the first place, if

$$0 \leqq \log N < 1,$$

we can approximate N by looking in the body of the Table of Common Logarithms for the closest entry to log N. Then N is approximately the number whose logarithm is this entry.

For example, given that

$$\log N = .8785,$$

we note that .8785 appears in the body of the table in the row marked 75 and in the column marked 6. Hence,

$$\log 7.56 \doteq .8785 \quad \text{and} \quad N \doteq 7.56.$$

If log N is not between 0 and 1, then we express log N as the sum of its fractional part and the greatest integer contained in it, that is,

$$\log N = A + k, \quad \text{where } 0 \leqq A < 1 \text{ and } k \text{ is an integer.}$$

Since A is between 0 and 1, we can find a positive number B whose logarithm is A from the table. Thus, $\log N = \log B + \log 10^k$ and

$$N = B \times 10^k, \quad \text{where } 1 \leqq B < 10 \text{ and } \log B = A.$$

For example, suppose that we are given

$$\log N = 1.8785.$$

Then the fractional part of log N is .8785, and the greatest integer contained in log N is 1. We may write

$$\log N = .8785 + 1.$$

From the preceding example, log 7.56 $\doteq$ .8785. Hence,

$$N \doteq 7.56 \times 10^1, \quad \text{or } 75.6.$$

Let us consider a second example. If

$$\log N = {}^{-}2.4522,$$

then

$${}^{-}3 < \log N < {}^{-}2.$$

Hence, $^{-}3$ is the greatest integer contained in log N, and

$${}^{-}2.4522 - {}^{-}3, \quad \text{or } .5478,$$

is the fractional part of log N. Thus,

$$\log N = .5478 - 3.$$

By the Table of Common Logarithms,

$$\log 3.53 \doteq .5478.$$

Therefore,

$$N \doteq 3.53 \times 10^{-3}, \quad \text{or } .00353.$$

When we represent log N in the form $A + k$, where $0 \leqq A < 1$ and k is an integer, we are expressing log N as the sum of its *mantissa* A and its *characteristic* k. The mantissa determines the digits in N, and the characteristic determines the placement of the decimal point.

If M and N are numbers such that $M = \log N$, then N is often called the *antilogarithm* of M, and we write

$$N = \text{antilog } M.$$

Thus, in the example above, .00353 $\doteq$ antilog ($^{-}2.4522$). Of course, if $M = \log N$, then $N = 10^M$ according to the definition of logarithms. Hence, antilog M is just 10^M.

Finding N from log N is difficult for some students. This section gives an opportunity for students to focus on that one problem, obtaining the entry in the table closest to the mantissa of log N, finding a three-digit value for N, and then locating the decimal point without getting involved in interpolating. Interpolation should be postponed until the meaning of the logarithm and the process of logarithmic computation are firmly fixed in the students' minds.

You may wish to emphasize here that the table is used to represent numbers as powers of 10, the laws of exponents for doing arithmetic, and again the table to find the decimal representation of a number expressed as a power of 10. Problem 1(a) could be written in the following way. Let

$$N = 87{,}500 \times 314.$$

Then

$$N \doteq 10^{4.9420} \times 10^{2.4969},$$
$$N \doteq 10^{4.9420+2.4969},$$
$$N \doteq 10^{7.4389},$$
$$N \doteq 27{,}500{,}000.$$

(See the bottom of page 302.)

The following example could be done in class to suggest a way to present the work on paper. Find

$$\sqrt{\frac{\sqrt{647} \times .0013}{181}}$$

using common logarithms.

Analysis:

Let

$$x = \sqrt{\frac{\sqrt{647} \times .0013}{181}},$$

then

$$\begin{aligned}\log x &= \tfrac{1}{2}[\log(\sqrt{647} \times .0013) - \log 181]\\ &= \tfrac{1}{2}[\log\sqrt{647} + \log .0013 - \log 181]\\ &= \tfrac{1}{2}[\tfrac{1}{2}\log 647 + \log .0013 - \log 181]\\ &= \tfrac{1}{2}[\tfrac{1}{2}\log(6.47 \times 10^2) + \log(1.3 \times 10^{-3}) - \log(1.81 \times 10^2)]\\ &\doteq \tfrac{1}{2}[\tfrac{1}{2}(.8109 + 2) + (.1139 + (^{-}3)) - (.2577 + 2)]\end{aligned}$$

$$\log x \doteq .1308 - 2,$$
$$x \doteq 10^{.1308} \times 10^{-2},$$
$$x \doteq 1.35 \times 10^{-2}, \quad \text{or } .0135.$$

Problem 1. Compute each of the following.

(a) $87{,}500 \times 314$ (b) $.0147 \div .397$

Solution.

(a) If we let N designate the desired product, then

$$\begin{aligned}\log N &= \log(87{,}500 \times 314)\\ &= \log 87{,}500 + \log 314.\end{aligned}$$

Thus,

$$\begin{array}{rcccl} \log 87{,}500 & = & \log(8.75 \times 10^4) & \doteq & .9420 + 4 \\ +\ \log 314 & = & \log(3.14 \times 10^2) & \doteq & .4969 + 2 \\ \hline & & \log N & \doteq & 1.4389 + 6 = .4389 + 7. \end{array}$$

Since $\log N$ has characteristic 7 and mantissa .4389,

$$N = B \times 10^7, \quad \text{where } \log B = .4389.$$

The mantissa .4389 is not in the body of the Table of Common Logarithms. The closest entry is $.4393 \doteq \log 2.75$. However, $\log B \doteq \log 2.75$ and $B \doteq 2.75$. Thus,

$$N \doteq 2.75 \times 10^7, \quad \text{or } 27{,}500{,}000.$$

(b) If N designates the desired quotient, then

$$\begin{aligned}\log N &= \log(.0147 \div .397)\\ &= \log .0147 - \log .397.\end{aligned}$$

Thus,

$$\begin{array}{rcccl} \log .0147 & = & \log(1.47 \times 10^{-2}) & \doteq & .1673 - 2 \\ -\ \log .397 & = & \log(3.97 \times 10^{-1}) & \doteq & .5988 - 1 \\ \hline \end{array}$$

In order to keep a positive mantissa when we subtract, we change $.1673 - 2$ to $1.1673 - 3$, as shown below.

$$\begin{array}{rcl} \log .0147 & \doteq & 1.1673 - 3 \\ -\ \log .397 & \doteq & .5988 - 1 \\ \hline & & .5685 - 2 \end{array}$$

Hence,

$$\log N = .5685 - 2$$

and

$$N \doteq B \times 10^{-2}, \quad \text{where } \log B = .5685.$$

Again, the mantissa .5685 is not in the Table of Common Logarithms. The closest entry is .5682 $\doteq$ log 3.70. Thus, $B \doteq 3.70$ and

$$N \doteq 3.70 \times 10^{-2}, \quad \text{or } .0370.$$

If we multiply 87,500 × 314 in Problem 1(a) we get 27,475,000, which is not the answer that we obtained by using logarithms. However, the answer we obtained by using logarithms is correct to three *significant digits;* that is, if we round off the numeral above, keeping the first three digits (reading from left to right), then we get 27,500,000 as an approximation to three significant digits. We replaced the block of digits 475 by 500 since 475 is closer to 500 than to 400.

Similarly, the answer we obtained for Problem 1(b) is an approximation of the correct answer to three significant digits. If we divide .0147 by .397, we get .03702 . . . Note that the three significant digits in this case are 3, 7, and 0, in that order. We wrote the answer in the form

$$.0370 \quad \text{rather than} \quad .037$$

to indicate that the last 0 was a significant digit.

When a physicist declares that the speed of light is 186,000 miles per second, he does not mean to imply that all six digits of this number are necessarily significant. Rather, he probably means that this is the approximate speed of light, accurate to three significant digits. In the early years of this century, the American physicist Michelson determined the speed of light, accurate to six significant digits, to be 186,234 miles per second.

Problem 2. Approximate $\sqrt[3]{.301}$ to three significant digits.

Solution. If we let

$$N = \sqrt[3]{.301},$$

then

$$\begin{aligned} \log N &= \log (.301)^{\frac{1}{3}} \\ &= \tfrac{1}{3} \log .301. \qquad \text{(LL-3)} \end{aligned}$$

Now

$$\begin{aligned} \tfrac{1}{3} \log .301 &= \tfrac{1}{3} \log (3.01 \times 10^{-1}) \\ &\doteq \tfrac{1}{3}(.4786 - 1) \\ &\doteq \tfrac{1}{3}(2.4786 - 3) \\ &\doteq .8262 - 1. \end{aligned}$$

Hence, $N \doteq B \times 10^{-1}$, where $\log B = .8262$.

Arithmetic:

$$\begin{array}{rl} 2\overline{).8109 + 2} & \\ .4054 + 1 & \\ .1139 - 3 & \text{add} \\ \hline .5193 - 2 & \\ .2577 + 2 & \text{subtract} \\ \hline 2).2616 - 4 & \\ .1308 - 2 & \end{array}$$

In Problem 1(b), the students should note the procedure used to avoid getting a negative fraction when subtracting logs. You may wish to show what would happen if this were not done,

$$\begin{array}{rl} .1673 - 2 & \\ .5988 - 1 & \text{subtract} \\ \hline {}^{-}.4315 - 1 & \end{array}$$

Now, before referring to the table of positive common logs, this log must be rewritten so no fraction is negative.

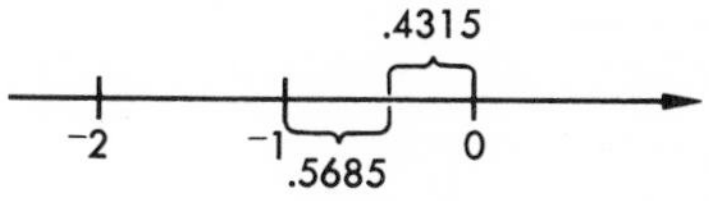

Since

$${}^{-}.4315 = .5685 - 1,$$

then

$${}^{-}.4315 - 1 = .5685 - 2,$$

which is the same answer as that obtained by the less tedious procedure suggested in the text.

Attention should be called to the statement about significant digits. In Problem 2, there is maneuvering such as that often used in computation involving roots. Again, you may wish to show what happens if the procedure given in the text is not followed:

$$\begin{aligned} \tfrac{1}{3}(.4786 - 1) &= .1595 - .3333 \\ &= {}^{-}.1738 \\ &= .8261 - 1. \end{aligned}$$

By the Table of Common Logarithms, $B \doteq 6.70$. Hence,

$$N \doteq 6.70 \times 10^{-1}, \quad \text{or } .670,$$

accurate to three significant digits.

Problem 3. Approximate $873 \div \sqrt[5]{.079}$ to three significant digits.

Solution. If

$$N = 873 \div \sqrt[5]{.079},$$

then

$$\begin{aligned} \log N &= \log 873 - \log \sqrt[5]{.079} \\ &= \log 873 - \tfrac{1}{5}\log .079. \end{aligned}$$

First, we find

$$\begin{aligned} \tfrac{1}{5}\log .079 &= \tfrac{1}{5}\log(7.9 \times 10^{-2}) \\ &\doteq \tfrac{1}{5}(.8976 - 2) \\ &\doteq \tfrac{1}{5}(3.8976 - 5) \\ &\doteq .7795 - 1 \end{aligned}$$

and

$$\log 873 \doteq 2.9410.$$

Continuing the solution of Problem 3, we obtain the following.

$$\begin{array}{rcr} \log 873 & \doteq & 2.9410 \\ -\ \tfrac{1}{5}\log .079 & \doteq & .7795 - 1 \\ \hline & & 2.1615 + 1 \end{array}$$

and

$$\log N \doteq .1615 + 3.$$

Therefore,

$$N = B \times 10^{3},$$

where

$$\log B \doteq .1615.$$

From the Table of Common Logarithms, $B \doteq 1.45$. Hence,

$$N = 1.45 \times 10^{3}, \quad \text{or } 1450,$$

accurate to three significant digits.

Problem 4. Compute $\sqrt[3]{^-.136}$.

Solution. We first observe that

$$\sqrt[3]{^-.136} = \sqrt[3]{(^-1)^3 \cdot .136}$$
$$= {}^-\sqrt[3]{.136}.$$

Since

$$\log \sqrt[3]{.136} = \tfrac{1}{3}\log .136$$
$$\doteq \tfrac{1}{3}(2.1335 - 3)$$
$$\doteq .7112 - 1,$$

we have

$$\sqrt[3]{.136} \doteq .514.$$

Therefore,

$$\sqrt[3]{^-.136} \doteq {}^-.514.$$

The Table of Common Logarithms makes it possible to express any positive real number as a power of 10. Wherever negative factors occur in a problem, the sign of the answer is determined and then the logarithmic computation is done using positive factors only.

Exercises

Find an approximate value of N in each of the following exercises.

1. $\log N = 2.5105$ 324
2. $\log N = .6513 + 1$ 44.8
3. $\log N = .8149 - 1$ .6530
4. $\log N = .3617 - 2$ .0230
5. $\log N = 3.0334$ 1080
6. $\log N = 7.9538 - 10$ .00899
7. $\log N = 14.8082 - 10$ 64,300
8. $\log N = 0.7042$ 5.06
9. $\log N = 3.8482 - 4$ .705
10. $\log N = 18.5752 - 20$ .0376
11. $\log N = {}^-.3698$ .4268
12. $\log N = {}^-2.6819$ .00208

Use logarithms to approximate each of the following numbers to three significant digits.

13. $(.317)(94.2)$ 29.9
14. $\sqrt[5]{1960}$ 4.55
15. $\dfrac{821}{37{,}500}$ .0219
16. $\dfrac{2.050}{.00045}$ 4560
17. $(.0126)(.115)$ .00145
18. $\sqrt[9]{764}$ 2.09

It is recommended that at least a few of Exercises 19–30 be assigned, and that the student be required to stick with them until he obtains the correct answers.

Exercises 31 and 32 should be assigned in order to help the student realize the need for logarithmic computation even in simple, ordinary formulas.

Quiz

Find an approximate value of N in each of the following exercises.

1. $\log N = 1.5988$ (ans: 39.7)
2. $\log N = 2.8451$ (ans: 700)
3. $\log N = .6561 - 1$ (ans: .453)
4. $\log N = 6.7649 - 8$ (ans: .0582)

Use logarithms to approximate each of the following numbers to three significant digits.

5. (.27)(281) (ans: 75.9)
6. $\dfrac{8.33}{.0328}$ (ans: 254)

Use logarithms to approximate each of the following numbers to three significant digits.

19. $\dfrac{(245)(7.53)}{(6.14)^2}$ 48.9 **20.** $\dfrac{16.8}{(0.871)^{\frac{1}{2}}}$ 18.0 **21.** $\left[\dfrac{\sqrt{647}\,(.0013)}{181}\right]^{\frac{1}{2}}$ .0135

22. $\sqrt[3]{\dfrac{3}{4}\left(\dfrac{275}{3.14}\right)}$ 4.03 **23.** $(4.71)^{-\frac{2}{3}}$ .356 **24.** $\sqrt[4]{7810}$ 9.40

25. $\sqrt{(.0417)(.123)}$ .0716 **26.** $\dfrac{5750}{9.32}$ 617 **27.** $(.00752)^{-\frac{3}{5}}$ 18.8

28. (186,000)(.445) 82,800 **29.** $\sqrt{\dfrac{(6.15)(37.7)}{255}}$ .954 **30.** $\sqrt[8]{\dfrac{705}{5.14}}$ 1.85

31. The formula for the volume V of a sphere with radius r units is $V = \frac{4}{3}\pi r^3$. Assuming the earth to be a perfect sphere with a radius of 3960 miles, determine the volume of the earth to three significant digits. (Use $\pi \doteq 3.14$.) 2.60×10^{11} cu mi

32. The number of seconds required for a complete swing of a pendulum is called the period of the pendulum. The period t seconds of a pendulum L feet long is given by the formula

$$t = 2\pi\sqrt{\frac{L}{g}},$$

where $g \doteq 32.2$. Find, to three significant digits, the period of a pendulum 3 feet long. 1.92 sec

33. The weight of a man d miles above the surface of the earth is given by the formula

$$W = \frac{W_0(4000)^2}{(4000 + d)^2},$$

where W_0 is the man's weight at the surface of the earth. Determine the approximate weight of a 160-pound man in a space capsule 500 miles above the earth. Find your own weight if you were in the capsule. 126 lb

34. When a principal P is invested at an annual interest rate of r per cent compounded k times a year, a formula for the amount A at the end of n years is

$$A = P\left(1 + \frac{r}{k}\right)^{nk}.$$

If the sum of \$1000 is invested at an annual rate of 4%, compute the amount A

(a) after 20 years if interest is compounded semiannually. \$2210
(b) after 20 years if interest is compounded quarterly. \$2210
(c) after 5 years in a bank which compounds interest daily. \$1200

35. Use the formula of the preceding exercise to find how many years it will take a sum of money invested at 4% compounded semiannually to double itself. 17.5 yr

36. A certain radioactive substance decays according to the formula

$$A = A_0 \times 2^{-\frac{t}{1500}}.$$

If the initial quantity A_0 is 425 milligrams, how much of the substance remains after 50 years? 415 mg

37. In 1950 the population of a certain town was 25,000. If the population growth is exponential, the population P after t years have elapsed is given by the formula

$$P = 25{,}000 \times \left(\tfrac{6}{5}\right)^{\frac{1}{10}t}.$$

(a) Find the population in 1955. 27,400

(b) How long will it take for the population to double? 38 yr

38. Heron's formula for the area of a triangle in terms of its three sides a, b, c, and semiperimeter s is

$$A = \sqrt{s(s - a)(s - b)(s - c)}.$$

Find, to three significant digits, the area of a triangle having sides of length 57 inches, 62 inches, and 43 inches. (The semiperimeter is one-half the sum of the lengths of the three sides.) 1180 sq in.

*7-8 LINEAR INTERPOLATION

Using the Table of Common Logarithms, we can find logarithms of numbers having three significant digits. If we are willing to interpolate, this table can be used to find products, quotients, and powers of numbers with four significant digits. How this interpolation is done will be shown below.

If you examine this table carefully, you will note that the *difference between consecutive numbers* in the table stays about the same in any particular row. For example, in the row

N	0	1	2	3	4	5	6	7	8	9
38	.5798	.5809	.5821	.5832	.5843	.5855	.5866	.5877	.5888	.5899

the differences between consecutive entries are as follows:

.0011, .0012, .0011, .0011, .0012, .0011, .0011, .0011, .0011.

Exercises 36, 37, and 38 also contain valuable information and are recommended for assignment.

***7-8 LINEAR INTERPOLATION**

The student should now understand what the logarithm of a number is and how to do computations using logarithms. Interpolation refines the approximation by adding one more digit to the answer and allowing one more digit in the numbers in the problem. This section is intended to strengthen the student's mastery of the topic and should not be too difficult.

The graph of $y = \log_{10} x$ and similar triangles may be used to show that

$$\log_{10} 3.827 = \log_{10} 3.82 + \tfrac{7}{10}(\log_{10} 3.83 - \log_{10} 3.82).$$

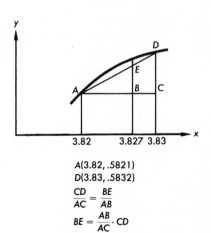

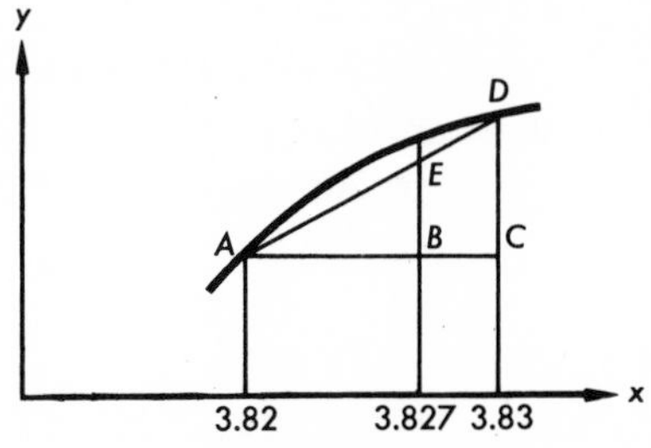

$A(3.82, .5821)$

$D(3.83, .5832)$

$$\frac{CD}{AC} = \frac{BE}{AB}$$

$$BE = \frac{AB}{AC} \cdot CD$$

$$BE = \tfrac{7}{10}(.0011)$$

TWISTER

Patrick Riley, an Irish watchmaker, was puzzled by a problem posed by a mathematical friend. The problem was as follows: A particular watch has a minute hand of length .499 inches and an hour hand of length .374 inches. When the hour hand was exactly at one and the minute hand at two, the minute hand stopped. What is the length of the arc formed by the hour hand from that moment until it reached the stopped minute hand? (Use only logarithms.)

Solution:

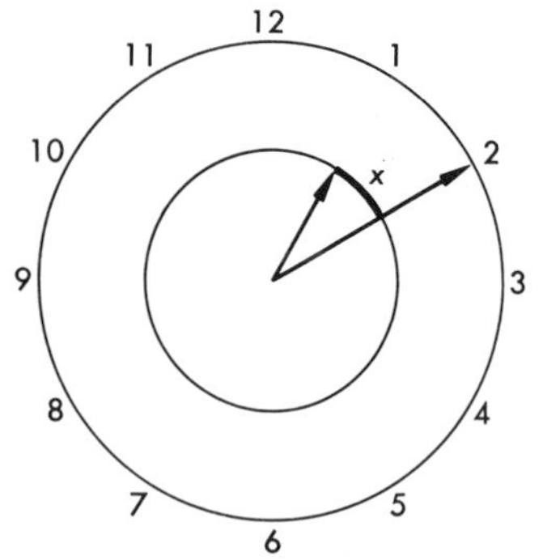

$$x = \tfrac{1}{12}(2)(\pi)(.374)$$
$$= 3.14(.0623)$$
$$\log x = \log 3.14 + \log .0623$$
$$= .4969 + (.7945 - 2)$$
$$= .2914 - 1$$
$$x \doteq .1956 \text{ inches}$$

Hence, if we graph the equation

$$y = \log x$$

every hundredth of a unit between $x = 3.80$ and $x = 3.89$, the graph will be, in essence, a straight line with slope

$$\frac{.0011}{.01}, \quad \text{or } .11.$$

Since, in this interval, the graph is essentially a straight line, we should be able to compute quite accurately the logarithms of numbers *between* entries of the table. For example, we may compute new entries between 383 and 384 as shown below.

N	0	1	2	3	4	5	6	7	8	9
383	.5832	.5833	.5834	.5835	.5836	.5838	.5839	.5840	.5841	.5842

We must realize, however, that these entries may be wrong by one unit in the last digit.

The process of approximating new entries in a table is called *linear interpolation.* It is apparent that we do not have to make up a whole new row, as we did above, to find some particular logarithm. For example, we can find log 3.836 as follows:

$$\log 3.836 \doteq \log 3.83 + \tfrac{6}{10}(.0011)$$
$$\doteq .5832 + .0007, \quad \text{or } .5839.$$

Given a number between 0 and 1 that does not appear in the Table of Common Logarithms, we can use linear interpolation to find a number having that logarithm and four-digit accuracy. For example, the number .6861 is not listed in the Table. Let us find N such that

$$\log N = .6861.$$

From the Table,

$$\log 4.85 \doteq .6857,$$
$$\log 4.86 \doteq .6866.$$

Since .6861 is between these two consecutive entries, N is between 4.85 and 4.86. Is N equal to 4.851, or to 4.852, and so on? Since

$$.6866 - .6857 = .0009$$

and

$$.6861 - .6857 = .0004,$$

the fourth digit of N should be the closest tenth of

$$\frac{.0004}{.0009}, \quad \text{or} \quad \frac{4}{9}.$$

The closest tenth is 4, and therefore,

$$N \doteq 4.854$$

to four significant digits.

Problem. Compute the following to four significant digits.

$$\frac{4.913 \times \sqrt{88.15}}{.0003021}$$

Solution. If we let

$$N = \frac{4.913 \times \sqrt{88.15}}{.0003021},$$

then

$$\begin{aligned} \log N &= \log (4.913 \times \sqrt{88.15}) - \log .0003021 \\ &= \log 4.913 + \log \sqrt{88.15} - \log .0003021. \end{aligned}$$

Using the Table of Common Logarithms, we interpolate for each logarithm separately.

1. $\log 4.913 \doteq .6911 + \frac{3}{10}(.0009) \doteq .6911 + .0003 = .6914$
2. $\begin{aligned}[t] \log \sqrt{88.15} &= \tfrac{1}{2}[(\log 8.815) + 1] \\ &\doteq \tfrac{1}{2}[.9450 + \tfrac{5}{10}(.0005) + 1] \\ &\doteq \tfrac{1}{2}[.9450 + .0002 + 1] \\ &= \tfrac{1}{2}[1.9452] = .9726 \end{aligned}$
3. $\begin{aligned}[t] \log .0003021 &= (\log 3.021) - 4 \\ &\doteq .4800 + \tfrac{1}{10}(.0014) - 4 \\ &\doteq .4800 + .0001 - 4 \doteq .4801 - 4 \end{aligned}$

Hence, we have

$$\begin{array}{rl} \log 4.913 & \doteq\ .6914 \\ + \ \log \sqrt{88.15} & \doteq\ .9726 \\ \hline & \ 1.6640 \end{array}$$

Therefore,

$$\begin{array}{rrl} & \log (4.913 \times \sqrt{88.15}) & \doteq 1.6640 \\ - & \log .0003021 & \doteq \ .4801 - 4 \\ \hline & \log N & \doteq 1.1839 + 4 \\ & & \doteq 5.1839 \end{array}$$

Thus,

$$N = B \times 10^5 \quad \text{where } \log B \doteq .1839.$$

Since

$$\begin{array}{ll} \log 1.52 & \doteq .1818 \\ \log B & \doteq .1839 \\ \log 1.53 & \doteq .1847 \end{array} \quad \left.\begin{array}{l} .0021 \\ .0029 \end{array}\right. \quad \text{and} \quad \tfrac{21}{29} \doteq \tfrac{7}{10},$$

it follows that

$$B \doteq 1.527.$$

Thus, finally,

$$N \doteq 1.527 \times 10^5.$$

We remind ourselves that the logarithms computed above enable us to write each number exponentially. Thus,

$$4.913 \doteq 0^{.6914}, \quad 88.15 \doteq 10^{1.9452}, \quad .0003021 \doteq 10^{.4801-4}.$$

Therefore,

$$\begin{aligned} N &\doteq \frac{10^{.6914} \times (10^{1.9452})^{\frac{1}{2}}}{10^{.4801-4}} \\ &\doteq \frac{10^{.6914} \times 10^{.9726}}{10^{.4801-4}} \\ &\doteq 10^{.6914+.9726-(.4801-4)} \\ &\doteq 10^{5.1839} \\ &\doteq 10^{.1839} \times 10^5. \end{aligned}$$

By looking under .1839 in the Table of Common Logarithms, we find that $10^{.1839} \doteq 1.527$. Hence,

$$N \doteq 1.527 \times 10^5.$$

Exercises

Use linear interpolation to find the logarithm of each of the following numbers to the nearest ten-thousandth.

1. 65.42 1.8157
2. .3537 .5486 − 1
3. 1.543 .1883
4. .04895 .6897 − 2
5. 120.4 2.0806
6. .005066 .7047 − 3
7. (18.78) × (2.609) 1.6902
8. (.4308) ÷ (.02031) 1.3266
9. $\sqrt{.5612}$ .8746 − 1

Use linear interpolation to find N to four significant digits in each of the following equations.

10. $\log N = .4719$ 2.964
11. $\log N = 1.5343$ 34.22
12. $\log N = .6097 - 1$ .4071
13. $\log N = 2.6742$ 472.3
14. $\log N = .8529 - 2$ .07127
15. $\log N = 3.9158$ 8238

Find x, given each of the following conditions.

16. $\log x = 1.5643$ 36.67
17. $10^x = .001234$ $^-2.9087$
18. $x = \log 81.53$ 1.9113
19. $\log x = {}^-.7654$ .1716
20. $x = 10^{\log .06789}$ .06789
21. $x = \log \frac{1}{2.564}$ $^-.4089$
22. $x = 10^{3.0472}$ 1115
23. $x = \left(\frac{1}{10}\right)^{2.4601}$ .003466
24. $\log x = \frac{1}{2} \log 576.0$ 24
25. $x = 10^{^-3.0012}$ .0009972
26. $\log x = \log .1432 - \log .4296$ $\frac{1}{3}$
27. $\log x = \frac{1}{3} \log .08432$ .4385

Use the method of linear interpolation to find answers correct to four significant digits for the expressions in Exercises 28–45.

28. $5.712 \times .09232$ .5274
29. $^-173.2 \div 7.32$ $^-23.66$
30. $\sqrt{1984}$ 44.54
31. $(1.025)^{14}$ 1.412
32. $\sqrt[5]{163.7}$ 2.772
33. $\sqrt{2.503 \times 16.24}$ 6.376
34. $(.3567 \times 4.108)^3$ 3.146
35. $\sqrt{(28.06)^2 - (20.39)^2}$ 19.27 (Hint: Factor first.)
36. $\dfrac{\sqrt{.5723}}{\sqrt[3]{^-4.218}}$ $^-.4682$
37. $(132.3)^{1.7}$ 4043
38. $\sqrt{518.4 \times .3142}$ 12.76
39. $\sqrt[5]{4816}$ 5.451
40. $\sqrt{(^-19.8)^2 + (23.4)^2}$ 30.65
41. $\dfrac{57.91 \times 80.24}{6.307}$ 736.7
42. $\sqrt[3]{\dfrac{72.24}{275.8}}$ .6399
43. $(423.1)^{-\frac{2}{7}}$ .1776
44. $\dfrac{(^-82.25) \times 47.17}{15.19 \times 49.93}$ $^-5.115$
45. $23.7 \times \dfrac{302}{325} \times \dfrac{14.7}{12.2}$ 26.53

Exercises

It is recommended that Exercises 16–27, and 35 on this page and Exercise 46 on the next page be assigned.

Exercises 47, 53, and 54 are important for their content and should also be assigned.

Quiz

Use linear interpolation to find the logarithm of each of the following numbers to the nearest ten-thousandth.

1. 7.955 (ans: .9006)
2. .03725 (ans: .5711 − 2)

Use linear interpolation to find N to four significant digits in each of the following equations.

3. $\log N = 1.7108$ (ans: 51.38)
4. $\log N = .4071 - 1$ (ans: .2553)
5. $N = 3.791 \times .4333$ (ans: 1.643)
6. $N = {}^-862.1 \div 4.207$ (ans: $^-204.9$)

*7–9 LOGARITHMS TO A BASE OTHER THAN 10

The student has solved equations of the form $x^2 = 9$. Can he solve the equation if the exponent rather than the base is unknown? That is, can he solve $2^x = 9$? If the 2 were only a 10 ($10^x = 9$), the equation would be instantly solvable using the table of common logarithms. The trick is to re-work the form of $2^x = 9$ until the table of common logarithms *is* usable. Since 2^x and 9 are the same number, $\log_{10} 2^x$ and $\log_{10} 9$ must be the same number. But

$$\log_{10} 2^x = x \log_{10} 2,$$

by the third law of logarithms. Hence,

$$x \log_{10} 2 = \log_{10} 9$$

and this is just a linear equation in x. From the log table, it can be found that $\log_{10} 2 = .3010$ and $\log_{10} 9 = .9542$. Hence,

$$x(.3010) = .9542$$

and

$$x = \frac{.9542}{.3010},$$

and so on. [The students should notice that $3 < x < 4$, which is convenient because $2^3 = 8$, $2^4 = 16$, and $8 < 9 < 16$.] You could have the class find $(.9542) \div (.301)$ both by long division and by means of logarithms.

At this point, it may be well to define the base for natural logarithms. Many students may have heard of natural logarithms or noticed them in handbooks of tables. You could have the class

46. Find each of the following logarithms.

(a) log (log 2) .4786 − 1 (b) log (log 6) .8911 − 1

(c) (log 2) · (log 6) .2342 (d) (log 2) ÷ (log 6) .3868

(e) log 2 + log 6 .0792 + 1 (f) $(\log 2)^2$ .0906

47. Using logarithms to approximate the squares of the legs and to compute the square root of their sum, find an approximation for the length of the hypotenuse of a right triangle if one leg is 235.1 inches long and the other is 15.24 inches long. 235.6 in.

48. Use logarithms to find an approximation to four significant digits of the area of the triangle in Exercise 47. 1792 sq in.

49. Find the approximate radius of a sphere whose volume is 137.7 cubic feet. (Use $\pi \doteq 3.142$ and $V = \frac{4}{3}\pi r^3$.) 3.204 ft

50. Find the approximate surface area ($A = 4\pi r^2$) of a sphere with a radius of 17.34 inches. 3778 sq in.

51. Find the approximate length of an edge of a cube whose volume is twice as big as the volume of a cube whose edge is 3 feet long. 3.78 ft

52. Find the radius of a circle with an area of 15 square inches. 2.185 in.

53. Use Heron's formula (Exercise 38, page 299) to find a four-digit approximation of the area of a triangle with sides of length 14.32 inches, 16.36 inches, and 15.71 inches. 102.7 sq in.

54. Find the approximate length of the side of an equilateral triangle which has an area of 136 square feet. 17.72 ft

*7–9 LOGARITHMS TO A BASE OTHER THAN 10

When we have a table of logarithms to the base 10, such as the Table of Common Logarithms, we can readily construct a table of logarithms to another base. For example, if we wish to approximate

$$\log_5 7,$$

we first observe that the two equations

$$N = \log_5 7 \quad \text{and} \quad 5^N = 7$$

are equivalent, according to the definition of a logarithm.

The solution of the second equation may be obtained in the following way. Two positive numbers are equal if, and only if, their logarithms to the base 10 are equal. Hence, the equation

$$\log 5^N = \log 7$$

is equivalent to each equation above. In turn, by the third law of logarithms, the equation

$$N \log 5 = \log 7$$

is equivalent to each equation above. This last equation is linear and has the solution

$$N = \frac{\log 7}{\log 5}.$$

Hence,

$$\log_5 7 = \frac{\log 7}{\log 5}.$$

From the Table of Common Logarithms,

$$\log_5 7 \doteq \frac{.8451}{.6990}.$$

We can compute the above quotient either by use of logarithms or by long division. In either case,

$$\log_5 7 \doteq 1.209.$$

In general, it can be shown that

$$\log_b N = \frac{\log N}{\log b}.$$

This equation can be used to convert logarithms from base 10 to base b.

Problem 1. Find an answer correct to four significant digits for each of the following.

(a) $\log_4 17$ (b) $\log_{0.5} 25$

Solution.

(a) $\log_4 17 = \dfrac{\log 17}{\log 4} \doteq \dfrac{1.2304}{0.6021} \doteq 2.044$

(b) $\log_{0.5} 25 = \dfrac{\log 25}{\log 0.5} \doteq \dfrac{1.3979}{(0.6990 - 1)} = \dfrac{1.3979}{{}^{-}0.3010} \doteq {}^{-}4.644$

develop the sequence defined by

$$s_n = \left(1 + \frac{1}{n}\right)^n, \; n = 1, 2, \ldots$$

and observe that

$$s_1 = (1 + 1)^1 = 2,$$
$$s_2 = (1 + \tfrac{1}{2})^2 = \tfrac{9}{4}, \ldots$$

is a sequence of increasing numbers, apparently bounded. Then the class could develop the sequence defined by

$$t_n = \left(1 + \frac{1}{n}\right)^{n+1}, \; n = 1, 2, \ldots$$

and observe that

$$t_1 = (1 + 1)^2 = 4,$$
$$t_2 = (1 + \tfrac{1}{2})^3 = \tfrac{27}{8}, \ldots$$

is a sequence of decreasing numbers, apparently bounded.

If the students have access to a computer, you could have them find s_n and t_n, $n = 1, \frac{1}{2}, \frac{1}{4}, \frac{1}{8}, \frac{1}{16}, \frac{1}{32}, \ldots, 1/(2^n)$ and watch these two sequences converge to the same limit. Now e may be defined to be the least upper bound on the set $\{s_n\}$ or the greatest lower bound on the set $\{t_n\}$. The number e is irrational, of course, but its rational approximation to nine decimal places is easy to remember:

2.718281828.

This is the second transcendental number in the mathematical experience of the student. Remind him that the other one, π, had a geometrical definition as the ratio of circumference to diameter of a circle. This one is defined to be the limit of a function which will concern him more when he studies calculus. The interested student may want to give a report on Napierian logarithms. Also, he may wish to read about hyperbolic functions, since they involve the exponential functions e^x and e^{-x}.

Quiz

Find an answer correct to four significant digits for each of the following.

1. $\log_2 8$ (ans: 3)
2. $\log_{1/4} 6$ (ans: $^{-}1.292$)
3. $\log_{1.931} 17$ (ans: 4.304)

Solve each equation for x.

4. $\log_{10} x^4 = 8$ (ans: 100)
5. $3^x = 8^{\log_7 7}$ (ans: 1.893)

Problem 2. Find x if $3^x = 2^{\log_4 2}$.

Solution. We first determine $\log_4 2$.

$$\log_4 2 = \frac{\log 2}{\log 4} \doteq \frac{0.3010}{.6021}, \quad \text{or } .5$$

Hence, the given equation is equivalent to the equation

$$3^x = 2^{.5}.$$

Using the third law of logarithms, we have

$$x \log 3 = .5 \log 2,$$

$$x = \frac{.5 \log 2}{\log 3} \doteq \frac{.5 \times 0.3010}{0.4771} \doteq \frac{.1505}{.4771}, \quad \text{or } .3154.$$

Exercises

For each of the following, find an answer correct to four significant digits.

1. $\log_3 10$ 2.096
2. $\log_{\frac{1}{2}} 5$ $^{-}2.332$
3. $\log_2 23$ 4.524
4. $\log_5 652$ 4.026
5. $\log_{2.718} 32$ 3.465
6. $3^{1.65}$ 6.126

In Exercises 7–15, solve each equation for x.

7. $5^x = 30^{3\log_2 4}$ 12.68
8. $5^{\log_5 x} = 2$ 2
9. $7^x = 27^{\log_3 3}$ 1.694
10. $2^x \cdot 16^3 = 4^{5\log_5 5}$ $^{-}2$
11. $100^{x \log_y y} = 35$ .772
12. $2^{x^2} = 27 \log_4 16$ 2.399
13. $\log_{10}(3x - 5) = 2$ 35
14. $\log_{10} x^3 = 12$ 10,000
15. $4^{\log_4 2} + 2^{\log_2 2} = 8^{\log_8 x}$ 4
16. Prove that the equation $\log_a b \cdot \log_b a = 1$ is true for every pair a, b of positive numbers other than 1. See Solution Manual.

Solve each of the following inequalities.

17. $2^x > 5$ $x > 2.322$
18. $3(2^x) \leqq 7$ $x \leqq 1.222$
19. $(\frac{1}{2})^x < .01$ $x > 6.644$

HISTORICAL NOTE

At the beginning of the seventeenth century, logarithms were invented for the specific purpose of aiding in astronomical computations. The Scotchman Napier (1550–1617) is usually given credit for their invention because they appeared in his *Descriptio*, published in 1614. However, the Swiss watchmaker Bürgi (1552–1632) discovered them independently at about the same time. The first table of logarithms is believed to have been published by Bürgi in 1620.

In 1624, the Englishman Briggs published a table of common logarithms of all integers from 1 to 20,000 and from 90,000 to 100,000. In this table, each logarithm was approximated to fourteen-decimal-place accuracy. In view of the limited mathematical knowledge of his period, this was quite an achievement. A portion of a page from this table is reproduced below.

Chilias vicesima.

Num. absolut.	Logarithmi.	Num. absolut.	Logarithmi.	Num. absolut.	Logarithmi.
19901	4,29887,48997,0470 2,18221,9843	19919	4,29926,75316,0861 2,18024,7908	19937	4,29965,98088,6701 2,17827,9533
19902	4,29889,67219,0313 2,18211,0197	19920	4,29928,93340,8769 2,18013,8460	19938	4,29968,15916,6234 2,17817,0284
19903	4,29891,85430,0510 2,18200,0563	19921	4,29931,11354,7229 2,18002,9024	19939	4,29970,33733,6518 2,17806,1045
19904	4,29894,03630,1073 2,18189,0939	19922	4,29933,29357,6253 2,17991,9598	19940	4,29972,51509,7563 2,17795,1817
19905	4,29896,21819,2012 2,18178,1327	19923	4,29935,47349,5851 2,17981,0184	19941	4,29974,69304,9380 2,17784,2600
19906	4,29898,39997,3339 2,18167,1725	19924	4,29937,65330,6035 2,17970,0781	19942	4,29976,87089,1980 2,17773,3394
19907	4,29900,58164,5064 2,18156,2135	19925	4,29939,83300,6816 2,17959,1388	19943	4,29979,04862,5374 2,17762,4198
19908	4,29902,76320,7199 2,18145,2555	19926	4,29942,01259,8204 2,17948,2006	19944	4,29981,22624,9572 2,17751,5014
19909	4,29904,94465,9754 2,18134,2987	19927	4,29944,19208,0210 2,17937,2636	19945	4,29983,40406,4586 2,17740,5841
19910	4,29907,12600,2741 2,18123,3430	19928	4,29946,37145,2846 2,17926,3276	19946	4,29985,58147,0427 2,17729,6679
19911	4,29909,30723,6171 2,18112,3883	19929	4,29948,55071,6122 2,17915,3927	19947	4,29987,75876,7106 2,17718,7527
19912	4,29911,48836,0054 2,18101,4348	19930	4,29950,72987,0049 2,17904,4590	19948	4,29989,93595,4633 2,17707,8387
19913	4,29913,66937,4402 2,18090,4823	19931	4,29952,90891,4639 2,17892,5263	19949	4,29992,11303,3020 2,17696,9257
19914	4,29915,85027,9225 2,18079,5310	19932	4,29955,08784,9902 2,17882,5947	19950	4,29994,29000,2277 2,17686,0139
19915	4,29918,03107,4535 2,18068,5808	19933	4,29957,26667,5849 2,17871,6643	19951	4,29996,46686,2416 2,17675,1031
19916	4,29920,21176,0343 2,18057,6316	19934	4,29959,44539,2492 2,17860,7349	19952	4,29998,64361,3447 2,17664,1934
19917	4,29922,39233,6659 2,18046,6835	19935	4,29961,62399,9841 2,17849,8066	19953	4,30000,82025,5381 2,17653,2849
19918	4,29924,57280,3494 2,18035,7367	19936	4,29963,80249,7907 2,17838,8794	19954	4,30002,99678,8230 2,17642,3774

KEY IDEAS AND KEY WORDS

The definition of the **logarithm function** to the base b, $\log_b$, is given by

$$\log_b s = r, \quad \text{where } b^r = s \qquad (\text{assuming } b > 0,\ b \neq 1).$$

The domain of $\log_b s$ is the set of all positive real numbers.

The **laws of logarithms** are as follows:

$$\log_b xy = \log_b x + \log_b y, \qquad \textbf{(LL-1)}$$

$$\log_b \frac{x}{y} = \log_b x - \log_b y, \qquad \textbf{(LL-2)}$$

$$\log_b x^r = r \log_b x. \qquad \textbf{(LL-3)}$$

Logarithms to the base 10 are called **common logarithms.** We understand

$$\log N \quad \text{to mean} \quad \log_{10} N.$$

The greatest integer contained in $\log N$ is called the **characteristic** of $\log N$, and the fractional part is called the **mantissa.** If N is expressed in scientific notation,

$$N = B \cdot 10^k, \quad \text{where } 1 \leqq B < 10.$$

Then

$$k = \text{characteristic} \quad \text{and} \quad \log B = \text{mantissa}$$

of $\log N$.

If we know $\log N$, we can find $\mathbf{log}_b\, \boldsymbol{N}$ with the aid of the following equation.

$$\log_b N = \frac{\log N}{\log b}$$

If M and N are numbers such that $M = \log N$, then N is called the **antilogarithm** of M.

CHAPTER REVIEW

See Solution Manual for graphs.

Tell which of the following statements are true and which are false. Correct the ones that you marked false.

1. If $r > s$, then $(^-2)^r > (^-2)^s$. False; $2^r > 2^s$

2. $\dfrac{\log 5}{\log 3} = \log 2$ False; $\dfrac{\log 5}{\log 3} = \log_3 5$

3. $\log (r + s) = \log r + \log s$ False; $\log rs = \log r + \log s$

4. $\log 3x = 3 \log x$ False; $\log 3x = \log 3 + \log x$

5. If $f(x) = \log (1 - x)$, the domain of x is $\{x \mid x < 1\}$. True

6. If $g(x) = \log (x^2 + 1)$, the domain of x is the set of real numbers. True

7. $\log x^n = (\log x)^n$ F; $\log x^n = n \log x$

8. $\log_9 3 = \dfrac{1}{\log_3 9}$ True

9. $\log \sqrt{\dfrac{a}{b^2}} = \dfrac{1}{2}(\log a - 2 \log b)$ True

10. $\log_4 16 = \dfrac{\log_2 16}{\log_2 4}$ True

Solve each of the following equations for x without referring to logarithm tables.

11. $\log 5 + \log 4 = \log x$ 20

12. $\log_7 x^5 - 3 \log_7 x = 2$ 7

13. $\log (4x - 1) - 2 \log x = \log 3$ $\frac{1}{3}$ or 1

14. $\log_3 42 - \log_3 8 = \log_3 x$ $\frac{21}{4}$

15. $2^{3x-2} = 64$ $\frac{8}{3}$

16. $\log_x \frac{1}{49} = {}^{-}2$ 7

17. $\log_8 x = \frac{4}{3}$ 16

18. $\log_{\frac{3}{2}} \frac{8}{27} = x$ $^{-}3$

Use logarithms to find approximations to four significant digits for each of the following numbers.

19. $45.32 \div 861.7$ .05259

20. $45{,}320 \times .008617$ 390.5

21. $\sqrt[3]{4532}$ 16.55

22. $(.4532)^2$ .2054

In Exercises 23–26, graph each of the equations. For what values of x is each equation defined?

23. $y = \log_{12} x$ $x > 0$

24. $y = \log_{12} |x|$ $x \neq 0$

25. $y = \log_3 (x + 2)$ $x > {}^{-}2$

26. $y = \log_3 (2 - x)$ $x < 2$

27. Solve each of the following equations for x.

(a) $\log_{10} (x + 1) - \log_{10} x = .3247$ .8993

(b) $3^{1+2x} = 5^{1-2x}$ .09434

28. The star Betelgeuse is approximately 1.59×10^{15} miles from the earth. How many years does it take light from Betelgeuse to reach us? 270.9 yrs

29. The speed of sound in water is 1.46×10^5 centimeters per second. If it takes a sound 2.00×10^{-2} seconds to travel from the surface of a body of water to the bottom and back, how deep is the water? 1.46×10^3 cm

CHAPTER TEST

1. Solve each of the following equations for N.

(a) $\log_2 \frac{1}{8} = N$ $^{-}3$ (b) $\log_5 N = {}^{-}3$ $\frac{1}{125}$ (c) $\log_N 16 = \frac{1}{2}$ 256

2. Sketch the graph of each of the following equations. For what values of x is each equation defined?

(a) $y = \log_3 x$ $x > 0$ (b) $y = \log_5 (x + 3)$ $x > {}^{-}3$

In Exercises 3–8, solve each equation for x.

3. $10^x = 235.4$ 2.3718

4. $\log x = 2.4561$ 285.8

5. $x = (43.85)^3$ 84,340

6. $x = \sqrt{.4385}$ .6622

7. $7^{x+1} = 49$ 1

8. $x = \log_3 7$ 1.771

9. Solve for n if $\log (15n + 1) + \log n = \log 2$. $\frac{1}{3}$

CHAPTER TEST

The material included in the Chapter Test was covered in the following sections:

Problem 1—Section 7-2
Problem 2—Section 7-3
Problem 3—Sections 7-5, 7-8
Problems 4-6—Sections 7-7, 7-8
Problem 7—Section 7-2
Problem 8—Section 7-9
Problem 9—Section 7-4

Answers to Chapter Test Problem 2

2. (a)

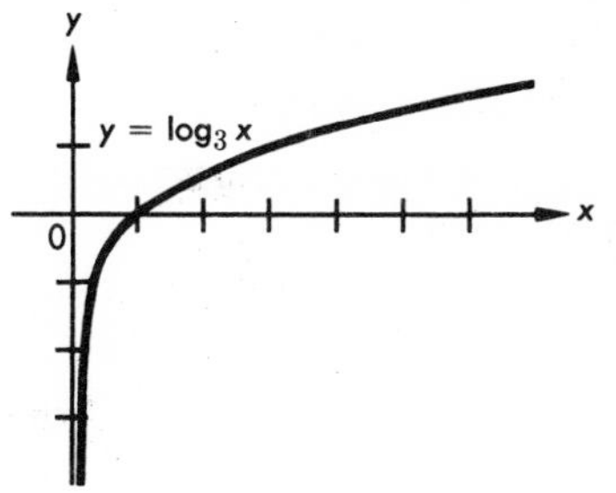

(b)

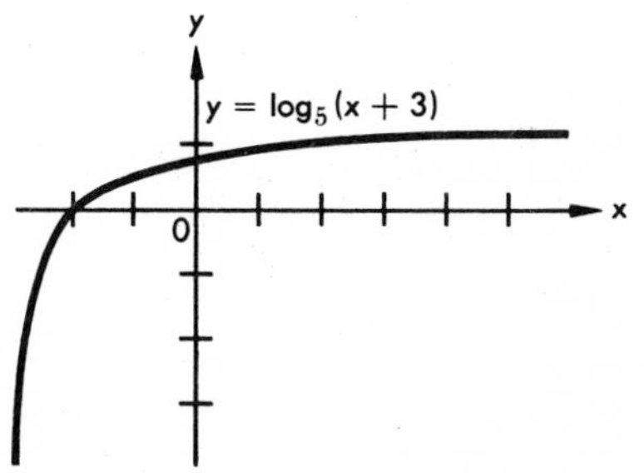

CUMULATIVE REVIEW II

In Cumulative Review Problem 9(b), use the table of logarithms to approximate $f(10)$, $f(20)$, $f(50)$, $f(100)$, and $f(1{,}000)$ to show that

$$\left(1+\frac{1}{x}\right)^x$$

approaches 2.72 as x takes on larger and larger values.

Cumulative Review II

See Solution Manual for graphs and proofs.

1. For what real values of x and y, if any, do the following pairs of algebraic expressions have the same value? $x = \left(\frac{^-1 \pm i\sqrt{3}}{2}\right)y$

   (a) xy^{-2} and $\frac{1}{xy^2}$ $x = \pm 1, y \neq 0$ (b) $x^{-1} + y^{-1}$ and $\frac{1}{x+y}$

2. A point P moves in a coordinate plane in such a way that its distance from the point $(^-1, 3)$ is always twice its distance from the point $(2, {}^-4)$. Prove that the path traced by P is a circle. Find the center and radius of the circle. $(3, \frac{^-19}{3})$ 5.08

3. On the same set of axes, sketch the graph of each of the following equations.

   (a) $y = x$ (b) $y = x^2$ (c) $y = x^3$ (d) $y = x^4$

4. Describe the graph of $y = x^n$, given that n is a positive integer. (Hint: Consider the cases n even and n odd separately.) See Solution Manual.

5. On the same set of axes, sketch the graph of each of the following equations.

   (a) $y = x^{^-1}$ (b) $y = x^{^-2}$ (c) $y = x^{^-3}$ (d) $y = x^{^-4}$

6. Describe the graph of $y = x^n$, given that n is a negative integer. See Solution Manual.

7. Find all points on the line $x = {}^-1$ that are at a distance of $\sqrt{17}$ units from the point $(^-2, 1)$. $(^-1, {}^-3), (^-1, 5)$

8. Let the functions f, g, and h be defined by the equations

$$f(x) = x^2, \quad g(x) = \frac{1}{x}, \quad h(x) = x^2 + \frac{1}{x}.$$

   (a) Graph f and g on the same set of axes.

   (b) Noting that $h(x) = f(x) + g(x)$, graph h on the same set of axes.

9. Let the function f be defined by

$$f(x) = \left(1 + \frac{1}{x}\right)^x, \quad x > 0.$$

   2 2.25 2.37 2.44 2.49 2.52

   (a) Find $f(1)$, $f(2)$, $f(3)$, $f(4)$, $f(5)$, and $f(6)$.

   (b) What do you observe about the behavior of $f(x)$ as x takes on larger and larger values? $(1+\frac{1}{x})^x$ approaches 2.72

10. Sketch the graph of each of the following equations.

   (a) $y = \dfrac{2^x + 2^{^-x}}{2}$ (b) $y = \dfrac{2^x - 2^{^-x}}{2}$

11. Let the functions f, g, and h be defined by the following equations.

$$f(x) = x^2 + 1, \quad g(x) = x^3 - 5x, \quad h(x) = \sqrt{4 - x^2}$$

(a) For each point (a, b) of the first quadrant on the graph of f, which of the points $(^-a, b)$, $(a, {}^-b)$, $(^-a, {}^-b)$, and (b, a) are also on the graph of f? $(^-a, b)$

(b) Answer the same question for the graph of g. $(^-a, {}^-b)$

(c) Answer the same question for the graph of h. $(^-a, b), (b, a)$

12. Solve each of the following equations.

(a) $(\log x)^2 - \log x^2 + 1 = 0$ 10

(b) $\log(\log x) = 2$ 10^{100}

(c) $(\log x)(\log x^2) + \log x^3 - 9 = 0$ $10\sqrt{10}$ or 10^{-3}

13. Find the solution set of each of the following expressions.

(a) $3^x = 5^x$ $x = 0$ (b) $3^x < 5^x$ $x > 0$ (c) $3^x > 5^x$ $x < 0$

Simplify each of the following by rationalizing the denominator.

14. $\dfrac{1}{\sqrt{2} - \sqrt{5}}$ $\frac{-1}{3}(\sqrt{2} + \sqrt{5})$

15. $\dfrac{1}{\sqrt{x + 1} - 1}$ $\frac{1}{x}(1 + \sqrt{x+1})$

16. For what real number or numbers k is the line $3x + ky = 15$ tangent to the circle $x^2 + y^2 = 9$? $k = \pm 4$

17. (a) How many digits are there in the numeral of 2^{50}? 16

(b) How many zeros precede the first significant digit in the decimal numeral of 2^{-50}? 15

18. The lengths of the sides of a triangle are 6, 8, and 12 inches. Find the length of the altitude drawn to the longest side. 3.56 in.

19. Sketch the graph of the function f defined by $f(x) = \sqrt{x^2}$. Describe the domain and range of f. Define f in terms of linear functions.
D = all reals; R = all non-negative reals; $f(x) = |x|$

20. If the birth rate of a nation is 12% and the death rate 2% per year, how many years (to the closest integer) will it take for the population to double? 7 yr

CHAPTER 8

Polynomials

The purpose of Chapter 8 is to give students an opportunity to review some of the materials on polynomials that were covered in first-year algebra, and to introduce polynomials as a mathematical system.

The introduction of polynomials parallels that of *i*-numbers and of complex numbers. First, a polynomial is defined and then, a procedure for doing arithmetic with two or more polynomials is described.

The following are some of the topics covered in Chapter 8:

- *The definition of addition and multiplication of polynomials*
- *The commutative and associative properties of multiplication and addition of polynomials*
- *The distributive law*
- *The existence of inverse and identity elements for addition and multiplication*
- *The properties of the zero polynomial*
- *The division algorithm*
- *The theory of zeros of a polynomial*
- *Synthetic division*
- *Factoring higher-degree polynomials*

It is suggested that one day be spent on each section, except for Section 8–9 on which you may wish to spend an additional day. Sections 8–10 and 8–11 are optional, but should be covered by those intending to continue in mathematics.

CHAPTER 8

The graphs of polynomials are reflected in many buildings, such as the elliptical dome of the Mormon Tabernacle in Salt Lake City. (Courtesy of the Church of Jesus Christ of Latter-Day Saints)

POLYNOMIALS

Seemingly different mathematical systems may have some common features. In geometry, for example, there is a certain dual relationship between points and planes in space. Two points determine a line, the line passing through them; and two (nonparallel) planes determine a line, their line of intersection. Similarly, two (nonparallel) lines determine a point, their point of intersection. They also determine a plane, the plane containing them.

In algebra, there is a close relationship between integers and polynomials. Just as there are prime integers, such as

$$2, \quad 3, \quad 5, \quad 41, \quad 103,$$

there are prime polynomials (with rational coefficients), such as

$$x - 2, \quad x^2 + 1, \quad 2x + 3, \quad x^3 + x + 1.$$

No integer in the above set can be factored in a nontrivial way ($5 = 5 \cdot 1$ is a trivial factorization), and no polynomial in the above set has a nontrivial factorization. Furthermore, every positive integer can be factored uniquely into a product of prime integers. For example,

$$120 = 2 \cdot 2 \cdot 2 \cdot 3 \cdot 5,$$
$$111{,}111 = 3 \cdot 7 \cdot 11 \cdot 13 \cdot 37.$$

Similarly, every polynomial can be factored uniquely into a product of prime polynomials. For example,

$$x^2 - x + 6 = (x - 3)(x + 2),$$
$$x^6 - 1 = (x - 1)(x + 1)(x^2 + x + 1)(x^2 - x + 1).$$

313

8–1 THE ALGEBRA OF POLYNOMIALS IN ONE VARIABLE

This material can be read alone without difficulty by the student. Then class discussion should clarify the main idea, which is a comparison of the algebra of polynomials with that of the integers. Both systems have closure and the rearrangement properties for addition and multiplication; subtraction is defined in both in the same manner; there are additive and multiplicative identity elements; and there are no multiplicative inverses. The arithmetic with polynomials involves arithmetic with real numbers, as did the arithmetic with complex numbers. Chapter 4 presented an opportunity to strengthen the understanding of Chapter 1. Chapter 8 demonstrates further that it is imperative to understand the structure of the real number system, since it is basic to the study of other systems.

The exercises may be covered orally, using some of those on page 321 as part of the first assignment, which should also include at least a part of Section 8–2.

If subscripts used on coefficients in the definition of a polynomial cause confusion, their necessity may be pointed up in the following way. Using different letters for each coefficient, a pattern may be written for each polynomial

zero degree: $a, a \neq 0$;

first degree: $ax + b$;

second degree: $ax^2 + bx + c$;

third degree: $ax^3 + bx^2 + cx + d$;

fourth degree: $ax^4 + bx^3 + cx^2 + dx + e$;

fifth degree: $ax^5 + bx^4 + cx^3 + dx^2 + ex + f$.

8–1 THE ALGEBRA OF POLYNOMIALS IN ONE VARIABLE

Algebraic expressions of the form

$$4x^3 - 3x^2 + 2, \quad \tfrac{1}{5}x^5 - x - 4, \quad 17x^{17} - 3x$$

are called polynomials in the variable x. Such expressions are not new to us, since we studied both linear and quadratic polynomials in one variable in previous chapters. In the present chapter, we wish to consider the algebraic system of all polynomials in one variable whose coefficients are real numbers.

After looking at the examples of polynomials above, you might have anticipated the following definition.

DEFINITION OF A POLYNOMIAL

A polynomial is an algebraic expression of the form

$$a_nx^n + a_{n-1}x^{n-1} + \cdots + a_1x + a_0$$

where n is a non-negative integer, x is a variable, and the coefficients $a_n, a_{n-1}, \ldots, a_1, a_0$ are real numbers.

The numbers $a_n, a_{n-1}, \ldots, a_1, a_0$ occurring in a polynomial are called its *coefficients*. Thus, a_n is called the coefficient of x^n, a_{n-1} the coefficient of x^{n-1}, and so on. The number a_n is called the *leading coefficient*; it is the coefficient of the highest power of x occurring in the polynomial. The number a_0 is called the *constant term* of the polynomial. If $a_n \neq 0$, then n is called the *degree* of the polynomial.

If $n = 0$ in the polynomial above, then the polynomial consists of just one term, a_0. Such a polynomial is called a *constant polynomial*. If $a_0 \neq 0$, the constant polynomial a_0 has degree 0. For a reason to be given later, the constant *polynomial* 0 *is not given a degree.*

If $n = 1$, the resulting polynomial

$$a_1x + a_0$$

is called a linear polynomial. Its degree is 1 if $a_1 \neq 0$. Of course, if $a_1 = 0$, this polynomial is equivalent to the constant polynomial a_0.

Each polynomial of degree 2 has the form

$$a_2x^2 + a_1x + a_0, \quad a_2 \neq 0.$$

We have called such algebraic expressions *quadratic polynomials.* A polynomial of degree 3 is called a *cubic polynomial* and has the form

$$a_3x^3 + a_2x^2 + a_1x + a_0, \quad a_3 \neq 0.$$

A polynomial of degree 4 is often called a *quartic polynomial.*

Let us consider the set of all polynomials in the variable x. Two polynomials in this set are considered equal if, and only if, they have the same degree and their corresponding coefficients are equal; that is,

$$a_nx^n + a_{n-1}x^{n-1} + \cdots + a_1x + a_0 \\ = b_nx^n + b_{n-1}x^{n-1} + \cdots + b_1x + b_0$$

if, and only if,

$$a_n = b_n, \quad a_{n-1} = b_{n-1}, \quad \ldots, \quad a_1 = b_1, \quad \text{and} \quad a_0 = b_0.$$

We would like to define the sum of two polynomials so that the rearrangement properties and the distributive law will hold. For example, we define

$$(2x^3 - 4x^2 + 5x + 1) + (^-x^3 + 11x^2 - 3x + 7) \\ = (2x^3 - x^3) + (^-4x^2 + 11x^2) + (5x - 3x) + (1 + 7) \\ = (2 - 1)x^3 + (^-4 + 11)x^2 + (5 - 3)x + (1 + 7) \\ = x^3 + 7x^2 + 2x + 8.$$

DEFINITION OF THE SUM OF TWO POLYNOMIALS

The sum of two polynomials is the polynomial which has as each of its coefficients the sum of the corresponding coefficients of the two polynomials.

To add two polynomials of different degrees, we shall assume that the missing terms have zero coefficients. For example,

$$(^-3x^2 + 1) + (5x^3 - x + 4) \\ = (0x^3 - 3x^2 + 0x + 1) + (5x^3 + 0x^2 - x + 4) \\ = (0 + 5)x^3 + (^-3 + 0)x^2 + (0 - 1)x + (1 + 4) \\ = 5x^3 - 3x^2 - x + 5.$$

According to this definition of addition, the set of all polynomials in the variable x is *closed* with respect to addition.

Six letters of the alphabet have been used for writing a fifth-degree polynomial. You could ask the students how many letters would be needed to write a polynomial of degree twenty-six. (Twenty-seven) Obviously, the possibilities for polynomials are greater than the number of letters in the alphabet. By using only one letter and letting a numerical subscript indicate the change, there will never be a shortage of coefficients for the powers of x.

The constant polynomial 0 is the *additive identity element* since the sum of 0 and any given polynomial is the given polynomial. We shall call 0 the *zero polynomial* since it plays the same role in the set of all polynomials as the number 0 does in the real number system.

Each polynomial has an *additive inverse*. For example, the additive inverse of $5x^3 - x + 4$ is $^-5x^3 + x - 4$, since their sum is 0. As usual, we shall call the additive inverse of a polynomial its opposite.

DEFINITION OF ADDITIVE INVERSE

The opposite, or additive inverse, of a polynomial is the polynomial which has as each of its coefficients the opposite of the corresponding coefficient of the given polynomial.

It can be verified that the same properties that are valid for addition in the real number system are valid for addition in the set of all polynomials: Addition of polynomials is *commutative* and *associative;* there is an *additive identity*, or *zero polynomial;* and each polynomial has an *opposite*. These properties are valid because addition of polynomials is defined in terms of addition of coefficients, which are real numbers, and addition of real numbers has these properties. For example, if

$$P = 3x^3 + 4x^2 + 10,$$
$$Q = 2x^2 + x + 5,$$

then

$$\begin{aligned} P + Q &= (3x^3 + 4x^2 + 10) + (2x^2 + x + 5) \\ &= 3x^3 + 6x^2 + x + 15 \end{aligned}$$

and

$$\begin{aligned} Q + P &= (2x^2 + x + 5) + (3x^3 + 4x^2 + 10) \\ &= 3x^3 + 6x^2 + x + 15. \end{aligned}$$

In general, if a_ix^i is a term of a polynomial P and b_ix^i is the corresponding term of a second polynomial Q, then $(a_i + b_i)x^i$ is the corresponding term in $P + Q$ and $(b_i + a_i)x^i$ is the corresponding term in $Q + P$. Since $a_i + b_i = b_i + a_i$ because of the commutative law of addition of real numbers, corresponding terms of $P + Q$ and $Q + P$ have equal coefficients. Hence, $P + Q = Q + P$. Thus, addition is commutative in the set of all polynomials. It is possible to prove the other properties of addition in a similar way.

We can define the multiplication of monomials (polynomials with one term) by means of the first law of exponents. For example, we define

$$(7x^2) \cdot (4x^3) = (7 \cdot 4)x^{2+3}, \quad \text{or } 28x^5.$$

In general,

$$(ax^i) \cdot (bx^j) = (ab)x^{i+j}.$$

We define the product of two polynomials as if the distributive law were valid. For example, we define

$$\begin{aligned}(4x^3 - 2x - 3) \cdot (3x^2 + 5) &= (4x^3 - 2x - 3)3x^2 + (4x^3 - 2x - 3)5\\ &= (4x^3 \cdot 3x^2) + ({}^-2x \cdot 3x^2) + ({}^-3 \cdot 3x^2) + (4x^3 \cdot 5)\\ &\quad + ({}^-2x \cdot 5) + ({}^-3 \cdot 5)\\ &= 12x^5 - 6x^3 - 9x^2 + 20x^3 - 10x - 15\\ &= 12x^5 + 14x^3 - 9x^2 - 10x - 15.\end{aligned}$$

Thus, the product consists of all terms obtained by multiplying each term of one polynomial by every term of the other polynomial.

DEFINITION OF THE PRODUCT OF TWO POLYNOMIALS

If

$$a_nx^n + a_{n-1}x^{n-1} + \cdots + a_1x + a_0$$

and

$$b_kx^k + b_{k-1}x^{k-1} + \cdots + b_1x + b_0$$

are any two polynomials, then their product is the polynomial whose terms are all monomials of the form

$$a_ib_jx^{i+j}, \quad \text{where } i = 0, 1, 2, \ldots, n \text{ and } j = 0, 1, 2, \ldots, k.$$

The symbols

$$a_ib_jx^{i+j}, \; i = 0, 1, 2, \ldots, n \text{ and } j = 0, 1, 2, \ldots, k,$$

may be examined for a specific case such as

$$a_ib_jx^{i+j}, \; i = 0, 1, 2 \text{ and } j = 0, 1,$$

by listing all the terms it yields. If $i = 0$, $j = 0, 1$, then

$$a_0b_0x^{0+0} = a_0b_0;$$
$$a_0b_1x^{0+1} = a_0b_1x.$$

If $i = 1$, $j = 0, 1$, then

$$a_1b_0x^{1+0} = a_1b_0x;$$
$$a_1b_1x^{1+1} = a_1b_1x^2.$$

If $i = 2$, $j = 0, 1$, then

$$a_2b_0x^{2+0} = a_2b_0x^2;$$
$$a_2b_1x^{2+1} = a_2b_1x^3.$$

Thus there are 3×2, or 6, terms in the product of a second- and a first-degree polynomial,

$$(a_2x^2 + a_1x + a_0)(b_1x + b_0).$$

Even though some of these combine to give a shorter form for the answer, in finding the product, six multiplications are actually performed.

How many products of monomials must be found when a third-degree polynomial is multiplied by a fourth-degree polynomial? (4×5, or 20, products)

The product of two polynomials may be found by a method very similar to that used in finding the product of two integers. This method is illustrated below.

$$
\begin{array}{rrrrrl}
x^2 & -\ 3x & +\ 4 & & & \\
2x^2 & +\ 2x & -\ 1 & & & \\
\hline
2x^4 & -\ 6x^3 & +\ 8x^2 & & & = 2x^2(x^2 - 3x + 4) \\
 & 2x^3 & -\ 6x^2 & +\ 8x & & = 2x(x^2 - 3x + 4) \\
 & & {}^{-}x^2 & +\ 3x & -\ 4 & = {}^{-}1(x^2 - 3x + 4) \\
\hline
2x^4 & -\ 4x^3 & +\ x^2 & +\ 11x & -\ 4 &
\end{array}
$$

According to this definition of multiplication, the set of all polynomials in x is *closed* with respect to multiplication. Although we shall not do so, we could prove that multiplication of polynomials is both *commutative* and *associative*. There is a *multiplicative identity element*, which is the constant polynomial 1, and the *distributive law* is valid. Does each nonzero polynomial have a multiplicative inverse, or reciprocal, which is also a polynomial? Although

$$\frac{1}{x}, \quad \text{or} \quad x^{-1},$$

is the reciprocal of x, the algebraic expression x^{-1} is not a polynomial. Remember that a polynomial in x is made up of terms of the form ax^n, where a is a real number and n is a *non-negative* integer. Actually, no polynomial of degree 1 or higher has a reciprocal which is a polynomial.

When we speak of the *algebra of polynomials*, we mean the set of polynomials together with the operations of addition and multiplication as described above.

The five basic properties of addition and multiplication given in Chapter 1, *with the exception of the multiplicative inverse property,* (*Inv-M*), *are valid for the algebra of polynomials.*

We might recall that, with the same exception, the system of integers also satisfies these five basic properties. Further similarities between the algebras of polynomials and integers will be described in this chapter.

The operation of *subtraction* is defined in the algebra of polynomials in the following way. If P and Q are polynomials, then

$$P - Q = P + {}^{-}Q,$$

where ^{-}Q designates the opposite, or additive inverse, of Q. For example,

$$\begin{aligned}(3x^2 - 7x + 2) - (2x^3 - 5x^2 + x - 8) &= (3x^2 - 7x + 2) + {}^{-}(2x^3 - 5x^2 + x - 8)\\ &= (3x^2 - 7x + 2) + ({}^{-}2x^3 + 5x^2 - x + 8)\\ &= {}^{-}2x^3 + 8x^2 - 8x + 10.\end{aligned}$$

If the nonzero polynomials

$$P = a_nx^n + a_{n-1}x^{n-1} + \cdots + a_1x + a_0, \quad a_n \neq 0,$$

and

$$Q = b_kx^k + b_{k-1}x^{k-1} + \cdots + b_1x + b_0, \quad b_k \neq 0,$$

are multiplied together, what is the degree of their product PQ? Since $a_n \neq 0$ and $b_k \neq 0$, their product $a_nb_k \neq 0$, and

$$(a_nx^n) \cdot (b_kx^k), \quad \text{or } a_nb_kx^{n+k},$$

is the term of highest degree in PQ. Thus, PQ has degree $n + k$. This result can be stated in the following manner.

The degree of the product of two nonzero polynomials is the sum of the degrees of the two polynomials.

The result above is true even if one of the polynomials is a nonzero constant. For example, if

$$P = 3 \quad \text{and} \quad Q = x^2 + 3x - 2,$$

then

$$PQ = 3x^2 + 9x - 6.$$

Since $0 + 2 = 2$, we see that the sum of the degrees of P and Q is the degree of PQ.

If we multiply a polynomial by the zero polynomial, the product is zero. For example,

$$0(x^2 + 3x - 2) = (0 \cdot x^2) + (0 \cdot 3x) + (0 \cdot {}^{-}2), \quad \text{or } 0.$$

This is the reason we did not assign a degree to the polynomial 0. If we had assigned a degree, say k, then the theorem above would demand that $k + 2 = k$. Since this theorem is false for every number k, we conclude that there is no degree that can be assigned to the zero polynomial.

It is suggested that attention be given to the paragraph at the bottom of the page on the degree of the zero polynomial.

Exercises for Discussion, page 320

Exercise for Discussion 1 may be done by two different students at the blackboard to illustrate the associative law.

Exercise for Discussion 4 is recommended for class discussion. If time is limited, it is suggested that at least Exercises for Discussion 1–5 be covered.

Answers to Exercises for Discussion 1–3

1. $(x - 3)[(x + 3)(2x + 5)]$
$= (x - 3)(2x^2 + 11x + 15)$
$= 2x^3 + 5x^2 - 18x - 45$
$= x^2(2x + 5) - 9(2x + 5)$
$= (x^2 - 9)(2x + 5)$
$= [(x - 3)(x + 3)](2x + 5)$
2. $(x - 3)[(x + 3) + (2x + 5)]$
$= (x - 3)(3x + 8)$
$= 3x^2 - x - 24$
$(x - 3)(x + 3) + (x - 3)(2x + 5)$
$= (x^2 - 9) + (2x^2 - x - 15)$
$= 3x^2 - x - 24$
3. The degree of the product of three polynomials is the sum of their degrees.

$$(a_nx^n + \cdots)(b_mx^m + \cdots)(c_px^p + \cdots) = a_nb_mc_px^{n+m+p} + \cdots$$

Exercises for Discussion, page 320

Exercise for Discussion 1 may be done by two different students at the blackboard to illustrate the associative law.

Exercise for Discussion 4 is recommended for class discussion. If time is limited, it is suggested that at least Exercises for Discussion 1–5 be covered.

Answers to Exercises for Discussion 1–3

1. $(x - 3)[(x + 3)(2x + 5)]$
   $= (x - 3)(2x^2 + 11x + 15)$
   $= 2x^3 + 5x^2 - 18x - 45$
   $= x^2(2x + 5) - 9(2x + 5)$
   $= (x^2 - 9)(2x + 5)$
   $= [(x - 3)(x + 3)](2x + 5)$
2. $(x - 3)[(x + 3) + (2x + 5)]$
   $= (x - 3)(3x + 8)$
   $= 3x^2 - x - 24$
   $(x - 3)(x + 3) + (x - 3)(2x + 5)$
   $= (x^2 - 9) + (2x^2 - x - 15)$
   $= 3x^2 - x - 24$
3. The degree of the product of three polynomials is the sum of their degrees.

$$(a_nx^n + \cdots)(b_mx^m + \cdots)(c_px^p + \cdots) = a_nb_mc_px^{n+m+p} + \cdots$$

Exercises, page 321

It is recommended that Exercises 2 and 3 be covered.

Exercises 14 and 15 should be assigned so that the students will not think that the a_i's must be integers. Also, he must not think that he can arbitrarily multiply by an integer without changing the product. With reference to Exercise 14, you could ask the students to compare the following products:

$$(x^2 - \tfrac{1}{2})(x^4 + \tfrac{1}{2}x^2 + \tfrac{1}{4}),$$
$$(2x^2 - 1)(x^4 + \tfrac{1}{2}x^2 + \tfrac{1}{4}),$$
$$(2x^2 - 1)(4x^4 + 2x^2 + 1),$$
$$(x^2 - \tfrac{1}{2})(4x^2 + 2x^2 + 1).$$

The following property is a consequence of the one stated above. It is also a property of the system of integers.

ZERO MULTIPLICATION

If P and Q are polynomials, then

$$PQ = 0 \quad \textit{if, and only if,} \quad P = 0 \textit{ or } Q = 0. \qquad \textit{(Zero-M)}$$

Proof. If either $P = 0$ or $Q = 0$, then $PQ = 0$. Conversely, if both $P \neq 0$ and $Q \neq 0$, then PQ cannot be the polynomial 0 since the polynomial PQ has a degree, whereas the polynomial 0 has no degree. Hence, if $PQ = 0$, then $P = 0$ or $Q = 0$.

Exercises for Discussion

1. Illustrate the associative law of multiplication in the set of polynomials, using the three polynomials

$$x - 3, \quad x + 3, \quad 2x + 5.$$

2. Illustrate the distributive law in the set of polynomials, using the three polynomials in Exercise 1.
3. Make a statement about the degree of the product of three polynomials, and prove it.
4. Consider the set of all fourth-degree polynomials in x:

$$a_4x^4 + a_3x^3 + a_2x^2 + a_1x + a_0, \quad a_4 \neq 0.$$

   (a) If a_4, a_3, a_2, a_1, and a_0 are real numbers, is the set closed with respect to any of the operations of arithmetic? If so, which? No
   (b) If a_4, a_3, a_2, a_1, and a_0 are positive real numbers, under which, if any, of the operations of arithmetic is the set closed? Addition

Perform the indicated operations with polynomials.

5. $(x^2 + 3x + 5) + (2x - 2)$ x^2+5x+3
6. $(3x^3 - 5x + 7) - (7 + 3x^3 - 5x)$ 0
7. $(x^3 + 2x + 3)(x^4 + 7)$ $x^7+2x^5+3x^4+7x^3+14x+21$
8. $0 \cdot (x + 5)$ 0

Exercises

1. Illustrate the associative law of addition in the set of polynomials, using the three polynomials See Solution Manual.

$$4x^2 - 3, \quad 7x^2 - 2x + 4, \quad 4x + 5.$$

2. Given two polynomials of unequal degree, what is the degree of their sum? Illustrate your answer with two examples. The degree of the polynomial of higher degree
3. Given two polynomials of equal degree, what can be said about the degree of their sum? Give examples to show the possible alternatives. Less than or equal to common degree

Perform the indicated operations with polynomials.

4. $(2x^2 - 3x + 5) + (x^3 - x + 7)$ $x^3+2x^2-4x+12$
5. $(4x^3 - x^2 + 3x - 2) + (^-3x^3 + 7x)$ $x^3-x^2+10x-2$
6. $(x^4 + 3x) + (12x^3 - 2x^2 + 5)$ $x^4+12x^3-2x^2+3x+5$
7. $(x^5 - 5x + 7) + (^-x^5 + 5x - 7)$ 0
8. $(x^2 + 2x - 5)(2x^2 - 4x + 3)$ $2x^4-15x^2+26x-15$
9. $(^-5x^3 + x^2 - 1)(x^3 - 2x + 4)$ $^-5x^6+x^5+10x^4-23x^3+4x^2+2x-4$
10. $(x^7 - 3x^5 + x^3 - x)(x^6 - x^4 + 3x^2 - 2)$ $x^{13}-4x^{11}+7x^9-13x^7+10x^5-5x^3+2x$
11. $0 \cdot (^-4x^5 + 7x^2 + 2)$ 0
12. $(4x^2 - 3x + 5) - (x^3 - 3x + 7)$ $^-x^3+4x^2-2$
13. $(7x^3 - 4x^2 + 2x - 4) - (7x^3 - 4x^2 - 4)$ $2x$
14. $(x^2 - \frac{1}{2})(x^4 + \frac{1}{2}x^2 + \frac{1}{4})$ $x^6-\frac{1}{8}$
15. $(x^3 + \frac{1}{2}x - \frac{1}{3})(x^3 + \frac{1}{2}x + \frac{1}{3})$ $x^6+x^4+\frac{1}{4}x^2-\frac{1}{9}$

8–2 THE DIVISION PROCESS

A quotient of two polynomials is not necessarily a polynomial, just as a quotient of two integers is not necessarily an integer. However, it is possible to divide one integer by another, obtaining both an integral quotient and an integral remainder. For example, 354 divided by 13 gives a quotient of 27 and a remainder of 3: $354 = (27 \times 13) + 3$.

In the same way, it is possible to divide one polynomial by another, obtaining a quotient and a remainder, each of which is a polynomial. For example, we can divide $6x^3 - 8x^2 + 5x - 1$ by $3x^2 - x + 2$.

$$\begin{array}{r|l}
 & 2x - 2 \\
\hline
3x^2 - x + 2 & 6x^3 - 8x^2 + 5x - 1 \\
 & 6x^3 - 2x^2 + 4x \\
\hline
 & ^-6x^2 + x - 1 \\
 & ^-6x^2 + 2x - 4 \\
\hline
 & ^-x + 3
\end{array}$$

If a student is not able to answer readily, you may be able to help him by asking for these products:

$\frac{3}{2} \cdot \frac{5}{7}$
$(2 \cdot \frac{3}{2}) \cdot \frac{5}{7}$
$\frac{3}{2} \cdot (7 \cdot \frac{5}{7})$
$(2 \cdot \frac{3}{2}) \cdot (7 \cdot \frac{5}{7})$.

Quiz

Perform the indicated operations with polynomials.

1. $(3x^3 - 2x^2 + 7) + (2x^3 - x + 1)$ (ans: $5x^3 - 2x^2 - x + 8$)
2. $(^-2x^2 + 13x - 1) + (x^4 - x^3 + 2x^2)$ (ans: $x^4 - x^3 + 13x - 1$)
3. $(x^6 + 2x^4 + 3x^2 + 1) - (x^5 - 2x^4 + 3x^2 + 1)$ (ans: $x^6 - x^5 + 4x^4$)
4. $(x^3 + x^2 + 1)(x^2 + x - 1)$ (ans: $x^5 + 2x^4 + x - 1$)
5. $(x^2 - \frac{1}{3})(x^4 + \frac{1}{3}x^2 + \frac{1}{9})$ (ans: $x^6 - \frac{1}{27}$)
6. $(^-2x^7 + x^5 - 3x^3 + 1) \cdot 0$ (ans: 0)

8–2 THE DIVISION PROCESS

In arithmetic, to divide b by a, multiples of a are subtracted from b until a remainder less than a is obtained. Thus,

$$612 = (26 \cdot 23) + 14$$

is found by subtracting $20 \cdot 23$ from 612, and then $6 \cdot 23$ from the first remainder. Since the second remainder is less than the divisor, the process terminates.

Similarly, it can be found that

$$5x^4 - 2x^2 - 9 = (5x^2 + 10x + 18)(x^2 - 2x) + (36x - 9)$$

by subtracting $5x^2(x^2 - 2x)$ from $5x^4 - 2x^2 - 9$, then subtracting

$10x(x^2 - 2x)$ from the first remainder, and then subtracting $18(x^2 - 2x)$ from the second remainder. Since the third remainder is of lower degree than the divisor, the process terminates.

$$
\begin{array}{r}
5x^2 + 10x + 18 \\
x^2 - 2x\,\overline{)\,5x^4 - 2x^2 - 9} \\
\underline{5x^4 - 10x^3} * \\
10x^3 - 2x^2 - 9 \\
\underline{10x^3 - 20x^2} \dagger \\
18x^2 - 9 \\
\underline{18x^2 - 36x} \ddagger \\
36x - 9
\end{array}
$$

$^*5x^2(x^2 - 2x)$
$\dagger 10x(x^2 - 2x)$
$\ddagger 18(x^2 - 2x)$

In dividing one integer by another, the quotient and the remainder are found as integers. Hence, the *size* of the remainder determines when the process ends. In dividing one polynomial by another, the quotient and the remainder are found as polynomials. Hence, the *degree* of the remainder determines when the process ends.

In other words,

$$6x^3 - 8x^2 + 5x - 1 = (2x - 2)(3x^2 - x + 2) + (^-x + 3).$$

The justification of this division process is essentially the same as the justification of long division. In this example, $2x - 2$ is the *quotient* and $^-x + 3$ is the *remainder*.

The quotient and remainder obtained when one integer is divided by another are unique. Symbolically, this means that if a and b are integers, with $b > 0$, then there is one, and only one, integer q and one, and only one, integer r such that

$$a = qb + r$$

and

$$0 \leqq r < b.$$

The integer q is the quotient and r is the remainder when a is divided by b.

Similarly, the quotient and remainder obtained by dividing one polynomial by another are unique. Thus, if A and B are polynomials in x, with $B \neq 0$, then there exist unique polynomials Q and R such that

$$A = (Q \cdot B) + R$$

with $R = 0$ or the degree of R less than the degree of B.

If the remainder $R = 0$, then $A = (Q \cdot B)$ and B is called a *divisor*, or *factor*, of A. We also say that A is a *multiple* of B. Of course, if the remainder $R \neq 0$, then B is not a divisor of A and A is not a multiple of B. In practice, on dividing one polynomial by another, we find the quotient and remainder by long division, as illustrated in the following problems.

Problem 1. Find the quotient and remainder on dividing the polynomial $3x^4 - 7x^2 + 2x$ by $x^2 + x - 3$.

Solution.

$$
\begin{array}{r}
3x^2 - 3x + 5 \\
x^2 + x - 3\,\overline{)\,3x^4 - 7x^2 + 2x} \\
\underline{3x^4 + 3x^3 - 9x^2} \\
^-3x^3 + 2x^2 + 2x \\
\underline{^-3x^3 - 3x^2 + 9x} \\
5x^2 - 7x \\
\underline{5x^2 + 5x - 15} \\
^-12x + 15
\end{array}
$$

In the division above, $3x^2 - 3x + 5$ is the quotient and $^-12x + 15$ is the remainder when $3x^4 - 7x^2 + 2x$ is divided by $x^2 + x - 3$. Note that we left space for the missing term of degree 3 and also for the missing constant term. We may express the results of this division process as follows:

$$3x^4 - 7x^2 + 2x = (3x^2 - 3x + 5)(x^2 + x - 3) + (^-12x + 15).$$

Note that the degree of the remainder is 1, *which is less than* 2, *the degree of the divisor.*

Problem 2. Find the quotient and remainder on dividing the polynomial $x^4 + x^3 + x^2 + 3x - 2$ by $2x^3 - 4x^2 + 3x - 2$.

Solution.

$$\begin{array}{r|l}
 & \tfrac{1}{2}x + \tfrac{3}{2} \\
2x^3 - 4x^2 + 3x - 2 & x^4 + x^3 + x^2 + 3x - 2 \\
 & x^4 - 2x^3 + \tfrac{3}{2}x^2 - x \\
\hline
 & 3x^3 - \tfrac{1}{2}x^2 + 4x - 2 \\
 & 3x^3 - 6x^2 + \tfrac{9}{2}x - 3 \\
\hline
 & \tfrac{11}{2}x^2 - \tfrac{1}{2}x + 1
\end{array}$$

Therefore, $\frac{1}{2}x + \frac{3}{2}$ is the quotient and $\frac{11}{2}x^2 - \frac{1}{2}x + 1$ is the remainder. We may express the results of this division process in the following way.

$$\begin{aligned} x^4 + x^3 + x^2 + 3x - 2 \\ &= (\tfrac{1}{2}x + \tfrac{3}{2})(2x^3 - 4x^2 + 3x - 2) + (\tfrac{11}{2}x^2 - \tfrac{1}{2}x + 1) \end{aligned}$$

Problem 3. Find the quotient and remainder on dividing the polynomial $2x^3 - 5x^2 + x - 1$ by $x - 3$.

Solution.

$$\begin{array}{r|l}
 & 2x^2 + x + 4 \\
x - 3 & 2x^3 - 5x^2 + x - 1 \\
 & 2x^3 - 6x^2 \\
\hline
 & x^2 + x - 1 \\
 & x^2 - 3x \\
\hline
 & 4x - 1 \\
 & 4x - 12 \\
\hline
 & 11
\end{array}$$

Thus, $2x^3 - 5x^2 + x - 1 = (2x^2 + x + 4)(x - 3) + 11$.

It is recommended that you go over Problem 2 in class and ask for the following to be done:

$(2x^3 - x^2 + 3x - 5) \div (3x - 1)$.
$(Q = \frac{2}{3}x^2 - \frac{1}{9}x + \frac{26}{27};$
$R = \frac{^-109}{27})$

In division of polynomials, the quotient may involve rational coefficients that are not integers, as may the dividend and divisor.

Exercises for Discussion

If time is limited, it is suggested that at least Exercises for Discussion 3 and 4 be covered.

Quiz

Find the quotient and remainder on dividing the first polynomial A in each of the following exercises by the second polynomial B. Then express the first polynomial A in the form $A = (Q \cdot B) + R$, with $R = 0$ or the degree of R less than the degree of B.

1. $7x + 20$ by $3x + 10$ (ans: $\frac{7}{3}(3x + 10) - \frac{10}{3}$)
2. $21x^2 - 7x + 15$ by $3x^2 - x$ (ans: $7(3x^2 - x) + 15$)
3. $x^3 + x^2 - 9x - 13$ by $x^2 - 2x - 4$ (ans: $(x + 3)(x^2 - 2x - 4) + (x - 1)$)
4. $3x^3 - 19x^2 + 22x - 10$ by $3x^2 - 4x + 2$ (ans: $(x - 5)(3x^2 - 4x + 2)$)
5. $x^4 - 9x^2 - 6x - 1$ by $x^2 + 3x + 1$ (ans: $(x^2 - 3x - 1)(x^2 + 3x + 1)$)

Exercises for Discussion

In each of the following exercises, find the quotient and remainder on dividing the first polynomial A by the second polynomial B. Then express the first polynomial A in the form $A = (Q \cdot B) + R$, with $R = 0$ or the degree of R less than the degree of B.

1. $4x^3 - 5x^2 + 3x - 2$ by $x + 1$ $(4x^2-9x+12)(x+1)-14$
2. $1 - x^2 + x^4$ by $1 - x$ $(^-x^3-x^2)(1-x)+1$
3. Factor $x^3 + x^2 - 4x - 4$ by first dividing by $x - 2$. $x^3+x^2-4x-4 = (x^2+3x+2)(x-2)=(x+1)(x+2)(x-2)$
4. Use the fact that

$$x^4 + 2x^3 + 5x^2 + 8x + 4$$
$$=(x^2+2x+1)(x^2+4) = (x+1)^2(x^2+4)$$

is divisible by $x^2 + 4$ to write the fourth-degree polynomial as a product of three polynomials.

Exercises

1. Factor $x^4 - 6x^2 + 5$ by first dividing by $x - 1$. $(x^2-5)(x+1)(x-1)$
2. Factor $x^5 + 2x^4 - 4x^3 - 8x^2$ by first dividing by x^2. $x^2(x+2)^2(x-2)$
3. Factor $x^3 + 5x^2 + 8x + 4$ by first dividing by $x + 1$. $(x+1)(x+2)^2$
4. Factor $x^4 - 2x^3 - 3x^2 + 4x + 4$ by first dividing by $(x + 1)^2$. $(x+1)^2(x-2)^2$
5. Use the fact that

$$x^5 + 6x^4 + 9x^3 + 8x^2 + 48x + 72$$

is divisible by $x^3 + 8$ to write the fifth-degree polynomial as a product of four polynomials. $(x+2)(x^2-2x+4)(x+3)^2$

Find the quotient and remainder on dividing the first polynomial A in each of the following exercises by the second polynomial B. Then express the first polynomial A in the form $A = (Q \cdot B) + R$, with $R = 0$ or the degree of R less than the degree of B.

6. $x^2 - 2x + 3$ by $x^2 + x - 2$ $1\cdot(x^2+x-2)+(^-3x+5)$
7. $3x + 1$ by $2x - 5$ $\frac{3}{2}(2x-5)+\frac{17}{2}$
8. x^3 by $x^2 + 7x - 11$ $(x-7)(x^2+7x-11)+(60x-77)$
9. $4x^2 - 9$ by $2x^2 - 7$ $2(2x^2-7)+5$
10. $3x^3 - 5x^2 + 2x - 1$ by $x^2 - 3x + 1$ $(3x+4)(x^2-3x+1)+(11x-5)$
11. $5x^4 - 3x + 8$ by $x^3 - 5x^2 + 2x - 1$ $(5x+25)(x^3-5x^2+2x-1)+(115x^2-48x+33)$
12. $2x^3 - 8x^2 + 9x - 2$ by $2x^2 - 4x + 1$ $(x-2)(2x^2-4x+1)$
13. $x^4 + 4$ by $x^2 - 2x + 2$

8-3 SYNTHETIC DIVISION

The division process can be considerably shortened if the divisor is a linear polynomial of the form $x - a$. For example, the solution of Problem 3 on page 323 can be shortened in the following way.

$$\begin{array}{r|rrrr}
 & 2x^2 & +\ x & +\ 4 & \\
\hline
x - 3 & 2x^3 & -\ 5x^2 & +\ x & -\ 1 \\
 & & {}^{-}6x^2 & & \\
\cline{3-3}
 & & x^2 & & \\
 & & & {}^{-}3x & \\
\cline{4-4}
 & & & 4x & \\
 & & & & {}^{-}12 \\
\cline{5-5}
 & & & & 11
\end{array}$$

We can shorten the division process by moving terms up under the dividend. The resulting array is shown below.

$$\begin{array}{r|rrrr}
 & 2x^2 & +\ x & +\ 4 & \\
\hline
x - 3 & 2x^3 & -\ 5x^2 & +\ x & -\ 1 \\
 & & {}^{-}6x^2 & -\ 3x & -\ 12 \\
\hline
 & 2x^3 & x^2 & 4x & 11
\end{array}$$

Note that in this latter array we have also put the leading term of the divisor, $2x^3$, on the bottom line. Next, we observe that the quotient $2x^2 + x + 4$ is repeated on the lower line, except that each term has been multiplied by x. Thus, we can omit the top line if we remember how it is obtained from the bottom line. We may also omit all powers of x, leaving the following array of coefficients.

$$\begin{array}{r|rrrr}
{}^{-}3 & 2 & {}^{-}5 & 1 & {}^{-}1 \\
 & & {}^{-}6 & {}^{-}3 & {}^{-}12 \\
\hline
 & 2 & 1 & 4 & 11
\end{array} \qquad \text{(subtract)}$$

The top row of the array consists of $^{-}3$, which comes from the polynomial $x - 3$, and the numbers 2, $^{-}5$, 1, and $^{-}1$, which are the coefficients (arranged in descending order) of the given polynomial, $2x^3 - 5x^2 + x - 1$.

Each number in the last row is obtained from the two numbers directly above it by subtracting the number in the middle row from the number directly above it. Each number in the middle row is obtained by multiplying the number preceding it in the bottom row by $^{-}3$. The bottom row of the array contains both the quotient and the remainder.

8-3 SYNTHETIC DIVISION

Students may ask why the process called synthetic division works. A method of proof is indicated by the following special case. Suppose a third-degree polynomial,

$$a_3x^3 + a_2x^2 + a_1x + a_0,$$

is divided by $x - r$ according to the rules in the text. The following array is obtained:

$$\begin{array}{r|rrrr}
r & a_3 & a_2 & a_1 & a_0 \\
 & & ra_3 & rb_1 & rb_2 \\
\hline
 & a_3 & b_1 & b_2 & b_3
\end{array}$$

where

$$b_1 = a_2 + ra_3$$
$$b_2 = a_1 + rb_1$$
$$b_3 = a_0 + rb_2.$$

Now it must be shown that the equation

$$a_3x^3 + a_2x^2 + a_1x + a_0 = (a_3x^2 + b_1x + b_2) \cdot (x - r) + b_3$$

is a true one. The right side is equivalent to

$$a_3x^3 + (b_1 - a_3r)x^2 + (b_2 - b_1r)x + (b_3 - b_2r).$$

From above, where each b_i is defined, it can be seen that

$$b_1 - ra_3 = a_2$$
$$b_2 - rb_1 = a_1$$
$$b_3 - rb_2 = a_0.$$

Substituting reduces the right side to

$$a_3x^3 + a_2x^2 + a_1x + a_0,$$

which is the same as the left side of the equation.

In connection with the division process, you may want to mention the Euclidean algorithm for finding the greatest common divisor of two integers or of two polynomials, and to compare the two systems in as many ways as possible. (See *Algebra*, by Johnson, Lendsey, and Slesnick, pages 143, 144 (Addison-Wesley), and *A Survey of Modern Algebra* by Birkhoff and MacLane, pages 18–20 and 76–77 (Macmillan)).

Thus, 2, 1, and 4 are the coefficients (in descending order) of the quotient $2x^2 + x + 4$, and the last number, 11, is the remainder.

One final simplification can be made when we realize that if we multiply by 3, and add, instead of multiplying by $^{-}3$, and subtracting, we obtain the same result. This new array is shown below.

$$\begin{array}{r|rrrr} 3 & 2 & ^{-}5 & 1 & ^{-}1 \\ & & 6 & 3 & 12 \\ \hline & 2 & 1 & 4 & 11 \end{array} \qquad \text{(add)}$$

The process described above for dividing a polynomial by $x - a$ is called *synthetic division.* Some further illustrations of its use are given below.

Problem 1. Find the quotient and remainder on dividing the polynomial $3x^4 - 11x^3 - 21x^2 + 3x + 17$ by $x - 5$.

Solution. We first write the coefficients of the dividend in order of decreasing powers of x. Then we write the number 5, from $x - 5$, as shown below.

$$\begin{array}{r|rrrrr} 5 & 3 & ^{-}11 & ^{-}21 & 3 & 17 \end{array}$$

Next, the leading coefficient, 3, is brought down to the bottom line, and the product of 3 and 5 is placed under the second term, $^{-}11$.

$$\begin{array}{r|rrrrr} 5 & 3 & ^{-}11 & ^{-}21 & 3 & 17 \\ & & 15 & & & \\ \hline & 3 & & & & \end{array}$$

We now *add* 15 to $^{-}11$ and place the sum on the bottom line. Continuing, we have the following.

$$\begin{array}{r|rrrrr} 5 & 3 & ^{-}11 & ^{-}21 & 3 & 17 \\ & & 15 & 20 & ^{-}5 & ^{-}10 \\ \hline & 3 & 4 & ^{-}1 & ^{-}2 & 7 \end{array}$$

The numbers 3, 4, $^{-}1$, and $^{-}2$ in the bottom line are the coefficients of the powers of x (given in descending order) in the quotient; the last number, 7, is the remainder. Since the dividend is a polynomial of degree 4 and the divisor of degree 1, the quotient is a polynomial of degree 3. Thus,

$$3x^3 + 4x^2 - x - 2$$

is the quotient and 7 is the remainder. We can express this result by the equation

$$3x^4 - 11x^3 - 21x^2 + 3x + 17 = (3x^3 + 4x^2 - x - 2)(x - 5) + 7.$$

Problem 2. Find the quotient and remainder on dividing the polynomial $^-5x^3 + 14x - 7$ by $x + 2$.

Solution. We note that the coefficient of x^2 in the dividend is zero, and that $x + 2 = x - {}^-2$. The synthetic division for this problem is shown below.

$^-2$	$^-5$	0	14	$^-7$
		10	$^-20$	12
	$^-5$	10	$^-6$	5

Therefore, $^-5x^2 + 10x - 6$ is the quotient and 5 is the remainder.

$$^-5x^3 + 14x - 7 = (^-5x^2 + 10x - 6)(x + 2) + 5.$$

Exercises for Discussion

1. Use synthetic division to find the quotient and remainder in each of the following divisions.

   (a) $(2x^3 - x^2 + 4x - 5) \div (x + 2)$

   (b) $(3x^4 - x^2 + 5) \div (x - 3)$

2. The integer 185 may be divided by 12 as follows: First divide 185 by 4 to obtain $185 = (46 \cdot 4) + 1$, and then divide the quotient, 46, by 3 to obtain $185 = [(15 \cdot 3) + 1]4 + 1$, or $185 = (15 \cdot 3 \cdot 4) + (1 \cdot 4) + 1$, or $185 = (15 \cdot 12) + 5$. Use such a procedure to find the quotient and remainder on dividing the following integers.

   (a) 833 by 15 (b) 479 by 28

3. The procedure of Exercise 2 can be applied to the division of polynomials, but synthetic division should be employed where the divisors are of the form $x - a$. Use this combination of procedures to perform each of the following divisions.

   (a) $x^2 - 4x + 2$ by $(x - 1)(x - 2)$

   (b) $2x^3 - 5x^2 + 4x - 7$ by $(x + 2)(x - 3)$

   (c) $x^5 - 5x^3 + 12x^2 - 10$ by $x^2 - 1$

Exercises for Discussion and Exercises

The exercises are easy, so a sampling will be sufficient, but be sure to include Exercises for Discussion 2 and 3 and Exercises 13 and 14.

Answers to Exercises for Discussion 1–3

1. (a)

$^-2$	2	$^-1$	4	$^-5$
		$^-4$	10	$^-28$
	2	$^-5$	14	$^-33$

Quotient: $2x^2 - 5x + 14$
Remainder: $^-33$

(b)

3	3	0	$^-1$	0	5
		9	27	78	234
	3	9	26	78	239

Quotient:

$3x^3 + 9x^2 + 26x + 78$

Remainder: 239

2. (a) $833 = (277 \cdot 3) + 2$
$= [(55 \cdot 5) + 2]3 + 2$
$= (55 \cdot 15) + 8$

(b) $479 = (119 \cdot 4) + 3$
$= [(17 \cdot 7)]4 + 3$
$= (17 \cdot 28) + 3$

3. (a) $x^2 - 4x + 2$
$= (x - 3)(x - 1) - 1$
$= [(x - 2) - 1](x - 1) - 1$
$= (x - 2)(x - 1) - x$

(b) $2x^3 - 5x^2 + 4x - 7$
$= (2x^2 - 9x + 22)(x + 2) - 51$
$= [(2x - 3)(x - 3) + 13] \times (x + 2) - 51$
$= (2x - 3)(x - 3)(x + 2) + (13x - 25)$

(c) $x^5 - 5x^3 + 12x^2 - 10$
$= (x^4 + x^3 - 4x^2 + 8x + 8) \times (x - 1) - 2$
$= [(x^3 - 4x + 12)(x + 1) - 4](x - 1) - 2$
$= (x^3 - 4x + 12)(x^2 - 1) + (^-4x + 2)$

Quiz

Use synthetic division to find the quotient and remainder on dividing the first polynomial A by the second polynomial B and express the results in the form

$$A = (Q \cdot B) + R,$$

with $R = 0$ or the degree of R less than the degree of B.

1. $4x^3 + 3x^2 - 2x + 1$ by $x - 1$ (ans: $(4x^2 + 7x + 5)(x - 1) + 6$)
2. $x^5 + x^4 + 3x^2 + 2x - 7$ by $x - 2$ (ans: $(x^4 + 3x^3 + 6x^2 + 15x + 32)(x - 2) + 57$)
3. $x^5 + 32$ by $x - 2$ (ans: $(x^4 + 2x^3 + 4x^2 + 8x + 16)(x - 2) + 64$)
4. $^-2x^4 + 4x^3 + x - 3$ by $x - 3$ (ans: $(^-2x^3 - 2x^2 - 6x - 17)(x - 3) - 54$)

8-4 POLYNOMIAL FUNCTIONS

You could introduce this section by defining a polynomial function and then asking the class to find the value of some specific function, such as

$$2x^3 - 3x^2 + 5x - 7$$

for an assortment of x's such as $^-5$, $^-3$, 0, 1, 4, and 10. The results could be recorded on the board. Then six students could be sent to

Exercises

In Exercises 1–12, use synthetic division to find the quotient and remainder on dividing the first polynomial A by the second polynomial B. Express the results in the form $A = (Q \cdot B) + R$, with $R = 0$ or the degree of R less than the degree of B.

1. $4x^2 - 3x + 7$ by $x - 2$ $(4x+5)(x-2)+17$
2. $2x^2 + 5x - 3$ by $x - 3$ $(2x+11)(x-3)+30$
3. $x^3 - 3x^2 + 4x + 8$ by $x + 1$ $(x^2-4x+8)(x+1)$
4. $3x^4 - 4x$ by $x + 2$ $(3x^3-6x^2+12x-28)(x+2)+56$
5. $x^5 - 3x^3 + 4x - 7$ by $x - 1$ $(x^4+x^3-2x^2-2x+2)(x-1)+5$
6. $^-2x^4 + 3x^3 - x^2 + 2x - 4$ by $x + 3$ $(^-2x^3+9x^2-28x+86)(x+3)-262$
7. $x^5 + 1$ by $x - 1$ $(x^4+x^3+x^2+x+1)(x-1)+2$
8. $x^5 + 32$ by $x + 2$ $(x^4-2x^3+4x^2-8x+16)(x+2)$
9. $x^4 + x^2 + 1$ by $x + 3$ $(x^3-3x^2+10x-30)(x+3)+91$
10. $^-3x^5 + 2x^2 - 2$ by $x - 2$ $(^-3x^4-6x^3-12x^2-22x-44)(x-2)-90$
11. $^-4x^3 + 3x + 5$ by $x + \frac{1}{2}$ $(^-4x^2+2x+2)(x+\frac{1}{2})+4$
12. $3x^4 - 4x^3 + x^2 + 6x + 17$ by $x - \frac{1}{3}$ $(3x^3-3x^2+6)(x-\frac{1}{3})+19$

△

13. Determine k so that when $2x^3 - x^2 + 3x + k$ is divided by $x - 1$, the remainder is zero. $k = {}^-4$
14. Determine a and b so that when $x^4 + x^3 - 7x^2 + ax + b$ is divided by $(x - 1)(x + 2)$, the remainder is zero. $a = {}^-5$, $b = 10$

8-4 POLYNOMIAL FUNCTIONS

A function f such that $f(x)$ is a polynomial in x is called a *polynomial function.* For example, the function f defined by

$$f(x) = x^3 + x^2 - x - 10$$

is a polynomial function. The domain of a polynomial function is usually understood to be the set of all real numbers. However, in the last section of this chapter, we shall consider polynomial functions which have the set of all complex numbers as their domain.

The polynomial $f(x)$ above can be divided by $x - 3$, yielding a quotient of $x^2 + 4x + 11$ and a remainder of 23, as shown by the following synthetic division.

$$\begin{array}{r|rrrr} 3 & 1 & 1 & ^-1 & ^-10 \\ & & 3 & 12 & 33 \\ \hline & 1 & 4 & 11 & 23 \end{array}$$

Hence,

$$f(x) = (x^2 + 4x + 11)(x - 3) + 23.$$

If we give x the value 3, then we obtain

$$f(3) = [3^2 + (4 \cdot 3) + 11](3 - 3) + 23 = (32 \cdot 0) + 23, \quad \text{or } 23.$$

In other words, $f(3)$ is the remainder when $f(x)$ is divided by $x - 3$. This result illustrates the following theorem.

REMAINDER THEOREM

If the polynomial $f(x)$ is divided by $x - r$, the remainder is $f(r)$.

The proof of this theorem is indicated in the example above. Thus, if the polynomial $f(x)$ is divided by $x - r$, the quotient is some polynomial $q(x)$, and the remainder R is a polynomial that is either zero or of lower degree than $x - r$. Since $x - r$ has degree 1, the remainder R is either 0 or of degree 0. In either case, R is a constant polynomial.

$$f(x) = q(x)(x - r) + R$$

When we assign to x the value r, we get

$$f(r) = q(r)(r - r) + R = (q(r) \cdot 0) + R = 0 + R, \quad \text{or } R.$$

This proves the theorem.

The remainder theorem provides us with a convenient method of computing values of a polynomial function. It is frequently easier to divide synthetically by $x - r$ than to let $x = r$ in $f(x)$ when we wish to compute $f(r)$. Thus, to find $f(r)$, we need find only the remainder on dividing $f(x)$ by $x - r$. The remainder may be computed by synthetic division, as shown in the following problem.

the board and asked for remainders when

$$2x^3 - 3x^2 + 5x - 7$$

is divided by $x + 5$, $x + 3$, x, $x - 1$, $x - 4$, or $x - 10$. With the divisions before them on the board and the table to refer to, the pattern will soon become apparent.

Problem 1. If $f(x) = x^4 - 2x^2 - 7x + 6$, find $f(^{-}2)$, $f(1)$, $f(2)$, and $f(5)$.

Solution. To obtain $f(^{-}2)$, we find the remainder on dividing $f(x)$ by $x - {}^{-}2$, as shown below. The other values of f are also computed below.

$$\begin{array}{r|rrrrr} ^{-}2 & 1 & 0 & ^{-}2 & ^{-}7 & 6 \\ & & ^{-}2 & 4 & ^{-}4 & 22 \\ \hline & 1 & ^{-}2 & 2 & ^{-}11 & 28 \end{array}$$

Thus, $f(^{-}2) = 28$.

$$\begin{array}{r|rrrrr} 1 & 1 & 0 & ^{-}2 & ^{-}7 & 6 \\ & & 1 & 1 & ^{-}1 & ^{-}8 \\ \hline & 1 & 1 & ^{-}1 & ^{-}8 & ^{-}2 \end{array}$$

Thus, $f(1) = {}^{-}2$.

$$\begin{array}{r|rrrrr} 2 & 1 & 0 & ^{-}2 & ^{-}7 & 6 \\ & & 2 & 4 & 4 & ^{-}6 \\ \hline & 1 & 2 & 2 & ^{-}3 & 0 \end{array}$$

Thus, $f(2) = 0$.

$$\begin{array}{r|rrrrr} 5 & 1 & 0 & ^{-}2 & ^{-}7 & 6 \\ & & 5 & 25 & 115 & 540 \\ \hline & 1 & 5 & 23 & 108 & 546 \end{array}$$

Thus, $f(5) = 546$.

A number r is called a zero of the polynomial $f(x)$ if $f(r) = 0$; that is, r is a zero of $f(x)$ if r is a solution of the polynomial equation

$$f(x) = 0.$$

For example, in Problem 1, a zero of the polynomial $f(x)$ is 2 since it was shown that $f(2) = 0$.

According to the remainder theorem, if we divide the polynomial $f(x)$ by $x - r$, we obtain a quotient $q(x)$ and a remainder $f(r)$, that is,

$$f(x) = q(x)(x - r) + f(r).$$

Given that r is a zero of $f(x)$, then $f(r) = 0$ and

$$f(x) = q(x)(x - r) + 0,$$

or

$$f(x) = q(x)(x - r).$$

Hence, $x - r$ is a *divisor*, or *factor*, of $f(x)$ if $f(r) = 0$. Conversely, if $x - r$ is a divisor of $f(x)$, then the remainder obtained on dividing $f(x)$ by $x - r$ must be 0. This remainder is $f(r)$ by the remainder theorem; hence, $f(r) = 0$, and we have proved the following theorem.

FACTOR THEOREM

The polynomial $x - r$ is a divisor, or factor, of the polynomial $f(x)$ if, and only if, r is a zero of $f(x)$.

Exercises for Discussion, pages 331 and 332

If time is limited, it is suggested that at least Exercises for Discussion 1, 3(a)–3(c), 4, 5(a), 5(b) and 6(b) be covered.

The Exercises for Discussion may be used for more than just drill on the use of the remainder and factor theorems. Exercise for Discussion 3 could include a test for symmetry about the y-axis, or symmetry about the origin, of the graph of $y = f(x)$, which will be discussed later. Exercise for Discussion 4 could contribute more to the same topic.

Exercise for Discussion 5 and Exercise 10 imply a relationship between pairs of zeros of a polynomial whose coefficients are all integers. The corresponding situation for complex zeros of a real polynomial is described on page 355.

Exercise for Discussion 6 and Exercises 9 and 11 imply a relationship between the rational zeros of a polynomial and the a_n and a_0 of the polynomial. (See pages 335 and 349.)

Answers to Exercise for Discussion 3, page 331

3. (a) $f(1) = 8$, $f(^{-}1) = 8$,
$f(2) = 32$, $f(^{-}2) = 32$,
$f(k) = k^4 + 3k^2 + 4$,
$f(^{-}k) = k^4 + 3k^2 + 4$;
even function

Problem 2. Which of the polynomials $x - 1$, $x + 1$, $x - \frac{1}{2}$, $x - 2$, and $x + 3$ are divisors of the polynomial

$$f(x) = 4x^3 + 16x^2 + 9x - 9?$$

Solution. We know that $x - 1$ will be a factor of $f(x)$ if 1 is a zero. Since

$$f(1) = 4 + 16 + 9 - 9, \quad \text{or } 20,$$

1 is not a zero of $f(x)$. Hence, $x - 1$ is not a divisor of $f(x)$. Also,

$$f(^-1) = {}^-4 + 16 - 9 - 9, \quad \text{or } {}^-6,$$

and $^-1$ is not a zero of $f(x)$. Therefore, $x - {}^-1$, or $x + 1$, is not a divisor of $f(x)$. Let us compute $f(\frac{1}{2})$, $f(2)$, and $f(^-3)$ by synthetic division.

$$\begin{array}{c|cccc} \frac{1}{2} & 4 & 16 & 9 & ^-9 \\ & & 2 & 9 & 9 \\ \hline & 4 & 18 & 18 & 0 \end{array} \qquad \begin{array}{c|cccc} 2 & 4 & 16 & 9 & ^-9 \\ & & 8 & 48 & 114 \\ \hline & 4 & 24 & 57 & 105 \end{array}$$

Thus, $f(\frac{1}{2}) = 0$. Thus, $f(2) = 105$.

$$\begin{array}{c|cccc} ^-3 & 4 & 16 & 9 & ^-9 \\ & & ^-12 & ^-12 & 9 \\ \hline & 4 & 4 & ^-3 & 0 \end{array}$$

Thus, $f(^-3) = 0$.

Clearly, $\frac{1}{2}$ and $^-3$ are zeros of $f(x)$, so that $x - \frac{1}{2}$ and $x + 3$ are divisors of $f(x)$. Since $f(2) \neq 0$, $x - 2$ is not a divisor of $f(x)$.

Exercises for Discussion

1. Given that $f(x) = 2x^3 - 3x^2 + 4x - 3$, find $f(0)$, $f(^-2)$, $f(5)$, and $f(^-4)$. $^-3$, $^-39$, 192, $^-195$
2. Given that $g(x) = x^4 - 7x^3 + 4x^2 + 5x$, find $g(0)$, $g(3)$, $g(^-3)$, and $g(6)$. 0, $^-57$, 291, $^-42$
3. If $f(^-r) = f(r)$ for every r in the domain of f, the function is said to be an *even function.* If $f(^-r) = {}^-f(r)$ for every r in the domain of f, the function is said to be an *odd function.* For each of the following functions, find $f(1)$ and $f(^-1)$, $f(2)$ and $f(^-2)$, $f(k)$ and $f(^-k)$, and then tell which are odd and which are even.

   (a) $f(x) = x^4 + 3x^2 + 4$ (b) $f(x) = 2x^3 - 3x$
   (c) $f(x) = 3x^4 - 2x^2 + x$ (d) $f(x) = x^6 + 3x^4 - 8$
   (e) $f(x) = 2x^5 - x^2$ (f) $f(x) = 1 - x^2 - x^4$

(b) $f(1) = {}^-1$, $f(^-1) = 1$, $f(2) = 10$, $f(^-2) = {}^-10$, $f(k) = 2k^3 - 3k$, $f(^-k) = {}^-2k^3 + 3k$; odd function

(c) $f(1) = 2$, $f(^-1) = 0$, $f(2) = 42$, $f(^-2) = 38$, $f(k) = 3k^4 - 2k^2 + k$, $f(^-k) = 3k^4 - 2k^2 - k$; neither

(d) $f(1) = {}^-4$, $f(^-1) = {}^-4$, $f(2) = 104$, $f(^-2) = 104$, $f(k) = k^6 + 3k^4 - 8$, $f(^-k) = k^6 + 3k^4 - 8$; even function

(e) $f(1) = 1$, $f(^-1) = {}^-3$, $f(2) = 60$, $f(^-2) = {}^-68$, $f(k) = 2k^5 - k^2$, $f(^-k) = {}^-2k^5 - k^2$; neither

(f) $f(1) = {}^-1$, $f(^-1) = {}^-1$, $f(2) = {}^-19$, $f(^-2) = {}^-19$, $f(k) = 1 - k^2 - k^4$, $f(^-k) = 1 - k^2 - k^4$; even function

Exercises, page 332

In Exercise 11, a special case may first be considered. If

$$3x^3 + 8x^2 - 2x + 3 = 0,$$

then

$$3x^3 + 8x^2 - 2x = {}^-3.$$

Since the even integers are closed under addition, subtraction, and multiplication, the left side of the equation is an even integer if x is an even integer, while the right side is odd. Hence, an even integer cannot be a zero of the polynomial $3x^3 + 8x^2 - 2x + 3$. On the other hand, though the odd integers are closed under multiplication, they are not closed under addition or subtraction. This means that each term of the polynomial would have to be examined in order to find out whether an odd integer could be a zero. If x is odd, then $3x^3$ is odd, $8x^2$ is even, $2x$ is even, and $3x^3 + 8x^2 - 2x$ is odd. Hence, an odd integer could be a zero of $3x^3 + 8x^2 - 2x + 3$. But if the example $2x^3 - 3x^2 + 9x - 5$ is considered, it can be shown by an argument similar to the one above that an odd integer cannot be a zero of $2x^3 - 3x^2 + 9x - 5$. Therefore, it depends on the coefficients a_n, $a_{n-1}, \ldots, a_1$ whether or not an odd integer can be a zero of

$$a_nx^n + a_{n-1}x^{n-1} + \ldots + a_1x + a_0,$$

with a_0 an odd integer and each a_i an integer.

Exercise 12 is recommended for discussion in class. Several examples may be used for each part, such as, for part (a)

$$p(x) = 2x^3 + 3x^2 + 4x + 6,$$

for part (b)

$$p(x) = {}^-2x^3 - 4x^2 - x - 5,$$

and for part (c)

$$p(x) = a_3x^3 + a_2x^2 + a_1x + 1.$$

In part (c), if $p(x) = 0$, then

$$a_3x^3 + a_2x^2 + a_1x + 1 = 0$$
$$a_3x^3 + a_2x^2 + a_1x = {}^-1.$$

It is known that a_3, a_2, a_1 are integers; x is replaced with an integer r, which is a zero of $p(x)$. Then

$$a_3r^3 + a_2r^2 + a_1r$$

is an integer and

$$r(a_3r^2 + a_2r + a_1) = {}^-1.$$

Since both factors on the left are integers, each is a divisor of $^-1$. Hence $r = 1$ or $r = {}^-1$.

The problem could also be considered in reverse. If $a_0 = 1$, r must be ± 1, but if $r = \pm 1$, it is not necessarily true that $a_0 = 1$. For example,

$$(x - 1)(2x^2 - 5x + 3) = 2x^3 - 7x^2 + 8x - 3,$$

where $a_0 = {}^-3$, but $r = 1$ is still a zero.

4. (a) If all the exponents in a polynomial are even, is the polynomial an even function? *Yes*

(b) If all the exponents in a polynomial are odd, is the polynomial an odd function? *Yes*

(c) Is every polynomial function either odd or even? *No* Illustrate your answer with an example. *(Examples vary.)*

(d) Is there any polynomial which is both odd and even? *Yes; $f(x) = 0$*

5. Use substitution to find which, if any, of the numbers $\sqrt{2}$, $\sqrt{3}$, $^-\sqrt{2}$, and $^-\sqrt{3}$ are zeros of the following polynomials.

(a) $x^3 + 3x^2 - 2x - 6$ *$\pm\sqrt{2}$* (b) $x^4 - 5x^2 + 6$ *$\pm\sqrt{2}, \pm\sqrt{3}$*

(c) $x^3 + (\sqrt{6} - \sqrt{2} - \sqrt{3})x^2 + (\sqrt{6} - 3\sqrt{2} - 2\sqrt{3})x + 6$ *$\sqrt{2}, \sqrt{3}$*

6. Use synthetic division to find which, if any, of the numbers $^-3$, $^-2$, $^-1$, 0, 1, 2, and 3 are zeros of the following polynomials.

(a) $x^3 - 4x^2 + x + 6$ *$^-1, 2, 3$* (b) $x^4 + x^3 - 3x^2 - 4x - 4$ *$^-2, 2$*

Exercises

1. Given that $p(y) = y^5 - y + 3$, find $p(10)$, $p(^-7)$, $p(1)$, and $p(5)$. *99,993; $^-16{,}797$; 3; 3123*

2. Given that $q(y) = 12y^3 + 7y^2 - 14y + 3$, find $q(^-2)$, $q(^-3)$, $q(3)$, and $q(5)$. *$^-37$; $^-216$; 348; 1608*

In Exercises 3–8, which, if any, of the numbers $^-3$, $^-2$, $^-1$, 0, 1, 2, and 3 are zeros of the polynomials?

3. $x - x^3$ *$^-1, 0, 1$* **4.** $y^3 + y + 1$ *None*

5. $3x^3 + 8x^2 - 2x + 3$ *$^-3$* **6.** $x^3 - 7x + 6$ *$^-3, 1, 2$*

7. $3x^4 + 8x^3 + 6x^2 + 3x - 2$ *$^-2$* **8.** $x^3 + 3x^2 - x - 3$ *$^-3, ^-1, 1$*

9. Which of the polynomials $(x - 1)$, $(x + 1)$, $(x - 4)$, and $(x + 3)$ are divisors, or factors, of the following polynomials?

(a) $x^3 - 2x^2 - 11x + 12$ *$(x-1), (x+3), (x-4)$* (b) $2x^3 + 3x^2 - 23x - 12$ *None*

(c) $2x^4 + x^3 + x^2 - x - 3$ *$(x-1), (x+1)$* (d) $x^4 + x^3 - 19x^2 + x - 20$ *$(x-4)$*

△ ———

10. Which, if any, of the numbers $2 + \sqrt{3}$, $3 + \sqrt{2}$, $^-3$, $2 - \sqrt{3}$, and $3 - \sqrt{2}$ are zeros of the following polynomials?

(a) $x^3 - x^2 - 11x + 3$ *$2+\sqrt{3}, {}^-3, 2-\sqrt{3}$* (b) $x^4 - 10x^3 + 32x^2 - 34x + 7$ *$2+\sqrt{3}, 2-\sqrt{3}, 3+\sqrt{2}, 3-\sqrt{2}$*

(c) $x^3 - 5x^2 + x + 7$ *$3+\sqrt{2}, 3-\sqrt{2}$*

(d) $x^3 + (\sqrt{2} - \sqrt{3} - 5)x^2 + (6 + 3\sqrt{3} - 2\sqrt{2} - \sqrt{6})x$ *$2+\sqrt{3}, 3-\sqrt{2}$*

11. If all the coefficients of a polynomial are integers and if the constant term is an odd integer, can an even integer be a zero of the polynomial? *No* Can an odd integer be a zero? *Yes* Justify your answers. *See Solution Manual.*

12. Consider a third-degree polynomial of the form

$$p(x) = a_3x^3 + a_2x^2 + a_1x + a_0$$

with a_3, a_2, a_1, a_0 all integers.

(a) Given that a_3, a_2, a_1, a_0 are all positive integers, what is the sign of each real zero of $p(x)$? *Negative*

(b) Given that a_3, a_2, a_1, a_0 are all negative integers, what is the sign of each real zero of $p(x)$? *Negative*

(c) Given that $a_0 = 1$ and r is an integral zero of $p(x)$, show that either $r = 1$ or $r = {}^-1$. *See Solution Manual.*

8-5 INTEGRAL ZEROS OF INTEGRAL POLYNOMIALS

A polynomial is called an *integral polynomial* if all of its coefficients are integers. For example,

$$2x^2 - 3x + 1 \quad \text{and} \quad 7x - 5$$

are integral polynomials. We note that both the sum,

$$(2x^2 - 3x + 1) + (7x - 5) = 2x^2 + 4x - 4,$$

and the product,

$$(2x^2 - 3x + 1)(7x - 5) = 14x^3 - 31x^2 + 22x - 5,$$

of these two polynomials are also integral polynomials. It is clear from this example that the set of all integral polynomials is *closed* with respect to addition and multiplication. Thus, there is an *algebra of integral polynomials* contained in the algebra of polynomials. The basic properties of our original algebra of polynomials are also valid for the algebra of integral polynomials. In particular, if an integer r is a zero of a polynomial $f(x)$, then r is called an *integral zero* of $f(x)$.

The problem in this section is that of finding integral zeros of integral polynomials. Let us attempt to develop a general procedure which, if followed, will yield all the integral zeros of an integral polynomial.

Quiz

Which, if any, of the numbers ${}^-3$, ${}^-2$, 0, 2, 3, $\sqrt{2}$, ${}^-\sqrt{2}$ are zeros of the following polynomials?

1. $x^4 + 3x^3 - 4x^2 - 12x$
   (ans: 0, ${}^-3$, 2, ${}^-2$)
2. $x^3 - 3x^2 - 2x + 6$
   (ans: $\sqrt{2}$, ${}^-\sqrt{2}$, 3)
3. $x^3 + (1 - \sqrt{2})x^2 - (6 + \sqrt{2})x + 6\sqrt{2}$
   (ans: $\sqrt{2}$, 2, ${}^-3$)
4. $x^3 - (3 + \sqrt{2})x^2 - 16x + 16(3 - \sqrt{2})$
   (ans: None)

8-5 INTEGRAL ZEROS OF INTEGRAL POLYNOMIALS

It should be emphasized that the test for integral zeros is necessary but still not sufficient. The students must understand clearly that there are as many possibilities for integral zeros as there are divisors of a_0 in the given polynomial. They will need to know this before taking up Exercises for Discussion 5 and 6 on page 337. Here the thinking shifts towards using the zeros of the polynomial to produce its linear factors.

This material should be covered carefully to prepare the way for the proof of the integral zero theorem on the next page.

Problem 1. Find all the integral zeros of the integral polynomial

$$f(x) = 2x^3 - 5x^2 - 27x + 10.$$

Solution. We can try to solve this problem by computing $f(0)$, $f(1)$, $f(^-1)$, $f(2)$, $f(^-2)$, $f(3)$, $f(^-3)$, and so on, until we find the zeros. For example, $f(0) = 10$, and therefore, 0 is not a zero. Also,

$$f(1) = 2 - 5 - 27 + 10, \quad \text{or } ^-20,$$

so that 1 is not a zero, and

$$\begin{aligned} f(^-1) &= 2(^-1)^3 - 5(^-1)^2 - 27(^-1) + 10 \\ &= {^-2} - 5 + 27 + 10, \quad \text{or } 30, \end{aligned}$$

so that $^-1$ is not a zero. We could continue searching for integral zeros in this way for a long time without finding any, because some integral polynomials do not have any integral zeros.

There is a way of eliminating certain integers from consideration as zeros. For example, let us express $f(x)$ in the form

$$f(x) = x(2x^2 - 5x - 27) + 10.$$

Then the integer r is a zero of $f(x)$ if, and only if,

$$r(2r^2 - 5r - 27) + 10 = 0,$$

or, equivalently,

$$r(2r^2 - 5r - 27) = {^-10}.$$

If r is an integer, then $2r^2 - 5r - 27$ must also be an integer because sums and products of integers are integers. By the equation above, r is a zero of $f(x)$ if, and only if, the product of the two integers r and $2r^2 - 5r - 27$ is $^-10$. Therefore, for r to be an integral zero of $f(x)$, it must be a *divisor* of $^-10$. Thus, the only *possible* integral zeros of $f(x)$ are the divisors of $^-10$. Since

$$1, \quad 2, \quad 5, \quad 10, \quad ^-1, \quad ^-2, \quad ^-5, \quad ^-10$$

are all the integral divisors of $^-10$ and 10, it follows that the only possible integral zeros of $f(x)$ are the eight integers listed above.

However, not all of these eight integers are zeros of $f(x)$, because 1 and $^-1$ have already been shown not to be zeros. Since

$$f(10) = (2 \cdot 10^3) - (5 \cdot 10^2) - (27 \cdot 10) + 10,$$

and the first term, $2 \cdot 10^3$, is much larger than the sum of the other three, we see that the sum of all four terms of $f(10)$ cannot be zero. Therefore, 10 is not a zero of $f(x)$. Similarly, $^{-}10$ is not a zero of $f(x)$.

We check by synthetic division to see which, if any, of the other four integers, 2, 5, $^{-}2$, and $^{-}5$, are zeros.

$$\begin{array}{r|rrrr} 2 & 2 & ^{-}5 & ^{-}27 & 10 \\ & & 4 & ^{-}2 & ^{-}58 \\ \hline & 2 & ^{-}1 & ^{-}29 & ^{-}48 \end{array} \qquad \begin{array}{r|rrrr} ^{-}2 & 2 & ^{-}5 & ^{-}27 & 10 \\ & & ^{-}4 & 18 & 18 \\ \hline & 2 & ^{-}9 & ^{-}9 & 28 \end{array}$$

$$\begin{array}{r|rrrr} 5 & 2 & ^{-}5 & ^{-}27 & 10 \\ & & 10 & 25 & ^{-}10 \\ \hline & 2 & 5 & ^{-}2 & 0 \end{array} \qquad \begin{array}{r|rrrr} ^{-}5 & 2 & ^{-}5 & ^{-}27 & 10 \\ & & ^{-}10 & 75 & ^{-}240 \\ \hline & 2 & ^{-}15 & 48 & ^{-}230 \end{array}$$

In only one case above, when $x = 5$, is the remainder 0. Hence, 5 is the only one of the four integers 2, 5, $^{-}2$, $^{-}5$ that is a zero of $f(x)$. We may conclude that 5 is the only integral zero of $f(x)$. Thus, we have solved our problem.

It is evident at a glance whether or not 0 is a zero of a polynomial; 0 is a zero if, and only if, the constant term of the polynomial is 0. Although we are not able to determine at a glance all the integral zeros of an integral polynomial, we can follow the procedure indicated in Problem 1 to determine the *possible* integral zeros. Thus, if

$$f(x) = a_n x^n + a_{n-1}x^{n-1} + \cdots + a_1 x + a_0$$

is an integral polynomial and r is an integral zero of $f(x)$, then

$$a_n r^n + a_{n-1}r^{n-1} + \cdots + a_1 r + a_0 = 0,$$
$$r(a_n r^{n-1} + a_{n-1}r^{n-2} + \cdots + a_1) + a_0 = 0,$$
$$r(a_n r^{n-1} + a_{n-1}r^{n-2} + \cdots + a_1) = {}^{-}a_0.$$

Therefore, r must be a divisor of $^{-}a_0$ or, alternatively, of a_0. This proves the following theorem.

INTEGRAL ZERO THEOREM

An integer is a zero of a given integral polynomial only if it is a divisor of the constant term of the polynomial.

TWISTER

A cubic box, each side of which is 1 foot long, is placed flat against a wall. A ladder of length $\sqrt{15}$ feet is placed in such a way that it touches both the wall and the free horizontal edge of the box. Using quadratics only, find at what height the ladder touches the wall.

Solution:

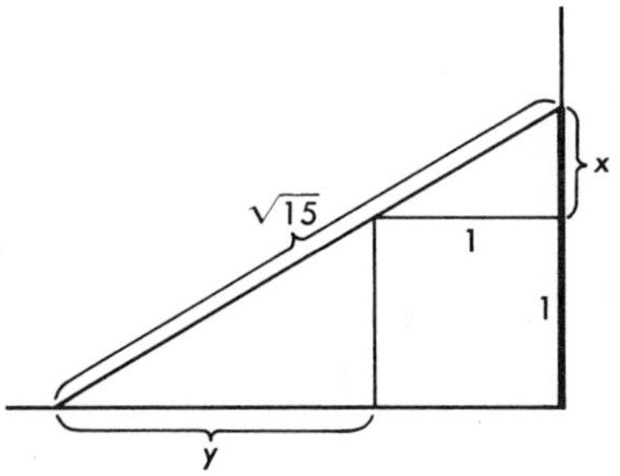

By using area,

$$xy = 1.$$

By the pythagorean theorem,

$$(x + 1)^2 + (y + 1)^2 = 15.$$

By substitution,

$$x^2 + 2x + 1 + \frac{1}{x^2} + \frac{2}{x} + 1 = 15.$$

Thus,

$$\left(x + \frac{1}{x}\right)^2 + 2\left(x + \frac{1}{x}\right) - 15 = 0,$$

and

$$x + \frac{1}{x} = 3 \text{ or } x^2 - 3x + 1 = 0.$$

Thus,

$$x = 2.618 \text{ or } x = .382.$$

The ladder will touch the wall 3.62 or 1.38 feet from the floor.

When the students appear to be reasonably adept at synthetic division, you may wish to show them the following abbreviated way to test several numbers in the same polynomial. It is done simply by keeping the second line of the synthetic division in one's head and writing only the third. Thus, if

$$p(x) = 2x^3 - x^2 - 13x - 6,$$

as in Exercise for Discussion 1 on page 337, only the writing below need be done.

x	2	$^-1$	$^-13$	$^-6$	$p(x)$
$^-6$	2	$^-13$	65	$^-396$	$p(^-6) = {}^-396$
$^-3$	2	$^-7$	8	$^-30$	$p(^-3) = {}^-30$
$^-2$	2	$^-5$	$^-3$	0	$p(^-2) = 0$
$^-1$	2	$^-3$	$^-10$	4	$p(^-1) = 4$
0				$^-6$	$p(0) = {}^-6$
1	2	1	$^-12$	$^-18$	$p(1) = {}^-18$
2	2	3	$^-7$	$^-20$	$p(2) = {}^-20$
3	2	5	2	0	$p(3) = 0$
6	2	11	53	312	$p(6) = 312$

We note that this theorem does *not* claim that every divisor, or even any divisor, of the constant term is a zero of the polynomial. For example, the only possible integral zeros of the integral polynomial $x^2 + x + 1$ are the divisors of the constant term 1, that is, 1 and $^-1$. Since

$$1^2 + 1 + 1 = 3 \quad \text{and} \quad (^-1)^2 + {}^-1 + 1 = 1,$$

neither 1 nor $^-1$ is a zero. Consequently, the polynomial $x^2 + x + 1$ has no integral zeros.

Problem 2. Find the integral zeros of the integral polynomial

$$f(x) = 3x^3 - 17x^2 - 8x + 12.$$

Solution. According to the integral zero theorem, the possible integral zeros are the divisors of the constant term 12:

$$\pm 1, \quad \pm 2, \quad \pm 3, \quad \pm 4, \quad \pm 6, \quad \pm 12.$$

Perhaps you can see that 12 and $^-12$ are not zeros, because the first term of $f(12)$ is much larger in absolute value than the sum of the other terms, and so is the first term of $f(^-12)$. Since

$$f(1) = 3 - 17 - 8 + 12, \quad \text{or } ^-10,$$

1 is not a zero. However,

$$f(^-1) = {}^-3 - 17 + 8 + 12, \quad \text{or } 0,$$

and therefore, $^-1$ is a zero.

Synthetic division can be used to show that 2, $^-2$, 3, $^-3$, 4, and $^-4$ are not zeros. However, we shall leave the details to you. Let us check 6 and $^-6$ as shown below.

$$\begin{array}{r|rrrr} 6 & 3 & ^-17 & ^-8 & 12 \\ & & 18 & 6 & ^-12 \\ \hline & 3 & 1 & ^-2 & 0 \end{array} \qquad \begin{array}{r|rrrr} ^-6 & 3 & ^-17 & ^-8 & 12 \\ & & ^-18 & 210 & ^-1212 \\ \hline & 3 & ^-35 & 202 & ^-1200 \end{array}$$

Evidently 6 is a zero, but $^-6$ is not. Therefore,

$$\{^-1, 6\}$$

is the set of all integral zeros of the given polynomial.

Exercises for Discussion

In Exercises 1–4, list the *possible* integral zeros of each polynomial. Then use synthetic division to see which, if any, actually are zeros of the polynomial.

1. $2x^3 - x^2 - 13x - 6$ Possible: $\pm 1, \pm 2, \pm 3, \pm 6$; actual: $^-2, 3$
2. $3x^3 + 23x^2 + 13x - 7$ Possible: $\pm 1, \pm 7$; actual: $^-1, ^-7$
3. $6x^3 + 29x^2 - 6x - 5$ Possible: $\pm 1, \pm 5$; actual: $^-5$
4. $x^3 + x^2 - x - 1$ Possible: ± 1; actual: $1, ^-1$
5. If r is a zero of a real polynomial $p(x)$, then by the factor theorem, $p(x) = (x - r)q(x)$, where $q(x)$ is a polynomial of degree 1 less than the degree of $p(x)$. Show that
   (a) if s is a zero of $q(x)$, then it is also a zero of $p(x)$.
   (b) if $s \neq r$ and if s is a zero of $p(x)$, then s is a zero of $q(x)$.
6. We can use the results of Exercise 5 to decrease the number of steps in the search for integral zeros. We could have shortened Problem 2 on page 336 after we had found that $^-1$ is a zero of $3x^3 - 17x^2 - 8x + 12$. If we use synthetic division to compute $f(^-1)$, we obtain $x + 1$ as a factor of this polynomial. We then display the other factor, $3x^2 - 20x + 12$. Thus, $3x^3 - 17x^2 - 8x + 12 = (x + 1)(3x^2 - 20x + 12)$. Additional zeros of the cubic are also zeros of the quadratic polynomial $3x^2 - 20x + 12$, which we can factor as $(x - 6)(3x - 2)$. Thus, $3x^3 - 17x^2 - 8x + 12 = (x + 1)(x - 6)(3x - 2)$, and all the zeros can be read off at a glance.

   Find all the integral zeros of each of the following polynomials, using the factor theorem and the results of Exercise 5 to shorten your work. If you can find nonintegral zeros of the polynomial, list them also.

   (a) $3x^3 - 4x^2 - 13x - 6$ $^-1, 3, \frac{^-2}{3}$
   (b) $x^3 + x^2 - 8x - 12$ $^-2, 3$
   (c) $x^3 - 8x^2 - 8x - 9$ $9, \frac{1}{2}(^-1 + \sqrt{3}i), \frac{1}{2}(^-1 - \sqrt{3}i)$
   (d) $2x^4 + 19x^3 - 8x^2 + 19x - 10$ $^-10, \frac{1}{2}, ^-i, i$

Exercises

Find all the integral zeros of each of the following integral polynomials.

1. $x^3 + x^2 + x - 1$ None
2. $x^3 + 2x^2 - 2x - 4$ $^-2$
3. $6x^3 - 67x^2 + 10x + 11$ 11
4. $15x^3 + 49x^2 + 8x - 12$ $^-3$
5. $2x^4 - 25x^3 + 60x^2 + 23x + 36$ $4, 9$
6. $x^4 + 4x^3 - 17x^2 - 20x + 60$ $^-6, 2$

Exercises for Discussion

If time is limited, it is suggested that at least Exercises for Discussion 1, 5, 6(b) and 6(d) be covered.

Answers to Exercise for Discussion 5

5. (a) If s is a zero of $q(x)$, then $q(s) = 0$. Since

$$\begin{aligned} p(x) &= (x - r)q(x), \\ p(s) &= (s - r)q(s) \\ &= (s - r) \cdot 0 \\ &= 0. \end{aligned}$$

Therefore, s is a zero of $p(x)$.

(b) If s is a zero of $p(x)$, then $p(s) = 0$. Since

$$\begin{aligned} p(x) &= (x - r)q(x), \\ p(s) &= (s - r)q(s). \end{aligned}$$

But $p(s) = 0$. Therefore,

$$(s - r)q(s) = 0,$$

but $s - r \neq 0$. Therefore,

$$q(s) = 0.$$

Quiz

Find all the integral zeros of each of the following integral polynomials.

1. $x^3 + 2x^2 + 1$ (ans: None)
2. $9x^3 + 9x^2 - x - 1$ (ans: $^{-}1$)
3. $2x^3 + 5x^2 - 4x - 3$ (ans: $^{-}3$, 1)
4. $12x^3 + 23x^2 - 3x - 2$ (ans: $^{-}2$)
5. $x^3 - 7x + 6$ (ans: 1, 2, $^{-}3$)

8-6 RATIONAL ZEROS OF RATIONAL POLYNOMIALS

The class may be asked for a proof of the rational zero theorem. It is not necessary that the synthetic division be carried as far as it can go each time. (See comments at the bottom of page 341.) As soon as a fraction appears on the third line, the student should stop.

Find all the integral zeros, if any, of each of the following integral polynomials. If you can find nonintegral zeros, list them also.

7. $x^4 - 10x^3 + 35x^2 - 50x + 24$ 1, 2, 3, 4
8. $x^4 + 8x^3 + 13x^2 - 16x - 30$ $^{-}3$, $^{-}5$, $\pm\sqrt{2}$
9. $x^5 - 4x^4 + x^3 + 10x^2 - 4x - 8$ $^{-}1$, 2
10. $x^4 - 12x^3 + 54x^2 - 68x + 81$ None

Find all the integral zeros of each of the following polynomials, and write each polynomial as a product of the factors you have obtained.

11. $x^4 + x^3 - 2x^2 + 4x - 24$ $\{^{-}3, 2\}$; $(x+3)(x-2)(x^2+4)$
12. $x^3 - 4x^2 + 7x - 60$ $\{5\}$; $(x-5)(x^2+x+12)$
13. $3x^3 + 14x^2 - 72x + 64$ $\{^{-}8, 2\}$; $(x+8)(x-2)(3x-4)$
14. $2x^3 - 5x^2 + 15x - 54$ $\{3\}$; $(x-3)(2x^2+x+18)$
15. $6x^4 + 23x^3 - 24x^2 - 68x + 48$ $\{^{-}4, ^{-}2\}$; $(x+4)(x+2)(6x^2-13x+6)$
16. $7x^4 + 33x^3 - 181x^2 + 33x + 72$ $\{^{-}8, 3\}$; $(x+8)(x-3)(7x^2-2x-3)$

8-6 RATIONAL ZEROS OF RATIONAL POLYNOMIALS

We shall call a polynomial $f(x)$ a *rational polynomial* if all the coefficients of $f(x)$ are rational numbers. It is evident that the set of all rational polynomials is *closed* with respect to addition and multiplication, and that there is an algebra of rational polynomials as well as an algebra of integral polynomials. The basic properties of our original algebra of polynomials are also valid for the algebra of rational polynomials. A zero r of a rational polynomial is called a *rational zero* if r is a rational number. In the preceding section, we were able to devise a method for finding all integral zeros of an integral polynomial. Now we shall indicate a similar method for determining all rational zeros of a rational polynomial.

Each rational polynomial $f(x)$ can be expressed as a product of a rational number and an integral polynomial $g(x)$. All we need do is consider each coefficient a_i of $f(x)$ as a quotient b_i/c_i of two integers and then find the least common multiple d of all denominators c_i. Then

$$f(x) = \frac{1}{d}\,g(x),$$

where all the coefficients of the polynomial $g(x)$ are now integers. For example, if

$$f(x) = \tfrac{1}{3}x^2 - \tfrac{3}{2}x + \tfrac{5}{6},$$

then the denominators 3, 2, and 6 of the coefficients have a least common multiple of 6. Hence,

$$f(x) = \tfrac{1}{6}(2x^2 - 9x + 5),$$

and the rational polynomial has been expressed as a product of the rational number $\frac{1}{6}$ and the integral polynomial $2x^2 - 9x + 5$.

If the rational polynomial $f(x)$ is expressed in the form

$$f(x) = \frac{1}{d}\, g(x)$$

as above, then for each real number r,

$$f(r) = \frac{1}{d}\, g(r).$$

Hence, $f(r) = 0$ if, and only if, $g(r) = 0$. Consequently, in looking for the rational zeros of the rational polynomial $f(x)$, we need only look for the rational zeros of the *integral* polynomial $g(x)$. Thus, let us consider the problem of finding all rational zeros of an integral polynomial.

Problem 1. Find all the rational zeros of the integral polynomial

$$g(x) = 6x^3 - x^2 - 2x - 15.$$

Solution. According to the integral zero theorem, the possible integral zeros of $g(x)$ are the divisors of $^-15$:

$$\pm 1, \quad \pm 3, \quad \pm 5, \quad \pm 15.$$

You may readily verify that not one of these eight integers is a zero of $g(x)$.

On the other hand, the synthetic division

$$\begin{array}{c|cccc} \frac{3}{2} & 6 & ^-1 & ^-2 & ^-15 \\ & & 9 & 12 & 15 \\ \hline & 6 & 8 & 10 & 0 \end{array}$$

shows that $\frac{3}{2}$ is a zero of $g(x)$.

Any rational number p/q, $q > 0$, expressed in lowest form is a zero of $g(x)$ if, and only if,

$$6\left(\frac{p}{q}\right)^3 - \left(\frac{p}{q}\right)^2 - 2\left(\frac{p}{q}\right) - 15 = 0,$$

or

$$6p^3 - p^2q - 2pq^2 - 15q^3 = 0. \qquad (1)$$

By adding $15q^3$ to each side of Eq. (1) and factoring p out of the left side of the resulting equation, we obtain the equivalent equation

$$p(6p^2 - pq - 2q^2) = 15q^3.$$

The left side of this equation is expressed as a product of the two integers p and $6p^2 - pq - 2q^2$. The right side is an integer $15q^3$. Hence, p is a divisor of $15q^3$. However, we had assumed that p and q were relatively prime. Therefore, p must be a divisor of $^-15$, the coefficient of q^3 in Eq. (1). If we start with Eq. (1), we can show that

$$6p^3 = q(p^2 + 2pq + 15q^2)$$

is an equivalent equation. By an argument similar to the one above, we see that the integer q is a divisor of $6p^3$ and hence, of 6, the coefficient of p^3.

Thus, we have shown that if the rational number p/q expressed in lowest form, with $q > 0$, is a zero of $g(x)$, then p must be a divisor of the constant term, $^-15$, and q is a positive divisor of the leading coefficient, 6.

The possible values of p are ± 1, ± 3, ± 5, and ± 15; those of q are 1, 2, 3, and 6. Hence, the possible rational zeros of $g(x)$, other than integers, are

$$\pm\tfrac{1}{2}, \quad \pm\tfrac{1}{3}, \quad \pm\tfrac{1}{6}, \quad \pm\tfrac{3}{2}, \quad \pm\tfrac{5}{2}, \quad \pm\tfrac{5}{3}, \quad \pm\tfrac{5}{6}, \quad \pm\tfrac{15}{2}.$$

These represent all nonintegral values of p/q. We used synthetic division to show that $\frac{3}{2}$ is a zero of $g(x)$. It can be shown that this is the only one of the sixteen rational numbers listed above that is a zero of $g(x)$. Therefore, $\frac{3}{2}$ is the only rational zero of $g(x)$.

The general theorem of integral polynomials illustrated by Problem 1 can be stated in the following way.

RATIONAL ZERO THEOREM

A rational number p/q, $q > 0$, expressed in lowest form is a zero of the integral polynomial

$$g(x) = a_n x^n + a_{n-1} x^{n-1} + \cdots + a_1 x + a_0$$

only if p is a divisor of the constant term a_0 and q is a divisor of the leading coefficient a_n.

Problem 2. Find the rational zeros of the integral polynomial

$$g(x) = 10x^3 - 17x^2 - 7x + 2.$$

Solution. According to the rational zero theorem, the possible rational zeros have the form p/q, where p is a divisor of 2 and q is a divisor of 10. Consequently, p can be ± 1 or ± 2, and q can be 1, 2, 5, or 10. Thus, the possible rational zeros of $g(x)$ are

$$\pm 1, \quad \pm\tfrac{1}{2}, \quad \pm\tfrac{1}{5}, \quad \pm\tfrac{1}{10}, \quad \pm 2, \quad \pm\tfrac{2}{5}.$$

Since $g(1) = {}^-12$ and $g({}^-1) = {}^-18$, neither 1 nor ${}^-1$ is a zero of $g(x)$. By the synthetic division given below, we see that

$$\{{}^-\tfrac{1}{2}, \tfrac{1}{5}, 2\}$$

is the set of all rational zeros of $g(x)$.

$$\begin{array}{r|rrrr} \frac{1}{2} & 10 & {}^-17 & {}^-7 & 2 \\ & & 5 & {}^-6 & {}^-\frac{13}{2} \\ \hline & 10 & {}^-12 & {}^-13 & {}^-\frac{9}{2} \end{array} \qquad \begin{array}{r|rrrr} {}^-\frac{1}{2} & 10 & {}^-17 & {}^-7 & 2 \\ & & {}^-5 & 11 & {}^-2 \\ \hline & 10 & {}^-22 & 4 & 0 \end{array}$$

$$\begin{array}{r|rrrr} \frac{1}{5} & 10 & {}^-17 & {}^-7 & 2 \\ & & 2 & {}^-3 & {}^-2 \\ \hline & 10 & {}^-15 & {}^-10 & 0 \end{array} \qquad \begin{array}{r|rrrr} {}^-\frac{1}{5} & 10 & {}^-17 & {}^-7 & 2 \\ & & {}^-2 & \frac{19}{5} & \\ \hline & 10 & {}^-19 & {}^-\frac{16}{5} & \end{array}$$

$$\begin{array}{r|rrrr} .1 & 10 & {}^-17 & {}^-7 & 2 \\ & & 1 & {}^-1.6 & \\ \hline & 10 & {}^-16 & {}^-8.6 & \end{array} \qquad \begin{array}{r|rrrr} {}^-.1 & 10 & {}^-17 & {}^-7 & 2 \\ & & {}^-1 & 1.8 & \\ \hline & 10 & {}^-18 & {}^-5.2 & \end{array}$$

$$\begin{array}{r|rrrr} 2 & 10 & {}^-17 & {}^-7 & 2 \\ & & 20 & 6 & {}^-2 \\ \hline & 10 & 3 & {}^-1 & 0 \end{array} \qquad \begin{array}{r|rrrr} {}^-2 & 10 & {}^-17 & {}^-7 & 2 \\ & & {}^-20 & 74 & {}^-134 \\ \hline & 10 & {}^-37 & 67 & {}^-132 \end{array}$$

$$\begin{array}{r|rrrr} .4 & 10 & {}^-17 & 7 & 2 \\ & & 4 & {}^-5.2 & \\ \hline & 10 & {}^-13 & 1.8 & \end{array} \qquad \begin{array}{r|rrrr} {}^-.4 & 10 & {}^-17 & {}^-7 & 2 \\ & & {}^-4 & 8.4 & \\ \hline & 10 & {}^-21 & 1.4 & \end{array}$$

You will note that we did not complete some of the divisions above, but stopped as soon as a nonintegral rational number appeared in the bottom row. Any further multiplication of this number and succeeding numbers by the rational number at the side will not yield an integer, and hence, the final remainder at the end of the row cannot be zero.

Exercises for Discussion and Exercises

Exercises for Discussion 7 and 8 and Exercise 14 are recommended for assignment. If time is limited, it is suggested that at least Exercises for Discussion 2, 5, 7 and 8 be covered.

Answers to Exercises for Discussion 1–6, 7(c)

1. Possible: $\pm 1, \pm\frac{1}{2}$; actual: $\frac{1}{2}$
2. Possible: $\pm 1, \pm\frac{1}{3}, \pm\frac{2}{3}, \pm 2$; actual: $\frac{1}{3}$
3. Possible: $\pm 1, \pm 2, \pm 3, \pm 6, \pm\frac{1}{10}, \pm\frac{1}{5}, \pm\frac{1}{2}, \pm\frac{2}{5}, \pm\frac{3}{5}, \pm\frac{6}{5}, \pm\frac{3}{10}, \pm\frac{3}{2}$; actual: $\frac{3}{5}, -\frac{1}{2}, -2$
4. Possible: $\pm 1, \pm\frac{1}{2}, \pm\frac{1}{3}, \pm\frac{1}{6}, \pm\frac{1}{9}, \pm\frac{1}{18}$; actual: $\frac{1}{2}, \frac{1}{3}$
5. Possible: $\pm 1, \pm 2, \pm 3, \pm 4, \pm 6, \pm 8, \pm 12, \pm 16, \pm 24, \pm 48, \pm\frac{1}{3}, \pm\frac{2}{3}, \pm\frac{4}{3}, \pm\frac{8}{3}, \pm\frac{16}{3}$; actual: none
6. Possible: $0, \pm 1, \pm\frac{1}{2}, \pm\frac{1}{3}, \pm\frac{1}{4}, \pm\frac{1}{6}, \pm\frac{1}{12}$; actual: $0, -\frac{1}{3}, \frac{1}{2}, -\frac{1}{2}$
7. (c) They are reciprocals of each other.

Quiz

Find all the rational zeros of each of the following polynomials.

1. $4x^3 - 4x^2 - x + 1$ (ans: $\frac{1}{2}, -\frac{1}{2}, 1$)
2. $x^2 - 7 + 4\sqrt{3}$ (ans: None)
3. $9x^4 - 28x^2 + 3$ (ans: $\frac{1}{3}, -\frac{1}{3}$)
4. $x^5 + x^4 - 5x^3 - 5x^2 + 6x + 6$ (ans: -1)

Exercises for Discussion

In Exercises 1–6, list the possible rational zeros of each integral polynomial. Then find which actually are zeros of the polynomial.

1. $2x^3 + x^2 + x - 1$
2. $3x^3 + 5x^2 + 4x - 2$
3. $10x^3 + 19x^2 - 5x - 6$
4. $18x^3 - 21x^2 + 8x - 1$
5. $3x^3 - 13x^2 + 52x - 48$
6. $12x^4 + 4x^3 - 3x^2 - x$

7. (a) Find the zeros of $2x^3 + 5x^2 - x - 6$. $-2, \frac{-3}{2}, 1$
   (b) Find the zeros of $2 + 5x - x^2 - 6x^3$. $\frac{-1}{2}, \frac{-2}{3}, 1$
   (c) Compare the zeros of the polynomials in parts (a) and (b).
   (d) If the zeros of $4x^3 + 3x^2 - 16x - 12$ are -2, $-\frac{3}{4}$, and 2, what do you expect the zeros of $4 + 3x - 16x^2 - 12x^3$ will be? Check to determine whether your answers are correct. $\frac{-1}{2}, \frac{-4}{3}, \frac{1}{2}$
8. What relation do you think the zeros of

$$a_nx^n + a_{n-1}x^{n-1} + \cdots + a_1x + a_0$$

have to the zeros of $a_n + a_{n-1}x + \cdots + a_1x^{n-1} + a_0x^n$?
They will be reciprocals of each other.

Exercises

Find all the rational zeros of each of the following polynomials.

1. $6x^3 - 11x^2 + 7x - 6$ $\frac{3}{2}$
2. $4x^4 - 3x^3 + 12x^2 + 2x + 3$ None
3. $20x^3 - 12x^2 - 3x + 2$ $\frac{-2}{5}, \frac{1}{2}$
4. $14x^4 - 45x^3 + 18x^2 + 12x - 5$ $\frac{-1}{2}, \frac{5}{7}$
5. $3x^3 + 13x^2 + 3x - 4$ -4
6. $2x^3 - 3x^2 + \frac{3}{2}x - \frac{1}{4}$ $\frac{1}{2}$
7. $10x^4 + 19x^3 - 5x^2 + 19x - 15$ $\frac{3}{5}, \frac{-5}{2}$
8. $12x^4 + 13x^3 - x^2 + 13x + 12$ $\frac{-3}{4}, \frac{-4}{3}$
9. $\frac{9}{8}x^4 - 3x^3 - x^2 + 4x + 4$ None
10. $x^4 + 4x^3 + 6x^2 + 4x + 1$ -1
11. $8x^4 - 28x^3 + 18x^2 + 27x - 27$ $-1, \frac{3}{2}$
12. $30x^3 + 49x^2 - 52x - 60$ $-2, \frac{-5}{6}, \frac{6}{5}$
13. $2 - 3x - 12x^2 + 20x^3$ $\frac{-2}{5}, \frac{1}{2}$

▲

14. Prove the rational zero theorem for $p(x) = a_3x^3 + a_2x^2 + a_1x + a_0$.
See Solution Manual.

8–7 IRRATIONALITY OF ROOTS

We can use the rational zero theorem to prove that certain real numbers are irrational. In geometry, you may have used the unique factorization theorem to prove that certain real numbers are irrational. We can also use the rational zero theorem to prove that certain real numbers are irrational. The procedure used in a proof of this type is illustrated below.

Problem 1. Prove that $\sqrt{3}$ is an irrational number.

Solution. Since

$$(\sqrt{3})^2 - 3 = 0,$$

the number $\sqrt{3}$ is a zero of the integral polynomial

$$x^2 - 3.$$

According to the rational zero theorem, the only possible rational zeros of this polynomial are

$$\pm 1 \quad \text{and} \quad \pm 3.$$

Not one of these four numbers is a zero of $x^2 - 3$. Therefore, the polynomial $x^2 - 3$ has no rational zeros. Hence, if $x^2 - 3$ does have real zeros, they must be irrational numbers. We know that $\sqrt{3}$ is a real zero of this polynomial. Consequently, $\sqrt{3}$ is an irrational number.

Problem 2. Find an integral polynomial of degree 3 having the three rational zeros $^-\frac{1}{5}$, $\frac{2}{3}$, and 3.

Solution. The cubic polynomial

$$f(x) = (x + \tfrac{1}{5})(x - \tfrac{2}{3})(x - 3)$$

has the given numbers as zeros, as does the polynomial $15f(x)$:

$$\begin{aligned} 15f(x) &= [5(x + \tfrac{1}{5})][3(x - \tfrac{2}{3})](x - 3) \\ &= (5x + 1)(3x - 2)(x - 3) \\ &= 15x^3 - 52x^2 + 19x + 6. \end{aligned}$$

Thus, $15f(x)$ is an integral polynomial of degree 3 with the given zeros.

8–7 IRRATIONALITY OF ROOTS

Problem 1 should be of interest to the class, as it presents a different way to prove that $\sqrt{3}$ is irrational. With what modifications could this method be used to prove $\sqrt{2}$ is irrational? $\sqrt{5}$? $\sqrt{5} - \sqrt{2}$? (See Problem 3 and Exercise for Discussion 3.)

In situations like that in Problem 2, errors are often made by students who are unable to recall whether the factor corresponding to the zero $^-\frac{1}{5}$ is $x - \frac{1}{5}$ or $x + \frac{1}{5}$. These students may be helped by the following:

If $^-\frac{1}{5}$ is a zero of $p(x)$, then $x = {}^-\frac{1}{5}$, and $x + \frac{1}{5} = 0$.
If $\frac{2}{3}$ is a zero of $p(x)$, then $x = \frac{2}{3}$, and $x - \frac{2}{3} = 0$.
If 3 is a zero of $p(x)$, then $x = 3$, and $x - 3 = 0$.
If these are the only zeros of $p(x)$, then

$$p(x) = (x + \tfrac{1}{5})(x - \tfrac{2}{3})(x - 3),$$

and $15p(x) = 0$ whenever $p(x) = 0$.

Problem 3. Find an integral polynomial having the real number $\sqrt{5} - \sqrt{3}$ as a zero. Prove that $\sqrt{5} - \sqrt{3}$ is an irrational number.

Solution. If we begin with the polynomial $x - (\sqrt{5} - \sqrt{3})$, which has $\sqrt{5} - \sqrt{3}$ as a zero, and multiply it by other polynomials, we shall always get polynomials having $\sqrt{5} - \sqrt{3}$ as a zero. What we must do is multiply it by other polynomials so that the product has integral coefficients. To do this, we obtain differences of squares in the following way.

$$\begin{aligned}(x - \sqrt{5} + \sqrt{3})(x - \sqrt{5} - \sqrt{3}) &= (x - \sqrt{5})^2 - (\sqrt{3})^2 \\ &= x^2 - 2\sqrt{5}x + 5 - 3 \\ &= x^2 - 2\sqrt{5}x + 2\end{aligned}$$

$$\begin{aligned}(x^2 - 2\sqrt{5}x + 2)(x^2 + 2\sqrt{5}x + 2) &= (x^2 + 2)^2 - (2\sqrt{5}x)^2 \\ &= x^4 + 4x^2 + 4 - 20x^2 \\ &= x^4 - 16x^2 + 4\end{aligned}$$

Thus, the integral polynomial

$$g(x) = x^4 - 16x^2 + 4$$

has $\sqrt{5} - \sqrt{3}$ as one of its zeros. Does $g(x)$ have any rational zeros? No, since ± 1, ± 2, and ± 4 are its only possible rational zeros, and not one of these six numbers is a zero. Hence, $\sqrt{5} - \sqrt{3}$ must be an irrational zero of $g(x)$. This proves that $\sqrt{5} - \sqrt{3}$ is an irrational number.

Exercises for Discussion

1. Find an integral polynomial of degree 3 for each of the following sets of zeros.

   (a) $\{2, {}^-2, 3\}$ $x^3 - 3x^2 - 4x + 12$ (b) $\{\frac{1}{2}, \frac{3}{2}, {}^-1\}$ $4x^3 - 4x^2 - 5x + 3$ (c) $\{3, {}^-1, \frac{2}{5}\}$ $5x^3 - 12x^2 - 11x + 6$

2. Find an integral polynomial of degree 4 for each of the following sets of zeros.

   (a) $\{1, 2, 3, 4\}$ $x^4 - 10x^3 + 35x^2 - 50x + 24$ (b) $\{1, \frac{1}{2}, \frac{1}{3}, \frac{1}{4}\}$ $24x^4 - 50x^3 + 35x^2 - 10x + 1$

3. For each of the following numbers, find an integral polynomial which has that number as a zero. Use the rational zero theorem and your polynomial to prove that the given number is irrational.

   (a) $\sqrt{2}$ (b) $\sqrt[3]{2}$ (c) $1 + \sqrt{2}$

Exercises for Discussion

If time is limited, it is suggested that at least Exercises for Discussion 1(b), 2(b), 3(b) and 3(c) be covered.

Answers to Exercise for Discussion 3

3. (a) $x^2 - 2$ has $\sqrt{2}$ for a zero, but its only possible rational zeros are ± 1 and ± 2. Since none of these is a zero, every zero must be irrational. Hence, $\sqrt{2}$, being a zero, is irrational.
   (b) $x^3 - 2$ has $\sqrt[3]{2}$ for a zero; the argument is the same as in (a).
   (c) $x^2 - 2x - 1$ has $1 + \sqrt{2}$ for a zero; the argument is the same as in (a).

Exercises

1. Find an integral polynomial of degree 3 for each of the following sets of zeros.
   $6x^3 - 11x^2 - 12x + 5$ $\quad$ $5x^3 + 12x^2 - 11x - 6$ $\quad$ $12x^3 + x^2 - 6x$
   (a) $\{\frac{1}{3}, -1, \frac{5}{2}\}$ (b) $\{-3, 1, -\frac{2}{5}\}$ (c) $\{\frac{2}{3}, 0, -\frac{3}{4}\}$
2. Find an integral polynomial of degree 4 for each of the following sets of zeros.
   $x^4 - 35x^2 + 90x - 56$ $\quad$ $ax^4 + bx^3 - 4ax^2 - 4bx,\ a \neq 0$
   (a) $\{1, 2, 4, -7\}$ (b) $\{2, 0, -2\}$ (several possibilities)
   (c) $\{-\frac{2}{3}, \frac{2}{3}, \frac{1}{5}, -\frac{1}{5}\}$ $\quad$ $225x^4 - 109x^2 + 4$
   (d) $\{1, -1, \frac{3}{4}, \frac{2}{5}\}$ $\quad$ $20x^4 - 23x^3 - 14x^2 + 23x - 6$
3. Prove that each of the following numbers is irrational.
   (a) $\sqrt{6}$ (b) $\sqrt[3]{13}$ (c) $\sqrt[n]{2}$, n any integer > 1
   See Solution Manual for 3-9 proofs.

△

In Exercises 4–9, for each given real number, find an integral polynomial having that number as a zero. Prove that the given real number is irrational.

4. $3 - \sqrt{5}$ $\quad x^2 - 6x + 4$
5. $\frac{1}{2} + \frac{1}{2}\sqrt{3}$ $\quad 2x^2 - 2x - 1$
6. $\sqrt{2} + \sqrt{3}$ $\quad x^4 - 10x^2 + 1$
7. $\sqrt{7} - \sqrt{2}$ $\quad x^4 - 18x^2 + 25$
8. $2 - \sqrt[3]{3}$ $\quad x^3 - 6x^2 + 12x - 5$
9. $\dfrac{1}{\sqrt[5]{2}}$ $\quad 2x^5 - 1$

8-8 FACTORING RATIONAL POLYNOMIALS

Every positive integer can be factored into a product of prime integers. For example,

$$60 = 2 \times 2 \times 3 \times 5.$$

We recall that an integer n greater than 1 is called a *prime* if n has no divisor d such that $1 < d < n$.

Similarly, every rational polynomial can be factored into a product of prime rational polynomials. A rational polynomial is called *prime* if it has no rational divisor $d(x)$ of positive degree less than the degree of $p(x)$. For example, the rational polynomial

$$p(x) = x^2 + x + 1$$

is prime, because it has no *rational* divisor of positive degree less than 2, that is, of degree 1. It has no rational divisor of degree 1 because it has no rational zero. Every rational polynomial of degree 1 is prime, since it cannot have a divisor of positive degree less than 1 because there is no positive integer less than 1.

Quiz

Find an integral polynomial of degree 3 for each of the following sets of zeros.

1. $\{-3, 3, 1\}$
   (ans: $x^3 - x^2 - 9x + 9$)
2. $\{\frac{1}{4}, -1, \frac{3}{2}\}$
   (ans: $8x^3 - 6x^2 - 11x + 3$)
3. $\{-4, 1, -\frac{2}{3}\}$
   (ans: $3x^3 + 11x^2 - 6x - 8$)
4. $\{\frac{1}{2}, 0, -\frac{1}{3}\}$
   (ans: $6x^3 - x^2 - x$)

8-8 FACTORING RATIONAL POLYNOMIALS

It is suggested that the three problems in this section be covered carefully as they contain a thorough presentation of the factoring of rational polynomials.

Problem 1. Factor the polynomial

$$p(x) = x^3 + 2x^2 - 5x - 6$$

into a product of primes.

Solution. The synthetic division

$$\begin{array}{r|rrrr} 2 & 1 & 2 & {}^-5 & {}^-6 \\ & & 2 & 8 & 6 \\ \hline & 1 & 4 & 3 & 0 \end{array}$$

shows that 2 is a zero of $p(x)$, and therefore, $x - 2$ is a divisor of $p(x)$. Furthermore, it shows that

$$p(x) = (x - 2)(x^2 + 4x + 3).$$

However, $x^2 + 4x + 3$ is not a prime rational polynomial since

$$x^2 + 4x + 3 = (x + 1)(x + 3).$$

Hence, $p(x)$ is factored into a product of prime rational polynomials as follows:

$$p(x) = (x - 2)(x + 1)(x + 3).$$

Problem 2. Factor the following polynomial into a product of primes.

$$f(x) = 2x^3 - x^2 + 13x + 7$$

Solution. The possible rational zeros of $f(x)$ are listed below.

$$\pm 1, \quad \pm 7, \quad \pm \tfrac{1}{2}, \quad \pm \tfrac{7}{2}$$

Clearly, no odd integer can be a zero, because if we let x be an odd integer in $f(x)$, three of the resulting terms are odd integers and one is an even integer. Such a sum must be odd, and hence cannot be zero. Thus, we need not check ± 1 or ± 7. The synthetic division

$$\begin{array}{r|rrrr} {}^-\tfrac{1}{2} & 2 & {}^-1 & 13 & 7 \\ & & {}^-1 & 1 & {}^-7 \\ \hline & 2 & {}^-2 & 14 & 0 \end{array}$$

shows that ${}^-\tfrac{1}{2}$ is a zero of $f(x)$, and therefore, that $x - {}^-\tfrac{1}{2}$ is a factor. Thus,

$$f(x) = (x + \tfrac{1}{2})(2x^2 - 2x + 14). \qquad (1)$$

We can factor the integer 2 out of the polynomial $2x^2 - 2x + 14$ and then multiply 2 and the factor $x + \tfrac{1}{2}$, obtaining first

$$(x + \tfrac{1}{2})(2)(x^2 - x + 7)$$

and then

$$f(x) = (2x + 1)(x^2 - x + 7). \qquad (2)$$

We cannot factor $x^2 - x + 7$ further, since it has no rational zeros. Hence, either (1) or (2) above yields a factorization of $f(x)$ into a product of prime rational polynomials.

Problem 3. Factor the polynomial

$$p(x) = 2x^3 + x - 1$$

into a product of primes.

Solution. The only possible rational zeros of $p(x)$ are ± 1 and $\pm \frac{1}{2}$. We leave it to you to verify that not one of these four numbers is a zero of $p(x)$. Hence, $p(x)$ has no rational divisor of degree 1. Can $p(x)$ have a rational divisor $f(x)$ of degree 2? If it does, then the quotient obtained on dividing $p(x)$ by $f(x)$ is a rational polynomial $g(x)$ of degree 1, and

$$p(x) = f(x)g(x).$$

However, $p(x)$ would then have a rational divisor $g(x)$ of degree 1, contrary to our discovery that $p(x)$ has no rational divisor of degree 1. Therefore, $p(x)$ cannot have a rational divisor of degree 2. Consequently, $p(x)$ is a prime and cannot be factored.

We could factor the polynomial $p(x)$ of Problem 3 as follows:

$$p(x) = 2(x^3 + \tfrac{1}{2}x - \tfrac{1}{2}).$$

However, we are looking for a factorization in which each factor has a positive degree. The factor 2, on the other hand, has degree 0.

Exercises for Discussion

Factor each of the following rational polynomials into a product of rational prime polynomials.

1. $2x^2 + x - 6$ $(2x - 3)(x + 2)$
2. $3x^2 - 5x - 9$ $3x^2 - 5x - 9$
3. $x^2 + 1$ $x^2 + 1$
4. $x^3 + 1$ $(x + 1)(x^2 - x + 1)$
5. $x^3 - 1$ $(x - 1)(x^2 + x + 1)$
6. $x^4 - 1$ $(x^2 + 1)(x - 1)(x + 1)$
7. $2x^3 + 3x^2 - 7x + 6$ $(x + 3)(2x^2 - 3x + 2)$
8. $2x^3 + 5x^2 - 22x + 15$ $(x - 1)(x + 5)(2x - 3)$
9. $x^3 + x^2 + x + 1$ $(x + 1)(x^2 + 1)$
10. $x^3 + 3x^2 + 3x + 1$ $(x + 1)^3$

In order to determine that

$$x^2 - x + 7$$

has no rational zeros, all the possibilities, ± 1, ± 7, may be checked by direct substitution, or the discriminant,

$$(-1)^2 - (4 \cdot 1 \cdot 7) = {}^-27,$$

may be computed, revealing that

$$x^2 - x + 7$$

has complex and not real zeros.

Problem 3 should be examined carefully, particularly the last paragraph.

Exercises for Discussion

If time is limited, it is suggested that at least Exercises for Discussion 2, 7, and 9 be covered.

Quiz

Factor each of the following rational polynomials into a product of rational prime polynomials.

1. $2x^3 - x^2 - x - 3$
   (ans: $(2x - 3)(x^2 + x + 1)$)
2. $x^3 - 7x - 6$
   (ans: $(x + 1)(x + 2)(x - 3)$)
3. $3x^3 - 9x^2 + 27x - 42$
   (ans: $3(x^2 - x + 7)(x - 2)$)
4. $27x^3 - 1$
   (ans: $(3x - 1)(9x^2 + 3x + 1)$)
5. $x^4 - 8x^3 + 24x^2 - 32x + 16$
   (ans: $(x - 2)^4$)

8-9 FURTHER FACTORING

In some courses this section may be omitted, and in others it may be postponed and used for one of the periodic reviews of the course. It also lends itself well to independent study. In order to do the exercises the students should follow exactly the development of the problem in the text.

Quiz

Factor each of the following rational polynomials into a product of rational prime polynomials.

1. $x^4 - 2x^3 - x^2 + 2x + 1$
   (ans: $(x^2 - x - 1)^2$)
2. $x^4 - 4x^3 + 6x^2 - 8x + 8$
   (ans: $(x^2 + 2)(x - 2)^2$)
3. $x^4 + x^3 - 7x^2 - x + 6$
   (ans: $(x - 2)(x + 1)(x + 3)(x - 1)$)
4. $x^4 + 5x^3 + 7x^2 + 5x + 6$
   (ans: $(x^2 + 1)(x + 2)(x + 3)$)

Exercises

Factor each of the following rational polynomials into a product of rational prime polynomials.

1. $3x^3 - 8x^2 + 11x - 10$ $(3x-5)(x^2-x+2)$
2. $x^3 + x^2 - 3$ x^3+x^2-3
3. $x^4 - 11x^3 + 30x^2 - 8x$ $x(x-4)(x^2-7x+2)$
4. $2x^4 - 17x^2 - 9$ $(2x^2+1)(x-3)(x+3)$
5. $16x^4 - 14x^3 - 15x^2$ $x^2(8x+5)(2x-3)$
6. $6x^4 + 7x^3 + 12x^2 + x - 2$ $(3x-1)(2x+1)(x^2+x+2)$
7. $4x^3 - 20x^2 + 17x - 4$ $(2x-1)^2(x-4)$
8. $3x^4 - 20x^3 + 13x^2 - 6x$ $x(x-6)(3x^2-2x+1)$
9. $x^4 - 5x^2 + 6$ $(x^2-3)(x^2-2)$
10. $x^4 + x^3 - 2x^2 + x - 1$ $(x-1)(x^3+2x^2+1)$
11. $x^4 + 8x^3 + 24x^2 + 32x + 16$ $(x+2)^4$
12. $15x^4 + 9x^2 - 6$ $3(5x^2-2)(x^2+1)$
13. $9x^3 + 21x^2 - 17x + 3$ $(3x-1)^2(x+3)$
14. $x^4 + 1$ x^4+1
15. $x^5 + 1$ $(x+1)(x^4-x^3+x^2-x+1)$
16. $64x^6 - 1$ $(2x-1)(2x+1)(4x^2+2x+1)\cdot(4x^2-2x+1)$
17. $8x^3 - 125$ $(2x-5)(4x^2+10x+25)$
18. $27x^3 + 1$ $(3x+1)(9x^2-3x+1)$

8-9 FURTHER FACTORING

If a rational polynomial has degree 4 or more, then it is more difficult to factor it into a product of primes. This is illustrated below.

Problem. Factor the polynomial

$$g(x) = x^4 + 2x^3 - 8x^2 + 18x - 9$$

into a product of primes.

Solution. The possible rational zeros are ± 1, ± 3, and ± 9. You can quickly verify that not one of these integers is a zero. Hence, $g(x)$ has no linear rational factors. This does not necessarily mean that $g(x)$ is a prime rational polynomial, because it is possible that $g(x) = p(x)q(x)$, where $p(x)$ and $q(x)$ are prime rational polynomials of degree 2. Since the coefficient of x^4 in $g(x)$ is 1, we might try polynomials of the form $x^2 + ax + b$ and $x^2 + cx + d$ to see whether there are integers a, b, c, and d such that

$$g(x) = (x^2 + ax + b)(x^2 + cx + d).$$

Since

$$(x^2 + ax + b)(x^2 + cx + d)$$
$$= x^4 + (a + c)x^3 + (ac + b + d)x^2 + (ad + bc)x + bd,$$

we must have

$$x^4 + (a + c)x^3 + (ac + b + d)x^2 + (ad + bc)x + bd$$
$$= x^4 + 2x^3 - 8x^2 + 18x - 9.$$

These polynomials are equal if, and only if, corresponding coefficients are equal. Thus, the integers a, b, c, and d must be solutions of the following system of equations.

$$\begin{cases} a + c = 2 \\ ac + b + d = {}^-8 \\ ad + bc = 18 \\ bd = {}^-9 \end{cases}$$

If b and d are integers and $bd = {}^-9$, then, assuming b to be the positive integer, we must have

$$b = 1,\ d = {}^-9; \quad \text{or} \quad b = 3,\ d = {}^-3; \quad \text{or} \quad b = 9,\ d = {}^-1.$$

When we give these values to b and d as indicated below, then the first three equations of the system above reduce to the following equations.

$b = 1,\ d = {}^-9$ $\quad$ $b = 3,\ d = {}^-3$ $\quad$ $b = 9,\ d = {}^-1$

$$\begin{cases} a + c = 2 \\ ac = 0 \\ {}^-9a + c = 18 \end{cases} \qquad \begin{cases} a + c = 2 \\ ac = {}^-8 \\ {}^-a + c = 6 \end{cases} \qquad \begin{cases} a + c = 2 \\ ac = {}^-16 \\ {}^-a + 9c = 18 \end{cases}$$

The systems of linear equations taken from each set of equations above may be solved in the following way.

$$\begin{cases} a + c = 2 \\ {}^-9a + c = 18 \end{cases} \qquad \begin{cases} a + c = 2 \\ {}^-a + c = 6 \end{cases} \qquad \begin{cases} a + c = 2 \\ {}^-a + 9c = 18 \end{cases}$$

$${}^-10a = 16 \qquad 2c = 8 \qquad 10c = 20$$

$$a = \tfrac{{}^-8}{5},\ c = \tfrac{18}{5} \qquad c = 4,\ a = {}^-2 \qquad c = 2,\ a = 0$$

In only one of three cases where values are given to b and d is the value of ac what it should be, and that is the middle system. There $ac = {}^-8$. Thus, $a = {}^-2$, $b = 3$, $c = 4$, $d = {}^-3$ is a solution of our system of equations, and

$$g(x) = (x^2 - 2x + 3)(x^2 + 4x - 3)$$

is a factorization of $g(x)$ into a product of prime rational polynomials.

*8-10 IRRATIONAL ZEROS

Some students have difficulty understanding why the graph of $y = p(x)$ crosses the x-axis at the zeros of $p(x)$. In order to help make this more clear, you could take

$$y = x^2 - 5x + 4$$

as an example. To find the x-intercepts of this graph, let $y = 0$, obtaining

$$0 = x^2 - 5x + 4.$$

Now the solution set is being found for the equation

$$x^2 - 5x + 4 = 0,$$

which is the same as the zeros of the polynomial $x^2 - 5x + 4$. The points (1, 0) and (4, 0) are on the graph, the solution set of the quadratic equation (and the zeros of the polynomial) is $\{1, 4\}$.

The assumptions here should be stated clearly. It can be concluded that if $p(a) < 0$ and $p(b) > 0$, then for some x between a and b, say $x = r$, $p(r) = 0$, because $p(x)$ has been restricted to polynomial functions. The polynomial functions happen to be continuous over the entire real number system; hence, $p(x)$ is defined for every real number x, but, in addition, when x is close to any number a, it is also known that $p(x)$ is close to $p(a)$. For a function continuous over an interval, say from $x = 1$ to $x = 2$, it is proved in analysis that if $p(1) = {}^-3$ and $p(2) = {}^+4$, then, as x runs through all numbers from 1 to 2, $p(x)$ will run through all values from ${}^-3$ to ${}^+4$ at least once. Of course, 0 is between ${}^-3$ and 4. Hence, $p(x) = 0$ for some x between 1 and 2.

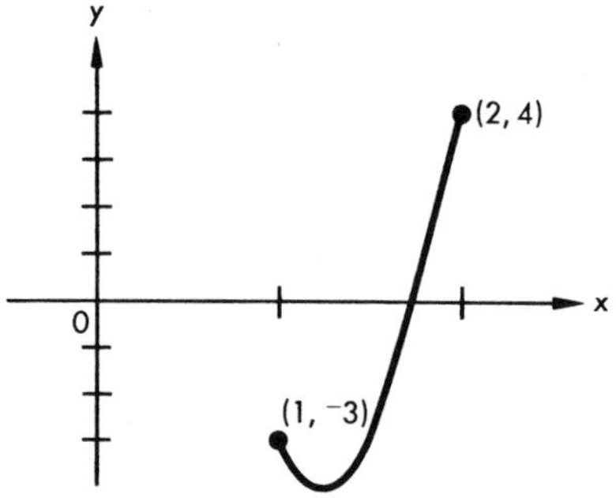

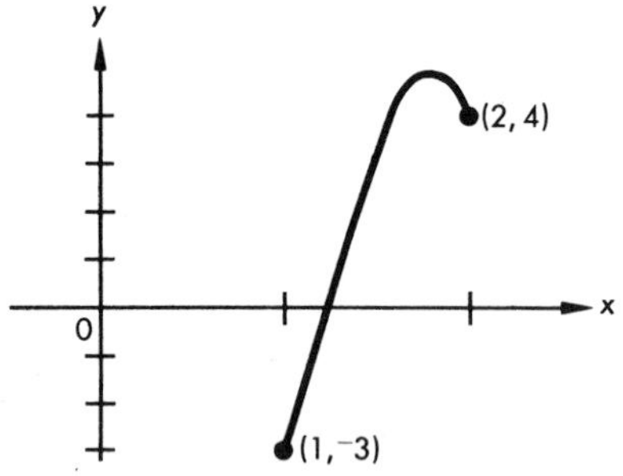

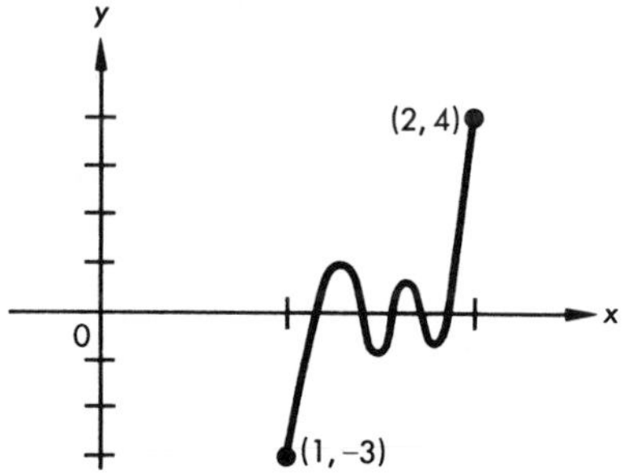

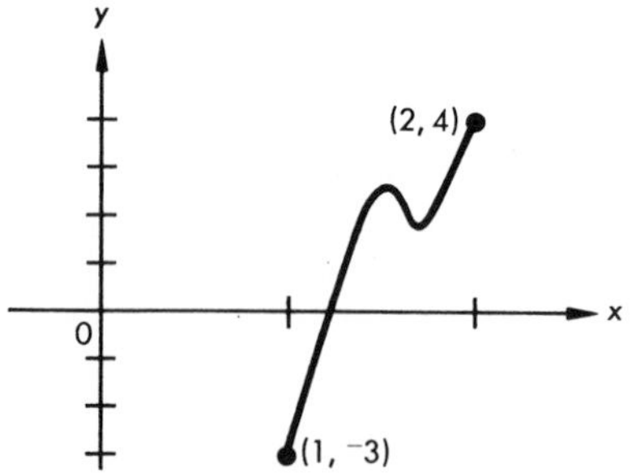

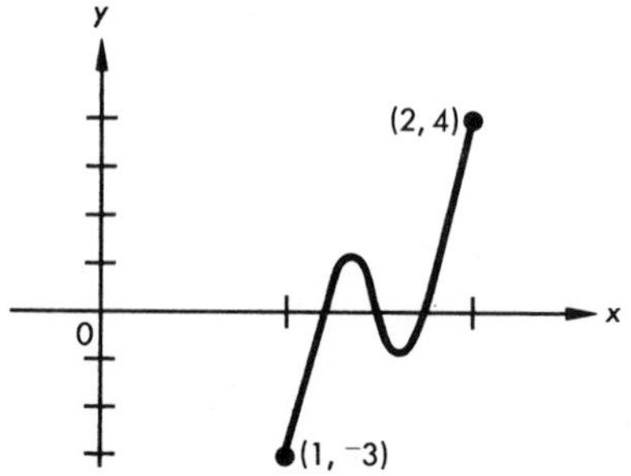

Exercises for Discussion

Factor each of the following rational polynomials into a product of rational prime polynomials.

1. $x^4 + 3x^3 + 4x^2 + 9x + 3$ $(x^2+3x+1)(x^2+3)$
2. $x^4 - x^3 - 13x^2 + x + 12$ $(x+1)(x-1)(x+3)(x-4)$

Exercises

Factor each of the following rational polynomials into a product of rational prime polynomials.

1. $x^4 - x^3 - 8x^2 + 6x + 8$ $(x^2-2x-2)(x^2+x-4)$
2. $x^4 + 2x^3 + 3x^2 + 2x + 1$ $(x^2+x+1)^2$
3. $x^4 + 4x^3 - 7x^2 - 22x + 24$ $(x-1)(x-2)(x+3)(x+4)$
4. $x^4 - 3x^3 + 4x^2 - 8x - 24$ $(x^2-2x-4)(x^2-x+6)$
5. $x^4 + 4x^3 - 16x^2 + 20x - 105$ $(x^2+5)(x-3)(x+7)$
6. $x^4 - 9x^2 - 4x + 12$ $(x-3)(x-1)(x+2)^2$
7. $x^4 + 7x^3 + x^2 - 63x - 90$ $(x+5)(x+2)(x+3)(x-3)$
8. $x^4 + 3x^2 + 2$ $(x^2+1)(x^2+2)$
9. $x^4 + 8x^3 + 16x^2 + 8x + 15$ $(x^2+1)(x+3)(x+5)$
10. $x^4 - 4x^3 - x^2 + 16x - 12$ $(x-1)(x-3)(x+2)(x-2)$

*8–10 IRRATIONAL ZEROS

Having developed a method for finding all rational zeros of a rational polynomial, we shall now try to find irrational zeros of a polynomial. Naturally, an *irrational zero* is a zero that is an irrational number. We can determine all the zeros of a quadratic polynomial by means of the quadratic formula. There are comparable formulas for finding all the zeros of a cubic or quartic polynomial, but we shall not present them here. This is as far as we can go, however, since it can be proved that there are no algebraic formulas for finding all the zeros of polynomials of degree 5 and higher. It is also true that there are no methods of the type described in the preceding two sections for determining irrational zeros of polynomials. For practical applications, it is often necessary to approximate the irrational zeros of a polynomial. There are many ways of doing this, one of which consists of the following steps.

The polynomial

$$p(x) = x^3 - 5x + 1$$

does not have any rational zeros. If we graph the polynomial equation $y = x^3 - 5x + 1$, we see that it probably has irrational zeros. This equation is graphed in the neighborhood of the origin in Fig. 8–1, with the aid of the following table of values.

x	$^-3$	$^-2\frac{1}{2}$	$^-2$	$^-1\frac{1}{2}$	$^-1$	$^-\frac{1}{2}$	0	$\frac{1}{2}$	1	$1\frac{1}{2}$	2	$2\frac{1}{2}$	3
y	$^-11$	$^-2\frac{1}{8}$	3	$5\frac{1}{8}$	5	$3\frac{3}{8}$	1	$^-1\frac{3}{8}$	$^-3$	$^-3\frac{1}{8}$	$^-1$	$4\frac{1}{8}$	13

The zeros of $p(x)$ are the x-coordinates of the points having y-coordinates 0; that is, the zeros of $p(x)$ are the x-coordinates of the points at which the graph intersects the x-axis.

If we assume that the graph of the equation $y = p(x)$ is a smooth connected curve such as that drawn in Fig. 8–1, then it is evident that there are three real zeros of $p(x)$, denoted by r_1, r_2, and r_3 in the figure. From the graph, it is apparent that

$$^-\tfrac{5}{2} < r_1 < {^-2}, \quad 0 < r_2 < \tfrac{1}{2}, \quad 2 < r_3 < \tfrac{5}{2}.$$

Since $p(x)$ has no rational zeros, each of the numbers r_1, r_2, and r_3 must be irrational. The inequalities above give us rational approximations of these zeros.

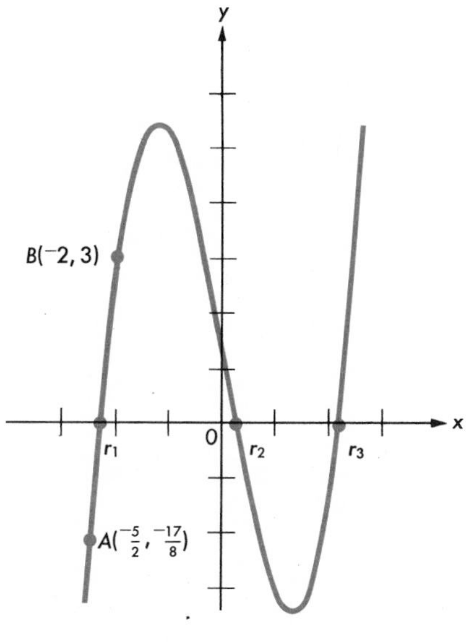

FIGURE 8–1

We can actually determine the approximate location of each zero by looking only at the table of values above. *Thus, there must be a zero between two numbers if the values of $p(x)$ at these two numbers have opposite sign.* Hence, it is clear that there is a zero r_1 of $p(x)$ between $^-\frac{5}{2}$ and $^-2$, since $p(^-\frac{5}{2}) < 0$ and $p(^-2) > 0$; and there must be a zero r_2 of $p(x)$ between 0 and $\frac{1}{2}$, since $p(0) > 0$ and $p(\frac{1}{2}) < 0$. Similarly, there is a third zero r_3 and $2 < r_3 < \frac{5}{2}$, since $p(2) < 0$ and $p(\frac{5}{2}) > 0$. Graphically, this means that the curve must cross the x-axis between a point of the curve above the x-axis and a point of the curve below the x-axis.

Each of the irrational zeros of the polynomial $p(x)$ above may be approximated more accurately by using linear interpolation. For example, let us find a more accurate rational approximation of r_1. The straight line joining the points $A(^-\frac{5}{2}, {^-\frac{17}{8}})$ and $B(^-2, 3)$ of Fig. 8–1 has slope

$$\frac{^-\frac{17}{8} - 3}{^-\frac{5}{2} + 2}, \quad \text{or} \quad \frac{41}{4}.$$

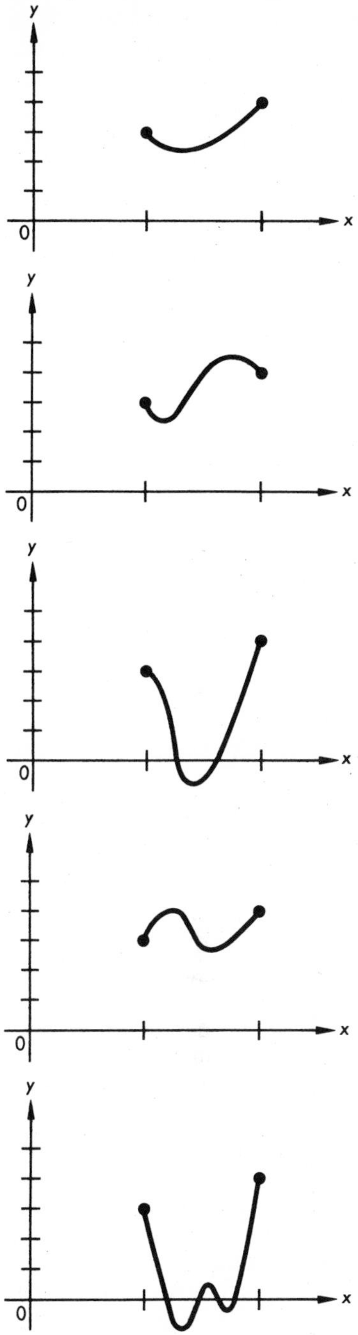

The graph of a continuous function is a smooth connected curve. You could have the class draw a smooth connected curve over the interval from 1 to 2, assuming that $p(1) = {^-3}$ and $p(2) = {^+4}$. It should be remembered that $p(x)$ is a function, and hence for each x there is a unique $p(x)$. Some possibilities are drawn on page 350. Now some smooth connected curves could be drawn over the same interval, assuming that $p(1) = 3$ and $p(2) = 4$. Some possibilities are presented on page 351. The possible number of zeros of $p(x)$ between $p(1)$ and $p(2)$ may be discussed, using these graphs.

The idea of linear interpolation is simple. The execution of the idea is tedious. The work may be done as a classroom project, where arithmetic can be checked every few minutes.

Exercises, page 353

In Exercise 2, where

$$p(x) = 6x^4 + 11x^3 - 4x - 1,$$

the student, unless alerted, would conclude that since $p(0) = {}^-1$ and $p(^-1) = {}^-2$, $p(x)$ must have no zero between $^-1$ and 0. However, in the next part of the exercise he would discover that there are actually two zeros, since

$$p(^-\tfrac{1}{3}) = 0$$

and

$$p(^-\tfrac{1}{2}) = 0.$$

Exercise 3 should be covered right after Exercise 2. You may wish to introduce the drawing of curves suggested earlier in the section after the student has completed Exercises 2 and 3. Some students learn more readily by being helped after having met with difficulty rather than by being taught how to avoid the difficulty beforehand.

If a student wants a formula for these zeros, you could ask him to do a report on Cardan's formulas for the cubic and quartic. Interesting material on this subject can be found in most books on the history of mathematics. The student could also investigate the question of formulas for the quintic by looking under the names of Galois and Abel.

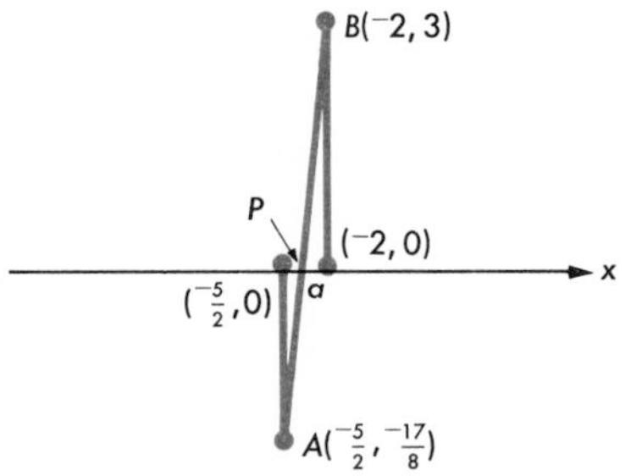

FIGURE 8–2

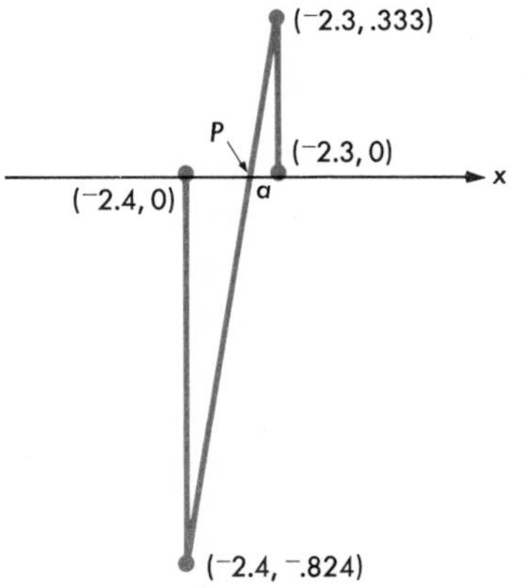

FIGURE 8–3

Figure 8–2 shows an enlarged picture of segment $\overline{AB}$. We choose as our next approximation of r_1 the coordinate of P, the point of intersection of segment $\overline{AB}$ and the x-axis. Since the slope of segment $\overline{PB}$ is $3/a$, where a is as indicated in Fig. 8–2, we must have

$$\frac{3}{a} = \frac{41}{4} \quad \text{and} \quad a = \frac{12}{41}, \quad \text{or .3 approximately.}$$

Hence, the x-coordinate of P is approximately $^-2 - .3$, or $^-2.3$. Therefore,

$$r_1 \doteq {}^-2.3.$$

To obtain a more accurate approximation of r_1, repeat this process using numbers closer to r_1.

$$p(^-2.4) = {}^-.824, \quad p(^-2.3) = .333$$

Hence, $^-2.4 < r_1 < {}^-2.3$. Now the line segment joining the points $(^-2.4, {}^-.824)$ and $(^-2.3, .333)$ has slope

$$\frac{^-.824 - .333}{^-2.4 + 2.3}, \quad \text{or } 11.57.$$

According to Fig. 8–3,

$$\frac{.333}{a} = 11.57 \quad \text{and} \quad a = \frac{.333}{11.57}, \quad \text{or } a \doteq .03.$$

Hence, $r_1 \doteq {}^-2.3 - .03$, or $r_1 \doteq {}^-2.33$.

You undoubtedly see how we could continue this process by computing $P(^-2.34)$ and $P(^-2.33)$ and once more using linear interpolation.

Exercises

$^{-}.9, .7, 3.1$; see Solution Manual.

1. Find one-decimal-place approximations of the irrational zeros of $p(x)$, given that $p(x) = x^3 - 3x^2 - x + 2$. Sketch the graph of $p(x)$.
2. (a) If $p(x) = 6x^4 + 11x^3 - 4x - 1$, find $p(0)$ $^{-}1$ and $p(^{-}1)$ $^{-}2$.
   (b) Does $p(x)$ have a zero r such that $^{-}1 < r < 0$? No
   (c) Find $p(^{-}\frac{1}{3})$ 0 and $p(^{-}\frac{1}{2})$ 0. Did you answer part (b) correctly?
3. Suppose that $p(x)$ is a real polynomial, $p(a) < 0$ and $p(b) > 0$.
   (a) Does $p(x)$ have exactly one real zero between a and b? Not necessarily
   (b) Does $p(x)$ have at least one real zero between a and b? Yes
   (c) Can $p(x)$ have an even number of real zeros between a and b? No
   (d) Can $p(x)$ have an odd number of real zeros between a and b? Yes

In Exercises 4–9 find a one-decimal-place approximation of the irrational zeros of each polynomial.

4. $x^3 + x - 1$ .7
5. $x^3 + 3x^2 + 1$ $^{-}3.1$
6. $x^3 - 2$ 1.3
7. $x^3 + 3x^2 + 4x + 5$ $^{-}2.2$
8. $x^4 - 4x^3 + 2$ .8, 4.0
9. $32x^3 - 36x^2 + 12x - 1$ All zeros are rational.
10. Find a two-decimal-place approximation of the real zero of $x^3 + x - 3$. 1.21
11. Find a two-decimal-place approximation of the positive real zero of $x^3 - 3x^2 - x - 6$. 3.71
12. Find a two-decimal-place approximation of the negative real zero of $x^3 + 3x^2 - 3x + 2$. $^{-}3.90$

*8-11 COMPLEX ZEROS OF REAL POLYNOMIALS

In this section, we shall discuss the complex zeros of a *real polynomial*, that is, of a polynomial whose coefficients are real numbers. According to the quadratic formula, every real quadratic polynomial has zeros. However, its zeros need not be real numbers. For example, the polynomial

$$x^2 - 4x + 5$$

has complex zeros

$$\frac{4 + \sqrt{-4}}{2} \quad \text{and} \quad \frac{4 - \sqrt{-4}}{2},$$

or

$$2 + i \quad \text{and} \quad 2 - i.$$

Quiz

Find a one-decimal-place approximation of the irrational zeros of each polynomial.

1. $x^2 + x - 1$ (ans: $^{-}1.6$, 0.6)
2. $x^3 - x^2 - 2x + 2$ (ans: $^{-}1.4$, 1.4)
3. $x^3 - 3$ (ans: 1.4)
4. $x^4 + x^3 + x^2 - 1$ (ans: .7)

***8-11 COMPLEX ZEROS OF REAL POLYNOMIALS**

The theorem of Gauss referred to on the following page is the so-called "fundamental theorem of algebra."

Several specific examples should be done with pairs of complex numbers that are conjugates of each other in order to illustrate the concepts stated on page 355 before the proof is actually tried. For example, if the numbers are $5 + 2i$ and $3 - 4i$, their sum is $8 - 2i$, and the conjugate of their sum is $8 + 2i$. On the other hand, their respective conjugates are $5 - 2i$ and

$3 + 4i$, and the sum of their conjugates is $8 + 2i$. Hence, the conjugate of the sum of the two complex numbers is the sum of their conjugates. Finally, you could have the class develop the following general proof and give reasons for each step.

$$\begin{aligned} &\overline{(a + bi) + (c + di)} \\ &\qquad = \overline{(a + c) + (b + d)i} \\ &\qquad = (a + c) - (b + d)i \\ &\qquad = (a - bi) + (c - di) \\ &\qquad = \overline{a + bi} + \overline{c + di} \end{aligned}$$

Furthermore, the product of $5 + 2i$ and $3 - 4i$ is $23 - 14i$, and the conjugate of their product is

$$23 + 14i.$$

However, the product of their respective conjugates is

$$(5 - 2i)(3 + 4i) \text{ or } 23 + 14i.$$

Hence, the conjugate of the product of the two complex numbers is the product of the conjugates. Again, let the class develop the following general proof, giving reasons for each step.

$$\begin{aligned} &\overline{(a + bi) \cdot (c + di)} \\ &\qquad = \overline{(ac - bd) + (bc + ad)i} \\ &\qquad = (ac - bd) - (bc + ad)i \\ &\qquad = (a - bi)(c - di) \\ &\qquad = \overline{a + bi} \cdot \overline{c + di} \end{aligned}$$

Since this polynomial has zeros $2 + i$ and $2 - i$, it has factors

$$x - (2 + i) \quad \text{and} \quad x - (2 - i)$$

according to the factor theorem:

$$x^2 - 4x + 5 = (x - 2 - i)(x - 2 + i).$$

One of the famous theorems of algebra, first proved in 1799 by the renowned German mathematician Gauss, states that *every polynomial of degree* 1 *or more has a zero.* Of course, the zeros of a polynomial need not be real numbers, as the example above shows. We shall not prove Gauss' theorem in this book, but we shall assume its truth.

If a real quadratic polynomial has two zeros, then it follows from the quadratic formula that both zeros are either real numbers or *conjugate complex numbers.* In the example above, $2 + i$ and $2 - i$ are conjugate complex numbers. Does a similar statement hold for real polynomials of degree higher than 2? Before we can answer this question, we must recall certain properties of conjugate complex numbers.

The complex number $a + bi$ has $a - bi$ as its conjugate. Let us denote the conjugate of each complex number r by $\bar{r}$. Thus,

$$\text{if } r = a + bi, \text{ then } \bar{r} = a - bi.$$

We are assuming, of course, that a and b are real numbers. For example,

$$\text{if } r = 5 + 4i, \text{ then } \bar{r} = 5 - 4i.$$

and

$$\text{if } s = 7 - 2i, \text{ then } \bar{s} = 7 + 2i.$$

Note that for the complex numbers r and s,

$$r + s = 12 + 2i, \quad \bar{r} + \bar{s} = 12 - 2i.$$

In other words, $\bar{r} + \bar{s}$ is the conjugate of $r + s$. Also,

$$\begin{aligned} rs &= (35 - 8i^2) + (28i - 10i), \quad \text{or } 43 + 18i. \\ \bar{r}\bar{s} &= (35 - 8i^2) + (^-28i + 10i), \text{ or } 43 - 18i. \end{aligned}$$

Hence, $\bar{r}\bar{s}$ is the conjugate of rs.

What we just demonstrated for two particular complex numbers can be shown to be valid for any two complex numbers. We state this result as follows.

If r and s are complex numbers, then the conjugate of their sum is the sum of their conjugates, and the conjugate of their product is the product of their conjugates. In symbols,

$$\overline{r+s} = \bar{r} + \bar{s} \quad \textit{and} \quad \overline{rs} = \bar{r}\bar{s}.$$

Given three complex numbers r, s, and t, we have

$$\overline{r+s+t} = (\overline{r+s}) + \bar{t} = \bar{r} + \bar{s} + \bar{t}.$$

A similar rule is valid for products. In general, it may be proved that *the conjugate of the sum of n complex numbers is the sum of their conjugates, and the conjugate of the product of n complex numbers is the product of their conjugates.* Consequently,

$$(\bar{r})^n = \overline{r^n}$$

for every complex number r and every positive integer n. The conjugate of a real number a (or $a + 0i$) is just a (or $a - 0i$). With these facts in mind, we can now prove the following theorem.

If p(x) is a real polynomial and if r is a complex zero of p(x), then $\bar{r}$ is also a zero of p(x).

To prove this, let $p(x) = a_nx^n + a_{n-1}x^{n-1} + \cdots + a_1x + a_0$, where the coefficients are real numbers. If t is any complex number, then

$$\begin{aligned} p(t) &= a_nt^n + a_{n-1}t^{n-1} + \cdots + a_1t + a_0, \\ \overline{p(t)} &= \overline{a_nt^n + a_{n-1}t^{n-1} + \cdots + a_1t + a_0} \\ &= \overline{a_nt^n} + \overline{a_{n-1}t^{n-1}} + \cdots + \overline{a_1t} + \overline{a_0} \\ &= \overline{a_n}\,\overline{t^n} + \overline{a_{n-1}}\,\overline{t^{n-1}} + \cdots + \overline{a_1}\,\overline{t} + \overline{a_0} \\ &= \bar{a}_n(\bar{t})^n + \bar{a}_{n-1}(\bar{t})^{n-1} + \cdots + \bar{a}_1\bar{t} + \bar{a}_0. \end{aligned}$$

However, $\bar{a}_n = a_n$, $\bar{a}_{n-1} = a_{n-1}$, and so on, since the coefficients of $p(x)$ are real numbers. Hence,

$$\overline{p(t)} = a_n(\bar{t})^n + a_{n-1}(\bar{t})^{n-1} + \cdots + a_1\bar{t} + a_0.$$

Before covering the proof of the property that complex zeros of real polynomials occur in conjugate pairs, you may wish to present the special case that if $1 + i$ is a zero of $x^2 - 2x + 2$, then $1 - i$ is also a zero of

$$x^2 - 2x + 2.$$

It may be seen by substitution that if

$$p(x) = x^2 - 2x + 2,$$

then $p(1 + i) = 0$. Since $\bar{0} = 0$, $\overline{p(1+i)} = 0$. Now

$$\begin{aligned} &\overline{p(1+i)} \\ &= \overline{(1+i)^2 - 2(1+i) + 2} \\ &= \overline{(1+i)(1+i)} + \overline{^-2} \cdot \overline{(1+i)} \\ &\quad + \bar{2} \\ &= \overline{(1+i)} \cdot \overline{(1+i)} + (^-2)(1-i) \\ &\quad + 2 \\ &= (1-i)^2 - 2(1-i) + 2 \\ &= p(1-i). \end{aligned}$$

Hence,

$$p(1-i) = 0$$

and $1 - i$ is a zero of $p(x)$. Now the proof may be tried in general.

The right side of this equation is $p(\bar{t})$, that is, the value of the polynomial $p(x)$ at the complex number $\bar{t}$. Thus, we have proved that

$$\overline{p(t)} = p(\bar{t}).$$

This equation is true for every complex number t and, in particular, for each complex zero r of $p(x)$. Hence,

$$\overline{p(r)} = p(\bar{r}).$$

Since $p(r) = 0$ and $\bar{0} = 0$, we know that $\overline{p(r)} = 0$. Hence, $p(\bar{r}) = 0$ by the equation above. This result proves that $\bar{r}$ also is a zero of $p(x)$ and thus, proves the theorem. This theorem is sometimes stated in an alternative form:

Complex zeros of real polynomials occur in conjugate pairs.

To illustrate this theorem, consider the real polynomial

$$p(x) = 2x^3 - 3x^2 + 2x + 2.$$

Both $1 + i$ and $1 - i$ are zeros of $p(x)$, as shown in the following synthetic division.

$$\begin{array}{r|rrrr} 1+i & 2 & ^-3 & 2 & 2 \\ & & 2+2i & ^-3+i & ^-2 \\ \hline & 2 & ^-1+2i & ^-1+i & 0 \end{array}$$

$$\begin{array}{r|rrrr} 1-i & 2 & ^-3 & 2 & 2 \\ & & 2-2i & ^-3-i & ^-2 \\ \hline & 2 & ^-1-2i & ^-1-i & 0 \end{array}$$

Thus, both $x - (1 + i)$ and $x - (1 - i)$ are divisors of $p(x)$. Since they are two different divisors of $p(x)$ of degree 1, it follows that their product is also a divisor of $p(x)$. Thus,

$$[x - (1 + i)][x - (1 - i)], \quad \text{or } [(x - 1) - i][(x - 1) + i],$$

is a divisor of $p(x)$. This product equals $(x - 1)^2 - i^2$, or

$$x^2 - 2x + 2.$$

We note that the product of these two complex polynomials is a real polynomial. You can easily verify that

$$p(x) = (x^2 - 2x + 2)(2x + 1).$$

You may wish to present to the students the fact that numbers of the form $a + b\sqrt{n}$, where a and b are integers and n is a square-free integer, are called quadratic integers. If $r = a + b\sqrt{n}$ is a quadratic integer, then

$$\bar{r} = a - b\sqrt{n}$$

is called the conjugate of r. You may wish to have your better students use the methods of this section to show that if $p(x)$ is an integral polynomial having a quadratic integer r as a zero, then $\bar{r}$ also is a zero of $p(x)$.

The following is a procedure for verifying that

$$p(x) = (x^2 - 2x + 2) \cdot (2x + 1).$$

Since

$$p(x) = 2x^3 - 3x^2 + 2x + 2,$$

and $x^2 - 2x + 2$ divides $p(x)$ exactly, we know that

$$(2x^3 - 3x^2 + 2x + 2) = (x^2 - 2x + 2)(ax + b).$$

If $ax^3 = 2x^3$, $a = 2$; if $2 \cdot b = 2$, $b = 1$; so $ax + b$ must equal $2x + 1$. Therefore,

$$p(x) = (x^2 - 2x + 2)(2x + 1).$$

The work may be checked by testing $^-\frac{1}{2}$ in

$$p(x) = 2x^3 - 3x^2 + 2x + 2$$

by synthetic division or substitution.

Thus, the polynomial $p(x)$ has two complex zeros, $1 + i$ and $1 - i$, and one real zero, $^{-}\frac{1}{2}$.

If $p(x)$ is any real polynomial of degree 2 or more, having a complex zero $r = a + bi$, $b \neq 0$, then both r and $\bar{r}$ ($\bar{r} = a - bi$, $b \neq 0$) are zeros of $p(x)$ by the theorem above. Therefore, $x - r$ and $x - \bar{r}$ are distinct divisors of $p(x)$ by the factor theorem. Hence, their product

$$(x - r)(x - \bar{r}) = x^2 - (r + \bar{r})x + r\bar{r},$$

or

$$[x - (a + bi)][x - (a - bi)] = x^2 - [(a + bi) + (a - bi)]x + (a + bi)(a - bi),$$

is a divisor of $p(x)$.

Since $r + \bar{r} = 2a$ and $r\bar{r} = a^2 + b^2$, the polynomial

$$f_1(x) = x^2 - 2ax + (a^2 + b^2)$$

is a *real polynomial.*

The polynomial $f_1(x)$ is a *prime real polynomial,* since it has no real factors of degree 1. Since $f_1(x)$ is a divisor of $p(x)$, and the quotient of a real polynomial by a real polynomial is real, we have

$$p(x) = f_1(x)q(x)$$

for some real polynomial $q(x)$.

If the real polynomial $q(x)$ is of positive degree, then it has a zero s by Gauss' theorem. If s is a real number, then $x - s$ is a real divisor of $q(x)$; if s is not real, then $q(x)$ has a real quadratic divisor $(x - s)(x - \bar{s})$. Thus,

$$q(x) = f_2(x)q_1(x),$$

where $f_2(x)$ is either $x - s$ or $(x - s)(x - \bar{s})$, whichever is real, and

$$p(x) = f_1(x)f_2(x)q_1(x).$$

We may continue this process with the real polynomial $q_1(x)$, provided that its degree is positive. Eventually, we will be able to factor $p(x)$ in the form

$$p(x) = f_1(x)f_2(x) \cdots f_n(x),$$

where each of the polynomials $f_1(x), f_2(x), \ldots, f_n(x)$ is real and of degree 1 or 2. Furthermore, each of these factors is a prime real polynomial in the sense that it cannot be further factored as a product of real polynomials of positive degree. This establishes the following property of real polynomials.

It is recommended that the material presented on this page be carefully discussed in class. A specific case may be used, such as

$$p(x) = x^5 + 2x^4 - 9x^3 - 8x^2 - 22x - 24,$$
$$p(x) = (x - 3)(x^4 + 5x^3 + 6x^2 + 10x + 8),$$
$$f_1(x) = x - 3,$$
$$q(x) = x^4 + 5x^3 + 6x^2 + 10x + 8,$$
$$q(x) = (x + 4)(x^3 + x^2 + 2x + 2),$$
$$f_2(x) = x + 4,$$
$$q_1(x) = x^3 + x^2 + 2x + 2,$$
$$q_1(x) = (x + 1)(x^2 + 2),$$
$$f_3(x) = x + 1,$$
$$q_2(x) = x^2 + 2.$$

Hence,

$$p(x) = (x - 3)(x + 4)(x + 1) \cdot (x^2 + 2).$$

Since every real polynomial of odd degree has at least one real zero, the graph of $y = p(x)$ in such cases must cross the x-axis at least once.

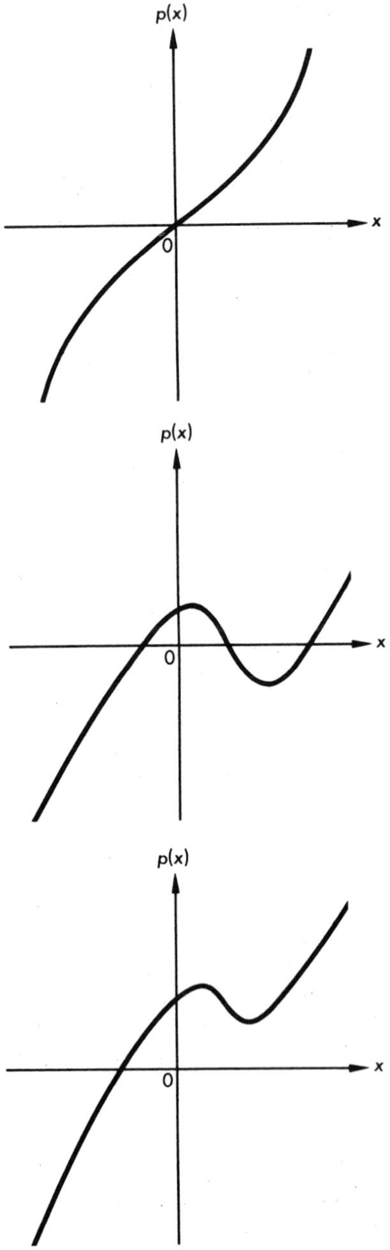

Some of the possibilities for the graph of a third-degree polynomial are presented in the figure above. In each example above, if

$$p(x) = a_3x^3 + a_2x^2 + a_1x + a_0,$$

Every real polynomial of positive degree can be factored into a product of prime real polynomials, each of degree 1 or 2.

The prime real polynomials of degree 2 have conjugate complex zeros, whereas those of degree 1 have real zeros. For example,

$$p(x) = (x^2 - 2x + 2)(x^2 - 4x + 5)(2x - 3)$$

is factored into prime real polynomials. Thus,

$$\begin{aligned} x^2 - 2x + 2 &\quad \text{has zeros} \quad 1 + i \quad \text{and} \quad 1 - i, \\ x^2 - 4x + 5 &\quad \text{has zeros} \quad 2 + i \quad \text{and} \quad 2 - i, \\ 2x - 3 &\quad \text{has zero} \quad \tfrac{3}{2}. \end{aligned}$$

If a real polynomial is of odd degree, such as the polynomial $p(x)$ above, and if $p(x) = f_1(x)f_2(x)\cdots f_n(x)$ where each of the factors $f_1(x), f_2(x), \ldots, f_n(x)$ is a real polynomial of degree 1 or 2, then some $f_i(x)$ must have degree 1, for otherwise, the degree of $p(x)$ would be

$$\overbrace{2 + 2 + \cdots + 2}^{n \text{ terms}}, \quad \text{or } 2n,$$

which is an even number, contrary to the assumption that $p(x)$ is of odd degree. Since some real factor of $p(x)$ has degree 1, $p(x)$ has a real zero by the factor theorem. We state this result in the following manner.

Every real polynomial of odd degree has at least one real zero.

Exercises

In each of the exercises below, there is a real polynomial and one of its zeros. Find the other zeros, and express the polynomial as a product of real prime polynomials.

1. $x^3 - 4x^2 + 9x - 10;\ 1 - 2i$ $1+2i,\ 2;\ (x-2)(x^2-2x+5)$
2. $3x^3 - 2x^2 + 3x - 2;\ i$ $-i,\ \frac{2}{3};\ (x^2+1)(3x-2)$
3. $x^3 - (6 + \sqrt{2})x^2 + (10 + 6\sqrt{2})x - 10\sqrt{2};\ 3 + i$ $3-i,\ \sqrt{2};\ (x^2-6x+10)(x-\sqrt{2})$
4. $x^4 + 1;\ \frac{\sqrt{2}}{2}(1 + i)$ $\frac{\sqrt{2}}{2}(1-i),\ \frac{-\sqrt{2}}{2}(1\pm i);\ (x^2-\sqrt{2}x+1)(x^2+\sqrt{2}x+1)$
5. $2x^4 + 5x^3 + 4x^2 + 3;\ -\frac{3}{2} + \frac{\sqrt{3}}{2}i$ $\frac{-3}{2} - \frac{\sqrt{3}}{2}i,\ \frac{1\pm\sqrt{7}i}{4};\ (x^2+3x+3)(2x^2-x+1)$

6. $x^3 + 8$; $^-2$ $1 \pm \sqrt{3}\,i$; $(x+2)(x^2-2x+4)$

7. $x^4 - 8x^3 + 41x^2 - 100x + 100$; $2 + 4i$ $2-4i$, $2 \pm i$; $(x^2-4x+20)(x^2-4x+5)$

8. $x^4 - 10x^3 + 50x^2 - 106x + 25$; $3 - 4i$
$3+4i$, $2 \pm \sqrt{3}$; $(x^2-6x+25)(x-2+\sqrt{3})(x-2-\sqrt{3})$

9. $2x^4 - 2x^3 + 9x^2 + 4x - 26$; $\frac{1}{2} + \frac{5}{2}i$
$\frac{1}{2} - \frac{5}{2}i$, $\pm\sqrt{2}$; $(2x^2-2x+13)(x-\sqrt{2})(x+\sqrt{2})$

In Exercises 10–19, find real polynomials of the smallest possible degree having the given numbers as zeros.

10. $7 - 2i$ $x^2-14x+53$

11. $^-\frac{1}{2} + \frac{3}{2}i$ $2x^2+2x+5$

12. $1 + \sqrt{2}$ $x-1-\sqrt{2}$

13. $^-2$, $\sqrt{3}$ $x^2+(2-\sqrt{3})x-2\sqrt{3}$

14. 0, i x^3+x

15. $3 + 4i$, 1 $x^3-7x^2+31x-25$

16. $^-\frac{1}{2}$, $i + 5$ $2x^3-19x^2+42x+26$

17. $i + 1$, $i - 1$ x^4+4

18. 1, i, $1 + i$
$x^5-3x^4+5x^3-5x^2+4x-2$

19. $^-2$, $^-1$, ^-i
$x^4+3x^3+3x^2+3x+2$

20. If $p(x) = x^3 - 3x^2 + 2ix + i - 1$, show that i is a zero but that ^-i is not a zero. Does this contradict one of the theorems of this section? See Solution Manual.

21. Let $p(x) = a_0 + a_1x + a_2x^2 + \cdots + a_nx^n$ be a polynomial with complex coefficients, and let $q(x) = \bar{a}_0 + \bar{a}_1x + \bar{a}_2x^2 + \cdots + \bar{a}_nx^n$. If r is a complex zero of $p(x)$, prove that $\bar{r}$ is a zero of $q(x)$. Illustrate this result using the polynomial of Exercise 20. See Solution Manual.

22. Factor the polynomial $x^6 + 1$ into a product of real prime polynomials.
$(x^2+1)(x^4-x^2+1)$

23. If r_1, r_2, and r_3 are the zeros of $x^3 + ax^2 + bx + c$, show that $r_1 + r_2 + r_3 = {^-a}$ and $r_1r_2r_3 = {^-c}$. See Solution Manual.

24. If r_1, r_2, r_3, and r_4 are the zeros of $x^4 + ax^3 + bx^2 + cx + d$, show that $r_1 + r_2 + r_3 + r_4 = {^-a}$ and $r_1r_2r_3r_4 = d$. See Solution Manual.

HISTORICAL NOTE

Formulas for solving quadratic, cubic, and quartic polynomial equations were discovered in the sixteenth century. Despite the efforts of mathematicians in the seventeenth and eighteenth centuries, similar formulas for solving fifth- or higher-degree polynomial equations were not found. The memoir of J. L. Lagrange (1736–1813), *Reflexions sur la resolutions algebrique des equations*, contained a systematic study of equation solving. This study was to prove extremely useful to the next generation of mathematicians who worked on the problem.

Three names are connected with the ultimate solution of the problem of solving fifth- and higher-degree polynomial equations: Abel, Ruffini, and Galois. Although the Norwegian mathematician N. H. Abel (1802–1829) died before his twenty-seventh birthday, he made fundamental

then what would the sign of a_3 have to be? (ans: positive)

Students have probably seen the $\sum$-sign for summation in a handbook or in current literature. You may wish to explain its use here. Some books write

$$p(x) = \sum_{i=0}^{n} a_ix^i,\ a_i \text{ real}.$$

The $\sum$-sign may be used to restate some of the properties of polynomials, such as

$$p(x) + q(x) = \sum_{i=0}^{n} a_ix^i + \sum_{i=0}^{n} b_ix^i = \sum_{i=0}^{n} (a_i + b_i)x^i.$$

It is recommended that Exercises 20 through 24 be assigned. The interested student may learn more about Exercises 23 and 24 by looking up the topic "symmetric functions" in a book on the theory of equations.

Quiz

In Exercises 1 and 2, there is a real polynomial and one of its zeros is given. Find the other zeros, and express the polynomial as a product of real prime polynomials.

1. $x^3 - 3x^2 + x - 3$; ^-i
(ans: i, 3; $(x^2 + 1)(x - 3)$)

2. $8x^3 - 12x^2 + 14x - 5$; $\frac{1}{2} + i$
(ans: $\frac{1}{2} - i$, $\frac{1}{2}$; $(4x^2 - 4x + 5) \times (2x - 1)$)

In Exercises 3 and 4, find real polynomials of the smallest possible degree having the given numbers as zeros.

3. $3 + i$
(ans: $x^2 - 6x + 10$)

4. 0, $i - 1$
(ans: $x^3 + 2x^2 + 2x$)

contributions to several fields of mathematics. In 1824, he published an algebraic proof of a most unusual theorem. His proof stopped all further attempts to find a formula which would give the solutions of a general quintic polynomial equation $x^5 + ax^4 + bx^3 + cx^2 + dx + e = 0$ in terms of powers and roots of its coefficients a, b, c, d, and e. His theorem stated simply that there is no such formula for solving general polynomial equations of degree 5 or higher! An Italian physician, P. Ruffini, proved essentially the same result in 1813. However, Abel was not aware of Ruffini's work.

One of the heartbreaking episodes of mathematical history is the story of the French mathematician E. Galois, who was killed in a political dual in 1832, a few months before his twenty-first birthday. Although he was a failure in school and in politics, he was reading the works of Lagrange at the age of sixteen and was discovering new results by the following year. He introduced the algebraic system called a *group*, and used it to give a definitive answer to the question of why polynomial equations of higher degree than 4 cannot be solved by a formula. He showed that if such an equation could be solved, then an associative finite group would have a certain structure. However, a group does not, in general, have this structure. His work led to an exhaustive study of group theory by later mathematicians, a study which is still going on at present.

KEY IDEAS AND KEY WORDS

A **polynomial** is an algebraic expression of the form

$$a_n x^n + a_{n-1} x^{n-1} + \cdots + a_1 x + a_0,$$

where n is a non-negative integer, x is a variable, and $a_n, a_{n-1}, \ldots, a_1, a_0$ are real or complex numbers. The numbers $a_0, a_1, \ldots, a_n$ are called the **coefficients** of the polynomial. In particular, a_n is called the **leading coefficient** and a_0 the **constant term.** If $a_n \neq 0$, then the polynomial is said to have **degree** n. The zero polynomial, 0, has no degree.

The set of all polynomials in a variable x with real or complex coefficients is **closed** under addition and multiplication. The five basic properties of addition and multiplication of the real number system, with the exception of the multiplicative inverse property, are valid for the algebra of polynomials.

For any given nonzero polynomials A and B, there exist unique polynomials Q and R such that $A = (B \cdot Q) + R$, with $R = 0$ or the degree of R less than the degree of B. We call Q the **quotient** and R the **remainder** on dividing A by B.

The **remainder theorem** states that if the polynomial $f(x)$ is divided by the polynomial $x - r$, then the remainder is $f(r)$.

The **factor theorem** states that the polynomial $x - r$ is a divisor, or factor, of a polynomial $f(x)$ if, and only if, $f(r) = 0$. We call r a **zero** of $f(x)$ if $f(r) = 0$.

A polynomial is called an **integral,** a **rational,** a **real,** or a **complex** polynomial depending upon whether its coefficients are integers, rational numbers, real numbers, or complex numbers.

According to the **integral zero theorem,** an integer k is a zero of an integral polynomial only if k is a divisor of a_0, the constant term.

By the **rational zero theorem,** a rational number p/q expressed in lowest form is a zero of an integral polynomial only if p is a divisor of the constant term a_0 and q is a divisor of the leading coefficient a_n.

The **complex zeros** of a real polynomial occur in **conjugate pairs.** Therefore, every real polynomial of odd degree has at least one real zero.

CHAPTER REVIEW

1. Use synthetic division to find the quotient and the remainder when $4x^3 - 5x + 1$ is divided by each of the following.

(a) $x - 2$ $4x^2 + 8x + 11;\ 23$ (b) $x + 3$ $4x^2 - 12x + 31;\ ^{-}92$

2. If $p(x) = 2x^3 - x^2 + 3x - 4$, find $p(^{-}2)$, $p(1)$, $p(3)$, and $p(4)$. $^{-}30,\ 0,\ 50,\ 120$

3. Find the zeros of each of the following polynomials.

(a) $6x^3 - x^2 - 12x - 5$ $\{^{-}1, \frac{^{-}1}{2}, \frac{5}{3}\}$ (b) $6x^4 - 11x^3 + 7x^2 - 22x + 24$ $\{\frac{4}{3}, \frac{3}{2}, \frac{^{-}1}{2} + \frac{1}{2}\sqrt{7}i, \frac{^{-}1}{2} - \frac{1}{2}\sqrt{7}i\}$

4. Find one-decimal-place approximations of the irrational zeros of the polynomial $3x^3 - 2x^2 - 11x + 7$. Graph the polynomial equation $y = 3x^3 - 2x^2 - 11x + 7$. $^{-}1.9, .6, 1.9$; see Solution Manual.

5. Find an integral polynomial of lowest possible degree for each of the following sets of zeros.

(a) $\{\frac{1}{2}, 3, ^{-}\frac{2}{3}\}$ $6x^3 - 17x^2 - 5x + 6$ (b) $\{1 + \sqrt{3}, 2i\}$ $x^4 - 2x^3 + 2x^2 - 8x - 8$

6. Prove that $\sqrt{2}/\sqrt{3}$ is irrational. See Solution Manual.

7. Factor each polynomial into a product of integral prime polynomials.

(a) $x^4 + 2x^3 - 25x^2 - 26x + 120$ $(x-2)(x+3)(x-4)(x+5)$ (b) $x^4 + 3x - 2$ $(x^2 + x - 1)(x^2 - x + 2)$

8. The real polynomial

$$x^4 - 6x^3 + 29x^2 - 24x + 100$$

has complex zero $3 - 4i$. Find the other three zeros. $3 + 4i, \pm 2i$

9. Illustrate the associative law of addition in the set of polynomials, using the three polynomials $8x^2 - 6$, $14x^2 - 4x + 8$, and $8x + 10$.
See Solution Manual.

10. Illustrate the associative law of multiplication in the set of polynomials, using the three polynomials $3y - 9$, $3y + 9$, and $6y + 15$.
See Solution Manual.

In Exercises 11–13, perform the indicated operations with polynomials.

11. $(x^3 + 3x^2 + 5x + 5) + (2x - 4)$ x^3+3x^2+7x+1

12. $(x^4 + x^2 + x)(x^4 + x^2 - x)$ $x^8+2x^6+x^4-x^2$

13. $(3x^3 + 5x - 4)(3x^2 + 5x - 4)$ $9x^5+15x^4+3x^3+13x^2-40x+16$

14. Determine k so that when $4x^3 - 2x^2 + 6x + 2k$ is divided by $2x - 2$, the remainder is 0. $k = {}^-4$

15. Determine c and d so that when $2y^4 + 2y^3 - 14y^2 + 2cy + 2d$ is divided by $(y - 1)(2y + 4)$, the remainder is 0. $c = {}^-5,\ d = 10$

Which of the polynomials $(2x - 2)$, $(2x + 2)$, $(2x - 8)$, and $(2x + 6)$ are divisors of the following polynomials?

16. $2x^3 - 4x^2 - 22x + 24$ $(2x-2), (2x-8), (2x+6)$

17. $4x^4 + 2x^3 + 2x^2 - 2x - 6$ $(2x-2), (2x+2)$

18. $4x^3 + 6x^2 - 46x - 24$ None

19. $2x^4 + 2x^3 - 38x^2 + 2x - 40$ $(2x-8)$

Find the rational zeros of each of the following polynomials.

20. $20x^3 - 34x^2 - 14x + 4$ $\{2, \frac{1}{5}, \frac{-1}{2}\}$

21. $2x^4 - \frac{3}{2}x^3 + 6x^2 + x + \frac{3}{2}$ None

Find an integral polynomial of degree 4 for each of the following sets of zeros.

22. $\{1, 0, {}^-1\}$ $x(x^2-1)(ax+b),\ a \neq 0$, a and b integers

23. $\{\frac{1}{2}, {}^-\frac{1}{2}, 1\}$ $(4x^2-1)(x-1)(ax+b)$, $a \neq 0$, a and b integers

24. $\{1, 2, 4, {}^-7\}$ $x^4-35x^2+90x-56$

25. $\{0, 1, {}^-2, 3\}$ $x^4-2x^3-5x^2+6x$

Determine the rational roots of the following equations.

26. $2x^3 - 7x^2 - 7x + 30 = 0$ $\{3, {}^-2, \frac{5}{2}\}$

27. $2x^5 - 11x^4 + 65x^2 + 31x = 0$ $\{0, \frac{-1}{2}\}$

28. $2x^4 - 3x^3 - 11x^2 + 3x + 9 = 0$ $\{1, {}^-1, 3, \frac{-3}{2}\}$

29. Use the fact that

$$x^8 - 6x^6 + 8x^4 + 6x^2 - 9$$

$(x^2-3)^2(x^2+1)(x+1)(x-1)$ as five polynomials

is divisible by $x^6 - 3x^4 - x^2 + 3$, which is, in turn, divisible by $x^2 - 3$, to write the eighth-degree polynomial as a product of four polynomials.

CHAPTER TEST

In Exercises 1 and 2, perform the indicated operations with polynomials.

1. $(3x^3 + 2x^2 + x + 2) + (\frac{1}{2}x^3 + 6x - 2)$ $\frac{7}{2}x^3 + 2x^2 + 7x$
2. $0 \cdot (3x^3 + 5x^2 + 5x + 3)$ 0
3. Given that
$$f(x) = x^5 - 3x^4 - x^2 + 7,$$
find $f(0)$, $f(1)$, and $f(^-2)$. 7, 4, $^-77$
4. Find the zeros of the polynomial
$$3x^3 - 4x^2 - 13x - 6. \quad \{\tfrac{^-2}{3}, {}^-1, 3\}$$
5. Find an integral polynomial having zeros $\frac{3}{4}$ and $\sqrt{2}$. $4x^3 - 3x^2 - 8x + 6$
6. Factor
$$6x^3 - 13x^2 + x + 2. \quad (x-2)(2x-1)(3x+1)$$
7. Prove that $\sqrt{2} + \sqrt{3}$ is an irrational number.
8. Factor
$$x^4 + 2x^3 - 4x^2 - 5x - 6. \quad (x^2 + x + 1)(x-2)(x+3)$$

CHAPTER TEST

The material included in the Chapter Test was covered in the following sections:

Problems 1, 2—Section 8-1
Problem 3—Section 8-4
Problem 4—Section 8-6
Problem 5—Section 8-7
Problem 6—Section 8-8
Problem 7—Section 8-7
Problem 8—Section 8-9

Answer to Chapter Test Problem 7

7. $(x + \sqrt{2} + \sqrt{3})(x + \sqrt{2} - \sqrt{3})$
$= (x + \sqrt{2})^2 - (\sqrt{3})^2$
$= x^2 + 2\sqrt{2}x + 2 - 3$
$= x^2 + 2\sqrt{2}x - 1$

$(x^2 - 1 + 2\sqrt{2}x)(x^2 - 1 - 2\sqrt{2}x)$
$= (x^2 - 1)^2 - (2\sqrt{2}x)^2$
$= x^4 - 2x^2 + 1 - 8x^2$
$= x^4 - 10x^2 + 1$

$x^4 - 10x^2 + 1$ has $\sqrt{2} + \sqrt{3}$ as a zero. Its only possible rational zeros are 1 and $^-1$, neither of which is zero. Hence, its zeros, including $\sqrt{2} + \sqrt{3}$, are irrational.

CHAPTER 9

Elements of Trigonometry

The purpose of this chapter is to reintroduce students to right triangle trigonometry in Section 9–1 and then to present the trigonometric functions as a class of periodic functions.

The following are some of the topics covered in Chapter 9:

- *Sine of an angle*
- *Cosine of an angle*
- *Function of an angle*
- *The wrapping function*
- *Period of the wrapping function*
- *Properties of the wrapping function*
- *Fundamental identities*
- *Radian measure and general angles*
- *Cofunctions*

You may find it necessary to spend two days on each section of this chapter, except for Sections 9–1 and 9–7, for which one day should be sufficient.

CHAPTER 9

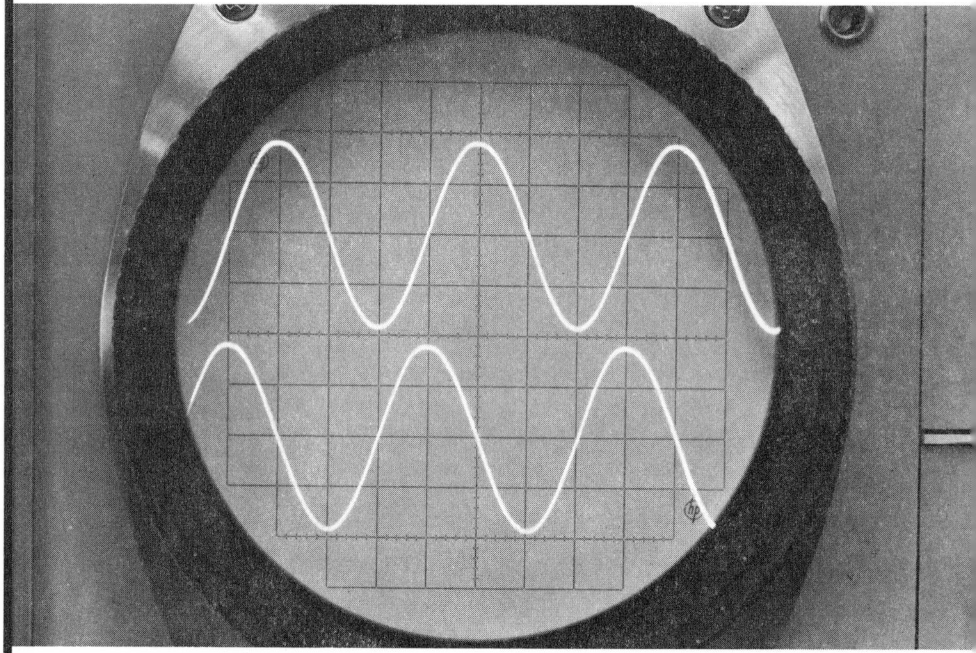

In the study of electrical currents, sine and cosine curves frequently appear on the screen of an oscilloscope. (Courtesy of Hewlett-Packard Company)

ELEMENTS OF TRIGONOMETRY

Until recently, the branch of mathematics called trigonometry was primarily concerned with the measurement of triangles. By definition, two triangles are similar if their angles are congruent in some order. Furthermore, a geometric theorem basic to the measurement of triangles states that two triangles are similar if, and only if, their corresponding sides have proportional lengths. Thus, the ratio of one side of a triangle to another side of the triangle does not depend on the size of the triangle, but only on its angles. These ratios are the original trigonometric functions of the angles of a triangle.

In its modern meaning, trigonometry is concerned with much more than the study of relationships between the sides and angles of triangles. It now includes the study of a class of periodic functions. Although it is true that these functions originally had domains consisting of angles of triangles, modern applications of these functions are far removed from triangles. In this chapter, we shall look at both the historical interpretation and the modern meaning of trigonometry.

365

9–1 TRIGONOMETRIC FUNCTIONS OF ACUTE ANGLES

The students ought to be familiar with the first three letters of the Greek Alphabet, α (alpha), β (beta), and γ (gamma).

The definitions of sine, cosine, and tangent should be reviewed. The students should be able to verbalize them in terms of lengths of the *opposite* and *adjacent* sides and the *hypotenuse* of a right triangle. For example, "sin α is the ratio of the length of the opposite side to the length of the hypotenuse."

Students may be asked to give other examples of right triangles with integral sides, for example, 6, 8, 10 and, in general, 3a, 4a, 5a may also be known to some students.

You may wish to have the students recall the definition of *function*, and it should be emphasized that sin α, cos α, and tan α really are mathematical functions. The trigonometric functions just defined have as their domain a set of *angles* instead of *numbers*.

The range when the domain is restricted to positive acute angles should be discussed.

You could draw an equilateral triangle such that a line from altitude to base results in two 30-60 right triangles in order to recall to the students the property that the hypotenuse is twice the length of the shorter leg. Even integers are obviously the most convenient choice for the lengths of the sides of an equilateral triangle.

9–1 TRIGONOMETRIC FUNCTIONS OF ACUTE ANGLES

Every acute angle α may be considered to be an angle of some right triangle ABC, as indicated in Fig. 9–1. If the vertices of a triangle are designated by A, B, and C, then we shall frequently denote the lengths of the opposite sides by a, b, and c, respectively, and the angles at vertices A, B, and C by α, β, and γ, respectively. The small square at vertex C of Fig. 9–1 indicates that the angle at C is a right angle.

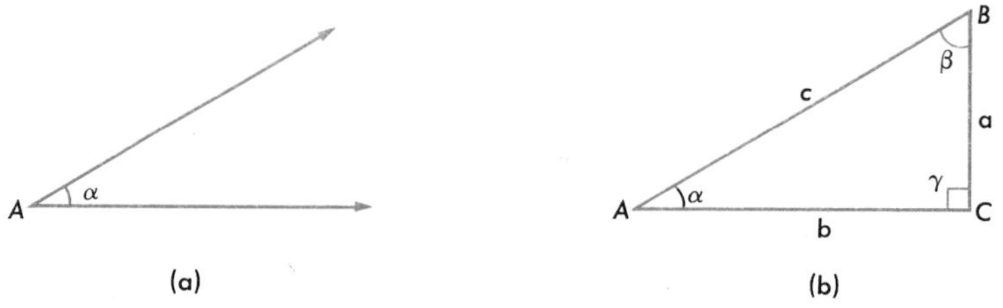

FIGURE 9–1

If α is an acute angle of the right triangle shown in Fig. 9–1, we can define the *sine* of α, the *cosine* of α, and the *tangent* of α in triangle ABC in the following manner.

$$\sin\alpha = \frac{a}{c}, \quad \cos\alpha = \frac{b}{c}, \quad \tan\alpha = \frac{a}{b}$$

In this way, we can associate with each acute angle α three numbers: sin α, cos α, and tan α. Note that we have abbreviated sine to sin, cosine to cos, and tangent to tan.

Although it appears that sin α, cos α, and tan α could depend on the size of the right triangle containing angle α, this is not the case, for if $A'B'C'$ is another right triangle with α as an acute angle (see Fig. 9–2), then it follows that triangles ABC and $A'B'C'$ are similar. Hence,

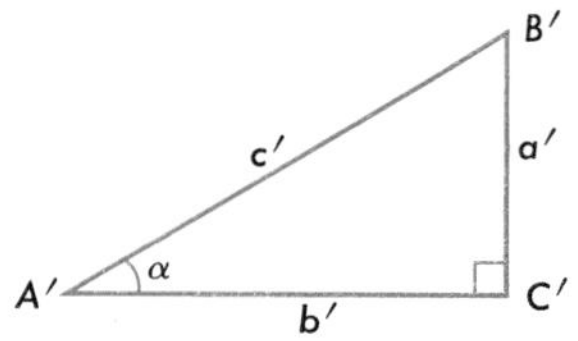

FIGURE 9–2

$$\frac{a}{c} = \frac{a'}{c'}, \quad \frac{b}{c} = \frac{b'}{c'}, \quad \frac{a}{b} = \frac{a'}{b'}.$$

This proves that sin α, cos α, and tan α do not depend on the size of the right triangle containing angle α.

One of the simplest right triangles having sides of integral lengths is the right triangle with sides 3, 4, and 5, as shown in Fig. 9–3. If we denote the smaller acute angle by α and the larger acute angle by β, then according to the definitions above,

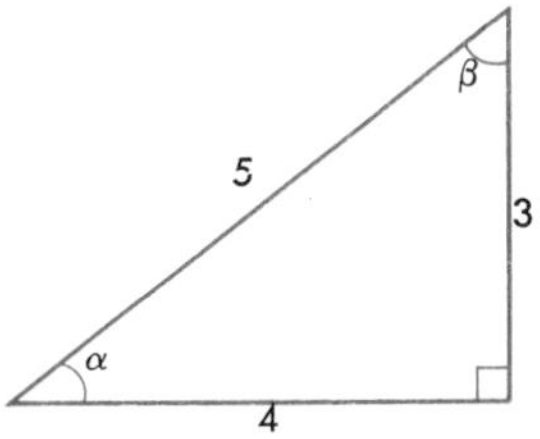

FIGURE 9–3

$$\sin \alpha = \tfrac{3}{5}, \quad \cos \alpha = \tfrac{4}{5}, \quad \tan \alpha = \tfrac{3}{4},$$
$$\sin \beta = \tfrac{4}{5}, \quad \cos \beta = \tfrac{3}{5}, \quad \tan \beta = \tfrac{4}{3}.$$

The correspondence that associates with each acute angle α the number $\sin \alpha$ is a *function*, called the *sine*. This function has the set of all acute angles as its domain and the set of positive real numbers less than 1 as its range. Similarly, *cosine* and *tangent* are *functions* having the same domain. The three functions sine, cosine, and tangent are called *trigonometric functions.*

Problem 1. Find the trigonometric functions of an angle of measure 60°.

Solution. The hypotenuse is twice as long as the shorter leg in a 30°–60° right triangle. If we assume that the hypotenuse has length 2 and the shorter leg length 1, then the length b of the other leg is $\sqrt{3}$ since

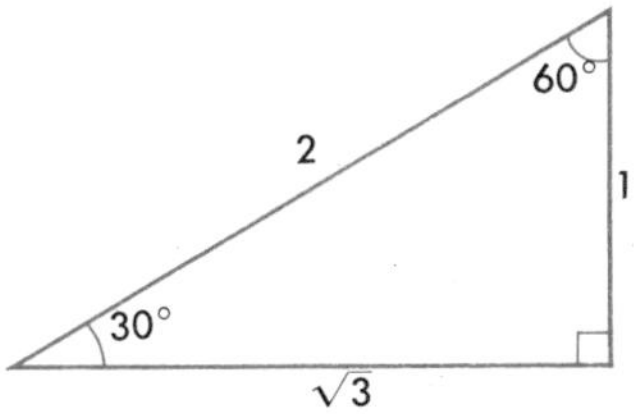

FIGURE 9–4

$$2^2 = 1^2 + b^2 \quad \text{and} \quad b = \sqrt{3}$$

by the pythagorean theorem. When we look at Fig. 9–4, we see that

$$\sin 60° = \frac{\sqrt{3}}{2}, \quad \cos 60° = \frac{1}{2}, \quad \tan 60° = \frac{\sqrt{3}}{1}.$$

Problem 2. Find the values of the $\cos \alpha$ and the $\tan \alpha$, given that α is acute and that $\sin \alpha = .3$.

Solution. Consider α as an angle of a right triangle (Fig. 9–5). The problem tells us that

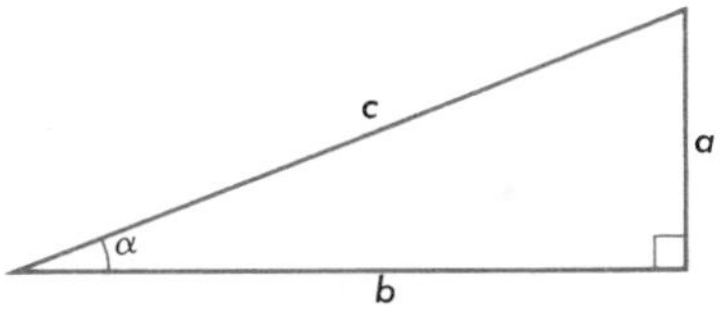

FIGURE 9–5

$$\sin \alpha = \frac{a}{c} = .3.$$

In Problem 2 below, a right triangle with $a = .3$ and $c = 1$ (or with $a = 3$, $c = 10$) could have been chosen, since the trigonometric functions do not depend on the size of the triangle. This approach might be simpler than the one given in the text.

Exercises for Discussion, page 368

It is important for the students to be able to sketch quickly the appropriate triangles for completing the table in Exercise for Discussion 1. They should also learn this table backwards and forwards, so that they will know from $\sin \alpha = \frac{1}{2}$ for acute angle α, that $\alpha = 30°$, and so on. Multiples of 30°, 45°, and 60° are the so-called *special angles*. The figure may be used to find the trigonometric functions of 45°.

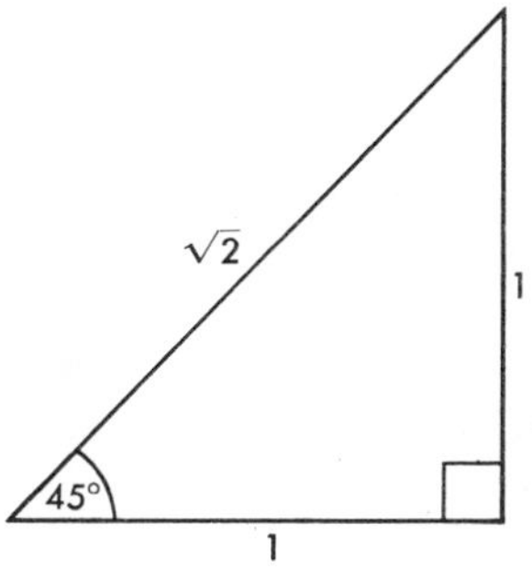

Answers to Exercises for Discussion 2–5

2. $\sin\alpha = \frac{5}{13} = \cos\beta$;
$\cos\alpha = \frac{12}{13} = \sin\beta$;
$\tan\alpha = \frac{5}{12}$; $\tan\beta = \frac{12}{5}$

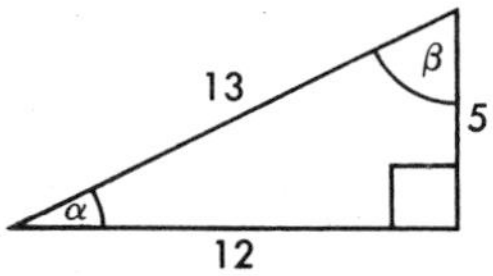

3. If $\tan\alpha = 12$, we can put a on the leg adjacent to α and $12a$ on the leg opposite α. The hypotenuse is then of length

$$\sqrt{(12a)^2 + a^2} = a\sqrt{145}.$$

$$\sin\alpha = \frac{12a}{a\sqrt{145}} = \frac{12}{145}\sqrt{145}$$

$$\cos\alpha = \frac{a}{a\sqrt{145}} = \frac{1}{145}\sqrt{145}$$

$$\tan\alpha = \frac{12a}{a} = 12.$$

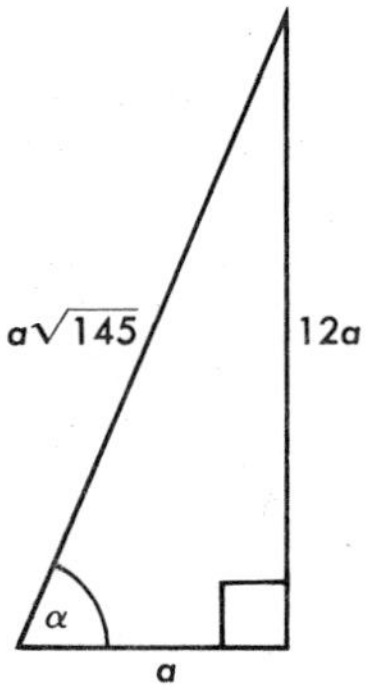

4. The other leg is

$$\sqrt{81 - 36} = \sqrt{45} = 3\sqrt{5}$$

inches long. Since $3\sqrt{5} > 6$, the acute angle opposite the 6 in. leg is the smaller.

$$\sin\alpha = \frac{6}{9} = \frac{2}{3}$$

$$\cos\alpha = \frac{3\sqrt{5}}{9} = \frac{1}{3}\sqrt{5}$$

$$\tan\alpha = \frac{6}{3\sqrt{5}} = \frac{2}{5}\sqrt{5}$$

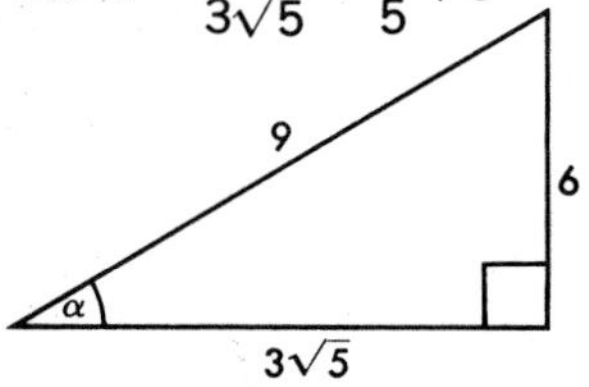

Hence, $a = .3c$. Since $a^2 + b^2 = c^2$, we have

$$\begin{aligned} b^2 &= c^2 - a^2 \\ &= c^2 - (.3c)^2, \quad \text{or } .91c^2. \end{aligned}$$

Thus,

$$b = c\sqrt{.91}.$$

Therefore,

$$\cos\alpha = \frac{b}{c} = \frac{c\sqrt{.91}}{c} = \sqrt{.91}, \quad \text{or} \quad \frac{\sqrt{91}}{10},$$

$$\tan\alpha = \frac{a}{b} = \frac{.3c}{c\sqrt{.91}} = \frac{.3}{\sqrt{.91}}, \quad \text{or} \quad \frac{3}{\sqrt{91}}, \quad \text{or} \quad \frac{3\sqrt{91}}{91}.$$

Exercises for Discussion

1. Complete the following table of values of trigonometric functions.

	30°	45°	60°
sine	$\frac{1}{2}$?	$\frac{1}{2}\sqrt{2}$?	$\frac{1}{2}\sqrt{3}$?
cosine	$\frac{1}{2}\sqrt{3}$?	$\frac{1}{2}\sqrt{2}$?	$\frac{1}{2}$?
tangent	$\frac{1}{3}\sqrt{3}$?	1 ?	$\sqrt{3}$?

Find the trigonometric functions of each angle described in Exercises 2–4.

2. The two acute angles of the right triangle whose sides are 5, 12, and 13 units long $\sin\alpha = \frac{5}{13} = \cos\beta$; $\cos\alpha = \frac{12}{13} = \sin\beta$; $\tan\alpha = \frac{5}{12}$; $\tan\beta = \frac{12}{5}$
3. The acute angle whose tangent is 12
4. The smaller acute angle of a right triangle with one leg of length 6 inches and with hypotenuse of length 9 inches

5. For an acute angle α of a right triangle, it is known that $\sin\alpha = \frac{3}{4}$ and that the length of the leg opposite angle α is 12. Find the lengths of the hypotenuse and the other leg.

Exercises

See Solution Manual for figures.

Find the trigonometric functions of each angle described in Exercises 1–7.

1. An angle of measure 30° $\sin 30° = \frac{1}{2}$; $\cos 30° = \frac{1}{2}\sqrt{3}$; $\tan 30° = \frac{1}{3}\sqrt{3}$
2. The two acute angles of the right triangle whose sides are 7, 24, and 25 units long
3. The acute angle whose sine is .2 $\sin\alpha = .2$; $\cos\alpha = \frac{2}{5}\sqrt{6}$; $\tan\alpha = \frac{1}{12}\sqrt{6}$
4. The acute angle whose cosine is .7 $\sin\alpha = \frac{1}{10}\sqrt{51}$; $\cos\alpha = .7$; $\tan\alpha = \frac{1}{7}\sqrt{51}$
5. The acute angle whose sine is .99 $\sin\alpha = .99$; $\cos\alpha = \frac{1}{100}\sqrt{199}$; $\tan\alpha = \frac{99}{199}\sqrt{199}$
6. The acute angle whose cosine is .001 $\sin\alpha = \frac{3\sqrt{111,111}}{1000}$; $\cos\alpha = .001$; $\tan\alpha = 3\sqrt{111,111}$
7. The larger acute angle of a right triangle with legs of 7 feet and 9 feet $\sin\alpha = \frac{9}{130}\sqrt{130}$; $\cos\alpha = \frac{7}{130}\sqrt{130}$; $\tan\alpha = \frac{9}{7}$

8. In $\triangle ABC$, the angle at A has measure 30° and the lengths of the two sides including angle A are 50 and 130, as shown in the figure.

(a) Find the length, h, of the altitude drawn to the base $\overline{AB}$ and find the area of $\triangle ABC$.
$h = 25$; area = 1625

(b) Show that $\triangle ABC$ is *not* a right triangle.
See Solution Manual.

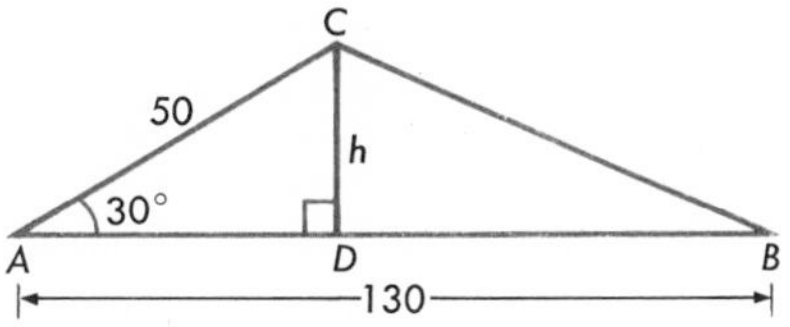

9. Prove that for each acute angle α, $(\sin \alpha)^2 + (\cos \alpha)^2 = 1$.
See Solution Manual.

10. Prove that for each acute angle α,

$$\tan \alpha = \frac{\sin \alpha}{\cos \alpha}.$$

See Solution Manual.

11. What is the measure of α if the tangent of α is equal to its own reciprocal?

12. Prove that if α and β are complementary angles, then

(a) $\sin \alpha = \cos \beta$. See Solution Manual.

(b) $\cos \alpha = \sin \beta$.

9–2 THE WRAPPING FUNCTION

Another way to approach the trigonometric functions is to relate them to points on a unit circle (that is, a circle of radius 1). In this approach, the domains of the sine and cosine functions are the set of all real numbers, rather than a set of acute angles. When considered in this way, the trigonometric functions are often called *circular functions*. We place the center of a unit circle at the origin of a cartesian coordinate system, and then place a number line (the s-axis) parallel to the y-axis, as shown in Fig. 9–6. We assume that all three number lines (the x-axis, the y-axis, and the s-axis) have the same unit of length.

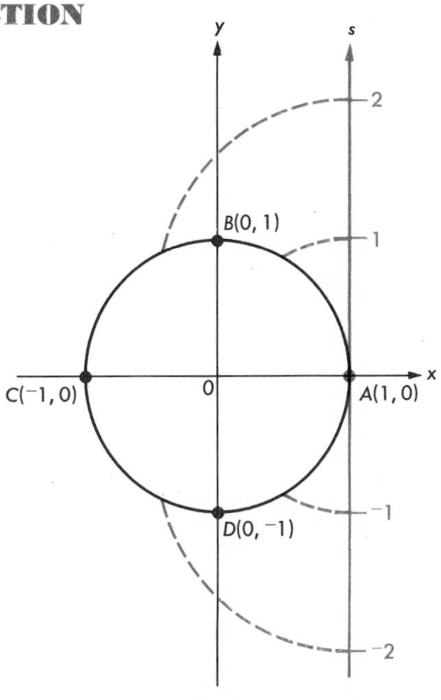

FIGURE 9–6

5. $\sin \alpha = \dfrac{12}{c} = \dfrac{3}{4}$

$3c = 48, \quad c = 16$

$b = \sqrt{c^2 - a^2}$

$= \sqrt{256 - 144} = 4\sqrt{7}$

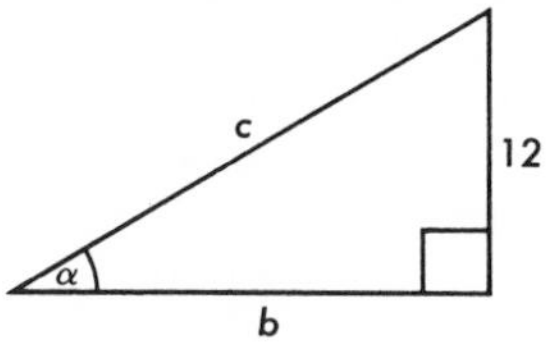

Answer to Exercise 2

2. $\sin \alpha = \frac{7}{25} = \cos \beta$;
$\cos \alpha = \frac{24}{25} = \sin \beta$;
$\tan \alpha = \frac{7}{24}$; $\tan \beta = \frac{24}{7}$

Quiz

1. Let β be the larger acute angle of a right triangle with sides 6, 8, and 10. Find

(a) $\sin \beta$ (ans: $\frac{8}{10}$ or $\frac{4}{5}$)

(b) $\cos \beta$ (ans: $\frac{6}{10}$ or $\frac{3}{5}$)

(c) $\tan \beta$ (ans: $\frac{8}{6}$ or $\frac{4}{3}$)

2. If α is an acute angle with

$$\cos \alpha = \tfrac{1}{4},$$

find

(a) $\sin \alpha$ $\left(\text{ans: } \dfrac{\sqrt{15}}{4}\right)$

(b) $\tan \alpha$ (ans: $\sqrt{15}$)

3. Draw quick sketches to find each of the following:

(a) sin 30° (ans: $\frac{1}{2}$)

(b) tan 45° (ans: 1)

(c) cos 60° (ans: $\frac{1}{2}$)

9–2 THE WRAPPING FUNCTION

It is suggested that you have a large drawing of Fig. 9–6 from the student text on the board, with scales marked on the axes in large units, and with the scale on the s-axis going from about $^-8$ to 8. You could mark with colored chalk the points on the x-axis which are integral multiples of $\pi/2$ units from the origin. (Thus the point located at approximately (1.6, 0) should be labelled $\pi/2$, the point $(^+3.1, 0)$ with label π, and so on.)

Individual students could be sent to the board to go through the motions of "wrapping" a thread around the unit circle to locate these various values of the function W.

Of course, a wooden disc and an actual string would make the demonstration more concrete but the students will benefit by visualizing the wrapping process mentally and will get the point.

Now imagine that the s-axis is an infinitely long thread which can be wrapped around the circle. The piece above the x-axis can be wrapped in a counterclockwise manner, and the piece below the x-axis can be wrapped in a clockwise manner. Then each point on the s-axis can be made to coincide with a point on the circle. In other words, this process defines a function W, called the *wrapping function*, which associates with each real number s (as the coordinate of a point on the s-axis) a *point* $W(s)$ on the unit circle. Because the thread is infinitely long and the circle has finite circumference 2π, the thread can be wrapped around the circle infinitely many times.

Each arc $\widehat{AB}$ of a unit circle has a length. For example, the arc $\widehat{AB}$ of Fig. 9–6 is a quarter circle, and hence, its length is $2\pi/4$, or $\pi/2$. Similarly, arc $\widehat{AC}$ is a semicircle with length π, and counterclockwise arc $\widehat{AD}$ is a three-quarter circle with length $3\pi/2$. Thus,

$$\begin{aligned} W(0) &= A(1, 0), \\ W\left(\frac{\pi}{2}\right) &= B(0, 1), \\ W(\pi) &= C(^-1, 0), \\ W\left(\frac{3\pi}{2}\right) &= D(0, ^-1), \\ W(2\pi) &= A(1, 0). \end{aligned}$$

If $s > 2\pi$, the piece of thread of length s is wrapped around the circle more than once. For example,

$$W(3\pi) = C(^-1, 0).$$

If the negative s-axis is wrapped around the circle, as shown in Fig. 9–7, we see that

$$\begin{aligned} W\left(^-\frac{\pi}{2}\right) &= D(0, ^-1), \\ W(^-\pi) &= C(^-1, 0), \\ W\left(^-\frac{3\pi}{2}\right) &= B(0, 1), \\ W(^-2\pi) &= A(1, 0), \\ W(^-3\pi) &= C(^-1, 0), \end{aligned}$$

and so on.

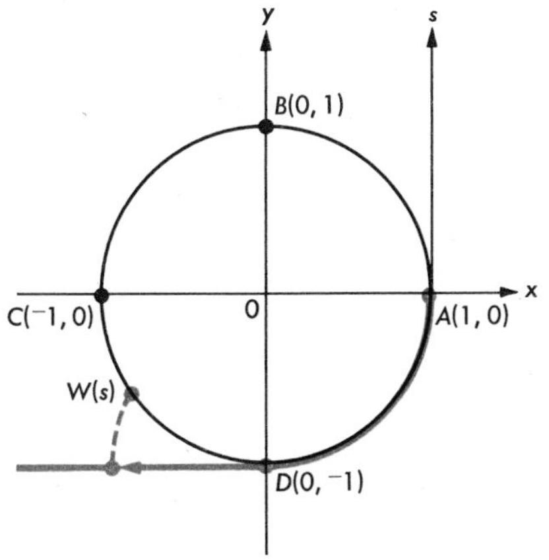

FIGURE 9-7

If we increase or decrease the length of a piece of thread by 2π, we end up at the same point on the unit circle. Thus, for every real number s,

$$W(s) = W(s + 2\pi), \quad W(s) = W(s - 2\pi).$$

On the other hand, if $0 < c < 2\pi$,

$$W(s) \neq W(s + c), \qquad W(s) \neq W(s - c).$$

Thus, the function W repeats itself every 2π, and 2π is the least positive number for which this is true. For this reason, we call the function W *periodic* and the number 2π its *period*.

The wrapping function W is periodic with period 2π.

If $0 \leqq s < 2\pi$, then $W(s)$ is the point on the unit circle such that the arc from A to $W(s)$, when traced counterclockwise, has length s. If $s > 2\pi$, then we subtract an integral multiple of 2π from s so that the difference is between 0 and 2π. In this manner, we can express $W(s)$ as $W(t)$ for some number t, where $0 \leqq t < 2\pi$, as shown in Fig. 9-8. If $s < 0$, then we add an integral multiple of 2π to s so that the sum t is between 0 and 2π. In either case, $W(s) = W(t)$ by the periodicity of W.

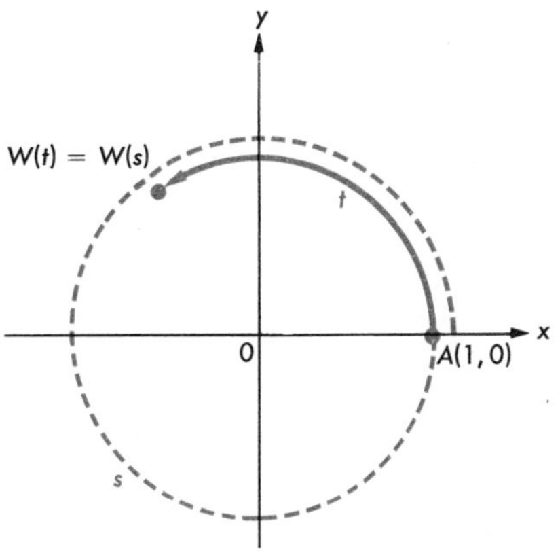

FIGURE 9-8

Here it may help to have handy a piece of string measured to be the length 2π of your board units. Then you could have a student go through the motions of first locating a point $W(s)$ for any s he chooses, and then indicating the point $W(s + 2\pi)$ as the point formed by then wrapping the string in a counter clockwise direction. For the point $W(s - 2\pi)$ it should be recalled that

$$s - 2\pi = s + {}^{-}2\pi$$

so that the string must be attached at the point $W(s)$ and wound clockwise.

Students will catch on rather quickly to the idea of subtracting out multiples of 2π until a number for s between 0 (inclusive) and 2π is reached. This procedure may be called "reducing modulo 2π" and likened to the modular arithmetic of integers with which some students will be familiar.

Here again are the special angle cases, but in a different setting so that directed segments enter the picture.

It is recommended that you avoid reverting to general angle notions (such as 270°, 450°, or ⁻180°) instead of arc-length, as the argument of the wrapping function. (The definitions of the trigonometric functions to be given in Section 9–4 in terms of the wrapping function are equivalent to those defining the trigonometric functions of a general angle whose radian measure is specified. See Section 9–7.) The advantage of using the present approach is to be able to emphasize later that the periodic functions are functions of numbers, that is, their domain is a set of real numbers rather than angles.

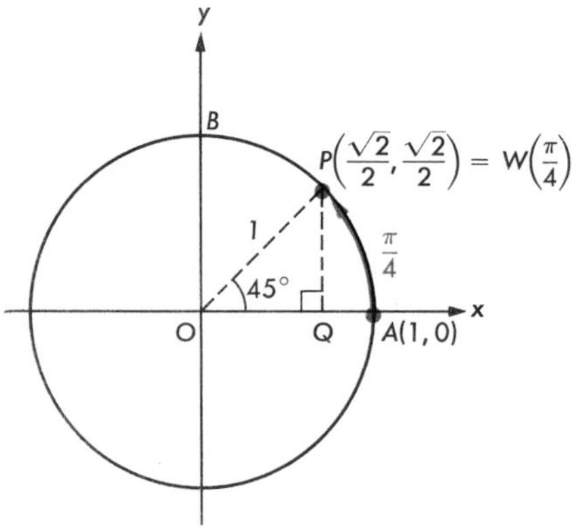

FIGURE 9–9

Problem 1. Find $W\left(\frac{\pi}{4}\right)$.

Solution. Since arc $\widehat{AP}$ is half of arc $\widehat{AB}$ (Fig. 9–9), the measure of $\angle POA$ must be 45°, and $\triangle OPQ$ is a 45° right triangle. We constructed the circle with a radius of 1; therefore, $\overline{OP}$ has length 1. From our previous work with a 45° right triangle,

$$OQ = QP$$

and

$$(OP)^2 = (QP)^2 + (OQ)^2.$$

Therefore,

$$QP = \frac{\sqrt{2}}{2}$$

and

$$W\left(\frac{\pi}{4}\right) = \left(\frac{\sqrt{2}}{2}, \frac{\sqrt{2}}{2}\right).$$

Problem 2. Find $W\left(\frac{^-3\pi}{4}\right)$.

Solution. The point

$$W\left(\frac{^-3\pi}{4}\right)$$

is halfway between the points $W(\pi)$ and $W(3\pi/2)$. We know from our previous work that the coordinates of all points in the third quadrant

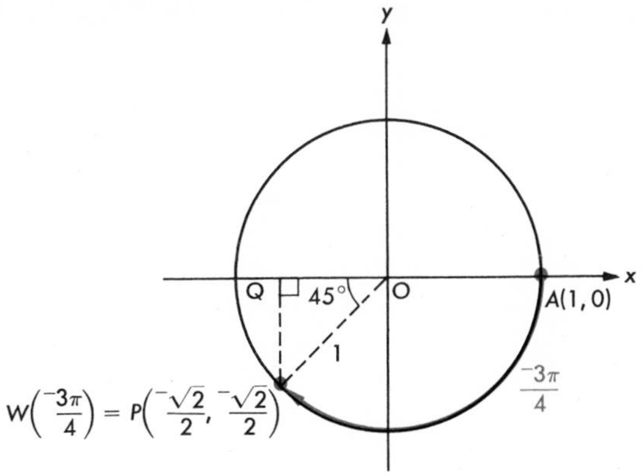

FIGURE 9–10

are negative. Since the measure of $\angle POQ$ is 45°, $\triangle OPQ$ is a 45° right triangle. (See Fig. 9–10.)

$$W\left(^-\frac{3\pi}{4}\right) = \left(^-\frac{\sqrt{2}}{2}, ^-\frac{\sqrt{2}}{2}\right)$$

Problem 3. Find $W\left(\frac{\pi}{6}\right)$.

Solution. Since arc $\widehat{AP}$ is a third of arc $\widehat{AB}$ (Fig. 9–11), the measure of $\angle POA$ is 30° and $\triangle OPQ$ is a 30°–60° right triangle. Therefore,

$$QP = .5, \quad OQ = \frac{\sqrt{3}}{2} \quad \text{and} \quad W\left(\frac{\pi}{6}\right) = \left(\frac{\sqrt{3}}{2}, \frac{1}{2}\right).$$

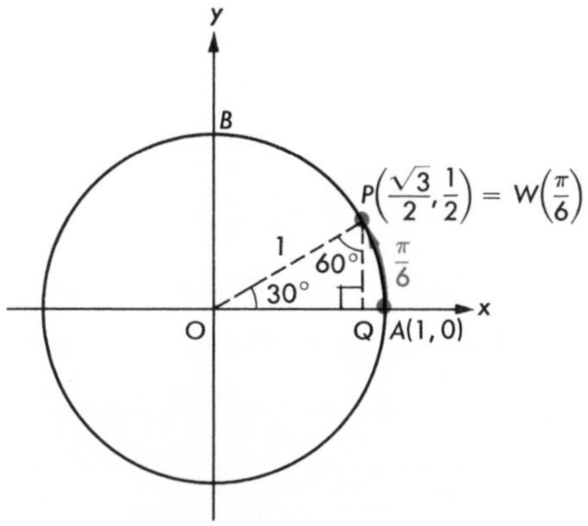

FIGURE 9–11

The problems of this section should be illustrated on the board using your drawing of the unit circle and going through the motions of wrapping to get each $W(s)$.

You may want to perform the motions for and obtain $W(^-s)$ for each of the s numbers in Problems 1–4 in anticipation of the next section.

You could have a student do each part of Problem 4 at the board without following the text solution, and then ask the class to read the solution and discuss it.

Problem 4. Find $W\left(\frac{21\pi}{4}\right)$ and $W\left(\frac{^-11\pi}{2}\right)$.

Solution. If we subtract $2(2\pi)$, or 4π, from $21\pi/4$, we get a number t between 0 and 2π:

$$t = \frac{21\pi}{4} - 4\pi, \quad \text{or} \quad \frac{5\pi}{4}.$$

By the periodicity of W,

$$W\left(\frac{21\pi}{4}\right) = W\left(\frac{5\pi}{4}\right).$$

Since $W(5\pi/4)$ is the same point as $W(^-3\pi/4)$, as shown in Fig. 9–10,

$$W\left(\frac{21\pi}{4}\right) = \left(\frac{^-\sqrt{2}}{2}, \frac{^-\sqrt{2}}{2}\right).$$

We must add $3(2\pi)$, or 6π, to $^-(11\pi)/2$ in order to obtain a number t between 0 and 2π:

$$t = \frac{^-11}{2}\pi + 6\pi = \frac{\pi}{2}.$$

By the periodicity of W,

$$W\left(\frac{^-11\pi}{2}\right) = W\left(\frac{\pi}{2}\right), \quad \text{or } (0, 1).$$

Exercises for Discussion

1. Complete the following table.

s	0	$\frac{\pi}{6}$	$\frac{\pi}{4}$	$\frac{\pi}{3}$	$\frac{\pi}{2}$
$W(s)$	(1, 0)	(?, ?) $\left(\frac{\sqrt{3}}{2}, \frac{1}{2}\right)$	(?, ?) $\left(\frac{\sqrt{2}}{2}, \frac{\sqrt{2}}{2}\right)$	(?, ?) $\left(\frac{1}{2}, \frac{\sqrt{3}}{2}\right)$	(0, 1)

s	$\frac{2\pi}{3}$	$\frac{3\pi}{4}$	$\frac{5\pi}{6}$	π
$W(s)$	(?, ?) $\left(\frac{^-1}{2}, \frac{\sqrt{3}}{2}\right)$	(?, ?) $\left(\frac{^-\sqrt{2}}{2}, \frac{\sqrt{2}}{2}\right)$	(?, ?) $\left(\frac{^-\sqrt{3}}{2}, \frac{1}{2}\right)$	($^-1$, 0)
s	$\frac{7\pi}{6}$	$\frac{5\pi}{4}$	$\frac{4\pi}{3}$	$\frac{3\pi}{2}$
$W(s)$	(?, ?) $\left(\frac{^-\sqrt{3}}{2}, \frac{^-1}{2}\right)$	(?, ?) $\left(\frac{^-\sqrt{2}}{2}, \frac{^-\sqrt{2}}{2}\right)$	(?, ?) $\left(\frac{^-1}{2}, \frac{^-\sqrt{3}}{2}\right)$	(0, $^-1$)
s	$\frac{5\pi}{3}$	$\frac{7\pi}{4}$	$\frac{11\pi}{6}$	2π
$W(s)$	(?, ?)	(?, ?)	(?, ?)	(1, 0)

2. Fill in the bottom row with real numbers t which lie in the interval $0 \leqq t < 2\pi$ and have the property $W(t) = W(s)$.

s	3π	$\frac{7\pi}{2}$	4π	$\frac{11\pi}{2}$	7π	10π
t	π?	$\frac{3\pi}{2}$?	0?	$\frac{3\pi}{2}$?	π?	0 ?

s	$^-2\pi$	$^-\frac{5\pi}{2}$	$^-3\pi$	$^-5\pi$	$^-7\pi$	$^-\frac{15\pi}{2}$
t	0?	$\frac{3\pi}{2}$?	π?	π?	π?	$\frac{\pi}{2}$?

3. Fill in the blanks of the following table for the wrapping function W by visualizing a thread wrapped around the unit circle in the manner described in the text. Make sketches on scratch paper.

s	3π	$\frac{7\pi}{2}$	4π	$\frac{11\pi}{2}$	7π	10π
$W(s)$	$(^-1, 0)$	? $(0, ^-1)$	? $(1, 0)$	? $(0, ^-1)$	? $(^-1, 0)$	? $(1, 0)$

s	$^-2\pi$	$^-\frac{5\pi}{2}$	$^-3\pi$	$^-5\pi$	$^-7\pi$	$^-\frac{15\pi}{2}$
$W(s)$	$(1, 0)$	? $(0, ^-1)$	? $(^-1, 0)$	? $(^-1, 0)$	? $(^-1, 0)$	? $(0, 1)$

Exercises

In Exercises 1–6, find a number t such that $0 \leqq t < 2\pi$ and $W(t) = W(s)$.

1. $s = \frac{13\pi}{6}$ $\frac{\pi}{6}$ 2. $s = \frac{19\pi}{6}$ $\frac{7\pi}{6}$ 3. $s = \frac{13\pi}{3}$ $\frac{\pi}{3}$

4. $s = \frac{^-22\pi}{3}$ $\frac{2\pi}{3}$ 5. $s = \frac{3\pi}{4}$ $\frac{3\pi}{4}$ 6. $s = \frac{^-15\pi}{4}$ $\frac{\pi}{4}$

7. For each number s in Exercises 1–6, find the coordinates of the point $W(s)$.

Find the coordinates of the point $P = W(s)$ for each value of s in Exercises 8–19.

8. $s = \frac{^-14\pi}{3}$ $\left(\frac{^-1}{2}, \frac{^-\sqrt{3}}{2}\right)$ 9. $s = \frac{11\pi}{3}$ $\left(\frac{1}{2}, \frac{^-\sqrt{3}}{2}\right)$ 10. $s = \frac{27\pi}{4}$ $\left(\frac{^-\sqrt{2}}{2}, \frac{\sqrt{2}}{2}\right)$

11. $s = \frac{^-7\pi}{4}$ $\left(\frac{\sqrt{2}}{2}, \frac{\sqrt{2}}{2}\right)$ 12. $s = \frac{41\pi}{6}$ $\left(\frac{^-\sqrt{3}}{2}, \frac{1}{2}\right)$ 13. $s = \frac{35\pi}{6}$ $\left(\frac{\sqrt{3}}{2}, \frac{^-1}{2}\right)$

14. $s = \frac{47\pi}{4}$ $\left(\frac{\sqrt{2}}{2}, \frac{^-\sqrt{2}}{2}\right)$ 15. $s = \frac{9\pi}{2}$ $(0, 1)$ 16. $s = \frac{^-11\pi}{3}$ $\left(\frac{1}{2}, \frac{\sqrt{3}}{2}\right)$

17. $s = \frac{^-27\pi}{4}$ $\left(\frac{^-\sqrt{2}}{2}, \frac{^-\sqrt{2}}{2}\right)$ 18. $s = \frac{23\pi}{6}$ $\left(\frac{\sqrt{3}}{2}, \frac{^-1}{2}\right)$ 19. $s = \frac{22\pi}{3}$ $\left(\frac{^-1}{2}, \frac{^-\sqrt{3}}{2}\right)$

Answers to Exercise 7

7. (1) $\left(\frac{\sqrt{3}}{2}, \frac{1}{2}\right)$; (2) $\left(\frac{^-\sqrt{3}}{2}, \frac{^-1}{2}\right)$;
(3) $\left(\frac{1}{2}, \frac{\sqrt{3}}{2}\right)$; (4) $\left(\frac{^-1}{2}, \frac{\sqrt{3}}{2}\right)$;
(5) $\left(\frac{^-\sqrt{2}}{2}, \frac{\sqrt{2}}{2}\right)$;
(6) $\left(\frac{\sqrt{2}}{2}, \frac{\sqrt{2}}{2}\right)$

Quiz

Find each of the following values of the wrapping function W.

1. $W(\pi/2)$ (ans: $(0, 1)$)
2. $W(^-\pi)$ (ans: $(^-1, 0)$)
3. $W(\pi/3)$ (ans: $(1/2, \sqrt{3}/2)$)
4. $W(^-2\pi/3)$ (ans: $(^-1/2, ^-\sqrt{3}/2)$)
5. $W(17\pi/4)$ (ans: $(\sqrt{2}/2, \sqrt{2}/2)$)

9–3 PROPERTIES OF THE WRAPPING FUNCTION

It is important to assure students that the properties of W listed in this section need not be memorized. They are introduced and numbered here for reference in the sections that follow.

With this assurance, the students should not find verification of the various properties difficult if they are willing to go through the motions of wrapping each time. In fact, they are apt to enjoy the discovery aspect of this section.

9–3 PROPERTIES OF THE WRAPPING FUNCTION

For every real number s, the points $W(s)$ and $W(^-s)$ are mirror images of each other, as shown in Fig. 9–12. This relationship can be stated as follows:

$$\textit{If } W(s) = (x, y), \quad \textit{then } W(^-s) = (x, ^-y). \qquad (1)$$

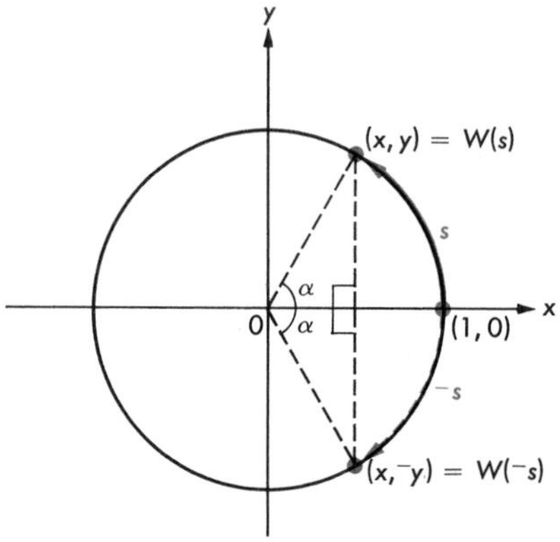

FIGURE 9–12

For example,

$$W\left(\frac{3\pi}{4}\right) = \left(^-\frac{\sqrt{2}}{2}, \frac{\sqrt{2}}{2}\right)$$

and

$$W\left(^-\frac{3\pi}{4}\right) = \left(^-\frac{\sqrt{2}}{2}, ^-\frac{\sqrt{2}}{2}\right).$$

The points $W(s)$ and $W(s + \pi/2)$ are also related. To illustrate this relation, let us consider $s = \pi/6$. Then $s + \pi/2 = 2\pi/3$. Since $s = \pi/6$, we can use the information we know about a 30°–60° right triangle (see Fig. 9–13) to find that

$$W\left(\frac{\pi}{6}\right) = \left(\frac{\sqrt{3}}{2}, \frac{1}{2}\right) \quad \text{and} \quad W\left(\frac{2\pi}{3}\right) = \left(^-\frac{1}{2}, \frac{\sqrt{3}}{2}\right).$$

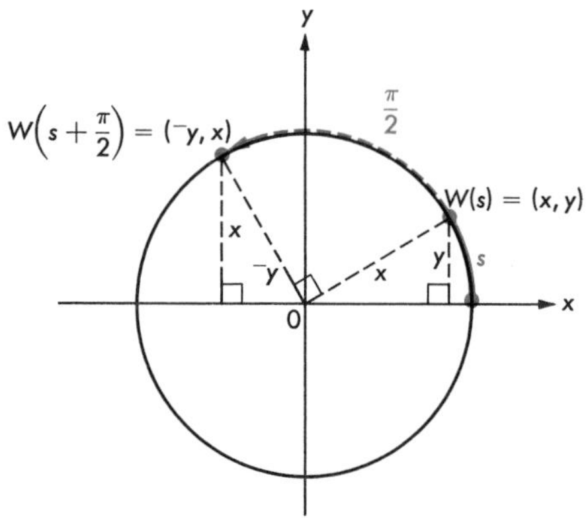

FIGURE 9–13

This relationship between $W(s)$ and $W(s + \pi/2)$ will always hold because the triangles involved will always be congruent. We state this relationship in the following way.

$$\textit{If } W(s) = (x, y), \textit{ then } W\left(s + \frac{\pi}{2}\right) = (^-y, x). \qquad (2)$$

In other words, the x-coordinate of $W(s)$ becomes the y-coordinate of $W(s + \pi/2)$, and the opposite of the y-coordinate of $W(s)$ becomes the x-coordinate of $W(s + \pi/2)$.

Since

$$s + \pi = \left(s + \frac{\pi}{2}\right) + \frac{\pi}{2},$$

we can use relationship (2) twice to obtain $W(s + \pi)$: If

$$W(s) = (x, y),$$

then

$$W\left(s + \frac{\pi}{2}\right) = (^-y, x)$$

and

$$W\left(\left(s + \frac{\pi}{2}\right) + \frac{\pi}{2}\right) = (^-x, {}^-y).$$

Also, $W(s + \pi) = W(s - \pi)$ by the periodicity of W. Thus, we have the following result.

$$\textit{If } W(s) = (x, y), \textit{ then } W(s + \pi) = W(s - \pi) = (^-x, {}^-y). \qquad (3)$$

We can use relationships (2) and (3) to find functional values of many other combinations of s and $\pi/2$. For example, if

$$W(s + \pi/2) = (^-y, x),$$

then $W(s - \pi/2) = W((s + \pi/2) - \pi) = (y, {}^-x)$ by relationship (3). Thus, by relationship (2), we have the following.

$$\textit{If } W(s) = (x, y), \textit{ then } W\left(s - \frac{\pi}{2}\right) = (y, {}^-x). \qquad (4)$$

Problem. If $W(s) = (x, y)$, what is $W(\pi/2 - s)$?

Solution. If $W(s) = (x, y)$, then

$$W\left(s - \frac{\pi}{2}\right) = (y, {}^-x)$$

and

$$W\left(\frac{\pi}{2} - s\right) = W\left(^-\left(s - \frac{\pi}{2}\right)\right) = (y, x).$$

While relationship (2) is valid whatever the original point $W(s)$ may be, it is undoubtedly easier to remember the relationship between $W(s)$ and $W(s + \pi/2)$, when needed, by picturing $W(s)$ as a point (x, y) in the first quadrant, with $W(s + \pi/2)$ then becoming the point $(^-y, x)$ in the second quadrant.

The relationship between $W(s)$ and $W(s + \pi)$ may, of course, be obtained directly by locating $W(s)$ and then $W(s + \pi)$ on the unit circle using the wrapping function. On the other hand, $W(s - \pi)$ may be obtained from $W(s + \pi)$ by using the periodicity of W, or from a drawing of $W(s)$ and $W(s - \pi)$.

Answers to Exercises for Discussion 1, 3–5, page 378

1.

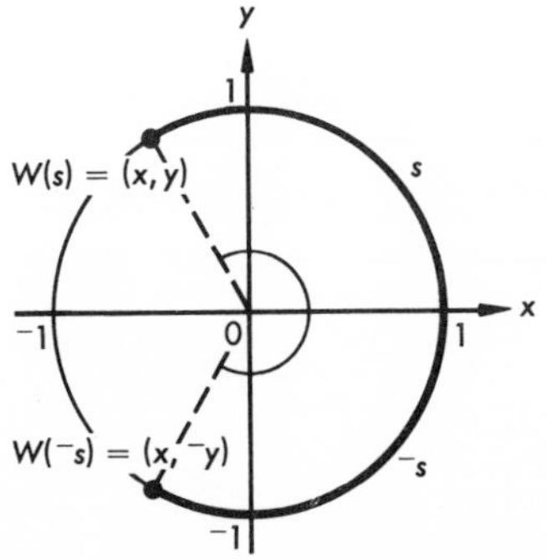

3. $P = W\left(\frac{\pi}{4}\right) = \left(\frac{\sqrt{2}}{2}, \frac{\sqrt{2}}{2}\right)$

$W\left(\frac{\pi}{4} + \frac{\pi}{2}\right) = W\left(\frac{3\pi}{4}\right)$

$= \left(\frac{^-\sqrt{2}}{2}, \frac{\sqrt{2}}{2}\right) = Q$

$Q = W\left(\frac{3\pi}{4}\right) = \left(\frac{^-\sqrt{2}}{2}, \frac{\sqrt{2}}{2}\right)$

$W\left(\frac{3\pi}{4} + \frac{\pi}{2}\right) = W\left(\frac{5\pi}{4}\right)$

$= \left(\frac{^-\sqrt{2}}{2}, \frac{^-\sqrt{2}}{2}\right) = R$

$R = W\left(\frac{5\pi}{4}\right) = \left(\frac{^-\sqrt{2}}{2}, \frac{^-\sqrt{2}}{2}\right)$

$W\left(\frac{5\pi}{4} + \frac{\pi}{2}\right) = W\left(\frac{7\pi}{4}\right)$

$= \left(\frac{\sqrt{2}}{2}, \frac{^-\sqrt{2}}{2}\right) = S$

$S = W\left(\frac{7\pi}{4}\right) = \left(\frac{\sqrt{2}}{2}, \frac{^-\sqrt{2}}{2}\right)$

$W\left(\frac{7\pi}{4} + \frac{\pi}{2}\right) = W\left(\frac{9\pi}{4}\right)$

$= \left(\frac{\sqrt{2}}{2}, \frac{\sqrt{2}}{2}\right) = P$

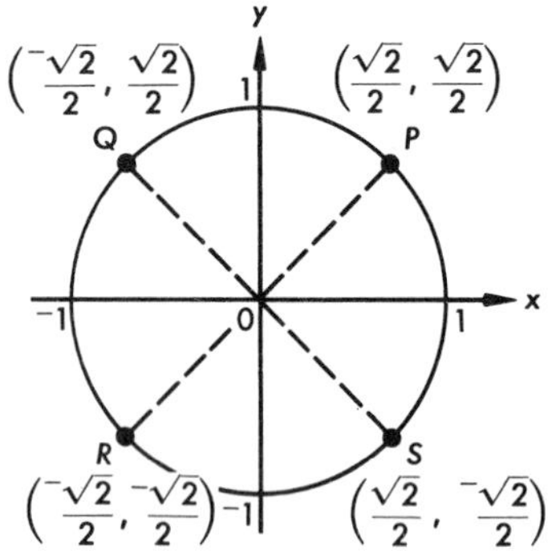

4.

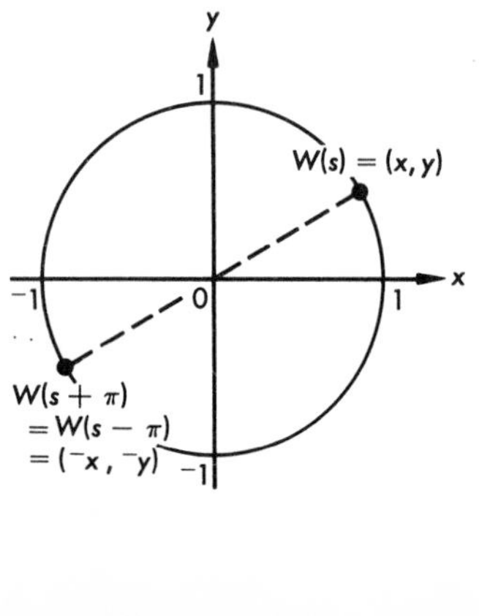

Exercises for Discussion

1. Suppose that s is a number between $\pi/2$ and π. Make a drawing like that of Fig. 9–12 to show the relationship between $W(s)$ and $W(^-s)$.

2. Verify the following relationship for $s = 0$, $s = \pi/2$, $s = \pi$, and $s = 3\pi/2$. $W(0) = (1, 0)$, $W(\frac{\pi}{2}) = (0, 1)$, $W(\frac{^-\pi}{2}) = (0, ^-1)$,

$$\text{If } W(s) = (x, y), \text{ then } W(^-s) = (x, ^-y).$$

$W(\pi) = (^-1, 0)$, $W(^-\pi) = (^-1, 0)$; $W(\frac{3\pi}{2}) = (0, ^-1)$, $W(\frac{^-3\pi}{2}) = (0, 1)$

3. Locate the point $P = W(\pi/4)$ on a graph of the unit circle and label this point with its coordinates. On the same graph, locate the following points and give their coordinates.

$$Q = W\left(\frac{3\pi}{4}\right), \quad R = W\left(\frac{5\pi}{4}\right), \quad S = W\left(\frac{7\pi}{4}\right)$$

On your sketch, draw dotted lines to help you find the coordinates of each point. Verify that the following relationship applied to P, Q, R, and S will yield coordinates of points Q, R, S, and P, respectively.

$$\text{If } W(s) = (x, y) \text{ then } W\left(s + \frac{\pi}{2}\right) = (^-y, x).$$

4. On a graph of the unit circle, show the relationship between the points $W(s)$ and $W(s \pm \pi)$. Derive the following relationship from your figure.

$$\text{If } W(s) = (x, y), \text{ then } W(s + \pi) = W(s - \pi) = (^-x, ^-y).$$

5. (a) Locate the point

$$P = W\left(\frac{\pi}{6}\right)$$

on a graph of the unit circle and label this point with its coordinate. On the same graph, locate the point

$$Q = W\left(\frac{7\pi}{6}\right)$$

and give its coordinates. Verify that if relationship (3) on page 377 is applied to P and Q, respectively, it will yield coordinates of the points Q and P, respectively.

(b) Follow the directions of part (a), using points

$$P = W\left(\frac{5\pi}{6}\right) \quad \text{and} \quad Q = W\left(\frac{11\pi}{6}\right).$$

Exercises

In Exercises 1–5, find the coordinates of each indicated point.

1. $W\left(\frac{3\pi}{4}\right)$, $W\left(-\frac{13\pi}{4}\right)$ $\left(\frac{-\sqrt{2}}{2}, \frac{\sqrt{2}}{2}\right)$; $\left(\frac{-\sqrt{2}}{2}, \frac{\sqrt{2}}{2}\right)$
2. $W\left(-\frac{2\pi}{3}\right)$, $W\left(\frac{4\pi}{3}\right)$ $\left(\frac{-1}{2}, \frac{-\sqrt{3}}{2}\right)$; $\left(\frac{-1}{2}, \frac{-\sqrt{3}}{2}\right)$
3. $W\left(\frac{7\pi}{6}\right)$, $W\left(\frac{31\pi}{6}\right)$ $\left(\frac{-\sqrt{3}}{2}, \frac{-1}{2}\right)$; $\left(\frac{-\sqrt{3}}{2}, \frac{-1}{2}\right)$
4. $W\left(-\frac{3\pi}{4}\right)$, $W(19\pi)$ $\left(\frac{-\sqrt{2}}{2}, \frac{-\sqrt{2}}{2}\right)$; $(-1, 0)$
5. $W(18\pi)$, $W(3\pi)$ $(1, 0)$; $(-1, 0)$

6. If the points $W(s)$ and $W(s')$ have the same coordinates, how are s and s' related? $s' = s + 2n\pi$, n an integer

7. Complete the following table.

s	0	$\frac{\pi}{6}$	$\frac{\pi}{4}$	$\frac{\pi}{3}$
$W(s)$	$(1, 0)$	$\left(\frac{\sqrt{3}}{2}, \frac{1}{2}\right)$	$\left(\frac{\sqrt{2}}{2}, \frac{\sqrt{2}}{2}\right)$	$\left(\frac{1}{2}, \frac{\sqrt{3}}{2}\right)$
$W(-s)$	$(1, 0)$ (?, ?)	$(\sqrt{3}/2, -1/2)$ (?, ?)	$(\sqrt{2}/2, -\sqrt{2}/2)$ (?, ?)	$(1/2, -\sqrt{3}/2)$ (_?_, _?_)
$s + \frac{\pi}{2}$	$\frac{\pi}{2}$?	$\frac{2\pi}{3}$?	$\frac{3\pi}{4}$?	$\frac{5\pi}{6}$?
$W\left(s + \frac{\pi}{2}\right)$	(?, ?) $(0, 1)$	(?, ?) $\left(\frac{-1}{2}, \frac{\sqrt{3}}{2}\right)$	(?, ?) $\left(\frac{-\sqrt{2}}{2}, \frac{\sqrt{2}}{2}\right)$	(?, ?) $\left(\frac{-\sqrt{3}}{2}, \frac{1}{2}\right)$
s	$\frac{\pi}{2}$	$\frac{2\pi}{3}$	$\frac{5\pi}{6}$	$\frac{3\pi}{4}$
$W(s)$	$(0, 1)$	$(-\frac{1}{2}, \sqrt{3}/2)$ (?, ?)	$(-\sqrt{3}/2, 1/2)$ (?, ?)	$(-\sqrt{2}/2, \sqrt{2}/2)$ (?, ?)
$W(-s)$	$(0, -1)$ (?, ?)	$(-\frac{1}{2}, -\sqrt{3}/2)$ (?, ?)	$(-\sqrt{3}/2, -1/2)$ (?, ?)	$(-\sqrt{2}/2, -\sqrt{2}/2)$ (?, ?)
$s + \frac{\pi}{2}$	π ?	$\frac{7\pi}{6}$?	$\frac{4\pi}{3}$?	$\frac{5\pi}{4}$?
$W\left(s + \frac{\pi}{2}\right)$	(?, ?) $(-1, 0)$	(?, ?) $\left(\frac{-\sqrt{3}}{2}, \frac{-1}{2}\right)$	(?, ?) $\left(\frac{-1}{2}, \frac{-\sqrt{3}}{2}\right)$	(?, ?) $\left(\frac{-\sqrt{2}}{2}, \frac{-\sqrt{2}}{2}\right)$

△

8. Use relationships (1) and (3) on pages 376 and 377 to find $W(\pi - s)$, given that $W(s) = (x, y)$. $(-x, y)$

5. (a) $P = W\left(\frac{\pi}{6}\right) = \left(\frac{\sqrt{3}}{2}, \frac{1}{2}\right)$

$$W\left(\frac{\pi}{6} + \pi\right) = W\left(\frac{7\pi}{6}\right) = W\left(\frac{\pi}{6} - \pi\right) = \left(\frac{-\sqrt{3}}{2}, \frac{-1}{2}\right) = Q$$

$$Q = W\left(\frac{7\pi}{6}\right) = \left(\frac{-\sqrt{3}}{2}, \frac{-1}{2}\right)$$

$$W\left(\frac{7\pi}{6} + \pi\right) = W\left(\frac{13\pi}{6}\right) = W\left(\frac{\pi}{6}\right) = W\left(\frac{7\pi}{6} - \pi\right) = \left(\frac{\sqrt{3}}{2}, \frac{1}{2}\right) = P$$

(b) $P = W\left(\frac{5\pi}{6}\right) = \left(\frac{-\sqrt{3}}{2}, \frac{1}{2}\right)$

$$W\left(\frac{5\pi}{6} + \pi\right) = W\left(\frac{11\pi}{6}\right) = W\left(\frac{5\pi}{6} - \pi\right) = \left(\frac{\sqrt{3}}{2}, \frac{-1}{2}\right) = Q$$

$$Q = W\left(\frac{11\pi}{6}\right) = \left(\frac{\sqrt{3}}{2}, \frac{-1}{2}\right)$$

$$W\left(\frac{11\pi}{6} + \pi\right) = W\left(\frac{17\pi}{6}\right) = W\left(\frac{5\pi}{6}\right) = W\left(\frac{11\pi}{6} - \pi\right) = \left(\frac{-\sqrt{3}}{2}, \frac{1}{2}\right) = P$$

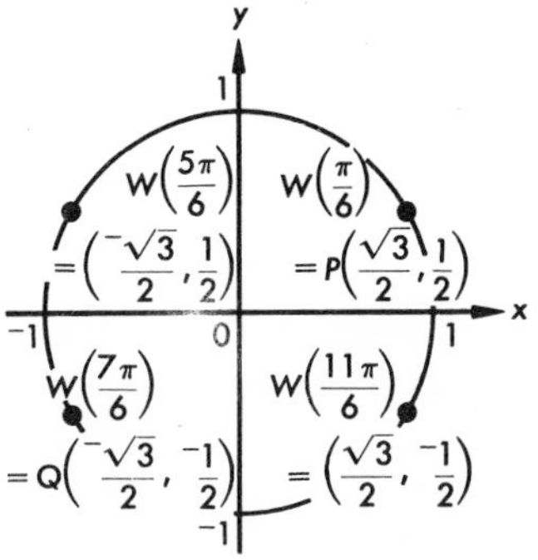

Quiz

1. Make a drawing of the unit circle locating the point $W(s)$ if s is some number between $\pi/2$ and π. Locate the points $W(^-s)$ and $W(s+\pi)$ on your drawing. If $W(s) = (a, b)$ then

$$W(^-s) = (?, ?)$$

and

$$W(s+\pi) = (?, ?)$$

(ans: $W(^-s) = (a, ^-b)$; $W(s+\pi) = (^-a, ^-b)$)

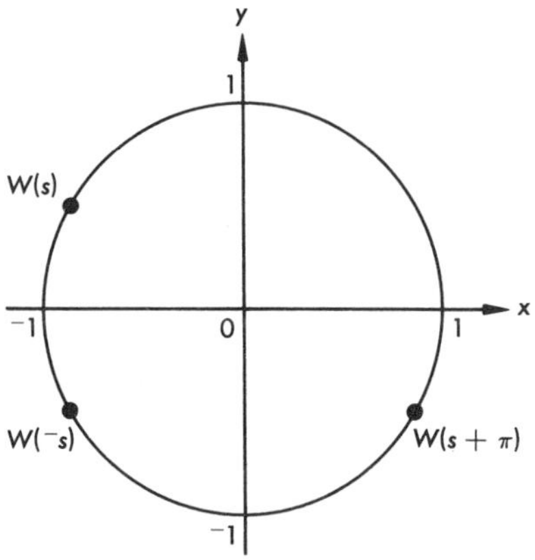

2. Find the following values of the wrapping function W.

(a) $W(\pi/3)$

$\left(\text{ans: } \left(\frac{1}{2}, \frac{\sqrt{3}}{2}\right)\right)$

(b) $W(^-\pi/3)$

$\left(\text{ans: } \left(\frac{1}{2}, \frac{^-\sqrt{3}}{2}\right)\right)$

(c) $W(2\pi - \pi/3)$

$\left(\text{ans: } \left(\frac{1}{2}, \frac{^-\sqrt{3}}{2}\right)\right)$

9–4 THE SINE AND COSINE

In this section, the convenience of the wrapping-function approach is emphasized. The cosine of s is simply the *abscissa* and the sine of s the *ordinate* of the point $W(s)$.

9–4 THE SINE AND COSINE

We recall that the wrapping function W associates with each number s a unique point $W(s)$ on the unit circle (Fig. 9–14). The coordinates of $W(s)$ are also functions of s; therefore, we can make the following definitions.

> ***DEFINITION OF SINE AND COSINE***
>
> $W(s)$ = *(cosine s, sine s)* *for every real number s*

According to the definition above, the x-coordinate of a point $W(s)$ on the unit circle is the cos s and the y-coordinate is the sin s, that is

$$\cos s = x \quad \text{and} \quad \sin s = y.$$

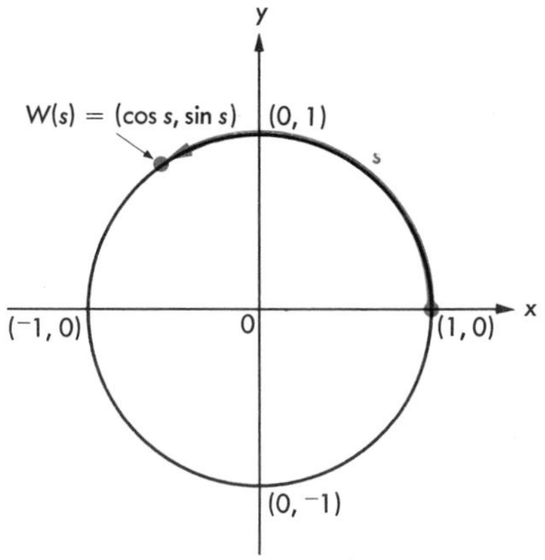

FIGURE 9–14

The function W is periodic with period 2π. Knowing this, we can show the truth of the following statement.

The sine and cosine are periodic functions; each has period 2π.

Problem 1. Find the sine and cosine of $\pi/4$, $\pi/3$, and $\pi/2$.

Solution. In Fig. 9–9, we saw that $W(\pi/4) = (\sqrt{2}/2, \sqrt{2}/2)$. Hence,

$$\sin\frac{\pi}{4} = \frac{\sqrt{2}}{2}, \quad \cos\frac{\pi}{4} = \frac{\sqrt{2}}{2},$$

and $W(\pi/3) = (1/2, \sqrt{3}/2)$. (See Fig. 9–15.) Therefore,

$$\sin\frac{\pi}{3} = \frac{\sqrt{3}}{2}, \quad \cos\frac{\pi}{3} = \frac{1}{2}.$$

Since $W(\pi/2) = (0, 1)$, we have

$$\sin\frac{\pi}{2} = 1, \quad \cos\frac{\pi}{2} = 0.$$

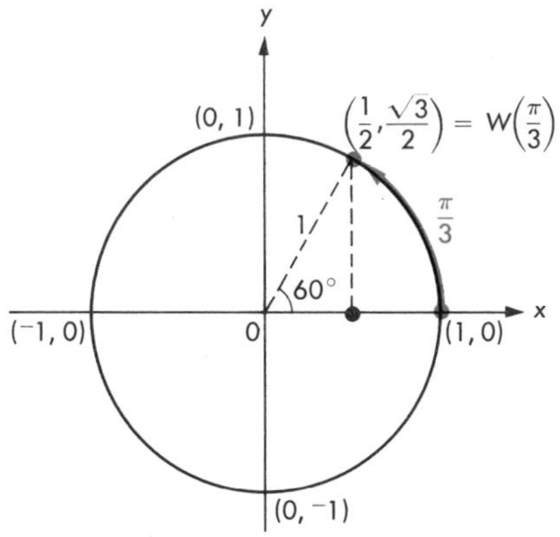

FIGURE 9–15

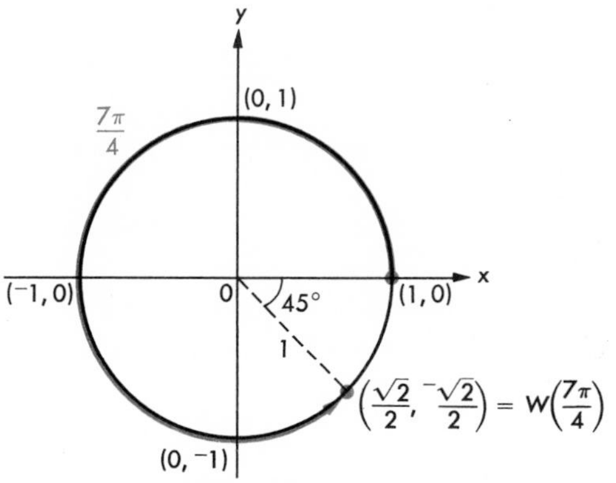

FIGURE 9–16

Problem 2. Find the sine and cosine of $55\pi/4$ and $^-10\pi/3$.

Solution. The greatest integral multiple of 2π contained in $55\pi/4$ is 6. Therefore,

$$W\left(\frac{55\pi}{4}\right) = W\left(\frac{55\pi}{4} - (6 \cdot 2\pi)\right), \text{ or } W\left(\frac{7\pi}{4}\right).$$

According to Fig. 9–16, $W(7\pi/4) = (\sqrt{2}/2, {}^-\sqrt{2}/2)$. Thus,

$$\sin\frac{55\pi}{4} = \frac{^-\sqrt{2}}{2}, \quad \cos\frac{55\pi}{4} = \frac{\sqrt{2}}{2}.$$

By the periodicity of W, we have

$$W\left(\frac{^-10\pi}{3}\right) = W\left(4\pi - \frac{10\pi}{3}\right), \text{ or } W\left(\frac{2\pi}{3}\right).$$

According to Fig. 9–17, $W(2\pi/3) = (^-1/2, \sqrt{3}/2)$.

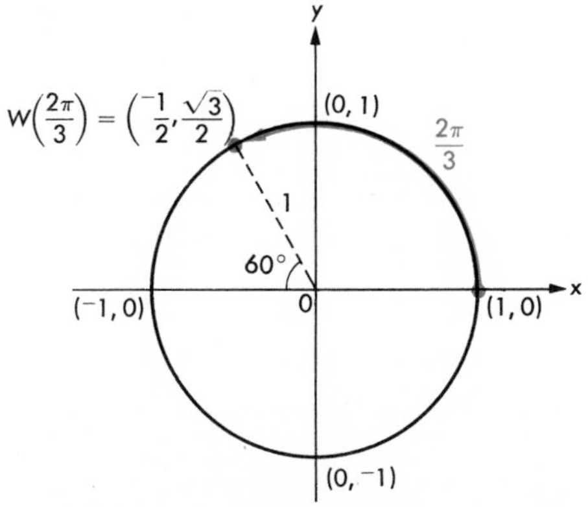

FIGURE 9–17

Finding $W(s)$ for a given s provides the answers to *two* questions:

$$\sin s = ? \text{ and } \cos s = ?$$

The problems and exercises of this section provide added practice in working with the special numbers which are integral multiples of $\pi/6$, $\pi/4$, and $\pi/3$.

By now the student should have become reasonably adept at finding what multiple of 2π to subtract or add to the given s. For example,

$$\frac{55\pi}{4} = 13\tfrac{3}{4}\pi$$

suggests subtracting 12π and

$$\frac{^-10\pi}{3} = {}^-3\tfrac{1}{3}\pi$$

suggests adding 4π.

Thus,

$$\sin\left(\frac{^-10\pi}{3}\right) = \frac{\sqrt{3}}{2}, \quad \cos\left(\frac{^-10\pi}{3}\right) = \frac{^-1}{2}.$$

The unit circle has equation

$$x^2 + y^2 = 1.$$

Therefore, for each real number s, the point $W(s)$ on the unit circle has coordinates $(\cos s, \sin s)$ which are a solution of the above equation. This can be stated in the following way.

FIRST FUNDAMENTAL IDENTITY

$\sin^2 s + \cos^2 s = 1$ *for every real number s* **(*FI*-1)**

The first fundamental identity is an important identity and, of course, implies that

$$\sin^2 s = 1 - \cos^2 s,$$

or

$$\cos^2 s = 1 - \sin^2 s,$$

which is the form in which it is often used (see Exercise 11).

Note that we write $\sin^2 s$ for $(\sin s)^2$ and $\cos^2 s$ for $(\cos s)^2$. The first fundamental identity is an example of an equation which is true for all numbers in the domains of the functions. In trigonometry, such an equation is frequently called an *identity.*

It follows from the first fundamental identity that $\sin^2 s \leqq 1$ and $\cos^2 s \leqq 1$. Hence,

$$^-1 \leqq \sin s \leqq 1 \quad \textit{for every real number } s,$$

$$^-1 \leqq \cos s \leqq 1 \quad \textit{for every real number } s.$$

To emphasize these inequalities, you could draw the unit circle on the board, ask for the definitions of sin *s* and cos *s*, and for a geometric argument to prove the inequalities. (No points on the unit circle lie outside the square with sides tangent to the circle at (1, 0), (0, 1), ($^-1$, 0), (0, $^-1$)).

In other words, the interval $\{x \mid {}^-1 \leqq x \leqq 1\}$ is the *range* of the cosine and $\{y \mid {}^-1 \leqq y \leqq 1\}$ is the range of the sine.

Exercises for Discussion

If time is limited, it is suggested that at least Exercises for Discussion 2, 3, 5, and 6 be covered.

For each s in Exercises 1–4, find $W(s)$, and give $\sin s$ and $\cos s$.

1. $\frac{9\pi}{4}$ — $W\left(\frac{9\pi}{4}\right) = \left(\frac{\sqrt{2}}{2}, \frac{\sqrt{2}}{2}\right)$; $\sin\frac{9\pi}{4} = \frac{\sqrt{2}}{2}$; $\cos\frac{9\pi}{4} = \frac{\sqrt{2}}{2}$

2. $\frac{5\pi}{6}$ — $W\left(\frac{5\pi}{6}\right) = \left(\frac{^-\sqrt{3}}{2}, \frac{1}{2}\right)$; $\sin\frac{5\pi}{6} = \frac{1}{2}$; $\cos\frac{5\pi}{6} = \frac{^-\sqrt{3}}{2}$

3. $^-\frac{\pi}{6}$ — $W\left(\frac{^-\pi}{6}\right) = \left(\frac{\sqrt{3}}{2}, \frac{^-1}{2}\right)$; $\sin\frac{^-\pi}{6} = \frac{^-1}{2}$; $\cos\frac{^-\pi}{6} = \frac{\sqrt{3}}{2}$

4. $\frac{4\pi}{3}$ — $W\left(\frac{4\pi}{3}\right) = \left(\frac{^-1}{2}, \frac{^-\sqrt{3}}{2}\right)$; $\sin\frac{4\pi}{3} = \frac{^-\sqrt{3}}{2}$; $\cos\frac{4\pi}{3} = \frac{^-1}{2}$

5. Complete the following table by telling whether the sin s and cos s are positive or negative numbers in each of the four quadrants in a cartesian coordinate system.

	I	II	III	IV
sin s	+	+ ?	− ?	− ?
cos s	+	− ?	− ?	+ ?

6. (a) When we say $\sin s = 1$, we mean that the y-coordinate of $W(s)$ is 1. Draw a sketch of the unit circle and locate all such points. How many points have this property? One point only: (0, 1)
(b) For what values of s in the interval $0 \leqq s < 2\pi$ is $\cos s = 1$? $s = 0$

Exercises

Find each of the following.

1. $\sin \frac{9\pi}{4}$ $\frac{\sqrt{2}}{2}$
2. $\cos\left(\frac{^-5\pi}{6}\right)$ $\frac{^-\sqrt{3}}{2}$
3. $\cos \frac{7\pi}{3}$ $\frac{1}{2}$
4. $\sin \frac{13\pi}{4}$ $\frac{^-\sqrt{2}}{2}$
5. $\cos \frac{3\pi}{2}$ 0
6. $\cos \frac{17\pi}{6}$ $\frac{^-\sqrt{3}}{2}$
7. $\sin \frac{5\pi}{6}$ $\frac{1}{2}$
8. $\sin(^-3\pi)$ 0
9. $\sin\left(\frac{^-5\pi}{6}\right)$ $\frac{^-1}{2}$
10. $\cos 4\pi$ 1

△

11. (a) If $\sin s = \frac{1}{2}$, use (FI-1) to find the two possible values of $\cos s$. $\frac{\sqrt{3}}{2}, \frac{^-\sqrt{3}}{2}$
(b) Since $\sin s$ in part (a) is positive, the point $W(s)$ must be in the first or second quadrant. Why? See Solution Manual.
(c) If $\sin s = \frac{1}{2}$ and $\pi/2 < s < \pi$, what is $\cos s$? $\frac{^-\sqrt{3}}{2}$
(d) Draw a sketch and find s for part (c). See Solution Manual.

12. (a) If $^-\pi/2 < s < 0$, is $\cos s$ positive or negative? Positive
(b) Given that s is in the interval $^-\pi/2 < s < 0$ and that $\cos s = \frac{3}{5}$, use (FI-1) to find $\sin s$. $\frac{^-4}{5}$

9-5 PROPERTIES OF SINE AND COSINE

Many identities follow from the properties of the wrapping function given in Section 9-4. The first fundamental identity, (FI-1), was stated in Section 9-4. The following are some other fundamental identities.

$$\sin(^-s) = {}^-\sin s \qquad (FI\text{-}2)$$

$$\cos(^-s) = \cos s \qquad (FI\text{-}3)$$

These follow directly from relationship (1) on page 376.

We call f an *odd function* if $f(^-x) = {}^-f(x)$ for every x in the domain

Answer to Exercise for Discussion 6(a)

6. (a)

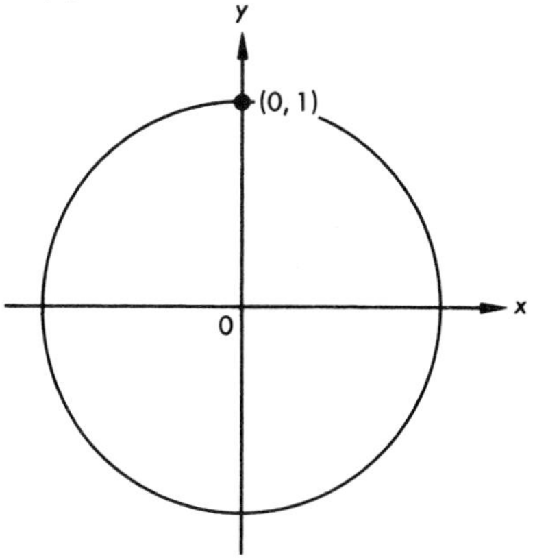

Quiz

Find each of the following.

1. $\sin \frac{7\pi}{4}$ $\left(\text{ans: } \frac{^-\sqrt{2}}{2}\right)$
2. $\sin \frac{7\pi}{3}$ $\left(\text{ans: } \frac{\sqrt{3}}{2}\right)$
3. $\cos(^-5\pi)$ (ans: $^-1$)
4. $\cos \frac{7\pi}{6}$ $\left(\text{ans: } \frac{^-\sqrt{3}}{2}\right)$
5. $\sin 5\pi$ (ans: 0)

9-5 PROPERTIES OF SINE AND COSINE

In order to recall the relationship of $W(^-s)$ to $W(s)$, you could draw the unit circle and label a point

$$W(s) = (a, b),$$

s in the first quadrant, and the point

$$W(^-s) = (a, {}^-b)$$

in the fourth quadrant.

of f. We call f an *even function* if $f(^-x) = f(x)$ for every x in the domain of f. By the second fundamental identity, *sine is an odd function*, and by the third fundamental identity, *cosine is an even function.*

If $W(s) = (\cos s, \sin s)$, then $W(s + \pi/2) = (^-\sin s, \cos s)$ by the second relationship on page 377. This leads us to the fourth and fifth fundamental identities.

$$\sin\left(s + \frac{\pi}{2}\right) = \cos s \qquad \text{(FI-4)}$$

$$\cos\left(s + \frac{\pi}{2}\right) = {}^-\sin s \qquad \text{(FI-5)}$$

Other identities are given below.

$$\sin(s \pm \pi) = {}^-\sin s \qquad \text{(FI-6)}$$

$$\cos(s \pm \pi) = {}^-\cos s \qquad \text{(FI-7)}$$

$$\sin\left(s - \frac{\pi}{2}\right) = {}^-\cos s \qquad \text{(FI-8)}$$

$$\cos\left(s - \frac{\pi}{2}\right) = \sin s \qquad \text{(FI-9)}$$

Problem. Find $\sin 4\pi/3$ and $\cos 7\pi/4$.

Solution.

$$\sin\frac{4\pi}{3} = \sin\left(\frac{\pi}{3} + \pi\right) = {}^-\sin\frac{\pi}{3} = \frac{^-\sqrt{3}}{2}$$

$$\cos\frac{7\pi}{4} = \cos\left(\frac{3\pi}{4} + \pi\right) = {}^-\cos\frac{3\pi}{4} = {}^-\cos\left(\frac{\pi}{4} + \frac{\pi}{2}\right) = \sin\frac{\pi}{4} = \frac{\sqrt{2}}{2}$$

The fundamental identities derived in this section will be used in the next chapter. Of those listed, the second, third, sixth, and seventh are the most useful in application and are easiest to recall from the

Again it should be emphasized that the fourth through the ninth fundamental identities need not be memorized. Rather, with s chosen conveniently, a quick sketch of the points $W(s)$ and $W(s + \pi/2)$, and so on, will yield these identities.

For the sixth and seventh fundamental identities, use s in the first quadrant to sketch $W(s)$ and

$$W(s + \pi).$$

Use s in the third quadrant to sketch the points $W(s)$ and

$$W(s - \pi).$$

Of course, the identities are valid in each case for *any* choice of s but these are the convenient ones to use.

These may, of course, be computed directly from $W(4\pi/3)$ and $W(7\pi/4)$ and results checked with those of the text in which the various identities have been illustrated.

properties of the wrapping function W. For example,

$$\sin\left(^{-}\frac{10\pi}{3}\right) = {}^{-}\sin\frac{10\pi}{3} \qquad \text{(FI-2)}$$
$$= {}^{-}\sin\left(\frac{10\pi}{3} - 2\pi\right)$$
$$= {}^{-}\sin\frac{4\pi}{3}$$
$$= {}^{-}\left({}^{-}\sin\frac{\pi}{3}\right) \qquad \text{(FI-6)}$$
$$= \frac{\sqrt{3}}{2}.$$

In the following exercises, you may find it more useful to learn these formulas rather than to refer to them in the text.

Exercises for Discussion

1. Derive (FI-8) and (FI-9) from relationship (4) on page 377.
2. Derive (FI-6) and (FI-7) from relationship (3) on page 377.
3. (a) Consider the polynomial function f, defined by
$f(^-x) = {}^-x^5 - 3(^-x)^3 + 4(^-x) = {}^-x^5 + 3x^3 - 4x = {}^-(x^5 - 3x^3 + 4x) = {}^-f(x)$
$$f(x) = x^5 - 3x^3 + 4x.$$
Show that f is an *odd* function.
(b) Show that the polynomial function g, defined by
$g(^-x) = 3(^-x)^4 + 2(^-x)^2 - 5 = 3x^4 + 2x^2 - 5 = g(x)$
$$g(x) = 3x^4 + 2x^2 - 5,$$
is an *even* function.
(c) Consider the polynomial function h, defined by
$$h(x) = x^3 - 3x^2 + x - 2.$$
Is h odd? No Is h even? No
4. (a) Make a verbal statement about all *odd* polynomial functions by generalizing Exercise 3(a). Odd polynomial functions have only odd powers of x appearing.
(b) Make a verbal statement about all *even* polynomial functions by generalizing Exercise 3(b). Even polynomial functions have only even powers of x appearing.
(c) Make a verbal statement about polynomial functions that are neither odd nor even by generalizing Exercise 3(c). Polynomial functions which have both odd and even powers of x are neither odd nor even.

Evaluate each of the following.

5. $\sin\left(^{-}\frac{5\pi}{4}\right)$ $\frac{\sqrt{2}}{2}$

6. $\cos\left(^{-}\frac{7\pi}{6}\right)$ $\frac{^-\sqrt{3}}{2}$

Answers to Exercises for Discussion 1 and 2

1. If $W(s) = (x, y)$, then
$$W\left(s - \frac{\pi}{2}\right) = (y, {}^-x).$$
Hence,
$$\sin\left(s - \frac{\pi}{2}\right) = {}^-x = {}^-\cos s$$
and
$$\cos\left(s - \frac{\pi}{2}\right) = y = \sin s.$$

2. If $W(s) = (x, y)$, then
$$W(s \pm \pi) = ({}^-x, {}^-y).$$
Hence,
$$\sin(s \pm \pi) = {}^-y = {}^-\sin s$$
and
$$\cos(s \pm \pi) = {}^-x = {}^-\cos s.$$

Exercises, page 386

The students may also do these exercises directly, as before, by picturing $W(s)$ for the specified s. However, certain of the fundamental identities, especially the second, third, sixth and seventh, are easily remembered, and this, of course, saves time.

Quiz

1. Draw the unit circle and locate point $W(s) = (a, b)$ for s in the first quadrant. Then locate point $W(s + \pi)$ and give its coordinates. State the two identities involving sines and cosines of s and $s + \pi$.
(ans: $\sin(s + \pi) = {}^-\sin s$
$\cos(s + \pi) = {}^-\cos s$)

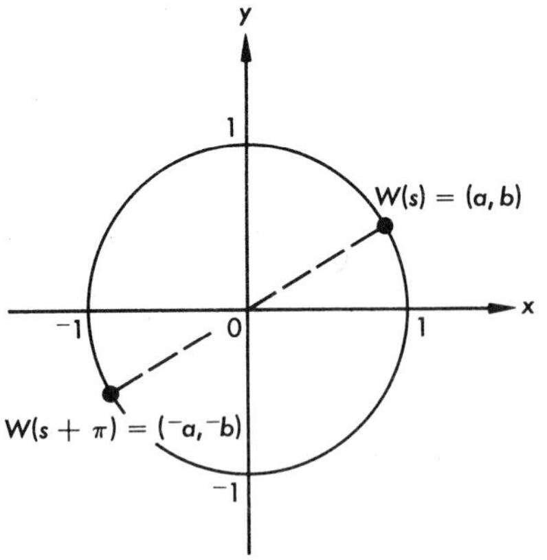

2. Choose a convenient s to illustrate $W(s) = (a, b)$ and $W(s - \pi)$ on the unit circle and state the identities involving sines and cosines of s and $s - \pi$.
(ans: $\sin(s - \pi) = {}^-\sin s$
$\cos(s - \pi) = {}^-\cos s$)

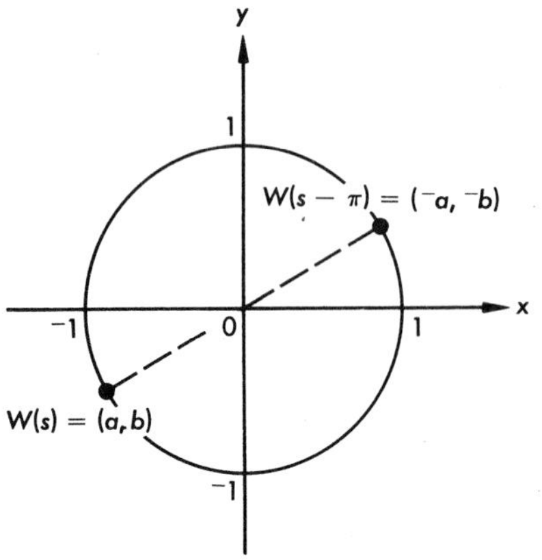

3. Complete
(a) $\sin({}^-s) =$ _?_ (ans: $^-\sin s$)
(b) $\cos({}^-s) =$ _?_ (ans: $\cos s$)

Exercises

Evaluate each of the following.

1. $\cos \frac{19\pi}{6}$ $\ {}^-\frac{\sqrt{3}}{2}$
2. $\sin({}^-23\pi)$ $\ 0$
3. $\cos({}^-17\pi)$ $\ {}^-1$
4. $\sin\left({}^-\frac{11\pi}{3}\right)$ $\ \frac{\sqrt{3}}{2}$
5. $\cos\left({}^-\frac{11\pi}{3}\right)$ $\ \frac{1}{2}$
6. $\sin\left({}^-\frac{17\pi}{6}\right)$ $\ {}^-\frac{1}{2}$
7. $\sin \frac{5\pi}{3}$ $\ {}^-\frac{\sqrt{3}}{2}$
8. $\cos \frac{11\pi}{6}$ $\ \frac{\sqrt{3}}{2}$
9. $\sin \frac{7\pi}{4}$ $\ {}^-\frac{\sqrt{2}}{2}$
10. $\cos \frac{2\pi}{3}$ $\ {}^-\frac{1}{2}$
11. $\sin \frac{4\pi}{3}$ $\ {}^-\frac{\sqrt{3}}{2}$
12. $\cos \frac{29\pi}{6}$ $\ {}^-\frac{\sqrt{3}}{2}$
13. $\cos\left({}^-\frac{5\pi}{6}\right)$ $\ {}^-\frac{\sqrt{3}}{2}$
14. $\sin\left({}^-\frac{11\pi}{6}\right)$ $\ \frac{1}{2}$
15. $\cos\left({}^-\frac{5\pi}{3}\right)$ $\ \frac{1}{2}$

△

State whether each of the following functions is odd, even, or neither.

16. $f(x) = 3x^3 - 4x$ *Odd*
17. $f(x) = 2x^6 + 4x^4 - 8$ *Even*
18. $f(x) = 6x^5 - 2x^2$ *Neither*
19. $f(x) = 1 - x^3 - 4x^5$ *Neither*

▲

See Solution Manual.

20. (a) Use (FI-2) and (FI-6) to prove that $\sin(\pi - s) = \sin s$.
(b) Prove that $\cos(\pi - s) = {}^-\cos s$.

9-6 THE OTHER TRIGONOMETRIC FUNCTIONS

For convenience, certain combinations of the sine and cosine are given names.

$$\textit{tangent } s = \frac{\textit{sine } s}{\textit{cosine } s}$$

$$\textit{cotangent } s = \frac{\textit{cosine } s}{\textit{sine } s}$$

$$\textit{secant } s = \frac{1}{\textit{cosine } s}$$

$$\textit{cosecant } s = \frac{1}{\textit{sine } s}$$

The domain of each of these four new functions is the set of all real numbers, excluding those numbers for which the function in the denominator is 0. For example,

$$\left\{s \mid s \neq \frac{\pi}{2} + n\pi,\ n \text{ an integer}\right\}$$

is the domain of both the tangent and the secant.

Problem 1. Find the circular functions of $\pi/4$ and $\pi/3$.

Solution.

$$\sin\frac{\pi}{4} = \frac{\sqrt{2}}{2}, \qquad \sin\frac{\pi}{3} = \frac{\sqrt{3}}{2},$$

$$\cos\frac{\pi}{4} = \frac{\sqrt{2}}{2}, \qquad \cos\frac{\pi}{3} = \frac{1}{2},$$

$$\tan\frac{\pi}{4} = \frac{\frac{\sqrt{2}}{2}}{\frac{\sqrt{2}}{2}} = 1, \qquad \tan\frac{\pi}{3} = \frac{\frac{\sqrt{3}}{2}}{\frac{1}{2}} = \sqrt{3},$$

$$\cot\frac{\pi}{4} = \frac{\frac{\sqrt{2}}{2}}{\frac{\sqrt{2}}{2}} = 1, \qquad \cot\frac{\pi}{3} = \frac{\frac{1}{2}}{\frac{\sqrt{3}}{2}} = \frac{\sqrt{3}}{3},$$

$$\sec\frac{\pi}{4} = \frac{1}{\frac{\sqrt{2}}{2}} = \sqrt{2}, \qquad \sec\frac{\pi}{3} = \frac{1}{\frac{1}{2}} = 2,$$

$$\csc\frac{\pi}{4} = \frac{1}{\frac{\sqrt{2}}{2}} = \sqrt{2}, \qquad \csc\frac{\pi}{3} = \frac{1}{\frac{\sqrt{3}}{2}} = \frac{2}{3}\sqrt{3}.$$

Observe that we have abbreviated tangent to tan, cotangent to cot, secant to sec, and cosecant to csc.

We shall leave the proof of the following identities for the exercises.

$$\sec^2 s = 1 + \tan^2 s \qquad (FI\text{-}10)$$

$$\csc^2 s = 1 + \cot^2 s \qquad (FI\text{-}11)$$

9–6 THE OTHER TRIGONOMETRIC FUNCTIONS

It should be noted that these newly defined functions, unlike sine and cosine, are not defined for every s.

You may wish to ask the students to fill in simplification steps in parts of the following problem:

$$\sec\frac{\pi}{4} = \frac{1}{\sqrt{2}/2} = \frac{2}{\sqrt{2}} = \frac{2}{\sqrt{2}}\cdot\frac{\sqrt{2}}{\sqrt{2}} = \sqrt{2},$$

in order to review the technique of rationalizing denominators.

It is recommended that you make use of Exercise for Discussion 1 in your explanation of the tenth fundamental identity.

In Problem 2, it is suggested that you make a sketch of the unit circle and $W(s)$ before discussing the solution in the text.

After going through steps of the text solution, you could sketch a right triangle with acute angle α having $\tan \alpha = \frac{1}{2}$ and use the technique of Section 9–1 to find $\sin \alpha$ and $\cos \alpha$. It should be made clear that these agree with the numerical value of $\sin s$ and $\cos s$. This is discovery material for Section 9–7.

Both Problem 3 and the exercises of the section provide a good review of the elementary algebraic operations with fractions and factoring. It may be necessary for you to discuss these concepts in the new setting.

Problem 4 illustrates a procedure which is often efficient, that of reducing an expression to one which involves only sines and cosines by using the definitions of tan, cot, sec, and csc.

Problem 2. If $\pi < s < 3\pi/2$ and $\tan s = \frac{1}{2}$, find the other trigonometric functions of s.

Solution. First,

$$\cot s = 2.$$

By the tenth fundamental identity, $\sec^2 s = \frac{5}{4}$. Since $\cos s < 0$ if $\pi < s < 3\pi/2$, the $\sec s$ must be less than 0 also. Hence,

$$\sec s = \frac{{}^-\sqrt{5}}{2}.$$

Therefore,

$$\cos s = \frac{{}^-2}{\sqrt{5}},$$

$$\sin s = \cos s \tan s = \frac{{}^-1}{\sqrt{5}}.$$

$$\csc s = {}^-\sqrt{5}.$$

Problem 3. Simplify the expression

$$\frac{1}{1 - \sin s} + \frac{1}{1 + \sin s}.$$

Solution. We proceed as follows:

$$\frac{1}{1 - \sin s} + \frac{1}{1 + \sin s} = \frac{(1 + \sin s) + (1 - \sin s)}{(1 - \sin s)(1 + \sin s)}$$

$$= \frac{2}{1 - \sin^2 s}.$$

Since $1 - \sin^2 s = \cos^2 s$ by the first fundamental identity, and $\sec^2 s = 1/\cos^2 s$, we obtain

$$\frac{2}{\cos^2 s}, \quad \text{or } 2 \sec^2 s,$$

as a simplified form of the given expression.

Problem 4. Prove that the following equation is an identity.

$$\csc s - \sin s = \cos s \cot s$$

Solution. What we really wish to show is that the expressions on the two sides of this equation are equivalent, that is, that one may be changed into the other by use of the fundamental identities. One way of doing this is shown below.

$$\begin{aligned}\csc s - \sin s &= \frac{1}{\sin s} - \sin s\\ &= \frac{1 - \sin^2 s}{\sin s}\\ &= \frac{\cos^2 s}{\sin s}\\ &= \cos s \cdot \frac{\cos s}{\sin s}\\ &= \cos s \cot s\end{aligned}$$

Hence, $\csc s - \sin s = \cos s \cot s$ for every s in the common domain of the cotangent and the cosecant.

Exercises for Discussion

1. Derive (FI-10). (Hint: Divide both sides of the equation in (FI-1) by $\cos^2 s$.)

2. (a) For what values of s is $\sin s = 0$? $s = n\pi$, n an integer
   (b) Find the domains of the cotangent and the cosecant.
   $\{s | s \neq \pi$, n an integer$\}$

In Exercises 3–5, use a sketch of the unit circle.

3. From the definition of $\sin s$ as the ordinate of the point $W(s)$, we see that the values of the sine function increase from 0 to 1 as s goes from 0 to $\pi/2$. What happens to the values of the cosine function as s goes from 0 to $\pi/2$? Values decrease from 1 to 0.

4. Given that s is in the interval

$$\left\{s \mid 0 \leqq s \leqq \frac{\pi}{2}\right\},$$

find the value or values of s for which

(a) $\sin s = \cos s$. $s = \frac{\pi}{4}$ (b) $\sin s < \cos s$. $0 \leqq s < \frac{\pi}{4}$ (c) $\sin s > \cos s$. $\frac{\pi}{4} < s \leqq \frac{\pi}{2}$

5. Describe the behavior of the tangent function in the interval
It increases from 0 through all positive real numbers.

$$\left\{s \mid 0 \leqq s < \frac{\pi}{2}\right\}.$$

Answer to Exercise for Discussion 1

1. $\cos^2 s + \sin^2 s = 1$

$$\frac{\cos^2 s}{\cos^2 s} + \frac{\sin^2 s}{\cos^2 s} = \frac{1}{\cos^2 s}$$

$$1 + \left(\frac{\sin s}{\cos s}\right)^2 = \left(\frac{1}{\cos s}\right)^2$$

$$1 + \tan^2 s = \sec^2 s$$

In Exercises 6 and 7, use a sketch of the unit circle.

6. Describe the behavior of the tangent function in the interval

$$\left\{s \mid \frac{\pi}{2} < s \leqq \pi\right\}.$$

It increases through all negative real numbers to 0.

7. What is the range of the tangent function; that is, what is the set of values of $\tan s$? *All real numbers*

8. Find the other five trigonometric functions of s in each of the following examples.

(a) $\cos s = \frac{\sqrt{5}}{5}$ and $0 < s < \frac{\pi}{2}$

$\sin s = \frac{2\sqrt{5}}{5}$, $\tan s = 2$, $\cot s = \frac{1}{2}$, $\sec s = \sqrt{5}$, $\csc s = \frac{\sqrt{5}}{2}$

(b) $\sin s = \frac{3\sqrt{10}}{10}$ and $0 < s < \pi$

$\cos s = \pm\frac{\sqrt{10}}{10}$, $\tan s = \pm 3$, $\cot s = \pm\frac{1}{3}$, $\sec s = \pm\sqrt{10}$, $\csc s = \frac{\sqrt{10}}{3}$

9. Complete the table by telling whether the tangent, cotangent, secant, and cosecant are positive or negative numbers in the four quadrants of a cartesian coordinate system.

	I	II	III	IV
tangent	+	− ?	+ ?	− ?
cotangent	+	− ?	+ ?	− ?
secant	+	− ?	− ?	+ ?
cosecant	+	+ ?	− ?	− ?

Exercises

In Exercises 1–8, find the other five trigonometric functions of s.

1. $\cos s = \frac{1}{\sqrt{2}}$ and $0 < s < \frac{\pi}{2}$

2. $\sin s = \frac{1}{2}$ and $\frac{\pi}{2} < s < \pi$

3. $\tan s = -2$ and $\frac{3\pi}{2} < s < 2\pi$

4. $\sin s = -1$

5. $\sec s = -\sqrt{2}$ and $\tan s < 0$

6. $\csc s = 3$ and $\cos s < 0$

7. $\tan s = 1$ and $\sin s < 0$

8. $\cos s = -1$

9. (a) What is the range of $\sin s$? *$\{y \mid -1 \leqq y \leqq 1\}$*

(b) What is the range of $\cos s$? *$\{x \mid -1 \leqq x \leqq 1\}$*

10. (a) What is the range of $\cot s$? *All real numbers*

(b) What is the range of $\sec s$? *$\{x \mid x \leqq -1 \text{ or } x \geqq 1\}$*

Answers to Exercises 1–8

1. $\sin s = \frac{\sqrt{2}}{2}$; $\tan s = 1$; $\cot s = 1$; $\sec s = \sqrt{2}$; $\csc s = \sqrt{2}$

2. $\cos s = \frac{-\sqrt{3}}{2}$; $\tan s = \frac{-\sqrt{3}}{3}$; $\cot s = -\sqrt{3}$; $\sec s = \frac{-2\sqrt{3}}{3}$; $\csc s = 2$

3. $\sin s = \frac{-2\sqrt{5}}{5}$; $\cos s = \frac{\sqrt{5}}{5}$; $\cot s = -\frac{1}{2}$; $\sec s = \sqrt{5}$; $\csc s = \frac{-\sqrt{5}}{2}$

4. $\cos s = 0$; $\tan s$ is undefined; $\cot s = 0$; $\sec s$ is undefined; $\csc s = -1$

5. $\sin s = \frac{\sqrt{2}}{2}$; $\cos s = \frac{-\sqrt{2}}{2}$; $\tan s = -1$; $\cot s = -1$; $\csc s = \sqrt{2}$

6. $\sin s = \frac{1}{3}$; $\cos s = \frac{-2\sqrt{2}}{3}$; $\tan s = \frac{-\sqrt{2}}{4}$; $\cot s = -2\sqrt{2}$; $\sec s = \frac{-3\sqrt{2}}{4}$

7. $\sin s = \frac{-\sqrt{2}}{2}$; $\cos s = \frac{-\sqrt{2}}{2}$; $\cot s = 1$; $\sec s = -\sqrt{2}$; $\csc s = -\sqrt{2}$

8. $\sin s = 0$; $\tan s = 0$; $\cot s$ is undefined; $\sec s = -1$; $\csc s$ is undefined

11. Simplify each of the following expressions.
(a) $\cos s \tan s$ *sin s*
(b) $\sec^2 s - \tan^2 s$ *1*
(c) $\dfrac{1}{\sec s - \tan s} - \dfrac{1}{\sec s + \tan s}$ *2 tan s*
(d) $\dfrac{\cot s}{\csc s}$ *cos s*
(e) $\sec s - \sin s \tan s$ *cos s*
(f) $\cot^2 s - \csc^2 s$ *⁻1*

12. Prove that each of the following equations is an identity.
(a) $(\sin s + \cos s)^2 = 1 + 2 \sin s \cos s$ *See Solution Manual.*
(b) $\dfrac{\sin s}{\csc s - \cot s} + \dfrac{\sin s}{\csc s + \cot s} = 2$
(c) $\dfrac{\sin s}{1 - \cos s} = \dfrac{1 + \cos s}{\sin s}$
(d) $\sin s \cos s - \sec s \sin s = {}^{-}\sin^2 s \tan s$
(e) $\tan s + \cot s = \sec s \csc s$
(f) $\dfrac{\cos s}{1 + \sin s} = \sec s - \tan s$

13. Show that the tangent function is an odd function. *See Solution Manual.*
14. Derive (FI-11).
See Solution Manual.

9–7 RADIAN MEASURE AND GENERAL ANGLES

In trigonometry, it is convenient for us to think of an angle in a more general way than we did in geometry. We still say that an angle is composed of two rays in a plane having a common endpoint V, called the vertex of the angle. However, let us suppose that we keep V fixed and rotate one of these rays to another position in the given plane. Then the angle is *swept out*. The ray with which we start is called the *initial side* of the angle, and the ray with which we end is called the *terminal side*. The curved arrow in Fig. 9–18 indicates that in the formation of the angle, initial side I is rotated in a counterclockwise

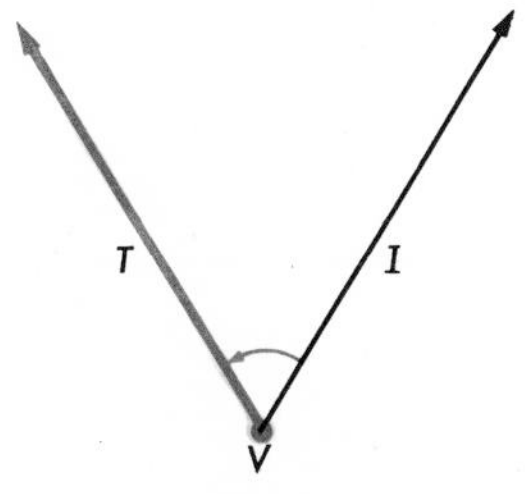

FIGURE 9–18

Quiz

1. Find the six trigonometric functions of $\frac{2}{3}\pi$.
(ans: $\sin(\frac{2}{3}\pi) = \dfrac{\sqrt{3}}{2}$
$\cos(\frac{2}{3}\pi) = {}^{-}\frac{1}{2}$
$\tan(\frac{2}{3}\pi) = {}^{-}\sqrt{3}$
$\cot(\frac{2}{3}\pi) = \dfrac{{}^{-}1}{\sqrt{3}} = \dfrac{{}^{-}\sqrt{3}}{3}$
$\sec(\frac{2}{3}\pi) = {}^{-}2$
$\csc(\frac{2}{3}\pi) = \dfrac{2}{\sqrt{3}} = \dfrac{2}{3}\sqrt{3}$)

2. Simplify $(\tan s \cdot \sin s) + \dfrac{1}{\sec s}$
(ans: sec s)

3. If $\cos s = \dfrac{4}{5}$ and $\dfrac{{}^{-}\pi}{2} < s < 0$, find $\tan s$. (ans: ${}^{-}\frac{3}{4}$)

9–7 RADIAN MEASURE AND GENERAL ANGLES

You may wish to draw a number of angles in standard position in such a way as to show the rotation each time. You could mention the amount of arc swept out on the unit circle from (1, 0) by each angle, and thus lead into the definition of radian measure.

Then you might ask what positive angle sweeps out an arc length of one-quarter, one-half, one-third, or one-sixth of the circumference. (ans: $\pi/2$, π, $2\pi/3$, $\pi/3$) Are any of these angles approximately 1 (radian) unit? (ans: $\pi/3$)

direction to terminal side T. An angle α is said to be in *standard position* relative to a cartesian coordinate system in a plane if the vertex of α is at the origin and the initial side of α is along the positive x-axis.

We shall assign a measure to each angle in the following way. The measure will be a positive number if the angle is formed by a counterclockwise rotation, and a negative number if the angle is formed by a clockwise rotation. There are two common ways of measuring angles: by degrees and by radians.

DEFINITION OF RADIAN MEASURE OF AN ANGLE

The length of arc swept out by an angle α on the unit circle is called the radian measure of α.

Since the circumference of a unit circle is 2π, an angle formed by one revolution (in a counterclockwise direction) of the terminal side has a radian measure of 2π. If the terminal side is rotated more than one complete revolution, the angle formed will have a radian measure of more than 2π. A straight angle has a radian measure π, and a right angle has radian measure $\pi/2$.

The measure of α is 1 radian if the arc of the unit circle swept out by α is of length 1 and if α is formed by a counterclockwise rotation. (See Fig. 9–19.) If the arc swept out by α had length 2, then α would have radian measure 2 or $^-2$, depending on whether α was formed by a counterclockwise or a clockwise rotation. From now on, when we

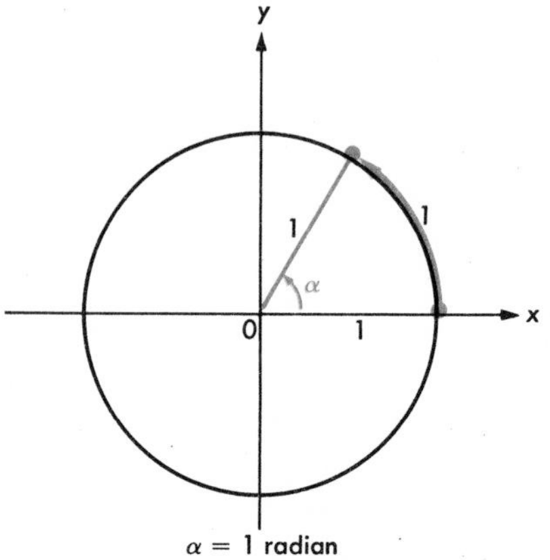

FIGURE 9–19

TWISTER

Jake jumped onto one end of a piece of tree trunk lying on the top of a hill. The impact caused the log to begin rolling down the hill. As it rolled, Jake managed to keep himself standing and slowly moved across the log to the other end, which he reached just as the log stopped at the bottom of the hill. The log was exactly 13 feet long, and it rolled 84 feet. How far did the boy actually travel if the log was 2 feet in diameter? 3 feet in diameter?

Solution: The problem suggests a right triangle with 84 feet on one side and 13 feet on the other. The hypotenuse is the distance which Jake actually traveled. By use of the pythagorean theorem, this distance is found to be 85 feet. The diameter of the log makes no difference.

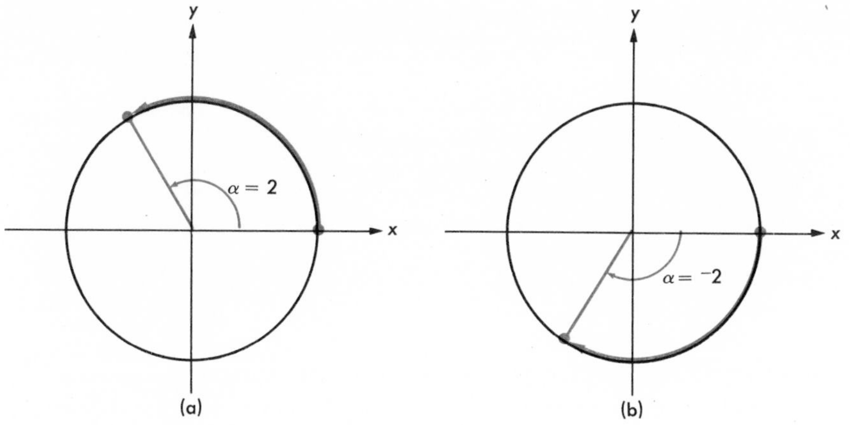

FIGURE 9–20

write $\alpha = 2$ without stating units, we mean than α has measure 2 radians. (See Fig. 9–20.)

If we start with the fact that a straight angle has measure 180°, or π radians, the formula

$$r = \frac{\pi}{180} d$$

gives the radian measure r of an angle in terms of its degree measure d.

We can solve the above formula for d in terms of r, obtaining

$$d = \frac{180}{\pi} r,$$

which gives the degree measure d of an angle in terms of its radian measure r. For example,

$$\text{if } r = \frac{\pi}{6}, \text{ then } d = 30°;$$

$$\text{if } r = 1, \text{ then } d = \frac{180}{\pi} \doteq 57.3°.$$

In other words $57.3° \doteq 1$ radian.

The first two columns of the Table of Values of Trigonometric Functions in the Appendix give the approximate radian measures of angles of measure 0°, 1°, 2°, . . . , 89°, 90°. Since π is irrational, it follows that if the degree measure of an angle is a rational number, then the radian measure is irrational, and vice versa.

It should be emphasized to the students that instead of memorizing these two formulas it will be easier for them simply to think of the straight angle measure in both systems. That is, 180 (degrees) corresponds to π (radians). Hence, 1 degree corresponds to $\pi/180$ of a radian, and $180/\pi$ of a degree corresponds to 1 radian.

Because of the way degree and radian units are related and because of the special angles which are multiples of 30, 45, and 60, one frequently works mostly with angles whose radian measures are multiples of $\pi/6$, $\pi/4$, and $\pi/3$. It is important for the student to be aware of the approximate numerical values of these radian measures. For example,

$$3.14/6 \doteq .52,$$
$$3.14/4 \doteq .79,$$
$$3.14/3 \doteq 1.05,$$

and so on.

There are now two different definitions of sin (and of cos) for an acute angle. Hence, it is important to show that the two definitions agree in that they both give the same answer.

Exercises for Discussion, page 395

If time is limited, it is suggested that at least Exercises for Discussion 2–4, 6, 8, and 9 be covered.

Answers to Exercises for Discussion 1–9, page 395

1. $\frac{2\pi}{3}$ radians $= \frac{2\pi}{3} \cdot \frac{180}{\pi}$ degrees
$= 120°$

2. $\frac{^-\pi}{4}$ radians $= \frac{^-\pi}{4} \cdot \frac{180}{\pi}$ degrees
$= {}^-45°$

3. $\frac{22\pi}{3}$ radians
$= \frac{22\pi}{3} \cdot \frac{180}{\pi}$ degrees
$= 1320°$

4. $^-90° = {}^-90 \cdot \frac{\pi}{180}$ radians
$= \frac{^-\pi}{2}$ radians

5. $40° = 40 \cdot \frac{\pi}{180}$ radians
$= \frac{2\pi}{9}$ radians

6. $450° = 450 \cdot \frac{\pi}{180}$ radians
$= \frac{5\pi}{2}$ radians

7. $\sin 30° = \frac{1}{2}$

$\cos 30° = \frac{\sqrt{3}}{2}$

$\tan 30° = \frac{1}{\sqrt{3}} = \frac{1}{3}\sqrt{3}$

$\cot 30° = \frac{\sqrt{3}}{1} = \sqrt{3}$

$\sec 30° = \frac{2}{\sqrt{3}} = \frac{2}{3}\sqrt{3}$

$\csc 30° = \frac{2}{1} = 2$

The trigonometric functions of a general angle can now be defined in the following way.

DEFINITION OF THE TRIGONOMETRIC FUNCTIONS OF A GENERAL ANGLE

If angle α has radian measure s, then we define

$$\sin \alpha = \sin s \quad \text{and} \quad \cos \alpha = \cos s.$$

The other functions of a general angle α are defined in terms of the sine α and cosine α, as before. For example, $\tan \alpha = \sin \alpha/\cos \alpha$.

If angle α is acute, and if α is in standard position as shown in Fig. 9–21, then α is an angle of right triangle ABC. Hence,

$$\sin \alpha = \frac{y}{1}, \quad \cos \alpha = \frac{x}{1}$$

by the definitions of the sine and cosine of an acute angle in Section 9–1. On the other hand, if α has radian measure s, then $W(s)$ is the point B. Since $W(s) = (\cos s, \sin s)$ and $B = (x, y)$, we have $x = \cos s$ and $y = \sin s$. Thus,

$$\sin \alpha = \sin s, \quad \cos \alpha = \cos s,$$

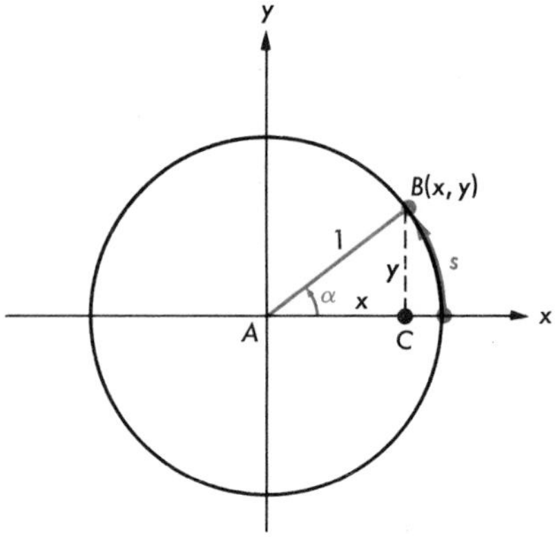

FIGURE 9–21

and the two definitions of sine and cosine agree for acute angles.

From now on, we shall consider the domains of the trigonometric functions as either a set of general angles or as a set of real numbers, whichever is more convenient. Whenever we write sin 30°, we mean the sine of an angle of measure 30°. If we write sin 3, we mean the sine of the number 3, or, equivalently, the sine of an angle of measure 3 radians.

The Table in the Appendix lists three-decimal-place approximations of $\sin \alpha$, $\cos \alpha$, and $\tan \alpha$ for $\alpha = 0°, 1°, 2°, \ldots, 89°, 90°$. For example,

$$\sin 24° \doteq .407, \quad \cos 44° \doteq .719, \quad \tan 77° \doteq 4.331.$$

Exercises for Discussion

Given the radian measure, find the degree measure for each angle below.

1. $\frac{2\pi}{3}$ **2.** $\frac{^{-}\pi}{4}$ **3.** $\frac{22\pi}{3}$

Given the degree measure, find the radian measure for each angle below.

4. $^{-}90°$ **5.** $40°$ **6.** $450°$

In each exercise, sketch, in standard position, the angle having the given measure. Find all trigonometric functions which exist for each angle.

7. $30°$ **8.** $^{-}150°$ **9.** $^{-}90°$

Exercises

See Solution Manual for figures.

Given the radian measure, find the degree measure for each angle below.

1. $\frac{8\pi}{9}$ 160° **2.** $\frac{7\pi}{4}$ 315° **3.** 2 $\left(\frac{360}{\pi}\right)^{\circ}$ **4.** $\frac{34\pi}{3}$ 2040°

Given the degree measure, find the radian measure for each angle below.

5. 200° $\frac{10\pi}{9}$ **6.** 450° $\frac{5\pi}{2}$ **7.** 330° $\frac{11\pi}{6}$ **8.** $^{-}150°$ $\frac{^{-}5\pi}{6}$

In each of the following exercises, sketch the angle in standard position, and find the three trigonometric functions: sine, cosine, and tangent.

9. 45° $\frac{\sqrt{2}}{2}, \frac{\sqrt{2}}{2}, 1$ **10.** 120° $\frac{\sqrt{3}}{2}, \frac{^{-}1}{2}, {}^{-}\sqrt{3}$ **11.** $^{-}60°$ $\frac{^{-}\sqrt{3}}{2}, \frac{1}{2}, {}^{-}\sqrt{3}$

12. 570° $\frac{^{-}1}{2}, \frac{^{-}\sqrt{3}}{2}, \frac{\sqrt{3}}{3}$ **13.** $^{-}210°$ $\frac{1}{2}, \frac{^{-}\sqrt{3}}{2}, \frac{^{-}\sqrt{3}}{3}$ **14.** 0° 0, 1, 0

15. 370°. .174, .985, .176 **16.** $^{-}280°$. .985, .174, 5.67 **17.** 756°. .588, .809, .727

In Exercises 18–23, find the sine and cosine of each number.

18. .628. .588, .809 **19.** .942. .809, .588 **20.** .803. .719, .695

21. .401. .391, .921 **22.** .262. .259, .966 **23.** 1.501. .998, .070

24. Show that the radian measure of α is See Solution Manual.

$\frac{a}{r}$.

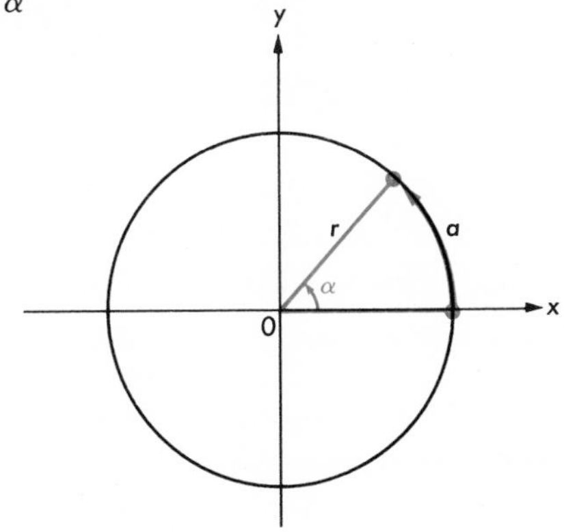

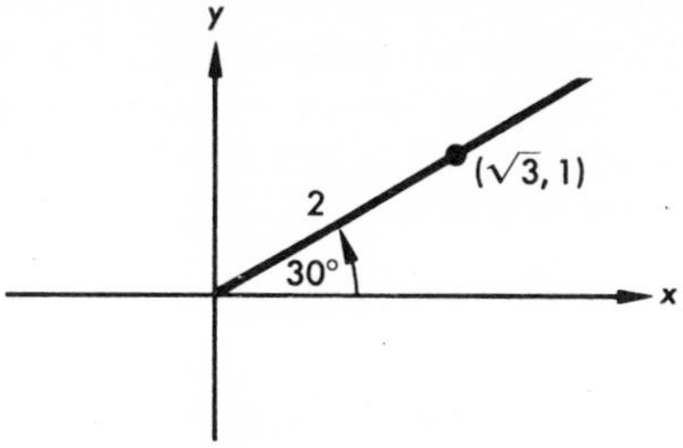

8. $\sin(^{-}150°) = {}^{-}\frac{1}{2}$

$\cos(^{-}150°) = \frac{^{-}\sqrt{3}}{2}$

$\tan(^{-}150°) = \frac{^{-}1}{\sqrt{3}} = \frac{^{-}1}{3}\sqrt{3}$

$\cot(^{-}150°) = \frac{^{-}\sqrt{3}}{1} = {}^{-}\sqrt{3}$

$\sec(^{-}150°) = \frac{^{-}2}{\sqrt{3}} = \frac{^{-}2}{3}\sqrt{3}$,

$\csc(^{-}150°) = {}^{-}\frac{2}{1} = {}^{-}2$

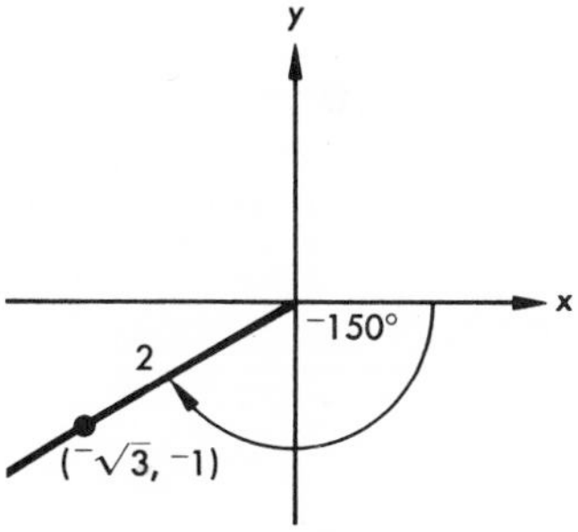

9. $\sin(^{-}90°) = {}^{-}1$

$\cos(^{-}90°) = 0$

$\tan(^{-}90°)$ undefined

$\cot(^{-}90°) = 0$

$\sec(^{-}90°)$ undefined

$\csc(^{-}90°) = {}^{-}1$

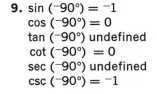

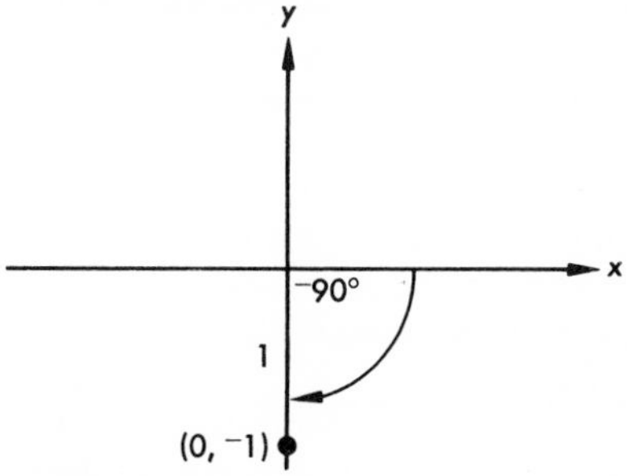

Exercises

In Exercises 18–23, it should be noted that these are all angles in the first quadrant, since $\pi/2 = 1.57$.

Quiz

1. Given the radian measure, find the degree measure for each angle below.
   (a) $\frac{5\pi}{4}$ (ans: 225°)
   (b) $\frac{^-9\pi}{2}$ (ans: $^-$810°)
   (c) $\frac{^-4\pi}{3}$ (ans: $^-$240°)
2. Given the degree measure, find the radian measure for each angle below.
   (a) 300° $\left(\text{ans: } \frac{5\pi}{3}\right)$
   (b) 540° (ans: 3π)
   (c) $^-$225° $\left(\text{ans: } \frac{^-5\pi}{4}\right)$
3. (a) Using 3.1416 for π, give the radian measure of the 60° angle correct to three decimal places. (ans: 1.047)
   (b) Give the degree measure of the angle of 1 radian correct to three decimal places. (ans: 57.296°)

9–8 FUNCTIONS AND COFUNCTIONS

While the cofunction identities are valid for any real number s, one usually calls them to mind by thinking of the case in which s is the (radian) measure of an acute angle in a right triangle. You may wish to present them in this way before introducing the treatment given in the text.

The derivations of the twelfth and fourteenth fundamental identities are not important in themselves, except as further examples of how previously developed properties of the wrapping function may be used to prove the identities for any value of s.

9–8 FUNCTIONS AND COFUNCTIONS

If an acute angle has measure α degrees, then its complement has measure $90 - \alpha$ degrees. Similarly, if an acute angle has radian measure s, then its complement has radian measure $\pi/2 - s$. The trigonometric functions of a number and its complement are related in the following way.

$$\begin{aligned} \sin\left(\frac{\pi}{2} - s\right) &= \sin\left(^-\left(s - \frac{\pi}{2}\right)\right) & \\ &= {}^-\sin\left(s - \frac{\pi}{2}\right) & \text{(FI-2)} \\ &= \cos s & \text{(FI-8)} \\ \cos\left(\frac{\pi}{2} - s\right) &= \cos\left(^-\left(s - \frac{\pi}{2}\right)\right) & \\ &= \cos\left(s - \frac{\pi}{2}\right) & \text{(FI-3)} \\ &= \sin s & \text{(FI-9)} \end{aligned}$$

Since these equations are true for every number s, they are identities.

$$\sin\left(\frac{\pi}{2} - s\right) = \cos s, \quad \cos\left(\frac{\pi}{2} - s\right) = \sin s \qquad (FI\text{-}12)$$

Similar identities can be derived for the other trigonometric functions.

$$\tan\left(\frac{\pi}{2} - s\right) = \cot s, \quad \cot\left(\frac{\pi}{2} - s\right) = \tan s \qquad (FI\text{-}13)$$

$$\sec\left(\frac{\pi}{2} - s\right) = \csc s, \quad \csc\left(\frac{\pi}{2} - s\right) = \sec s \qquad (FI\text{-}14)$$

The sine and cosine are called *cofunctions* of each other; that is, cosine is the cofunction of sine, and sine is the cofunction of cosine. Similarly, the tangent and cotangent are cofunctions, and the secant and cosecant are cofunctions. In terms of cofunctions, the twelfth, thirteenth, and fourteenth fundamental identities can be expressed as follows: If f is any one of the six trigonometric functions and cof is its cofunction, then

$$f\left(\frac{\pi}{2} - s\right) = cof\ s.$$

For example,

$$\sin\frac{\pi}{6} = \cos\left(\frac{\pi}{2} - \frac{\pi}{6}\right) = \cos\frac{\pi}{3},$$

$$\cot\frac{3\pi}{8} = \tan\left(\frac{\pi}{2} - \frac{3\pi}{8}\right) = \tan\frac{\pi}{8},$$

$$\sec 42° = \csc(90° - 42°) = \csc 48°.$$

If an angle has measure α between 0° and 180°, then its *supplement* has measure $180 - \alpha$ degrees. Similarly, if an acute angle has radian measure s, then its supplement has radian measure $\pi - s$. Using the second, third, sixth, and seventh fundamental identities, we can easily establish the following identity.

$$\sin(\pi - s) = \sin s, \quad \cos(\pi - s) = {}^-\cos s \qquad \text{(FI-15)}$$

For example,

$$\cos\frac{5\pi}{6} = \cos\left(\pi - \frac{\pi}{6}\right) = {}^-\cos\frac{\pi}{6}, \quad \text{or} \quad \frac{^-\sqrt{3}}{2}.$$

Exercises for Discussion

1. Fill in the blank in each of the following problems.

   (a) $\cos\frac{\pi}{10} = \sin$ $\frac{2\pi}{5}$?

   (b) $\csc\frac{2\pi}{3} = \sec$ $\frac{^-\pi}{6}$?

   (c) $\tan 48° = \cot$ 42° ?

2. Use the Table of Values of Trigonometric Functions in the Appendix, when necessary, and give the values of the trigonometric functions in each part of Exercise 1. (a) .951 (b) 1.15 or $\frac{2\sqrt{3}}{3}$ (c) 1.111

3. Use the Table of Values of Trigonometric Functions to find the complement of each of the following angles having the given radian measure.

   (a) .646 1.571 − .646 = .925 (b) 1.047 1.571 − 1.047 = .524 (c) 1.309 1.571 − 1.309 = .262

4. Give a three-decimal-place approximation for the sine and cosine of each angle and its complement in Exercise 3.

5. From (FI-15), derive similar identities relating the other four trigonometric functions of s and $\pi - s$.

Again, you may wish to picture for the students an acute angle of radian measure s, and a second-quadrant angle with radian measure $\pi - s$, on the unit circle in order to illustrate the fifteenth fundamental identity.

Exercises for Discussion

If time is limited, it is suggested that at least Exercises for Discussion 1–3(a), 4(a), 5–7, and 9–11 be covered.

Answers to Exercises for Discussion 4, 5

4. (a) $\sin .646 = \cos .925 = .602$
$\cos .646 = \sin .925 = .799$

(b) $\sin 1.047 = \cos .524 = .866$
$\cos 1.047 = \sin .524 = .500$

(c) $\sin 1.309 = \cos .262 = .966$
$\cos 1.309 = \sin .262 = .259$

5. $$\tan(\pi - s) = \frac{\sin(\pi - s)}{\cos(\pi - s)} = \frac{\sin s}{^-\cos s} = {}^-\tan s$$

$$\cot(\pi - s) = \frac{\cos(\pi - s)}{\sin(\pi - s)} = \frac{^-\cos s}{\sin s} = {}^-\cot s$$

$$\sec(\pi - s) = \frac{1}{\cos(\pi - s)} = \frac{1}{^-\cos s} = {}^-\sec s$$

$$\csc(\pi - s) = \frac{1}{\sin(\pi - s)} = \frac{1}{\sin s} = \csc s$$

Answer to Exercise 19

19. (13) $\frac{\sqrt{2}}{2}$, (14) .510; (15) 2; (16) $\frac{\sqrt{3}}{3}$; (17) 1.39; (18) .946

Quiz

1. Find each of the following.
   (a) $\sin\frac{3\pi}{4}$ $\left(\text{ans: } \frac{\sqrt{2}}{2}\right)$
   (b) $\cos\frac{3\pi}{4}$ $\left(\text{ans: } \frac{^{-}\sqrt{2}}{2}\right)$
   (c) $\tan\frac{3\pi}{4}$ (ans: $^{-}1$)

2. Fill in the blanks in the following.
   (a) sin 27° = cos __?__ (ans: 63°)
   (b) tan 71° = cot __?__ (ans: 19°)

3. Given sin 10° = .174, cos 10° = .985, tan 10° = .176, find
   (a) sin 170°, cos 170°, tan 170° (ans: .174, $^{-}$.985, $^{-}$.176)
   (b) sin 80°, cos 80° (ans: .985, .174)

Use the identities involving the circular functions of a number and its supplement to evaluate each of the following. Consult the Table of Values of Trigonometric Functions, when necessary.

6. $\sin\frac{2}{3}\pi = \sin\frac{\pi}{3} = \frac{\sqrt{3}}{2}$ **7.** $\tan\frac{3}{4}\pi = {}^{-}\tan\frac{\pi}{4} = {}^{-}1$ **8.** $\cos\frac{5}{6}\pi = {}^{-}\cos\frac{\pi}{6} = \frac{^{-}\sqrt{3}}{2}$

9. cos 113° = $^{-}$cos 67° = $^{-}$.391 **10.** sin 170° = sin 10° = .174 **11.** tan 151° = $^{-}$tan 29° = $^{-}$.554

12. cos 94° = $^{-}$cos 86° = $^{-}$.070 **13.** tan 91° = $^{-}$tan 89° = $^{-}$57.290 **14.** sin 150° = sin 30° = .500 or $\frac{1}{2}$

Exercises

Using the Table of Values of Trigonometric Functions, when necessary, find the value of the following functions.

1. $\sin\frac{13\pi}{6}$ $\frac{1}{2}$	**2.** $\cos\frac{9\pi}{4}$ $\frac{\sqrt{2}}{2}$	**3.** $\tan 3\pi$ 0
4. $\cos\frac{8\pi}{3}$ $\frac{^{-}1}{2}$	**5.** $\sec\frac{11\pi}{4}$ $^{-}\sqrt{2}$	**6.** sin 130° .766
7. cos 95° $^{-}$.087	**8.** tan 113° $^{-}$2.356	**9.** tan 463° $^{-}$4.331
10. cos 540° $^{-}$1	**11.** cos 455° $^{-}$.087	**12.** sin 450° 1

Fill in the blanks in Exercises 13–18.

13. $\sin\frac{\pi}{4} = \cos$ __?__ $\frac{\pi}{4}$ **14.** cot 63° = tan __?__ 27°

15. $\sec\frac{\pi}{3} = \csc$ __?__ $\frac{\pi}{6}$ **16.** $\tan\frac{\pi}{6} = \cot$ __?__ $\frac{\pi}{3}$

17. csc 46° = sec __?__ 44° **18.** cos 19° = sin __?__ 71°

19. Using the Table of Values of Trigonometric Functions, when necessary, give the values of the trigonometric functions in Exercises 13–18.

20. Find the complement of each of the following angles for the given radian measure. Give a three-decimal-place approximation for the sine and cosine of each angle and its complement.

(a) .314 1.257; sin .314 = cos 1.257 = .309; cos .314 = sin 1.257 = .951
(b) 1.204 .367; sin 1.204 = cos .367 = .934; cos 1.204 = sin .367 = .358
(c) 1.431 .140; sin 1.431 = cos .140 = .990; cos 1.431 = sin .140 = .139

KEY IDEAS AND KEY WORDS

The trigonometric functions are defined in terms of the **wrapping function W,** which assigns to each real number s a point $W(s)$ on a unit circle. By definition of **sine** and **cosine,** the coordinates of $W(s)$ are $(\cos s, \sin s)$. The other trigonometric functions, **tangent, cotangent, secant,** and **cosecant,** are defined in terms of sine and cosine:

$$\tan s = \frac{\sin s}{\cos s}, \qquad \cot s = \frac{\cos s}{\sin s},$$

$$\sec s = \frac{1}{\cos s}, \qquad \csc s = \frac{1}{\sin s}.$$

The sine and cosine are **periodic functions** with period 2π. In other words, the following equations are true for every real number s.

$$\sin s = \sin(s + 2\pi), \qquad \cos s = \cos(s + 2\pi)$$

The following are the **fundamental identities.**

$$\sin^2 s + \cos^2 s = 1 \qquad \textbf{(FI-1)}$$

$$\sin(^-s) = {}^-\sin s \qquad \textbf{(FI-2)}$$

$$\cos(^-s) = \cos s \qquad \textbf{(FI-3)}$$

$$\sin\left(s + \frac{\pi}{2}\right) = \cos s \qquad \textbf{(FI-4)}$$

$$\cos\left(s + \frac{\pi}{2}\right) = {}^-\sin s \qquad \textbf{(FI-5)}$$

$$\sin(s \pm \pi) = {}^-\sin s \qquad \textbf{(FI-6)}$$

$$\cos(s \pm \pi) = {}^-\cos s \qquad \textbf{(FI-7)}$$

$$\sin\left(s - \frac{\pi}{2}\right) = {}^-\cos s \qquad \textbf{(FI-8)}$$

$$\cos\left(s - \frac{\pi}{2}\right) = \sin s \qquad \textbf{(FI-9)}$$

$$\sec^2 s = 1 + \tan^2 s \qquad \textbf{(FI-10)}$$

$$\csc^2 s = 1 + \cot^2 s \qquad \textbf{(FI-11)}$$

$$\sin\left(\frac{\pi}{2} - s\right) = \cos s, \quad \cos\left(\frac{\pi}{2} - s\right) = \sin s \qquad \textbf{(FI-12)}$$

$$\tan\left(\frac{\pi}{2} - s\right) = \cot s, \quad \cot\left(\frac{\pi}{2} - s\right) = \tan s \qquad \textbf{(FI-13)}$$

$$\sec\left(\frac{\pi}{2} - s\right) = \csc s, \quad \csc\left(\frac{\pi}{2} - s\right) = \sec s \qquad \textbf{(FI-14)}$$

$$\sin(\pi - s) = \sin s, \quad \cos(\pi - s) = {}^-\cos s \qquad \textbf{(FI-15)}$$

If α sweeps out an arc of the unit circle of length s, then we call s the **radian measure** of angle α. Then π radians $= 180°$.

CHAPTER REVIEW

In Exercises 1–15, find each number.

1. $\sin(^-\pi)$ 0
2. $\tan\frac{2\pi}{3}$ $^-\sqrt{3}$
3. $\cos\frac{\pi}{2}$ 0
4. $\sec\frac{3\pi}{4}$ $^-\sqrt{2}$
5. $\sin(^-5\pi)$ 0
6. $\sin\left(^-\frac{7\pi}{6}\right)$ $\frac{1}{2}$
7. $\tan\frac{7\pi}{4}$ $^-1$
8. $\cos 180°$ $^-1$
9. $\sin 270°$ $^-1$
10. $\sec 210°$ $\frac{^-2\sqrt{3}}{3}$
11. $\tan 225°$ 1
12. $\csc 240°$ $\frac{^-2\sqrt{3}}{3}$
13. $\cot 135°$ $^-1$
14. $\sin\left(^-\frac{9\pi}{2}\right)$ $^-1$
15. $\cos\left(^-\frac{11\pi}{6}\right)$ $\frac{\sqrt{3}}{2}$

TWISTER

Mr. Franklin, an elderly eccentric, kept a considerable amount of money hidden under the floorboards in one particular room of his house. This room was $6\sqrt{5}$ feet wide, which was two-thirds of its length. A fireplace on one long wall was situated exactly in the center of the wall and took up one-third of it. The door into the room was directly opposite one corner of the fireplace. To find one of his favorite hiding places, Mr. Franklin walked four-fifths of the distance from the center of the door to the corner of the fireplace not opposite the door, turned 90 degrees toward the other corner of the fireplace, and walked one-half of the distance he had already come. His hiding place was somewhere along the long wall containing the fireplace. Where?

Solution: His hiding place was at the corner of the fireplace directly opposite the door.

16. Show that

$$W\left(\frac{11\pi}{4}\right) = W\left(\frac{^-5\pi}{4}\right).$$

17. Given that

$$W\left(\frac{\pi}{4}\right) = P,$$

determine the coordinates (x, y) of P.

18. Show that if n is an integer, then $W(s + 2\pi n) = W(s)$.

19. Graph $W(s)$ for

$$s = \frac{7\pi}{6},\quad \frac{^-5\pi}{6},\quad \frac{5\pi}{12},\quad \frac{21\pi}{4},\quad 17\pi,\quad \frac{^-5\pi}{4},\quad 2,\quad ^-3.$$

20. Are there real numbers s such that $\sin s = 2$?

Simplify each of the following expressions.

21. $\sec s \cos s - \cos^2 s$

22. $\dfrac{\cot^2 s}{1 - \sin^2 s}$

23. $\dfrac{\cot^2 s}{1 + \cot^2 s}$

24. $1 - \dfrac{\sin^2 s}{1 + \cos s}$

25. $\dfrac{\tan^2 s + 1}{\cot^2 s + 1}$

Prove the following identities.

26. $\sin s \sec s \cot s = 1$

27. $\cos^4 s - \sin^4 s = \cos^2 s - \sin^2 s$

28. $\cot^2 s - \cos^2 s = \cos^2 s \cot^2 s$

29. $\dfrac{\cos s}{1 + \sin s} + \dfrac{1 + \sin s}{\cos s} = 2 \sec s$

30. $\dfrac{1 - \tan^2 s}{1 - \cot^2 s} = 1 - \sec^2 s$

Find the values of the following trigonometric functions. In each case, convert radian measure to degree measure.

31. $\cos\left(\frac{^-\pi}{3}\right)$

32. $\sin \frac{7\pi}{6}$

33. $\tan\left(\frac{^-3\pi}{4}\right)$

34. $\cot\left(\frac{^-\pi}{2}\right)$

CHAPTER TEST

The material included in the Chapter Test was covered in the following sections:

Problem 1—Section 9-1
Problems 2-4—Section 9-8
Problems 5-7—Sections 9-4, 9-5
Problem 8(a)—Section 9-2
Problem 8(b)—Section 9-3
Problems 9, 10—Section 9-6

Express each of the following in terms of a trigonometric function of s.

35. $\sin(90° + s)$ cos s | **36.** $\cos(180° - s)$ $^{-}$cos s

37. $\sin(180° + s)$ $^{-}$sin s | **38.** $\cos(360° - s)$ cos s

39. $\sin(^{-}s)$ $^{-}$sin s | **40.** $\sin\left(\frac{\pi}{2} - s\right)$ cos s

41. $\tan(\pi + s)$ tan s

In Exercises 42–46, which of the functions are odd? Which are even? Which are neither odd nor even?

42. $f(x) = \sec x$ Even | **43.** $f(x) = x \sin x$ Even

44. $f(x) = \sin x$ Odd | **45.** $f(x) = x \cos x$ Odd

46. $f(x) = x + \cos x$ Neither

CHAPTER TEST

1. Fill in the following table of values of the sine, cosine, and tangent functions of an acute angle. Illustrate your answers with sketches of appropriate right triangles.

θ	30°	45°	60°
$\sin\theta$	$\frac{1}{2}$?	$\frac{\sqrt{2}}{2}$?	$\frac{\sqrt{3}}{2}$?
$\cos\theta$	$\frac{\sqrt{3}}{2}$?	$\frac{\sqrt{2}}{2}$?	$\frac{1}{2}$?
$\tan\theta$	$\frac{\sqrt{3}}{3}$?	1 ?	$\sqrt{3}$?

Find each number in Exercises 2–7.

2. $\sin 120°$ $\frac{\sqrt{3}}{2}$ **3.** $\cos 135°$ $^{-}\frac{\sqrt{2}}{2}$ **4.** $\tan 150°$ $^{-}\frac{\sqrt{3}}{3}$

5. $\sin\frac{5\pi}{4}$ $^{-}\frac{\sqrt{2}}{2}$ **6.** $\sin\frac{^{-}2\pi}{3}$ $^{-}\frac{\sqrt{3}}{2}$ **7.** $\cos\left(\frac{^{-}\pi}{2}\right)$ 0

8. (a) Given that $W\left(\frac{\pi}{3}\right) = Q$, determine the coordinates of Q. $\left(\frac{1}{2}, \frac{\sqrt{3}}{2}\right)$

(b) What are the coordinates of $W\left(\frac{^{-}\pi}{3}\right)$? $\left(\frac{1}{2}, \frac{^{-}\sqrt{3}}{2}\right)$

Prove each of the following identities.

9. $\sec s \csc s - 2\cos s \csc s = \tan s - \cot s$

10. $(\sec^2 s)(1 - \cos^2 s) = \tan^2 s$

Answers to Chapter Test Problems 1, 9, 10

1.

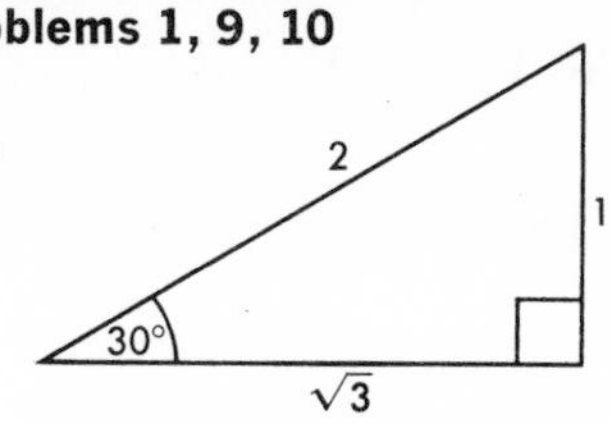

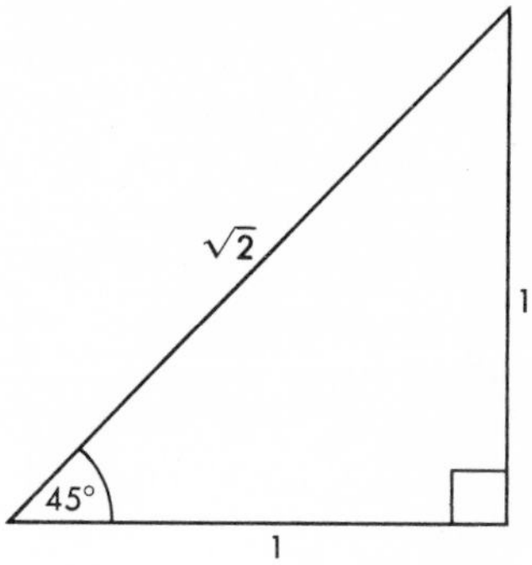

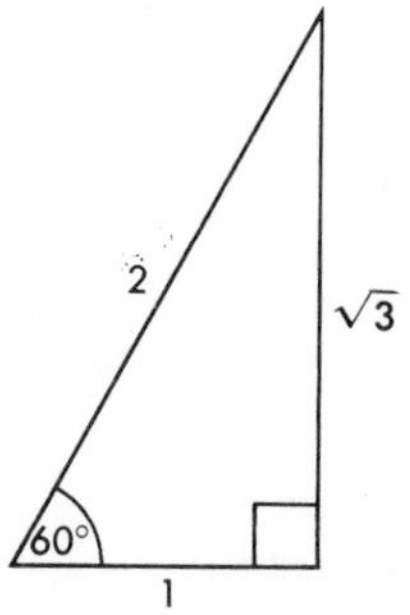

9. $\sec s \csc s - 2\cos s \csc s$

$$= \frac{1}{\cos s}\cdot\frac{1}{\sin s} - 2\cos s\cdot\frac{1}{\sin s}$$

$$= \frac{1 - 2\cos^2 s}{\cos s \sin s}$$

$$= \frac{1 - \cos^2 s - \cos^2 s}{\cos s \sin s}$$

$$= \frac{\sin^2 s - \cos^2 s}{\cos s \sin s}$$

$$= \frac{\sin^2 s}{\cos s \sin s} - \frac{\cos^2 s}{\cos s \sin s}$$

$$= \frac{\sin s}{\cos s} - \frac{\cos s}{\sin s}$$

$$= \tan s - \cot s$$

10. $(\sec^2 s)(1 - \cos^2 s)$

$$= \frac{1}{\cos^2 s}\cdot\sin^2 s$$

$$= \frac{\sin^2 s}{\cos^2 s}$$

$$= \tan^2 s$$

CHAPTER 10

Topics in Trigonometry

The purpose of Chapter 10 is to extend the material on trigonometry that was begun in Chapter 9, and to provide an opportunity for the student to solve triangles by using the laws of sine and cosine, to find the solutions of trigonometric equations, and to study inverse trigonometric functions. The following are some of the topics covered in Chapter 10:

- *Law of cosines*
- *Law of sines*
- *The addition formulas*
- *Double angle formulas*
- *Half angle formulas*
- *Solutions of trigonometric equations*
- *Graphs of trigonometric functions*
- *Amplitude of a trigonometric function*
- *Period of a trigonometric function*
- *Arccosine*
- *Arcsine*
- *Arctangent*
- *DeMoivre's theorem*

It may be necessary to allow more than one day for Sections 10–2, 10–5, and 10–8. Section 10–9 is optional but should be covered by those intending to continue in mathematics.

CHAPTER 10

Trigonometric functions are used extensively in the study of electricity. Shown above is a Van de Graaff, or electrostatic, generator. (Courtesy of Lockheed Missiles and Space Company)

TOPICS IN TRIGONOMETRY

There are many interesting relations, or identities, among the trigonometric functions. Some of these identities were developed in Chapter 9. For example,

$$\sin^2 s + \cos^2 s = 1.$$

Others will be developed in this chapter. For example,

$$\sin (u + v) = \sin u \cos v + \cos u \sin v.$$

According to this identity,

$$\begin{aligned} \sin 75^\circ &= \sin (45^\circ + 30^\circ) \\ &= \sin 45^\circ \cos 30^\circ + \cos 45^\circ \sin 30^\circ. \end{aligned}$$

Since the exact trigonometric functions of 30° and 45° are known, we can find sin 75° exactly.

If we are given a variable y as a function of x, we can sometimes express x as a function of y. The resulting function is called the inverse of the given function. For example, if $y = f(x)$ is defined by

$$y = 3x - 5,$$

then we can solve this equation for x in terms of y: $x = g(y)$. We obtain

$$x = \tfrac{1}{3}(y + 5).$$

Thus, the functions f and g are inverses of each other.

The trigonometric functions have inverses which are frequently used in mathematics. In this chapter, we shall study inverse trigonometric functions.

403

10–1 LAW OF COSINES

Before starting this section, you may wish to drill the class in assigning coordinates to a point in the coordinate plane which lies on the terminal side of an angle in standard position. Start with points on the unit circle. For example, the point one unit from the origin on the terminal side of the 60° angle has coordinates

$$(\cos 60°, \sin 60°) = (1/2, \sqrt{3}/2).$$

The point on the terminal side of this angle but 10 units from the origin has coordinates

$$(10 \cos 60°, 10 \sin 60°) = (5, 5\sqrt{3}).$$

In general, the point at a distance a units from the origin on the terminal side of an angle of α radians has coordinates $(a \cos \alpha, a \sin \alpha)$.

In presenting the law of cosines, you may wish to draw a figure in which the angle at A is obtuse, instead of using the figure in the text, in order to find out whether this will bring any objections from the class. The coordinates of C are still $(b \cos \alpha, b \sin \alpha)$. (See Exercise for Discussion 1 in this section.)

Problem 2 on page 405 illustrates one of the principal uses of the law of cosines. The law may be used to determine any one of the angles of a triangle, given the lengths of its three sides.

Exercises for Discussion, page 406

If time is limited, it is suggested that at least Exercises for Discussion 4, 7, and 8 be covered.

10–1 LAW OF COSINES

The sides and angles of every triangle are related in ways that will be discussed in this section. Since the sum of the measures of the angles of a triangle is 180°, each angle of a triangle has a measure between 0° and 180°. Let ABC be a given triangle, and let a coordinate system be placed in the plane of the triangle so that angle α at vertex A is in standard position. Then the vertices of the given triangle will have the coordinates shown in Fig. 10–1.

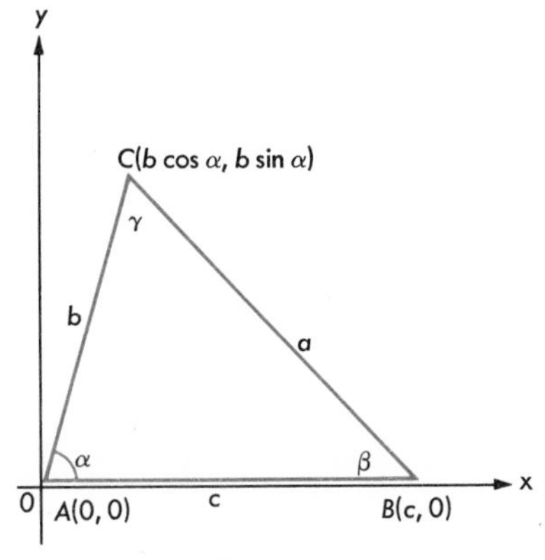

FIGURE 10–1

According to the distance formula, a, the distance between points B and C is given by

$$a = \sqrt{(b \cos \alpha - c)^2 + (b \sin \alpha - 0)^2}.$$

Hence,

$$a^2 = b^2 (\cos \alpha)^2 - 2bc \cos \alpha + c^2 + b^2 (\sin \alpha)^2,$$
$$a^2 = b^2 (\cos^2 \alpha + \sin^2 \alpha) + c^2 - 2bc \cos \alpha,$$

and since $\cos^2 \alpha + \sin^2 \alpha = 1$,

$$a^2 = b^2 + c^2 - 2bc \cos \alpha.$$

This is a proof of the following law.

LAW OF COSINES

If α, β, and γ are the angles of a triangle and a, b, and c are the lengths of the respective opposite sides, then

$$a^2 = b^2 + c^2 - 2bc \cos \alpha.$$

We can interchange a and b, and α and β, to obtain the formula

$$b^2 = a^2 + c^2 - 2ac \cos \beta.$$

In a similar way, we can interchange a and c, and α and γ, to obtain the formula

$$c^2 = a^2 + b^2 - 2ab \cos \gamma.$$

The law of cosines is sometimes called the generalized pythagorean theorem. For example, if $\alpha = 90°$, then $\cos \alpha = 0$, and the law of cosines becomes the pythagorean theorem: $a^2 = b^2 + c^2$.

Problem 1. Find a for the triangle in Fig. 10–2.

Solution. By the law of cosines,

$$a^2 = 3^2 + 4^2 - (2 \cdot 3 \cdot 4 \cos 60°).$$

Since $\cos 60° = \frac{1}{2}$,

$$a^2 = 9 + 16 - 12,$$
$$a^2 \doteq 13,$$

and $a = \sqrt{13}$.

This problem illustrates one of the principal uses of the law of cosines. The law helps us find the length of one side of a triangle if we are given the lengths of the other two sides and the measure of the angle formed by them.

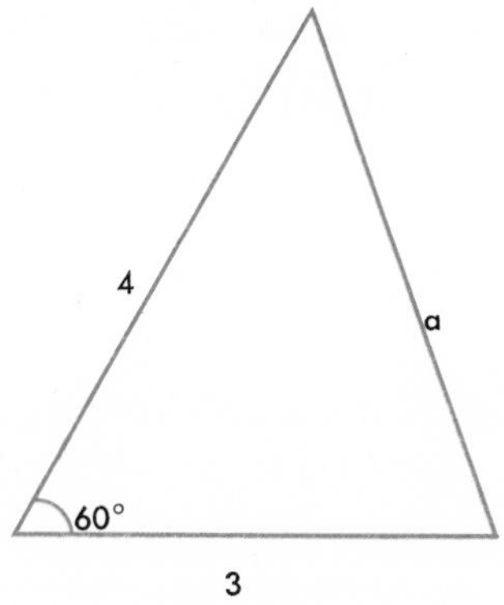

FIGURE 10–2

Problem 2. If the sides of a triangle have lengths 12, 9, and 5, find approximate measures of the angles.

Solution. If the vertices and angles of this triangle are labeled as shown in Fig. 10–3, then by the law of cosines,

$$12^2 = 9^2 + 5^2 - (2 \cdot 9 \cdot 5 \cos \alpha),$$
$$144 = 81 + 25 - (90 \cos \alpha),$$
$$\cos \alpha = {}^{-}\tfrac{38}{90}.$$

Thus, $\cos \alpha \doteq {}^{-}.422$. The fact that $\cos \alpha$ is negative indicates that α is obtuse. Since $\cos (180° - \alpha) = {}^{-}\cos \alpha \doteq .422$, we see that $(180° - \alpha) \doteq 65°$ and $\alpha \doteq 115°$.

We can find the other angles of triangle ABC in a similar way. Thus,

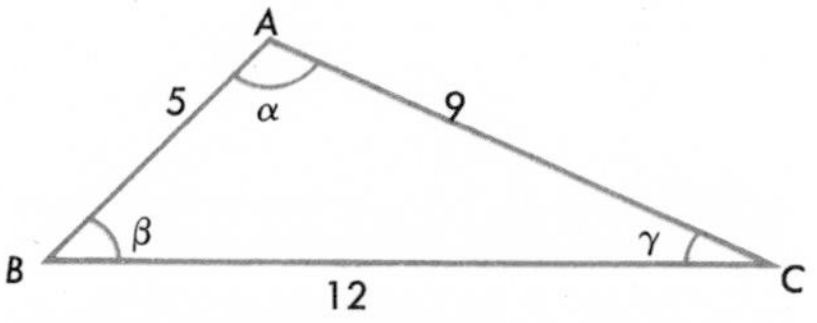

FIGURE 10–3

$$9^2 = 12^2 + 5^2 - (2 \cdot 5 \cdot 12 \cos \beta),$$
$$\cos \beta = \tfrac{88}{120}, \quad \text{or } .733.$$

Hence, $\beta \doteq 43°$. Now γ has measure $180 - (115 + 43)°$, or $\gamma \doteq 22°$. Thus, the angles of the triangle are $\alpha \doteq 115°$, $\beta \doteq 43°$, $\gamma \doteq 22°$.

Answers to Exercises for Discussion 1–4, page 406

1. By the distance formula,

$$a = \sqrt{(b \cos \alpha - c)^2 + (b \sin \alpha - 0)^2}$$
$$a^2 = b^2 \cos^2 \alpha - 2bc \cos \alpha + c^2 + b^2 \sin^2 \alpha$$
$$a^2 = b^2 + c^2 - 2bc \cos \alpha$$

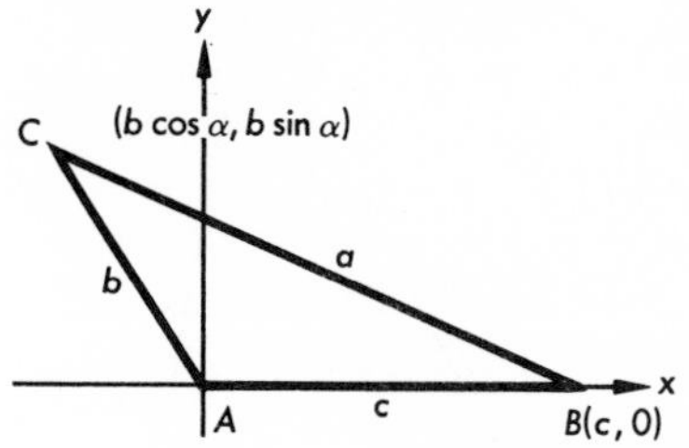

2. $c^2 = a^2 + b^2 - 2ab \cos \gamma$
$= 9 + 49 - 42 \cos 40°$
$\doteq 25.828$
$c \doteq 5.08$

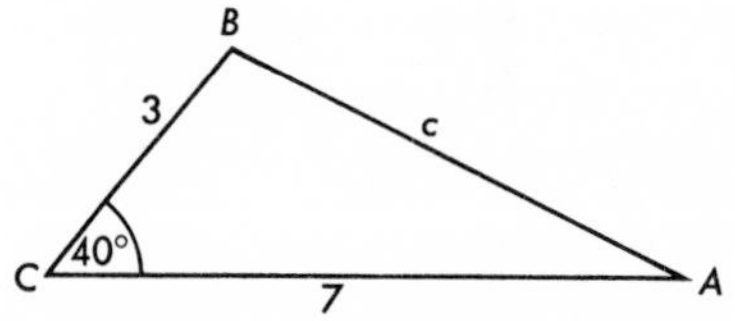

3. $a^2 = b^2 + c^2 - 2bc \cos \alpha$

$$\cos \alpha = \frac{b^2 + c^2 - a^2}{2bc} = \frac{43}{48} \doteq .896$$
$\alpha \doteq 26°$

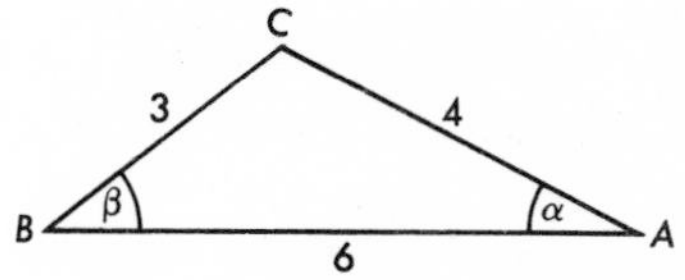

4. $a^2 = b^2 + c^2 - 2bc \cos \alpha$
$= 9 + 16 - 24 \cos 120°$
$= 25 + 24 \cos 60° = 37$
$a \doteq 6.08$

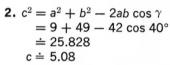

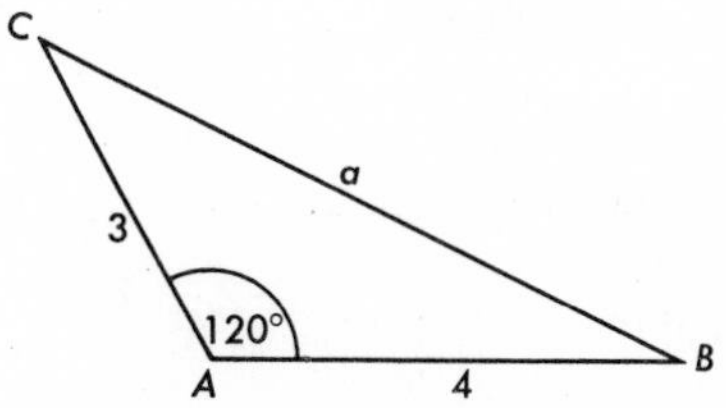

Answers to Exercises for Discussion 5–8

5. $a^2 = b^2 + c^2 - 2bc \cos \alpha$
$= 9 + 4 - 12 \cos 60°$
$= 7$
$a \doteq 2.65$

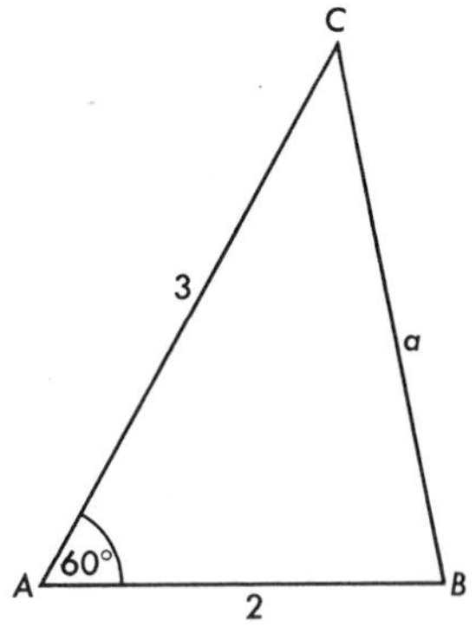

6. $b^2 = a^2 + c^2 - 2ac \cos \beta$

$$\cos \beta = \frac{a^2 + c^2 - b^2}{2ac} = \frac{128}{160} = .800$$

$\beta \doteq 37°$

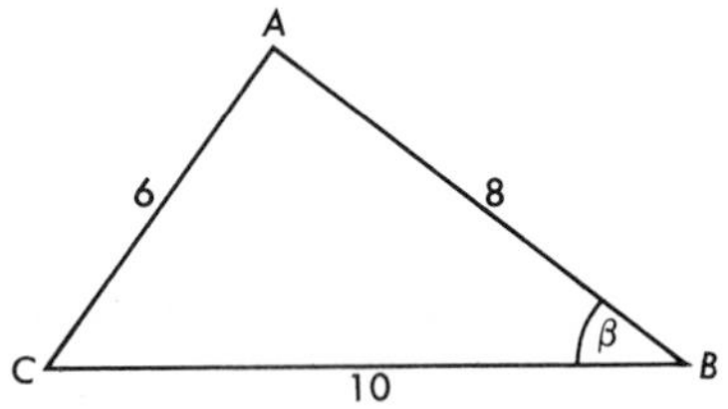

7. $d^2 = (40)^2 + (70)^2 - 2(40)(70) \cos 144°$
$= 1600 + 4900 + 5600 \cos 36°$
$\doteq 6500 + 5600(.809)$
$= 11030.4$
$d \doteq 105$ feet

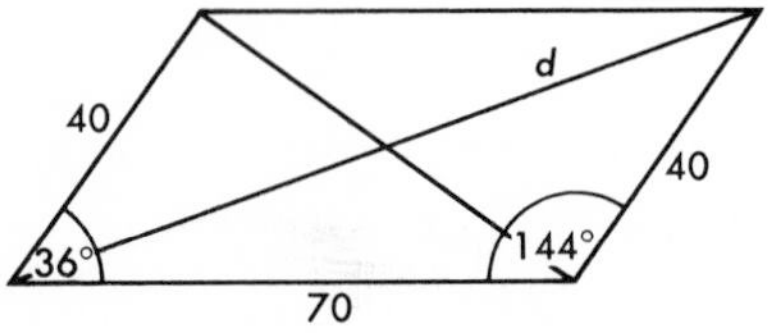

Exercises for Discussion

1. Draw $\triangle ABC$ with an obtuse angle at A in standard position. Follow the method of the proof in the text to prove the law of cosines for this triangle.

In each exercise of Exercises 2–6, A, B, and C designate the vertices of a triangle; α, β, and γ designate the measures of the corresponding angles; and a, b, and c designate the lengths of the corresponding opposite sides.

2. Find c, given that $a = 3$, $b = 7$, $\gamma = 40°$.

3. Find α, given that $a = 3$, $b = 4$, $c = 6$.

4. Find a, given that $b = 3$, $c = 4$, $\alpha = 120°$.

5. Find a, given that $b = 3$, $c = 2$, $\alpha = 60°$.

6. Find β, given that $a = 10$, $c = 8$, $b = 6$.

7. The sides of a parallelogram are 40 feet and 70 feet long, and the smallest angle has measure 36°. Find the length of the longer diagonal.

8. A triangular lot bounded by three streets has a frontage of 300 feet on one street, 250 feet on the second, and 420 feet on the third street. Find the measure of the smallest angle between two streets bounding the lot.

Exercises

In Exercises 1–5, A, B, and C designate the vertices of a triangle; α, β, and γ designate the measures of the corresponding angles; and a, b, and c designate the lengths of the corresponding opposite sides.

1. Find c, given that $b = 4$, $a = \sqrt{3}$, $\gamma = 150°$. $c = 5.57$

2. Find α, given that $a = 4$, $b = 6$, $c = 7$. $\alpha = 35°$

3. Find c, given that $a = 5$, $b = 5\sqrt{2}$, $\gamma = 45°$. $c = 5$

4. Find c, given that $a = 5$, $b = 5\sqrt{2}$, $\gamma = 135°$. $c = 11.18$

5. Find the smallest angle, given that $a : b : c = 2 : 3 : 4$. 29°

△

---

6. A parallelogram with one angle of measure 120° has sides of length 50 feet and 80 feet. Find the length of the shorter diagonal. 70 ft

7. Prove that if $\triangle ABC$ has an obtuse angle at C, then $c^2 > a^2 + b^2$. See Solution Manual.

8. Two planes, one flying at 450 miles per hour and the other at 300 miles per hour, left an airport at the same time. Three hours later, they were 1200 miles apart. What was the measure of the angle between their flight paths? 61°

10–2 LAW OF SINES

Each triangle T has an area $A(T)$, given by

$$A(T) = \tfrac{1}{2}bh,$$

where h is the length of the altitude of the triangle drawn from vertex B. If α is acute, then $\sin \alpha = h/c$ and

$$h = c \sin \alpha$$

from Fig. 10–4. This suggests the following formula.

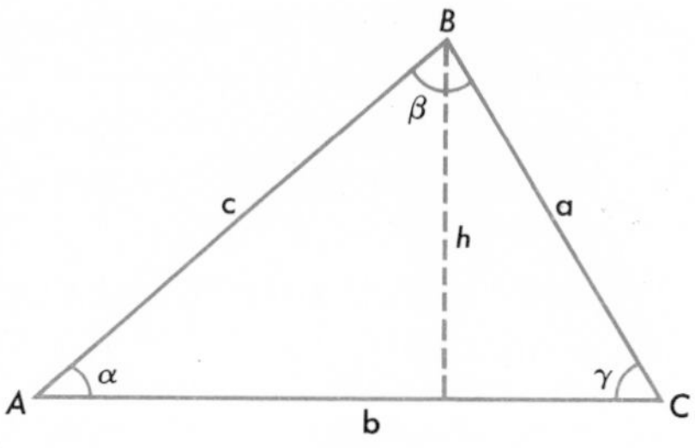

FIGURE 10–4

FORMULA FOR THE AREA OF A TRIANGLE T

$$A(T) = \frac{1}{2}bc \sin \alpha$$

Although we proved this formula on the assumption that α is acute, the formula is valid even if $\alpha = 90°$ or $\alpha > 90°$. Thus, if $\alpha = 90°$, then $\sin \alpha = 1$. The formula $A(T) = \frac{1}{2}bc$ is the one most frequently used in finding the area of a right triangle. In the exercises, you will be asked to prove that the formula is true when $\alpha > 90°$.

The formula for $A(T)$ is true for any two sides and the included angle. Thus, we also have

$$A(T) = \tfrac{1}{2}ac \sin \beta.$$

From these two formulas for $A(T)$, we obtain the true equation

$$\tfrac{1}{2}bc \sin \alpha = \tfrac{1}{2}ac \sin \beta,$$

or, multiplying each side by $2/abc$, we have

$$\frac{\sin \alpha}{a} = \frac{\sin \beta}{b}.$$

This is a proof of the following important law.

8. The smallest angle, which is α, is opposite the shortest side.

$$a^2 = b^2 + c^2 - 2bc \cos \alpha$$

$$\cos \alpha = \frac{b^2 + c^2 - a^2}{2bc} = \frac{(300)^2 + (420)^2 - (250)^2}{2(300)(420)} \doteq .809$$

$$\alpha \doteq 36°$$

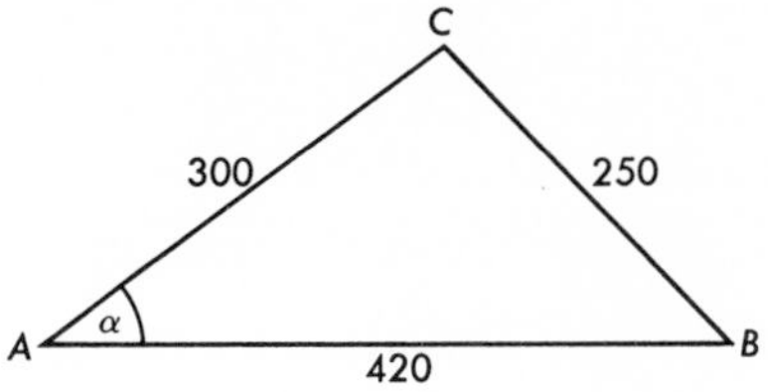

Quiz

Using the notation of the text,

1. Find c if $a = 10$, $b = 20$, $\gamma = 60°$. (ans: $10\sqrt{3}$)
2. Find c if $a = 10$, $b = 20$, $\gamma = 120°$. (ans: $10\sqrt{7}$)
3. Find $\cos \alpha$ if $a = 4$, $b = 6$, $c = 8$. (ans: $\frac{7}{8}$)
4. Show that $\triangle ABC$ in Exercise 3 is obtuse. (ans: $\cos \gamma = -\frac{1}{4} < 0$)

10–2 LAW OF SINES

You may wish to draw $\triangle ABC$ of Fig. 10–4 with α in standard position and then ask the students to give the coordinates of B as was done in Section 10–1. This could also be done for an obtuse angle. It can be seen that h, the y-coordinate of B, is $c \sin \alpha$. This demonstration will help students with Exercise 16 in this section.

The second form of the formula for $A(t)$ may be obtained by using β as the angle to place in standard position.

LAW OF SINES

If α, β, and γ are the angles of a triangle, and a, b, and c are the lengths of the respective opposite sides, then

$$\frac{\sin \alpha}{a} = \frac{\sin \beta}{b}.$$

We may interchange b and c, and β and γ, to obtain the law of sines in another form:

$$\frac{\sin \alpha}{a} = \frac{\sin \gamma}{c}.$$

Problem 1. Find the length of a for $\triangle ABC$, shown in Fig. 10–5.

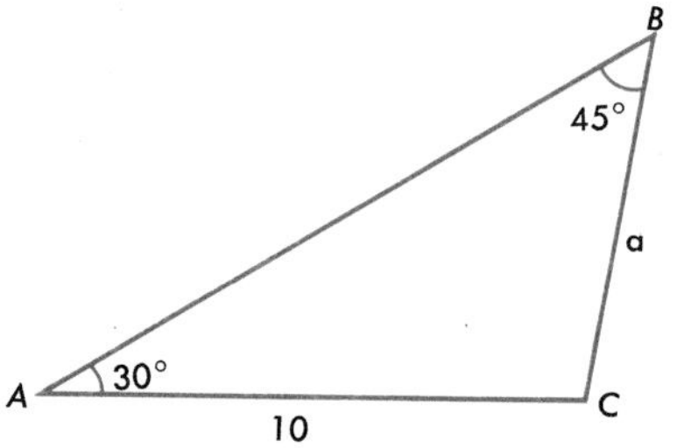

FIGURE 10–5

Solution. By the law of sines,

$$\frac{\sin 30°}{a} = \frac{\sin 45°}{10}.$$

Since

$$\sin 30° = \tfrac{1}{2} \text{ and } \sin 45° = 1/\sqrt{2},$$

we obtain

$$a = 5\sqrt{2}.$$

This problem shows that we can use the law of sines to find the length of one side of a triangle if we are given the length of another side and the measures of two angles of the triangle.

Problem 2. We can also use the law of sines to find the other parts of a triangle if we are given the lengths of two sides and the measure of an angle opposite one of them. For example, let $\alpha = 30°$, $a = 8$, and $b = 12$. Find the other angles and the third side of the triangle.

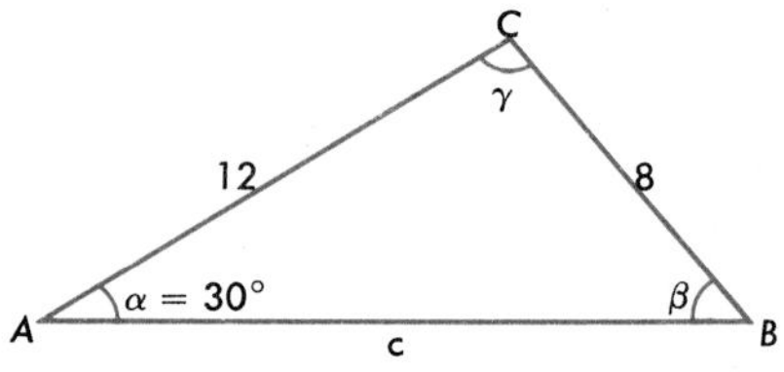

FIGURE 10–6

Solution. If the vertices and angles of the triangle are labeled as shown in Fig. 10–6, then by the law of sines,

$$\frac{\sin 30°}{8} = \frac{\sin \beta}{12}.$$

Problem 2 presents the so-called "ambiguous case" in that, given two sides and the angle opposite one of them, two different triangles may satisfy these conditions.

Bright students may ask if there are always two solutions, given two sides and the angle opposite one of them. The answer is no. For example, $\alpha = 30°$, $a = 10$, $b = 20$ is a 30–60 right triangle since the law of sines gives $\sin \beta = 1$. Two solutions are *possible* when the side opposite the angle is shorter than the side adjacent to the angle.

Students may then ask if there is always at least one triangle under the above conditions. Again the answer is no. For example, $\alpha = 30°$, $a = 10$, $b = 21$, for which the law of sines gives $\sin \beta = \frac{21}{20}$, is impossible. You could draw the supposed triangle in order to make this point clear.

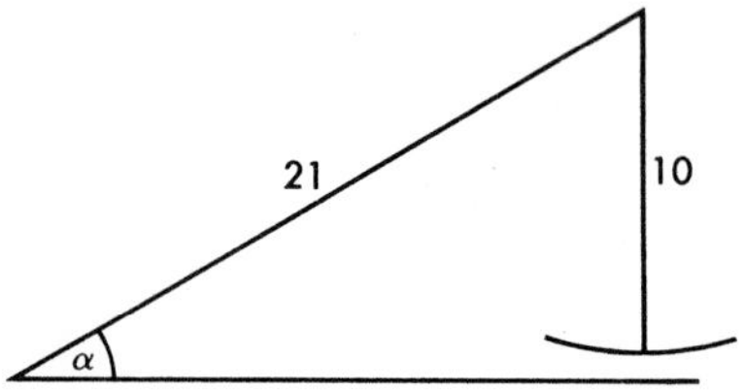

It is important to note that the law of sines will automatically discover these exceptional cases.

Since $\sin 30° = \frac{1}{2}$,

$$\sin \beta = \tfrac{3}{4}, \quad \text{or } .75.$$

From the Table of Values of Trigonometric Functions in the Appendix, we see that $\beta \doteq 49°$. Now γ has measure $180° - (30 + 49)°$, or $\gamma \doteq 101°$.

If c is the third side of the triangle, then

$$\frac{\sin 101°}{c} = \frac{\sin 30°}{8}.$$

We can find sin 101°, using the identity

$$\sin (180 - \gamma)° = \sin \gamma.$$

Therefore,

$$\sin 101° = \sin (180 - 101)°, \quad \text{or } \sin 79°.$$

From the Table in the Appendix, $\sin 79° \doteq 982$. Hence,

$$\frac{.982}{c} = \frac{.5}{8}$$

and

$$c \doteq 15.7.$$

Thus, the other angles of the triangle in Fig. 10–6 are $\beta \doteq 49°$ and $\gamma \doteq 101°$, and the other side is $c \doteq 15.7$.

However, since $\sin (180° - \beta) = \sin \beta$, then $(180 - 49)°$, or $131°$, is also an angle with sine of .75. Thus, $\beta \doteq 131°$ is another possible solution. In other words, the problem has two possible solutions. The second solution is shown in Fig. 10–7.

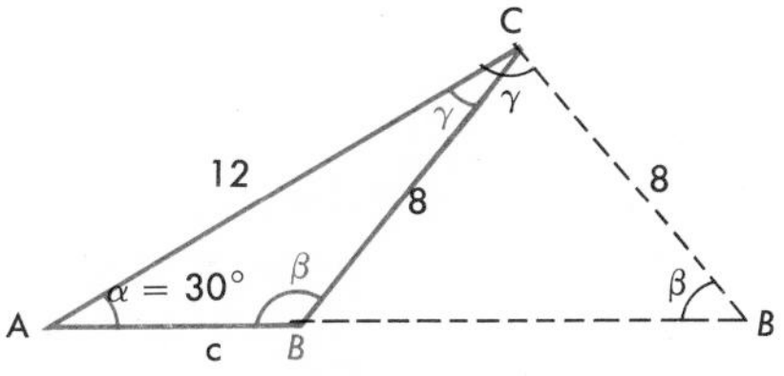

FIGURE 10–7

In this case, γ has measure $180 - (30 + 131)$ degrees, or $\gamma \doteq 19°$. To find c, we have

$$\frac{\sin 19°}{c} = \frac{\sin 30°}{8}.$$

From the Table, $\sin 19° \doteq .326$. Hence, $c \doteq 5.2$. The other angles of the triangle in Fig. 10–7 are $\beta \doteq 131°$, $\gamma \doteq 19°$, and the other side is $c \doteq 5.2$.

However, it can happen that there is a unique solution even without a right triangle. This will be so either when the side opposite the angle is longer than the adjacent side, or when the length of the third side is given so that it is easy to decide whether or not a solution would be sensible. (See Exercise for Discussion 5 in this section.)

In Problem 3 on the next page a log-trig table will eliminate the extra step of first obtaining

$$\sin 63° \doteq .891,$$

Thus

$$\log \sin 63° \doteq .9499 - 1,$$

directly from the log-sin tables.

The problems and exercises of this section provide some review of logarithmic computation, as does Problem 3.

Exercises for Discussion, page 411

If time is limited, it is suggested that at least Exercises for Discussion 4–9 be covered.

Answer to Exercise for Discussion 1, page 411

1. $\dfrac{\sin \alpha}{a} = \dfrac{\sin \gamma}{c}$

$$c = \frac{a \sin \gamma}{\sin \alpha}$$

$$= \frac{5\sqrt{6}\,(1/\sqrt{2})}{\sqrt{3}/2} = 10$$

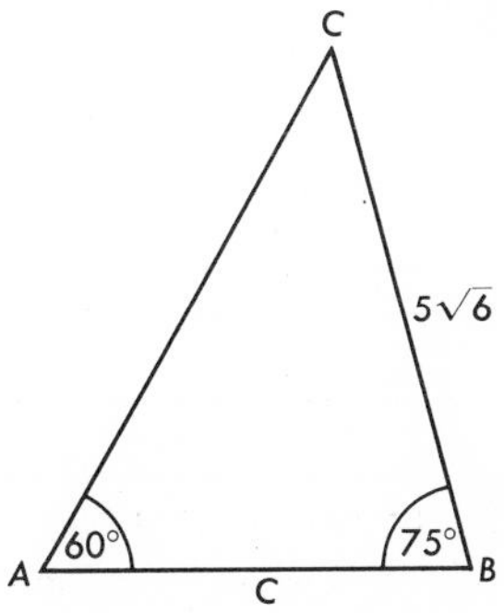

Answers to Exercises for Discussion 2–5, 7, page 411

2. $\dfrac{\sin\alpha}{a} = \dfrac{\sin\beta}{b}$

$$\sin\alpha = \frac{a\sin\beta}{b} = \frac{4\sin 30^\circ}{5} = \frac{4(.500)}{5} = .400$$

$\alpha \doteq 24^\circ$,
$\gamma \doteq 126^\circ$

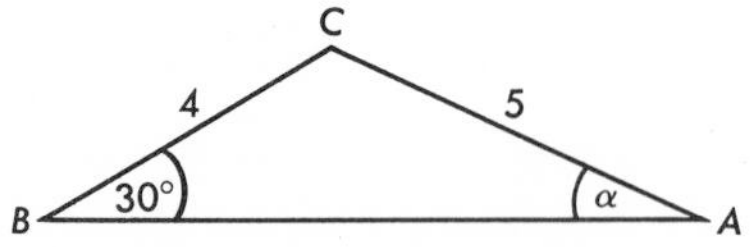

3. $\beta = 180^\circ - (\alpha + \gamma)$
$= 180^\circ - (50^\circ + 55^\circ)$
$= 75^\circ$

$\dfrac{\sin\beta}{b} = \dfrac{\sin\alpha}{a}$

$$b = \frac{a\sin\beta}{\sin\alpha} = \frac{30\sin 75^\circ}{\sin 50^\circ} \doteq \frac{30(.966)}{.766} = 37.8$$

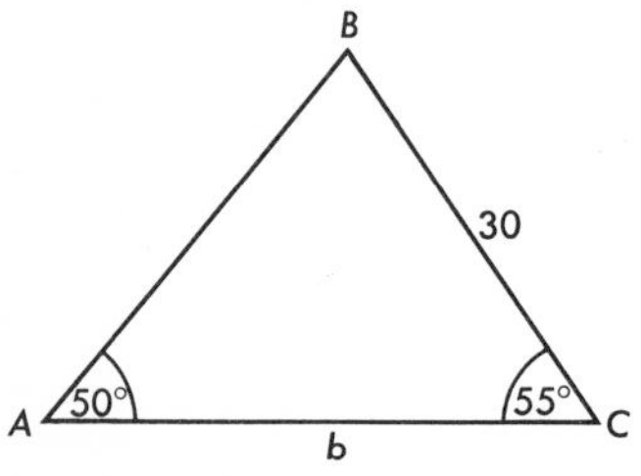

4. $\dfrac{\sin\beta}{b} = \dfrac{\sin\gamma}{c}$

$$\sin\gamma = \frac{c\sin\beta}{b} = \frac{10(.5)}{7} = \frac{5}{7} \doteq .714$$

$\gamma \doteq 46^\circ$ or $\gamma \doteq (180 - 46)^\circ$
$= 134^\circ$

The law of sines is ideally suited for logarithmic computation. Thus, from the law of sines, we have

$$\log\left(\frac{\sin\alpha}{a}\right) = \log\left(\frac{\sin\beta}{b}\right),$$

or

$$\log\sin\alpha - \log a = \log\sin\beta - \log b.$$

Given values of three of the four variables in the equation above, we can quickly compute the value of the other variable. This is illustrated in the following problem.

Problem 3. Vertices A and B of $\triangle ABC$ are on one bank of a river and vertex C is on the opposite bank, as shown in Fig. 10–8. The distance between A and B is 200 feet, and the angles at A and B have measures 33° and 63°, respectively. Find the distance between C and A, and the distance between C and B. Also, find the width of the river.

Solution. The angle at C has measure $180^\circ - (33 + 63)^\circ$, or 84°. If b designates the distance from A to C, then

$$\frac{\sin 63^\circ}{b} = \frac{\sin 84^\circ}{200}$$

by the law of sines. From the Table, we find that $\sin 63^\circ \doteq .891$ and $\sin 84^\circ \doteq .995$. Therefore,

$$\log .891 - \log b = \log .995 - \log 200,$$

or

$$\log b = \log 200 + \log .891 - \log .995.$$

From the Table of Common Logarithms, $\log 200 \doteq .3010 + 2$ and $\log .891 \doteq .9499 - 1$. Therefore,

$$\log 200 + \log .891 \doteq 1.2509 + 1.$$

Also, $\log .995 \doteq .9978 - 1$. Therefore,

$$\log 200 + \log .891 - \log .995 = \log b \doteq .2531 + 2.$$

Hence, by the Table of Common Logarithms,

$$b \doteq 179 \text{ feet.}$$

If a denotes the distance from B to C in Fig. 10–8, then

$$\frac{\sin 33°}{a} = \frac{\sin 84°}{200}.$$

Since $\sin 33° \doteq .545$, we have

$$\log a = \log 200 + \log .545 - \log .995.$$

From the Table of Common Logarithms,

$$\log 200 + \log .545 - \log .995 = \log a \doteq .0396 + 2.$$

Hence, by the Table of Common Logarithms,

$$a \doteq 110 \text{ feet}.$$

If w denotes the width of the river, then

$$\sin 33° = \frac{w}{b}$$

and

$$\log w = \log b + \log \sin 33°.$$

From our previous work,

$$\log b = 2.2531$$

and

$$\log \sin 33° = .7364 - 1.$$

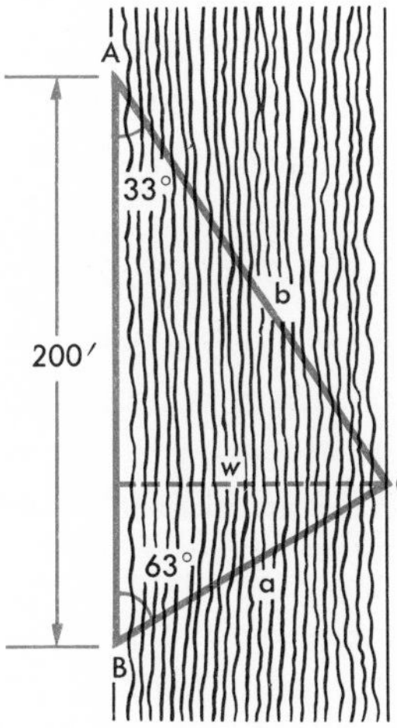

FIGURE 10–8

Therefore, $\log w = \log b + \log \sin 33° = 2.9895 - 1$, or 1.9895. Hence, $w \doteq 97.6$ feet.

Exercises for Discussion

In each exercise of Exercises 1–5, A, B, and C designate the vertices of a triangle; α, β, and γ designate the measures of the corresponding angles; and a, b, and c designate the lengths of the corresponding opposite sides.

1. Find c, given that $\alpha = 60°$, $\beta = 75°$, $a = 5\sqrt{6}$.
2. Find γ, given that $a = 4$, $b = 5$, $\beta = 30°$.
3. Find b, given that $\alpha = 50°$, $\gamma = 55°$, $a = 30$.
4. Find γ, given that $b = 7$, $c = 10$, $\beta = 30°$.
5. Find γ, given that $b = 7$, $c = 10$, $\alpha = 30°$.
6. Find the area of the triangle in Exercise 5. $A = \frac{1}{2} bc \sin\alpha = \frac{1}{2}\cdot 7 \cdot 10 \sin 30° = 35 \cdot \frac{1}{2} = 17.5$
7. Find the area of the two possible triangles of Exercise 4.

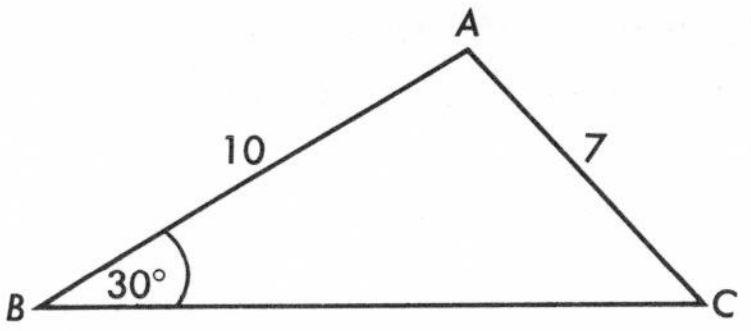

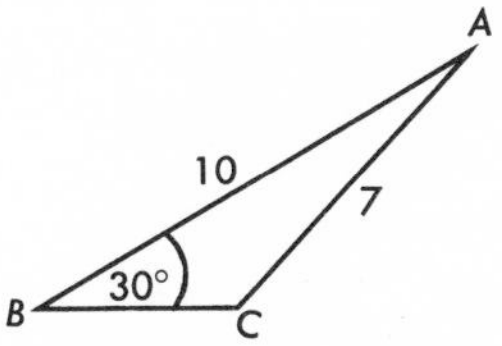

5. $a^2 = b^2 + c^2 - 2bc \cos\alpha$
$= 49 + 100 - 2\cdot 7\cdot 10 \cos 30°$
$\doteq 149 - 140(.866)$
$= 27.76$
$a \doteq 5.27$

$$\frac{\sin\gamma}{c} = \frac{\sin\alpha}{a}$$

$$\sin\gamma = \frac{c \sin\alpha}{a} = \frac{10 \sin 30°}{5.27} = \frac{10(.5)}{5.27} = \frac{5}{5.27} = .949$$

$\gamma \doteq 72°$ or $\gamma \doteq 108°$

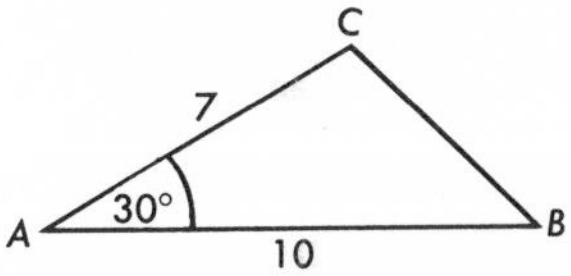

But since the longest side must be opposite the greatest angle, $\gamma \doteq 108°$.

7. $A = \frac{1}{2}bc \sin\alpha$
$= \frac{1}{2}\cdot 7 \cdot 10 \sin \times [180° - (30° + 46°)]$
$= 35 \sin 104°$
$= 35 \sin 76°$
$\doteq 35(.970)$
$= 33.95$

or

$A = \frac{1}{2}\cdot 7 \cdot 10 \sin \times [180° - (30° + 134°)]$
$= 35 \sin 16°$
$\doteq 35(.276)$
$= 9.66$

Answers to Exercises for Discussion 8, 9

8. $75° = 63° + \sigma$

$\sigma = 12°$

$$\frac{\sin 63°}{p} = \frac{\sin 12°}{40}$$

$$p = \frac{40 \sin 63°}{\sin 12°}$$

$$\doteq \frac{40(.891)}{.208}$$

$$\doteq 171 \text{ feet}$$

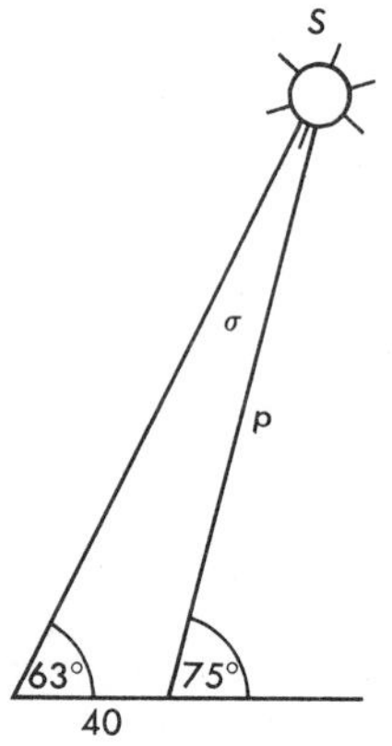

9.
$$\begin{cases} \dfrac{h}{x} = \tan 47° \\ \dfrac{h}{x + 2500} = \tan 21° \end{cases}$$

$$\begin{cases} h = x \tan 47° \\ h = (x + 2500) \tan 21° \end{cases}$$

$$\begin{cases} x = \dfrac{h}{\tan 47°} \\ h = x \tan 21° + 2500 \tan 21° \end{cases}$$

$$\begin{cases} x = \dfrac{h}{\tan 47°} \\ h = \dfrac{h \tan 21°}{\tan 47°} + 2500 \tan 21° \end{cases}$$

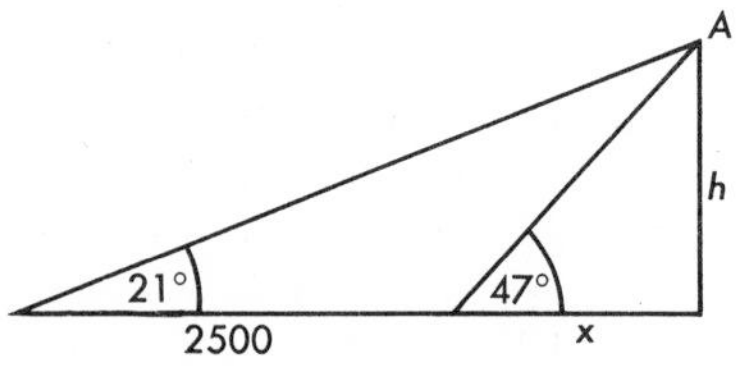

8. A telegraph pole casts a shadow 40 feet long when the angle of elevation of the sun is 63°. The pole leans 15° from the vertical, directly toward the sun. Find the length of the pole.

9. From a ship, the angle of elevation of a point A at the top of a cliff is 21°. After the ship has sailed 2500 feet directly toward the foot of the cliff, the angle of elevation of A is 47°. Find the height of the cliff.

Exercises

In each exercise of Exercises 1–12, A, B, and C designate the vertices of a triangle; α, β, and γ designate the measures of the corresponding angles; and a, b, and c designate the lengths of the corresponding opposite sides.

1. Find a, given that $\alpha = 30°$, $\beta = 135°$, $b = 10\sqrt{2}$. $a = 10$
2. Find c, given that $\alpha = 30°$, $\beta = 105°$, $a = 3\sqrt{2}$. $c = 6$
3. Find β, given that $a = 12$, $b = 8\sqrt{3}$, $\alpha = 60°$. $\beta = 90°$
4. Given that $\beta = 60°$, $a = 10$, $b = 9\sqrt{3}$, find the other side and the angles of the triangle. $\alpha \doteq 34°$; $\gamma \doteq 86°$; $c = 17.96$
5. Given that $\beta = 30°$, $b = 9$, $c = 15$, find the other side and the angles of the triangle. $\gamma \doteq 56°$; $\gamma' \doteq 124°$; $\alpha \doteq 94°$; $\alpha' \doteq 26°$; $a = 17.96$, $a' = 7.88$
6. Find the area of the triangle or triangles of Exercise 5. 29.55; 67.35
7. Find c, given that $\alpha = 110°$, $\beta = 55°$, $a = 30$. $c = 8.26$
8. Find a, given that $\beta = 28°$, $\gamma = 41°$, $c = 100$. $a = 142.4$
9. Find c, given that $\alpha = 37°$, $\beta = 53°$, $a = 60$. $c = 99.7$
10. Find γ, given that $a = 9$, $c = 10$, $\alpha = 55°$. $\gamma = 65°$ or $115°$
11. Find b and then α, given that $a = 12$, $c = 9$, $\beta = 63°$. $b = 11.27$; $\alpha \doteq 72°$
12. Find b, α, and γ, given that $a = \sqrt{2}$, $c = 8$, $\beta = 45°$. $b = 7.07$; $\alpha \doteq 8°$; $\gamma = 127°$
13. Find the area of the triangle in Exercise 11. 48.1
14. Find the area of the triangle in Exercise 12. 4
15. A 10-foot ladder must make an angle of 30° with the ground if it is to reach a certain window. What angle must a 20-foot ladder make with the ground to reach the same window? 14°
16. Prove that the following formula for the area of a triangle T is true if $\alpha > 90°$. See Solution Manual.

$$A(T) = \tfrac{1}{2}bc \sin \alpha$$

△

17. A surveyor runs a line due east from A to B, but he cannot continue the line in an easterly direction because of an obstacle. Therefore, he runs a line 800 feet long from B to C in a direction 24° east of south, and then runs another line CD in a direction 47° east of north. How long should CD be if D is to be due east of B? 1072

18. The two diagonals of a parallelogram have lengths 10 and 7. The diagonals meet at a 60° angle. Find the lengths of the sides of the parallelogram and the measure of its angles. 4.44; 7.40; 67°; 113°

19. On a coordinate plane, plot the three points

$$A(^{-}2, 7),\quad B(6, 1),\quad C(^{-}6, ^{-}4)$$

73°; 47°; 60°

and draw $\triangle ABC$. Find the measure of the three angles of this triangle.

20. Find length a in the figure. $a = 60$

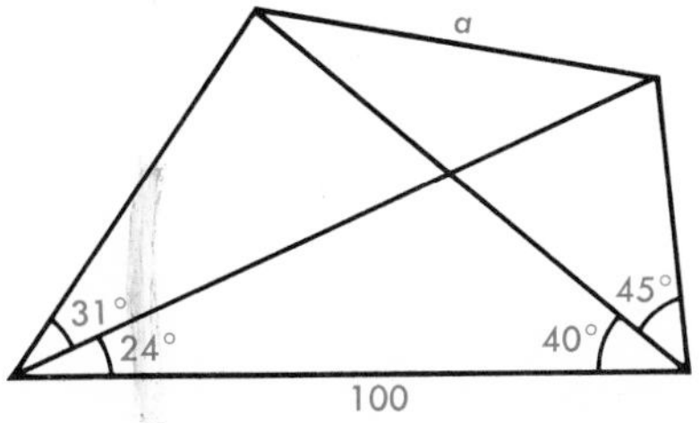

21. (a) Find a formula for the area of a parallelogram with two of its adjacent sides of length b and c, given that the included angle of the sides has a measure of α. $A = bc \sin \alpha$

(b) Find the area of the parallelogram, given that $b = 365$, $c = 489$, $\alpha = 132°$. 132,614.4

22. In the figure, $PABC$ is a parallelogram with two adjacent sides of length 300 and 450 forming a 47° angle. The arrows suggest an application to the following physical problem: Two forces, one of 300 pounds and the other of 450 pounds, acting on an object at P with a 47° angle between their directions, have the same effect as one force acting on P in the direction of the diagonal PB. The length of the diagonal gives the magnitude of this resultant force. Find the magnitude of the resultant force and the measure of the angle it makes with the 450-pound force. 690 pounds; 19°

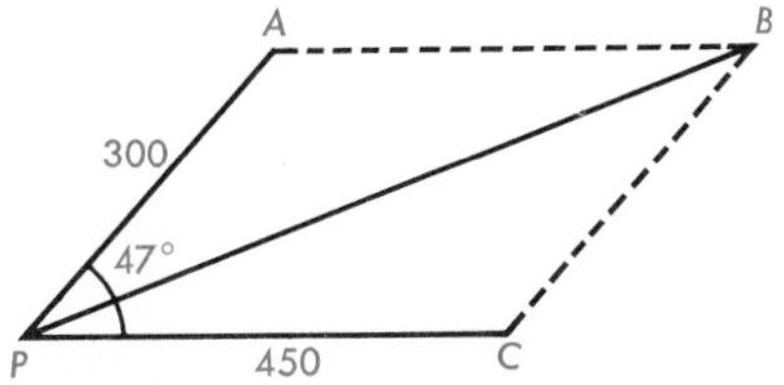

▲

$P = 2nr \sin\left(\frac{180}{n}\right)^{\circ}$

23. A regular polygon of n sides is inscribed in a circle of radius r. Using trigonometric functions, derive a formula for the perimeter of the polygon.

24. Given that k is the proportionality number $\sin \alpha / a$, encountered in the law of sines, and that $r = 1/(2k)$, prove that r is the radius of the circle circumscribed about $\triangle ABC$. See Solution Manual.

Solving the second equation in the last system for h we obtain

$$h - \frac{h \tan 21°}{\tan 47°} = 2500 \tan 21°$$

$$h\left(1 - \frac{\tan 21°}{\tan 47°}\right) = 2500 \tan 21°$$

$$h\left(\frac{\tan 47° - \tan 21°}{\tan 47°}\right) = 2500 \tan 21°$$

$$h = 2500 \tan 21° \times \left(\frac{\tan 47°}{\tan 47° - \tan 21°}\right)$$

$$= \frac{2500 \tan 21° \tan 47°}{\tan 47° - \tan 21°}$$

$$\doteq \frac{2500(.384)(1.072)}{1.072 - .384}$$

$$h \doteq 1496 \text{ feet.}$$

Exercises

Five or six of these exercises should be enough for any individual assignment because of the time needed for computation. It is recommended that different sets of exercises be assigned to different groups of students. You could ask for volunteers to put examples of the different cases on the board.

Quiz

1. Find the area of $\triangle ABC$ if

$$\gamma = 150°,\ a = 10,\ b = 16$$

(ans: 40)

2. Find the length of side c given

$$\alpha = 30°,\ \gamma = 135°,\ a = 10$$

(ans: $10\sqrt{2}$)

3. If $\beta = 30°$, $a = 10\sqrt{3}$, $b = 10$, find two triangles ABC (give angles and lengths of sides) satisfying these conditions. (ans: $\alpha = 60°$, $\beta = 30°$, $\gamma = 90°$, $a = 10\sqrt{3}$, $b = 10$, $c = 20$; or $\alpha = 120°$, $\beta = 30°$, $\gamma = 30°$, $a = 10\sqrt{3}$, $b = 10$, $c = 10$)

10-3 THE ADDITION FORMULAS

When you begin the discussion of this section, you may wish to recall the definition of sin s and cos s in terms of the wrapping function $W(s)$ for any real number s.

10-3 THE ADDITION FORMULAS

In this section, we shall develop formulas for finding trigonometric functions of *sums* and *differences* of numbers. For any real numbers u and v, there correspond points $W(u)$ and $W(v)$ on the unit circle, as shown in Fig. 10-9. If $0 < u < v < 2\pi$, then the arc from $W(u)$ to $W(v)$ has length $v - u$. Therefore, there is a central angle α of the circle whose radian measure is $v - u$.

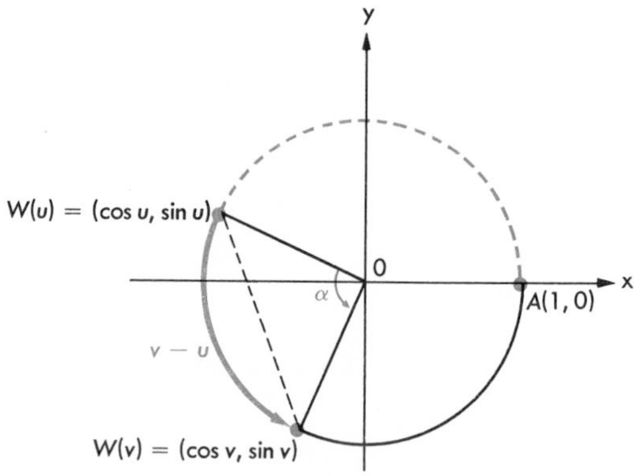

FIGURE 10-9

In connection with the drawing in Fig. 10-9, this equation is just the law of cosines applied to the triangle with vertices at 0, $W(u)$, and $W(v)$.

We can follow the method used in proving the law of cosines to show that the distance d between points $W(u)$ and $W(v)$ can be given by the equation

$$\begin{aligned} d^2 &= 1^2 + 1^2 - (2 \cdot 1 \cdot 1 \cdot \cos \alpha) \\ &= 2 - 2 \cos \alpha. \end{aligned}$$

Since α has radian measure $v - u$, we have proved that

$$d^2 = 2 - 2 \cos (v - u).$$

You could ask students to recall the distance formula for the distance between two points (x_1, y_1) and (x_2, y_2) in a coordinate plane. (See page 211.)

On the other hand, we can compute the distance between $W(u)$ and $W(v)$ by using the distance formula.

$$\begin{aligned} d^2 &= (\cos v - \cos u)^2 + (\sin v - \sin u)^2 \\ &= \cos^2 v - 2 \cos v \cos u + \cos^2 u \\ &\quad + \sin^2 v - 2 \sin v \sin u + \sin^2 u \\ &= (\sin^2 u + \cos^2 u) + (\sin^2 v + \cos^2 v) \\ &\quad - 2(\cos v \cos u + \sin v \sin u) \\ &= 1 + 1 - 2(\cos v \cos u + \sin v \sin u) \end{aligned}$$

We now have two different formulas for the distance between points $W(u)$ and $W(v)$ which we combine to obtain the equation

$$2 - 2\cos(v - u) = 2 - 2(\cos v \cos u + \sin v \sin u).$$

By simplifying, we obtain the first *addition formula* of trigonometry.

FIRST ADDITION FORMULA

$$\cos(v - u) = \cos v \cos u + \sin v \sin u \qquad (A\text{-}1)$$

Although the first addition formula, (A-1), was proved on the assumption that $0 < u < v < 2\pi$, it can be shown that it is true for all values of u and v. Although we have used the term *radian measure* in the proof of the first addition formula, the formula continues to be true if we think of u and v as the degree measure of angles.

The following problem indicates how the first addition formula can be used to find the cosine of certain angles and numbers.

Problem 1. Find cos 15°.

Solution. Because $15 = 45 - 30$ and we know the sine and cosine of angles of measure 45° and 30°, we can use the first addition formula to find cos 15°.

$$\cos 15° = \cos 45° \cos 30° + \sin 45° \sin 30°$$

We substitute the known values of the sine and cosine of 45° and 30° and obtain

$$\cos 15° = \left(\frac{\sqrt{2}}{2} \cdot \frac{\sqrt{3}}{2}\right) + \left(\frac{\sqrt{2}}{2} \cdot \frac{1}{2}\right),$$

or

$$\cos 15° = \tfrac{1}{4}(\sqrt{6} + \sqrt{2}).$$

This is the exact value of cos 15°. Using the Table of Square Roots, we obtain

$$\sqrt{6} \doteq 2.449 \quad \text{and} \quad \sqrt{2} \doteq 1.414.$$

Hence,

$$\cos 15° \doteq \tfrac{1}{4}(3.863), \text{ or } .966.$$

Does this result agree with the entry in the Table of Values of Trigonometric Functions?

It is important that the first addition formula and the remaining three formulas of the section be learned by the student. They are the fundamental building blocks for all the identities to follow in later sections.

In particular, they should know the identity for the case $v = u$:

$$\cos(u - u) = \cos 0$$
$$\cos 0 = \cos u \cos u + \sin u \sin u = \cos^2 u + \sin^2 u = 1.$$

The derivations of the formulas on the following page need not be learned by the students. Exercise 20 on page 417, in which the fourth addition formula is derived, will probably interest only the brighter students.

Answers to Exercises for Discussion 1–9, 11, page 416

1. $\cos(v + u) = \cos(v - {}^-u) = \cos v \cos({}^-u) + \sin v \sin({}^-u) = \cos v \cos u + \sin v({}^-\sin u) = \cos v \cos u - \sin v \sin u$

2. $\sin 105° = \sin(60° + 45°) = \sin 60° \cos 45° + \cos 60° \sin 45° = \frac{\sqrt{3}}{2} \cdot \frac{\sqrt{2}}{2} + \frac{1}{2} \cdot \frac{\sqrt{2}}{2} = \tfrac{1}{4}(\sqrt{6} + \sqrt{2})$

3. $\tan 105° = \dfrac{\sin 105°}{\cos 105°}$

$= \dfrac{\sin 105°}{\cos (60° + 45°)}$

$= \dfrac{\sin 105°}{\cos 60° \cos 45° - \sin 60° \sin 45°}$

$= \dfrac{\frac{1}{4}(\sqrt{6} + \sqrt{2})}{\frac{1}{2} \cdot \frac{\sqrt{2}}{2} - \frac{\sqrt{3}}{2} \cdot \frac{\sqrt{2}}{2}}$

$= \dfrac{\sqrt{6} + \sqrt{2}}{\sqrt{2} - \sqrt{6}} \cdot \dfrac{\sqrt{2} + \sqrt{6}}{\sqrt{2} + \sqrt{6}}$

$= \dfrac{2 + 2\sqrt{12} + 6}{2 - 6}$

$= {}^{-}2 - \sqrt{3}$

4. $\tan (5\pi/12) = \dfrac{\sin (5\pi/12)}{\cos (5\pi/12)}$

$= \dfrac{\sin (\pi/4 + \pi/6)}{\cos (\pi/4 + \pi/6)}$

$= \dfrac{\sin \frac{\pi}{4} \cos \frac{\pi}{6} + \cos \frac{\pi}{4} \sin \frac{\pi}{6}}{\cos \frac{\pi}{4} \cos \frac{\pi}{6} - \sin \frac{\pi}{4} \sin \frac{\pi}{6}}$

$= \dfrac{\frac{\sqrt{2}}{2} \cdot \frac{\sqrt{3}}{2} + \frac{\sqrt{2}}{2} \cdot \frac{1}{2}}{\frac{\sqrt{2}}{2} \cdot \frac{\sqrt{3}}{2} - \frac{\sqrt{2}}{2} \cdot \frac{1}{2}}$

$= \dfrac{\sqrt{3} + 1}{\sqrt{3} - 1} \cdot \dfrac{\sqrt{3} + 1}{\sqrt{3} + 1}$

$= \dfrac{3 + 2\sqrt{3} + 1}{3 - 1}$

$= 2 + \sqrt{3}$

5–6 $\sin u = \frac{2}{3}$ $\quad \cos v = \frac{3}{7}$
$\cos u = {}^{-}\frac{1}{3}\sqrt{5}$ $\quad \sin v = \frac{2}{7}\sqrt{10}$

5. $\cos (u + v)$

$= \cos u \cos v - \sin u \sin v$

$= \dfrac{{}^{-}\sqrt{5}}{3} \cdot \dfrac{3}{7} - \dfrac{2}{3} \cdot \dfrac{2\sqrt{10}}{7}$

$= {}^{-}\frac{1}{21}(3\sqrt{5} + 4\sqrt{10})$

6. $\sin (u + v)$

$= \sin u \cos v + \cos u \sin v$

$= \dfrac{2}{3} \cdot \dfrac{3}{7} + \dfrac{{}^{-}\sqrt{5}}{3} \cdot \dfrac{2\sqrt{10}}{7}$

$= \frac{2}{21}(3 - 5\sqrt{2})$

The addition formulas given below can be derived from the first addition formula, (A-1). However, instead of including the proofs, we shall outline them in the exercises.

SECOND, THIRD, AND FOURTH ADDITION FORMULAS

$$\cos (v + u) = \cos v \cos u - \sin v \sin u \qquad (A\text{-}2)$$

$$\sin (v - u) = \sin v \cos u - \cos v \sin u \qquad (A\text{-}3)$$

$$\sin (v + u) = \sin v \cos u + \cos v \sin u \qquad (A\text{-}4)$$

Problem 2. Find $\sin \dfrac{11\pi}{12}$.

Solution. Since

$$\frac{11\pi}{12} = \frac{2\pi}{3} + \frac{\pi}{4},$$

$$\sin \frac{11\pi}{12} = \sin\left(\frac{2\pi}{3} + \frac{\pi}{4}\right)$$

$$= \sin \frac{2\pi}{3} \cos \frac{\pi}{4} + \cos \frac{2\pi}{3} \sin \frac{\pi}{4}$$

$$= \left(\frac{\sqrt{3}}{2} \cdot \frac{\sqrt{2}}{2}\right) + \left(\frac{{}^{-}1}{2} \cdot \frac{\sqrt{2}}{2}\right)$$

$$= \frac{1}{4}(\sqrt{6} - \sqrt{2}).$$

Exercises for Discussion

1. Use the formulas $\cos ({}^{-}u) = \cos u$, $\sin ({}^{-}u) = {}^{-}\sin u$, and (A-1) to prove (A-2). This proof consists of writing $\cos (v + u)$ as $\cos (v - {}^{-}u)$.

Find the exact value of each of the following.

2. $\sin 105°$ 3. $\tan 105°$ 4. $\tan \dfrac{5\pi}{12}$

Given that $\sin u = \frac{2}{3}$ and $\cos v = \frac{3}{7}$, with $\pi/2 < u < \pi$ and $0 < v < \pi/2$, find each of the following.

5. $\cos (u + v)$ 6. $\sin (u + v)$

Given that $csc\ u = \frac{7}{3}$, $\cos u < 0$, $\tan v = {}^{-}\frac{3}{2}$, and $\cos v > 0$, find each of the following.

7. $\sin (u - v)$ 8. $\cos (u - v)$ 9. $\tan (u - v)$

Use the addition formulas to simplify each of the following.

$\cos(\pi - u) = \cos \pi \cos u + \sin \pi \sin u$

10. $\cos (\pi - u)$ $= ({}^{-}1)\cos u + (0)\sin u$ $= {}^{-}\cos u$ 11. $\tan\left(\dfrac{5\pi}{2} + u\right)$

Exercises

Find the exact value of each of the following.

1. $\sin 15°$ $\frac{1}{4}(\sqrt{6}-\sqrt{2})$
2. $\tan 15°$ $2-\sqrt{3}$
3. $\sin 75°$ $\frac{1}{4}(\sqrt{6}+\sqrt{2})$
4. $\cos 75°$ $\frac{1}{4}(\sqrt{6}-\sqrt{2})$
5. $\tan 75°$ $2+\sqrt{3}$
6. $\tan 195°$ $2-\sqrt{3}$
7. $\cos \frac{7\pi}{12}$ $\frac{1}{4}(\sqrt{2}-\sqrt{6})$
8. $\tan \frac{7\pi}{12}$ $^{-}2-\sqrt{3}$
9. $\tan \frac{29\pi}{12}$ $2+\sqrt{3}$

If $\sin u = \frac{3}{5}$ and $\cos v = \frac{5}{13}$, with $\pi/2 < u < \pi$ and $0 < v < \pi/2$, find each of the following.

10. $\cos(u + v)$ $\frac{^{-}56}{65}$
11. $\sin(u + v)$ $\frac{^{-}33}{65}$
12. $\tan(u + v)$ $\frac{33}{56}$

If $\sec u = \frac{25}{7}$, $\tan u < 0$, $\tan v = {}^{-}\frac{4}{3}$, and $\sin v > 0$, find each of the following.

13. $\cos(u - v)$ $\frac{^{-}117}{125}$
14. $\sin(u - v)$ $\frac{44}{125}$
15. $\tan(u - v)$ $\frac{^{-}44}{117}$

Use the addition formulas to simplify each of the following.

16. $\cos\left(\frac{3\pi}{2} - u\right)$ $^{-}\sin u$
17. $\sin(2\pi - u)$ $^{-}\sin u$
18. $\tan(\pi - u)$ $^{-}\tan u$
19. $\cos\left(u + \frac{3\pi}{2}\right)$ $\sin u$

△

20-33 See Solution Manual.

20. Use the formulas $\cos(\pi/2 - v) = \sin v$, $\sin(\pi/2 - v) = \cos v$, and (A-1) to prove formula (A-4). The proof consists of writing $\sin(v + u)$ first as $\cos[\pi/2 - (v + u)]$ and then as $\cos[(\pi/2 - v) - u]$.

21. Prove formula (A-3).

22. Use the fundamental identity $\tan s = \sin s/\cos s$, (A-2), and (A-4) to show that

(a) $\tan(v + u) = \dfrac{\sin v \cos u + \cos v \sin u}{\cos v \cos u - \sin v \sin u}$.

(b) $\tan(v + u) = \dfrac{\tan v + \tan u}{1 - \tan v \tan u}$.

23. Use the formula $\tan({}^{-}u) = {}^{-}\tan u$ and the formula of Exercise 22(b) to show that

$$\tan(v - u) = \frac{\tan v - \tan u}{1 + \tan v \tan u}.$$

7-9 $\csc u = \frac{7}{3}$, $\sin u = \frac{3}{7}$

$\tan v = {}^{-}\frac{3}{2}$, $\cos u = \frac{^{-}2\sqrt{10}}{7}$

$\sin v = \frac{^{-}3}{\sqrt{13}}$, $\cos v = \frac{2}{\sqrt{13}}$

7. $\sin(u - v)$

$$= \sin u \cos v - \cos u \sin v = \frac{3}{7}\cdot\frac{2}{\sqrt{13}} - \frac{^{-}2\sqrt{10}}{7}\cdot\frac{^{-}3}{\sqrt{13}} = \frac{6}{7\sqrt{13}}(1 - \sqrt{10}) = \frac{6\sqrt{13}}{91}(1 - \sqrt{10})$$

8. $\cos(u - v)$

$$= \cos u \cos v + \sin u \sin v = \frac{^{-}2\sqrt{10}}{7}\cdot\frac{2}{\sqrt{13}} + \frac{3}{7}\cdot\frac{^{-}3}{\sqrt{13}} = \frac{1}{7\sqrt{13}}({}^{-}4\sqrt{10} - 9) = \frac{^{-}\sqrt{13}}{91}(4\sqrt{10} + 9)$$

9. $$\tan(u - v) = \frac{\sin(u - v)}{\cos(u - v)} = \frac{\frac{6\sqrt{13}}{91}(1 - \sqrt{10})}{\frac{^{-}\sqrt{13}}{91}(4\sqrt{10} + 9)} = \frac{^{-}6(1 - \sqrt{10})}{4\sqrt{10} + 9} = \tfrac{6}{79}(49 - 13\sqrt{10})$$

11. $\sin\left(\frac{5\pi}{2} + u\right)$

$$= \sin\frac{5\pi}{2}\cos u + \cos\frac{5\pi}{2}\sin u = \cos u$$

$\cos\left(\frac{5\pi}{2} + u\right)$

$$= \cos\frac{5\pi}{2}\cos u - \sin\frac{5\pi}{2}\sin u = {}^{-}\sin u$$

$$\tan\left(\frac{5\pi}{2} + u\right) = \frac{\sin\left(\frac{5\pi}{2} + u\right)}{\cos\left(\frac{5\pi}{2} + u\right)} = \frac{^{-}\cos u}{\sin u} = {}^{-}\cot u$$

Quiz

1. Use $15° = 60° - 45°$ to find $\sin 15°$. (ans: $(\sqrt{6} - \sqrt{2})/4$)
2. Verify that the formulas for $\sin(u - v)$ and $\cos(u - v)$ are valid when $u = v$.

   (ans: $\sin(u - u)$ $= \sin u \cos u - \cos u \sin u$ $= 0$
   and
   $\sin 0 = 0$

   $\cos(u - u)$ $= \cos u \cdot \cos u + \sin u \sin u$ $= 1$
   and
   $\cos 0 = 1$)
3. Use the addition formulas to verify the following identities:

   (a) $\cos(\pi + x) = {}^{-}\cos x$
   (ans: $\cos(\pi + x)$ $= \cos \pi \cos x - \sin \pi \sin x$ $= {}^{-}\cos x$)

   (b) $\sin(\pi + x) = {}^{-}\sin x$

   (ans: $\sin(\pi + x)$ $= \sin \pi \cos x + \cos \pi \sin x$ $= {}^{-}\sin x$)

10–4 DOUBLE-ANGLE AND HALF-ANGLE FORMULAS

The formulas of this section are used mainly as theoretical tools. For example, the first and second half-angle formulas are especially useful in the technique of integration in calculus. However, their application in evaluating sin 15°, cos 75°, and so on, may be more meaningful to the student at this time. The students should know how to derive these formulas from the addition formulas.

Prove each of the following identities.

24. $\cos(u + v)\cos(u - v) = \cos^2 u - \sin^2 v$

25. $\sin(u + v)\sin(u - v) = \sin^2 u - \sin^2 v$

26. $\cos\left(\frac{\pi}{4} - u\right) = \frac{1}{\sqrt{2}}(\cos u + \sin u)$

27. $\frac{\cos(u + v)}{\cos(u - v)} = \frac{1 - \tan u \tan v}{1 + \tan u \tan v}$

Use the fundamental identities of Section 9–5 and the addition formulas in this section to prove each of the following.

28. (FI-4) **29.** (FI-5) **30.** (FI-6)

31. (FI-7) **32.** (FI-8) **33.** (FI-9)

10–4 DOUBLE-ANGLE AND HALF-ANGLE FORMULAS

If in the second addition formula, (A-2), we let $u = v$, then we obtain the equation

$$\cos(v + v) = \cos v \cos v - \sin v \sin v,$$

which is equivalent to the equation below.

FIRST DOUBLE-ANGLE FORMULA

$$\cos 2v = \cos^2 v - \sin^2 v. \qquad \text{(D-1)}$$

If we know $\cos v$ and $\sin v$, we can use the first double-angle formula, (D-1), to find $\cos 2v$. The second double-angle formula can be derived from the fourth addition formula, (A-4).

SECOND DOUBLE-ANGLE FORMULA

$$\sin 2v = 2 \sin v \cos v \qquad \text{(D-2)}$$

Problem 1. Given that $0 < v < \pi/2$ and that $\sin v = \frac{5}{6}$, find $\sin 2v$ and $\cos 2v$.

Solution. Before we can use the first and second double-angle formulas, we must find $\cos v$. By the first fundamental identity,

$$\sin^2 v + \cos^2 v = 1.$$

Then

$$\cos^2 v = 1 - \sin^2 v = 1 - (\tfrac{5}{6})^2, \quad \text{or } \tfrac{11}{36}.$$

Hence,

$$\cos v = \frac{\sqrt{11}}{6} \quad \text{or} \quad \cos v = \frac{^-\sqrt{11}}{6}.$$

However, since $0 < v < \pi/2$, $\cos v > 0$. Thus, $\cos v = \sqrt{11}/6$. Now we can use the double angle-formulas to obtain

$$\sin 2v = 2 \cdot \frac{5}{6} \cdot \frac{\sqrt{11}}{6}, \quad \text{or } \frac{5\sqrt{11}}{18},$$

$$\cos 2v = \left(\frac{\sqrt{11}}{6}\right)^2 - \left(\frac{5}{6}\right)^2,$$

$$\cos 2v = \frac{11}{36} - \frac{25}{36}, \quad \text{or } \frac{^-14}{36}, \quad \text{or } \frac{^-7}{18}.$$

Two different forms of the first double-angle formula can be obtained by using the first fundamental identity, (FI-1). Thus, if we replace $\cos^2 v$ by $1 - \sin^2 v$ in the first double-angle formula, we get

$$\cos 2v = 1 - 2\sin^2 v. \tag{1}$$

If we replace $\sin^2 v$ by $1 - \cos^2 v$, we get

$$\cos 2v = 2\cos^2 v - 1. \tag{2}$$

Formulas (1) and (2) can be solved for $\sin^2 v$ and $\cos^2 v$, respectively:

$$\sin^2 v = \tfrac{1}{2}(1 - \cos 2v),$$
$$\cos^2 v = \tfrac{1}{2}(1 + \cos 2v).$$

If we let $u = 2v$, and hence, $v = u/2$, in the identities above, we obtain the *half-angle formulas* below.

FIRST AND SECOND HALF-ANGLE FORMULAS

$$\cos^2 \frac{u}{2} = \frac{1}{2}(1 + \cos u) \qquad (H\text{-}1)$$

$$\sin^2 \frac{u}{2} = \frac{1}{2}(1 - \cos u) \qquad (H\text{-}2)$$

If we know $\cos u$ and the quadrant in which $W(u/2)$ lies, we can use the first and second half-angle formulas to find $\sin u/2$ and $\cos u/2$, as illustrated in Problem 2.

It is important for the students to realize that the double-angle formulas provide means to express, say, $\cos 6\theta$ in terms of sines and cosines of 3θ, and the half-angle formulas enable one to express, for example, $\sin^2 5\theta$ in terms of $\cos 10\theta$.

Exercises for Discussion

If time is limited, it is suggested that at least Exercises for Discussion 1–6 be covered.

Answers to Exercises for Discussion 2–8

2. $\tan 2v = \dfrac{\sin 2v}{\cos 2v}$

$= \dfrac{2 \sin v \cos v}{\cos^2 v - \sin^2 v}$

$= \dfrac{2\dfrac{\sin v \cos v}{\cos^2 v}}{\dfrac{\cos^2 v}{\cos^2 v} - \dfrac{\sin^2 v}{\cos^2 v}}$

$= \dfrac{2 \tan v}{1 - \tan^2 v}$

3. $\sin 3u = \sin(2u + u)$
$= \sin 2u \cos u + \cos 2u \sin u$
$= (2 \sin u \cos u) \cos u + (1 - 2 \sin^2 u) \sin u$
$= 2 \sin u \cos^2 u + \sin u - 2 \sin^3 u$
$= 2 \sin u(1 - \sin^2 u) + \sin u - 2 \sin^3 u$
$= 2 \sin u - 2 \sin^3 u + \sin u - 2 \sin^3 u$
$= 3 \sin u - 4 \sin^3 u$

4. $\cos u = {}^-\sqrt{1 - \sin^2 u}$
$= {}^-\sqrt{1 - (\frac{5}{13})^2} = {}^-\sqrt{1 - \frac{25}{169}}$
$= {}^-\sqrt{\frac{144}{169}} = {}^-\frac{12}{13}$

5. $\sin 2u = 2 \sin u \cos u$
$= 2(\frac{5}{13})({}^-\frac{12}{13}) = {}^-\frac{120}{169}$

6. $\tan u = \dfrac{\sin u}{\cos u} = \dfrac{{}^-5/13}{12/13} = {}^-\frac{5}{12}$

$\tan 2u = \dfrac{2 \tan u}{1 - \tan^2 u} = \dfrac{2({}^-\frac{5}{12})}{1 - ({}^-\frac{5}{12})^2}$

$= \dfrac{{}^-120}{144 - 25} = {}^-\frac{120}{119}$

7. $\sin \dfrac{u}{2} = \sqrt{\frac{1}{2}(1 - \cos u)}$
$= \sqrt{\frac{1}{2}[1 - ({}^-\frac{12}{13})]}$
$= \sqrt{\frac{25}{26}} = \frac{5}{26}\sqrt{26}$

Problem 2. Find the sine and cosine of $5\pi/8$.

Solution. If we let $u = 5\pi/4$,

$$\sin^2 \frac{5\pi}{8} = \frac{1}{2}\left(1 - \cos \frac{5\pi}{4}\right) = \frac{1}{2}\left(1 - \frac{{}^-\sqrt{2}}{2}\right) = \frac{1}{4}(2 + \sqrt{2}).$$

Since $W(5\pi/8)$ is in the second quadrant and the sine is positive in this quadrant,

$$\sin \frac{5\pi}{8} = \frac{1}{2}\sqrt{2 + \sqrt{2}}.$$

Similarly,

$$\cos^2 \frac{5\pi}{8} = \frac{1}{4}(2 - \sqrt{2})$$

and

$$\cos \frac{5\pi}{8} = {}^-\frac{1}{2}\sqrt{2 - \sqrt{2}},$$

since the cosine is negative in the second quadrant.

Exercises for Discussion

1. Derive (D-2) from (A-4).

$\sin 2v = \sin(v + v)$
$= \sin v \cos v + \cos v \sin v$
$= 2 \sin v \cos v$

2. Use (D-1) and (D-2) to show that

$$\tan 2v = \frac{2 \tan v}{1 - \tan^2 v}.$$

3. Show that $\sin 3u = 3 \sin u - 4 \sin^3 u$. (Hint: $3u = 2u + u$.)

Given that $\sin u = \frac{5}{13}$ and $\pi/2 < u < \pi$, evaluate each trigonometric function in Exercises 4–7.

4. $\cos u$
5. $\sin 2u$
6. $\tan 2u$
7. $\sin \dfrac{u}{2}$

8. Use the half-angle formulas to find the values of the six trigonometric functions of the angle with measure $22\frac{1}{2}°$.

Exercises

Given that $\cos u = \frac{3}{5}$ and $0 < u < \pi/2$, evaluate each of the following.

1. $\sin u$ $\frac{4}{5}$
2. $\tan u$ $\frac{4}{3}$
3. $\sin 2u$ $\frac{24}{25}$
4. $\cos 2u$ $\frac{-7}{25}$
5. $\tan 2u$ $\frac{-24}{7}$
6. $\sin \frac{u}{2}$ $\frac{1}{5}\sqrt{5}$
7. $\cos \frac{u}{2}$ $\frac{2}{5}\sqrt{5}$
8. $\tan \frac{u}{2}$ $\frac{1}{2}$

Given that $\tan u = \frac{24}{7}$ and $\sin u < 0$, evaluate each of the following.

9. $\sin u$ $\frac{-24}{25}$
10. $\cos u$ $\frac{-7}{25}$
11. $\cos 2u$ $\frac{-527}{625}$
12. $\tan \frac{u}{2}$ $\frac{-4}{3}$

Given that $\sec u = \frac{7}{5}$ and $\tan u < 0$, evaluate each trigonometric function in Exercises 13–15.

13. $\sin u$ $\frac{-2}{7}\sqrt{6}$
14. $\tan 2u$ $^{-}20\sqrt{6}$
15. $\tan \frac{u}{2}$ $\frac{-1}{6}\sqrt{6}$

16. Use the half-angle formulas to find the values of the six trigonometric functions of the angle with measure 15°.

17. (a) Find a formula for $\tan^2 u/2$ in terms of $\cos u$. $\frac{1-\cos u}{1+\cos u}$

(b) Show that

$$\tan \frac{u}{2} = \frac{1 - \cos u}{\sin u}.$$

See Solution Manual.

△

18–24 See Solution Manual.

Prove each of the following identities.

18. $\cos 3u = 4 \cos^3 u - 3 \cos u$

19. $\sqrt{1 + \sin 2u} = |\sin u + \cos u|$

20. $\dfrac{\cos 2\delta}{\sin \delta} - \dfrac{\sin 2\delta}{\cos \delta} = \dfrac{2 \cos 3\delta}{\sin 2\delta}$

21. $\dfrac{1 + \tan^2 \phi}{2 \tan \phi} = \csc 2\phi$

22. $\dfrac{\sin 2\theta}{1 - \cos 2\theta} = \cot \theta$

Given that α, β, and γ are the angles of a triangle, prove the identities in Exercises 23 and 24.

23. $\tan \alpha + \tan \beta + \tan \gamma = \tan \alpha \tan \beta \tan \gamma$

$$\tan \frac{\alpha}{2} \tan \frac{\beta}{2} + \tan \frac{\beta}{2} \tan \frac{\gamma}{2} + \tan \frac{\gamma}{2} \tan \frac{\alpha}{2} = 1$$

8. $\sin^2 22\frac{1}{2}° = \frac{1}{2}(1 - \cos 45°)$
$= \frac{1}{2}(1 - \sqrt{2}/2)$
$= \frac{1}{4}(2 - \sqrt{2})$

$\cos^2 22\frac{1}{2}° = \frac{1}{2}(1 + \cos 45°)$
$= \frac{1}{2}(1 + \sqrt{2}/2)$
$= \frac{1}{4}(2 + \sqrt{2})$

$\sin 22\frac{1}{2}° = \frac{1}{2}\sqrt{2 - \sqrt{2}}$

$\cos 22\frac{1}{2}° = \frac{1}{2}\sqrt{2 + \sqrt{2}}$

$\tan 22\frac{1}{2}° = \sqrt{\dfrac{2 - \sqrt{2}}{2 + \sqrt{2}}}$
$= \sqrt{2} - 1$

$\cot 22\frac{1}{2}° = \dfrac{1}{\sqrt{2} - 1}$
$= \sqrt{2} + 1$

$\sec 22\frac{1}{2}° = \dfrac{2}{\sqrt{2 + \sqrt{2}}}$
$= \sqrt{4 - 2\sqrt{2}}$

$\csc 22\frac{1}{2}° = \dfrac{2}{\sqrt{2 - \sqrt{2}}}$
$= \sqrt{4 + 2\sqrt{2}}$

Answer to Exercise 16

16. $\sin 15° = \frac{1}{2}\sqrt{2 - \sqrt{3}}$
$\cos 15° = \frac{1}{2}\sqrt{2 + \sqrt{3}}$
$\tan 15° = 2 - \sqrt{3}$
$\cot 15° = 2 + \sqrt{3}$
$\sec 15° = 2\sqrt{2 - \sqrt{3}}$
$\csc 15° = 2\sqrt{2 + \sqrt{3}}$

Quiz

1. If $\sin \alpha = \frac{3}{5}$ and $0 < \alpha < \frac{\pi}{2}$, find $\sin 2\alpha$, $\cos 2\alpha$. (ans: $\frac{24}{25}$, $\frac{7}{25}$)
2. Find $\sin \frac{\pi}{8}$, $\cos \frac{\pi}{8}$. (ans: $\frac{1}{2}\sqrt{2 - \sqrt{2}}$, $\frac{1}{2}\sqrt{2 + \sqrt{2}}$)
3. Find $\cos 105°$ by using the second half-angle formula. (ans: $\cos 105° = {}^{-}\sin 15° = {}^{-}\frac{1}{2}\sqrt{2 - \sqrt{3}}$)

10-5 TRIGONOMETRIC EQUATIONS

This section furnishes an excellent review of the preceding sections as well as of fundamental algebraic processes.

Attention should be called to the statement that solutions in one period of the functions involved are being sought. The equation

$$2\sin^2 x - \sin x - 1 = 0$$

is a quadratic in $\sin x$. The number of solutions for $\sin x$ could therefore be two, one, or none. In this case, it can be seen that $\sin x = {}^{-}\frac{1}{2}$ or $\sin x = 1$. Each of these trigonometric equations actually has an infinite solution set, which could be described in the following way. From $\sin x = {}^{-}\frac{1}{2}$,

$$\{x \mid x = \tfrac{7}{6}\pi + 2\pi n,\ n = 0, \pm 1, \pm 2, \ldots\} \cup \{x \mid x = \tfrac{11}{6}\pi + 2\pi n,\ n = 0, \pm 1, \pm 2, \ldots\}$$

is obtained. From $\sin x = 1$,

$$\{x \mid x = \tfrac{1}{2}\pi + 2\pi n,\ n = 0, \pm 1, \pm 2, \ldots\}$$

is obtained. It has been agreed that the solutions be listed for one period of $\sin x$. Hence they are written in each of the three sets for which $n = 0$, $\{\frac{7}{6}\pi, \frac{1}{2}\pi, \frac{11}{6}\pi\}$.

In Problem 2 on the opposite page, the class may be asked why both sides of ${}^{-}\cos^2 x = 2\cos x$ are not divided by $\cos x$, obtaining just ${}^{-}\cos x = 2$. This equation is not equivalent to the original one since the solution set $\{x \mid \cos x = 0\}$ is not in the solution set of ${}^{-}\cos x = 2$.

25. (a)–(g) See Solution Manual.

25. Given triangle ABC and point D on $\overline{AB}$ as shown in the figure,

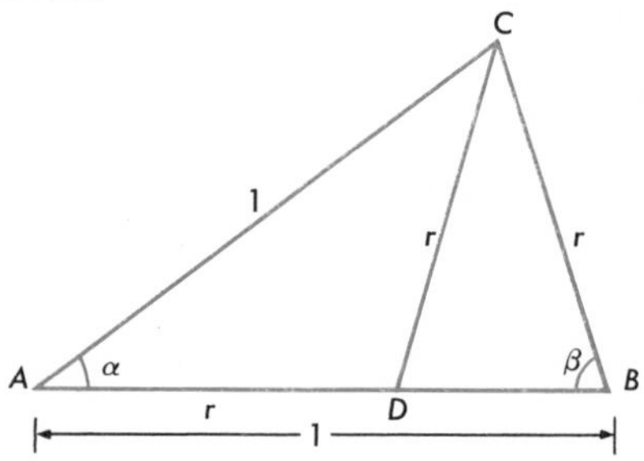

(a) show that triangle ABC is similar to triangle CBD with proportionality factor r.
(b) show that the length of $\overline{DB}$ is r^2.
(c) show that $2r = \sqrt{5} - 1$.
(d) show that $\beta = 2\alpha$.
(e) show that α has measure 36°.
(f) show that $\sin\alpha = \frac{1}{4}\sqrt{10 - 2\sqrt{5}}$.
(g) show that $\cos\alpha = \frac{1}{4}(1 + \sqrt{5})$.
(h) find the trigonometric functions of β.

$\sin\beta = \frac{1}{4}\sqrt{10+2\sqrt{5}}$; $\cos\beta = \frac{-1}{4}(1-\sqrt{5})$; $\tan\beta = \frac{1}{4}(1+\sqrt{5})\sqrt{10+2\sqrt{5}}$; $\cot\beta = \frac{1}{20}(5-\sqrt{5})\sqrt{10+2\sqrt{5}}$; $\sec\beta = 1+\sqrt{5}$; $\csc\beta = \frac{1}{5}\sqrt{50-10\sqrt{5}}$

10-5 TRIGONOMETRIC EQUATIONS

An equation that involves trigonometric functions, such as

$$2\sin^2 x - \sin x - 1 = 0,$$

is called a *trigonometric equation.* If this trigonometric equation has any solutions, then it has infinitely many, since the trigonometric functions are all periodic. Therefore, in solving such an equation, we shall seek the solutions in one period of the functions involved unless we are instructed otherwise.

Problem 1. Solve the equation $2\sin^2 x - \sin x - 1 = 0$.

Solution. Let us find every number x, with $0 \leqq x < 2\pi$, for which this equation is true. Basically, the given equation is quadratic in $\sin x$:

$$2(\sin x)^2 - (\sin x) - 1 = 0.$$

In other words, it has the same form as the quadratic equation

$$2y^2 - y - 1 = 0.$$

We solve these two equations side by side to illustrate that the method is the same.

$$2y^2 - y - 1 = 0 \qquad 2\sin^2 x - \sin x - 1 = 0$$
$$(2y + 1)(y - 1) = 0 \qquad (2\sin x + 1)(\sin x - 1) = 0$$

The solution set of each of these equations is given below.

$$\{y \mid 2y + 1 = 0\} \cup \{y \mid y - 1 = 0\}$$
$$\{^-\tfrac{1}{2}\} \cup \{1\}, \quad \text{or} \quad \{^-\tfrac{1}{2}, 1\}$$
$$\{x \mid 2 \sin x + 1 = 0\} \cup \{x \mid \sin x - 1 = 0\}$$
$$\{x \mid \sin x = {^-\tfrac{1}{2}}\} \cup \{x \mid \sin x = 1\}$$

For $0 \leqq x < 2\pi$, the equation

$$\sin x = \frac{^-1}{2} \quad \text{has solution set} \quad \left\{\pi + \frac{\pi}{6}, 2\pi - \frac{\pi}{6}\right\},$$

and the equation

$$\sin x = 1 \quad \text{has solution set} \quad \left\{\frac{\pi}{2}\right\}.$$

Hence, $\{\pi/2, 7\pi/6, 11\pi/6\}$ is the solution set of the given trigonometric equation in one period of the sine.

Problem 2. Solve the equation $\sin^2 x = 1 + 2 \cos x$.

Solution. We can obtain an equivalent equation containing only cosines by replacing $\sin^2 x$ by $1 - \cos^2 x$, according to the first fundamental identity, (FI-1).

$$1 - \cos^2 x = 1 + 2 \cos x$$

This equation is equivalent, in turn, to each of the following.

$$^-\cos^2 x = 2 \cos x$$
$$0 = \cos^2 x + 2 \cos x$$
$$0 = \cos x(\cos x + 2)$$

Hence, the solution set of the given equation is

$$\{x \mid \cos x = 0\} \cup \{x \mid \cos x + 2 = 0\}.$$

Since $^-1 \leqq \cos x \leqq 1$ for every x, the equation $\cos x + 2 = 0$ has solution set $\emptyset$. Thus, the solution set is

$$\{x \mid \cos x = 0\}.$$

If $0 \leqq x < 2\pi$, then the solution set is $\{\pi/2, 3\pi/2\}$.

Exercises for Discussion, page 424

If time is limited, it is suggested that at least Exercises for Discussion 2, 5, 7, and 8 be covered.

Answers to Exercises for Discussion 2–8, page 424

2. $2 \sin^2 x - 5 \sin x - 3 = 0$
$(2 \sin x + 1)(\sin x - 3) = 0$

$\{x \mid 2 \sin x + 1 = 0$ or $\sin x - 3 = 0\}$
$= \{x \mid \sin x = {^-\tfrac{1}{2}}$ or $\sin x = 3\}$

The solution set of $\sin x = {^-\tfrac{1}{2}}$ is $\{\tfrac{7}{6}\pi, \tfrac{11}{6}\pi\}$ and that of $\sin x = 3$ is $\emptyset$. Thus

$\{x \mid \sin x = {^-\tfrac{1}{2}}$ or $\sin x = 3\}$
$= \{\tfrac{7}{6}\pi, \tfrac{11}{6}\pi\}$.

3. $\{x \mid 4 \sin^2 x = 3\}$
$= \{x \mid \sin^2 x = \tfrac{3}{4}\}$
$= \{x \mid \sin x = \tfrac{1}{2}\sqrt{3}$ or $\sin x = {^-\tfrac{1}{2}}\sqrt{3}\}$
$= \{\tfrac{1}{3}\pi, \tfrac{2}{3}\pi, \tfrac{4}{3}\pi, \tfrac{5}{3}\pi\}$

4. $\{x \mid \cos 2x = 1\}$
$= \{x \mid 2x = 0 \text{ or } 2\pi\}$
$= \{x \mid x = 0 \text{ or } \pi\}$
$= \{0, \pi\}$

5. $\{x \mid 4 \sin x \cos x = 1\}$
$= \{x \mid 2 \sin 2x = 1\}$
$= \{x \mid \sin 2x = \tfrac{1}{2}\}$
$= \{x \mid 2x = \tfrac{1}{6}\pi, \tfrac{5}{6}\pi, \tfrac{13}{6}\pi, \tfrac{17}{6}\pi\}$
$= \{\tfrac{1}{12}\pi, \tfrac{5}{12}\pi, \tfrac{13}{12}\pi, \tfrac{17}{12}\pi\}$

6. $\{x \mid 3 \cos 4x = 5\}$
$= \{x \mid \cos 4x = \tfrac{5}{3}\} = \emptyset$,

since no number greater than 1 is in the range of the cosine.

7. $\{x \mid 2 \cos (x + \tfrac{1}{3}\pi) = 1\}$
$= \{x \mid \cos (x + \tfrac{1}{3}\pi) = \tfrac{1}{2}\}$
$= \{x \mid x + \tfrac{1}{3}\pi = \tfrac{1}{3}\pi \text{ or } \tfrac{5}{3}\pi\}$
$= \{0, \tfrac{4}{3}\pi\}$

8. $\{x \mid 2\tan x = 1 - \tan^2 x\}$

$$= \left\{x \mid \frac{2\tan x}{1-\tan^2 x} = 1\right\}$$
$$= \{x \mid \tan 2x = 1\}$$
$$= \{x \mid 2x = \tfrac{1}{4}\pi, \tfrac{5}{4}\pi, \tfrac{9}{4}\pi, \tfrac{13}{4}\pi\}$$
$$= \{\tfrac{1}{8}\pi, \tfrac{5}{8}\pi, \tfrac{9}{8}\pi, \tfrac{13}{8}\pi\}$$

Exercises

The instructions say to find all x, $0 \leqq x < 2\pi$. To do this for a problem like Exercise 6, one could look at the infinite solution set for $\sin 3x = \frac{1}{2}$. Thus,

$$3x = \tfrac{1}{6}\pi + 2\pi n, n = 0, \pm 1, \pm 2, \ldots$$
$$x = \tfrac{1}{18}\pi + \tfrac{2}{3}\pi n, n = 0, \pm 1, \pm 2, \ldots$$

may be written, and then the x's corresponding to $n = 0, 1, 2$ taken, since all of these will be less than 2π. Also, from $\sin 3x = \frac{1}{2}$,

$$3x = \tfrac{5}{6}\pi + 2\pi n, n = 0, \pm 1, \pm 2, \ldots$$
$$x = \tfrac{5}{18}\pi + \tfrac{2}{3}\pi n, n = 0, \pm 1, \pm 2, \ldots$$

is obtained, and again the x's corresponding to $n = 0, 1, 2$ may be taken. Thus there are six solutions in the interval $0 \leqq x < 2\pi$. They are $\{\frac{1}{18}\pi, \frac{13}{18}\pi, \frac{25}{18}\pi, \frac{5}{18}\pi, \frac{17}{18}\pi, \frac{29}{18}\pi\}$.

Answers to Exercises 13 and 17

13. $\left\{\frac{\pi}{24}, \frac{5\pi}{24}, \frac{7\pi}{24}, \frac{11\pi}{24}, \frac{13\pi}{24}, \frac{17\pi}{24}, \frac{19\pi}{24}, \frac{23\pi}{24}, \frac{25\pi}{24}, \frac{29\pi}{24}, \frac{31\pi}{24}, \frac{35\pi}{24}, \frac{37\pi}{24}, \frac{41\pi}{24}, \frac{43\pi}{24}, \frac{47\pi}{24}\right\}$

17. $\left\{\frac{\pi}{9}, \frac{2\pi}{9}, \frac{4\pi}{9}, \frac{5\pi}{9}, \frac{7\pi}{9}, \frac{8\pi}{9}, \frac{10\pi}{9}, \frac{11\pi}{9}, \frac{13\pi}{9}, \frac{14\pi}{9}, \frac{16\pi}{9}, \frac{17\pi}{9}\right\}$

Exercises for Discussion

Solve each of the following trigonometric equations for $0 \leqq x < 2\pi$.

1. $\sin x = \frac{1}{2}$ $\{\frac{\pi}{6}, \frac{5\pi}{6}\}$
2. $2\sin^2 x - 5\sin x - 3 = 0$
3. $4\sin^2 x = 3$
4. $\cos 2x = 1$
5. $4\sin x\cos x = 1$
6. $3\cos 4x = 5$
7. $2\cos\left(x + \frac{\pi}{3}\right) = 1$
8. $2\tan x = 1 - \tan^2 x$

Exercises

Solve each of the following trigonometric equations for $0 \leqq x < 2\pi$.

1. $2\cos x = {}^{-}\sqrt{3}$ $\{\frac{5\pi}{6}, \frac{7\pi}{6}\}$
2. $\tan^2 x = 1$ $\{\frac{\pi}{4}, \frac{3\pi}{4}, \frac{5\pi}{4}, \frac{7\pi}{4}\}$
3. $\tan^2 x - 3\tan x + 2 = 0$ $\{1.107, 4.249, \frac{\pi}{4}, \frac{5\pi}{4}\}$
4. $\cos^2 x - 1 = 2\sin x$ $\{0, \pi\}$
5. $\cos x - 2\sin^2 x + 1 = 0$ $\{\frac{\pi}{3}, \frac{5\pi}{3}, \pi\}$
6. $2\sin 3x = 1$ $\{\frac{\pi}{18}, \frac{5\pi}{18}, \frac{13\pi}{18}, \frac{17\pi}{18}, \frac{25\pi}{18}, \frac{29\pi}{18}\}$
7. $3\tan^2\left(x + \frac{\pi}{4}\right) = 1$ $\{\frac{7\pi}{12}, \frac{11\pi}{12}, \frac{19\pi}{12}, \frac{23\pi}{12}\}$
8. $2\cos\left(2x + \frac{\pi}{2}\right) = 1$ $\{\frac{7\pi}{12}, \frac{11\pi}{12}, \frac{19\pi}{12}, \frac{23\pi}{12}\}$
9. $2\sin x + 2\cos x = \tan x + 1$ $\{\frac{\pi}{3}, \frac{5\pi}{3}, \frac{3\pi}{4}, \frac{7\pi}{4}\}$
10. $\sin x\cos x + 1 = \sin x + \cos x$ $\{0, \frac{\pi}{2}\}$
11. $\tan^2 x + 4\tan x = 1$ $\{.232, 3.374, 1.803, 4.945\}$
12. $4\sin x + 3\cos x = 5$ $\{.927\}$
13. $4\cos^2 4x = 3$
14. $5\cos^2 x = \cos x$ $\{\frac{\pi}{2}, \frac{3\pi}{2}, 1.369, 4.914\}$
15. $\sin x\cos x = 2\cos x$ $\{\frac{\pi}{2}, \frac{3\pi}{2}\}$
16. $\sin^2 x = 3\cos^2 x$ $\{\frac{\pi}{3}, \frac{2\pi}{3}, \frac{4\pi}{3}, \frac{5\pi}{3}\}$
17. $4\cos^2(3x + \pi) = 1$
18. $(\sin x + 2)(\tan 2x + 1) = 0$ $\{\frac{3\pi}{8}, \frac{7\pi}{8}, \frac{11\pi}{8}, \frac{15\pi}{8}\}$

△

In Exercises 19–22, solve each trigonometric equation for $0 \leqq x < 2\pi$.

19. $4\sin^2 x + 1 = 3\tan^2 x$ $\{\frac{\pi}{4}, \frac{3\pi}{4}, \frac{5\pi}{4}, \frac{7\pi}{4}\}$
20. $\sin x = \cos x$ $\{\frac{\pi}{4}, \frac{5\pi}{4}\}$
21. $\sin 3x\cos x + \cos 3x\sin x = 1$ $\{\frac{\pi}{8}, \frac{5\pi}{8}, \frac{9\pi}{8}, \frac{13\pi}{8}\}$
22. $\sqrt{3}\sin 3x + \cos 3x = 2$ $\{\frac{\pi}{9}, \frac{7\pi}{9}, \frac{13\pi}{9}\}$
23. Solve the following system of trigonometric equations for all ordered pairs (x, y) having $0 \leqq x < 2\pi$. $\{(\frac{\pi}{6}, 1), (\frac{5\pi}{6}, 1)\}$

$$\begin{cases} y = 2 - 2\sin x \\ y = 2\sin x \end{cases}$$

24. Find the solution set of the following system of equations.

$$\begin{cases} y = \sin x - 1 \\ y^2 = \frac{1}{2}\sin x \end{cases}$$

$\{(\frac{\pi}{6}, \frac{-1}{2}), (\frac{5\pi}{6}, \frac{-1}{2})\}$

10-6 GRAPHS OF THE TRIGONOMETRIC FUNCTIONS

Every reader of this book has probably seen a *sine curve*, either on the screen of an oscilloscope or in some related way. In this section, we shall sketch the sine curve and the other trigonometric curves.

Because of the periodicity of the sine and cosine, we need only graph each function over one period in order to be able to describe its graph completely. Actually, since

$$\sin(\pi + s) = {}^{-}\sin s,$$

the graph of the sine from π to 2π is the "negative" of its graph from 0 to π. The same is true for the cosine. Thus, we can get a rough idea of the graph of the sine function from the short table of values below.

x	0	$\frac{\pi}{6}$	$\frac{\pi}{3}$	$\frac{\pi}{2}$	$\frac{2\pi}{3}$	$\frac{5\pi}{6}$	π
$\sin x$	0	$\frac{1}{2}$	$\frac{\sqrt{3}}{2}$	1	$\frac{\sqrt{3}}{2}$	$\frac{1}{2}$	0

We have sketched the graph of the sine function from $^{-}3\pi$ to 3π in Fig. 10-10, using this table and our remarks above.

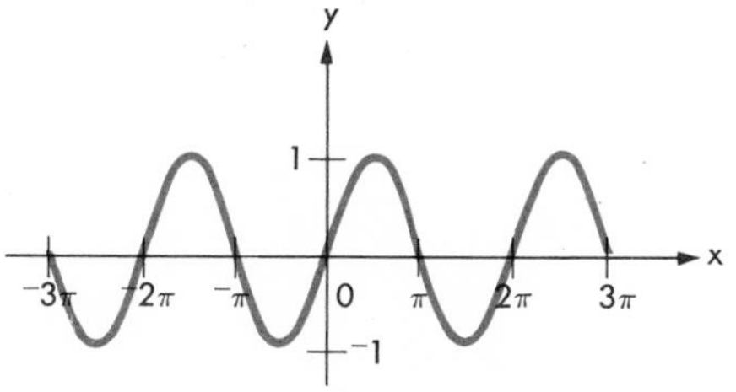

$y = \sin x$

FIGURE 10-10

The *cosine curve* is often described as being "90° out of phase" with the sine curve. Thus, if we move the sine curve of Fig. 10-10 a distance of $\pi/2$ units (equivalent to 90°) to the left, the resulting curve is the graph of the cosine function. We can see that this is so by using the fourth addition formula, (A-4), and letting $v = x$ and $u = \pi/2$.

$$\sin\left(x + \frac{\pi}{2}\right) = \sin x \cos \frac{\pi}{2} + \cos x \sin \frac{\pi}{2}$$
$$= \sin x \cdot 0 + \cos x \cdot 1$$

Quiz

Solve each of the following trigonometric equations for $0 < x < 2\pi$.

1. $2\cos^2 x + 3\cos x + 1 = 0$
   (ans: $\{\frac{2}{3}\pi, \frac{4}{3}\pi, \pi\}$)
2. $\sin^2 x = 1 + 3\cos x$
   (ans: $\{\frac{1}{2}\pi, \frac{3}{2}\pi\}$)
3. $\sin 2x = 1$
   (ans: $\{\frac{1}{4}\pi, \frac{3}{4}\pi\}$)

10-6 GRAPHS OF THE TRIGONOMETRIC FUNCTIONS

An xy-coordinate system could be drawn on the board, and from the definition

$$\sin\theta = \frac{y}{r},$$

$\sin\theta$ could be found for each θ in the table below. (See also the first figure at the top of the next page.)

θ	0	$\frac{1}{6}\pi$	$\frac{1}{4}\pi$	$\frac{1}{3}\pi$	$\frac{1}{2}\pi$
$\sin\theta$	0	0.50	0.71	0.87	1.00

θ	$\frac{2}{3}\pi$	$\frac{3}{4}\pi$	$\frac{5}{6}\pi$	π
$\sin\theta$	0.87	0.71	0.50	0

θ	$\frac{7}{6}\pi$	$\frac{5}{4}\pi$	$\frac{4}{3}\pi$	$\frac{3}{2}\pi$
$\sin\theta$	$^{-}0.50$	$^{-}0.71$	$^{-}0.87$	$^{-}1.00$

θ	$\frac{5}{3}\pi$	$\frac{7}{4}\pi$	$\frac{11}{6}\pi$	2π
$\sin\theta$	$^{-}0.87$	$^{-}0.71$	$^{-}0.50$	0

The work of making this table offers a good review of the signs of the trigonometric functions in the different quadrants, the properties of 30-60 right triangles, and of right isosceles triangles. Sets of angles, such as $\{\frac{1}{6}\pi, \frac{5}{6}\pi, \frac{7}{6}\pi, \frac{11}{6}\pi\}$ may be considered at one time so that the connection between the functions of θ and those of a related positive acute angle are also reviewed.

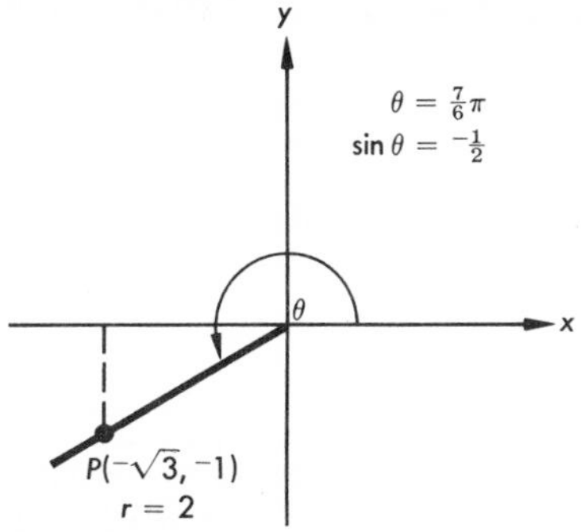

When graphing $f(\theta) = \sin\theta$, a scale may be chosen for the vertical axis, and π marked on the horizontal axis where 3 would be on the vertical axis. The two scales are approximately the same as can be seen by the figure below. It is important that the students understand fully the range and period of $f(\theta) = \sin\theta$ on the basis of this table and graph.

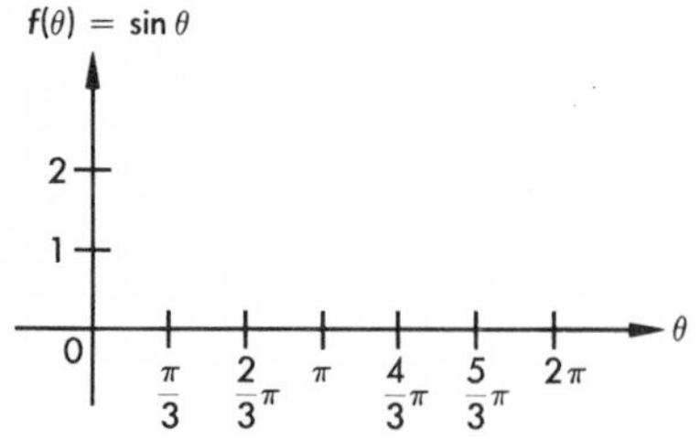

Perhaps a table of values would help the students to see that the cosine wave leads the sine wave by $\pi/2$ units. You could use three rows in the table, the first for x, the second for $x + \pi/2$, and the third for $\cos x = \sin(x + \pi/2)$, from values already obtained in the sine table on the previous page.

Making a table of values may help the students to understand the graph of tan x. Use values close to $\pi/2$, or, in degree measure, close to 90° (such as 75°, 80°, and 85°) and then use the table in the Appendix to indicate the behavior of tan x as x approaches 90°.

Exercises for Discussion, page 427

If time is limited, it is suggested that at least Exercises for Discussion 1 and 2 be covered.

Hence,

$$\cos x = \sin\left(x + \frac{\pi}{2}\right).$$

The cosine curve is sketched in Fig. 10–11.

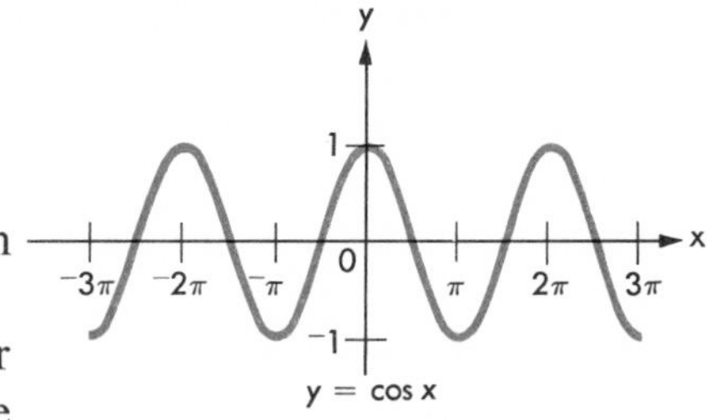

FIGURE 10–11

The tangent function has a smaller period than either the sine or the cosine. Because

$$\tan x = \tan(x + \pi)$$

for every real number x, and π is the smallest positive number for which such an equation is true, the period of the tangent function is π. If we recall that the range of the tangent function is the set of all real numbers, then we realize that the graph of the tangent function is unbounded. The graph consists of an infinite number of branches, which are all alike. One of these branches occurs between $x = {}^-\pi/2$ and $x = \pi/2$.

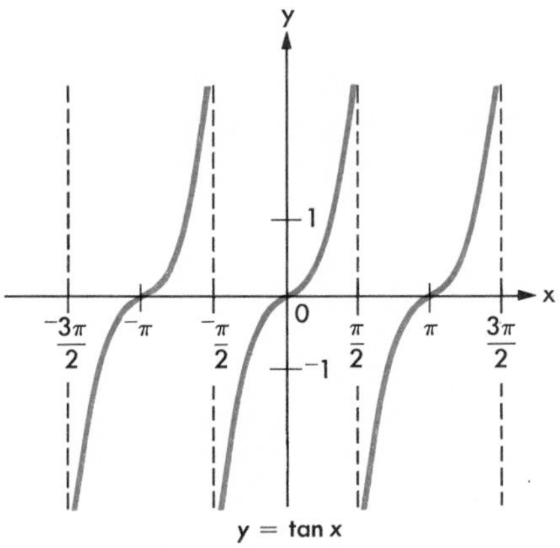

FIGURE 10–12

The lines $x = \pi/2$, $x = 3\pi/2$, $x = {}^-\pi/2$, $x = {}^-3\pi/2$, and so on, are called *asymptotes* of the graph. We have sketched the graph in Fig. 10–12, using the Table of Values of Trigonometric Functions in the Appendix. Since

$$\text{secant } x = \frac{1}{\text{cosine } x},$$

the domain of the secant is the set

$$\{x \mid \cos x \neq 0\} = \left\{x \mid x \neq \frac{2n+1}{2}\pi,\ n \text{ an integer}\right\}.$$

Also, since $|\cos x| \leqq 1$, we have $|\sec x| \geqq 1$ for every number x in its domain. In fact, the range of secant is the set

$$\{y \mid y \geqq 1\} \cup \{y \mid y \leqq {}^-1\}.$$

We can graph the secant from the cosine by taking reciprocals of ordinates. For every point (a, b) on the graph of the cosine, with $b \neq 0$, the point $(a, 1/b)$ is on the graph of the secant. Thus, as $|b|$ gets closer to zero, $|1/b|$ gets larger. In other words, the vertical lines $x = (2n + 1)\pi/2$, $n = 0, \pm 1, \pm 2, \ldots$, are asymptotes of the graph. A sketch of the graph is shown in Fig. 10–13.

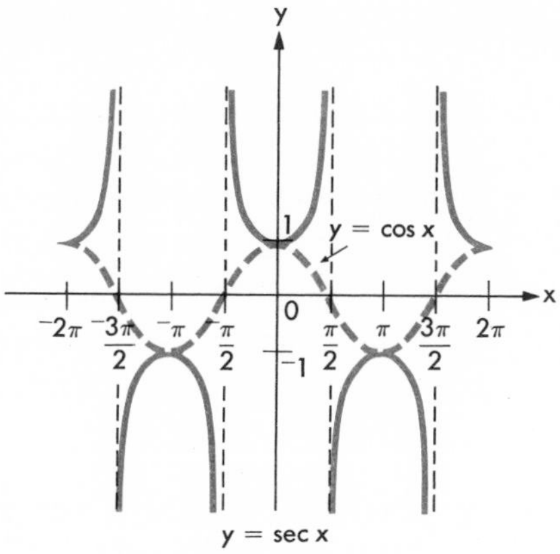

FIGURE 10–13

Exercises for Discussion

1. Graph the cotangent function.
2. Graph the cosecant function.
3. Sketch graphs of the sine and cosine functions. Use only the values of these functions at the following numbers.

$$x = k \cdot \frac{\pi}{2}, \quad k \text{ an integer}$$

Exercises

See Solution Manual for graphs.

1. On the same set of axes, sketch graphs of each of the following equations.
   (a) $y = \sin x$ (b) $y = {}^-\sin x$ (c) $y = \sin ({}^-x)$
2. On the same set of axes, sketch graphs of each of the following equations.
   (a) $y = \cos x$ (b) $y = 2 \cos x$ (c) $y = 2 + \cos x$

△

3. Graph the sine curve and the cosine curve on the same set of axes. Complete the following table and then graph the equation

$$y = \sin x + \cos x.$$

x	0	$\frac{\pi}{4}$	$\frac{\pi}{2}$	$\frac{3\pi}{4}$	π	$\frac{5\pi}{4}$	$\frac{3\pi}{2}$	$\frac{7\pi}{4}$	2π
$\sin x + \cos x$	$0 + 1$	$\frac{\sqrt{2}}{2} + \frac{\sqrt{2}}{2}$	1 ?	0 ?	⁻1 ?	$\sqrt{2}$?	⁻1 ?	0 ?	1 ?

Answers to Exercises for Discussion 1–3

1.

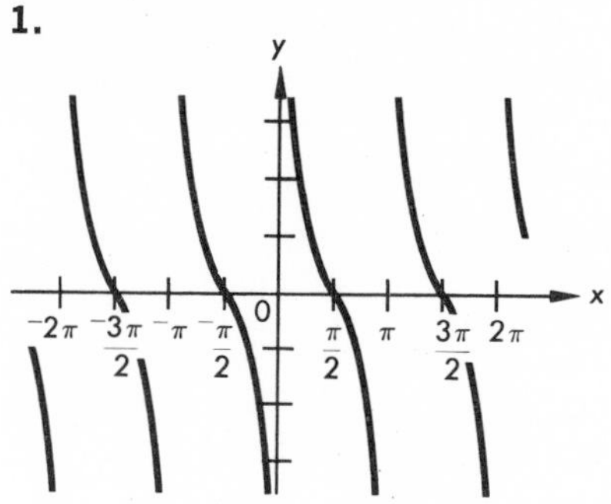

2.

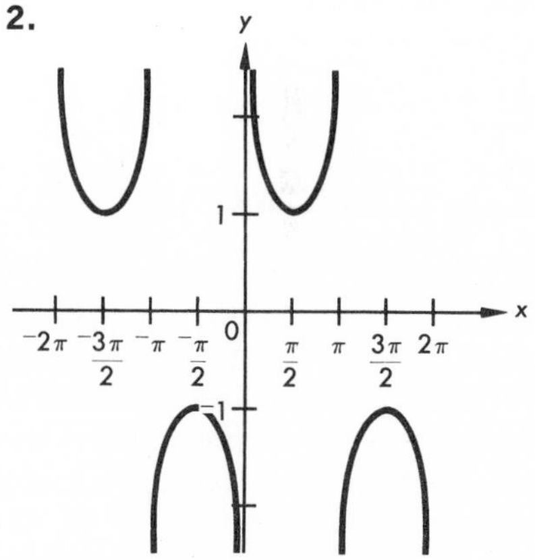

3.

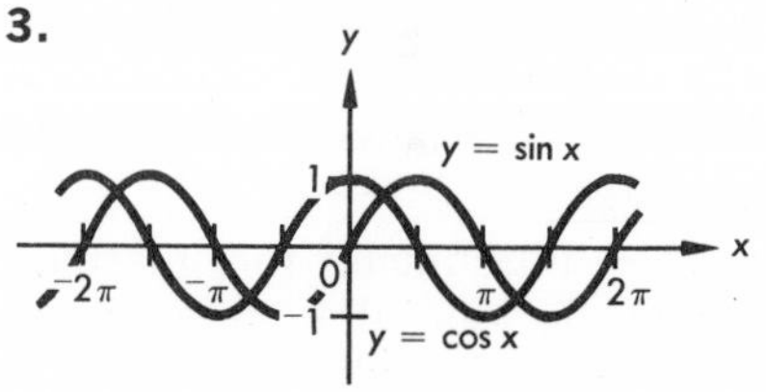

Exercises

Exercises 2(b) and 4 are discovery material for the subject matter of the next section. You may wish to have students make tables of values to graph each part. Before starting on Section 10–7, you could ask for a generalization of these exercises. For example, what effect do the constants 10 and 4 have on the graph of $y = 10 \cos x$ or $y = 10 \sin x$? The graph of $y = \sin 4x$?

Quiz

1. Sketch a graph of the sine function and, on the same axes, draw the graph of the cosine function using a dashed line. Have the horizontal axis scale of your graphs go from $^{-}2\pi$ to 2π.

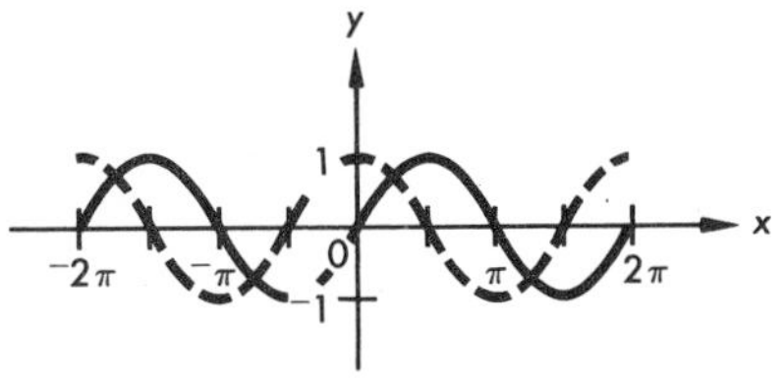

10–7 AMPLITUDES AND PERIODS OF TRIGONOMETRIC FUNCTIONS

In preparation for this section, you may wish to refer to Wahlert's chapter on musical sounds in *Introduction to Mathematics*, 2nd edition, by Cooley, Gans, Kline, and Wahlert (Houghton Mifflin), as you will find it especially rewarding. You could also recommend it later to interested students, and perhaps have one or two give reports on it in class.

When introducing this material, it may be helpful to refer to the table and the graph of sin θ in the previous section and consider in what way the table and the graph would be altered if $g(\theta) = 2 \sin \theta$, $g(\theta) = 1 + \sin \theta$, or $g(\theta) = {}^{-}\sin \theta$ were taken. You could describe in general the graph of $g(\theta) = k \sin \theta$ or $g(\theta) = k + \sin \theta$, k being any nonzero number. Then you could consider what would happen to the table and to the graph if

$$g(\theta) = \sin k\theta,$$

k any nonzero real number, were taken.

4. Make a table of values for plotting the graph of the equation $y = \sin 2x$. For x, use the numbers in the interval $0 \leqq x < \pi/2$ which are integral multiples of $\pi/12$. Make your graph cover the interval $0 \leqq x < 2\pi$. Compare this graph with that of the equation $y = \sin x$.

5. Sketch a graph of the equation $y = \sin x$. On the same set of axes, graph the equation $y = \sin(x + \pi)$. How can the graph of $y = \sin x$ be shifted to produce the graph of $y = \sin(x + \pi)$?
   Shift π units to the left.

10–7 AMPLITUDES AND PERIODS OF TRIGONOMETRIC FUNCTIONS

Equations of the form

$$y = a \sin bx, \quad a \text{ and } b \text{ positive numbers,}$$

are commonplace in the theory of electricity and wave motion. Let us analyze the graph of such an equation by analyzing the function f, defined by

$$f(x) = a \sin bx, \quad a \text{ and } b \text{ positive numbers.}$$

The range of f is the set

$$\{y \mid {}^{-}a \leqq y \leqq a\}.$$

This is so because the range of the sine function is the set

$$\{y \mid {}^{-}1 \leqq y \leqq 1\}.$$

We call a the *amplitude* of the function f. In the same way, we call $|a|$ the amplitude of the functions $a \sin bx$ and $a \cos bx$, whether a is positive or not.

To show that f is periodic, we seek the smallest positive number k such that

$$f(x + k) = f(x) \quad \text{for every number } x.$$

In this case, since $f(x + k) = a \sin[b(x + k)] = a \sin(bx + bk)$, we want to find the smallest positive number k such that

$$\sin(bx + bk) = \sin bx \quad \text{for every number } x.$$

However, the sine function has period 2π. Therefore, the smallest positive number bk such that $\sin bx = \sin(bx + bk)$ for every number x is 2π. Hence, $bk = 2\pi$ and $k = 2\pi/b$.

In other words, the function f, defined by

$$f(x) = a \sin bx, \ a \text{ and } b \text{ positive numbers,}$$

is periodic with period $2\pi/b$. In the same way, if b is not positive, $a \sin bx$ and $a \cos bx$ are periodic with period $2\pi/\ b$.

Problem 1. Discuss and sketch the graph of the equation

$$y = 2 \sin 3x.$$

Solution. From our remarks above, we know that the function f, defined by

$$f(x) = 2 \sin 3x,$$

has amplitude 2 and period $2\pi/3$. Thus, we can sketch its graph from the following table of values. (See Fig. 10–14.)

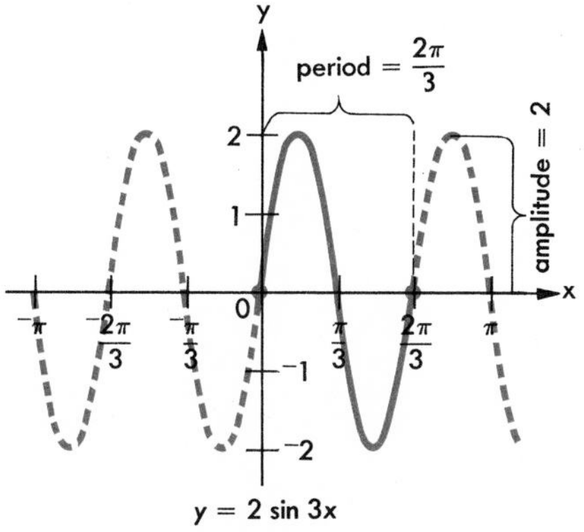

FIGURE 10–14

x	0	$\frac{\pi}{18}$	$\frac{\pi}{9}$	$\frac{\pi}{6}$	$\frac{2\pi}{9}$	$\frac{5\pi}{18}$	$\frac{\pi}{3}$
$2 \sin 3x$	0	1	$\sqrt{3}$	2	$\sqrt{3}$	1	0

Problem 2. Discuss and sketch the graph of the equation

$$y = 3 \cos 2x.$$

Solution. The function g, defined by

$$g(x) = 3 \cos 2x,$$

has amplitude 3 and period $2\pi/2$, or π. Thus, we can sketch its graph from the following table of values. (See Fig. 10–15.)

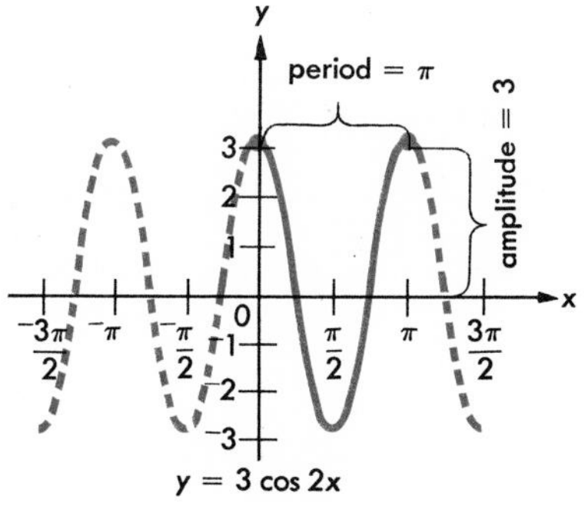

FIGURE 10–15

x	0	$\frac{\pi}{12}$	$\frac{\pi}{6}$	$\frac{\pi}{4}$	$\frac{\pi}{3}$	$\frac{5\pi}{12}$	$\frac{\pi}{2}$
$3 \cos 2x$	3	$\frac{3\sqrt{3}}{2}$	$\frac{3}{2}$	0	$-\frac{3}{2}$	$\frac{-3\sqrt{3}}{2}$	-3

The graphic method of adding ordinates (see top of page 431) may be shown by putting the graphs of Problems 1 and 2 on the same axes on the board and using a board compass or divider to add the ordinates of one to the corresponding ordinates of the other.

Exercises for Discussion, page 431

If time is limited, it is suggested that at least Exercises for Discussion 3–5, 7, and 8 be covered.

Answers to Exercises for Discussion 1–8, page 431

1. 2π; 4

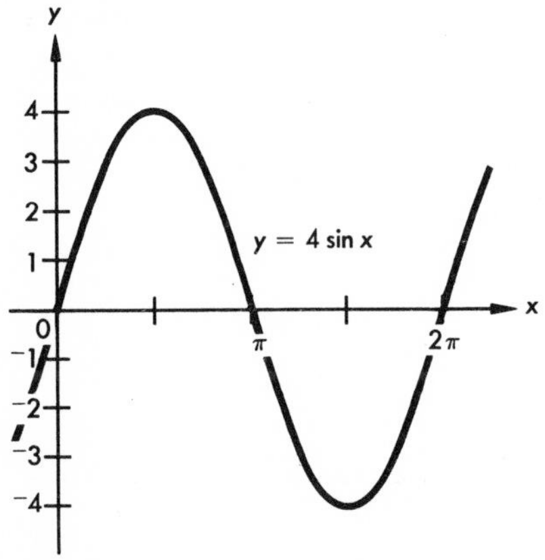

2. π; 3

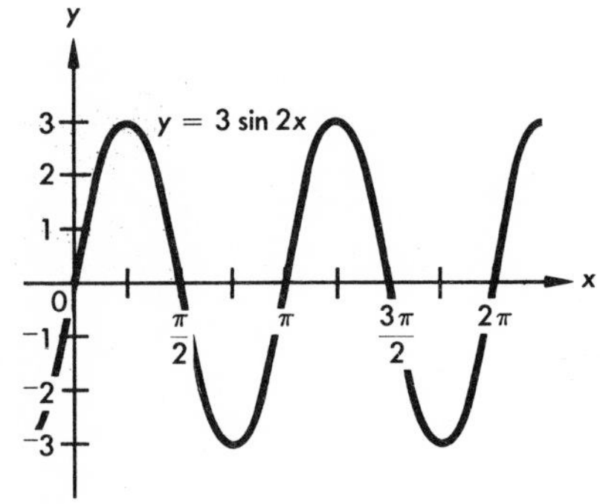

3. π; 2

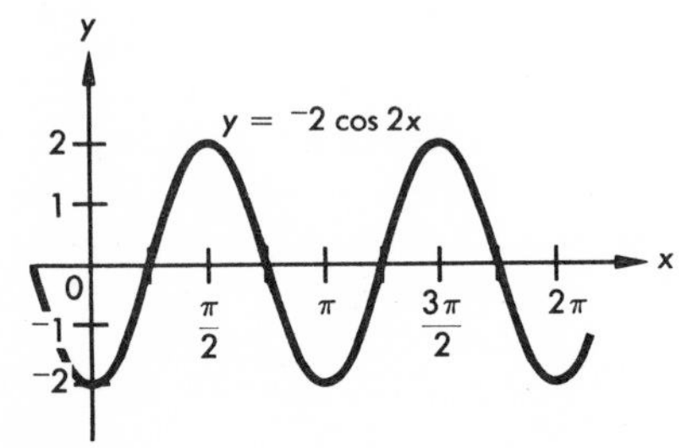

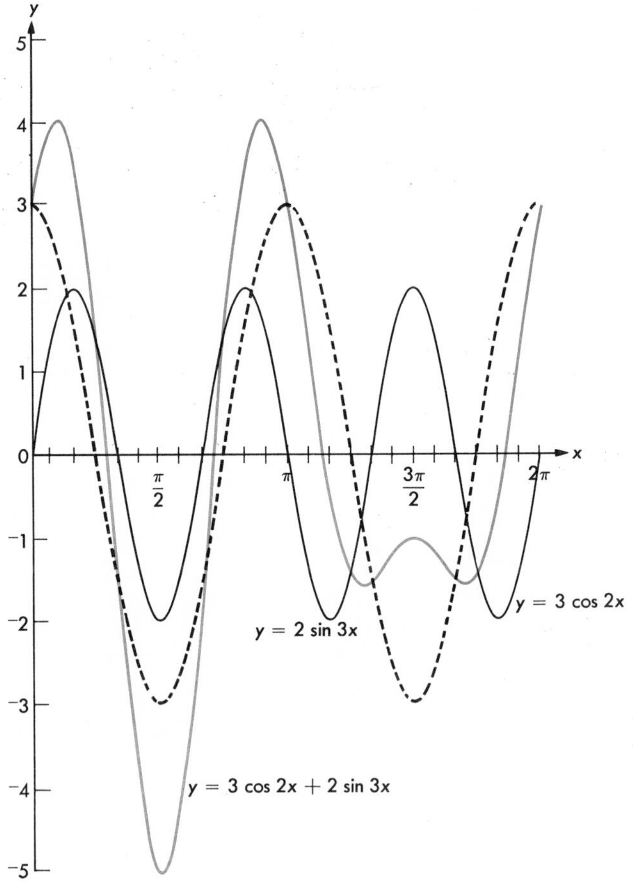

FIGURE 10–16

Problem 3. Discuss and sketch the graph of the equation

$$y = 2 \sin 3x + 3 \cos 2x.$$

Solution. The function h, defined by

$$h(x) = 2 \sin 3x + 3 \cos 2x,$$

is simply the sum of the functions f and g, defined in Problems 1 and 2, respectively. Although 2π is not the period of f or g, these functions do repeat their values every 2π. Hence, the function h repeats its values every 2π. Therefore, the function h is periodic with period less than or equal to 2π. Because the graph of f has three identical pieces in the interval $\{x \mid 0 \leqq x \leqq 2\pi\}$ and the graph of g has two such pieces in this interval, we can argue that the graph of h has the greatest common divisor of two and three, or one, identical piece, in an interval of 2π. In other words, h has period 2π.

We can construct the graph of h from the graphs of f and g by the method of adding ordinates. This method is illustrated by a few points in the table below. The graph of the function is shown in Fig. 10–16.

x	0	$\frac{\pi}{6}$	$\frac{\pi}{3}$
$2 \sin 3x + 3 \cos 2x$	$0 + 3$	$2 + \frac{3}{2}$	$0 + \frac{^-3}{2}$
$h(x)$	3	$\frac{7}{2}$	$\frac{^-3}{2}$

Exercises for Discussion

In Exercises 1–6, graph each equation. Give the period and amplitude of each function.

1. $y = 4 \sin x$
2. $y = 3 \sin 2x$
3. $y = {}^-2 \cos 2x$
4. $y = \sin \left(\frac{x}{2}\right)$
5. $y = |\sin x|$
6. $y = 2 + \sin x$
7. Sketch the graph of the equation $y = \tan x$, and use it to sketch the graph of the equation $y = \tan (x + \pi/2)$ on the same axes.
8. Graph the function $y = 2 \sin \pi x$, and give its period and amplitude.

Exercises

See Solution Manual for graphs.

Give the period and amplitude of each function, and then graph the function.

1. $y = \sin {}^-x$ 2π; 1
2. $y = {}^-3 \cos x$ 2π; 3
3. $y = 4 \cos \frac{2x}{3}$ 3π; 4
4. $y = 3\,|\cos x|$ π; 3
5. $y = {}^-2\,|\sin x|$ π; 2
6. $y = 3 - 3 \cos x$ 2π; 3
7. $y = 3 + 3 \sin x$ 2π; 3
8. $y = \sin \left(x - \frac{\pi}{2}\right)$ 2π; 1
9. $y = \sin 2(x - \pi)$ π; 1
10. $y = 2 \sin (x - \pi)$ 2π; 2
11. $y = 3 \sin (\pi - x)$ 2π; 3

△

Give the period of each function and then graph the function.

12. $y = \sin x + \sin 2x$ 2π
13. $y = \sin x + \cos x$ 2π
14. $y = \sin 2x + \cos 3x$ 2π

4. 4π; 1

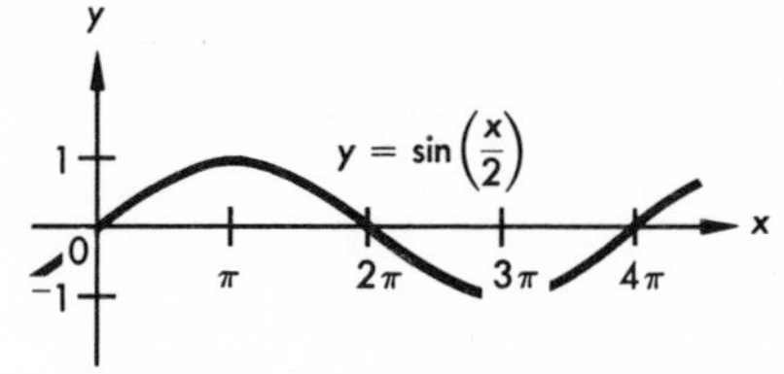

5. π; 1

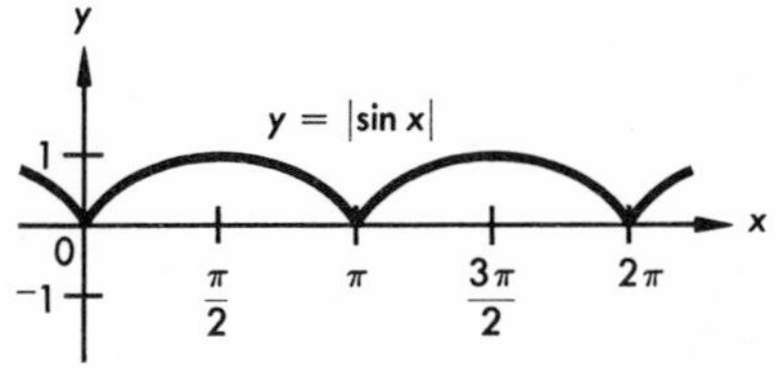

6. 2π; 1

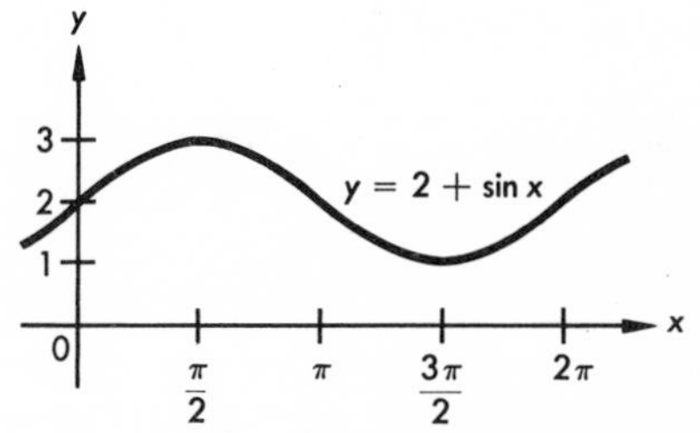

7.

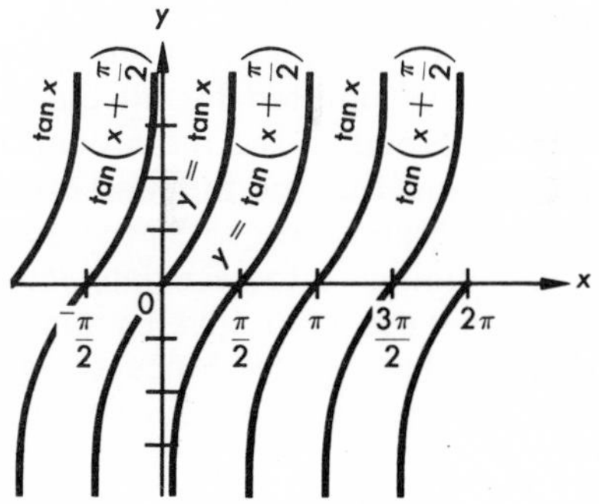

8. 2; 2

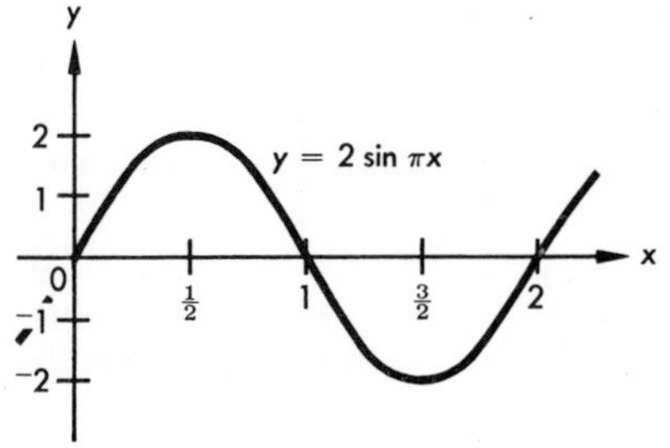

Quiz

1. Give the amplitude and period of each of the following functions:
   (a) $f(x) = 3 \sin x$ (ans: 3, 2π)
   (b) $g(x) = 2 \sin 2x$ (ans: 2; π)
   (c) $h(x) = \frac{1}{2} \cos 2x$ (ans: $\frac{1}{2}$, π)
2. Sketch the graph of $y = \sin x$ and on the same axis sketch $y = 2 \sin x$ and $y = \sin 2x$ for $0 \leqq x \leqq 2\pi$.

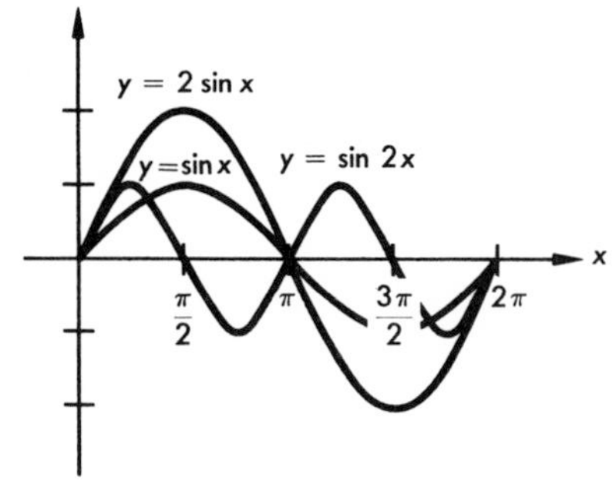

10–8 INVERSE TRIGONOMETRIC FUNCTIONS

This section is tricky and may well have to be omitted for all but advanced groups. The main point to be made is that the thinking is now reversed, and the goal is to decide what number s to associate with x such that $\cos s = x$, given a number x with $^-1 \leqq x \leqq 1$. Since $\cos s$ is the abscissa of the point $W(s)$ on the unit circle, the simplest way to arrive at points with abscissas lying between $^-1$ and 1 is probably to use the wrapping function for s lying on the interval $0 \leqq s \leqq \pi$, and arccosine x is consequently defined to be that number s lying between 0 and π (inclusive) for which $\cos s = x$, where arccosine is interpreted verbally to mean "arc whose cosine is". Of course, $\cos(s + 2\pi)$, $\cos(s - 2\pi)$, and generally, $\cos(s \pm 2n\pi)$, for any integer n, also have the value x as has been

15. If a, b, and c are numbers such that $a^2 + b^2 = c^2$, and if s is a number such that $\sin s = b/c$ and $\cos s = a/c$, prove that

$$a \sin x + b \cos x = c \sin(x + s)$$

for every real number x. *See Solution Manual.*

Use your answer to Exercise 15 to rewrite each of the following equations, and then graph the equation.

16. $y = \sqrt{3} \sin x + \cos x$ — $2 \sin(x + \frac{\pi}{6})$

17. $y = \sin x - \cos x$ — $\sqrt{2} \sin(x - \frac{\pi}{4})$

10–8 INVERSE TRIGONOMETRIC FUNCTIONS

For each number x in the interval $I = \{x | ^-1 \leqq x \leqq 1\}$, there exists an arc $\widehat{AP}$ of length s, with $0 \leqq s \leqq \pi$, as shown in Fig. 10–17. Since $x = \cos s$, it is natural to call s the *arc whose cosine is* x and denote s by *arccosine x.*

DEFINITION OF ARCCOSINE

arccosine $x = s$, where $\cos s = x$ and $0 \leqq s \leqq \pi$

The domain of arccosine is the interval $^-1 \leqq x \leqq 1$.

Similarly, for each number y in $J = \{y | ^-1 \leqq y \leqq 1\}$, there exists an arc $\widehat{AP}$ of length s, with $^-\pi/2 \leqq s \leqq \pi/2$, as shown in Fig. 10–18.

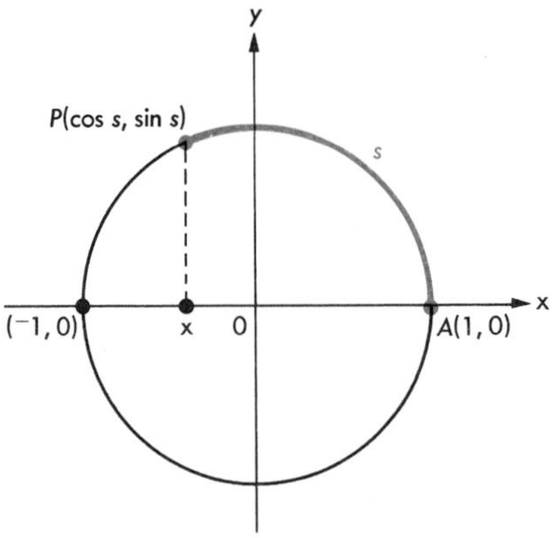

FIGURE 10–17

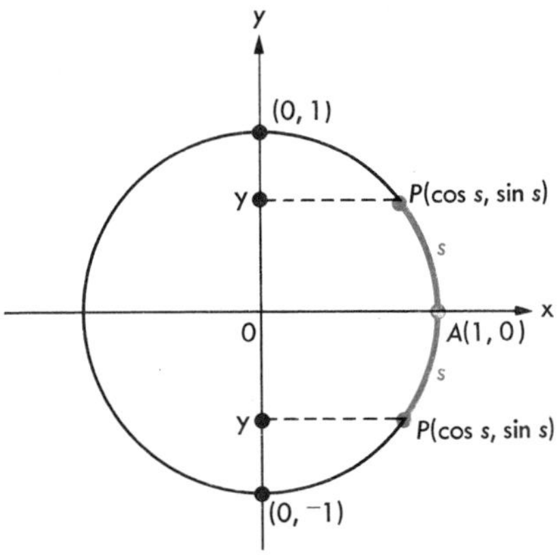

FIGURE 10–18

The arc $\widehat{AP}$ is understood to have a positive length if P is above the x-axis and a negative length if P is below the x-axis. Both cases are shown in Fig. 10–18. Since $y = \sin s$ in either case, we call s the *arcsine y.*

DEFINITION OF ARCSINE

$$\text{arcsine } y = s, \text{ where } \sin s = y \text{ and } {}^-\frac{\pi}{2} \leqq s \leqq \frac{\pi}{2}$$

The domain of arcsine is the interval $^-1 \leqq y \leqq 1$.

In the same way that we abbreviated sine and cosine, we shall abbreviate arccosine to *arccos* and arcsine to *arcsin.*

Problem. Find $\arccos \frac{1}{2}$, arcsin 1, $\arccos\left(\frac{^-\sqrt{2}}{2}\right)$, and $\arcsin\left(\frac{^-\sqrt{3}}{2}\right)$

Solution. Since

$$\cos\frac{\pi}{3} = \frac{1}{2} \text{ and } 0 \leqq \frac{\pi}{3} \leqq \pi, \arccos\frac{1}{2} = \frac{\pi}{3}.$$

Since

$$\sin\frac{\pi}{2} = 1 \text{ and } {}^-\frac{\pi}{2} \leqq \frac{\pi}{2} \leqq \frac{\pi}{2}, \arcsin 1 = \frac{\pi}{2}.$$

Since

$$\cos\frac{3\pi}{4} = \frac{^-\sqrt{2}}{2} \text{ and } 0 \leqq \frac{3\pi}{4} \leqq \pi, \arccos\left(\frac{^-\sqrt{2}}{2}\right) = \frac{3\pi}{4}.$$

Since

$$\sin\left({}^-\frac{\pi}{3}\right) = \frac{^-\sqrt{3}}{2} \text{ and } {}^-\frac{\pi}{2} \leqq {}^-\frac{\pi}{3} \leqq \frac{\pi}{2}, \arcsin\left(\frac{^-\sqrt{3}}{2}\right) = {}^-\frac{\pi}{3}.$$

The cosine and arccosine functions are related to each other by the following equations.

cos (arccos x) = x for every number x in $\{x \mid {}^-1 \leqq x \leqq 1\}$
arccos (cos s) = s for every number s in $\{s \mid 0 \leqq s \leqq \pi\}$

If f and g are functions defined by

$$f(s) = \cos s, \text{ domain } f = \{s \mid 0 \leqq s \leqq \pi\},$$
$$g(x) = \arccos x, \text{ domain } g = \{x \mid {}^-1 \leqq x \leqq 1\},$$

then

$$f(g(x)) = x \text{ for all } x \text{ in domain } g,$$
$$g(f(s)) = s \text{ for all } s \text{ in domain } f.$$

seen, but the requirement that one number be selected (whose cosine is x) to be called arccosine x forces a choice.

When the analogous problem is faced of choosing a number arcsine x (an arc whose sine is x) for x any number in the interval

$$^-1 \leqq x \leqq 1,$$

it is necessary to readjust one's thinking. Since sin s is the ordinate of the point $W(s)$, the wrapping function does not produce ordinates which encompass the interval $^-1 \leqq x \leqq 1$ for $0 \leqq s \leqq \pi$. Instead sin s goes from 0 to 1, then back from 1 to 0 as s goes from 0 to π. On the other hand, if one starts with s at $^-\pi/2$, goes to 0, and on to $\pi/2$ it is found that sin s, the ordinate of $W(s)$, covers the interval of values from $^-1$ to 1. Hence arcsine of x is defined as the number s lying in the interval $^-\pi/2 \leqq s \leqq \pi/2$ for which $\sin s = x$.

It happens that the arctangent of x may be defined in a way analogous to that used for the case of arcsine.

Probably the main value of this section is to raise questions in the mind of the student and, granted that he can assimilate this material, to provide him with some review of the trigonometric functions of the so-called "special" angles. Several encounters with the idea of inverse function will certainly be needed before the student can grasp the notions of this section, and only when he later confronts the calculus of the periodic functions will the significance of the particular choice of domain for the inverse trigonometric functions become apparent.

Any two functions f and g which are related in this way are called *inverse functions.* It is important to realize *f is not the cosine function,* since the domain of f is $\{s \mid 0 \leqq s \leqq \pi\}$ whereas the domain of cosine is the set of all real numbers. However, f and cosine have the same values over the domain of f. The graphs of f and g are shown in Fig. 10–19.

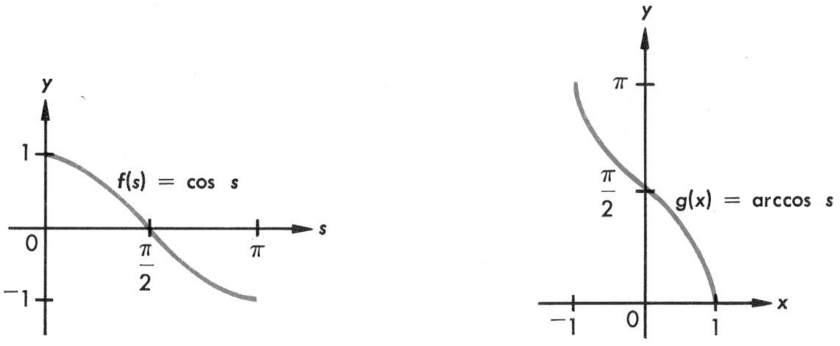

FIGURE 10–19

The sine and arcsine functions satisfy similar equations.

$$\textit{sin (arcsin } y) = y \textit{ for every number } y \textit{ in } \{y \mid {}^{-}1 \leqq y \leqq 1\}$$

$$\textit{arcsin (sin } s) = s \textit{ for every number } s \textit{ in } \left\{s \,\middle|\, \frac{{}^{-}\pi}{2} \leqq s \leqq \frac{\pi}{2}\right\}$$

Therefore, if we define functions f and g by

$$f(s) = \sin s, \text{ domain } f = \left\{s \,\middle|\, \frac{{}^{-}\pi}{2} \leqq s \leqq \frac{\pi}{2}\right\},$$

$$g(x) = \arcsin x, \text{ domain } g = \{x \mid {}^{-}1 \leqq x \leqq 1\},$$

the functions f and g are inverses of each other. These functions are graphed in Fig. 10–20.

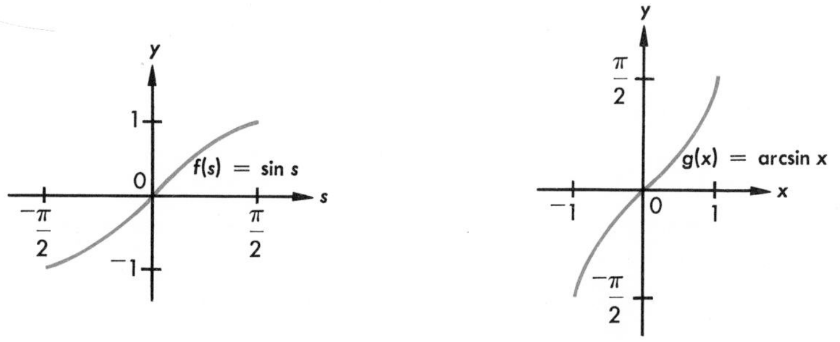

FIGURE 10–20

Each trigonometric function has an arc-function defined in a way similar to those above. For example, we have the following definition of arctangent.

DEFINITION OF ARCTANGENT

arctan x = y, where tan y = x and $\frac{^{-}\pi}{2} < y < \frac{\pi}{2}$.

The domain of arctangent is the set R of all real numbers.

The graph of the arctangent function is the graph of the equation

$$x = \tan y, \quad \frac{^{-}\pi}{2} < y < \frac{\pi}{2},$$

as shown in Fig. 10–21.

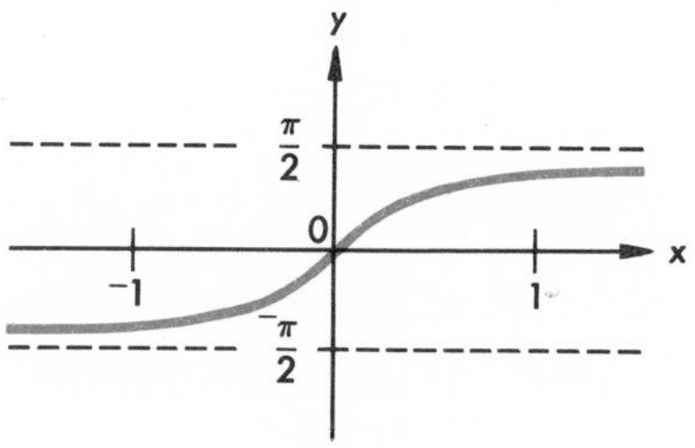

$y = \arctan x$

FIGURE 10–21

Exercises for Discussion

Find each of the following. Use the Table of Values of Trigonometric Functions, if necessary.

1. $\arcsin \frac{1}{2}$
2. $\arccos\left(\frac{^{-}\sqrt{3}}{2}\right)$
3. $\arctan \sqrt{2}$
4. $\arctan 10$
5. $\arcsin\left(\frac{^{-}1}{\sqrt{2}}\right)$
6. $\arcsin \frac{2}{3}$
7. $\arccos(^{-}\frac{1}{2})$
8. $\arccos 0$
9. $\arctan(^{-}12)$

Evaluate each of the following.

10. $\tan(\arctan {}^{-}1)$
11. $\cos(\arctan {}^{-}1)$
12. $\sec\left(\arcsin \frac{^{-}\sqrt{3}}{2}\right)$
13. $\sin\left(\arccos \frac{^{-}5}{13}\right)$

In Exercises 14–16, find arc tan (tan *s*) for each given number *s*.

14. $s = \frac{3\pi}{4}$
15. $s = \frac{11\pi}{4}$
16. $s = \frac{^{-}9\pi}{4}$

17. Prove the following identity.

$$\arctan\frac{1}{5} + \arctan\frac{2}{3} = \frac{\pi}{4}$$

Answer to Exercise for Discussion 17

17. Let $A = \arctan \frac{1}{5}$ and $B = \arctan \frac{2}{3}$.

Then $\tan A = \frac{1}{5}$ and $\tan B = \frac{2}{3}$

$$\tan(A + B) = \frac{\tan A + \tan B}{1 - \tan A \tan B} = \frac{\frac{1}{5} + \frac{2}{3}}{1 - \frac{1}{5}\cdot\frac{2}{3}} \cdot \frac{15}{15} = \frac{3 + 10}{15 - 2} = \frac{13}{13} = 1$$

$$A + B = \arctan 1$$

Thus,

$$\arctan\frac{1}{5} + \arctan\frac{2}{3} = \frac{\pi}{4}.$$

Quiz

Give the value of each of the following:

1. arcsine $\frac{1}{2}$ (ans: $\pi/6$)
2. arccos $(^-\frac{1}{2})$ (ans: $2\pi/3$)
3. arctan $(^-1)$ (ans: $^-\pi/4$)
4. arcsin $(^-\sqrt{3}/2)$ (ans: $^-\pi/3$)

Exercises

Find each of the following. Use the Table of Values of Trigonometric Functions, if necessary.

1. $\arcsin \frac{\sqrt{3}}{2}$ $\frac{\pi}{3}$

2. $\arctan (^-\sqrt{2})$ $^-.960$

3. $\arccos (^-1)$ π

4. $\arctan \sqrt{3}$ $\frac{\pi}{3}$

5. $\arcsin 0$ 0

6. $\arcsin \frac{3}{5}$ $.646$

7. $\arccos (^-\frac{4}{5})$ 2.496

8. $\arctan (^-\frac{5}{12})$ $^-.401$

Find arctan (tan s) for each given number s.

9. $s = \frac{\pi}{4}$ $\frac{\pi}{4}$

10. $s = \frac{5\pi}{4}$ $\frac{\pi}{4}$

11. $s = \frac{^-7\pi}{4}$ $\frac{\pi}{4}$

12. $s = \frac{^-3\pi}{4}$ $\frac{\pi}{4}$

13. $s = \frac{^-\pi}{4}$ $\frac{^-\pi}{4}$

Evaluate each of the following.

14. $\sin (\arctan {^-1})$ $\frac{^-\sqrt{2}}{2}$

15. $\csc (\arcsin \frac{1}{2})$ 2

16. $\cot (\arccos {^-\frac{3}{5}})$ $\frac{^-3}{4}$

17. $\tan (\arcsin \frac{7}{25})$ $\frac{7}{24}$

△

18. For which numbers s in Exercises 9–13 is arctan (tan s) $= s$? $\frac{\pi}{4}, \frac{^-\pi}{4}$

19. For which numbers s is arctan (tan s) $= s$? $\{s \mid \frac{^-\pi}{2} < s < \frac{\pi}{2}\}$

20. For which numbers x is tan (arctan x) $= x$? $\{x \mid x \neq \frac{(2n+1)\pi}{2}$, n an integer$\}$

▲

Complete each of the following statements:

21. $\sin (\arcsin x) = x$ for every number x in the set

$\{x \mid \underline{\ ?\ }\}$. $\{x \mid x \text{ is real}\}$

22. $\arcsin (\sin s) = s$ for every number s in the set

$\{s \mid \underline{\ ?\ }\}$. $\{s \mid \frac{^-\pi}{2} \leq s \leq \frac{\pi}{2}\}$

Show that each equation in Exercises 23 and 24 is true.

23–24 See Solution Manual.

23. $\arcsin \frac{12}{13} + \arcsin \frac{4}{5} = \arccos {^-\frac{33}{65}}$

24. $2 \arctan \frac{1}{3} + \arctan \frac{1}{7} = \arctan 1$

25. Find the solution set of the equation

$$\arctan 3x + \arctan x = \arctan 2. \quad \{\tfrac{1}{3}, {^-1}\}$$

*10-9 TRIGONOMETRIC FORM OF COMPLEX NUMBERS

Every complex number has the form $a + bi$ where a and b are real numbers and $i^2 = {}^-1$. As we saw in Chapter 4, the complex numbers can be used as coordinates in the complex number plane. Thus, each point P having coordinates (a, b) in a cartesian coordinate system has coordinate $a + bi$ in the associated complex number plane. If P is not the origin, that is, if $a + bi \neq 0$, then P is on the terminal side of some angle θ in standard position, as shown in Fig. 10-22. If

$$r = |a + bi| = \sqrt{a^2 + b^2},$$

then

$$\frac{a}{\cos\theta} = \frac{r}{1} \quad \text{and} \quad \frac{b}{\sin\theta} = \frac{r}{1}$$

by the definition of similar triangles. Hence,

$$a = r\cos\theta, \quad b = r\sin\theta$$

and

$$a + bi = r\cos\theta + (r\sin\theta)i,$$

or

$$a + bi = r(\cos\theta + i\sin\theta).$$

We call $r(\cos\theta + i\sin\theta)$ a *trigonometric form* of the complex number $a + bi$. (See Fig. 10-23.) In a trigonometric form of $a + bi$, the positive number r is the *absolute value* of $a + bi$ and θ is an *angle* associated with $a + bi$. The number 0 has trigonometric form $0(\cos\theta + i\sin\theta)$ for any angle θ.

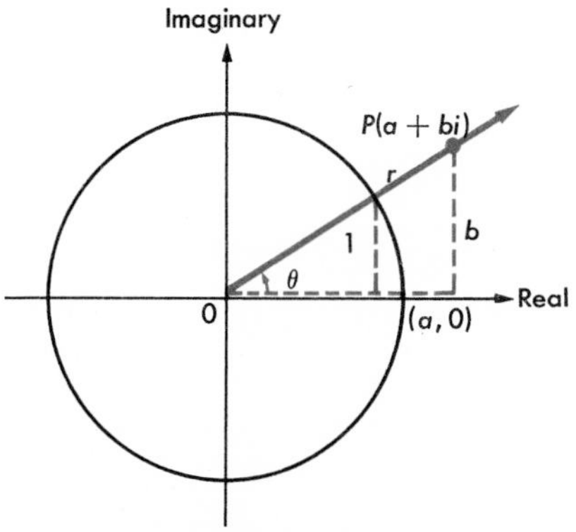

FIGURE 10-22

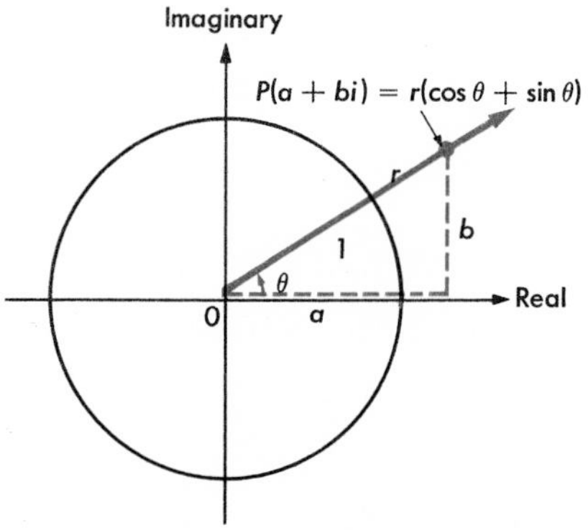

FIGURE 10-23

*10-9 TRIGONOMETRIC FORM OF COMPLEX NUMBERS

Students find this topic easy and interesting. Once before a detour was taken, so to speak, before performing an assigned task in arithmetic. A table of logarithms was used to express two or more positive real numbers as powers of 10; then the powers of 10 were multiplied just by adding exponents to obtain the new power of 10.

Now trigonometric functions are being used to write two complex numbers in a new form so that multiplication can be performed partly by adding, partly by multiplying. It happens that the greatest advantage is in raising to powers. The most interesting aspect is that the ability to find and discuss the n nth roots of a complex number has now been gained.

TWISTER

In a relatively obscure work, an unknown geometer proved the following theorem: "The square of the side opposite the mundangle is equal to the sum of the squares of the other two sides added to the product of those two sides multiplied by the square root of three." What is a mundangle?

Solution: The theorem states that

$$a^2 = b^2 + c^2 + \sqrt{3}\, bc,$$

where a is the side opposite the mundangle A. By the law of cosines,

$$a^2 = b^2 + c^2 - 2bc \cos A,$$

whence,

$$\cos A = -\frac{\sqrt{3}}{2}.$$

Therefore, a mundangle is an angle of 150°.

Problem 1. Find a trigonometric form of each of the following.

(a) 4 (b) ^-3i
(c) $2 + 2i$ (d) $1 - \sqrt{3}i$

Solution. Each of these complex numbers is plotted in Fig. 10–24. We read the following trigonometric forms from the figure.

(a) $4 = 4(\cos 0° + i \sin 0°)$
(b) $^-3i = 3(\cos 270° + i \sin 270°)$
(c) $2 + 2i = 2\sqrt{2}\,(\cos 45° + i \sin 45°)$
(d) $1 - \sqrt{3}i = 2(\cos {}^-60° + i \sin {}^-60°)$

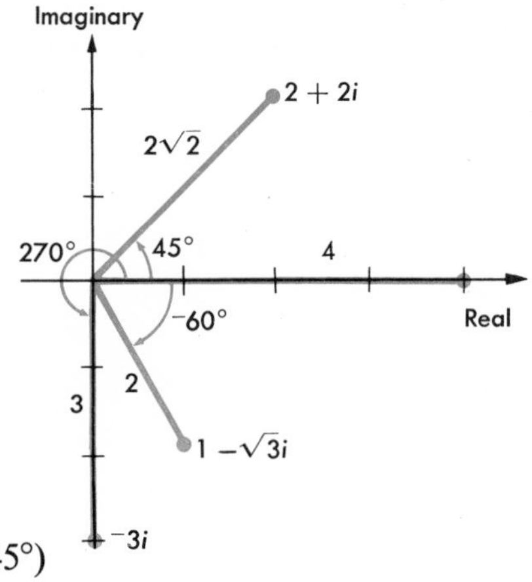

FIGURE 10–24

The angle θ is not unique because the sine and cosine are periodic functions. For example, we could just as well have expressed $1 - \sqrt{3}i$ in the trigonometric form

$$1 - \sqrt{3}\, i = 2(\cos 300° + i \sin 300°)$$

since $\sin {}^-60° = \sin 300°$ and $\cos {}^-60° = \cos 300°$.

If w and z are two complex numbers having trigonometric forms

$$w = r(\cos \theta + i \sin \theta),$$
$$z = s(\cos \phi + i \sin \phi),$$

then a trigonometric form of their product wz may be found by multiplying the two complex numbers and using the second and fourth addition formulas.

$$\begin{aligned} wz &= r(\cos \theta + i \sin \theta) \cdot s(\cos \phi + i \sin \phi) \\ &= rs(\cos \theta + i \sin \theta)(\cos \phi + i \sin \phi) \\ &= rs[(\cos \theta \cos \phi - \sin \theta \sin \phi) + i(\cos \theta \sin \phi + \sin \theta \cos \phi)] \end{aligned}$$

Thus,

$$wz = rs[\cos (\theta + \phi) + i \sin (\theta + \phi)].$$

This result can be stated in words in the following manner.

A trigonometric form of the product of two complex numbers is found by multiplying absolute values and adding angles of the two complex numbers.

The following theorem is named after De Moivre, a seventeenth-century French mathematician.

De MOIVRE'S THEOREM

$$[r(\cos\theta + i\sin\theta)]^n = r^n(\cos n\theta + i\sin n\theta)$$

for every real number r, every angle θ, and every positive integer n

We shall postpone the proof of this theorem until Chapter 13.

Problem 2. Use De Moivre's theorem to find

(a) $(2 + 2i)^5$. (b) $(1 - \sqrt{3}i)^6$.

Solution.

(a) By Problem 1, $2 + 2i = 2\sqrt{2}\,(\cos 45° + i\sin 45°)$. Hence, by De Moivre's theorem,

$$\begin{aligned}(2 + 2i)^5 &= [2\sqrt{2}\,(\cos 45° + i\sin 45°)]^5\\ &= (2\sqrt{2})^5[\cos(5\cdot 45°) + i\sin(5\cdot 45°)]\\ &= 128\sqrt{2}\,(\cos 225° + i\sin 225°).\end{aligned}$$

Since both sin 225° and cos 225° are equal to $^-\sqrt{2}/2$, we have

$$\begin{aligned}(2 + 2i)^5 &= 128\sqrt{2}\left(^-\frac{\sqrt{2}}{2} - i\frac{\sqrt{2}}{2}\right)\\ &= {}^-128 - 128i.\end{aligned}$$

(b) By Problem 1, $1 - \sqrt{3}\,i = 2(\cos {}^-60° + i\sin {}^-60°)$. Hence, by De Moivre's theorem,

$$\begin{aligned}(1 - \sqrt{3}\,i)^6 &= 2^6\,[\cos(6\cdot {}^-60°) + i\sin(6\cdot {}^-60°)]\\ &= 64(\cos {}^-360° + i\sin {}^-360°).\end{aligned}$$

Since $\cos {}^-360° = 1$ and $\sin {}^-360° = 0$, we obtain

$$(1 - \sqrt{3}\,i)^6 = 64.$$

In other words, $1 - \sqrt{3}\,i$ is a complex sixth root of 64. Incidentally, 2 and $^-2$ are the only real sixth roots of 64.

De Moivre's theorem for the case $n = 2$ is, of course, based on the rule for multiplying two (equal) complex numbers. You may wish to have students obtain the identity for $n = 3$ by considering the product of the square ($n = 2$) of the complex number with itself. Most students will agree that the theorem appears plausible for any n by building up in this way to that power.

In Problem 2, you could ask for volunteers who would prefer to obtain the result directly by raising $2 + 2i$ to the fifth power.

The following problem shows the way in which we can use De Moivre's theorem to find roots of complex numbers.

Problem 3. Find the square roots of

(a) i. (b) $^{-}2 + 2\sqrt{3}i$.

Solution.

(a) The complex number i has trigonometric form

$$i = \cos 90° + i \sin 90°.$$

If $r(\cos\theta + i\sin\theta)$ is a square root of i, then its square must be i:

$$[r(\cos\theta + i\sin\theta)]^2 = \cos 90° + i\sin 90°.$$

Hence, using De Moivre's theorem, we must have

$$r^2(\cos 2\theta + i\sin 2\theta) = \cos 90° + i\sin 90°.$$

In Section 4–2 of Chapter 4, we saw that $a + bi = c + di$ if, and only if, $a = c$ and $b = d$. Thus, $r = 1$ and $2\theta = 90°$, or $\theta = 45°$, and the resulting complex number,

$$1(\cos 45° + i\sin 45°),$$

will be a square root of i. Consequently, $\sqrt{2}/2 + i\sqrt{2}/2$ is a square root of i. Given one square root of a number, the only other square root is the negative of the first one. Hence,

Students may check answers by squaring these numbers, and thus at the same time reviewing algebraic operations with complex numbers.

$$\frac{\sqrt{2}}{2} + \frac{\sqrt{2}}{2}i \quad\text{and}\quad ^{-}\frac{\sqrt{2}}{2} - \frac{\sqrt{2}}{2}i$$

are the square roots of i.

(b) The trigonometric form of $^{-}2 + 2\sqrt{3}i$ is $4(\cos 120° + i\sin 120°)$. If

$$[r(\cos\theta + i\sin\theta)]^2 = 4(\cos 120° + i\sin 120°),$$

then

$$r^2(\cos 2\theta + i\sin 2\theta) = 4(\cos 120° + i\sin 120°),$$

with $r = 2$ and $\theta = 60°$. Thus,

$$2(\cos 60° + i\sin 60°), \quad\text{or } 2\left(\frac{1}{2} + \frac{\sqrt{3}}{2}i\right),$$

is a square root of $^{-}2 + 2\sqrt{3}i$. Hence, the two square roots of $^{-}2 + 2\sqrt{3}i$ are

$$1 + \sqrt{3}i \quad\text{and}\quad ^{-}1 - \sqrt{3}i.$$

Exercises

Find a trigonometric form of each of the following complex numbers.

1. $^-1 + \sqrt{3}i$ $2(\cos 120° + i \sin 120°)$
2. $\sqrt{2} - \sqrt{2}i$ $2(\cos 315° + i \sin 315°)$
3. $2i$ $2(\cos 90° + i \sin 90°)$
4. $^-5$ $5(\cos 180° + i \sin 180°)$
5. ^-5i $5(\cos 270° + i \sin 270°)$
6. $^-1 - i$ $\sqrt{2}(\cos 225° + i \sin 225°)$
7. $\sqrt{3} + 3i$ $2\sqrt{3}(\cos 60° + i \sin 60°)$
8. π $\pi(\cos 0° + i \sin 0°)$
9. $5 - 5i$ $5\sqrt{2}(\cos 315° + i \sin 315°)$

Find the product of each of the following pairs of complex numbers, and write the product in the form $a + bi$.

10. $3(\cos 20° + i \sin 20°)$ and $4(\cos 70° + i \sin 70°)$ $12i$
11. $\frac{1}{2}(\cos 42° + i \sin 42°)$ and $6(\cos {}^-42° + i \sin {}^-42°)$ 3
12. $5(\cos 15° + i \sin 15°)$ and $4(\cos 165° + i \sin 165°)$ $^-20$
13. $2(\cos 10° + i \sin 10°)$ and $7(\cos 50° + i \sin 50°)$ $7 + 7\sqrt{3}i$
14. $3(\cos 300° + i \sin 300°)$ and $5(\cos 330° + i \sin 330°)$ ^-15i
15. $2(\cos 20° + i \sin 20°)$ and $3(\cos 25° + i \sin 25°)$ $3\sqrt{2} + 3\sqrt{2}i$

Use De Moivre's theorem to find each of the following.

16. $[2(\cos 30° + i \sin 30°)]^3$ $8i$
17. $[\sqrt[3]{3}(\cos 20° + i \sin 20°)]^9$ $^-27$
18. $(2 - 2i)^4$ $^-64$
19. $(\sqrt{3} + i)^6$ $^-64$
20. $(^-3 + \sqrt{3}i)^3$ $24\sqrt{3}i$
21. $(^-3 - 3i)^3$ $54 - 54i$
22. $(\sqrt{2} + \sqrt{2}i)^7$ $64\sqrt{2} - 64\sqrt{2}i$
23. $(\sqrt[5]{3} - \sqrt[5]{3}i)^{10}$ ^-288i

In Exercises 24–29, use De Moivre's theorem to find each of the following.

24. The cube roots of $27i$ $^-3i,\ \frac{^-3}{2}\sqrt{3} + \frac{3}{2}i,\ \frac{3}{2}\sqrt{3} + \frac{3}{2}i$
25. The square roots of ^-4i $^-\sqrt{2} + \sqrt{2}i,\ \sqrt{2} - \sqrt{2}i$
26. The eighth roots of 16 $\sqrt{2},\ 1+i,\ \sqrt{2}i,\ ^-1+i,\ ^-\sqrt{2},\ ^-1-i,\ ^-\sqrt{2}i,\ 1-i$
27. The cube roots of $^-8$ $^-2,\ 1+\sqrt{3}i,\ 1-\sqrt{3}i$
28. The fourth roots of i
29. The fifth roots of $3 - \sqrt{3}i$, leaving your answers in trigonometric form
30. (a) Find the sixth roots of 1.
    (b) Which of the roots in part (a) are also cube roots of 1?
    (c) Which of the roots in part (a) are also square roots of 1? $1, {}^-1$
31. Prove De Moivre's theorem when $n = 4$ and $n = 3$. See Solution Manual.

Answers to Exercises 28–30(b)

28. $.924 + .383i;\ {}^-.383 + .924i;\ {}^-.924 - .383i;\ .383 - .924i$
29. $\sqrt[10]{12}(\cos 66° + i \sin 66°)$;
$\sqrt[10]{12}(\cos 138° + i \sin 138°)$;
$\sqrt[10]{12}(\cos 210° + i \sin 210°)$;
$\sqrt[10]{12}(\cos 282° + i \sin 282°)$;
$\sqrt[10]{12}(\cos 354° + i \sin 354°)$
30. (a) $1,\ \frac{1}{2} + \frac{1}{2}\sqrt{3}i,\ {}^-\frac{1}{2} + \frac{1}{2}\sqrt{3}i,\ {}^-1,\ {}^-\frac{1}{2} - \frac{1}{2}\sqrt{3}i,\ \frac{1}{2} - \frac{1}{2}\sqrt{3}i$
(b) $1,\ {}^-\frac{1}{2} + \frac{1}{2}\sqrt{3}i,\ {}^-\frac{1}{2} - \frac{1}{2}\sqrt{3}i$

Quiz

1. Find a trigonometric form for each of the following complex numbers:
   (a) $^-3$ (ans: $3(\cos 180° + i \sin 180°)$)
   (b) $^-1 + i$ (ans: $\sqrt{2}(\cos 135° + i \sin 135°)$)
   (c) $\sqrt{3} - i$ (ans: $2(\cos 330° + i \sin 330°)$)
   (d) $5i$ (ans: $5(\cos 90° + i \sin 90°)$)
2. Find $(^-1 + i)^4$ using De Moivre's theorem and your result in 1(b). (ans:
$[\sqrt{2}(\cos 135° + i \sin 135°)]^4$
$= (\sqrt{2})^4(\cos 540° + i \sin 540°)$
$= 4(\cos 180° + i \sin 180°)$
$= {}^-4$

KEY IDEAS AND KEY WORDS

If α, β, and γ are the angles and a, b, and c are the lengths of the respective opposite sides of a triangle, then each of the following laws is true.

Law of cosines

$$a^2 = b^2 + c^2 - 2bc \cos \alpha$$

Law of sines

$$\frac{\sin \alpha}{a} = \frac{\sin \beta}{b}$$

The **addition formulas** relate the trigonometric functions of sums and differences of two numbers (or angles) to the functions of the individual numbers (or angles). These formulas can be stated in the following manner.

First, second, third, and fourth addition formulas

$$\cos (v - u) = \cos v \cos u + \sin v \sin u \qquad \text{(A-1)}$$

$$\cos (v + u) = \cos v \cos u - \sin v \sin u \qquad \text{(A-2)}$$

$$\sin (v - u) = \sin v \cos u - \cos v \sin u \qquad \text{(A-3)}$$

$$\sin (v + u) = \sin v \cos u + \cos v \sin u \qquad \text{(A-4)}$$

Special instances of the addition formulas are the double-angle formulas and the half-angle formulas.

First and second double-angle formulas

$$\cos 2v = \cos^2 v - \sin^2 v \qquad \text{(D-1)}$$

$$\sin 2v = 2 \sin v \cos v \qquad \text{(D-2)}$$

First and second half-angle formulas

$$\cos^2 \frac{u}{2} = \frac{1}{2}(1 + \cos u) \qquad \text{(H-1)}$$

$$\sin^2 \frac{u}{2} = \frac{1}{2}(1 - \cos u) \qquad \text{(H-2)}$$

The **inverse trigonometric functions, arcsine, arccosine,** and **arctangent,** are defined in the following way.

$$\arcsin x = s, \text{ where } \sin s = x \text{ and } -\frac{\pi}{2} \leqq s \leqq \frac{\pi}{2}$$

$$\arccos x = s, \text{ where } \cos s = x \text{ and } 0 \leqq s \leqq \pi$$

$$\arctan x = s, \text{ where } \tan s = x \text{ and } -\frac{\pi}{2} < s < \frac{\pi}{2}$$

TWISTER

A dog buried a bone in a vacant lot which contained three eucalyptus trees, each 100 feet from the other two. Two of these trees were in a north-south line. A boy, watching the dog, decided to make a map showing exactly where the dog had buried his "treasure." He placed it at 15 feet due north from the southernmost tree, and 26 feet due west from that point. Is the bone buried within the triangle formed by the trees?

Solution: The two parts of the route to the bone form a right triangle with sides 15 feet and 26 feet. If the third tree lies to the east of the other two, the bone is obviously outside the triangle. Otherwise, since the angle opposite the 26-foot side is arctan 26/15, which is greater than 60 degrees, and since the trees form angles of 60 degrees with each other, the bone will lie outside the triangle.

CHAPTER REVIEW

In Exercises 1–4, $\triangle ABC$ has sides of lengths a, b, and c with opposite angles α, β, and γ.

1. Find c, given that $a = 3$, $b = 2$, $\gamma = 120°$. $c = 4.36$

2. Find α, given that $a = 5$, $b = 7$, $c = 8$. $\alpha \doteq 38°$

3. Find a, given that $\alpha = 30°$, $\beta = 105°$, $c = 10$. $a = 5\sqrt{2}$

4. Find the area of the triangle in Exercise 1. $\frac{3\sqrt{3}}{2}$

If $\sin u = \frac{2}{7}$ and $\cos v = \frac{7}{11}$, with $\pi/2 < u < \pi$ and $0 < v < \pi/2$, find each of the following.

5. $\cos(u - v)$ $\quad \frac{1}{77}(-21\sqrt{5} + 12\sqrt{2})$

6. $\sin(u - v)$ $\quad \frac{1}{77}(14 + 18\sqrt{10})$

7. $\tan(u - v)$ $\quad \frac{14 + 18\sqrt{10}}{12\sqrt{2} - 21\sqrt{5}}$

If $\cos u = \frac{3}{10}$, $\tan u < 0$, $\tan v = -\frac{10}{17}$, and $\sin v > 0$, find each of the following.

8. $\sin(u + v)$ $\quad \frac{17\sqrt{91} + 30}{10\sqrt{389}}$

9. $\cos(u + v)$ $\quad \frac{-51 + 10\sqrt{91}}{10\sqrt{389}}$

10. $\tan(u + v)$ $\quad \frac{17\sqrt{91} + 30}{10\sqrt{91} - 51}$

Use the half-angle formulas to find the sine, cosine, and tangent of each of the following.

11. $\frac{\pi}{8}$ $\quad \sin\frac{\pi}{8} = \frac{1}{2}\sqrt{2 - \sqrt{2}}$, $\cos\frac{\pi}{8} = \frac{1}{2}\sqrt{2 + \sqrt{2}}$, $\tan\frac{\pi}{8} = \sqrt{2} - 1$

12. $\frac{3\pi}{8}$ $\quad \sin\frac{3\pi}{8} = \frac{1}{2}\sqrt{2 + \sqrt{2}}$, $\cos\frac{3\pi}{8} = \frac{1}{2}\sqrt{2 - \sqrt{2}}$, $\tan\frac{3\pi}{8} = \sqrt{2} + 1$

Use the double-angle formulas to find the sine, cosine, and tangent of each of the following.

13. $\frac{2\pi}{3}$ $\quad \sin\frac{2\pi}{3} = \frac{\sqrt{3}}{2}$, $\cos\frac{2\pi}{3} = \frac{-1}{2}$, $\tan\frac{2\pi}{3} = -\sqrt{3}$

14. $\frac{5\pi}{3}$ $\quad \sin\frac{5\pi}{3} = \frac{-\sqrt{3}}{2}$, $\cos\frac{5\pi}{3} = \frac{1}{2}$, $\tan\frac{5\pi}{3} = -\sqrt{3}$

Given $\cos v = -\frac{2}{3}$, with $\pi/2 < v < \pi$, find each of the following.

15. $\sin 2v$ $\quad \frac{-4\sqrt{5}}{9}$

16. $\tan \frac{1}{2}v$ $\quad \sqrt{5}$

Simplify each of the following expressions.

17. $\dfrac{\cos 2x}{\cos x + \sin x}$ $\quad \cos x - \sin x$

18. $\sin x \cos 2x + \cos x \sin 2x$ $\quad \sin 3x$

19. $\sin 2x \tan x + \cos 2x$ $\quad 1$

20. $2\sin^2\frac{x}{2} + \cos x$ $\quad 1$

For each of the following, find the solution set which lies within the interval $0 \leqq x < 2\pi$.

21. $2\sin^2 x - 5\sin x - 3 = 0$ $\quad \{\frac{7\pi}{6}, \frac{11\pi}{6}\}$

22. $\cos^2 x - 2\cos x = 0$ $\quad \{\frac{\pi}{2}, \frac{3\pi}{2}\}$

23. $\sec^2\theta - \tan\theta = 1$ $\quad \{0, \frac{\pi}{4}, \pi, \frac{5\pi}{4}\}$

Draw the graph and state the period and amplitude of each of the following functions. See Solution Manual.

24. $f(x) = 5\sin 4x$ $\quad \frac{\pi}{2}; 5$

25. $g(x) = 3\cos 2x$ $\quad \pi; 3$

26. $h(x) = 3(1 + \cos 2x)$ $\quad \pi; 3$

Find each of the following.

27. $\arcsin \frac{3}{2}$ Does not exist

28. $\arccos\ (^{-}\frac{1}{2})$ $\frac{2\pi}{3}$

29. $\arctan\ (^{-}1)$ $\frac{^{-}\pi}{4}$

30. $\arcsin\ (^{-}\frac{1}{2})$ $\frac{^{-}\pi}{6}$

31. $\arccos\ (^{-}1)$ π

32. $\tan\ (\arccos\ ^{-}\frac{3}{7})$ $\frac{^{-}2}{3}\sqrt{10}$

33. $\sec\ (\arcsin\ ^{-}\frac{1}{2})$ $\frac{2}{3}\sqrt{3}$

34. $\cot\ (\text{arccot}\ ^{-}1)$ $^{-}1$

In Exercises 35–38, prove each identity. 35-40 See Solution Manual.

35. $\csc 2\theta + \cot 2\theta = \cot \theta$

36. $\dfrac{2 \tan \theta}{1 + \tan^2 \theta} = \sin 2\theta$

37. $\cos^4 u - \sin^4 u = \cos 2u$

38. $\dfrac{2 \sin^2 u - 1}{\sin u \cos u} = \tan u - \cot u$

In Exercises 39 and 40, show that each equation is true.

39. $\arctan 2 - \arctan 1 = \arctan \frac{1}{3}$

40. $\arcsin \frac{4}{5} = \pi - 2 \arctan 2$

41. Find the sixth roots of 64. $2,\ 1+\sqrt{3}i,\ ^{-}1+\sqrt{3}i,\ ^{-}2,\ 1-\sqrt{3}i,\ ^{-}1-\sqrt{3}i$

42. (a) Express the following complex number in trigonometric form. $\cos 135° + i \sin 135°$

$$^{-}\frac{1}{\sqrt{2}} + \frac{1}{\sqrt{2}}i$$

(b) Find, in trigonometric form, the cube roots of the complex number of part (a). $\cos 45° + i \sin 45°;\ \cos 165° + i \sin 165°;\ \cos 285° + i \sin 285°$

(c) Express one of the roots in part (b) in the form $a + bi$. $1/\sqrt{2} + (1/\sqrt{2})i$

43. (a) If an arc 10 feet long subtends an angle of 2 radians at the center of a circle, find its radius. 5 feet

(b) Find the area of the circular sector in part (a). 25 sq ft

44. City B is due north of City A. To fly from city A to city B, one must take a plane from city A to city C, which is 50° east of north from A at a distance of 150 miles, and then fly 200 miles to city B. How far due north is City B from City A? 260 miles

45. A parallelogram has two sides of lengths 50 and 100. One angle of the parallelogram has measure 120°. Find the length of the longer diagonal and the angle made by this diagonal and the longer side. $d \doteq 132;\ \alpha = 19°$

CHAPTER TEST

The material included in the Chapter Test was covered in the following sections:

Problem 1—Section 10-1
Problems 2, 3—Section 10-2
Problems 4, 5—Section 10-4
Problem 6—Section 10-3
Problem 7—Section 10-5
Problem 8—Section 10-7
Problems 9-11—Section 10-8
Problem 12—Section 10-2

Answers to Chapter Test Problems 1, 2, 4, 5, 8, 12, page 445

1. 21.8

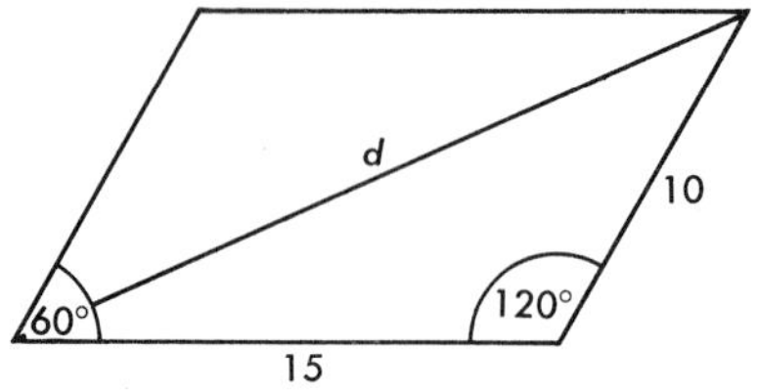

2. Impossible

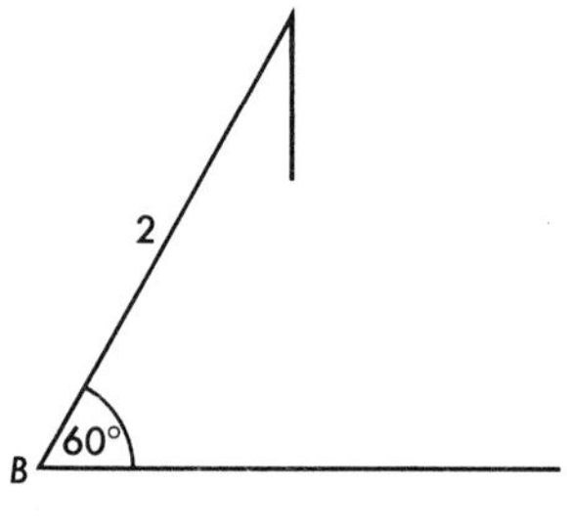

CHAPTER TEST

1. Find the longer diagonal of a parallelogram having sides of lengths 10 and 15 and one angle of measure 60°.
2. Find α in $\triangle ABC$, given that $a = 2$, $b = 1$, $\beta = \pi/3$.
3. Find the area of $\triangle ABC$, given that $a = 2$, $b = 4$, $\gamma = 30°$. 2
4. From the addition formulas, $\cos(v + u) = \cos v \cos u - \sin v \sin u$ and $\sin(u + v) = \sin v \cos u + \cos v \sin u$, derive the double-angle formulas for sine and cosine.

In Exercises 5 and 6, prove each identity.

5. $\sin 2\theta = \tan\theta(1 + \cos 2\theta)$
6. $\dfrac{\cos(v - u) + \sin(v + u)}{\cos u + \sin u} = \cos v + \sin v$ (See below.)
7. For the following equation, find the part of the solution set that lies in the interval $0 \leqq x < 2\pi$. $\{\frac{7\pi}{6}, \frac{11\pi}{6}\}$

$$2\sin^2 x - 5\sin x - 3 = 0$$

8. Graph the function $f(x) = 3\sin 2x$, using that part of the domain of f for which $0 \leqq x < 2\pi$.

In Exercises 9–11, find each number.

9. $\arcsin(^-1)$ $\frac{^-\pi}{2}$ 10. $\arccos 0$ $\frac{\pi}{2}$ 11. $\arctan(^-\frac{1}{2})$ $^-.471$

12. A vertical telegraph pole is supported by two guy wires, each running from the top of the pole to the ground. One wire is 70 feet long and makes an angle of 55° with the ground. If the second wire is 60 feet long, what angle does it make with the ground?

6. $\dfrac{\cos(v-u)+\sin(v+u)}{\cos u+\sin u} = \dfrac{(\cos v\cos u+\sin v\sin u)+(\sin v\cos u+\cos v\sin u)}{\cos u+\sin u}$

$= \dfrac{(\cos v\cos u+\sin v\cos u)+(\sin v\sin u+\cos v\sin u)}{\cos u+\sin u}$

$= \dfrac{\cos u(\cos v+\sin v)+\sin u(\sin v+\cos v)}{\cos u+\sin u}$

$= \dfrac{(\cos v+\sin v)(\cos u+\sin u)}{\cos u+\sin u}$

$= \cos v+\sin v$

4. $\sin(u + v)$
$= \sin v\cos u + \cos v\sin u$
Let $u = v$.
$\sin(v + v)$
$= \sin v\cos v + \cos v\sin v$
$\sin 2v = 2\sin v\cos v$
$\cos(u + v)$
$= \cos u\cos v - \sin u\sin v$
Let $u = v$.
$\cos(v + v)$
$= \cos v\cos v - \sin v\sin v$
$\cos 2v$
$= \cos^2 v - \sin^2 v$

5. $\sin 2\theta$
$= 2\sin\theta\cos\theta$
$= 2\sin\theta\cos\theta \cdot \dfrac{\cos\theta}{\cos\theta}$
$= \dfrac{\sin\theta}{\cos\theta} \cdot 2\cos^2\theta$
$= \tan\theta(\cos^2\theta + \cos^2\theta)$
$= \tan\theta[\cos^2\theta + (1 - \sin^2\theta)]$
$= \tan\theta[1 + (\cos^2\theta - \sin^2\theta)]$
$= \tan\theta(1 + \cos 2\theta)$

8.

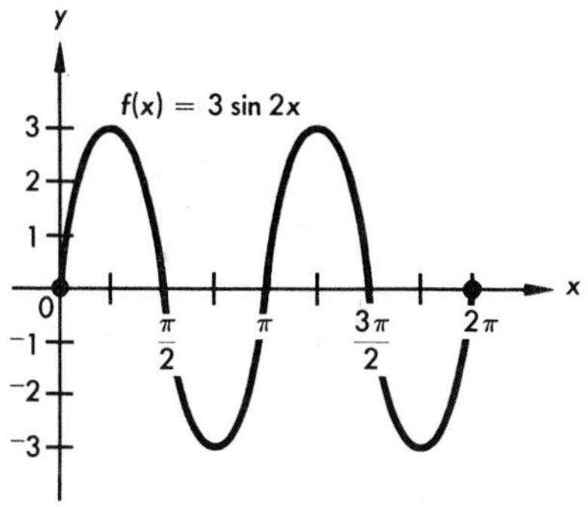

12. 73°

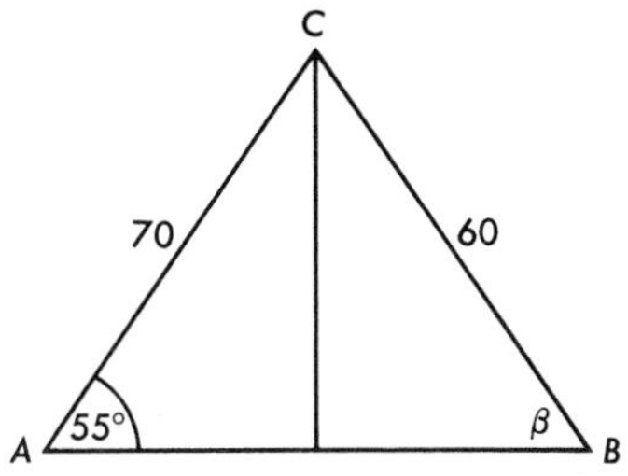

CHAPTER 11

Problems of Counting

The purpose of Chapter 11 is to give the student an opportunity to study methods of counting the number of objects in a large collection, which in general is a matter of devising a systematic procedure for listing the members of the collection. In this process of listing objects one notes certain patterns which enable one to arrive at a total number of objects in the collection without actually completing the listing. Some of these patterns occur frequently enough to be formulated in terms of general rules or principles to obtain the count of such collections. The following are some of the topics covered in Chapter 11:

- *Tree diagrams*
- *Sequential counting principle*
- *Mutually exclusive cases*
- *Alternative cases principle*
- *Combinations*
- *Permutations*
- *Factorials*
- *Binomial theorem*
- *Pascal's triangle*

It is suggested that one day be spent on each section of this chapter.

CHAPTER 11

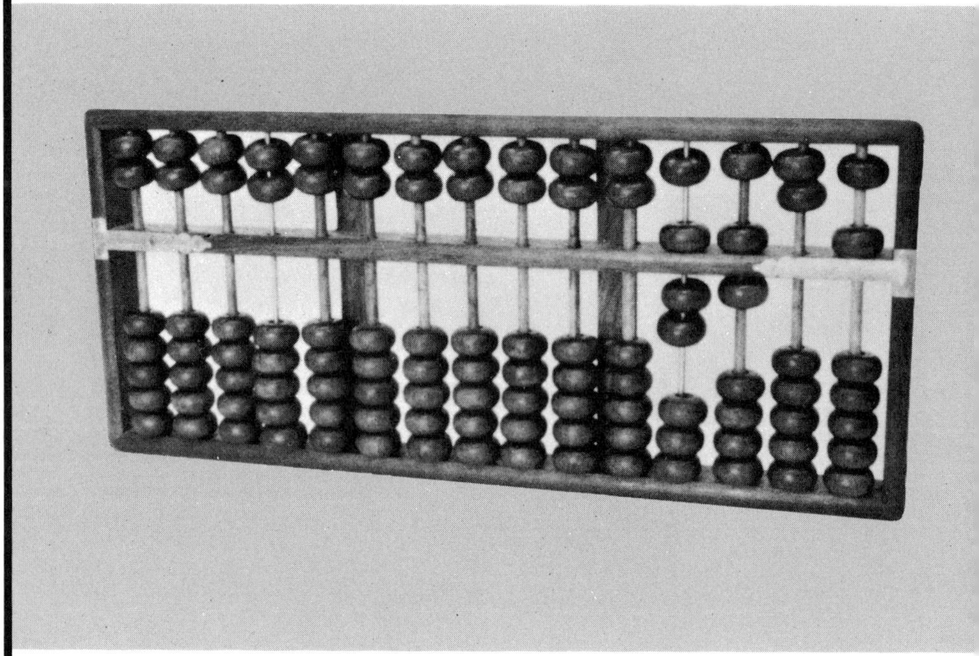

The abacus is a primitive instrument used in counting. Calculations are made by sliding the counters along the rods.

PROBLEMS OF COUNTING

In this chapter, we shall develop some systematic ways of counting the number of elements in certain types of sets. Consider, for example, the set of all possible license plates that can be made with two letters and four or fewer digits on each plate. Basic counting principles can be used to determine the exact number of license plates that can be made before the same arrangement of letters and digits is repeated.

Problems in which it is necessary to make such counts arise in many branches of mathematics. However, counting principles are most frequently used in the branch of mathematics that is called probability theory.

447

11-1 SEQUENTIAL COUNTING PRINCIPLE

The importance of actually starting a list of items to be counted (or, at least, thinking about what such a list would contain) before attempting to make a count, should be emphasized to the students repeatedly throughout this chapter.

After the student has completed many examples in which he actually lists all the different ways of carrying out the instructions, he should verify that the sequential counting principle (or the counting principle for cases of alternatives which is presented in the next section) correctly gives the number in his list.

Students are usually quick to grasp the idea of a tree diagram and find it a welcome aid.

11-1 SEQUENTIAL COUNTING PRINCIPLE

The procedure for solving a counting problem is usually twofold. First, we devise a *scheme* for listing the set of objects to be counted; then we look for *patterns* in this scheme so that we can compute the count without actually pointing to the objects one by one. This procedure is implemented by some basic counting principles which we shall illustrate in the following problems.

Problem 1. Consider a set of four discs in which the discs are numbered 1, 2, 3, and 4. How many two-digit numbers can be represented by placing two discs side by side?

Solution. We might choose any one of the four discs as a start. Then to the right of this disc we could place any one of the three remaining discs. The *tree diagram* of Fig. 11–1 suggests our scheme.

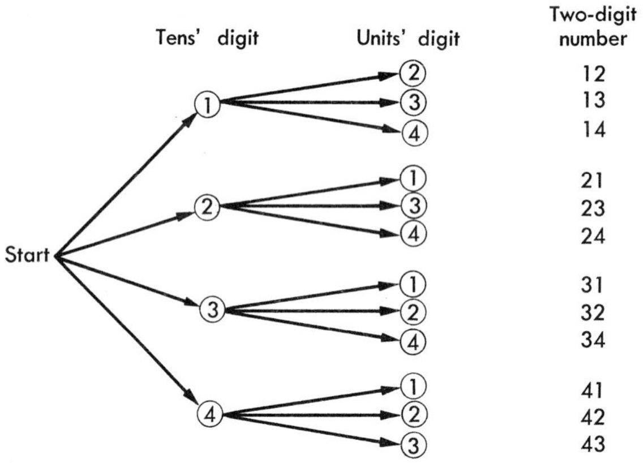

FIGURE 11–1

The arrows drawn from the word "start" point to the four possible discs of our first choice. The numeral on each of these discs will be a tens' digit of our number. Three arrows are drawn from each disc of our first choice, indicating the possible discs of our second choice. Our second choice must be different from our first choice. The numeral on each disc of our second choice will be a units' digit of our number. To the right of the tree, we have listed the numbers represented by our various choices. This list is formed by reading off the digits in order along each path (that is, along a succession of branches) of the tree. The total number of two-digit numbers so formed is 12, the total number of paths. The total number of paths is the product of the number of arrows drawn in the first stage and the number of arrows drawn in the second stage.

If more than two actions are performed, then the tree will have more than two branching stages, as the following problem illustrates.

Problem 2. How many four-digit numbers can be formed with the set of four discs of Problem 1?

Solution. The tree diagram used to count the number of possibilities in this problem has four branching stages: The stages represent, in turn, the choice of the thousands' digit of the number, the hundreds' digit, the tens' digit, and finally the units' digit.

Since there are four arrows drawn in the first stage, three arrows drawn from each disc in the second stage, two arrows drawn from each disc in the third stage, and one arrow drawn from each disc in the final stage, there are

$$4 \cdot 3 \cdot 2 \cdot 1, \quad \text{or } 24,$$

paths in this tree. Thus, 24 four-digit numbers can be formed. It should be noted that there are many other orders in which the four actions can be performed. We might select the tens' digit first (4 ways), the hundreds' digit second (3 ways), the units' digit third (2 ways), and finally the thousands' digit (1 way). The number of paths is nonetheless $4 \cdot 3 \cdot 2 \cdot 1$, or 24.

A succession of two or more actions performed in a definite order is called a *sequence* of actions. The number of possible results of a sequence of actions in a given problem may often be counted by using the following fundamental principle.

SEQUENTIAL COUNTING PRINCIPLE

Given that two or more actions are performed in a definite order, that the first action produces m possible results, and that for each of these results, the second action produces n possible results, and that for each of these results, the third action produces p results, and so on, then the number of possible results of this sequence of actions is the product of the numbers m, n, p, and so on.

Each action referred to in the sequential counting principle is performed at a *branching stage* of a tree diagram, and each result of a sequence of actions is a *path* of the diagram. Problem 3 is another example of this principle.

You may wish to have a student draw the tree, or part of the tree, for Problem 2 on the board. Students usually understand right away that an incomplete tree diagram will frequently suffice.

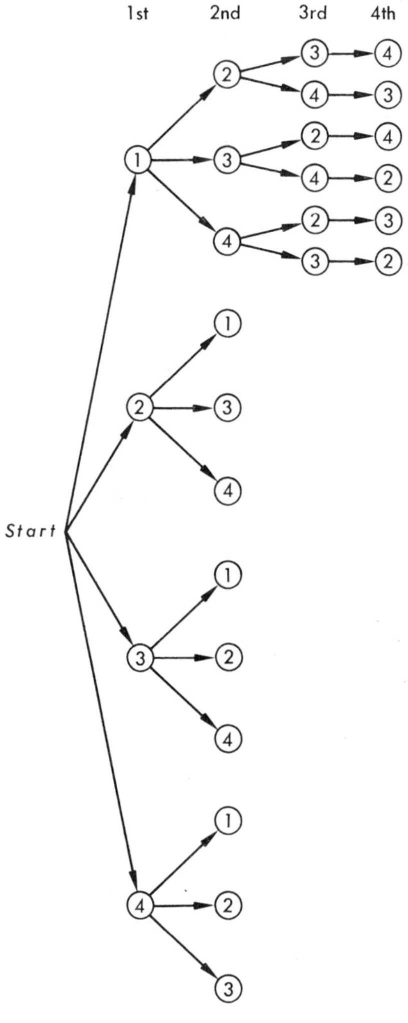

$4 \cdot 3 \cdot 2 \cdot 1 = 24$

You may wish to have the tree for Problem 3 put on the board.

Problem 3. How many two-digit numbers can be formed if only the digits 1, 2, 3, and 4 are used?

Solution. This problem might at first glance appear to be the same as Problem 1. However, the number 44 fulfills the conditions of this problem but not those of Problem 1, where two *different* discs had to be used to form each number. If we let the first action be that of selecting the tens' digit and the second action be that of selecting the units' digit of our number, then there are 4 possible results of the first action, and for each of these results there are 4 possible results of the second action. Hence, there are 4×4, or 16, possible results of this sequence of actions; that is, there are 16 two-digit numbers that can be formed.

The tree diagram for Problem 3 is similar to that drawn in Fig. 11–1 for Problem 1. The difference is that four branches, instead of three, are drawn in the second stage from each first-stage endpoint.

Exercises for Discussion

If time is limited, it is suggested that at least Exercises for Discussion 2–4 be covered.

Exercises for Discussion

1. Jane tosses a penny, a dime, and a quarter, in turn. We designate the result of each toss with H for heads and T for tails.
   (a) Make a tree diagram that shows the results of Jane's tosses. At the end of each path, write three letters to indicate the result of the sequence of tosses. Thus, HTH will be at the end of one path indicating that the penny landed H, the dime landed T, and the quarter landed H.
   (b) How many results are there? 8
   (c) In how many of the results do exactly two heads show? 3
   (d) In how many of the results do three heads show? 1
   (e) In how many of the results do at least two heads show? 4
2. John and Tom had their birthdays guessed by a mind reader at a carnival. The mind reader wrote the month and day of each boy's birthday on the same card. Ignore leap years in answering the questions below.
   (a) How many possible guesses can the mind reader make in writing the card? $(365)(365) = 133{,}225$
   (b) If the mind reader is told that the boys have different birthdays, how many guesses can he make? $(365)(364) = 132{,}860$
3. How many four-digit numbers can be formed if only the digits 1, 2, 3, and 4 are used, if each number must begin and end with an even digit, and
   (a) if repetition of digits is not allowed? $2 \times 1 \times 2 \times 1 = 4$
   (b) if repetition of digits is allowed? $2 \times 2 \times 4 \times 4 = 64$

Answer to Exercise for Discussion 1(a)

1. (a)

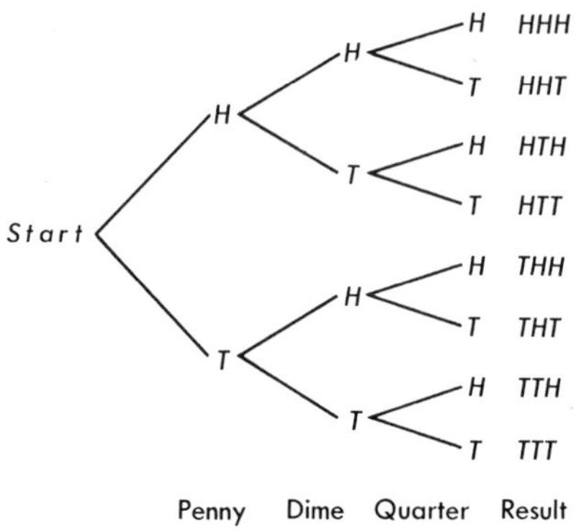

4. Given the set of digits {4, 5, 6},
  (a) how many two-digit numbers can be formed? $3 \times 3 = 9$
  (b) how many even two-digit numbers can be formed? $3 \times 2 = 6$
  (c) how many odd two-digit numbers can be formed? $3 \times 1 = 3$
  (d) draw a tree diagram for part (*b*).

Exercises

1. If the mind reader of the second problem in the Exercises for Discussion is told that both boys were born in June but have different birthdays, how many guesses can he make? 870

2. If you are given a set of five discs, numbered 1, 3, 5, 6, and 9,
  (a) how many two-digit numbers can you represent by placing two discs side by side? 20
  (b) how many four-digit numbers can you represent by placing four discs in a row? 120
  (c) how many five-digit numbers can you represent by placing five discs in a row? 120

3. Given the set of digits {1, 3, 6, 8, 9} and the condition that repetition of digits is not allowed,
  (a) how many two-digit numbers can be formed? 20
  (b) how many even two-digit numbers can be formed? 8
  (c) how many three-digit numbers can be formed? 60
  (d) how many odd three-digit numbers can be formed? 36

4. Given that repetition of digits is allowed, answer each question in Exercise 3. (a) 25 (b) 10 (c) 125 (d) 75

5. (a) In how many different ways can a student answer a multiple-choice exam, if the exam consists of five questions and each question has three possibilities which are listed as *a*, *b*, and *c*? 243
  (b) Answer the question in part (a), assuming that the student never makes the same lettered choice for two consecutive answers. 48

6. John's mother always puts in his lunch box one white-bread sandwich, one brown-bread sandwich, a piece of fruit, and a dessert. Her sandwich fillings are peanut butter, jam, egg salad, cheese, ham, and sliced chicken. For fruit, she selects a banana, an orange, an apple, or a pear. Her desserts are chocolate cake and molasses cookies.
  (a) If his mother puts a different filling in each sandwich, how many lunches can John have before he eats the same lunch twice? 240
  (b) If she does not always use a different filling in each sandwich, how many different lunches can John have? 288

Answer to Exercise for Discussion 4(d)

4. (d)

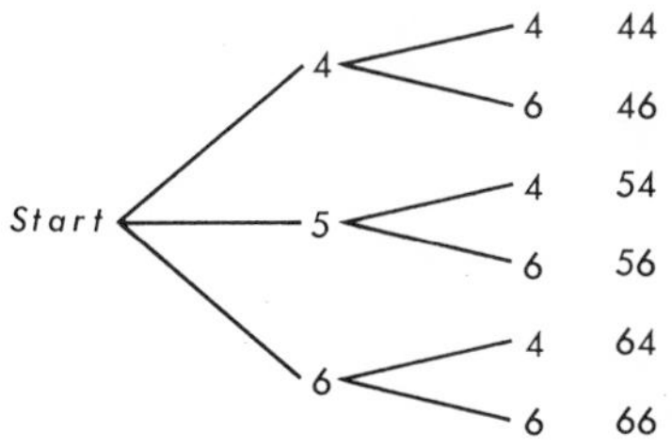

Quiz

Using only the odd digits 1, 3, 5, 7, 9:

1. How many three-digit numbers can be formed not allowing repetition of digits? (ans: 60)

2. How many three digit numbers can be formed allowing repeated digits? (ans: 125)

3. How many three-digit numbers, allowing repetition of digits, end in the digit 5? (ans: 25)

4. How many three-digit numbers, allowing repetition of digits, are less than 400? (ans: 50)

11-2 ALTERNATIVE CASES PRINCIPLE

It should be emphasized that the question of when to multiply numbers and when to add them may be answered only by first thinking through the actions needed to form the proposed list. For example, in forming two-digit numbers, it is natural to think of choosing a first digit and then with each such choice to select a second digit (sequential counting principle). In making a list of monograms which will have sets either of two initials or of three, one first concentrates on the list of two-initial monograms and then on another list of three-initial monograms (alternative cases principle). In other words, the language itself indicates which principle is involved. If one is asked to do *first* one thing *and then* another, then two things must be done in order and the total number of outcomes counted. This is the sequential counting principle. If one is asked to do *either* one thing *or* another, but not both, and then to count the possibilities at his disposal, that is the alternative cases principle.

11-2 ALTERNATIVE CASES PRINCIPLE

The next problem illustrates the need for separating some counting problems into various cases, called *mutually exclusive cases,* before applying the sequential counting principle.

Problem. If repetition of digits is not allowed, how many numbers can be formed by using the digits 5, 6, 7, and 8?

Solution. We can form one-digit numbers, two-digit numbers, three-digit numbers, and four-digit numbers; each of these mutually exclusive cases involves a different sequence of actions, starting with one action for one-digit numbers and ending with four actions for four-digit numbers. Using the sequential counting principle, we determine the number of results of the sequence of actions in each case below.

Cases	Count
One-digit numbers	4
Two-digit numbers	$4 \cdot 3$, or 12
Three-digit numbers	$4 \cdot 3 \cdot 2$, or 24
Four-digit numbers	$4 \cdot 3 \cdot 2 \cdot 1$, or 24

If tree diagrams are drawn, the first case has a one-stage tree, the second case a two-stage tree, the third case a three-stage tree, and the fourth case a four-stage tree. To obtain the solution of the problem, we find the *sum* of the counts listed above: $4 + 12 + 24 + 24$, or 64. Thus, 64 different numbers can be formed.

The four cases of this problem are called mutually exclusive since each case refers to a type of number entirely different from those in the other cases. In other words, the appearance of a number in one set *excludes* the possibility of its being in the set of another case. Thus, each number is a one-digit, or a two-digit, or a three-digit, or a four-digit number, but it cannot be more than one of these types at once.

We have illustrated the following fundamental principle for counting mutually exclusive cases.

ALTERNATIVE CASES PRINCIPLE

If an action can be analyzed into several mutually exclusive cases, say into cases 1, 2, 3, and so on, and if there are m possible results of performing the action in case 1, n possible results of performing the action in case 2, p possible results of performing the action in case 3, and so on, then the total number of possible results of the action is the sum of the numbers m, n, p, and so on.

Exercises for Discussion

1. How many numbers of one, two, or three digits can be formed if only the numerals 1, 2, and 3 are used and
   (a) if repetition of digits is not allowed? $3+3\cdot2+3\cdot2\cdot1=3+6+6=15$
   (b) if repetition of digits is allowed? $3+3\cdot3+3\cdot3\cdot3=3+9+27=39$
2. (a) How many different individuals can there be, each with two initials and no two with the same ordered pair of initials? $26\times26=676$
   (b) How many different members can there be in an organization if each person has three initials and no two persons have the same initials in the same order? $26\times26\times26=17,576$
   (c) How many different monograms should an embroiderer prepare so that he will have a monogram for any person with two or three initials? $676+17,576=18,252$
3. There are exactly four different roads from town A to town B and three from town B to town C. There are also two routes from town A to town C that bypass town B.
   (a) How many possible routes are there from A to C that bypass B? 2
   (b) How many possible routes are there from A to C that pass through B? $4\times3=12$
   (c) How many possible routes are there from A to C? $2+12=14$
   (d) How many possible trips are there from A to C and back to A? $14\times14=196$

Exercises

1. If only the digits 2, 3, 6, 7, and 9 are used and if repetition of digits is allowed,
   (a) how many numbers of no more than five digits can be formed? 3905
   (b) how many of the numbers in part (a) are even? 1562
   (c) how many of the numbers in part (a) are three-digit numbers? 125

In Exercises 2–6, consider a pair of dice that consists of a red die and a green die. The red die and then the green die are thrown, and the number of dots showing on the top face of each is noted.

2. Make a list that has an ordered pair representing the result of each sequence; the first member of each ordered pair will represent the number of dots showing on the red die. You should have 36 different pairs in your list.
3. In Exercise 2, how many results are there in which the total number of dots showing is 7? 6
4. In Exercise 2, how many results are there in which the total number of dots showing is 11? 2
5. In Exercise 2, how many results are there in which the total number of dots showing is 7 or 11? 8
6. In Exercise 2, how many results are there in which the total number of dots showing is less than or equal to 4? 6

Exercises for Discussion

If time is limited, it is suggested that at least Exercises for Discussion 2 and 3 be covered.

Answer to Exercise 2

2. (1, 1), (1, 2), (1, 3), (1, 4), (1, 5), (1, 6), (2, 1), (2, 2), (2, 3), (2, 4), (2, 5), (2, 6), (3, 1), (3, 2), (3, 3), (3, 4), (3, 5), (3, 6), (4, 1), (4, 2), (4, 3), (4, 4), (4, 5), (4, 6), (5, 1), (5, 2), (5, 3), (5, 4), (5, 5), (5, 6), (6, 1), (6, 2), (6, 3), (6, 4), (6, 5), (6, 6)

Quiz

Given the set of odd digits {1, 3, 5, 7, 9}:

1. If repetition of digits is not allowed, how many numbers of three or fewer digits may be formed? (ans: 85)
2. How many numbers of three or fewer digits can be formed, allowing repetitions of digits? (ans: 155)
3. A red die and a green die are each thrown once. The result can be noted each time as an ordered pair of numbers, giving the number on the red die as the first element of the pair.
   (a) How many ordered pairs are there? (ans: 36)
   (b) How many ordered pairs give a total of 7? Exhibit a complete list of such pairs. (ans: 6: {(1, 6), (2, 5), (3, 4), (4, 3), (5, 2), (6, 1)})

Suppose that license plates for certain years always start with two letters which may be alike. The letters are followed by four numerals, which can be the digits 0, 1, 2, . . . , 9. Repetition of digits is allowed. (You may give your answers with products of integers indicated instead of computed.)

7. How many different license plates can be issued if no zeros are permitted to appear between the letters and the first nonzero numeral? $26^2 \cdot 9 \cdot 10^3$

8. How many different license plates can be issued without the restriction made in Exercise 7? $26^2 \cdot 10^4$

9. How many different license plates can be issued without the restriction made in Exercise 7 if there is no repetition of letters and no repetitions of numerals? $26 \cdot 25 \cdot 10 \cdot 9 \cdot 8 \cdot 7$

10. How many different license plates are available, under the conditions stated in Exercise 9 if the letters I, O, and Q are not used? $23 \cdot 22 \cdot 10 \cdot 9 \cdot 8 \cdot 7$

△

In Exercises 11–18, numbers are to be formed from the digits 0, 1, 2, 3, 4, 5, 6, 7, 8, and 9, without repetition of digits. The first digit of each number must, of course, be nonzero.

11. How many three-digit numbers can be formed starting with the digit 1? 72

12. How many three-digit numbers can be formed? 648

13. How many five-digit numbers can be formed that end with the digit 0? 3024

14. How many five-digit numbers can be formed so that the last digit is an even number but not zero? 10,752

15. How many even five-digit numbers can be formed? $9 \cdot 8 \cdot 7 \cdot 6 \cdot 1 + 8 \cdot 8 \cdot 7 \cdot 6 \cdot 4$

16. How many numbers can be formed to satisfy the requirement that each number must be less than 300? 235

17. How many odd five-digit numbers can be formed, with odd and even digits alternating? 1200

18. How many five-digit numbers can be formed in which no two consecutive digits are either both even or both odd? 2160

11–3 COMBINATIONS AND PERMUTATIONS

If a set S consists of the first five letters of the alphabet, then we may use set notation to indicate S:

$$S = \{a, b, c, d, e\}.$$

In this notation, *the order in which we write the elements of S is immaterial.* Thus, we could just as well indicate the elements of the set S in another order. For example, $S = \{a, c, e, b, d\}$.

11–3 COMBINATIONS AND PERMUTATIONS

The purpose of this section is to identify the different sorts of counting situations involved in listing combinations and in listing permutations. Again, the emphasis is on the actual listing, not the count of items in the list.

A combination of n objects is just a set with n elements. The n objects

In listing the elements of a set, we never display any element more than once. For example, we would never write $\{3, 3, 3\}$ for the set of digits of the number 333. Rather, we would write $\{3\}$ and say that the number 333 was formed by repeated use of the single digit 3 of the set $\{3\}$.

Consider the subsets

$$U = \{a, c, e\}, \quad V = \{c, b\}, \quad W = \{a\}$$

of the set $S = \{a, b, c, d, e\}$.

Since the subset W of S has exactly one element, we shall call it a 1-subset of S. Similarly, U is called a 3-subset and V is called a 2-subset of S, according to the following definition.

DEFINITION OF A COMBINATION

If S is a set with n elements and if T is a subset of S containing r elements, then T is called an r-subset of S. Such a set T is also called a combination of r objects from a set of n objects.

We note that an n-subset of a set of n objects is the set itself. Also, we never speak of a combination of r objects from a set of n objects unless $r \leqq n$.

Problem 1. List all possible combinations of three letters from the set S:

$$S = \{a, b, c, d\}.$$

Solution. It is helpful to use an organized procedure rather than to proceed at random. Therefore, we shall pick one letter, say a, and list all of the combinations of three letters that contain this letter.

$$\{a, b, c\} \qquad \{a, c, d\}$$
$$\{a, b, d\}$$

Notice that we did not list $\{a, c, b\}$ in the second column because the set $\{a, c, b\}$ is the same as the set $\{a, b, c\}$, which we had already listed. Now let us list the sets containing b that we have not already listed.

$$\{b, c, d\}$$

Thus, the total number of combinations of three letters from S is 4. An easy way to check is to see if we used each letter an equal number of times. In this case, each letter is used 3 times.

may be lined up in different ways. Each line-up, or arrangement without repetition, is called a permutation of the n objects. A tree diagram quickly illustrates that a single combination or selection of n objects gives rise to $n!$ arrangements with all n objects in each arrangement, or permutation. It is suggested that instead of simply stating these facts you could lead up to them by taking a set of 1 element and listing all its arrangements, then a set of 2 elements with all its arrangements, and so on.

Set	Arrangements
a	*a*
a, *b*	*ab*, *ba*
a, *b*, *c*	*abc*, *acb*, *bac*, *bca*, *cab*, *cba*

The list remains the key to understanding, even if the student only begins to make the list and indicates how it should be continued.

In Problem 1, the reason the check works is, of course, that no one of the four letters has any reason to be more or less favored than any other letter.

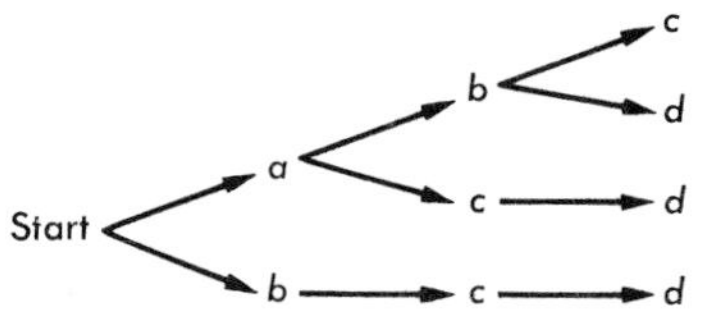

List of combinations

$\{a, b, c\}$

$\{a, b, d\}$

$\{a, c, d\}$

$\{b, c, d\}$

FIGURE 11-2

It should be made clear to the students that using the tree-diagram approach for making a list of combinations is a tricky procedure and its use for this purpose should not be belabored.

The tree diagram of Fig. 11–2 illustrates the actions involved in selecting each combination. In drawing this diagram, we have to be sure that *no two paths contain the same three elements.* For example, we could not have a branch going from d to a in the last stage of the bottom path, for this would give us the combination $\{c, d, a\}$ which is the same combination as $\{a, c, d\}$.

Sometimes we are interested in indicating a specific order for the objects of a set. For example, the outcome of a race is announced by listing the names of the participants in the order in which they finish the race. Thus, the list

Tom, Frank, Joe, Archibald

indicates that Tom won the race, Frank was second, Joe was third, and Archibald was last. Such strings of elements are called *arrangements* of elements from a set.

As another example, the expressions *abcde* and *aabcb* are arrangements of five elements taken from the set $\{a, b, c, d, e, f\}$. The arrangement *abcde* is called an *arrangement of five elements without repetition,* and *aabcb* is called an *arrangement of five elements with repetition.*

Another way of designating arrangements follows the notation for *ordered pairs* of numbers. Thus, the arrangement *aabcb* may be written as (a, a, b, c, b). We call (a, a, b, c, b) an *ordered* 5-*tuple.* In general, if an arrangement of r elements $a_1, a_2, \ldots, a_r$ of a set is taken in the order in which we have written them, then this arrangement is designated by the *ordered r-tuple* $(a_1, a_2, \ldots, a_r)$. Two ordered r-tuples $(a_1, a_2, \ldots, a_r)$ and $(b_1, b_2, \ldots, b_r)$ of elements of a set are equal if, and only if, $a_1 = b_1$, $a_2 = b_2, \ldots, a_r = b_r$. For example, the ordered 3-tuples (1, 2, 3) and (1, 2, 3) are equal, but the ordered 3-tuples (1, 2, 3) and (2, 1, 3) are different. Each numeral for an integer consists of an ordered r-tuple of digits.

Arrangements without repetition are called permutations. In this definition, r and n are positive integers with $r \leq n$.

DEFINITION OF A PERMUTATION

A permutation of r objects from a set of n objects is an arrangement without repetition of r objects from the set of n objects.

Problem 2. List all possible permutations of three objects from the set

$$S = \{a, b, c, d\}.$$

Solution. The tree diagram of Fig. 11–3 illustrates the three actions involved in selecting each permutation. According to the sequential counting principle, we count the number of permutations and obtain $4 \cdot 3 \cdot 2$, or 24.

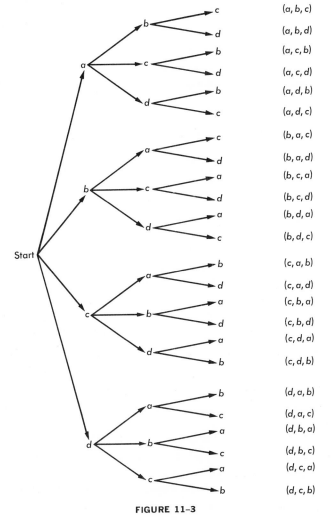

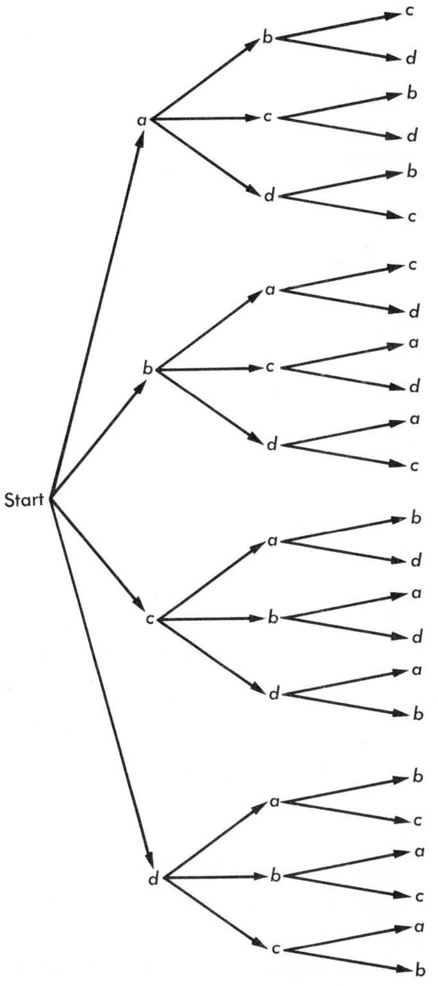

(a, b, c)
(a, b, d)
(a, c, b)
(a, c, d)
(a, d, b)
(a, d, c)
(b, a, c)
(b, a, d)
(b, c, a)
(b, c, d)
(b, d, a)
(b, d, c)
(c, a, b)
(c, a, d)
(c, b, a)
(c, b, d)
(c, d, a)
(c, d, b)
(d, a, b)
(d, a, c)
(d, b, a)
(d, b, c)
(d, c, a)
(d, c, b)

FIGURE 11–3

The efficacy of the tree diagram for forming lists of permutations lies in its property of portraying actions performed in an ordered sequence. Thus, selecting letters *a*, *b*, *c*, in that order, is a different sequence from the selection *c*, *b*, *a*.

Exercises for Discussion, page 458

If time is limited, it is suggested that at least Exercises for Discussion 3–5 be covered.

Answers to Exercises for Discussion 1 and 3(a), page 458

1. *abc* *acd* *abd* *bcd*
acb *adc* *adb* *bdc*
bac *cad* *bad* *cbd*
bca *cda* *bda* *cdb*
cab *dac* *dab* *dbc*
cba *dca* *dba* *dcb*
Same

3. (a) $\{B, C, D\}$, $\{B, C, E\}$, $\{B, C, J\}$, $\{B, D, E\}$, $\{B, D, J\}$, $\{B, E, J\}$, $\{C, D, E\}$, $\{C, D, J\}$, $\{C, E, J\}$, $\{D, E, J\}$

Answers to Exercises 1(a), 1(b), 2, page 459

1. (a) 67, 68, 69, 76, 78, 79, 86, 87, 89, 96, 97, 98

(b) 678, 698, 768, 798, 786, 796, 876, 896, 976, 986, 968, 978

2. (a) $\{A, B, C\}$, $\{A, B, D\}$, $\{A, B, E\}$, $\{A, B, F\}$, $\{A, C, D\}$, $\{A, C, E\}$, $\{A, C, F\}$, $\{A, D, E\}$, $\{A, D, F\}$, $\{A, E, F\}$, $\{B, C, D\}$, $\{B, C, E\}$, $\{B, C, F\}$, $\{B, D, E\}$, $\{B, D, F\}$, $\{B, E, F\}$, $\{C, D, E\}$, $\{C, D, F\}$, $\{C, E, F\}$, $\{D, E, F\}$

(b) $\{A, E, B\}$, $\{A, E, C\}$, $\{A, E, D\}$, $\{A, E, F\}$, $\{B, C, D\}$, $\{B, C, E\}$, $\{B, C, F\}$, $\{B, D, E\}$, $\{B, D, F\}$, $\{B, E, F\}$, $\{C, D, E\}$, $\{C, D, F\}$, $\{C, E, F\}$, $\{D, E, F\}$

Answers to Exercises 4, 5, 7(a), page 459

4. Girls parts: *AD, AE, DE, DA, EA, ED*; boys parts: *BC, BF, BG, CB, CF, CG, FB, FC, FG, GB, GC, GF*; complete casts: each of girls with each of boys—72 possible casts
5. (a) (1, 1), (1, 2), (1, 3), (1, 4), (2, 1), (2, 2), (2, 3), (2, 4), (3, 1), (3, 2), (3, 3), (3, 4), (4, 1), (4, 2), (4, 3), (4, 4)
   (b) (1, 1), (1, 2), (1, 3), (1, 4), (2, 1), (2, 2), (2, 3), (3, 1), (3, 2), (4, 1)
7. (a) $\{\{K, P\}, \{O, H, V\}\}$, $\{\{K, O\}, \{P, H, V\}\}$, $\{\{K, H\}, \{P, O, V\}\}$, $\{\{K, V\}, \{P, O, H\}\}$, $\{\{P, O\}, \{K, H, V\}\}$, $\{\{P, H\}, \{K, O, V\}\}$, $\{\{P, V\}, \{K, O, H\}\}$, $\{\{O, H\}, \{K, P, V\}\}$, $\{\{O, V\}, \{K, P, H\}\}$, $\{\{H, V\}, \{K, P, O\}\}$

Quiz

1. Using only the set of numerals $\{1, 2, 3, 4\}$, list the 3-sets, or combinations of 3 numerals, from this set.
   (ans: $\{1, 2, 3\}$, $\{1, 2, 4\}$, $\{1, 3, 4\}$, $\{2, 3, 4\}$)
2. For each of your combinations in Exercise 1, give a list of all the permutations of this 3-set.
   (ans:

123	124	134	234
132	142	143	243
213	214	314	324
231	241	341	342
312	412	413	423
321	421	431	432)

Exercises for Discussion

1. In four columns, list the set of all permutations of the 3 elements of each combination found in Problem 1 (page 455). How does your list of 24 permutations compare with that in Problem 2 (page 457)?
2. (a) List all possible combinations of two objects from the set $T = \{w, x, y, z\}$. $\{w, x\}, \{w, y\}, \{w, z\}, \{x, y\}, \{x, z\}, \{y, z\}$
   (b) List all possible permutations of two objects from T.
   wx, xw, wy, yw, wz, zw, xy, yx, xz, zx, yz, zy
3. Five students, Bob, Charles, Dick, Elsie, and Jane, are candidates for membership on a committee which will have three members.
   (a) Make a list of all possible committees.
   (b) Make a list of all possible committees which have Bob, Dick, and one of the girls as members. $\{B, D, E\}$, $\{B, D, J\}$
4. In a psychology experiment, a rat is placed at the entrance of a T maze, from which he runs either to the left, L, or the right, R. (See the figure.)
   LLL, LLR, LRL, LRR, RLL, RLR, RRL, RRR
   (a) Suppose that this experiment is performed 3 times. List the possible paths of the rat (for example, *LRL*, and so on).
   (b) If food is always placed at L, how many of these paths could the rat take to receive food at least 2 of the 3 times? 4
   (c) Suppose that the food is placed at L, R, and L, in turn, and answer the question in part (b). 4

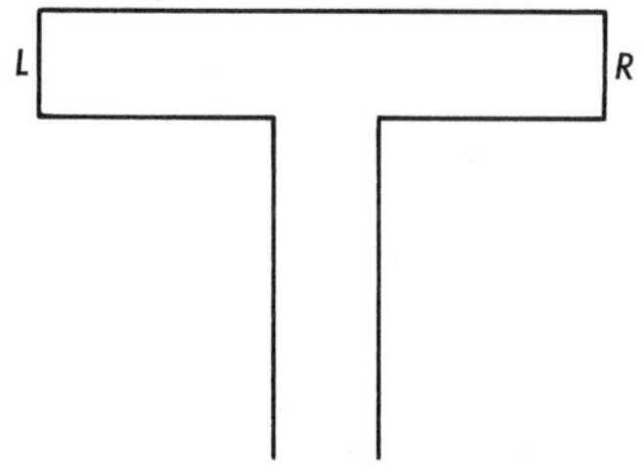

5. State whether each of the following lists is a list of combinations, a list of permutations, or a list of elements of neither type.
   (a) A list of all possible ways of placing 6 people in a line for a photograph Permutations
   (b) A list of all possible football teams formed from a squad of 25 men, each of whom is versatile enough to play any position Combinations
   (c) A list of all possible bridge hands Combinations
   (d) A list of all possible ways of placing 3 books on a shelf when 9 different books are available Permutations
   (e) A list of all possible selections of 3 books from a reading list containing 9 recommended books Combinations
   (f) A list of all possible ways in which 2 ordinary dice can land in 1 toss of the dice Neither
   (g) A list of all the three-digit numbers in which no digits are repeated Permutations
   (h) A list, from 10 contestants, of the winners of first, second, and third prizes Permutations
   (i) A list of all possible ways in which 3 boys and 5 girls may be seated in a row with both end seats occupied by boys Neither

Exercises

1. In this exercise, you are to form numbers with digits from the set {6, 7, 8, 9}. Repetition of digits is not allowed.
   (a) Make a list of all possible two-digit numbers.
   (b) Make a list of all possible even three-digit numbers.
   (c) Make a list of all possible even four-digit numbers in which even and odd digits alternate. 7698, 9678, 7896, 9876

2. Committees having 3 men each are to be formed from a list of 6 men denoted by *A*, *B*, *C*, *D*, *E*, and *F*.
   (a) Make a list of all possible committees.
   (b) Make a list of all possible committees, given that *A* agrees to serve only if *E* also serves.

3. Using the symbols *H* and *T* for heads and tails, respectively, make a list of all possible results of tossing a penny 3 times in succession.
   HHH, HHT, HTH, HTT, TTT, TTH, THT, THH

4. A one-act play has 2 parts for boys and 2 parts for girls. Make a list of all possible casts for the play, choosing members from the following set of applicants.

   {Alice, Bob, Charles, Diane, Elsie, Frank, George}

5. A four-faced die can be made by writing the numbers 1, 2, 3, and 4 on the faces of a regular tetrahedron. Two such dice are manufactured, one painted blue and the other yellow, and both are tossed once. The number read is that on the face which lands down.
   (a) Make a list of all possible ways in which the pair of dice can land, listing each way as an ordered pair of numbers.
   (b) Make a list of all possible ways in which the pair of dice can land with the sum of the numbers on the down faces less than 6.

6. State whether each of the lists you made in Exercises 1–5 is a list of combinations, a list of permutations, or a list of neither type.
   (1) Permutations (2) Combinations (3) Neither
   (4) Permutations (5) Neither

△

7. (a) Set $S = \{K, P, O, H, V\}$ is to be partitioned into two subsets. The first subset will contain two elements of *S*, and the second subset will contain the remaining three elements of *S*. For example, $\{\{K, O\}, \{P, H, V\}\}$ is one such partition. Make a list of all such partitions of *S*.
   (b) The element *V* is removed from the set *S*, and the remaining set of four elements is partitioned into two subsets, each containing two elements. Make a list of all such partitions.
   {K,P}, {O,H}; {K,O}, {P,H}; {K,H}, {P,O}

3. Use a tree diagram to obtain a list of all permutations of 3 numerals drawn from the set {1, 2, 3, 4} and compare it with your complete list in Exercise 2.

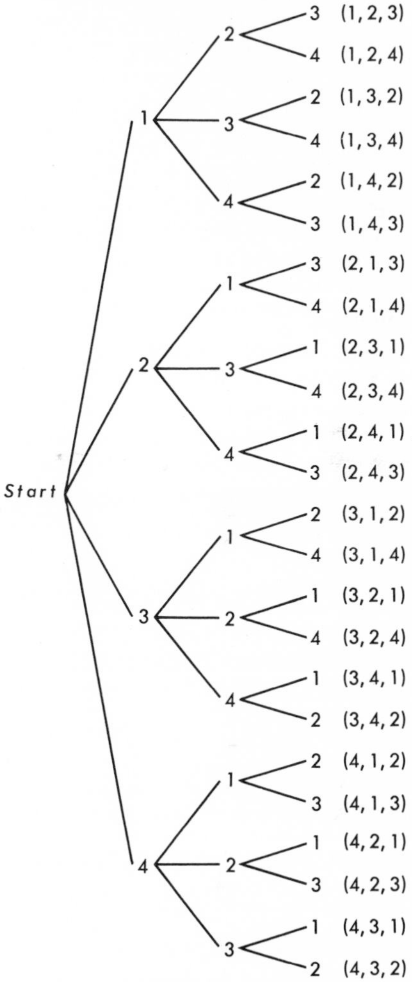

(ans: same list)

4. Do either of the lists in Exercises 2 and 3 contain all three-digit numbers which can be formed from the set of numerals

   {1, 2, 3, 4}?

   How many such numbers are there? (ans: no; 64)

11-4 FORMULAS FOR COUNTING PERMUTATIONS AND COMBINATIONS

Students tend to clutch at counting formulas instead of first analyzing the situation at hand, and thinking of a list. You may need to refer to Sections 11–1 and 11–2 constantly in order to make clear to the students the fundamental principles involved.

The student's success with the probability chapter will depend on his success with counting in these first four sections. Each exercise should be analyzed in class, and diagrams drawn whenever possible.

11-4 FORMULAS FOR COUNTING PERMUTATIONS AND COMBINATIONS

In the problems of the preceding section, we saw that the *number* of permutations of 3 objects from a set of 4 objects is 24, and the *number* of combinations of 3 objects from a set of 4 objects is 4. It is convenient to introduce symbols for such numbers. Thus, let

$_nP_r$ *denote the number of permutations of r objects from a set of n objects.*

$_nC_r$ *denote the number of combinations of r objects from a set of n objects.*

Using this notation, we know from the preceding section that $_4P_3 = 24$ and $_4C_3 = 4$. Other symbols commonly used are P^n_r and $P(n, r)$ instead of $_nP_r$; and C^n_r, $C(n, r)$, and $\binom{n}{r}$ in place of $_nC_r$.

Problem 1. Find $_nP_r$.

Solution. We are asked to find the number of permutations of r objects from a set consisting of n objects. We can imagine the r stages of a tree diagram that could be used to list all such permutations. There are n branches in the first stage; for each branch of the first stage, there are $n - 1$ branches in the second stage; for each branch of the second stage, there are $n - 2$ branches in the third stage; and so on. By the sequential counting principle, the total number of permutations of r objects from a set of n objects is

$$_nP_r = \overbrace{n \cdot (n - 1) \cdot (n - 2) \cdot \ldots}^{r \text{ factors}}$$

In the sequence that starts out

$$n, \quad n - 1, \quad n - 2, \quad n - 3, \quad n - 4, \ldots,$$

the second element is $n - 1$, the third is $n - 2$, and the fifth is $n - 4$. It follows that the rth element is $n - (r - 1)$, or $n - r + 1$. Thus, the number of permutations of r objects from a set of n objects is given by the following formula.

$$_nP_r = n(n - 1)(n - 2) \cdot \ldots \cdot (n - r + 1)$$

Remember that $_nP_r$ is represented as a product of r successive integers, the largest of which is n.

For example, ${}_5P_3$ is a product of 3 successive integers, the largest of which is 5, that is,

$${}_5P_3 = 5 \cdot 4 \cdot 3, \quad \text{or } 60.$$

Also,

$${}_{10}P_4 = 10 \cdot 9 \cdot 8 \cdot 7, \quad \text{or } 5040,$$

$${}_{52}P_{13} = 52 \cdot 51 \cdot 50 \cdot \ldots \cdot (52 - 13 + 1)$$

$$= \overbrace{52 \cdot 51 \cdot 50 \cdot \ldots \cdot 40}^{13 \text{ factors}}.$$

The formula for the number of permutations of n objects from a set of n objects is of particular interest. If we let $r = n$ in the formula above for ${}_nP_r$, then $n - r + 1 = n - n + 1$, or 1, and

$${}_nP_n = n \cdot (n - 1) \cdot (n - 2) \cdot \ldots \cdot 1.$$

In other words, ${}_nP_n$ is the *product of the first n positive integers.*

Before covering Problem 2, you may first wish to refer to Exercise for Discussion 1 on page 458. Here, ${}_4C_3 = 4$ and ${}_4P_3 = 24$. Furthermore, the 24 permutations were obtained by rearranging in ${}_3P_3$ ways each of the four combinations. It is recommended that another one or two numerical problems be done before you teach the general case. For example, you could compute ${}_6C_3$ and ${}_{10}C_4$, and so on.

Problem 2. Find ${}_5C_2$.

Solution. We can imagine the set of five objects to be $S = \{a, b, c, d, e\}$. Let us determine how ${}_5P_2$ and ${}_5C_2$ are related. The number of permutations of 2 objects from the set S is

$${}_5P_2 = 5 \cdot 4, \quad \text{or } 20.$$

Note that there are two permutations of each 2-subset of S; that is, the permutations of the 2-subset $\{b, e\}$ of S are (b, e) and (e, b). Since there are ${}_5C_2$ 2-subsets of S and since there are two permutations of each 2-subset, there are $2 \cdot {}_5C_2$ permutations of two objects from the set S, that is,

$$2 \cdot {}_5C_2 = {}_5P_2$$

and

$${}_5C_2 = \frac{{}_5P_2}{2} = \frac{20}{2}, \quad \text{or } 10.$$

Similarly, we may obtain a formula for ${}_nC_r$ from that for ${}_nP_r$ by performing a two-action procedure to count the number of permutations having r objects from a set of n objects. The first action is to select an r-subset from the set of n objects, and the second action is to form permutations of all r objects of the r-subset. There are ${}_nC_r$ r-subsets and ${}_rP_r$ permutations of the r-objects of each of these subsets. Hence, by the sequential counting principle there are

$${}_nC_r \cdot {}_rP_r$$

It should be emphasized that the formulas for ${}_nC_r$ and ${}_nP_r$ do not replace the necessity of first analyzing the problem to see what kinds of objects are being counted (Section 11–2). For example, the number of objects to be listed in Exercises for Discussion 5(f) and 5(i) on page 458 is not given by either of these formulas.

permutations of r objects from a set of n objects. Because we know that the above product is ${}_nP_r$, we have the following formula for the number of combinations of r objects from a set S consisting of n objects.

$$ {}_nC_r \cdot {}_rP_r = {}_nP_r, \quad or \quad {}_nC_r = \frac{{}_nP_r}{{}_rP_r} $$

For example,

$$ {}_4C_3 = \frac{{}_4P_3}{{}_3P_3} = \frac{4 \cdot 3 \cdot 2}{3 \cdot 2 \cdot 1}, \text{ or } 4. $$

There are 4 combinations of 3 objects from a set of 4 objects.

$$ {}_7C_4 = \frac{{}_7P_4}{{}_4P_4} = \frac{7 \cdot 6 \cdot 5 \cdot 4}{4 \cdot 3 \cdot 2 \cdot 1} = 7 \cdot 5, \text{ or } 35. $$

There are 35 combinations of 4 objects from a set of 7 objects.

Exercises for Discussion

1. Evaluate each of the following.

(a) ${}_{10}P_3$ $10 \cdot 9 \cdot 8 = 720$ (b) $\frac{{}_9P_4}{{}_4P_4}$ $\frac{9 \cdot 8 \cdot 7 \cdot 6}{4 \cdot 3 \cdot 2 \cdot 1} = 126$ (c) ${}_9C_4$ $\frac{{}_9P_4}{{}_4P_4} = 126$

2. In how many ways can 4 different books be arranged on a shelf? $4 \cdot 3 \cdot 2 \cdot 1 = 24$

3. From a group of 8 students, how many different committees of 4 students can be formed? ${}_8C_4 = \frac{8 \cdot 7 \cdot 6 \cdot 5}{4 \cdot 3 \cdot 2 \cdot 1} = 70$

4. If there is no repetition of letters, how many three-letter arrangements can be made from the letters in the word "cloudy"? ${}_6P_3 = 6 \cdot 5 \cdot 4 = 120$

5. Answer Exercise 4, allowing for repetition of letters. $6 \cdot 6 \cdot 6 = 216$

6. A panel consisting of 1 girl and 2 boys is to be elected from a slate consisting of 5 girls and 10 boys. How many different panels are possible? ${}_5C_1 \times {}_{10}C_2 = \frac{5}{1} \cdot \frac{10 \cdot 9}{2 \cdot 1} = 225$

7. (a) In how many ways can 7 people be lined up in one row for a photograph? ${}_7P_7 = 7 \cdot 6 \cdot 5 \cdot 4 \cdot 3 \cdot 2 \cdot 1 = 5040$

(b) In how many ways can the 7 people be lined up if one of them, say C, has to be in the middle? ${}_6P_6 = 6 \cdot 5 \cdot 4 \cdot 3 \cdot 2 \cdot 1 = 720$

(c) How many lineups of the 7 people have C in the middle and two other people, A and B, always taking the end positions? $2 \times {}_4P_4 = 2 \cdot 4 \cdot 3 \cdot 2 \cdot 1 = 48$

Exercises

1. Evaluate each of the following.
   (a) ${}_8P_3$ 336 (b) ${}_7P_7$ 5040 (c) ${}_{16}P_1$ 16
   (d) ${}_{20}C_{20}$ 1 (e) ${}_{16}C_1$ 16 (f) ${}_9C_5$ 126
2. How many four-digit numbers can be formed if repetition of digits is not allowed and if only the numerals shown in each exercise are used?
   (a) 1, 2, 3, 4? 24 (b) 0, 1, 2, 3? 18
3. Answer both parts of Exercise 2, allowing for repetition. (a) 256 (b) 192
4. How many committees of 4 people can be formed from a group of 10 people? 210
5. In how many ways can 6 different books be arranged on a shelf? 720
6. (a) How many different committees of 4 students can be formed from 8 students? 70
   (b) How many of these contain one particular student A? 35
   (c) How many committees include A and exclude B? 20
   (d) How many include both A and B? 15
   (e) How many exclude both A and B? 15
7. (a) Suppose that a penny is tossed 5 times and that the succession of results is represented by H's and T's. Determine how many different sequences of results of the 5 tosses are possible. 32
   (b) In how many of these sequences is a head showing on both the first and last toss? 8
8. A small class consists of 3 boys and 5 girls.
   (a) In how many ways can they all be seated in a row if both end seats are occupied by boys? 4320
   (b) In how many ways can a committee of 3 be chosen from the class? 56
   (c) How many of the committees in part (b) will contain 1 boy and 2 girls? 30
   (d) How many of the committees in part (b) will contain 3 boys? 1
   (e) How many of the committees in part (b) will contain 3 girls? 10
9. From a set of 10 different entries in a contest, 3 are to be chosen to receive first, second, and third prize. In how many ways can these prizes be awarded? 720
10. Out of a group of 10 boys and 7 girls, 3 boys and 2 girls are to be selected to represent a school. In how many ways can the selection be made? 2520
11. Given that ${}_nP_5 = 6720$, find ${}_nC_5$. 56
12. Given that ${}_nP_5 = 6({}_nP_3)$, find n. $n = 6$
13. John has 3 boxes, one red, one white, and one blue. He has 9 different objects. In how many ways can he put 3 objects in each box? (Hint: This is a three-stage counting process, involving one stage for each box and using combinations at each stage.) 10,080

Exercises

It is recommended that most of these exercises be discussed in class. Often the discovery of one's errors in making a miscount is even more instructive than performing the correct count. The students should first explain what sorts of objects they have in a list to be counted. Often writing down a few typical items of the list will suggest a procedure for making the count.

Quiz

1. Evaluate each of the following:
   (a) ${}_8P_4$ (ans: 1680)
   (b) ${}_8C_4$ (ans: 70)
   (c) ${}_5P_5$ (ans: 120)
   (d) ${}_5C_5$ (ans: 1)
2. How many panels of three students can be chosen from a group of six students? (ans: 20)
3. How many three-letter arrangements are possible using the letters of the word FORCE and not allowing repetitions? (ans: 60)

TWISTER

King Arthur sat at his Round Table on three successive nights with his knights—Basil, Cecil, Dudley, Edwin, Francis, and Galahad. On no occasion did anybody have as his neighbor someone who had sat next to him before. On the first evening, they sat in alphabetical order around the table. But afterwards, King Arthur arranged the next two sittings so that Basil was as near to him as possible while Galahad was as far away as possible. How did he seat the knights?

Solution: On the second evening, he arranged the knights and himself in the following order: A, F, B, D, G, E, C. On the third evening, they sat thus: A, E, B, G, C, F, D.

△

14. If the 3 boxes in Exercise 13 are colored red and are indistinguishable, then it makes no difference in which box John puts a particular set of 3 objects. In how many ways can he now put 3 of his 9 different objects in each box? 1680

15. One section of each of the eleventh grade English, algebra, and Latin courses will be meeting at 9 A.M., 11 A.M., and 1 P.M. In how many ways can a student arrange his schedule so that he can take these three courses? 6

16. At each of the times, 7, 7:30, 8, and 8:30 P.M., there are always three different half-hour programs on different channels: a Western, a mystery, and a musical show. No program scheduled on one channel ever appears on another channel.

(a) In how many ways can a person spend his evening hours from 7 to 9 P.M. if he watches television? 81

(b) In how many ways can he watch shows from 7 to 9 P.M. and never see a Western? 16

(c) In how many ways can he watch shows from 7 to 9 P.M. and see at least one Western? 65

(d) In how many ways can he watch shows from 7 to 9 P.M. and see nothing but Westerns? 1

17. In how many ways can 7 people line up if two of them, A and B, always stand next to each other? 1440

18. From a set of books consisting of 3 different novels and 5 different biographies, 2 novels and 3 biographies are selected.

(a) How many selections are there? 30

(b) In how many different ways can the books selected be lined up on a shelf? 120

▲

19. (a) Find the sum ${}_4C_4 + {}_4C_3 + {}_4C_2 + {}_4C_1$. 15

(b) Interpret the sum in part (a) in terms of counting the number of nonempty subsets of a set of 4 objects. See Solution Manual.

(c) Make a tree diagram to check your answer to part (b), using the set $\{a, b, c, d\}$. Use four branching stages, one for each element, writing a if a is to be a member of the subset, and writing $\bar{a}$ if a is not to be a member, and so on. See Solution Manual.

20. The circular disc shown at the right is to be pinned through its center to a board and spun around this center pin. The numbers 1, 2, 3, 4 are to be assigned to the four points marked with crosses. In how many ways can this be done? (Hint: The assignments (1, 2, 3, 4) and (2, 3, 4, 1) produce the same effect when the disc is spun.) 6

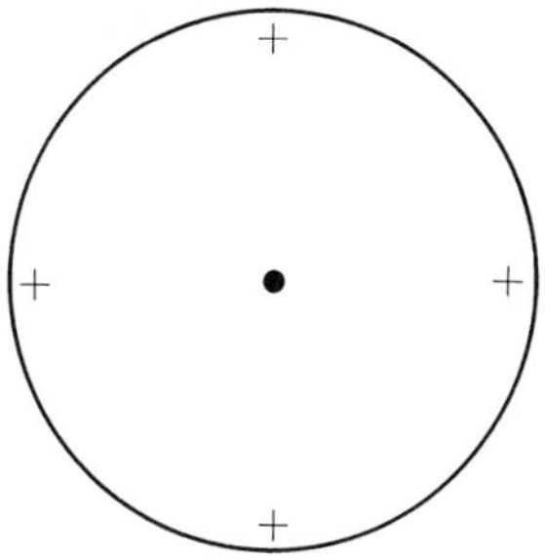

21. Consider that the *rim* of the disc in Exercise 20 represents a bracelet that has no clasp, and the points marked with crosses indicate the position of 4 round beads of different colors. How many possible bracelets are there? (Hint: Remember to turn the bracelet over.) 3

22. In how many arrangements can 6 people be seated in 6 chairs placed at a round table

(a) if one particular position is designated as head of the table? 720

(b) without the restriction in part (a)? 120

11-5 FACTORIALS

The formulas for ${}_nP_r$ and ${}_nC_r$ may be written in a simpler way if we use the notation of factorials.

> ***THE NOTATION OF FACTORIALS***
>
> ***For each positive integer n, the product of the first n positive integers is called n factorial and is denoted by n!.***
>
> $$n! = n(n-1)(n-2)\cdot \ldots \cdot 2\cdot 1$$

For example,

$$1! = 1,$$
$$2! = 2\cdot 1, \quad \text{or } 2,$$
$$3! = 3\cdot 2\cdot 1, \quad \text{or } 6,$$
$$6! = 6\cdot 5\cdot 4\cdot 3\cdot 2\cdot 1, \quad \text{or } 720.$$

The factorial numbers grow large very rapidly as we extend this list. For example,

$$10! = 3{,}628{,}800.$$

11-5 FACTORIALS

The material of this section can be read easily by the student. If possible, you could bring to class a table of factorials and log factorials. Students are impressed by the way these numbers rapidly increase.

If we know the value of the factorial of an integer, we can quickly compute the value of the factorial of the next integer. For example,

$$\begin{aligned} 7! &= 7 \cdot 6 \cdot 5 \cdot 4 \cdot 3 \cdot 2 \cdot 1 \\ &= 7 \cdot 6! \\ &= 7 \cdot 720, \quad \text{or } 5040. \end{aligned}$$

In other words,

$$(n + 1)! = (n + 1) \cdot n!$$

for every positive integer n.

The formula for ${}_nP_r$ can be expressed in factorials. We recall that

$${}_nP_n = n!,$$

but if $r < n$, then

$${}_nP_r = n(n - 1)(n - 2) \cdot \ldots \cdot (n - r + 1),$$

$${}_nP_r = \frac{n(n - 1)(n - 2) \cdot \ldots \cdot 2 \cdot 1}{(n - r)(n - r - 1) \cdot \ldots \cdot 2 \cdot 1},$$

$${}_nP_r = \frac{n!}{(n - r)!}.$$

In order to obtain the second equation for ${}_nP_r$, the first equation should be multiplied by

$$\frac{n - r!}{n - r!}.$$

For example,

$${}_7P_2 = \frac{7!}{5!} = 42.$$

In evaluating ${}_7P_2$, we do not compute 7! and 5! and then divide 7! by 5!. Instead, we proceed in the following way.

$$\frac{7!}{5!} = \frac{7 \cdot 6 \cdot 5 \cdot 4 \cdot 3 \cdot 2 \cdot 1}{5 \cdot 4 \cdot 3 \cdot 2 \cdot 1}$$

$$\frac{7!}{5!} = 7 \cdot 6$$

In general,

$${}_nP_r = \frac{n!}{(n - r)!} = n(n - 1) \cdot \ldots \cdot (n - r + 1).$$

The formula

$${}_nP_r = \frac{n!}{(n - r)!}$$

is valid as long as $r < n$. If we let $r = n$ in this formula, we obtain the equation

$$_nP_n = \frac{n!}{(n-n)!}, \quad \text{or } _nP_n = \frac{n!}{0!}.$$

We can define 0! so that the equation above is true. Since $_nP_n = n!$, we define

$$0! = 1.$$

The definition $0! = 1$ is in the same category as the definition of negative and zero exponents; that is, they are a matter of convenience. Of course 0! has no meaning in terms of the definition of $n!$ for n a positive integer.

With 0! defined in this way, the formula

$$_nP_r = \frac{n!}{(n-r)!}$$

is true for every pair n, r of positive integers, provided that $r \leqq n$.

We can also find a formula in terms of factorials for the number of combinations of r objects from a set of n objects. From the preceding section,

$$_nC_r = \frac{_nP_r}{_rP_r}.$$

Hence,

$$_nC_r = \frac{n!/(n-r)!}{r!},$$

or

$$_nC_r = \frac{n!}{r!(n-r)!}.$$

This is called the *symmetric form* of the formula for $_nC_r$. It is valid for every pair r, n of positive integers when $r \leqq n$. For example,

$$_7C_2 = \frac{7!}{2!5!}.$$

Thus,

$$_7C_2 = \frac{7 \cdot 6}{2 \cdot 1}, \quad \text{or } 21.$$

The equation $_nC_r = {_nC_{n-r}}$ is verified by using the symmetric form of the formula for $_nC_r$.

$$_nC_r = \frac{n!}{r!(n-r)!}$$

$$_nC_{n-r} = \frac{n!}{(n-r)!(n-(n-r))!}, \quad \text{or } \frac{n!}{(n-r)!r!}$$

Hence, $_nC_r = {_nC_{n-r}}$. Thus, $_{90}C_{88} = {_{90}C_2}$, or 4005.

For convenience, we *define* ${}_nC_0$ to be equal to ${}_nC_n$. Since ${}_nC_n = 1$, we have

$$ {}_nC_0 = 1 $$

by definition. Therefore, the formula

$$ {}_nC_r = {}_nC_{n-r} $$

is true for every positive integer n and every non-negative integer r with $r \leqq n$.

Exercises for Discussion

1. Evaluate each of the following.

(a) $\dfrac{6!}{2!3!}$ $\dfrac{6\cdot5\cdot4}{2\cdot1} = 60$ (b) $\dfrac{8!}{7!}$ 8

(c) ${}_{1000}C_0$ 1 (d) ${}_{1000}C_{999}$ 1000

2. Simplify each of the following.

(a) $\dfrac{(n+3)!}{n!}$ $(n+3)(n+2)(n+1)$ (b) $(n-r-2)!(n-r-1)(n-r)$ $(n-r)!$

3. Given that ${}_nC_7 = {}_nC_5$, find the value of ${}_nC_9$.

4. Show that ${}_nC_{r-1} + {}_nC_r = {}_{n+1}C_r$.

5. Show that

$$ \frac{1}{n!} + \frac{1}{(n+1)!} = \frac{n+2}{(n+1)!}. $$

Exercises

1. Evaluate each of the following.

(a) $\dfrac{300!262!}{260!302!}$ $\dfrac{34191}{45451}$ (b) $8! - 7!$ 35,280 (c) ${}_8C_6 \cdot {}_6C_4 \cdot {}_4C_2 \cdot {}_2C_2$ 2520

2. Simplify each of the following.

(a) $\dfrac{(n-2)!}{n!}$ $\dfrac{1}{(n-1)n}$ (b) ${}_nC_{n-2}$ $\dfrac{n(n-1)}{2}$ (c) $\dfrac{(2n)!}{n!}$ $2^n(2n-1)(2n-3)\ldots 5\cdot3\cdot1$

3. Given that ${}_nC_{12} = {}_nC_8$, find ${}_nC_{17}$ and ${}_{22}C_n$. 1140; 231

4. Given the following, find n.

$$ \frac{n!}{(n-3)!} = 210 \quad n = 7 $$

Answers to Exercises for Discussion 3–5

3. ${}_nC_7 = {}_nC_{n-7} = {}_nC_5$. Therefore, $n - 7 = 5$ and $n = 12$,

$$ {}_nC_9 = {}_{12}C_9 = 220 $$

4.
$$ \begin{aligned} {}_nC_r + {}_nC_{r-1} &= \frac{n!}{r!(n-r)!} + \frac{n!}{(r-1)![n-(r-1)]!} \\ &= \frac{n!(n+1-r) + n!(r)}{[(n+1)-r]!r!} \\ &= \frac{(n+1)!}{[(n+1)-r]!r!} \\ &= {}_{n+1}C_r \end{aligned} $$

5.
$$ \begin{aligned} \frac{1}{n!} + \frac{1}{(n+1)!} &= \left(\frac{1}{n!}\right)\cdot\left(\frac{n+1}{n+1}\right) + \frac{1}{(n+1)!} \\ &= \frac{n+1}{(n+1)!} + \frac{1}{(n+1)!} \\ &= \frac{(n+1)+1}{(n+1)!} \\ &= \frac{n+2}{(n+1)!} \end{aligned} $$

5. In how many ways can 8 different novels be arranged on a shelf? 40,320
6. From the set {1, 2, 3, 4, 5, 6}, in how many ways can one choose two numbers whose sum is even? 6
7. In how many ways can 5 students,

George, John, Charles, Mary, Joanne,

stand in a line in which boys and girls alternate? 12
8. Answer the question in Exercise 7 for 6 students, supposing that another girl, Ruth, joins the group. 72

9. In how many ways can 8 different keys be put on a key ring which is made so that the keys slide around the complete ring? 2520
10. Remembering that a number is divisible by 9 only if the sum of its digits is divisible by 9, and given that repetition of digits is allowed, how many three-digit numbers, each divisible by 9, can be formed if only the numbers 0, 1, 3, 6, 8, 9 are used? 26
11. Given n points in a plane, no three of which are collinear, how many lines can be drawn joining the points in pairs? $\frac{n(n-1)}{2}$
12. Derive the formula

$$_nC_r = {_nC_{n-r}}$$

See Solution Manual.

by considering the lists of objects for which each side of the equality provides the count.

11-6 THE BINOMIAL THEOREM

In this section, we shall show how our counting techniques can be used to derive an important formula of algebra. This formula is used to raise a binomial, such as $x + y$, to a positive integral power. For example, we may check by multiplication that each of the following formulas is true.

$$(x + y)^2 = x^2 + 2xy + y^2$$
$$(x + y)^3 = x^3 + 3x^2y + 3xy^2 + y^3$$
$$(x + y)^4 = x^4 + 4x^3y + 6x^2y^2 + 4xy^3 + y^4$$
$$(x + y)^5 = x^5 + 5x^4y + 10x^3y^2 + 10x^2y^3 + 5xy^4 + y^5$$

Quiz

1. Evaluate each of the following:
(a) 6! (ans: 720)
(b) $\frac{6!}{3!}$ (ans: 120)
(c) 6! − 3! (ans: 714)
2. Find a common denominator for the fractions and write their sum as a quotient of the form

$$\frac{n!}{r!(n-r)!} = {_nC_r}$$

without evaluating the factorials:

$$\frac{6!}{2!4!} + \frac{6!}{3!3!} \quad \left(\text{ans: } \frac{7!}{3!4!}\right)$$

11-6 THE BINOMIAL THEOREM

Students may have become so used to combining middle terms in $(x + y)^2$ that they do not think of the distributive law as operating in this multiplication. You may find it helpful to go through the details of writing

$$(x + y)(x + y) = x(x + y) + y(x + y) = x^2 + xy + yx + y^2.$$

The students should see that this is the same result as that obtained by selecting, in turn, each possible term of the first factor $(x + y)$ to multiply by each possible term of the second factor $(x + y)$.

In the same manner, $(x + y)^3$ and $(x + y)^4$ may be obtained. (Presumably, the students checking formulas at the bottom of the previous page did not use this method, but instead found $(x + y)^3$ as $(x^2 + 2xy + y^2)(x + y)$ and $(x + y)^4$ as $(x^2 + 2xy + y^2)(x^2 + 2xy + y^2)$.)

The coefficients of the various terms appearing on the right side of each equation above are called *binomial coefficients*. Thus, the last equation has binomial coefficients

$$1, \quad 5, \quad 10, \quad 10, \quad 5, \quad 1,$$

in that order. Note the symmetric way in which the numbers appear in this 6-tuple.

For each positive integer n,

$$(x + y)^n = \overbrace{(x + y) \cdot (x + y) \cdot \ldots \cdot (x + y)}^{n \text{ factors}}.$$

Using the distributive law, we can multiply out the right side of this equation in the following way. First, select an x or y from each of the n binomial factors and multiply the n chosen quantities together. Then make another selection of an x or a y from each of the n binomial factors and multiply them together, and continue this process until you have made your selections in every possible way. Finally, add together all the products so formed. The result will be a formula for $(x + y)^n$.

The tree diagram of Fig. 11–4 illustrates the above procedure for finding $(x + y)^2$. Hence,

$$(x + y)^2 = x^2 + 2xy + y^2.$$

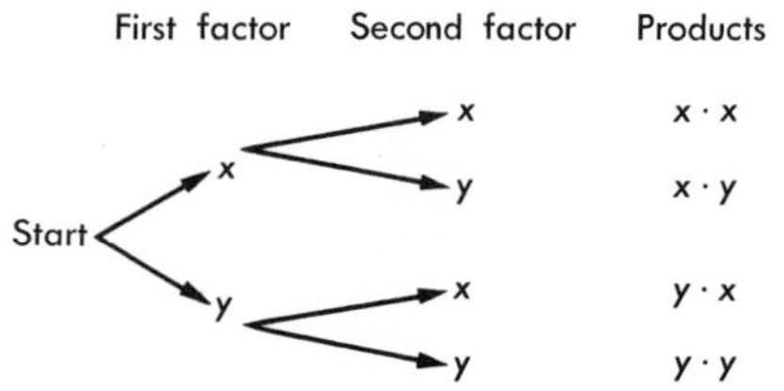

$(x+y)^2 = (x+y)(x+y) = x^2+2xy+y^2$

FIGURE 11–4

We find $(x + y)^3$ in a similar way, as shown by the tree diagram in Fig. 11–5.

The products occurring in the last column of Fig. 11–5 are of four different types:

$$x^3, \quad x^2y, \quad xy^2, \quad y^3.$$

Hence, the expanded form of $(x + y)^3$ is a sum of terms of these types; the number of terms of each type is the coefficient of the term in the

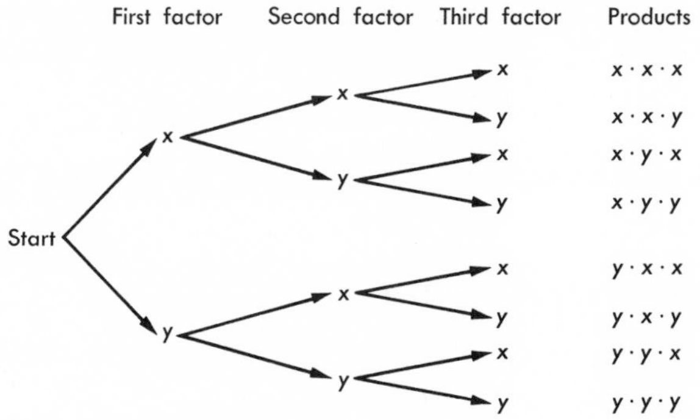

$$(x+y)^3 = (x+y)(x+y)(x+y)$$
$$= xxx+xxy+xyx+xyy+yxx+yxy+yyx+yyy$$
$$= x^3+3x^2y+3xy^2+y^3$$

FIGURE 11-5

sum. A method of finding the binomial coefficients of the expanded form of $(x + y)^3$ without the aid of a tree diagram is indicated in the table. In this table and throughout the rest of the chapter, we shall use the symbol

$$\binom{n}{r} \text{ instead of } {}_nC_r.$$

We recall that by definition, ${}_nC_0 = 1$. Hence, by definition, $\binom{n}{0} = 1$.

$(x + y)(x + y)(x + y)$		
Type of term	Procedure	Number of ways
x^3	Select x from every factor, y from no factor.	1, or $\binom{3}{0}$
x^2y	Select y from exactly one factor.	$\binom{3}{1}$
xy^2	Select y from exactly two factors.	$\binom{3}{2}$
y^3	Select y from every factor.	$\binom{3}{3}$

According to the above table,

$$(x + y)^3 = \binom{3}{0}x^3 + \binom{3}{1}x^2y + \binom{3}{2}xy^2 + \binom{3}{3}y^3.$$

This result agrees with our previous formula for $(x + y)^3$, since

$$\binom{3}{0} = 1, \qquad \binom{3}{1} = \frac{3}{1}, \text{ or } 3,$$

$$\binom{3}{2} = \frac{3 \cdot 2}{2 \cdot 1}, \text{ or } 3, \qquad \binom{3}{3} = \frac{3 \cdot 2 \cdot 1}{3 \cdot 2 \cdot 1}, \text{ or } 1.$$

Students may ask why $\binom{3}{2}$ or ${}_3C_2$, and not ${}_3P_2$, count the number of ways of selecting y from exactly two factors. These $\binom{3}{2} = 3$ ways may be listed as {1st, 2nd}, {1st, 3rd}, {2nd, 3rd}. The list which ${}_3P_2 = 6$ would count is a list such as (1, 2), (2, 1), (1, 3), (3, 1), (2, 3), (3, 2), which is clearly inappropriate.

The proof of the binomial theorem is no more difficult than that for the special case $(x + y)^3$ but there seems to be little advantage in having the student involve himself in the extra notation of the general case. You may want to try it in class, after asking first for the terms with y, with y^2, then with y^k, and so on.

The pattern for the expansion of

$$(x + y)^n$$

is suggested by this example. We state it in the form of a theorem.

THE BINOMIAL THEOREM

For every pair x, y of real numbers and every positive integer n,

$$(x + y)^n =$$

$$\binom{n}{0} x^n + \binom{n}{1} x^{n-1}y + \binom{n}{2} x^{n-2}y^2 + \cdots + \binom{n}{k} x^{n-k}y^k + \cdots + \binom{n}{n-2} x^2y^{n-2} + \binom{n}{n-1} xy^{n-1} + \binom{n}{n} y^n.$$

The expansion above for $(x + y)^n$ is easy to remember if we keep in mind the succession of terms. Each term has the form

$$\binom{n}{k} x^{n-k}y^k.$$

To obtain all the terms, we let k assume the successive values 0, 1, 2, . . . , n. Note that the sum of the degrees of x and y in each term is n since $(n - k) + k = n$.

Problem 1. Expand

$$(2a + 3b)^3$$

by the binomial theorem and simplify the terms of the expansion.

Solution. The expressions $2a$ and $3b$ can be substituted for x and y in the formula for the binomial expansion. We have

$$\begin{aligned}(2a + 3b)^3 &= \binom{3}{0}(2a)^3 + \binom{3}{1}(2a)^2(3b) + \binom{3}{2}(2a)(3b)^2 + \binom{3}{3}(3b)^3 \\ &= 1(8a^3) + 3(4a^2)(3b) + 3(2a)(9b^2) + 1(27b^3) \\ &= 8a^3 + 36a^2b + 54ab^2 + 27b^3.\end{aligned}$$

Problem 2. Expand $(3c^2 - d)^4$ and simplify.

Solution. We write $3c^2 - d$ as $3c^2 + {}^-d$ so that $3c^2$ can be the x of the formula and ${}^-d$ can be the y. Then

$$\begin{aligned}(3c^2 - d)^4 &= \binom{4}{0}(3c^2)^4 + \binom{4}{1}(3c^2)^3({}^-d) + \binom{4}{2}(3c^2)^2({}^-d)^2 \\ &\quad + \binom{4}{3}(3c^2)({}^-d)^3 + \binom{4}{4}({}^-d)^4 \\ &= 1(81c^8) + 4(27c^6)({}^-d) + 6(9c^4)(d^2) \\ &\quad + 4(3c^2)({}^-d^3) + 1(d^4) \\ &= 81c^8 - 108c^6d + 54c^4d^2 - 12c^2d^3 + d^4.\end{aligned}$$

Exercises for Discussion

In Exercises 1–3, use the binomial theorem to expand each expression, and then simplify.

1. $(x + y)^6$ 2. $(3x - 2y)^3$ 3. $(1 + .01)^4$

4. In the simplification of the expansion of $(2a - b)^8$, the exponent of b in a particular term is 3.
   (a) Is this term the third or fourth in the expansion? Fourth
   (b) What is the complete term including its sign? $^-1792\, a^5b^3$
   (c) Write the complete term of the expansion which has 6 as the exponent of b. $\binom{8}{6}(2a)^2(-b)^6 = 112a^2b^6$

Exercises

In Exercises 1–6, use the binomial theorem to expand each expression, and then simplify. 1-4 See Solution Manual.

1. $(x - y)^8$ 2. $(a + b)^7$ 3. $(p - q)^5$
4. $(1 + x)^5$ 5. $(1 - .02)^3$ .941192 6. $(1 + x^2)^3$ $1+3x^2+3x^4+x^6$

7. Without writing out the entire expansion in any of the following cases, find the specified terms in their simplest forms.
   (a) The fifth term of the expansion of $(7x - 2y)^6$ $11{,}760x^2y^4$
   (b) The third term of the expansion of $(2c + \frac{1}{2}d)^7$ $168c^5d^2$
   (c) The term in the expansion of

$$\left(x - \frac{1}{x}\right)^8$$

   which does not contain an x 70

Exercises for Discussion

If time is limited, it is suggested that at least Exercise for Discussion 4 be covered.

Answers to Exercises for Discussion 1–3

1. $x^6 + 6x^5y + 15x^4y^2 + 20x^3y^3 + 15x^2y^4 + 6xy^5 + y^6$
2. $27x^3 - 54x^2y + 36xy^2 - 8y^3$
3. $1 + 4(.01) + 6(.01)^2 + 4(.01)^3 + (.01)^4 = 1.04060401$

The form of the binomial expansion in Exercise 10 could be used for an introduction to the case of n not a positive integer and its use to approximate numbers such as $\sqrt{1.02}$, $\sqrt[3]{7.5}$, and so on, although Exercise 11 uses only the positive integral case.

Quiz

Use the binomial theorem to expand each expression, and then simplify:

1. $(a + b)^4$ (ans: $a^4 + 4a^3b + 6a^2b^2 + 4ab^3 + b^4$)
2. $(2x - 3y)^3$ (ans: $8x^3 - 36x^2y + 54xy^2 - 27y^3$)
3. $(1 + x^2)^5$ (ans: $1 + 5x^2 + 10x^4 + 10x^6 + 5x^8 + x^{10}$)

11-7 PASCAL'S TRIANGLE

This section could be assigned as independent reading, but Exercise for Discussion 1 is worth a few minutes of class time in order to verbalize this equality for application to Pascal's triangle.

8. (a) Write the term in the expansion of

$$\left(\frac{1}{x^2} - 2x^2\right)^6$$

which does not contain an x. $^{-}160$

(b) Write the two middle terms in the expansion of

$$\left(\frac{2}{3}a - \frac{3}{2}b\right)^7. \quad \frac{-70}{3}a^4b^3;\ \frac{105}{2}a^3b^4$$

9. Write and simplify each of the following. $x^7\sqrt{x} + 10x^6 + 40x^4\sqrt{x}$

(a) The first three terms in the expansion of $(x\sqrt{x} + 2)^5$

(b) The first five terms in the expansion of $(3 - 2\sqrt{x})^7$

$2187 - 10{,}206\sqrt{x} + 20{,}412x - 22{,}680x\sqrt{x} + 15{,}120x^2$

△

10. (a) Show that the first four terms of the binomial expansion can be written in the form See Solution Manual.

$$(x + y)^n = x^n + \frac{n}{1}x^{n-1}y + \frac{n(n-1)}{1\cdot 2}x^{n-2}y^2 + \frac{n(n-1)(n-2)}{1\cdot 2\cdot 3}x^{n-3}y^3 + \cdots$$

(b) Write the next two terms of the expansion begun in part (a).

11. (a) Use the first three terms of the binomial expansion of $(1 - .01)^5$ to find an approximation of $(.99)^5$. .951

(b) Compute an approximation of $(1.04)^6$. 1.26528

(c) Check your approximations in parts (a) and (b) by using logarithms. .9506; 1.265

11-7 PASCAL'S TRIANGLE

We are now in a position to explain the symmetry noted in the set of binomial coefficients of the expansion of $(x + y)^n$. In this expansion, the coefficients, in the order in which they appear in the binomial theorem, are

$$\binom{n}{0}, \binom{n}{1}, \binom{n}{2}, \binom{n}{3}, \ldots, \binom{n}{n-3}, \binom{n}{n-2}, \binom{n}{n-1}, \binom{n}{n}.$$

The first coefficient is equal to the last; the second is equal to the next to the last; the third is equal to the third from the last; and so on. Remember that

$$\binom{n}{k} = \binom{n}{n-k}$$

for every value of k, with $0 \leq k \leq n$.

The symmetry of the binomial coefficients is often displayed in the form given below.

$$
\begin{array}{ll}
(x+y)^1 & \binom{1}{0} \quad \binom{1}{1} \\
(x+y)^2 & \binom{2}{0} \quad \binom{2}{1} \quad \binom{2}{2} \\
(x+y)^3 & \binom{3}{0} \quad \binom{3}{1} \quad \binom{3}{2} \quad \binom{3}{3} \\
(x+y)^4 & \binom{4}{0} \quad \binom{4}{1} \quad \binom{4}{2} \quad \binom{4}{3} \quad \binom{4}{4} \\
(x+y)^5 & \binom{5}{0} \quad \binom{5}{1} \quad \binom{5}{2} \quad \binom{5}{3} \quad \binom{5}{4} \quad \binom{5}{5}
\end{array}
$$

If we enter the value of each combination symbol in the array above and place a 1 at the top of the array, we obtain the triangular array started below. This infinite triangular array of numbers is called *Pascal's triangle* in honor of the French mathematician and philosopher Blaise Pascal (1623–1662).

$$
\begin{array}{c}
1 \\
1 \quad 1 \\
1 \quad 2 \quad 1 \\
1 \quad 3 \quad 3 \quad 1 \\
1 \quad 4 \quad 6 \quad 4 \quad 1 \\
1 \quad 5 \quad 10 \quad 10 \quad 5 \quad 1 \\
- \quad - \quad - \quad - \quad - \quad - \quad -
\end{array}
$$

If you look at the simplified form of the binomial expansions in Problems 1 and 2 on pages 472 and 473, you will see that the simplified coefficients do not exhibit the symmetry of Pascal's triangle of binomial coefficients. In Problem 1, for example, the coefficients of this expansion lack symmetry because the coefficients 2 and 3 of the expressions $2a$ and $3b$ appear in the expansion in various powers.

Exercises for Discussion

1. By evaluating each of the binomial symbols, show that the equation

$$\binom{n+1}{r} = \binom{n}{r-1} + \binom{n}{r}$$

is true for every integer $n > 1$ and every integer r, with $1 \leqq r \leqq n$.

2. Use the results of Exercise 1 to extend the triangle in the text to include the row of coefficients for $(x+y)^8$.

Exercises for Discussion

Exercise for Discussion 1 contains the well-known trick for writing the next row in Pascal's triangle. Thus, if one is down to

1 5 10 10 5 1

one then writes

1 6 15 20 15 6 1

Answers to Exercises for Discussion 1, 2

1. $\binom{n}{r-1} + \binom{n}{r}$

$$= \frac{n(n-1)\cdots(n-r+2)}{1\cdot 2\cdot 3\cdots(r-1)} + \frac{n(n-1)\cdots(n-r+1)}{1\cdot 2\cdot 3\cdots r}$$

$$= \frac{[n(n-1)\cdots(n-r+2)] \times [r+(n-r+1)]}{1\cdot 2\cdot 3\cdots(r-1)r}$$

$$= \frac{(n+1)(n)(n-1)\cdots(n-r+2)}{1\cdot 2\cdot 3\cdots r}$$

$$= \binom{n+1}{r}$$

2. 1 6 15 20 15 6 1
1 7 21 35 35 21 7 1
1 8 28 56 70 56 28 8 1

Answer to Exercises 2, 4(c)

2. $x^5 - 10x^4y + 40x^3y^2 - 80x^2y^3 + 80xy^4 - 32y^5$

4. (c) $\{a\}$ $2^1 - 1 = 1$
$\{a\}, \{b\}, \{a, b\}$ $2^2 - 1 = 3$
$\{a\}, \{b\}, \{c\}, \{a, b\}, \{a, c\}, \{b, c\}, \{a, b, c\}$ $2^3 - 1 = 7$
$\{a\}, \{b\}, \{c\}, \{d\}, \{a, b\}, \{a, c\}, \{a, d\}, \{b, c\}, \{b, d\}, \{c, d\}, \{a, b, c\}, \{a, b, d\}, \{a, c, d\}, \{b, c, d\}$
$\{a, b, c, d\}$ $2^4 - 1 = 15$

Quiz

Write Pascal's triangle including the row of coefficients for $(x + y)^6$ and use this to obtain the binomial expansion of each of the following:

1. $(2a - 3b)^3$ (ans: $8a^3 - 36a^2b + 54ab^2 - 27b^3$)
2. $(1 + 2x)^6$ (ans: $1 + 12x + 60x^2 + 160x^3 + 240x^4 + 192x^5 + 64x^6$)

Exercises

1. Use Pascal's triangle to obtain the binomial expansion of $(2a + 3b)^4$. Simplify the resulting expression. $16a^4 + 96a^3b + 216a^2b^2 + 216ab^3 + 81b^4$
2. Obtain the binomial expansion of $(x - 2y)^5$ and simplify.
3. Given a principal of \$100 invested at compound interest at the yearly rate of 4%, with interest compounded quarterly, use the binomial theorem to find the amount of money in the account at the end of 2 years. (Hint: At the end of the first quarter-year, the amount is $100(1 + .01)$; after the second quarter-year, it is $100(1 + .01)^2$; and so on.)
\$108.29

△

4. (a) Use the binomial expansion of $(1 + 1)^n$ to show that if n is a positive integer, then See Solution Manual.

$$2^n = \binom{n}{0} + \binom{n}{1} + \binom{n}{2} + \cdots + \binom{n}{n}.$$

(b) Since $\binom{n}{0} = 1$, the expression See Solution Manual.

$$\binom{n}{1} + \binom{n}{2} + \binom{n}{3} + \cdots + \binom{n}{n} = 2^n - 1$$

is equivalent to the equation in part (a). Explain how the second equation above gives a formula for the total number of nonempty subsets of a set of n objects.

(c) Test the formula of part (b) by listing the nonempty subsets of each of the following sets: $\{a\}$, $\{a, b\}$, $\{a, b, c\}$, and $\{a, b, c, d\}$.

5. (a) Use the binomial theorem to expand $(1 - 1)^n$ to show that
See Solution Manual.

$$\binom{n}{0} - \binom{n}{1} + \binom{n}{2} - \binom{n}{3} + \cdots (^-1)^n \binom{n}{n} = 0.$$

(b) Test the formula in part (a) for several rows of Pascal's triangle.
$1 - 1 = 0$; $1 - 2 + 1 = 0$; $1 - 3 + 3 - 1 = 0$; $1 - 4 + 6 - 4 + 1 = 0$; $1 - 5 + 10 - 10 + 5 - 1 = 0$; ...

▲

6. In the expansion of the trinomial $(x + y + z)^5$, we obtain a sum of terms. Each term is formed by selecting any one of the symbols x, y, or z from each of the five factors and then forming their product. For example, $xxyzz$ and $zyxxz$ are terms of the expansion, each of which is equal to the expression x^2yz^2.
(a) How many terms of the form x^2yz^2 occur in the expansion? 30
(b) What is the coefficient of the term xy^3z in the expansion? 20
7. Collect like terms and write the complete expansion of $(a + b + c)^3$.
$a^3 + b^3 + c^3 + 3a^2b + 3a^2c + 3ab^2 + 3ac^2 + 3b^2c + 3bc^2 + 6abc$

KEY IDEAS AND KEY WORDS

There are two fundamental counting principles.

Sequential counting principle

Given that two or more actions are performed in a definite order, that the first action produces m possible results, and that for each of these results, the second action produces n possible results, and that for each of these results, the third action produces p results, and so on, then the number of possible results of this sequence of actions is the product of the numbers m, n, p, and so on.

Alternative cases principle

If an action can be analyzed into several mutually exclusive cases, say into cases 1, 2, 3, and so on, and if there are m possible results of performing the action in case 1, n possible results of performing the action in case 2, p possible results of performing the action in case 3, and so on, then the total number of possible results of the action is the sum of the numbers m, n, p, and so on.

A subset T of a set S with n elements is called an **r-subset** of S if T contains r elements. Subset T is also called a **combination** of r-objects from a set of n objects. The symbols

$$_nC_r \quad \text{and} \quad \binom{n}{r}$$

are used to denote the **number of combinations** of r objects from a set of n objects.

A **permutation** of r objects from a set S of n objects is an arrangement without repetition of r objects from S. The symbol $_nP_r$ denotes the **number of permutations** of r objects from a set of n objects.

If we use the **factorial notation**

$$n! = n(n-1)(n-2)\cdot \ldots \cdot 2 \cdot 1,$$

we can obtain the following formulas.

$$_nP_r = n(n-1)(n-2)\cdot \ldots \cdot (n-r+1) = \frac{n!}{(n-r)!}$$

$$_nC_r = \frac{_nP_r}{_rP_r} = \frac{n!}{r!(n-r)!}$$

$$_nC_r = {_nC_{n-r}}$$

The **binomial theorem** states that the equation

$$(x+y)^n = \binom{n}{0}x^n + \binom{n}{1}x^{n-1}y + \cdots + \binom{n}{k}x^{n-k}y^k + \cdots + \binom{n}{n}y^n$$

is true for all real numbers x and y and every positive integer n.

TWISTER

Anne, Beth, Carol, Debbie, Elaine, and Faith are at their monthly card game. The game they play requires partners, and, as they are seated at a round table, each girl pairs with the girl next to her. In this way, Anne and Beth, Carol and Debbie, and Elaine and Faith are partners for the first game. However, with each new game, they must have a different partner. They decide that they can play five games without playing twice with the same partner. How should they move around the table and which girls should move, so that the fewest possible moves are made for these five games, assuming that Elaine refuses to move at all?

Solution: For the first two games it is not necessary for anyone to move. After the second game, Anne and Debbie change places and so do Beth and Faith. They can then play two more games without moving. For the fifth game, Anne and Faith change and also Beth and Carol.

Answers to Chapter Review Problems 13–24

13. $8x^3 + 60x^2y + 150xy^2 + 125y^3$
14. $1 - 4x + 6x^2 - 4x^3 + x^4$
15. $x^7 - 7x^6y + 21x^5y^2 - 35x^4y^3 + 35x^3y^4 - 21x^2y^5 + 7xy^6 - y^7$
16. $16x^4 + 96x^3y + 216x^2y^2 + 216xy^3 + 81y^4$
17. $\frac{x^5}{y^5} - 5\frac{x^4}{y^4} + 10\frac{x^3}{y^3} - 10\frac{x^2}{y^2} + 5\frac{x}{y} - 1$
18. $16x^4 + 32x^3y + 24x^2y^2 + 8xy^3 + y^4$
19. $243x^5 - \frac{405}{2}x^4y + \frac{135}{2}x^3y^2 - \frac{45}{4}x^2y^3 + \frac{15}{16}xy^4 - \frac{1}{32}y^5$
20. $\frac{a^4}{16} - \frac{a^3b}{6} + \frac{a^2b^2}{6} - \frac{2ab^3}{27} + \frac{b^4}{81}$
21. $x^5 + \frac{5}{2}x^4y + \frac{5}{2}x^3y^2 + \frac{5}{4}x^2y^3 + \frac{5}{16}xy^4 + \frac{1}{32}y^5$
22. $\frac{1}{16}t^4 + \frac{1}{6}t^3v + \frac{1}{6}t^2v^2 + \frac{2}{27}tv^3 + \frac{1}{81}v^4$
23. $x^{10} + 10x^9\sqrt{y} + 45x^8y + 120x^7y\sqrt{y} + 210x^6y^2 + 252x^5y^2\sqrt{y} + 210x^4y^3 + 120x^3y^3\sqrt{y} + 45x^2y^4 + 10xy^4\sqrt{y} + y^5$
24. $a^5 - 10a^4b + 40a^3b^2 - 80a^2b^3 + 80ab^4 - 32b^5$

CHAPTER REVIEW

In Exercises 1–9, evaluate each expression. $1000 \cdot 999 \cdot 998 \cdot \ldots \cdot 989$

1. $\frac{1000!}{988!}$
2. ${}_{200}C_{198}$ 19,900
3. $\binom{5}{4}\binom{10}{8}$ 225
4. ${}_{10}P_3$ 720
5. $\frac{8!}{2!6!}$ 28
6. ${}_{1000}C_{1000}$ 1
7. $\frac{100!}{2! \cdot 98!}$ 4950
8. $\binom{27}{0}$ 1
9. $\binom{107}{1}$ 107

10. (a) How many committees of 2 people can be formed from a group of 10? 45
    (b) How many committees of 2 or more people can be formed from a group of 10? 1013
11. How many three-digit numbers can be formed if numerals from the set $\{0, 1, 2, 3, 4\}$ are used and
    (a) if no repetition of digits is allowed? 48
    (b) if repetition is allowed? 100
    (c) if repetition is allowed and the numbers must be even integers? 60
12. (a) From a collection of 6 novels and 5 nonfiction books, how many different selections of 2 novels and 3 nonfiction books can be made? 150
    (b) In how many ways can your selection of books be arranged on a shelf if the novels are separated from the nonfiction books? 24
    (c) In how many ways can your selection be arranged on the shelf if the restriction of part (b) is removed? 120

Use the binomial theorem to expand each of the following, and then simplify.

13. $(2x + 5y)^3$
14. $(1 - x)^4$
15. $(x - y)^7$
16. $(2x + 3y)^4$
17. $\left(\frac{x}{y} - 1\right)^5$
18. $(2x + y)^4$
19. $\left(3x - \frac{1}{2}y\right)^5$
20. $\left(\frac{a}{2} - \frac{b}{3}\right)^4$
21. $\left(x + \frac{1}{2}y\right)^5$
22. $\left(\frac{1}{2}t + \frac{1}{3}v\right)^4$
23. $(x + \sqrt{y})^{10}$
24. $(a - 2b)^5$

Write and simplify each of the following.

25. The fourth term in the expansion of $(2x - 3y^2)^8$ $-48,384x^5y^6$
26. The term of the expansion of $[x - (2/x)]^6$ which does not contain an x -160
27. The second term of $(3x + 2y)^5$ $810x^4y$
28. The third term of $(\frac{1}{2}x + y)^6$ $\frac{15}{16}x^4y^2$
29. The middle term of $(x^2 - y^2)^4$ $6x^4y^4$
30. The fifth term of $(2 - 3t)^7$ $22,680t^4$
31. The sixth term of $(3\sqrt{x} + \sqrt[5]{y})^5$ y

CHAPTER TEST

1. Evaluate $\frac{5! + 4!}{6!}$. $\frac{1}{5}$
2. Evaluate ${}_{20}C_{17}$. 1140
3. Evaluate ${}_4C_0 \cdot {}_3C_2 + {}_4C_1 \cdot {}_3C_1 + {}_4C_2 \cdot {}_3C_0$. 21
4. Express the following as a quotient with factorials only.

$${}_{11}C_4 \cdot {}_7C_3 \cdot {}_4C_2 \cdot {}_2C_2 \quad \frac{11!}{4!\,3!\,2!\,2!}$$

5. How many three-digit numbers can be formed if only numerals from the set {1, 2, 3, 4} are used and if
   (a) repetition of numerals is not allowed? 24
   (b) repetition is allowed? 64
6. If 3 girls and 4 boys are lined up in a row for a photograph, how many arrangements are possible? In how many of these arrangements, do boys and girls alternate? 5040; 144
7. Using the binomial theorem, expand and simplify $(x^2 - 2y)^4$.
8. Find the coefficient of y^6 in the expansion of $(5x - 2y)^7$ and simplify. 2240x

CHAPTER TEST

The material included in the Chapter Test was covered in the following sections:

Problem 1—Section 11-5
Problem 2—Sections 11-4, 11-5
Problems 3, 4—Section 11-5
Problem 5—Sections 11-1, 11-4
Problem 6—Section 11-3
Problems 7, 8—Section 11-6

Answer to Chapter Test Problem 7

7. $x^8 - 8x^6y + 24x^4y^2 - 32x^2y^3 + 16y^4$

CHAPTER 12

Probability

The purpose of this chapter is to give the student an opportunity to study probability theory as a model for experiments resulting in one of a finite number of outcomes. This theory, called the probability theory of finite spaces, is remarkably simple in its form relation and in its demands on mathematical background. It requires far less scaffolding, for example, than is needed for euclidean geometry. The following are some of the topics found in Chapter 12:

- *Finite probability spaces*
- *Equiprobable weights*
- *Probability of an event*
- *Complement of a set*
- *Complementary events*
- *Addition theorem of probabilities*
- *Mutually exclusive events*
- *Independent events*
- *Binomial distribution*
- *The birthday problem*

It is suggested that one day be spent on each section of this chapter, except for Sections 12-3 and 12-5 on which it may be beneficial to spend an extra day. Section 12-6 should be treated as an optional section and may be assigned for individual study.

CHAPTER 12

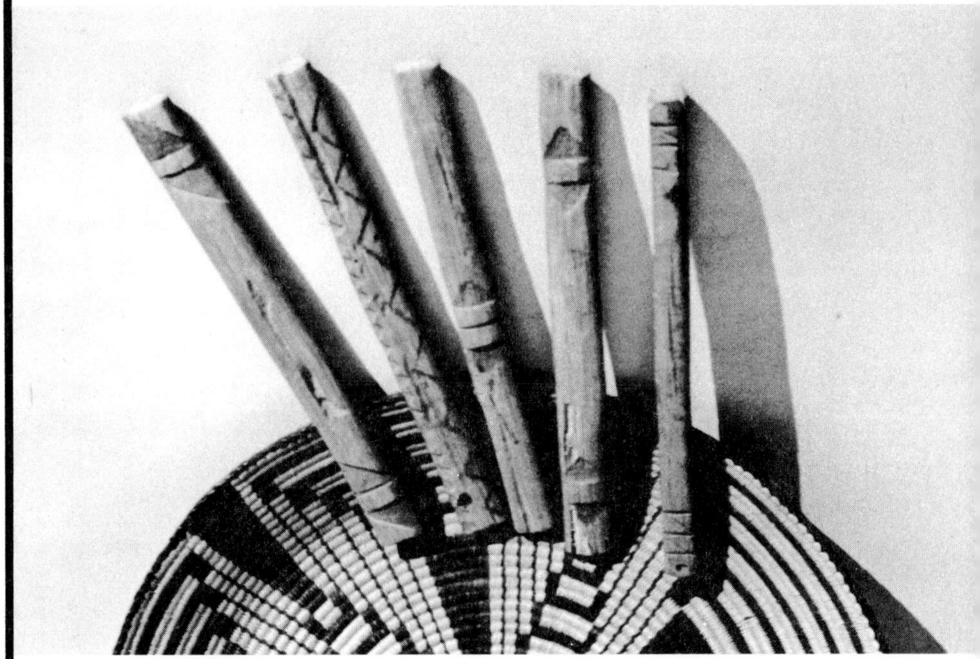

Counting sticks are used by the Pima Indians in a gambling game called *kints*. The sticks, with various numbers of notches, are made from the wood of the sahuaro cactus. (Courtesy of the Heard Museum)

PROBABILITY

Like geometry, number theory, and algebra, the modern theory of probability is a branch of mathematics. In its present form, it starts with a set of undefined terms and axioms, from which theorems are deduced and additional concepts are defined. In its early beginnings, probability, like geometry, was an empirical study consisting of a collection of solutions to problems. Whereas geometry originated from the search to answer questions such as "How large is this piece of land"? probability originated from attempts to answer questions such as "How often will this event happen?"

481

12-1 INTUITIVE NOTIONS

This section deliberately places heavy reliance on the student's intuition in his first introduction to probability theory. You may wish to have some actual experiments conducted in the room, before or after school, based on the problems in the text. Compare the data of the experiment with the mathematical theory. Wherever feasible, a complete listing of outcomes, with those that are favorable being circled, is recommended. Students can find interesting background reading in encyclopedias and histories of mathematics by looking in the index for the topic, or for such names as de Mère, Pascal, D'Alembert, Fermat, Cardan, Laplace. In particular, the *American Mathematical Monthly*, (67), 1960, pp. 409–419 contains an article by Oysteen Ore, entitled "Pascal and the Invention of Probability Theory". Also recommended is a book by Ore, entitled *Cardano, the Gambling Scholar*, 1953 (Princeton University Press). Other items of interest may be found in the bibliography in the text.

12–1 INTUITIVE NOTIONS

Conversation is sprinkled with statements such as "Smith will probably be elected mayor," "Chances are good that today will be another hot one," and "It's a toss-up between the two teams." In the first two statements, the speaker feels that a particular outcome, while not guaranteed, is more likely to happen than not. The third statement indicates that the speaker has no such intuition concerning what may happen.

In many instances, more precise statements about outcomes can be made. For example, suppose that the letter A is painted on each of five faces of a cube and the letter B is painted on the sixth face. If the cube is rolled on a tabletop, then it is far more likely that an A, rather than a B, will appear on top when the cube stops rolling. The fact that there are five chances out of six for an A to be on top may be translated into the following mathematical statement: The probability of an A is $\frac{5}{6}$.

Problem 1. An ordinary die is rolled once. (a) What is the probability of a 3 on the top face of the die? (b) What is the probability of a number less than or equal to 3 on the top face?

Solution. The faces of an ordinary die are numbered 1 through 6. In a roll of the die, it seems natural to expect that one particular face is as likely to appear on top as any other face. Of these *six* equally weighted possibilities, just *one* leads to the case of a 3 on top. Thus, for part (a), we say that the probability of a 3 is $\frac{1}{6}$.

The number on the top face will be less than or equal to 3 if it is either a 1, 2 or a 3. Thus, the probability for part (b) is $\frac{3}{6}$ or $\frac{1}{2}$.

Problem 2. An urn contains 100 balls which differ only in color. Of these 100 balls, 75 are red and 25 are white. One ball is drawn from the urn. (a) What is the probability that the ball drawn from the urn is red? (b) What is the probability that the ball drawn is white?

Solution. There is an equal chance that any one of the 100 balls will be selected from the urn. Because there are 75 red balls and 25 white balls, 75 of these cases will result in a red ball being drawn and 25 in a white ball being drawn. Hence, the answers to (a) and (b) are $\frac{75}{100}$, or $\frac{3}{4}$, and $\frac{25}{100}$, or $\frac{1}{4}$, respectively.

Problem 3. From a set of four discs numbered 1, 2, 3, and 4, respectively, two discs are selected at random and placed side by side to form a two-digit number. (a) What is the probability that the discs selected will form the two-digit number 32? (b) What is the probability that they will form a two-digit number which does not contain the digit 2?

Solution. This problem differs from the first two problems in that a set of equally weighted outcomes is not immediately apparent. We select two discs from the given four discs and place the two that are selected side by side. The phrase *at random* suggests that we consider all such possible selections as equally likely. From the counting principles of the last chapter, we know that there are $4 \cdot 3$, or 12, ordered pairs of discs that could be so presented. Only one of these pairs would result in the two-digit number 32, so we say that the probability of this result is $\frac{1}{12}$. In part (b), several of the pairs would not contain the digit 2 (for example, 34, 41, 14, and so on). Resorting again to elementary counting practices, we see that $3 \cdot 2$, or 6, of the pairs do *not* contain the digit 2. Thus, the answer to the question in part (b) is $\frac{6}{12}$, or $\frac{1}{2}$.

The students should be aware that the counting principles of Chapter 11 will frequently be used to analyze lists of outcomes of experiments in Chapter 12.

Exercises for Discussion

Analyze each of the following problems in a way that will enable you to give the same weight to each outcome of a set of all possible outcomes. Then determine the number of equally likely cases that lead to the correct result.

1. A green die and a red die are each rolled once and their top faces noted.

(a) Complete the following table of the 36 possible outcomes, writing them as ordered pairs in a rectangular array. The first number in the ordered pair is the number of dots on the top face of the green die and the second is the number of dots on the top face of the red die.

Red

	(1, 1)	(1, 2)	(1, 3)	(1, 4)	(1, 5)	(1, 6)
	(2, 1)	(2, ? 2)	(2, ? 3)	(2, ? 4)	(2, ? 5)	(2, ? 6)
Green	(3, ? 1)	(3, ? 2)	(3, ? 3)	(3, ? 4)	(3, ? 5)	(3, ? 6)
	(4, ? 1)	(4, ? 2)	(4, ? 3)	(4, ? 4)	(4, ? 5)	(4, ? 6)
	(5, ? 1)	(5, ? 2)	(5, ? 3)	(5, ? 4)	(5, ? 5)	(5, ? 6)
	(6, ? 1)	(6, ? 2)	(6, ? 3)	(6, ? 4)	(6, ? 5)	(6, 6)

(b) What is the probability of "snake eyes," that is, of a 1 on the top face of each die? $\frac{1}{36}$

(c) What is the probability of a 5 on the top face of the red die and a 6 on the green die? $\frac{1}{36}$

(d) What is the probability of a 5 on the top face of one die and a 6 on the other? $\frac{2}{36} = \frac{1}{18}$

(e) What is the probability of a total of 11 on the two top faces? $\frac{2}{36} = \frac{1}{18}$

(f) What is the probability of a total of 7 on the two top faces? $\frac{6}{36} = \frac{1}{6}$

Exercises for Discussion

In Exercise for Discussion 1(b)–1(f), if probability $\frac{1}{36}$ is assigned to each of the points found in 1(a), the remaining answers are obtained by counting the number of points belonging to each of the respective events.

Answer to Exercise for Discussion 3

3. Since each number appears on exactly two of the six faces of the supposedly symmetrical die, we assign probability $\frac{2}{6} = \frac{1}{3}$ to each of these numbers. Thus the probability of a 2 showing is $\frac{1}{3}$; the probability of either a 1 or a 2 showing is $\frac{1}{3} + \frac{1}{3} = \frac{2}{3}$.

Exercises

It is recommended that most of the assigned exercises be discussed in class before starting Section 12–2.

In Exercises 5, 6, and 8, the students will tend to start counting cases leading to the outcome whose probability is required, rather than thinking of a list of all possible outcomes. They should be required to specify all possible outcomes of the experiment before worrying about the specific outcome or outcomes. (See Section 12–2.)

Quiz

1. In rolling an ordinary die once, what is the probability of an even number on the top face? Of a number greater than 4? (ans: $\frac{3}{6}$, or $\frac{1}{2}$; $\frac{2}{6}$, or $\frac{1}{3}$)
2. In one toss of two pennies a list of outcomes could be formed in either of the following ways:
   (a) $\{(H, H), (H, T), (T, H), (T, T)\}$, where H stands for heads, and T for tails.
   (b) {Two heads, one head and one tail, two tails}

   The mathematician, D'Alembert, used list (b) and concluded that the probability of one head and one tail is $\frac{1}{3}$. Do you agree? Why or why not?
   (ans: No; if one of the pennies were red and the other green, it would be easy to see that the case of one head and one tail has

Assigning probability $\frac{1}{52}$ to each possible draw, the required probabilities are:

2. Suppose that a card is drawn from a well-shuffled bridge deck containing 52 cards. What is the probability of an ace? a spade? the ace of spades? $4/52 = 1/13$; $13/52 = 1/4$; $1/52$
3. An ordinary die is painted and the numbers changed so that two opposite faces bear a 1, two other opposite faces bear a 2, and the remaining faces bear a 3. If the die is rolled once, what is the probability of a 2 on the top face? of either a 1 or a 2?

Exercises

1. On a trick die, the face that ordinarily bears a 1 has a 6 painted on it, but the other faces are unchanged. If the die is rolled once, what is the probability of an odd number on the top face? of an even number? $\frac{1}{3}$; $\frac{2}{3}$
2. A nickel and a dime are each tossed once and their top faces noted.
   (a) Make a table showing all possible outcomes, writing them as ordered pairs in a rectangular array. (H, H) (T, H) / (H, T) (T, T)
   (b) What is the probability of heads on both coins? $\frac{1}{4}$
3. Suppose that a card is drawn from a well-shuffled bridge deck from which the red aces and red queens have been removed. What is the probability of
   (a) an ace? $\frac{1}{24}$ (b) a heart? $\frac{11}{48}$ (c) the queen of spades? $\frac{1}{48}$
4. A fake coin has heads on both sides. If this coin is tossed once, what is the probability of heads? of tails? 1; 0
5. From a set of five discs numbered 1, 2, 3, 4, 5, respectively, one disc is selected at random and the number on its face recorded. The disc is then returned to the set. Following the same procedure, a second selection is made and a two-digit number is recorded.
   (a) What is the probability of the two-digit number 41 being recorded? $\frac{1}{25}$
   (b) What is the probability of a two-digit *even* number being recorded? $\frac{2}{5}$
6. From a set of six discs numbered from 1 to 6, two discs are selected at random and placed side by side to form a two-digit number. What is the probability of an *odd* two-digit number? $\frac{1}{2}$ of a two-digit number less than 30? $\frac{1}{3}$ of a two-digit number such that the sum of its digits is 7? $\frac{1}{5}$
7. From a set of nine discs numbered from 1 to 9, one disc is selected at random.
   (a) What is the probability of a prime number on the disc? (Note: 1 is not considered to be a prime number.) $\frac{4}{9}$
   (b) What is the probability of an odd number on the disc? $\frac{5}{9}$
   (c) What is the probability of a multiple of 3 as the number on the disc? $\frac{1}{3}$
8. There are four roads connecting towns A and B and three roads connecting towns B and C. In addition, there are two roads which bypass B to connect A and C. If a person selects a route, at random, to get from A to C, what is the probability of a route that bypasses B? $\frac{1}{7}$

12-2 EVENTS IN FINITE PROBABILITY SPACES WITH EQUIPROBABLE WEIGHTS

Each of the problems in the first section concerns an experiment that is performed with a set of objects. In the problems on page 482, a die is rolled, a ball is drawn from an urn, and two discs are selected and placed side by side. Each experiment results in a finite set of possible outcomes. We are willing to give equal weight to each of these outcomes, that is, we agree that the set with which we are working is a set of equally likely outcomes. A set of outcomes in which equal weight is assigned to each outcome is called a *finite probability space with equiprobable weights.* It is customary to call the outcomes *points* of the space. Thus, the space in Problem 1 on page 482 has 6 equally weighted points and the space in Problem 3 on pages 482 and 483 has 12 such points, each of which is an ordered pair of numbers.

Probability questions arising from such experiments concern various *events,* such as *top face* 3 or *top face a number less than or equal to* 3. In this terminology, events are *subsets* of the probability space of the experiment. Thus, in Problem 1 on page 482, the event *top face* 3 is the subset $\{3\}$ of the probability space, and the event *top face less than or equal to* 3 is the subset $\{1, 2, 3\}$. The numbers we gave as *probabilities* for these two events were $\frac{1}{6}$ and $\frac{3}{6}$, or $\frac{1}{2}$, respectively. These numbers are ratios of the number of points in the corresponding event to the total number of points in the space.

DEFINITION OF THE PROBABILITY OF AN EVENT

In an experiment, if S is the finite probability space with equiprobable weights and E is a subset of S, then we may define the probability of an event E, denoted by P(E), in the following manner.

$$P(E) = \frac{\text{number of points in } E}{\text{number of points in } S}$$

When we attempt to answer a probability question, we first specify the probability space. This enables us to count the total number of equally likely outcomes, or points, of the space, and the number of points in various subsets of this space. Since E is a subset of S, it follows from the definition that the probability of an event is a number between 0 and 1. If E is the space S, we have $P(E) = 1$, but if E is the empty set, then $P(E) = 0$ (see Exercise 4 in Section 12-1).

two possible ways to occur, whereas the cases either of two heads or of two tails each have only one way in which to happen. Therefore, the list in (b), unlike that in (a), is not a list of equally weighted outcomes of the experiment. Using list (a), the probability of one head and one tail is $\frac{2}{4}$, or $\frac{1}{2}$, and that of either two heads or two tails is $\frac{1}{4}$.)

12-2 EVENTS IN FINITE PROBABILITY SPACES WITH EQUIPROBABLE WEIGHTS

Students should be reminded of their study of geometry where they started with a set of undefined terms and axioms or postulates, which were assumed true without proof. For the theory of probability, *space* and *point* are undefined terms and the fundamental assumption is that all points of the space are to be equally weighted; that is, no point of the space counts more than any other point. In probability terminology, this is the *equally likely* case for outcomes (points). A more general theory for finite space would postulate only that each point has a non-negative weight assigned to it, with the condition that the sum of the weights of all the points of the space is 1.

Events are defined to be subsets of points of the probability space and the probability of an event is defined as the ratio of the number of points in the event to the number of points in the whole space. From this definition, it is clear that the first step in applying it is one of determining what the points of the space are and then finding the total number of such points. In the more general theory mentioned above, the probability of an event would be the sum of the weights assigned to points of the event.

Answers to Exercises for Discussion 1 and 4

1. (*H*, *H*, *H*), (*H*, *H*, *T*), (*H*, *T*, *H*), (*H*, *T*, *T*), (*T*, *H*, *H*), (*T*, *H*, *T*), (*T*, *T*, *H*), (*T*, *T*, *T*). Assigning probability $\frac{1}{8}$ to each of these points, the solutions are obtained by direct count of the number of points representing the various events: $\frac{1}{8}$; $\frac{3}{8}$; $\frac{3}{8}$; $\frac{1}{8}$

4. (a) There are

$$\binom{52}{2} = 1326$$

possibilities to draw a set of 2-subsets from a bridge deck.

(b) There are

$$\binom{4}{2} = 6$$

2-subsets consisting of two jacks; hence, the probability is

$$\frac{6}{1326} = \frac{1}{221}.$$

(c) There are $4 \cdot 4 = 16$ ways to select one queen and one jack to form a 2-subset of this composition; hence, the pobability is

$$\frac{16}{1326} = \frac{8}{663}.$$

Quiz

The following exercises are concerned with draws from a set of nine discs, numbered from 1 to 9.

1. One of the discs is selected. What is the probability of:
   (a) A number greater than 7? (ans: $\frac{2}{9}$)
   (b) A number divisible by three? (ans: $\frac{3}{9}$, or $\frac{1}{3}$)
2. A set of two discs is selected.
   (a) How many 2-subsets from the set of nine discs are there? (ans: 36)
   (b) What is the probability of an odd sum on the pair selected? (ans: $\frac{5}{9}$)

Exercises for Discussion

1. Using ordered triples and denoting the coordinates by the symbols *H* or *T*, list the 8 equally likely outcomes of an experiment in which 3 pennies are tossed. What is the probability of 3 heads? 2 heads and 1 tail? 1 head and 2 tails? no heads?
2. Two girls and three boys are lined up in a row for a picture. If each arrangement has equiprobable weight, what is the probability that the boys and girls alternate? (Hint: Let points of *S* be permutations of 5 individuals out of a group of 5 people.) $\frac{3!\,2!}{5!} = \frac{1}{10}$
3. All possible numbers having one or two digits are formed from the digits 1, 2, 3, and 4, and no digits are repeated. Each resulting number is written on a separate disc. From the collection of discs, one disc is drawn at random. What is the probability of a digit 3 in the number on the disc selected? $\frac{1+(1\cdot 3)+(3\cdot 1)}{4+(4\cdot 3)} = \frac{7}{16}$
4. A set of 2 cards is drawn at random from a deck of 52 cards.
   (a) How many possibilities are there for such a draw?
   (b) What is the probability of a draw of 2 jacks?
   (c) What is the probability of a draw with 1 jack and 1 queen?

Exercises

1. From a group of 3 girls and 4 boys, a committee of two members is to be chosen. If each committee has equiprobable weight, what is the probability of a committee consisting of
   (a) a boy and a girl? $\frac{4}{7}$ (b) 2 boys? $\frac{2}{7}$
   (c) 2 girls? $\frac{1}{7}$
2. Five discs, numbered 1 to 5, are selected one at a time at random. What is the probability that the discs are drawn in the order 1, 2, 3, 4, 5? $\frac{1}{120}$ What is the probability that the first two discs are 1, 2, in that order? $\frac{1}{20}$
3. (a) How many possible three-digit numbers can be formed, using only numerals from the set

   $$\{1, 2, 3, 4, 5\}$$

   if repetition of digits is not allowed? 60

   (b) From the set of possible three-digit numbers in part (a), one element is chosen at random. What is the probability of a number beginning with the digit 1? $\frac{1}{5}$ beginning with an even digit? $\frac{2}{5}$
4. Answer the questions of Exercise 3, given that repetition of digits is allowed. (a) 125 (b) $\frac{1}{5}$; $\frac{2}{5}$
5. In a family of 3 children, what is the probability of all 3 children being boys? $\frac{1}{8}$ What is the probability of 2 girls and 1 boy? $\frac{3}{8}$ 2 boys and 1 girl? $\frac{3}{8}$ 3 girls? $\frac{3}{8}$

6. If a red die and a green die are thrown, what is the probability that the red die shows a number greater than 3 and the green die shows a number less than 3? $\frac{1}{6}$

7. A lot of 50 items contains 5 defective and 45 nondefective items. A sample set of 3 of these items is selected from the lot and tested. What is the probability that all 3 items in the sample are defective? that none are defective? that exactly 1 is defective? that at least 2 are defective? $\frac{1}{1960}$; $\frac{1419}{1960}$; $\frac{99}{392}$; $\frac{23}{980}$

8. An urn contains 100 balls, of which 20 are white, 20 green, and 60 red. A set of 2 balls is drawn from the urn. What is the probability of drawing
(a) 2 green balls? $\frac{19}{495}$ (b) 1 green ball and 1 red ball? $\frac{8}{33}$
(c) 2 balls which are not green? $\frac{316}{495}$ (d) 2 balls of different color? $\frac{56}{99}$

9. A lunch counter has 6 seats, numbered 1 to 6. Three people come in and take seats, at random, at the empty counter. What is the probability that the seats numbered 1, 2, and 3 are occupied? $\frac{1}{20}$ that 3 seats are occupied and that there are no empty seats between them? $\frac{1}{5}$

12–3 COMPLEMENTARY EVENTS AND ADDITION THEOREMS

Since events are subsets of a probability space, we may use the algebra of subsets to answer probability questions. A useful device for picturing the relationships between various subsets of a set is the Venn diagram.† For example, let $S = \{a, b, c, d, e, f\}$ be a probability space of six equally likely outcomes, and let A be the following subset of S.

$$A = \{a, b, c, d\}$$

In Fig. 12–1, the six points which comprise set S are enclosed in a rectangle and the four points of S which comprise the subset A are enclosed in the circle labeled A. By definition, the probability of A, $P(A)$, is $\frac{4}{6}$, or $\frac{2}{3}$. The points of S which are *not in A* also form a subset $\overline{A}$, called the *complement of A*. In Fig. 12–1, the points of $\overline{A}$ are those points of S *outside* the circle A, that is, $\overline{A} = \{e, f\}$. Note that $P(\overline{A}) = \frac{2}{6}$, or $\frac{1}{3}$, which is $1 - P(A)$, or $1 - \frac{2}{3}$. In fact, the following theorem is true for any subset A of a probability space S.

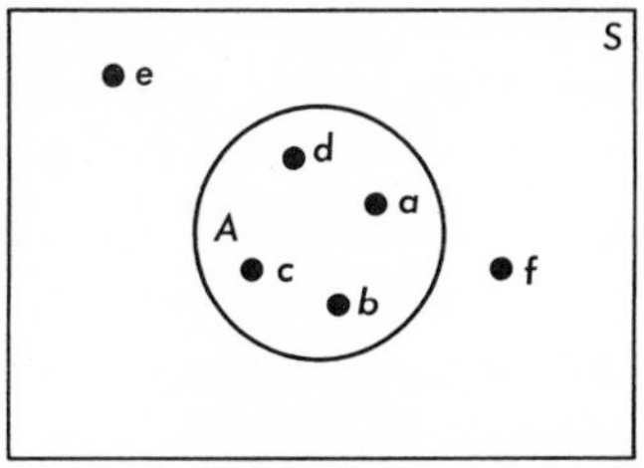

FIGURE 12–1

† The Venn diagram is named in honor of the English logician, John Venn (1834–1883).

3. Two discs are drawn from the set of nine discs and are placed side by side to form a two-digit number.
(a) How many two-digit numbers may be so formed? (ans: 72)
(b) What is the probability of the event, *an even two-digit number*? (ans: $\frac{4}{9}$)

12–3 COMPLEMENTARY EVENTS AND ADDITION THEOREMS

The theorems of this section provide formulas for computing the probability of an event in terms of probabilities of other related events whose probabilities may be more easily obtained.

The notion of complement of a set will probably be a new one to the student. Venn diagrams may be found useful here and later in the section to recall the union and intersection of sets.

The Venn diagram of Fig. 12–2 may be drawn on the board so that the students can arrive at the numerical value of $P(A \cup B)$ in the two ways suggested by this theorem: first, by counting directly the number of points in $A \cup B$ and dividing by the number of points in S, and second, by adding the numbers $n(A)$ and $n(B)$ and then subtracting $n(A \cap B)$ before dividing by $n(S)$.

A second diagram could be drawn with different numbers of points in A, B, $A \cap B$, and S, and the procedures above repeated.

THEOREM ON COMPLEMENTARY EVENTS

If A is an event in the probability space S, and $\overline{A}$ is its complement, then $P(\overline{A}) = 1 - P(A)$.

Proof. Let $n(S)$ be the number of points in the probability space S. Let $n(A)$ and $n(\overline{A})$ be the number of points in A and $\overline{A}$, respectively. Then $n(A) + n(\overline{A}) = n(S)$, since $\overline{A}$ contains all the points of S not in A. Hence, we have

$$n(\overline{A}) = n(S) - n(A),$$

and upon dividing both sides of this equation by $n(S)$,

$$P(\overline{A}) = 1 - P(A).$$

Before illustrating the usefulness of this theorem, we shall state a second probability theorem.

ADDITION THEOREM OF PROBABILITIES

If A and B are subsets of a probability space S, then

$$P(A \cup B) = P(A) + P(B) - P(A \cap B).$$

In particular, *if $A \cap B$ is the empty set, then*

$$P(A \cup B) = P(A) + P(B).$$

Proof. Recall that the *union*, $A \cup B$, of subsets A and B is the set consisting of all points in A or in B and that the *intersection*, $A \cap B$, is the set of all points that are common to both A and B. Let $n(A)$, $n(B)$, $n(A \cup B)$, and $n(A \cap B)$ be the number of points of S in each of the corresponding subsets, A, B, $A \cup B$, and $A \cap B$. From the Venn diagram in Fig. 12–2, we see that adding the numbers $n(A)$ and $n(B)$ counts the points in $A \cap B$ twice. Thus,

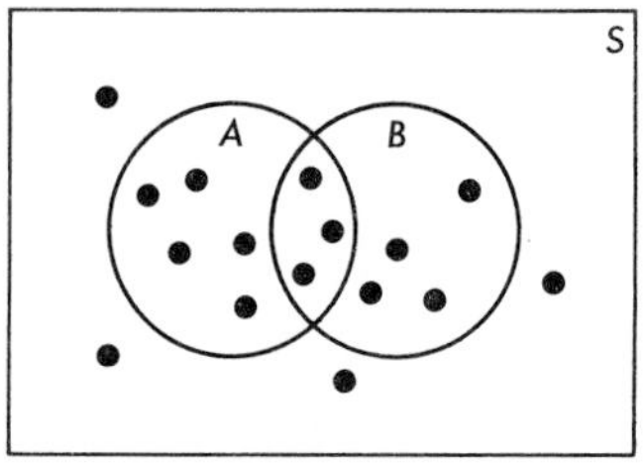

FIGURE 12–2

$$n(A) + n(B) - n(A \cap B)$$

gives us the correct number of points in $A \cup B$, that is,

$$n(A \cup B) = n(A) + n(B) - n(A \cap B).$$

After dividing both sides of this equation by $n(S)$, we obtain

$$P(A \cup B) = P(A) + P(B) - P(A \cap B).$$

If $A \cap B$ is the empty set, we have $P(A \cap B) = 0$, so that the addition formula becomes

$$P(A \cup B) = P(A) + P(B) \quad \text{if} \quad A \cap B = \emptyset.$$

Sets A and B, for which $A \cap B = \emptyset$ are called *disjoint* sets. In probability terminology, disjoint sets A and B, representing events in a probability space, are called *mutually exclusive events.*

DEFINITION OF MUTUALLY EXCLUSIVE EVENTS

If A and B are sets in a probability space and $A \cap B = \emptyset$, then A and B are called mutually exclusive events.

The event $A \cup B$, representing the union of any two events A, B of a probability space, can be called the event *at least one of A or B*, and the event $A \cap B$ can be called *both A and B*.

Problem. In a single roll of two dice, what is the probability of at least one six on the top faces?

Solution. In Exercise for Discussion 1 of Section 12–1, we analyzed an experiment in which there are 36 equally likely outcomes from a toss of two dice. The event A, *at least one six*, consists of those ordered pairs with first coordinate 6, or second coordinate 6, or possibly both coordinates 6. The complementary event, $\overline{A}$, is the set of all ordered pairs in which *neither* coordinate is 6. By elementary counting procedures, we quickly compute

$$n(\overline{A}) = 5 \cdot 5, \quad \text{or } 25,$$

so that $P(\overline{A}) = \frac{25}{36}$, and hence, $P(A) = 1 - P(\overline{A})$, or $\frac{11}{36}$, according to the theorem on complementary events.

In this problem, we could have represented the event A as

$$A = B_1 \cup B_2,$$

where B_1 is the event *six on the first die*, and B_2 is the event *six on the second die*. Then $n(B_1) = n(B_2) = 6$ and $n(B_1 \cap B_2) = 1$, so that by the addition theorem of probabilities,

$$P(A) = P(B_1) + P(B_2) - P(B_1 \cap B_2)$$
$$= \tfrac{6}{36} + \tfrac{6}{36} - \tfrac{1}{36}, \quad \text{or } \tfrac{11}{36}.$$

You may wish to draw a Venn diagram with *A* and *B* disjoint sets and verify this special case of the addition theorem of probabilities directly. Watch for logical fallacies in finding complementary events. (See Chapter 15 on negation of statements in logic.) You could ask the class for the complementary event to *both faces six,* which is *at least one face not six*. Or, in a list of outcomes involving all possible three-digit numbers, you could ask for the complementary event to *at least two of the three digits are alike,* that is, a repeated-digit pair, which is *all digits different*.

Answers to Exercises for Discussion 2, 3(a), and 4(a)

2. $\dfrac{4+13-1}{52} = \dfrac{4}{13}$; $\dfrac{26}{52} = \dfrac{1}{2}$

3. (a)

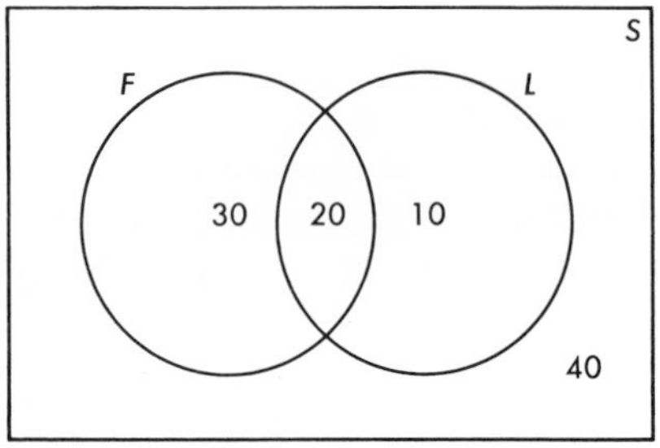

4. (a)

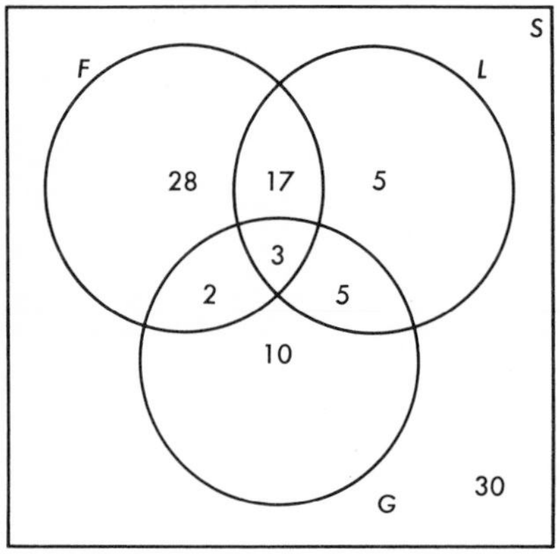

Quiz

1. What is the probability of at least one head in three tosses of a penny? (ans: $\frac{7}{8}$)
2. If a single card is drawn from a bridge deck of 52 cards, what is the probability of a heart or a club? Of a heart or a queen? Of neither a heart nor a queen? (ans: $\frac{1}{2}$; $\frac{4}{13}$; $\frac{9}{13}$)

Exercises for Discussion

1. In tossing two dice, what is the probability of a sum of numbers different from 7 on the top faces? $\frac{36-6}{36} = \frac{5}{6}$
2. If a single card is drawn from a bridge deck of 52 cards, what is the probability of an ace or a spade? of a heart or a spade?
3. A high school has 100 students, of whom 50 are enrolled in French, 30 are enrolled in Latin, and 20 are enrolled in both French and Latin.
   (a) Make a Venn diagram, letting S represent the set of 100 students and enclosing subsets F and L in two overlapping circles in S. In the set $F \cap L$, write the number of students taking both French and Latin: $n(F \cap L)$. Then write the number of elements in each of the remaining three regions in the rectangle S. These regions represent sets $F \cap \overline{L}$ (students taking French, but not Latin), $\overline{F} \cap L$ (students taking Latin, but not French), and $\overline{F} \cap \overline{L}$ (students taking neither French nor Latin).
   (b) If one student is chosen at random from the class, what is the probability that the student chosen is taking at least one of the languages? is taking neither language? $\frac{60}{100} = \frac{3}{5}$; $\frac{40}{100} = \frac{2}{5}$
4. Suppose that we are given more information about the class described in Exercise 3: 20 students take German, 5 take both French and German, 8 take both German and Latin, and 3 take all three languages.
   (a) Make a Venn diagram with three overlapping circles representing sets L, F, and G (German). Working from the inside of the circles to the outside, compute the number of elements of the eight disjoint sets in S.
   (b) What is the probability that a student selected at random from the class is a student of French, but is not a student of either of the other two languages? is a student of none of these three languages?
   $\frac{28}{100} = \frac{7}{25}$ $\frac{30}{100} = \frac{3}{10}$

Exercises

See Solution Manual for figures.

1. From the set of 4 aces, 2 are drawn at random. What is the probability that in the pair selected, at least 1 of the cards is a red ace? $\frac{5}{6}$
2. A carton containing 12 eggs has 1 rotten egg. If three eggs are chosen at random from the box, what is the probability that the rotten egg will be one of the eggs chosen? $\frac{1}{4}$
3. If a fair coin is tossed 5 times, how many equally weighted outcomes are there? What is the probability that at least 1 head will show in the 5 tosses? at most 1 head? 32; $\frac{31}{32}$; $\frac{3}{16}$
4. A certain class of 80 students boasts 20 honor students and 30 school athletes. Forty students in the class do not indulge in sports and are not honor students. If a student is selected at random to represent the class, what is the probability that he is both an honor student and a school athlete? $\frac{1}{8}$ that he is in at least one of these two special categories? $\frac{1}{2}$

5. The registrar of a school of 500 students reports the following enrollments: French, 300; German, 200; Latin, 180. He reports that duplication of names occurs in 70 cases with French and German, in 80 cases with French and Latin, in 60 cases with German and Latin, and that there are 50 students taking all three languages. Why is there reason to question his arithmetic? 520 students instead of 500

6. In a group of 100 girls, 40 are blondes and the rest are brunettes. Fifty of the girls have blue eyes, and the others have brown eyes. There are 10 blue-eyed blondes. If a boy dates one of these 100 girls, choosing her name by lot, what are his chances of going out with a brown-eyed brunette? $\frac{1}{5}$

7. A group of 250 people is classified according to nationality (native or foreign); age group (adult or child); sex (male or female). In the group, there are 20 native children of whom 10 are boys. There are 30 native males and 40 foreign men. Of the whole group, 100 are native, 100 are children, and 100 are males. In selecting one person at random from this group, what is the probability that the person selected is

   (a) a native woman? $\frac{6}{25}$ (b) a foreign girl? $\frac{1}{5}$

8. An integer is chosen at random from the first 20 positive integers. What is the probability that the integer chosen is divisible by 4 or by 6? (Try to do this exercise in two ways.) $\frac{7}{20}$

12-4 INDEPENDENT EVENTS

We shall now consider two different, but related, experiments.

Problem. An urn contains 3 red balls and 4 white balls.

1. Two balls are drawn in succession from the urn, and the first ball *is not* replaced before the second is drawn.
2. Two balls are drawn in succession from the urn, and the first ball *is* replaced before the second is drawn.

In each experiment, what are the probabilities of the following events?

(a) A, first ball red
(b) B, second ball red
(c) $A \cap B$, both balls red

Solution. In Experiment 1, we take a sample space, S_1, consisting of the set of all ordered pairs, without replacement of balls, from the set of 7 balls. We use equiprobable assignment of weights to the points in S_1. Therefore, $n(S_1) = 7 \cdot 6$, or 42.

12-4 INDEPENDENT EVENTS

It is possible to arrive at the notion of independent events by using an approach different from the one in the text, that is, by introducing conditional probabilities. Thus, the conditional probability of an event A, given an event B, denoted by $P(A \mid B)$ is defined to be

$$P(A \cap B)/P(B).$$

A is said to be independent of B if $P(A \mid B) = P(A)$. It also follows then that if A is independent of B, $P(A \cap B) = P(A) \cdot P(B)$ and B is independent of A. Our definition of independent events A and B as events for which

$$P(A \cap B) = P(A) \cdot P(B)$$

can be shown to be equivalent to this alternative definition given above.

Event A consists of all ordered pairs of the form (R, R) or (R, W):

$$n(A) = (3 \cdot 2) + (3 \cdot 4), \quad \text{or } 18,$$
$$P(A) = \tfrac{18}{42}, \quad \text{or } \tfrac{3}{7}.$$

Event B consists of all ordered pairs of the form (R, R) or (W, R):

$$n(B) = (3 \cdot 2) + (4 \cdot 3) = 18,$$
$$P(B) = \tfrac{18}{42}, \quad \text{or } \tfrac{3}{7}.$$

The elements of $A \cap B$ consist only of ordered pairs of the type (R, R):

$$n(A \cap B) = 3 \cdot 2, \quad \text{or } 6,$$
$$P(A \cap B) = \tfrac{6}{42}, \quad \text{or } \tfrac{1}{7}.$$

In Experiment 2, we take a sample space S_2 consisting of the set of all ordered pairs, with replacement of balls, from the set of 7 balls. We use equiprobable assignment of weights to the points in S_2. Therefore,

$$n(S_2) = 7 \cdot 7, \quad \text{or } 49,$$
$$n(A) = (3 \cdot 3) + (3 \cdot 4), \quad \text{or } 21,$$
$$P(A) = \tfrac{21}{49}, \quad \text{or } \tfrac{3}{7},$$
$$n(B) = (3 \cdot 3) + (4 \cdot 3), \quad \text{or } 21,$$
$$P(B) = \tfrac{21}{49}, \quad \text{or } \tfrac{3}{7},$$
$$n(A \cap B) = 3 \cdot 3, \quad \text{or } 9,$$
$$P(A \cap B) = \tfrac{9}{49}.$$

Notice that in each experiment, the probability of a red ball on the second draw is the same as that of a red ball on the first draw. This seems obvious in the second experiment because the first ball is replaced before the second is drawn. However, it is less obvious in the first experiment because the chances of drawing a red ball on the second draw seem to depend on the color of the first ball drawn.

The difference between the two experiments becomes evident when we try to relate the probability of the event $A \cap B$, both balls red, to the probabilities of the separate events A and B. In Experiment 2, we see that

$$P(A \cap B) = P(A) \cdot P(B) \quad \text{since} \quad \tfrac{9}{49} = \tfrac{3}{7} \cdot \tfrac{3}{7}.$$

In other words, if we know only the probabilities of events A and B, we can find the probability of $A \cap B$ by multiplying these two probabilities. This illustrates the following property of pairs of events.

In this first experiment, the probability of *second ball red* is still $\frac{3}{7}$ which was the probability of *first ball red*. The reason for student's surprise at this result is that one tends to think in terms of conditional probabilities mentioned on the previous page. If this were an experiment dealing with conditional probability, the conditional probability of second ball red, given first ball red would be $\frac{1}{3}$ and the conditional probability of second ball red given first white would be $\frac{1}{2}$.

Thus, if two events A and B are known to be independent, in order to compute $P(A \cap B)$, one multiplies the two probabilities $P(A)$ and $P(B)$. Conversely, in order to test for independence of events A and B, one would compute $P(A)$, $P(B)$, $P(A \cap B)$ and check to see if

$$P(A \cap B) = P(A) \cdot P(B).$$

If this equality is true, A and B are independent; otherwise, A and B are dependent.

DEFINITION OF INDEPENDENT EVENTS

Two events A and B in a sample space S are said to be independent if, and only if,

$$P(A \cap B) = P(A) \cdot P(B).$$

In the first experiment in Problem 1, we see that

$$P(A \cap B) \neq P(A) \cdot P(B) \quad \text{since} \quad \tfrac{1}{7} \neq \tfrac{3}{7} \cdot \tfrac{3}{7}.$$

Thus, in this experiment, A and B are *dependent*, rather than *independent*, events. The definition above may be extended to more than two events. Three events A, B, and C of a sample space S are said to be completely independent if, and only if, any two of these events are independent and

$$P(A \cap B \cap C) = P(A) \cdot P(B) \cdot P(C).$$

Four events A, B, C, and D are said to be completely independent if, and only if, any three of the events are completely independent and

$$P(A \cap B \cap C \cap D) = P(A) \cdot P(B) \cdot P(C) \cdot P(D).$$

We could extend the definition to include any finite number of events.

Exercises for Discussion

1. Three fair coins are tossed. Let A be the event *at least two heads*, let B be the event *at most two heads*, and let C be the event *same face on all three coins.* $P(A) = \frac{4}{8} = \frac{1}{2}$; $P(B) = \frac{7}{8}$; $P(C) = \frac{2}{8} = \frac{1}{4}$; $P(A \cap C) = \frac{1}{8}$;
   (a) Compute $P(A)$, $P(B)$, $P(C)$, $P(A \cap C)$, and $P(B \cap C)$. $P(B \cap C) = \frac{1}{8}$
   (b) Are events A and C independent? $P(A \cap C) = \frac{1}{8} = \frac{1}{2} \cdot \frac{1}{4} = P(A) \cdot P(C)$; yes
   (c) Are events B and C independent? $P(B \cap C) = \frac{1}{8} \neq \frac{7}{8} \cdot \frac{1}{4} = P(B) \cdot P(C)$; no
2. The table below shows a two-way classification of a group of 100 people according to sex and age.

	45 or older	less than 45	Total
Men	39	21	60
Women	26	14	40
Total	65	35	100

   The marginal totals on the right of the table are the totals of the rows and the marginal totals at the bottom of the table are the totals of the columns. Suppose that a person is chosen, at random, from this group and let D be the event *45 or older* and M the event *male.* Are the events D and M independent? Are D and $\overline{M}$? $\overline{D}$ and M? $\overline{D}$ and $\overline{M}$?

Answer to Exercise for Discussion 2

2. $P(D) = \frac{65}{100}$;
$P(M) = \frac{60}{100}$;
$P(\overline{D}) = \frac{35}{100}$;
$P(\overline{M}) = \frac{40}{100}$
$P(D \cap M) = \frac{39}{100} = P(D) \cdot P(M)$;
$P(D \cap \overline{M}) = \frac{26}{100} = P(D) \cdot P(\overline{M})$
$P(\overline{D} \cap M) = \frac{21}{100} = P(\overline{D}) \cdot P(M)$;
$P(\overline{D} \cap \overline{M}) = \frac{14}{100} = P(\overline{D}) \cdot P(\overline{M})$

Thus, all four pairs of events are independent.

Quiz

1. From the set of 13 spades, two cards are drawn in succession without replacing the first before drawing the second. Use the set of ordered pairs of cards drawn as your probability space. What is the probability of:
   (a) An ace on the first draw? (ans: $\frac{1}{13}$)
   (b) A king on the second draw? (ans: $\frac{1}{13}$)
   (c) An ace on the first and king on the second draw? (ans: $\frac{1}{156}$)
   (d) Are the events *ace on first draw* and *king on second draw* independent? (ans: no)
2. In Exercise 1, suppose the first card drawn is replaced before the second is drawn. What are the points of this probability space and how many are there? Answer the questions of parts (a), (b), (c), (d) of Exercise 1 for this exercise. (ans: ordered pairs with repetitions allowed; 169; (a) $\frac{1}{13}$; (b) $\frac{1}{13}$; (c) $\frac{1}{169}$; (d) yes)

Exercises

1. (a) Two fair coins are tossed. Let A be the event *not more than one head* and B the event *at least one of each face*. Show that A and B are dependent events. See Solution Manual.

   (b) Three fair coins are tossed. Let A' and B' be the events in this space corresponding to the events A and B in part (a). Are A' and B' independent or dependent events? Independent

2. Two dice are tossed. Show that the event *even on first die* and the event *both dice fall alike* are independent. See Solution Manual.

3. Each of the three-digit code numbers 100, 010, 001, and 111 is written on a disc. From the set of 4 discs, one is chosen at random. Let A_1, A_2, and A_3 be the events *first digit* 1, *second digit* 1, *third digit* 1, respectively. Show that each pair of events A_1 and A_2, A_1 and A_3, A_2 and A_3 is independent but that the set of all three events is not a completely independent set. See Solution Manual.

4. (a) One card is drawn from a bridge deck of 52 cards. Let A be the event *ace* and B be the event *spade*. Show that events A and B are independent. Are A and B mutually exclusive? No; see Solution Manual.

   (b) Let C be the event *king* in the experiment of part (a). Show that events A and C are mutually exclusive and are not independent. See Solution Manual.

5. Using the definitions of independence and of mutually exclusive events, prove the following statement: If A and B are independent events, then they are not mutually exclusive. Assume that $P(A) \neq 0$ and $P(B) \neq 0$. See Solution Manual.

6. A die is tossed 3 times. Let event A be all ordered triples resulting from an even first toss (e, x, x); let event B be those resulting from an odd second toss (x, o, x); let event C be those resulting from a six on the third toss $(x, x, 6)$. Find each of the following.

$$n(S),\quad n(A),\quad n(B),\quad n(C),\quad n(A \cap B),$$
$$n(A \cap C),\quad n(B \cap C),\quad n(A \cap B \cap C)$$

216, 108, 108, 36, 54, 18, 18, 9

7. In Exercise 6, are the three events A, B, and C completely independent? Yes

8. In a certain school, examination results showed that 12% of the students failed French, 10% failed chemistry, and 2% failed both French and chemistry. A student is selected, at random, from the school roll. Are the events *student failed French* and *student failed chemistry* independent? No

9. A die is tossed 3 times. What is the probability that the first toss will show odd, the second toss even, and the third toss a six? $\frac{1}{24}$

12-5 BINOMIAL DISTRIBUTION

The principal usefulness of the concept of independence is that it allows us to compute the probability of an intersection of several events once we know the probability of each of these individual events. An example of this is given by the *independent trials process.*

Suppose that an experiment is performed n times and that care is taken to make certain that the same conditions apply each time. This gives us a set of *n independent trials of an experiment*, or an *independent trials process*. Examples of independent trials processes are coin tossing, dice throwing, and repeated drawing of balls with replacement. Because of the independence property, the probability space of such a process can be built sequentially. In other words, probabilities can be assigned to the points of the space by *multiplying* the probabilities of the points of the common spaces of the independent trials.

Problem 1. It is believed that, of a large group of people, opinions on a certain proposal are divided so that about 60% of the people are for the proposal and about 40% are against it. If 5 people are chosen at random and asked their opinion, what is the probability that of these 5 people, 3 are for and 2 are against the proposal?

Solution. If we assume that the 5 individuals do not influence one another in giving their answers, we may consider this an independent trials process, consisting of 5 trials in which a person is asked his opinion. On each trial there is a 60%, or $\frac{3}{5}$, probability of response for the proposal and a 40%, or $\frac{2}{5}$, probability of response against it. As we perform the 5 trials, we shall work with arrangements of the type *FFFAA*, *FFAFA*, and so on, representing sequences of replies for and against. Since the trials are independent, we have

$$P(FFFAA) = \tfrac{3}{5}\cdot\tfrac{3}{5}\cdot\tfrac{3}{5}\cdot\tfrac{2}{5}\cdot\tfrac{2}{5}, \quad \text{or } (\tfrac{3}{5})^3(\tfrac{2}{5})^2,$$

$$P(FFAFA) = \tfrac{3}{5}\cdot\tfrac{3}{5}\cdot\tfrac{2}{5}\cdot\tfrac{3}{5}\cdot\tfrac{2}{5}, \quad \text{or } (\tfrac{3}{5})^3(\tfrac{2}{5})^2,$$

and so on. Since *each* sequence of replies is to have 3 F's and 2 A's, the probability of any one of these sequences will be the same as the two we computed: $(\frac{3}{5})^3(\frac{2}{5})^2$. Hence, to complete this problem, we need to *count* the number of sequences, each of which has 3 F's and 2 A's. This is a problem in *combinations*, since we want the number of ways of selecting a 3-subset of the spaces numbered 1 to 5. We shall put the F's in these spaces, and use the remaining 2 spaces for A's. There are $\binom{5}{3}$ such combinations and the answer to our question is

$$\tbinom{5}{3}(\tfrac{3}{5})^3(\tfrac{2}{5})^2, \quad \text{or } \tfrac{216}{625}.$$

12-5 BINOMIAL DISTRIBUTION

In this section the student will again encounter the binomial expansion discussed in Chapter 11 (see page 497) from which the particular probability formulas of this section get the name binomial probabilities. After struggling with the elusive logic involved in individual probability problems, students will appreciate the fact that it is possible to classify a whole group of experiments as *independent trial experiments*, for which probability questions have formula solutions.

Problem 1 belongs to a large class of experiments involving independent trials processes for which there exist formulas for computing probabilities. The most famous of these formulas is given in the following theorem.

In the binomial distribution theorem, the two extreme cases, $k = 0$ and $k = n$ are more easily handled on their own merits without benefit of the binomial probability formulas. Thus $k = 0$, or *no* successes in n trials, is clearly all n failures and has probability q^n; and $k = n$, or n successes in n trials, has probability p^n. Of course, the formulas for $k = 0$ and $k = n$ give these same results.

BINOMIAL DISTRIBUTION THEOREM

If a sequence of n independent trials of an experiment is performed, and if each trial results in one of two possible outcomes, called success and failure, with the probability of success given to be p and that of failure given to be q, then the probability of exactly k successes in the n trials is

$$\binom{n}{k} p^k q^{n-k} \quad \textit{for} \quad k = 0, 1, 2, \ldots, n.$$

Proof. Since the sum of the probabilities of the outcomes of each trial must be 1, we have $p + q = 1$, or

$$q = 1 - p.$$

Suppose that R is the event of exactly k successes in n trials in the probability space of all ordered n-tuples selected from the set $\{S, F\}$, where S stands for success and F for failure. Then one point of R is

$$\underbrace{SS\cdots S}_{k \text{ symbols}} \quad \underbrace{FF\cdots F}_{n-k \text{ symbols.}}$$

Because the trials are independent, the probability assigned to this point is

$$p^k q^{n-k}.$$

The number of arrangements of the kS's and $(n - k)F$'s in an ordered n-tuple is the number of combinations of k objects from a set of n objects,

$$\binom{n}{k}.$$

Hence,

$$P(R) = \binom{n}{k} p^k q^{n-k},$$

as stated in the theorem.

An easy way to remember the binomial distribution theorem is to expand $(q + p)^n$ by the binomial theorem:

$$(q + p)^n = \binom{n}{0} q^n + \binom{n}{1} q^{n-1}p + \cdots + \binom{n}{k} q^{n-k}p^k + \cdots + \binom{n}{n} p^n.$$

Then the term containing p^k is the probability of exactly k successes in n trials of our experiment. Since $q + p = 1$, the sum of the probabilities in the binomial distribution is 1.

A sequence of independent trials of the same experiment, each trial having *success* and *failure* as its two possible outcomes, is often called a *sequence of Bernoulli trials.*†

Problem 2. Find the probability of obtaining more than 2 but fewer than 6 successes in 12 Bernoulli trials of an experiment in which the probability of success in each trial is $\frac{1}{3}$.

Solution. The event A, more than 2 but fewer than 6 successes, consists of the three mutually exclusive events; B, exactly 3 successes; C, exactly 4 successes; and D, exactly 5 successes. Hence,

$$P(A) = P(B) + P(C) + P(D)$$
$$= \binom{12}{3}\left(\frac{1}{3}\right)^3\left(\frac{2}{3}\right)^9 + \binom{12}{4}\left(\frac{1}{3}\right)^4\left(\frac{2}{3}\right)^8 + \binom{12}{5}\left(\frac{1}{3}\right)^5\left(\frac{2}{3}\right)^7.$$

This expression simplifies to

$$P(A) = \frac{1331 \times 2^8}{3^{12}}.$$

Using logarithms, we obtain

$$\log P(A) = \log 1331 + 8 \log 2 - 12 \log 3$$
$$\doteq 3.1242 + 2.4080 - 5.7252$$
$$\doteq .8070 - 1.$$

Hence,

$$P(A) \doteq .641.$$

† The Swiss mathematician James Bernoulli (1654–1705) made important contributions to the early phases of the development of probability theory. He was a member of the most famous family of mathematicians in history.

The fact that the binomial expansion displays in turn each of the cases of probability of exactly k successes in n dependent trials, for $k = 0$ to n, is, of course, the reason for calling these *binomial probabilities* and for calling the collection of these, the *binomial distribution*.

Here is an opportunity for review of the combinatorial symbols (also called binomial coefficients) and the use of logarithms.

The process average fraction defective is usually determined by dividing the total number of defectives by the total number of articles produced over a considerable period of time in the previous history of the production. It might also be a hypothetical figure (ratio) toward which the company is striving and whose determination is subject to change according to the results of various test runs.

The inspection of manufactured articles in a factory might be considered a sequence of Bernoulli trials. The two outcomes for each article inspected could be either acceptance, if the article is satisfactory, or rejection, if it is defective. The probability that an article will be rejected is called the *process average fraction defective*. The following problem corrects a fallacy often committed in interpreting the meaning of process average fraction defective.

Problem 3. In a certain manufacturing process, the process average fraction defective is $\frac{1}{20}$. Is it correct to infer from this number that there is exactly 1 defective in each run of 20?

Solution. To answer this question, let A be the event *exactly* 1 *defective in each* 20 *trials* in a Bernoulli model for which $n = 20$ and $p = .05$.

$$P(A) = \binom{20}{1}(.05)(.95)^{19}$$
$$\doteq .3725$$

Hence, the chances are only about 3 in 8 that a run of 20 produces exactly 1 defective.

Problem 4. How many times must a coin be tossed for the chances to be 99% or better that at least 1 head shows?

Solution. If we take n Bernoulli trials with probability of success $\frac{1}{2}$ on each trial and if A is the event *at least one head*, then we wish to determine the smallest positive integer n such that

$$P(A) \geqq .99.$$

It is easier to work with the complementary event $\overline{A}$, *no head shows*,

$$P(\overline{A}) = \binom{n}{0}\left(\frac{1}{2}\right)^0\left(\frac{1}{2}\right)^n = \left(\frac{1}{2}\right)^n.$$

Using $P(A) = 1 - P(\overline{A})$, we obtain

$$1 - \left(\frac{1}{2}\right)^n \geqq .99.$$

We must find the smallest possible integer n that is a solution of this inequality. The inequalities below are equivalent to the one above.

$$.01 \geqq (\tfrac{1}{2})^n$$
$$2^n \geqq 100$$

The smallest positive integer n such that $2^n \geqq 100$ is 7. Therefore, the coin must be tossed 7 times to make the chances 99% or better of at least 1 head showing.

Trial and error is probably the best way of solving the inequality $2^n \geqq 100$ for n a positive integer, although logarithms may be used. Thus $2^n \geqq 100$, if and only if, $n \log 2 \geqq \log 100$; that is,

$$n \geqq \frac{2}{\log 2},$$

and so on.

Exercises for Discussion

1. A coin is tossed 5 times. Using the binomial distribution formulas, find the probability of the events A, *exactly four heads*, and B, *at least one head*. $P(A) = \binom{5}{4}\left(\frac{2}{3}\right)^4\left(\frac{1}{2}\right) = \frac{5}{32}$, $P(B) = 1 - \binom{5}{0}\left(\frac{1}{2}\right)^5 = 1 - \frac{1}{32} = \frac{31}{32}$
2. A certain team has probability $\frac{2}{3}$ of winning whenever it plays.
   (a) What is the probability that the team will win exactly 4 out of 5 games? $\binom{5}{4}\left(\frac{2}{3}\right)^4\left(\frac{1}{3}\right) = \frac{80}{243}$
   (b) What is the probability that the team will win at most 4 out of 5 games?
   (c) What is the probability that the team will win 4 games out of 5 if it has already won the first 2 games of the series of 5 games?
3. Expand the binomial $(.8 + .2)^4$ and interpret each term of this expansion as a probability in the space of a specified number of Bernoulli trials of a particular experiment.
4. (a) What is the probability of obtaining at least one six in 4 tosses of a fair die?
   (b) What is the probability of obtaining at least one double-six in 24 tosses of 2 fair dice.
5. How many times must a fair die be thrown to make the probability greater than $\frac{9}{10}$ that at least one six shows?

Exercises

1. What is the probability of getting 3 or more sixes in 4 tosses of a die? $\frac{7}{432}$ of getting at most 3 sixes in the 4 throws? $\frac{1295}{1296}$
2. A baseball player's batting average is .250. What is the probability that he gets exactly 2 hits in 4 times at bat? that he gets at least 1 hit in 4 times at bat? $\frac{175}{256}$ $\frac{27}{128}$
3. Over a period of time, it is found that 10% of the fuses produced by a certain manufacturing process are defective. Using logarithms to compute your answers, find the probability that in a sample of 10 fuses selected from the production line there will be
   (a) no defectives. .35
   (b) at least 1 defective. .65
   (c) at most 1 defective. .74
4. Ten students are polled to determine their approval or disapproval of a suggested design for the class ring. If the opinions of the class as a whole are equally divided on this issue, what is the probability that 8 or more of the students polled say that they approve? .05
5. How many tosses of a fair coin are required if the probability that at least 1 head will appear is to be greater than $\frac{9}{10}$? 4 tosses

Exercises for Discussion

If time is limited, it is suggested that at least Exercises for Discussion 2–4 be covered.

Answers to Exercises for Discussion 2(b)–5

2. (b) *At most 4* is the complement of *not all 5*; hence,

$$1 - \left(\tfrac{2}{3}\right)^5 = \tfrac{211}{243}.$$

(c) $P\{$4 successes out of 5 | first two successes$\}$

$$= P\{\text{2 out of 3 are successes}\}$$

$$= \binom{3}{2}\left(\tfrac{2}{3}\right)^2\left(\tfrac{1}{3}\right) = \tfrac{4}{9}.$$

3. $(.8)^4 + 4(.8)^3(.2) + 6(.8)^2(.2)^2 + 4(.8)(.2)^3 + (.2)^4 = 1$

The probability of j successes in 4 Bernoulli trials with success probability .2 on each trial is given by the $(j + 1)$-term of the expansion of $(.8 + .2)^4$.

4. *At least one six* is the complement of *no sixes*; hence,

$$P_1 = 1 - \left(\tfrac{5}{6}\right)^4 \doteq .52.$$

At least one double-six is the complement of *no double-sixes*; hence,

$$P_2 = 1 - \left(\tfrac{35}{36}\right)^{24} \doteq .49.$$

5. Find n such that

$$1 - \left(\tfrac{5}{6}\right)^n > .9 \text{ or } \left(\tfrac{5}{6}\right)^n < .1.$$

Using logs, $n \geqq 13$.

Quiz

1. In a sequence of four Bernoulli trials with success probability $\frac{1}{5}$ on each trial, find the probability of:
   (a) exactly one success (ans: $\frac{256}{625}$)
   (b) no successes (ans: $\frac{256}{625}$)
   (c) no failures (ans: $\frac{1}{625}$)
   (d) fewer than three successes (ans: $\frac{608}{625}$)
2. Expand the binomial $(\frac{1}{3} + \frac{2}{3})^3$ and interpret each of the four terms as a binomial probability in a sequence of Bernoulli trials. (ans: $(\frac{1}{3})^3 + 3(\frac{1}{3})^2(\frac{2}{3}) + 3(\frac{1}{3})(\frac{2}{3})^2 + (\frac{2}{3})^3$)

$$(\tfrac{1}{3})^3 = P(\text{3 successes})$$
$$3(\tfrac{1}{3})^2(\tfrac{2}{3}) = P(\text{2 successes})$$
$$3(\tfrac{1}{3})(\tfrac{2}{3})^2 = P(\text{1 success})$$
$$(\tfrac{2}{3})^3 = P(\text{no successes})$$

in three Bernoulli trials with success probability $\frac{1}{3}$ on each trial.)

6. Three independent trials of an experiment are performed. Each trial results in one of two outcomes, success or failure. Let p be the (unknown) probability of success on each trial.
   (a) Use the binomial distribution formulas to obtain a formula giving the probability P of at most 1 success in the 3 trials as a function of p; call this result $P(p)$. $P = (1-p)^2(1+2p)$
   (b) Make a table of values of your function P, listing $P(p)$ for p = .1, .2, .3, .4, .5, .6, .7, .8, .9. Find also $P(0)$ and $P(1)$ and interpret these two probabilities in terms of the experiment being performed. .97, .90, .78, .65, .50, .35, .22, .10, .03; 1; 0
   (c) Graph the function P from your table of values in part (b), using the horizontal axis for values of p and the vertical axis for values of $P(p)$. See Solution Manual.
   (d) Describe briefly how the probability of at most 1 success in 3 Bernoulli trials changes as the success probability p for each trial increases. Probability decreases.

In Exercises 7–9, computation will be facilitated if tables of binomial distributions are used. A section of such a table for 10 Bernoulli trials is given below. The column headings of the table list various values of the success probability p for binomial distributions with $n = 10$, and the row leaders list the successive values of k from 0 to 10. For example, the entry .146 in column $p = .25$ and row $k = 4$ gives the probability to three decimal places of exactly 4 successes in 10 Bernoulli trials when, in each of these trials, the success probability is $p = .25$, that is,

$$\binom{10}{4}(.25)^4(.75)^6 \doteq .146.$$

k \ p	.1	.25	.50	.75	.90
0	.349	.056	.001	.000	.000
1	.387	.188	.010	.000	.000
2	.194	.282	.044	.000	.000
3	.057	.250	.117	.003	.000
4	.011	.146	.205	.016	.000
5	.001	.058	.246	.058	.001
6	.000	.016	.205	.146	.011
7	.000	.003	.117	.250	.057
8	.000	.000	.044	.282	.194
9	.000	.000	.010	.188	.387
10	.000	.000	.001	.056	.349

7. Ten articles are selected at different times during the day at a factory producing large quantities of the product. If 2 or fewer defectives are found, the day's run is judged ready to sell. If more than 2 defectives are found, the day's run is subjected to further inspection and the machinery is overhauled.

   (a) What is the probability that the day's run will be accepted when the actual process average fraction defective is .50? .055

   (b) What is the probability that the day's run will be accepted when the actual process average fraction defective is .75? 0

   (c) What is the probability that the day's run will be accepted when the actual process average fraction defective is .90? 0

   (d) What is the probability that the decision to overhaul the machinery will be made when the actual process average fraction defective is .1? .070

   (e) What is the probability that the decision to overhaul the machinery will be made when the actual process average fraction defective is .25? .474

8. Joy claims that she can call the toss of a fair coin correctly more than half the time. To test her claim, you can devise the following experiment and decision plan. You will toss the coin 10 times, each time asking Joy to state in advance which way the coin will land. If she is correct 7 or more of the 10 times, you will agree with her claim; otherwise, you will say she is just guessing. Using the table of binomial probabilities given in the text, answer the following questions.

   (a) Under your decision plan, what is the probability that you will give Joy credit for her claim when she is actually just guessing each time? .172

   (b) Under your plan, what is the probability that you will accuse Joy of just guessing when she actually has a *success probability* (probability of being right in calling a toss) of $\frac{3}{4}$? .225

9. The standard treatment for a certain disease leads to cures in $\frac{1}{4}$ of the cases. A new treatment is devised which is said to produce cures in $\frac{3}{4}$ of the cases. The new treatment is tested on 10 people having the disease. If 7 or more are cured, the new treatment will be adopted. If 3 or fewer people are cured, the new treatment will be discarded as not worth further research. If the number cured is 4, 5, or 6, then judgment on the new treatment will be deferred but studies investigating its properties will continue.

   (a) Find the probability of *each* of these 3 possible actions, given that the new treatment is no more effective than the original treatment, that is, given that $p = \frac{1}{4}$ for the 10 Bernoulli trials. .004; .22; .776

   (b) Find the probabilities of each of the actions if the new treatment is actually as effective as was claimed. .776; .22; .004

TWISTER

When the ballots are being counted in an election contest between two candidates, what is the probability that the candidate who eventually wins will always lead his opponent?

Solution: If x votes are cast for the winner and y votes for the loser, the probability is

$$\frac{x-y}{x+y}.$$

*12-6 THE BIRTHDAY PROBLEM

The birthday problem is one which is especially appropriate for programming on a digital computer. If one is available, the following program may be used to illustrate the power of a loop in affecting the computation required to give the break-even point $n = 23$.

```
10  READ K
15  LET S = 365
20  LET C = 1
25  FOR N = 2 TO K
30  LET S = S - 1
35  LET R = S/365
40  LET C = C * R
45  NEXT N
50  LET P = 1 - C
55  PRINT "N =" N, "P =" P
60  GO TO 10
65  DATA 10, 22, 23, 24, 25, 30,
    40, 50, 60
100 END
```

(This program is in BASIC, a computer language developed by Dartmouth College and closely related to FORTRAN of which it is a simplified version.)

*12-6 THE BIRTHDAY PROBLEM

One of the famous problems in the field of probability is the so-called birthday problem.

Problem. A clerk registering voters notices that in a group of 20 or 30 people, he frequently finds at least two people who have the same birthday. Explain why this is so.

Solution. In attempting to explain this phenomenon, let us ignore those people born on February 29, that is, let us assume that there are 365 days in each year.

Before dealing with the clerk's observation, we consider the following simpler problem. In a random group of 3 people, what is the probability that at least 2 have the same birthday? To answer this question, we conduct the experiment of asking each person the date of his birthday. Then an appropriate space S is the set of all ordered triples, with repetition, of the first 365 positive integers. These integers represent the days of the year from January 1 through December 31. Thus, we have

$$n(S) = 365 \cdot 365 \cdot 365, \quad \text{or } 365^3.$$

The event A whose probability we are trying to find is *at least two birthdays the same*. Rather than finding $P(A)$, let us find $P(\overline{A})$, where $\overline{A}$ is the complementary event *all three birthdays different*. We may derive $P(\overline{A})$ in the following way. Since $\overline{A}$ is the set of all ordered triples in S, without repetition, we have

$$n(\overline{A}) = {}_{365}P_3, \quad \text{or } 365 \cdot 364 \cdot 363.$$

Hence,

$$P(\overline{A}) = \frac{365 \cdot 364 \cdot 363}{365^3}, \quad \text{or } \frac{364 \cdot 363}{365^2}.$$

Finally, since A and $\overline{A}$ are complementary sets in S,

$$P(A) = 1 - P(\overline{A}) = 1 - \frac{364 \cdot 363}{365^2}, \quad \text{or } \frac{1093}{133{,}225}.$$

Since $P(A) \doteq .008$, we conclude that there is less than 1 chance in 100 that at least 2 of the group of 3 people have the same birthday.

If we start with a random group of r people and ask each person the date of his birthday, then this experiment suggests a sample space S of ordered r-tuples, with repetition, from the first 365 positive integers and

$$n(S) = 365^r.$$

If A is the event *at least two birthdays the same*, then the complementary event $\overline{A}$ is *all r birthdays different*. In the same way that we found $P(\overline{A})$ above, we obtain

$$P(\overline{A}) = \frac{365 \cdot 364 \cdot \ldots \cdot (365 - r + 1)}{365^r},$$

$$P(A) = 1 - P(\overline{A}).$$

It is not easy to compute $P(A)$ if r is large. Of course, $P(\overline{A})$ can be approximated by means of logarithms if r is not too large.

To return to the original problem, it may be shown that

$$P(\overline{A}) \doteq .493 \quad \text{if} \quad r = 23,$$
$$P(A) \doteq .507 \quad \text{if} \quad r = 23.$$

In other words, in a group of 23 people, the probability that at least two people have the same birthday is greater than $\frac{1}{2}$. Consequently, the clerk's observations are supported by the theory of probability. Incidentally, if a group contains 60 people, the probability that at least two people have the same birthday exceeds .99.

Exercises

1. Find to 2 significant digits the probability that in a group of 6 people, at least 2 have the same birthday. .04
2. (a) If you are in a room containing 5 people, what is the probability that at least 1 person will have the same birthday as yours? (Note: This is *not* the same birthday problem as that in this section.) $1 - \left(\frac{364}{365}\right)^5$
   (b) How large a group of people is needed for the probability to be greater than $\frac{1}{2}$ that at least 1 of the group will have the same birthday as yours? $n \geqq 251$

HISTORICAL NOTE

It is generally believed that the science of probability originated in the correspondence between two great mathematicians of the seventeenth century, Pascal (1623–1662) and Fermat (1601–1665). These two men began to exchange ideas when they were asked questions by the French nobleman Chevalier de Méré, whose gambling experiences seemed to contradict his attempts at mathematical reasoning about dice and cards. However, Sydney Gould,† in a recent translation of Cardan's *Liber de Ludo Aleae* (*Book on Games of Chance*), written around 1520, makes a strong case for beginning the historical study of probability with the colorful figure of Cardan.

† *The Book on Games of Chance*, Gerolamo Cardano (Cardan), translated by Sydney H. Gould, 1961, Holt, Rinehart and Winston, Inc., N. Y.

Quiz

In a group of five people, what is the probability that at least two have the same birthday?
(ans: 0.027)

TWISTER

There was at one time an exclusive club in Boston, for which only men who had been to Harvard or Princeton were eligible. It was observed at one time that 75 of the members were Harvardites, 60% were Princetonions, while 20% had attended both schools. What was the total membership of the club?

Solution: There were 60 members who attended only Harvard; 75 who attended only Princeton; and 15 who attended both schools, for a total membership of 150.

The theory of probability has attracted the attention of many outstanding mathematicians in its brief history. Important contributions were made by the famous mathematical family of Bernoullis, by De Moivre (1667–1754) and Laplace (1749–1827), and by the Russian mathematicians Chebyshev (1821–1894), Markov (1856–1922), and Liapunov (1858–1918). Today, probability, together with its related branches of research, such as mathematical statistics, game theory, and operations research, is an important field of study in mathematics.

KEY IDEAS AND KEY WORDS

A set of all possible outcomes of an experiment in which each outcome is given equal weight is called a **probability space with equiprobable measure.** Each possible outcome of such an experiment is called a **point** of the space. If S is the probability space of such an experiment and E is a subset of S, then we may define the probability of an event E, denoted by $P(E)$, in the following manner.

$$P(E) = \frac{\text{number of points in } E}{\text{number of points in } S}, \quad \text{or} \quad \frac{n(E)}{n(S)}$$

If A and B are events in a probability space S, we have the following related events: $\overline{A}$, the **complement** of A; $A \cup B$, the **union** of A and B; and $A \cap B$, the **intersection** of A and B. Furthermore, we have

$$P(\overline{A}) = 1 - P(A)$$

and

$$P(A \cup B) = P(A) + P(B) - P(A \cap B).$$

If $A \cap B = \emptyset$, the empty set, we say that A and B are **mutually exclusive** events. In this particular case, $P(A \cap B) = P(\emptyset)$, or 0, and we have

$$P(A \cup B) = P(A) + P(B) \quad \text{when} \quad A \cap B = \emptyset.$$

Two events A and B are said to be **independent events** if

$$P(A \cap B) = P(A) \cdot P(B).$$

Events which are not independent are called **dependent events.**

A sequence of independent trials of an event in which each trial results in success or failure, with probability of success p on each trial, is called a sequence of **Bernoulli trials.** The **binomial distribution theorem** states that in a sequence of n Bernoulli trials with probability of success p, the probability of *exactly* k successes in the n trials is given by

$$\binom{n}{k} p^k (1-p)^{n-k} \quad \text{for} \quad k = 0, 1, 2, \ldots, n.$$

CHAPTER REVIEW

1. In tossing four coins, what is the probability of

(a) exactly 3 heads? $\frac{1}{4}$

(b) at least 3 heads? $\frac{5}{16}$

(c) at most 1 head? $\frac{5}{16}$

2. An algebra class is composed of 7 blondes and 11 brunettes. Of the 9 boys in the class, 5 are brunettes. One class member is selected at random. What is the probability that the individual selected is a blond girl? $\frac{1}{6}$

3. Assuming equal probability for boy or girl, what is the probability in a 3-child family of 2 boys and a girl? $\frac{3}{8}$

4. A bargain counter has 4 pair of socks, but the socks of each pair have become separated. If you pull out 2 socks at random, what is the probability that they form a matching pair? $\frac{1}{7}$

5. Let A and B be two independent events with $P(A \cap B) = \frac{1}{6}$ and $P(A \cup B) = \frac{2}{3}$. Find $P(A)$ and $P(B)$. Is there more than one possible answer? $P(A) = \frac{1}{2}$, $P(B) = \frac{1}{3}$, or $P(A) = \frac{1}{3}$, $P(B) = \frac{1}{2}$

6. In the World Series, the first team to win 4 games is the winner. Suppose that the stronger of two teams has probability $\frac{2}{3}$ of winning each game, independent of the outcome of any other game. Assume that a game cannot end in a tie. Show that the probability that the series will end in 4 games is 0.21, correct to two decimal places. .21

7. (a) How many committees of 5 students can be formed from a class of 7 girls and 8 boys? 3003

(b) What is the probability that 1 particular boy, A, will be a member of the committee? $\frac{1}{3}$

(c) What is the probability that the committee will have more boys than girls? $\frac{82}{143}$

8. If 3 cards are drawn from the suit of 13 hearts, what is the probability that the selection will contain the ace or the king, or both? $\frac{11}{26}$

9. What is the probability of getting at least one 6 in 4 tosses of an ordinary die? of getting exactly one 6 in the 4 tosses? $\frac{671}{1296}$; $\frac{125}{324}$

10. A set of balls numbered from 1 to 15 is placed in an urn and 2 balls are drawn simultaneously. What is the probability that the sum of their numbers is 10? $\frac{4}{105}$

11. If in Exercise 10, one ball is drawn and replaced and then a second ball drawn, what is the probability that the sum of the numbers is 10? $\frac{1}{25}$

12. Let A be the event *head on first coins* and B be the event *coins show different faces* in the probability space of a toss of two ordinary coins. Show that A and B are independent events. See Solution Manual.

CHAPTER TEST

The material included in the Chapter Test was covered in the following sections:

Problem 1—Section 12–3
Problem 2—Sections 12–2, 12–3
Problem 3—Section 12–5
Problem 4—Section 12–2
Problem 5—Section 12–4

Answer to Chapter Test Problem 1

1. $\frac{1}{5}$

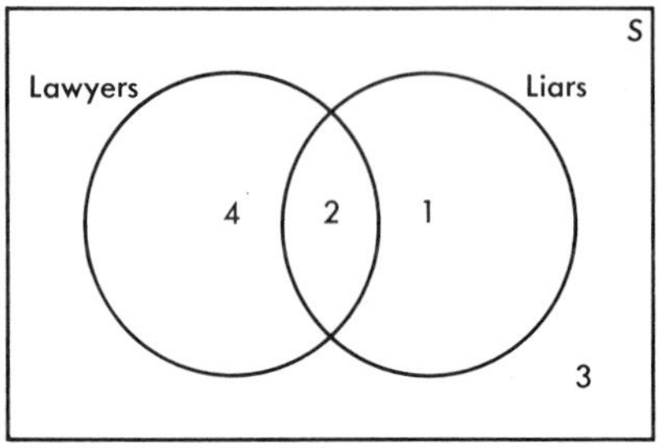

CHAPTER TEST

1. A small club has 10 members of whom 6 are lawyers, 3 are liars, and 3 of the members are neither lawyers nor liars. If one slip of paper is selected from a hat containing the 10 names on slips of paper, what is the probability that the name selected will be that of a lawyer-liar?

2. From an urn containing 5 white and 3 red balls, 3 balls are drawn. There is no replacement of balls.
   (a) How many possible subsets of 3 balls can be drawn? 56
   (b) What is the probability of drawing 2 white balls and 1 red ball? $\frac{15}{28}$
   (c) What is the probability of drawing 3 red balls? $\frac{1}{56}$
   (d) What is the probability of drawing at least 1 red ball? $\frac{23}{28}$

3. A fair die is rolled 4 times. Use the binomial distribution formulas to find the probability of rolling
   (a) exactly 3 sixes. $\frac{5}{324}$
   (b) at most 3 sixes. $\frac{1295}{1296}$
   (c) no sixes. $\frac{625}{1296}$
   (d) not more than 1 six. $\frac{1125}{1296}$

4. Three boys and three girls are lined up in a row for a picture.
   (a) How many arrangements of the 6 people are there? 720
   (b) What is the probability of the girls and boys being lined up in the following order: *GBGBGB*? $\frac{1}{20}$
   (c) What is the probability of boys and girls alternating in the lineup? $\frac{1}{10}$

5. If A and B are independent events in a probability space S such that $P(A \cap B) = \frac{1}{6}$ when $n(S) = 18$ and $n(B) = 9$, find each of the following.
   (a) $P(B)$ $\frac{1}{2}$
   (b) $P(A)$ $\frac{1}{3}$
   (c) $n(A)$ 6

Cumulative Review III

1. The cubic polynomial $4x^3 + 3x^2 + ax + b$, with a and b real numbers, has $^-1 + i\sqrt{3}$ as a zero. Find the other zeros and determine the values of a and b. $^-1 - i\sqrt{3}$; $\frac{5}{4}$; $a = 6$, $b = {}^-20$

2. If you have 6 pairs of shoes, in how many ways could you choose a right shoe and a left shoe which do not form a pair? 30

3. Let U be the set of all points (x, y) in a rectangular coordinate plane and let

$$D = \{(x, y) \mid x^2 + y^2 \leqq 4\},$$
$$L = \{(x, y) \mid x + y = 2\},$$
$$R = \{(x, y) \mid x + y > 2\}.$$

   Graph each of the following sets in U. See <u>Solution Manual.</u>
   (a) D
   (b) L
   (c) $D \cap L$
   (d) $R \cap L$
   (e) R
   (f) $D \cap R$

4. Three dice are rolled.

(a) What is the probability that their sum is greater than or equal to 16? 5/108

(b) What is the probability that their sum is less than or equal to 17? 215/216

5. Find the set of zeros for each of the following polynomials, and write each polynomial as a product of real prime factors.

(a) $x^3 - 4x^2 + x + 6$ (b) $2x^3 + 5x^2 - x - 1$

(c) $x^4 - 6x^3 + 10x^2 - 6x + 9$ $\{3, \pm i\}$; $(x-3)^2(x^2+1)$

(d) $4x^4 + x^2 - 3x + 1$ $\{\frac{1}{2}, \frac{1}{2}(^-1 \pm \sqrt{3}i)\}$; $(2x-1)^2(x^2+x+1)$

6. Three colors of paint are available for painting a group of 10 houses, and there are 5 houses on each side of a street. Each house is to be painted 1 color only. How many ways of painting the houses are there if at most 2 different colors are to be used for the houses on the same side of the street? 8649

7. Approximate to one-decimal-place accuracy a positive real zero of the polynomial $x^3 - 3x - 3$. 2.1

8. If A is an event in a sample space with probability $\frac{2}{3}$, we say that the odds for A are 2:1 and the odds against A are 1:2. In general, for an event E with probability $p > \frac{1}{2}$, the odds for E are $p{:}q$, where $q = 1 - p$; if E has probability $p < \frac{1}{2}$, the odds against E are $q{:}p$; if E has probability $p = \frac{1}{2}$, the odds are 1:1, or *the odds are even.*

(a) Suppose that you throw a pair of dice once. Find the odds against obtaining a total less than 5. 5:1

(b) Suppose that A and B play the following game: A draws a card from an ordinary bridge deck and then B draws a card from the remaining set of cards. If the cards are of the same suit, B wins; otherwise, A wins. What are the odds in favor of A? 13:4

9. Determine the values of a and b so that $2x^3 - x^2 + ax + b$ will be divisible by $(x + 2)(x - 4)$. $a = {}^-22$, $b = {}^-24$

10. Find the solution set for the system of equations

$$\begin{cases} x^2 - y = 2, \\ y^2 - x = 2. \end{cases}$$

$(2, 2), (^-1, ^-1), \left(\frac{^-1+\sqrt{5}}{2}, \frac{^-1-\sqrt{5}}{2}\right), \left(\frac{^-1-\sqrt{5}}{2}, \frac{^-1+\sqrt{5}}{2}\right)$

11. Express $(1 + i)^{10}$ as a complex number in the form $a + bi$. $32i$

12. In shuffling a deck of 52 cards, 4 are accidentally dropped. What is the probability that the missing cards are all of the same suit? $\frac{44}{4165}$

13. Prove that $\sqrt[4]{6}$ is irrational. See Solution Manual.

14. What is the probability of a one appearing on the top face 2 times in 6 tosses of an ordinary die? $\frac{3125}{15,552}$

15. (a) If $2 - i$ and $\sqrt{3}$ are zeros of the polynomial

$$x^5 - 4x^4 + 2x^3 + 12x^2 - 15x,$$

what are the other zeros? $0, 2+i, {}^-\sqrt{3}$

(b) Write an equation of a rational polynomial of lowest possible degree having $^-2$ and $4 + \sqrt{5}$ as two of its zeros. $x^3 - 6x^2 - 5x + 22$

Answers to Cumulative Review Problems 5(a), 5(b)

5. (a) $\{^-1, 2, 3\}$; $(x + 1)(x - 2)(x - 3)$

(b) $\{\frac{1}{2}, \frac{1}{2}(^-3 \pm \sqrt{5})\}$ $(2x - 1) \times (2x + 3 + \sqrt{5}) \times (2x + 3 - \sqrt{5})$

16. How many three-digit numbers greater than 200 can be formed with the digits 1, 2, 3, 4, 5, and 6 if repetition of digits is not allowed? 100

17. Jane asks 7 people to come to a party at her house.

(a) In how many ways can she select the 7 people from a group of 10 acquaintances? 120

(b) In how many ways can she make her selection if 2 of the 10 people refuse to attend the party together? 64

18. In the sample space of 2 throws of a die, let A, B, and C be the following events.

A, odd number on the first throw

B, odd number on the second throw

C, odd sum on the two throws

See *Solution Manual.*

Show that any pair of the set of events A, B, C is independent, but that this is not a completely independent set of three events.

19. What values must m and n have if the polynomial $x^2 + 3x + 4$ is to be a factor of $x^4 + mx^2 + n$? $m = {}^-1$, $n = 16$

20. A triangle has vertices $P(0, 0)$, $Q(12, 0)$, and $R(6, {}^-6\sqrt{3})$. The midpoints of the three sides are joined to form a triangle with vertices A, B, and C. Find the perimeter of triangles PQR and ABC. 36, 18

21. Graph $y = 2^x + 1$ and $y = 2^x$ on the same set of axes. See *Solution Manual.*

22. Graph $y = 2^{x+1}$ and $y = 2^x$ on the same set of axes. See *Solution Manual.*

23. Given that triangle ABC is isosceles, with $AB = BC = a$, $AC = b$, and angle ABC of measure 20°, show that $a^3 + b^3 = 3a^2b$. See *Solution Manual.*

24. If s and t are numbers such that $0 \leqq s < t \leqq \pi/2$, show that

$$\sin\left(\frac{s+t}{2}\right) > \frac{\sin s + \sin t}{2}.$$

See *Solution Manual.*

What does this imply about the graph of the sine?
Concave downward from 0 to π

25. Given that r is an irrational number and that a, b, c, and d are rational numbers, under what conditions on a, b, c, and d is the number

$$\frac{(ar + b)}{(cr + d)}$$

also rational? $ad = bc$

26. Let a, b, c, and d be distinct integers and

$$p(x) = (x - a)(x - b)(x - c)(x - d) - 4.$$

If it is known that the polynomial $p(x)$ has a rational zero r, then show that r must equal $\frac{(a + b + c + d)}{4}$. See Solution Manual.

27. Graph the system of inequalities

$$\begin{cases} |y| \leqq \sqrt{x^2 + 9}, \\ -\sqrt{y^2 + 9} \leqq x \leqq \sqrt{y^2 + 9}. \end{cases}$$ See Solution Manual.

28. Graph the solution set of the following system of inequalities. See Solution Manual.

$$\begin{cases} 4y^2 - x^2 + 16y \leqq 0 \\ 9x^2 + y^2 - 2y > 24 \end{cases}$$

29. Draw and describe the graph of each of the following inequalities. See Solution Manual.

(a) $x^2 > y^2 + 4$

(b) $|x| < y^2 + 4$

(c) $x \leqq \sqrt{y^2 + 4}$

(d) $|x| \geqq \sqrt{y^2 + 4}$

30. For what values of k does the graph of $y^2 = k^2$ intersect the graph of

$$\frac{y^2}{a^2} - \frac{x^2}{b^2} = 1$$

in at least two points? $k \leqq {}^{-}a$ or $k \geqq a$

CHAPTER 13

Mathematical Induction

The purpose of Chapter 13 is to introduce a property of the positive integers called mathematical induction. It is introduced gradually so that all the students will gain some comprehension, if not complete understanding, of the principle of induction. To increase the value of the study, induction is first used in the proof of propositions already known to the students from the theory of polynomial equations and from geometry.

Propositions from number theory and combinatorial analysis are examined to keep the study of induction itself relevant to the study of key ideas in mathematics.

Formulas for summing arithmetic series are proven by mathematical induction.

Geometric series are introduced as they arise naturally in the practical problem of compounding interest. Infinite geometric series allow one to consider convergence of an increasing sum such as

$$1 + \tfrac{1}{2} + \tfrac{1}{4} + \tfrac{1}{8} + \ldots + \frac{1}{2^{n-1}} + \ldots$$

toward a limit, which in this case is 2.

The following are some of the topics covered in Chapter 13:

- *The number of zeros of a nonzero real polynomial*
- *The induction property*
- *The sum of the first n positive odd integers*
- *The fourth law of exponents*
- *Topics from number theory*

CHAPTER 13

The theory of Queues is used extensively in studying traffic problems. (Courtesy of the Redwood Empire Association)

MATHEMATICAL INDUCTION

The system of integers has a special property that does not belong to the rational, real, or complex number systems. This distinctive property, called the induction property, is concerned with the counting of the positive integers. Roughly speaking, it states that every positive integer can be reached by starting with 1 and counting the integers *in order:* 1; 1 + 1, or 2; 2 + 1, or 3; 3 + 1, or 4; 4 + 1, or 5; and so on. Thus, we eventually count to 100, to 1000, to 1,000,000, and to 10^{100}. Although we could not actually count to a number as large as 10^{100} in a lifetime, we can imagine having a machine which could.

The rational number system is countable in the sense that the set of positive rational numbers can be put in a one-to-one correspondence with the set of positive integers. However, it is not possible to do this in such a way that the rational numbers appear *in order*. In other words, there is no way of lining up the positive rational numbers

$$a_1, a_2, a_3, a_4, a_5, a_6, \ldots$$

so that

$$a_1 < a_2 < a_3 < a_4 < a_5 < a_6 \ldots$$

If this were possible, then there would exist consecutive rational numbers. However, we know that between any two distinct rational numbers, there is always another rational number. For example, the arithmetic average of two rational numbers is between the numbers. For similar reasons, the real and complex number systems do not have an induction property.

- *Arithmetic series*
- *Geometric series*
- *Infinite geometric series*

It is suggested that one day be spent on Section 13–1 and one day on Section 13–2, but it probably will be necessary to spend two days on the remaining sections. Even though Section 13–6 is a starred section, it is recommended that it be covered by all of your students.

13–1 PROBLEMS INVOLVING INDUCTION

This section contains an easy, informal approach to induction, with two examples—one related to the subject of polynomials (already covered in Chapter 8), and one related to problems of counting (covered in Chapter 11). An attempt is made to instill two ideas in the minds of the students through the explanation in the text and through the exercises. First, there is the fact that a proposition or statement to be proved by induction is really an infinite set of theorems, one theorem for each natural number. Second, although such a task cannot be *concluded* by direct substitution, the job is begun by checking the proposition for the first few of the natural numbers, observing that no matter how many have been checked, there is always a *next* one.

In an above-average class, the discussion of this section may be completed in one full class period and the assignment made from the next section.

13–1 PROBLEMS INVOLVING INDUCTION

To understand better the need in mathematics for an induction property, we shall first study two problems whose solutions depend on induction. Our first problem concerns the number of real zeros of a real polynomial. Each real polynomial $ax + b$ of degree 1 has one real zero: $x = {}^{-}b/a$. However, each real polynomial

$$p(x) = ax^2 + bx + c$$

of degree 2 does not necessarily have two real zeros. For example, if its discriminant $b^2 - 4ac$ is less than 0, then according to the quadratic formula, it has no real zeros. If $b^2 - 4ac = 0$, then $p(x)$ has one real zero; if $b^2 - 4ac > 0$, then $p(x)$ has two real zeros. In any event, every real polynomial of degree 2 has *at most* two real zeros.

Now let us consider a real polynomial $p(x)$ of degree 3 and determine how many real zeros it can have. If r is a real zero of $p(x)$, then by the factor theorem, $x - r$ is a real divisor of $p(x)$. Hence,

$$p(x) = (x - r)q(x)$$

for a real polynomial $q(x)$ of degree 2. If c is a real zero of $p(x)$, then $p(c) = 0$ and $(c - r)q(c) = 0$. If $c \neq r$, then $c - r \neq 0$ and $q(c)$ must be equal to 0. Thus, each real zero of $p(x)$ except r is also a zero of the quadratic polynomial $q(x)$. Since r may also be a zero of $q(x)$, $p(x)$ has at most one more real zero than $q(x)$. However, $q(x)$ has at most two real zeros, so $p(x)$ has at most three. Hence, we have proved that *every real polynomial of degree 3 has at most three real zeros.*

In view of the results above, we are led to the following conjecture.

Proposition 1. *The number of real zeros of a nonzero real polynomial is at most equal to the degree of the polynomial.*

Before attempting to give a proof of this theorem (which we shall do in Section 13–2), let us look at another similar problem.

Our second problem, or proposition, is geometric in nature, because it concerns the number of lines that can be drawn through two or more points of a set of points in a plane. If the set Q contains only one point, then no line can be drawn that satisfies the conditions. If Q contains the two points A and B, then there is one line that can be drawn, as shown in Fig. 13–1. If Q contains three points, or

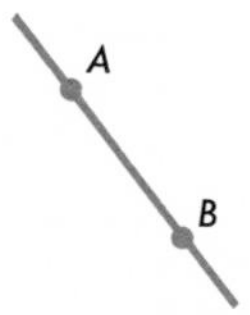

FIGURE 13–1

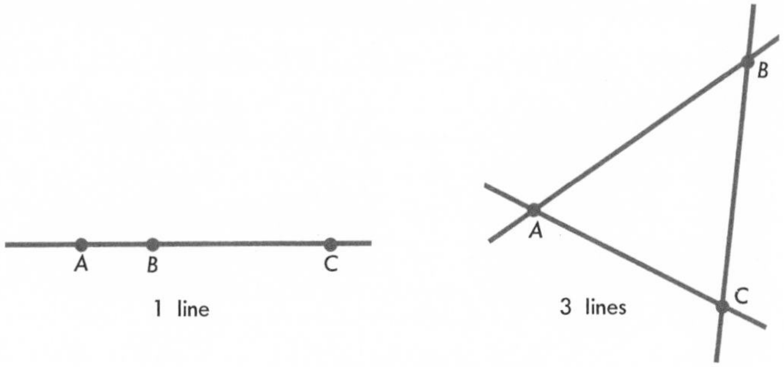

FIGURE 13-2

$Q = \{A, B, C\}$, then either the three points of Q are collinear or they are not. In the first case, there is only one line that can be drawn through two or more of the points of Q; in the second case, there are three lines that can be drawn through two or more of the points of Q. Both cases are shown in Fig. 13-2.

There are three possible alternatives if set Q contains four points:

$$Q = \{A, B, C, D\}.$$

The three alternatives are shown in Fig. 13-3. We note that if no three of the points of Q are collinear, then there are six lines that can be drawn through two of the points of Q.

Each of the cases shown above is one of an infinite number of possibilities described in the following statement.

Proposition II. *If Q is a set of n points in a plane, then the number of lines that can be drawn through two or more of the points of Q is at most equal to $\frac{1}{2}n(n-1)$.*

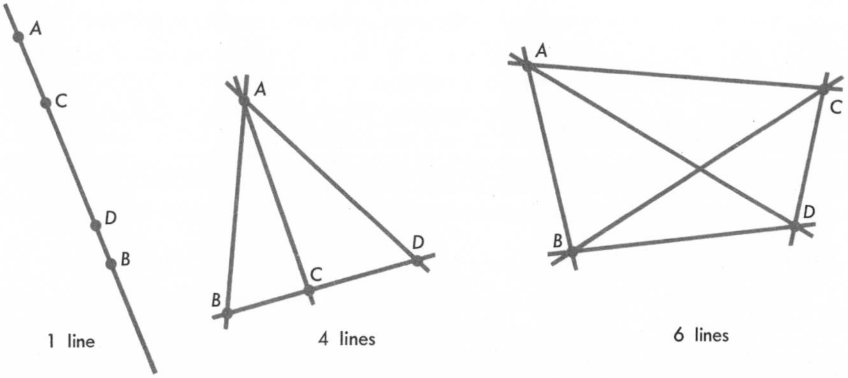

FIGURE 13-3

Exercises for Discussion, page 514

It is suggested that all of the Exercises for Discussion be done carefully in class.

In Exercise for Discussion 3, explain fully the role of n. First, n designates any counting number. Hence, $n = 1, 2, 3, 4, 5, 6, \ldots$ and so on. On the left side of the equation, $n(n+1)^2$ is a formula for the nth term of the sum. If $n = 1$,

$$n(n+1)^2 = 1 \cdot (1+1)^2 = 1 \cdot 2^2$$

and this is the first term on the left side. If n = 2,

$$n(n+1)^2 = 2 \cdot (2+1)^2 = 2 \cdot 3^2$$

and this is the second term on the left side. If $n = 3$,

$$n(n+1)^2 = 3(3+1)^2 = 3 \cdot 4^2$$

and this is the third term on the left side.

Stress that each term on the left is a function of n, that the value of the term can be found as soon as the position of the term in the sum is known. You could write

$$t(n) = n(n+1)^2$$

and this may be called the *term function* of the pattern, for each term on the left.

On the right side of the equation

$$\tfrac{1}{12}n(n+1)(n+2)(3n+5)$$

is a formula for giving the sum of the first n terms on the left. Thus, if one wants to know what

$$1 \cdot 2^2 + 2 \cdot 3^2 + 3 \cdot 4^2$$

equals, since these terms are the first three on the left, their sum may be found by substituting 3 for n in the formula on the right:

$$\tfrac{1}{12}(3(3+1)(3+2)[(3 \cdot 3)+5]) = \tfrac{1}{12} \cdot 3 \cdot 4 \cdot 5 \cdot 14, \quad \text{or } 70.$$

The work may be checked in the following way:

$$(1 \cdot 4) + (2 \cdot 9) + (3 \cdot 16) = 4 + 18 + 48 = 70.$$

You could write

$$S(n) = \tfrac{1}{12}n(n+1)(n+2)(3n+5)$$

to emphasize that the sum of the numbers on the left is a *function* of n. If it is known how many terms are to be added, it is not necessary to find the exact value of each term and then add; instead the number n may be substituted into $S(n)$ and the corresponding sum may be found.

Answers to Exercises for Discussion 1, 2(d), 3

1. Let $p(x)$ be a real polynomial of degree 4. If r is a zero of $p(x)$, then $x - r$ is a factor of $p(x)$; and $p(x) = (x - r)q(x)$, where $q(x)$ is of degree 3. But, by hypothesis, $q(x)$ has at most three real zeros. Hence, $p(x)$ has at most four real zeros.

2. (d) $n = 4$ $\quad 5 + 4 + 3 + 2 + 1 = 15 = \dfrac{5 \cdot 6}{2}$

$n = 5$ $\quad 6 + 5 + 4 + 3 + 2 + 1 = 21 = \dfrac{6 \cdot 7}{2}$

$n = 6$ $\quad 7 + 6 + 5 + 4 + 3 + 2 + 1 = 28 = \dfrac{7 \cdot 8}{2}$

3. $n = 3$ $\quad 1 \cdot 2^2 + 2 \cdot 3^2 + 3 \cdot 4^2 = 4 + 18 + 48 = 70$

$\tfrac{1}{12} \cdot 3 \cdot 4 \cdot 5 \cdot 14 = 70$

$n = 4$ $\quad 1 \cdot 2^2 + 2 \cdot 3^2 + 3 \cdot 4^2 + 4 \cdot 5^2 = 70 + 100 = 170$

$\tfrac{1}{12} \cdot 4 \cdot 5 \cdot 6 \cdot 17 = 170$

$n = 5$ $\quad 1 \cdot 2^2 + 2 \cdot 3^2 + 3 \cdot 4^2 + 4 \cdot 5^2 + 5 \cdot 6^2 = 170 + 180 = 350$

$\tfrac{1}{12} \cdot 5 \cdot 6 \cdot 7 \cdot 20 = 350$

The following table of values compares n, the number of points in Q, and $\frac{1}{2}n(n-1)$, the maximum number of lines that can be drawn through the points of Q.

n	$\frac{1}{2}n(n-1)$
2	$\frac{1}{2} \cdot 2 \cdot (2-1)$, or 1
3	$\frac{1}{2} \cdot 3 \cdot (3-1)$, or 3
4	$\frac{1}{2} \cdot 4 \cdot (4-1)$, or 6

Each of these values is in agreement with our discoveries above: If Q contains four points, then at most six lines can be drawn through two or more of the points of Q; if Q contains three points, then at most three lines can be drawn; and so on. In other words, Proposition II is true if n equals 1, 2, 3, or 4.

We could proceed to try to prove Proposition II by showing that it is true for $n = 5$, $n = 6$, and so on. However, we would never arrive at a complete proof in this way, since such a proof would involve an infinite number of steps. A valid proof of Proposition II will be given in the next section.

Exercises for Discussion

1. If a polynomial $p(x)$ of degree 4 has a real zero r, then

$$p(x) = (x - r)q(x)$$

for some polynomial $q(x)$ of degree 3. Remembering that $q(x)$ has at most three real zeros, prove that $p(x)$ has at most four real zeros.

2. A set of dominoes contains each possible combination of numbers from double zero to double six exactly once. There are 28 dominoes in a set.

(a) How many dominoes would you need to have each possible combination of numbers from double zero to double two exactly once? [handwritten: 3+2+1 = 6]

(b) How many dominoes would you need to have each possible combination of numbers from double zero to double three exactly once? [handwritten: 4+3+2+1 = 10]

(c) Devise a proposition, or formula, for the number of dominoes you would need to have each possible combination of numbers from double zero to double n, where n is any positive integer. [handwritten: (n+1)+n+...+1 = ½(n+1)(n+2)]

(d) Show that your formula is correct for $n = 4$, 5, and 6.

3. Show that the formula

$$1 \cdot 2^2 + 2 \cdot 3^2 + 3 \cdot 4^2 + \cdots + n(n+1)^2 = \tfrac{1}{12}n(n+1)(n+2)(3n+5)$$

is true for $n = 3$, 4, and 5.

Exercises

1. If S is a set of five points in a plane, then the following configurations are possible.

(a) The five points of S are collinear. 1

(b) Some four, but not all five, points of S are collinear. 5

(c) Two different sets of three points of S are collinear. 6

(d) There is one set, but not two sets, of three collinear points of S. 8

(e) No three points of S are collinear. 10

In each configuration above, find the number of lines that can be drawn through two or more points of S. In each case, make a sketch. See Solution Manual.

2. Consider the following proposition: For every finite set S of three or more points in a plane, the number of triangles having points of S as vertices is at most equal to $\frac{1}{6}n(n-1)(n-2)$, where n is the number of points in set S. Show that this proposition is true for every set S containing See Solution Manual.

(a) 3 points. (b) 4 points. (c) 5 points.

3. (a) Six boys are entered in a chess tournament. How many games are played if each boy plays one game with each of the other boys? 15

(b) Devise a formula for the number of games played if n boys are entered in the tournament. Let n be a positive integer greater than 1. $\frac{n(n-1)}{2}$

(c) Verify your conjecture for $n = 2, 3, 4, 5$, and 6. See Solution Manual

4. One of two consecutive positive integers is even and one is odd. Their product, therefore, is divisible by 2.

(a) Will the product of three consecutive integers be divisible by 2? Why? Yes; at least one must be even.

(b) Will the product of three consecutive integers be divisible by 3? Why? Yes; exactly one must be divisible by three.

(c) What is the largest integer that divides a product of any three consecutive positive integers? 6

(d) State a proposition about the divisibility of a product of any three consecutive positive integers.

(e) Show that the statement you made in part (d) is true for several products. See Solution Manual.

5. (a) What is the largest integer that divides a product of four consecutive positive integers? 24

(b) State a proposition about the divisibility of a product of any four consecutive positive integers.

(c) Show that your statement is true for several products. See Solution Manual.

6. (a) What is the largest integer that divides a product of any n consecutive positive integers? $n!$

(b) State a proposition about the divisibility of a product of any n consecutive positive integers.

(c) Show that your proposition is true for $n = 3, 4, 5$, and 6. See Solution Manual.

Exercises

It is suggested that something from geometry with illustrations be included in the assignment, such as Exercise 1, and also something from number theory, such as Exercise 4.

Exercise 3 is related to the chapter on counting.

These exercises are all important in that they are typical of situations where mathematical induction is the form of proof that applies.

Answers to Exercises 4(d), 5(b), 6(b)

4. (d) The product $n(n+1)(n+2)$ of the three consecutive integers n, $n+1$, $n+2$ is divisible by 6.

5. (b) The product

$$n(n+1)(n+2)(n+3)$$

of the four consecutive integers n, $n+1$, $n+2$, $n+3$ is divisible by 24.

6. (b) The product

$$k(k+1)(k+2)\ldots(k+n-1)$$

of the n consecutive integers

$$k, k+1, k+2, \ldots, k+n-1$$

is divisible by $n!$

Quiz

1. Evaluate the sum

$$S_n = 1 + 2 + 2^2 + \cdots + 2^{n-1}$$

for $n = 1, 2, 3, 4$, and make a conjecture for a simpler expression for S_n.
(ans: 1, 3, 7, 15; $S_n = 2^n - 1$)

13–2 THE INDUCTION PROPERTY

Now the attempt is begun in earnest to prove that every statement in an infinite set of statements is true. The proof is based on a belief that if one starts to collect a subset of the positive integers, and if one selects the smallest positive integer, 1, and, therefore, every time one picks any positive integer, he automatically picks the succeeding positive integer, then the subset omits not one from the set of positive integers. The material of this section should be discussed with the class, after they have read and studied it at home. Then you could send a good student to the board to prove Proposition I. Have him speak in complete, clear sentences. Then another good student could go to the board to present a proof of Proposition II. In correcting the errors of these students, you will probably help to clear up any misunderstandings the class may have.

13–2 THE INDUCTION PROPERTY

The induction property of the set of positive integers can be stated in the following way. It is a fundamental property whose truth we shall assume.

INDUCTION PROPERTY

If a set S of positive integers contains* 1*, and if whenever S contains an integer k, it also contains the integer k* + 1*, then S must be the set of all positive integers.

The only set that can fulfill the conditions stated in the induction property is the set of all positive integers. The conditions on S are that

1. S contains only positive integers.
2. S contains 1.
3. if any positive integer k is an element of S, then the next larger integer, $k + 1$, is also an element of S.

Suppose we know that a set P satisfies these conditions and contains 1, 2, and 3. Since set P contains 3, according to the third condition, set P must contain $3 + 1$, or 4. If P contains 4, then it must contain $4 + 1$, or 5, and so on. Thus, P must be the set of all positive integers.

Let us show how the induction property may be used to prove Proposition I:

The number of real zeros of a nonzero real polynomial is at most equal to the degree of the polynomial.

We have already noted that this proposition actually consists of an infinite set of propositions, which we shall designate by P_1, P_2, P_3, and so on. They can be stated in the following manner.

P_1: The number of real zeros of each real polynomial of degree 1 is at most one.

P_2: The number of real zeros of each real polynomial of degree 2 is at most two.

P_3: The number of real zeros of each real polynomial of degree 3 is at most three.

We could proceed in this way indefinitely. Thus, for each positive integer n, P_n is given by the following proposition.

P_n: The number of real zeros of each real polynomial of degree n is at most n.

We have already proved that P_1, P_2, and P_3 are true propositions. For each positive integer, the proposition P_n is either true or false. Let us consider the set of positive integers n for which P_n is true. We might call this set S. Thus,

$$S = \{n \mid P_n \text{ is true}\}.$$

If we can prove that S is the set of all positive integers, then we shall have proved that every proposition P_n is true. Hence, we shall have proved that Proposition I is true. To prove that S is the set of all positive integers, we shall use the induction property.

Since P_1, P_2, and P_3 are true, the integers 1, 2, and 3 are in set S. Let us now prove that for every integer k in S, the integer $k + 1$ is also in set S. Thus, let k be an element of S. If k is in S, the following proposition is true.

P_k: The number of real zeros of each real polynomial of degree k is at most k.

We want to show that $k + 1$ is also in S. If it is in S, the following proposition is true.

P_{k+1}: The number of real zeros of each real polynomial of degree $k + 1$ is at most $k + 1$.

In attempting to show that P_{k+1} is true, let $p(x)$ be a real polynomial of degree $k + 1$. If $p(x)$ has no real zeros, then the number of real zeros of $p(x)$ is less than $k + 1$. If $p(x)$ has a real zero r, then $x - r$ is a divisor of $p(x)$ by the factor theorem, and

$$p(x) = (x - r)q(x)$$

for some real polynomial $q(x)$ of degree k. If c is another zero of $p(x)$, with $c \neq r$, then $p(c) = 0$, and therefore,

$$(c - r)q(c) = 0.$$

Since $c - r \neq 0$, we must have $q(c) = 0$. Consequently, every zero of $p(x)$ except r is a zero of $q(x)$. It is also true, of course, that every zero of $q(x)$ is a zero of $p(x)$. Thus, the real zeros of $p(x)$ are r and the additional real zeros of $q(x)$.

How many real zeros does $q(x)$ have? Since $q(x)$ has degree k and P_k is true, $q(x)$ has *at most* k real zeros. Now $p(x)$ has at most one

Here the use of k may be related to the use of a, b, c in

$$ax^2 + bx + c = 0.$$

A quadratic equation like

$$3x^2 - 5x - 7 = 0$$

is solved by completing the square, but it gives no information as to the solution set of any other quadratic equation. However, if

$$ax^2 + bx + c = 0$$

is solved by completing the square, formulas for the solution set of all quadratics are obtained:

$$\left\{\frac{-b + \sqrt{b^2 - 4ac}}{2a}, \frac{-b - \sqrt{b^2 - 4ac}}{2a}\right\}.$$

Here, proving P_3 gives no information about P_4 or P_5, and so on. In order to circumvent the problem, a statement of our own making is proved: If P_k is true, then P_{k+1} must be true. Now when one returns to P_3, it is seen that P_4 must be true, P_5 must be true, and so on. Students encountering this technique for the first time often have the uncomfortable feeling that to assume P_k is true, is to assume that which we are trying to prove. However, it must be proved that for any n which is an element of S, P_n implies P_{n+1}. The correct, logical way to do this is to assume *temporarily* P_k for *arbitrary* k and to show that P_{k+1} follows.

more real zero than $q(x)$ does, and therefore, it has *at most* $k + 1$ real zeros. This proves that proposition P_{k+1} is true, and hence, that $k + 1$ is in set S.

We have shown that set S contains the integer 1, and that whenever S contains the integer k, it also contains the integer $k + 1$. Hence, S is the set of all positive integers by the induction property. Thus, we have proved that Proposition I is true. A proof of this type is called a proof by *mathematical induction.*

We turn now to Proposition II. It also consists of an infinite set of propositions: P_1, P_2, P_3, and so on. In each of these propositions, Q is a set of points in a plane.

P_1: If the number of points in Q is 1, then the number of lines that can be drawn through two or more points of Q is at most $\frac{1}{2} \cdot 1 \cdot (1 - 1)$, or 0.

P_2: If the number of points in Q is 2, then the number of lines that can be drawn through two or more points of Q is at most $\frac{1}{2} \cdot 2 \cdot (2 - 1)$, or 1.

P_3: If the number of points in Q is 3, then the number of lines that can be drawn through two or more points of Q is at most $\frac{1}{2} \cdot 3 \cdot (3 - 1)$, or 3.

In general, for each positive integer n, proposition P_n can be stated in the following way.

P_n: If the number of points in Q is n, then the number of lines that can be drawn through two or more points of Q is at most $\frac{1}{2}n(n - 1)$.

For each positive integer, the proposition P_n is either true or false. We collect together into one set S every positive integer n such that P_n is true; that is, we let

$$S = \{n \mid P_n \text{ is true}\}.$$

As we showed in the preceding section, propositions P_1, P_2, P_3, and P_4 are true. We know then that the integers 1, 2, 3, and 4 are in S. We shall have proved that Proposition II is true when we have proved that S is the set of all positive integers. Since 1 is in S, we must still prove that for every integer k in S, the integer $k + 1$ is also in S.

Exercises for Discussion, page 520

It is recommended that the Exercises for Discussion be covered carefully in class.

Answers to Exercises for Discussion 1(b)–1(d), 1(h), page 520

1. (b) P_k: If Q has k points and $k \geqq 3$, then the number of triangles having the points of Q as vertices is at most $\frac{1}{6}k(k - 1)(k - 2)$.
   (c) P_{k+1}: If Q has $k + 1$ points and $k \geqq 2$, then the number of triangles having points of Q as vertices is at most $\frac{1}{6}(k + 1)k(k - 1)$.
   (d) We select A and two points of T as the three vertices. We may select the two points of T in ${}_kC_2$ ways.
   (g) ${}_kC_2 + \frac{1}{6}k(k - 1)(k - 2)$
   $= \frac{1}{2}k(k - 1) + \frac{1}{6}k(k - 1) \times (k - 2)$
   $= \frac{1}{2}k(k - 1)[1 + \frac{1}{3}(k - 2)]$
   $= \frac{1}{2}k(k - 1)\left[\frac{3 + k - 2}{3}\right]$
   $= \frac{1}{6}k(k - 1)(k + 1)$
   (h) The number of triangles in set Q is at most the number in set T plus the number determined by point A and points of T. This sum is equal to $\frac{1}{6}k(k - 1)(k + 1)$. Hence, P_{k+1} is true. By the induction property, P_n is true.

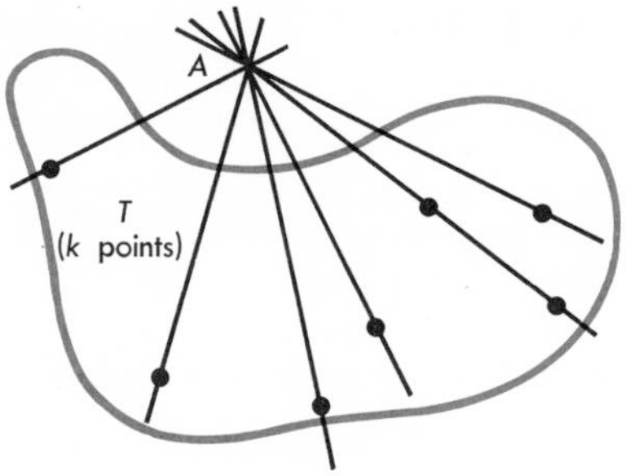

FIGURE 13-4

We first assume that the integer k is in S, that is, that P_k is true. We shall attempt to prove that $k + 1$ is in S, that is, that P_{k+1} is true. The proposition P_{k+1} is stated below.

P_{k+1}: If the number of points in Q is $k + 1$, then the number of lines that can be drawn through two or more points of Q is at most $\frac{1}{2}(k + 1)[(k + 1) - 1]$, or $\frac{1}{2}k(k + 1)$.

To prove that P_{k+1} is true, let Q be a set of $k + 1$ points and let A be one of the points of Q. The other k points of set Q form a set T. Since T has k points and since P_k is true, there are *at most*

$$\tfrac{1}{2}k(k - 1)$$

lines that can be drawn through two or more points of T. In addition to these lines, what lines can be drawn through two or more points of Q? Each line is drawn through point A and some point of set T, as shown in Fig. 13-4. Since set T contains k points, there are *at most* k lines drawn through point A and some point of set T. Thus, there are *at most*

$$\tfrac{1}{2}k(k - 1) + k$$

lines that can be drawn through two or more points of set Q. The expression above is equivalent to each of the following.

$$\tfrac{1}{2}[k(k - 1) + 2k], \quad \tfrac{1}{2}[k(k - 1 + 2)], \quad \tfrac{1}{2}k(k + 1)$$

Hence, at most $\frac{1}{2}k(k + 1)$ lines can be drawn through two or more points of Q. This proves that P_{k+1} is true.

We have proved that the integer 1 is in set S, and that whenever k is in S, then $k + 1$ is also in S. Therefore, S is the set of all positive integers by the induction property, and we have proved by mathematical induction that Proposition II is true.

Answer to Exercise for Discussion 2, page 520

2. $\frac{n(n-1)}{2}$ for $n \geqq 2$

$n = 2$: ${}_2C_2 = 1$, $\frac{2(2-1)}{2} = 1$

$n = 3$: ${}_3C_2 = 3$, $\frac{3(3-1)}{2} = 3$

$n = 4$: ${}_4C_2 = 6$, $\frac{4(4-1)}{2} = 6$

$n = 5$: ${}_5C_2 = 10$, $\frac{5(5-1)}{2} = 10$

Let $T(n)$ be the number of games played when n boys are in the tournament. Let

$$S = \left\{n \mid T(n) = \frac{n(n-1)}{2}\right\};$$

2 is in S.

Let k be an element of S; then

$$T(k) = \frac{k(k-1)}{2}.$$

For $k + 1$ entries in the tournament, there are k additional games to be played, namely, the games played by the one new boy with each of the original k boys. Hence,

$$T(k+1) = T(k) + k = \frac{(k+1)k}{2},$$

and $k + 1$ is in S.

Since 2 is in S and since, whenever k is in S, $k + 1$ is in S, it follows by the induction property that S is the set of all positive integers greater than or equal to 2.

It is recommended that most of the exercises be presented by students and discussed, but that only a few be written out in detail. In order for the student to benefit from the writing it is important to mark these papers carefully and to require that they be done over and over until correct.

Exercises

It is suggested that one of the proofs from the Exercises be put on the board each day by a student with all the details included that would be expected on his paper.

Exercise 5 on page 521 could be assigned to the best students for extra credit.

Quiz

1. Use mathematical induction to show that the nth odd natural number is $2n - 1$. (ans: For each positive integer n, let P_n be the following proposition: P_n: the nth odd natural number is $2n - 1$. Next, let

$$S = \{n \mid P_n \text{ is true}\}.$$

Now 1 is in set S, since the first odd natural number is

$$2(1) - 1 = 1.$$

If k is an integer in set S, then the following proposition is true: P_k: the kth odd natural number is $2k - 1$. To show that $k + 1$ is in S, we must show that the following proposition is true: P_{k+1}: the $(k + 1)$th odd natural number is

$$2(k + 1) - 1 = 2k + 1.$$

Since the $(k + 1)$th odd natural number will be 2 greater than the kth odd number, the former will be equal to $(2k - 1) + 2$ or $2k + 1$. We have proved that 1 is in S, and that whenever k is in S, $k + 1$ is also in S. Hence, by the induction property, S is the set of all positive integers. This means that every proposition P_n is true.)

Exercises for Discussion

1. Let Q be a set of points in a plane and P_n be the following proposition.

   P_n: If Q has n points and $n \geqq 3$, then the number of triangles having points of Q as vertices is at most $\frac{1}{6}n(n - 1)(n - 2)$.

   Complete the proof of this proposition by following the steps below.

   (a) Show that P_3, P_4, and P_5 are true. *See Section 13-1, Exercise 2.*

   (b) State proposition P_k. Assume that proposition P_k is true.

   (c) State proposition P_{k+1}.

   (d) To prove that P_{k+1} is true, let T be a set of k points in Q and A be any point of Q not in T. Why are there at most ${}_kC_2$ triangles which have A as one vertex and points of T as the other two vertices?

   (e) ${}_kC_2 = \frac{?}{2}$ *k(k − 1)*

   (f) The maximum number of triangles having points of T as vertices is $\frac{1}{6}k(\underline{k - ?1})(\underline{k - ?2})$.

   (g) Show that ${}_kC_2 + \frac{1}{6}k(k - 1)(k - 2) = \frac{1}{6}k(k - 1)(k + 1)$.

   (h) Use part (g) to show that P_{k+1} is true. Why is P_n now true for every positive integer n?

2. Suppose that n boys are entered in a chess tournament. How many games are played if each boy plays one game with each of the other boys? Show that the formula

$$\frac{n(n - 1)}{2}$$

gives the correct number when $n = 2, 3, 4$, and 5. Use mathematical induction to prove that this formula is true for every positive integer.

Exercises

See Solution Manual for proofs.

1. Devise a formula to determine the number of dominoes in the set that runs from double zero to double n. Prove your formula by mathematical induction. $\frac{(n+1)(n+2)}{2}$, $n \geqq 1$

2. If a convex polygon has n sides, how many diagonals does it have? Prove your formula by mathematical induction. $\frac{n(n-3)}{2}$, $n \geqq 3$

3. The sum of the measures of the angles of a triangle is a measure of 180°. Generalize this result to give the sum of the measures of the angles of any polygon. Prove your formula by mathematical induction. $[(n-2)180]^\circ$

4. In bowling, the pins are arranged in four rows with one pin in the first row, two pins in the second row, three pins in the third row, and four pins in the fourth row. This makes a total of ten pins. Suppose that we arrange the pins in n rows, with one pin in the first row, two in the second row, three in the third row, and so on, with n pins in the nth row. How many pins are there all together? Prove your formula by mathematical induction.

5. Use mathematical induction to prove that $x - y$ is a factor of $x^n - y^n$ for all positive integral values of n.

13-3 FURTHER EXAMPLES OF INDUCTION

Since mathematical induction is a property of the integers, it is often used to prove other properties of the integers. In this section, we shall give a few examples of this use of the induction property.

Problem 1. Prove that the sum of the first n positive odd integers is n^2 for every positive integer n.

Solution. Although we cannot actually add one number, the sum of the first *one* positive odd integer is understood to be the first positive odd integer, 1. Since

$$1 = 1^2,$$

the sum of the first one positive odd integer is 1^2. The sum of the first *two* positive odd integers is

$$1 + 3 = 4, \quad \text{or } 2^2.$$

The sum of the first *three* is

$$1 + 3 + 5 = 9, \quad \text{or } 3^2.$$

Thus, the sum of the first n positive odd integers is n^2 when n is equal to 1, 2, or 3. Therefore, if we let

$$S = \{n \mid \text{the sum of the first } n \text{ positive odd integers is } n^2\},$$

then 1, 2, and 3 are in S. We wish to prove that S is the set P of all positive integers.

13-3 FURTHER EXAMPLES OF INDUCTION

It should be made clear that the induction property is *postulated* for the system of natural numbers (here identified with the positive integers). It does not even make sense for the system of integers, rationals, irrationals, and so on. In the beginning, according to the Italian mathematician, Peano, there were five postulates for the positive integers. The principle of mathematical induction is based on the fifth postulate. These five postulates, with definitions of addition and multiplication based on them, suffice for proving all the properties (such as commutativity, and so on) of the positive integers. From the integers, the system of rational numbers is constructed as the set of all pairs of integers (a, b), where the rational number (a, b) is a solution of the equation $bx = a$. Finally, the system of real numbers is constructed as the set of all infinite decimals. Hence, the Peano postulates form the very foundation of the real number system. The class should be encouraged to do some reading on this subject. (See Birkhoff and MacLane, *A Survey of Modern Algebra*.)

It is recommended that Problem 1 be carefully developed in class.

Colored chalk and square brackets may be used for the following:

$$\overbrace{[1 + 3 + 5 + \cdots + (2k - 1)]}^{\text{Indicated sum of first } k \text{ terms}} + \underbrace{(2k + 1)}_{(k+1)\text{st term}}$$

$$\underbrace{\overbrace{[k^2]}^{\text{Sum of first } k \text{ terms}} + (2k + 1)}_{\text{Sum of } k+1 \text{ terms}}$$

$$= (k + 1)^2.$$

This problem lays the groundwork for the study of arithmetic series in Section 13–4.

Problem 3 and others of its type should be very interesting to the students. You may wish to use it to review factoring by use of the distributive law.

Problem 4 should be discussed since it reviews an important theorem in trigonometry. If you omitted the theorem previously, you may wish to take it up here.

By the induction property, we can prove that $S = P$ by showing that whenever k is in S, then $k + 1$ is also in S. If k is in S, the sum of the first k positive odd integers is k^2. In other words,

$$1 + 3 + 5 + \cdots + (2k - 1) = k^2.$$

Since the kth odd integer is denoted by $2k - 1$, the $(k + 1)$-odd integer is denoted by $(2k - 1) + 2$, or $2k + 1$. Therefore, the sum of the first $k + 1$ positive odd integers is $2k + 1$ more than the sum of the first k positive odd integers. Since the sum of the first k positive odd integers is k^2, the sum of the first $k + 1$ is $k^2 + (2k + 1)$, or $(k + 1)^2$. In other words,

$$\begin{aligned} 1 + 3 + 5 + \cdots + (2k - 1) + (2k + 1) &= k^2 + 2k + 1 \\ &= (k + 1)^2. \end{aligned}$$

Since the sum of the first $k + 1$ positive odd integers is $(k + 1)^2$, $k + 1$ is in S. Since 1 is in S, and $k + 1$ is in S whenever k is in S, we know that, by the induction property, S is the set of all positive integers. Therefore, the sum of the first n positive odd integers is n^2 for every positive integer n.

We can use mathematical induction to prove the five laws of exponents, (LE-1) through (LE-5), for positive integral exponents. Before we begin, let us review the definition of exponents: For each number x, $x^1 = x$, $x^2 = x \cdot x$, and whenever x^k is defined, then x^{k+1} is defined by

$$x^{k+1} = x^k \cdot x.$$

Problem 2. Prove the fourth law of exponents, (LE-4):

$$(x \cdot y)^n = x^n \cdot y^n$$

for all numbers x and y and every positive integer n.

Solution. For each positive integer n, let P_n be the following proposition.

P_n: The equation $(x \cdot y)^n = x^n \cdot y^n$ is true for every pair x, y of numbers.

Next, let

$$S = \{n \mid P_n \text{ is true}\}.$$

Now 1 is in set S, since the equation

$$(x \cdot y)^1 = x^1 \cdot y^1$$

is true for every pair x, y of numbers by the definition of the first power of a number: $(x \cdot y)^1 = x \cdot y$, $x^1 = x$, $y^1 = y$, and therefore, $(x \cdot y)^1 = x^1 \cdot y^1$. If k is an integer in set S, then the following proposition is true.

$\boldsymbol{P_k}$: The equation $(x \cdot y)^k = x^k \cdot y^k$ is true for every pair x, y of numbers.

To show that $k + 1$ is in S, we must show that the following proposition is true.

$\boldsymbol{P_{k+1}}$: The equation $(x \cdot y)^{k+1} = x^{k+1} \cdot y^{k+1}$ is true for every pair x, y of numbers.

To show that P_{k+1} is true, we return to the definition of the $(k + 1)$-power of any number. Thus, by definition,

$$(x \cdot y)^{k+1} = (x \cdot y)^k \cdot (x \cdot y), \quad x^{k+1} = x^k \cdot x, \quad y^{k+1} = y^k \cdot y.$$

Hence, each of the following equations is true for every pair x, y of numbers.

$$\begin{aligned} (x \cdot y)^{k+1} &= (x \cdot y)^k \cdot (x \cdot y) && \text{(Def-Exp)} \\ (x \cdot y)^{k+1} &= (x^k \cdot y^k) \cdot (x \cdot y) && \text{(since } P_k \text{ is true)} \\ (x \cdot y)^{k+1} &= (x^k \cdot x) \cdot (y^k \cdot y) && \text{(R-M)} \\ (x \cdot y)^{k+1} &= x^{k+1} \cdot y^{k+1} && \text{(Def-Exp)} \end{aligned}$$

Since this last equation is true, P_{k+1} is true.

We have proved that 1 is in S, and that whenever k is in S, $k + 1$ is also in S. Hence, by the induction property, S is the set of all positive integers. This means that every proposition P_n is true. Thus, we have proved the fourth law of exponents.

In Problem 3, we shall use mathematical induction to prove a result of number theory.

Problem 3. Prove that the integer $7^{2n} - 1$ is divisible by 48 for every positive integer n.

Solution. If $n = 1$, then the given integer is $7^2 - 1$, or 48. Hence, it is divisible by 48. If $n = 2$, the given integer is $7^4 - 1$, or 2400. Since $2400 = 48 \cdot 50$, $7^4 - 1$ is divisible by 48. Therefore, the integers 1 and 2 are in set S, defined by

$$S = \{n \mid 7^{2n} - 1 \text{ is divisible by } 48\}.$$

To complete the given proof, we must show that S is the set of all positive integers.

Exercises for Discussion, page 525

If time is limited, it is suggested that at least Exercises for Discussion 1 and 3 be covered.

Answers to Exercises for Discussion 1(b), 2(b), 2(c), 3(b)–4, page 525

1. (b) P_1 is true: $\dfrac{1(2)}{1} = 1$

Assume P_k is true:

$$1 + 2 + \cdots + k = \frac{k(k+1)}{2}$$

Prove P_{k+1} is true:

$$1 + 2 + \cdots + k + (k+1) = \frac{(k+1)(k+2)}{2}$$

Proof:

$$\begin{aligned} 1 + 2 + \cdots + k + (k+1) &= \frac{k(k+1)}{2} + (k+1) \\ &= (k+1)\left(\frac{k}{2} + 1\right) \\ &= (k+1)\left(\frac{k+2}{2}\right) \\ &= \frac{(k+1)(k+2)}{2} \end{aligned}$$

Hence, by the induction property, P_n is true.

2. (b)

$$\begin{aligned} 1 &= 1^2 = 1^2 \\ 9 &= 3^2 = (1+2)^2 \\ 36 &= 6^2 = (1+2+3)^2 \\ 100 &= 10^2 \\ &= (1+2+3+4)^2 \\ 1^3 + 2^3 + 3^3 + \cdots + n^3 &= (1+2+3+\cdots+n)^2 \end{aligned}$$

Thus,

$$1^3 + 2^3 + 3^3 + \cdots + n^3 = \left[\frac{n(n+1)}{2}\right]^2.$$

(c) P_1 is true: $\left[\frac{1(1+1)}{2}\right]^2 = 1$

Assume P_k is true:

$$1^3 + 2^3 + 3^3 + \cdots + k^3 = \left[\frac{k(k+1)}{2}\right]^2$$

Prove P_{k+1} is true:

$$1^3 + 2^3 + 3^3 + \cdots + k^3 + (k+1)^3 = \left[\frac{(k+1)(k+2)}{2}\right]^2$$

Proof: $1^3 + 2^3 + 3^3 + \cdots + k^3 + (k+1)^3$

$$= \left[\frac{k(k+1)}{2}\right]^2 + (k+1)^3$$

$$= (k+1)^2\left[\frac{k^2}{4} + (k+1)\right]$$

$$= (k+1)^2\left(\frac{k^2+4k+4}{4}\right)$$

$$= (k+1)^2\left(\frac{k+2}{2}\right)^2$$

$$= \left[\frac{(k+1)(k+2)}{2}\right]^2$$

Hence, P_{k+1} is true whenever P_k is true. By the induction property, P_n is true.

3. (b)

$$\frac{1}{1} = \frac{3}{3}$$

$$\frac{5}{1+2} = \frac{5}{3}$$

$$\frac{14}{1+2+3} = \frac{7}{3}$$

$$\frac{30}{1+2+3+4} = \frac{9}{3}$$

From these results we conjecture:

$$\frac{1^2 + 2^2 + 3^2 + \cdots + n^2}{1 + 2 + 3 + \cdots + n} = \frac{2n+1}{3}.$$

If k is an element of S, then $7^{2k} - 1$ is divisible by 48. If q designates the quotient obtained by dividing $7^{2k} - 1$ by 48, then q is an integer such that

$$7^{2k} - 1 = 48q, \quad \text{or } 7^{2k} = 1 + 48q.$$

Is $k + 1$ also in S? In other words, is 48 a divisor of $7^{2(k+1)} - 1$? To answer this question, we observe that

$$\begin{aligned} 7^{2(k+1)} - 1 &= 7^{2k+2} - 1 \\ &= (7^{2k} \cdot 7^2) - 1 \\ &= (1 + 48q)7^2 - 1 \\ &= 7^2 + (48q \cdot 7^2) - 1 \\ &= 49 + (48q \cdot 7^2) - 1 \\ &= 48 + (48q \cdot 7^2) \\ &= 48(1 + 49q). \end{aligned}$$

Since $1 + 49q$ is an integer, this last equation shows that 48 is a divisor of $7^{2(k+1)} - 1$. Therefore, $k + 1$ is in set S.

Since 1 is in set S, and since, whenever k is in S, then $k + 1$ is also in S, the set S is the set of all positive integers by the induction property. This proves that $7^{2n} - 1$ is divisible by 48 for every positive integer n.

Problem 4. Prove De Moivre's theorem:

$$[r(\cos\theta + i\sin\theta)]^n = r^n(\cos n\theta + i\sin n\theta)$$

for every positive integer n.

Solution. Let set S contain every positive integer n for which the equation above is true. Since

$$[r(\cos\theta + i\sin\theta)]^1 = r^1[(\cos 1\cdot\theta) + (i\sin 1\cdot\theta)]$$

is true, 1 is in S. Let k be an integer in S, so that the equation

$$[r(\cos\theta + i\sin\theta)]^k = r^k(\cos k\theta + i\sin k\theta)$$

is true. We wish to prove that the following equation is also true.

$$[r(\cos\theta + i\sin\theta)]^{k+1} = r^{k+1}[\cos(k+1)\theta + i\sin(k+1)\theta]$$

By definition of the $(k + 1)$-power of a number,

$$[r(\cos\theta + i\sin\theta)]^{k+1} = [r(\cos\theta + i\sin\theta)]^k[r(\cos\theta + i\sin\theta)].$$

Using the known value of the kth power of $r(\cos\theta + i\sin\theta)$ and the method of finding a trigonometric form of the product of two complex numbers, we may find the $(k+1)$-power of $r(\cos\theta + i\sin\theta)$ as follows:

$$\begin{aligned}[r(\cos\theta + i\sin\theta)]^{k+1} &= [r(\cos\theta + i\sin\theta)]^k[r(\cos\theta + i\sin\theta)]\\ &= [r^k(\cos k\theta + i\sin k\theta)][r(\cos\theta + i\sin\theta)]\\ &= r^k \cdot r[\cos(k\theta+\theta) + i\sin(k\theta+\theta)]\\ &= r^{k+1}[\cos(k+1)\theta + i\sin(k+1)\theta].\end{aligned}$$

We have proved that $k+1$ is also in set S.

Since 1 is in set S, and since, whenever the integer k is in S, $k+1$ is also in S, the set S is the set of all positive integers by the induction property. This proves De Moivre's theorem.

Exercises for Discussion

1. (a) Complete the following formula for the sum of the first n positive integers.

$$1 + 2 + 3 + \cdots + n = \frac{n(?)}{2}$$

(b) Prove that the formula you completed in part (a) is true for all positive integers n.

2. (a) Find each of the following sums.

$$1^3, \quad 1^3 + 2^3, \quad 1^3 + 2^3 + 3^3, \quad 1^3 + 2^3 + 3^3 + 4^3$$

(b) Complete the following formula for the sum of the first n positive cubes.

$$1^3 + 2^3 + 3^3 + \cdots + n^3 = \left(\frac{?}{?}\right)^2$$

(c) Prove that the formula you completed in part (b) is true for all positive integers n.

3. (a) Find the following sums.

$$1^2, \quad 1^2 + 2^2, \quad 1^2 + 2^2 + 3^2, \quad 1^2 + 2^2 + 3^2 + 4^2$$

(b) Complete the description of

$$R = \left\{n \mid 1^2 + 2^2 + 3^2 + \cdots + n^2 = \frac{(?)(n+1)(2n+1)}{6}\right\}.$$

(c) Use the induction property to prove that R is the set of all positive integers.

4. Prove that if x is a real number and m is an arbitrary positive integer, then $x^m \cdot x^n = x^{m+n}$, (LE-1), is true for every positive integer n.

Therefore,

$$\begin{aligned}1^2 + 2^2 + 3^2 + \cdots + n^2 &= \left(\frac{2n+1}{3}\right)(1 + 2 + 3 + \cdots + n),\\ &= \left(\frac{2n+1}{3}\right)\left[\frac{n(n+1)}{2}\right],\\ &= \frac{n(n+1)(2n+1)}{6}.\end{aligned}$$

$$R = \left\{n \mid 1^2 + 2^2 + 3^2 + \cdots + n^2 = \frac{n(n+1)(2n+1)}{6}\right\}$$

(c) $1 = \frac{1}{6} \cdot 1 \cdot 2 \cdot 3$, so 1 is in R. Let k be in R; then

$$\begin{aligned}1^2 + 2^2 + \cdots + k^2 + (k+1)^2 &= \tfrac{1}{6}k(k+1)(2k+1) + (k+1)^2\\ &= \frac{k+1}{6}[(2k+1)\cdot k + 6 \times (k+1)]\\ &= \tfrac{1}{6}(k+1)(2k+3)(k+2).\end{aligned}$$

Thus, 1 is in R, and $k+1$ is in R whenever k is in R; by the induction property, R is the set of all positive integers.

4. $x^m \cdot x^1 = x^{m+1}$. Hence, P_1 is true. Assume P_k is true:

$$x^m \cdot x^k = x^{m+k}$$

Prove P_{k+1} is true:

$$x^m \cdot x^{k+1} = x^{m+k+1}$$

Proof:

$$\begin{aligned}x^m \cdot x^{k+1} &= x^m(x^k \cdot x^1)\\ &= (x^m x^k)x\\ &= x^{m+k} \cdot x\\ &= x^{m+k+1}\end{aligned}$$

Hence, P_{k+1} is true when P_k is true. Thus, P_n is true by the induction property.

Exercises

Exercise 2 should make for a lively class discussion.

Exercise 9 should also be included as the fact it presents is important.

Exercises 12 and 13 could be used for honors work.

The fact that the laws of exponents require proof by mathematical induction is important, and merits discussion whether Exercises 14–16 are assigned or not.

Quiz

1. Using induction show that

$$1 \cdot 2 \cdot 3 + 2 \cdot 3 \cdot 4 + \cdots + n(n+1)(n+2) = \frac{n(n+1)(n+2)(n+3)}{4}$$

for all positive integers n. (ans: For each positive integer n, let P_n be the following proposition:

$$P_n\colon 1 \cdot 2 \cdot 3 + 2 \cdot 3 \cdot 4 + \cdots + n(n+1)(n+2) = \frac{n(n+1)(n+2)(n+3)}{4}.$$

Next, let $S = \{n \mid P_n \text{ is true}\}$. Now 1 is in set S, since

$$1 \cdot 2 \cdot 3 = \frac{1(1+1)(1+2)(1+3)}{4}.$$

If k is an integer in set S, then the following proposition is true:

$$P_k\colon 1 \cdot 2 \cdot 3 + 2 \cdot 3 \cdot 4 + \cdots + k(k+1)(k+2) = \frac{k(k+1)(k+2)(k+3)}{4}.$$

To show that $k+1$ is in S, we must show that the following proposition is true:

$$P_{k+1}\colon 1 \cdot 2 \cdot 3 + 2 \cdot 3 \cdot 4 + \cdots k(k+1)(k+2) + (k+1)(k+2)(k+3) = \frac{(k+1)(k+2)(k+3)(k+4)}{4}.$$

Exercises

1. Use the induction property to prove that $(^-1)^n = 1$ if n is a positive even integer. (Hint: Let $Q = \{w \mid (^-1)^{2w} = 1 \text{ is true}\}$.)
2. Use the induction property to prove that $(^-1)^n = {}^-1$ if n is a positive odd integer.
3. Prove that the integer $5^{2n} - 1$ is divisible by 24 for every positive integer n.
4. Prove that the integer $4^n + (^-1)^{n-1}$ is divisible by 5 for every positive integer n.
5. Prove that for every integer $n > 0$, the integer $n^3 + 5n$ is divisible by 6.
6. Let $V = \{n \mid n^2 - n + 11 \text{ is a prime number}\}$.
   (a) How many of the first ten positive integers are in V?
   (b) Do you think that V is the set of all positive integers?
   (c) Is 11 in V?
   (d) Which part of the induction property does V satisfy?
7. Let

$$U = \left\{n \mid 5 + 10 + 15 + \cdots + 5n = \frac{5n(n+1)}{2} + (1-n)(2-n)(3-n)\right\}.$$

   (a) How many of the first four positive integers are in U?
   (b) Is U the set of all positive integers?
8. Let G be the set of positive even integers which can be expressed as the sum of two prime numbers. (Note: 1 is not a prime.)
   (a) Which of the positive even integers less than 20 are in G?
   (b) Which of the positive even integers less than 40 are in G?
   (c) Which positive even integers do you think are in G?

△

9. Prove that $(1+a)^n > 1 + na$ for every integer $n \geqq 1$ and every number $a > 0$. Is this inequality true for every integer $n > 1$ and some negative number a?
10. Prove by mathematical induction that $2^n > n$ for every positive integer n.
11. Let r be a positive real number. Prove by mathematical induction that
    (a) if $r > 1$, then $r^n > 1$ for every positive integer n.
    (b) if $r < 1$, then $r^n < 1$ for every positive integer n.

12. Prove by mathematical induction that

$$1 \cdot 2^2 + 2 \cdot 3^2 + 3 \cdot 4^2 + \cdots + n \cdot (n+1)^2 = \tfrac{1}{12}n(n+1)(n+2)(3n+5)$$

for every positive integer n.

13. Let $W = \{n \mid 4 + 8 + 12 + \cdots + 4n = 2n(n+1) + 3\}$.

(a) Is $k + 1$ in W whenever k is in W?
(b) Do you think that W is the set of all positive integers?
(c) Is 1 in W?
(d) Which part of the induction property does W satisfy?

14. Prove that if x is a nonzero real number and m is an arbitrary positive integer, then

$$\frac{x^m}{x^n} = x^{m-n} \qquad \text{(LE-2)}$$

is true for every positive integer $n \leqq m$.

15. Prove that if x is a real number and m is a positive integer,

$$(x^m)^n = x^{mn} \qquad \text{(LE-3)}$$

is true for every positive integer n.

16. Prove that if x and y are real numbers, and $y \neq 0$, then

$$\left(\frac{x}{y}\right)^n = \frac{x^n}{y^n} \qquad \text{(LE-5)}$$

is true for every positive integer n.

13–4 ARITHMETIC SERIES

On pages 521 and 522, we proved that the sum of the first n positive odd integers is n^2:

$$1 + 3 + 5 + \cdots + (2n - 1) = n^2$$

for every positive integer n. In the same way, we can prove that the sum of the first n positive even integers is $n^2 + n$:

$$2 + 4 + 6 + \cdots + 2n = n^2 + n$$

for every positive integer n. Each of the equations above is called a *summation formula.* The left side of each equation is an example of an *arithmetic series.*

Since P_k is true, then

$$1 \cdot 2 \cdot 3 + 2 \cdot 3 \cdot 4 + \cdots k(k+1)(k+2) + (k+1)(k+2)(k+3) = \frac{k(k+1)(k+2)(k+3)}{4} + (k+1)(k+2)(k+3) = \frac{(k+1)(k+2)(k+3) \times (k+4)}{4}.$$

It has been proven that 1 is in S and that whenever k is in S, $k + 1$ is also in S. Hence, by the induction property, S is the set of all positive integers. This means that every proposition P_n is true.)

13–4 ARITHMETIC SERIES

The objective here is not just to obtain formulas and use them over and over. On one hand, the aim is to use the inductive property to prove that a given formula generates an infinite number of true statements, one for every positive integer. On the other hand, the aim is also to use some formulas (which have already been proved by induction) and a little ingenuity with the properties of the real numbers to derive further formulas without having to use induction. In particular, both methods are used to establish the formula for the sum of the first n terms of an arithmetic series. The definition of an arithmetic series and these two procedures should be emphasized rather than the formula

$$A(n) = na + \frac{d}{2}(n^2 - n).$$

It should be impressed upon the student from the beginning that the important thing is the definition of the arithmetic series. Several could be written on the board. For example,

$$^-1 + 1 + 3 + 5 + 7 + 9 + \cdots$$
$$^-10 - 7 - 4 - 1 + 2 + 5 + 8 + \cdots$$

The students should observe that any term is the average of the neighboring terms. In the first series,

$$3 = \frac{1+5}{2}, \quad 1 = \frac{^-1+3}{2},$$
$$7 = \frac{5+9}{2}.$$

In the second series,

$$^-7 = \frac{^-10-4}{2}, \quad 2 = \frac{^-1+5}{2},$$
$$5 = \frac{2+8}{2}.$$

This is revealed in the pattern

$$a + (a + d) + (a + 2d) + \cdots$$

where

$$a + d = \frac{a + (a + 2d)}{2}.$$

It should be noted by the students that any two terms of a series will describe the series, for the general pattern only involves two variables. Thus, if 7 is the 11th term and 20 is the 14th term, then

$$\begin{cases} 7 = a + 10d, \\ 20 = a + 13d, \end{cases}$$

and the series is uniquely determined.

ARITHMETIC SERIES

An algebraic expression of the form

$$a + (a + d) + (a + 2d) + \cdots + [a + (n - 1)d]$$

is called an arithmetic series with n terms. The number a is called the first term, and the number d is called the difference of this series.

We note that each term of an arithmetic series except the first is obtained from the preceding term by adding d to it. In other words, the *difference* between a term and its predecessor is d.

The values of a and d for the arithmetic series listed above are given below.

$$1 + 3 + 5 + \cdots + (2n - 1); \quad a = 1, d = 2$$
$$2 + 4 + 6 + \cdots + 2n; \quad a = 2, d = 2$$

Problem 1. Derive a formula for the sum of an arithmetic series, given that the first term is 5 and the difference is 4.

Solution. This arithmetic series starts out as follows:

$$5 + 9 + 13 + 17 + 21 + 25 + \cdots$$

Thus, the first term is $4 + 1$; the second term is $(4 \cdot 2) + 1$; the third term is $(4 \cdot 3) + 1$; and so on. Hence, the nth term is $4n + 1$ for each positive integer n. Therefore,

$$5 + 9 + 13 + \cdots + (4n + 1)$$

describes an arithmetic series with n terms for which $a = 5$ and $d = 4$. This series can be denoted by A_n,

$$A_n = 5 + 9 + 13 + \cdots + (4n + 1).$$

We now wish to find a simpler expression for A_n. We note that, in particular,

$$A_1 = 5,$$
$$A_2 = 5 + 9, \quad \text{or } 14,$$
$$A_3 = 5 + 9 + 13, \quad \text{or } 27.$$

Making use of the fact that each term of A_n is 1 more than a multiple of 4, we can rearrange the terms of A_n in the following way.

$$A_n = (4 + 1) + (8 + 1) + (12 + 1) + \cdots + (4n + 1)$$

$$= (4 + 8 + 12 + \cdots + 4n) + \overbrace{(1 + 1 + 1 + \cdots + 1)}^{n \text{ terms}}$$

$$= 2(2 + 4 + 6 + \cdots + 2n) + n$$

Now we may use the summation formula for the sum of the first n positive even integers to obtain

$$A_n = 2(n^2 + n) + n, \quad \text{or } A_n = 2n^2 + 3n.$$

This result is the desired summation formula for A_n. For example, if this series has twenty terms, then

$$5 + 9 + 13 + \cdots + 81 = (2 \cdot 20^2) + (3 \cdot 20), \quad \text{or } 860,$$

according to the summation formula above.

If we were given the arithmetic series

$$A_n = 5 + 9 + 13 + \cdots + (4n + 1)$$

and the summation formula

$$A_n = 2n^2 + 3n$$

without any supporting evidence of its truth, then we could prove that the formula is true by mathematical induction in the following way. Let S be the set consisting of every positive integer n for which the equation $A_n = 2n^2 + 3n$ is true. We may verify that 1 is in S; thus,

$$A_1 = 5 \quad \text{and} \quad (2 \cdot 1^2) + (3 \cdot 1) = 5$$

so that the equation $A_1 = (2 \cdot 1^2) + (3 \cdot 1)$ is true. Next, let k be an integer in S. Hence, the equation

$$A_k = 2k^2 + 3k$$

is true. If $k + 1$ is in S, then the equation

$$A_{k+1} = 2(k + 1)^2 + 3(k + 1)$$

must also be true. Remember that, by definition,

$$A_{k+1} = 5 + 9 + 13 + \cdots + [4(k + 1) + 1]$$

Problem 1 on the opposite page produces a sum formula for just one arithmetic series, but reveals a method for finding a sum formula applicable to any arithmetic series:

$$a + (a + d) + (a + 2d) + \cdots$$

This formula is found in Problem 2 on page 530.

You may want to omit the second proof by induction and continue on to Problem 2.

is an arithmetic series with $k + 1$ terms. Since the sum of the first k terms of A_{k+1} is A_k, the equation

$$A_{k+1} = A_k + [4(k + 1) + 1]$$

is true. Replacing A_k by $2k^2 + 3k$, we obtain the true equation

$$A_{k+1} = 2k^2 + 3k + (4k + 5).$$

Thus, the equations

$$A_{k+1} = (2k^2 + 4k + 2) + (3k + 3)$$

and

$$A_{k+1} = 2(k + 1)^2 + 3(k + 1)$$

are true. This proves that $k + 1$ is in set S. Hence, by mathematical induction, we have completed the proof that S is the set of all positive integers. Therefore, the formula

$$A_n = 2n^2 + 3n$$

is true for every positive integer n.

The students should not have any difficulty in following Problem 2 after Problem 1 has been discussed.

Problem 2. Derive a formula for the sum of any arithmetic series.

Solution. Let A_n designate the arithmetic series having n terms, first term a, and difference d.

$$A_n = a + (a + d) + (a + 2d) + \cdots + [a + (n - 1)d]$$

Then

$$A_1 = a,$$
$$A_2 = a + (a + d),$$
$$A_3 = a + (a + d) + (a + 2d).$$

In the preceding problem, we found a summation formula for a particular arithmetic series. We can find a summation formula for a general arithmetic series in the same way. Thus,

$$A_n = \overbrace{(a + a + a + \cdots + a)}^{n \text{ terms}} + [d + 2d + \cdots + (n - 1)d]$$

$$= na + \frac{d}{2}[2 + 4 + \cdots + 2(n - 1)].$$

By the formula for the sum of the first n positive even integers,

$$2 + 4 + \cdots + 2(n - 1) = (n - 1)^2 + (n - 1),$$

or

$$2 + 4 + \cdots + 2(n - 1) = n^2 - n.$$

Hence, the *formula for the sum of an arithmetic series* is

$$a + (a + d) + (a + 2d) + \cdots + [a + (n - 1)d] = na + \frac{d}{2}(n^2 - n).$$

For variety, let us use mathematical induction to prove that this formula is true for every positive integer n. As we did above, we shall let

$$A_n = a + (a + d) + (a + 2d) + \cdots + [a + (n - 1)d].$$

Then we wish to prove that the equation

$$\boldsymbol{P_n}\text{:}\quad A_n = na + \frac{d}{2}(n^2 - n)$$

is true for every positive integer n. The equation

$$\boldsymbol{P_1}\text{:}\quad A_1 = (1 \cdot a) + \frac{d}{2}(1^2 - 1)$$

is true since each side of this equation is equal to a.

Next, let us assume that k is selected so that P_k is true.

$$\boldsymbol{P_k}\text{:}\quad A_k = ka + \frac{d}{2}(k^2 - k).$$

We shall then prove that P_{k+1} is also true.

$$\boldsymbol{P_{k+1}}\text{:}\quad A_{k+1} = (k + 1)a + \frac{d}{2}[(k + 1)^2 - (k + 1)]$$

$$= (k + 1)a + \frac{d}{2}(k^2 + k).$$

Note that A_{k+1} has precisely one more term than A_k; the last term of A_{k+1} is d more than the last term of A_k:

$$A_{k+1} = A_k + [a + (k - 1)d + d],$$

or

$$A_{k+1} = A_k + (a + kd).$$

In a minimum course, or with below-average students, the proof by induction may be omitted. Instead, the students could practice using the formula.

After replacing A_k by its equal from P_k above, we obtain the true equations

$$A_{k+1} = ka + \frac{d}{2}(k^2 - k) + (a + kd),$$

$$A_{k+1} = (ka + a) + \left[\frac{d}{2}(k^2 - k) + kd\right],$$

$$A_{k+1} = (ka + a) + \frac{d}{2}[(k^2 - k) + 2k],$$

or

$$A_{k+1} = (k + 1)a + \frac{d}{2}(k^2 + k).$$

Consequently, P_{k+1} is true, and the summation formula for an arithmetic series is true for every positive integer n by mathematical induction.

For example, the arithmetic series that starts out $3 + 10 + 17 + \cdots$ has summation formula

$$3 + 10 + 17 + \cdots + [3 + 7(n - 1)] = 3n + \tfrac{7}{2}(n^2 - n),$$

or

$$3 + 10 + 17 + \cdots + [3 + 7(n - 1)] = \tfrac{1}{2}(7n^2 - n).$$

If we wish to find the sum of the first 12 terms of this series, we let $n = 12$ and obtain the following.

$$3 + 10 + 17 + \cdots + 80 = \tfrac{1}{2}[(7 \cdot 144) - 12], \quad \text{or } 498$$

Exercises for Discussion

It is suggested that you go over all of the Exercises for Discussion before assigning the Exercises on the next page.

Exercises for Discussion

1. Each of the following sums is the beginning of an arithmetic series. Find the nth term of each series for the specified value of n.
   (a) $3 + 8 + 13 + \cdots, \quad n = 10$ 48
   (b) $^-2 - 5 - 8 - \cdots, \quad n = 12$ $^-35$

2. Find the sum of each of the arithmetic series described below.
   (a) $13 + 20 + 27 + \cdots + 146$ 1590
   (b) $a = 7,\ d = 4,\ n = 12$ 348

3. The terms of an arithmetic series between the first and the last term are called *arithmetic means*. If the series contains only three terms, the middle one is called *the arithmetic mean* of the other two.
   (a) Find the arithmetic mean of $^-1$ and 2. $\frac{1}{2}$
   (b) Find six arithmetic means between 4 and 25. 7, 10, 13, 16, 19, 22

4. If t designates the nth term of an arithmetic series, find a formula for A_n which contains a, n, and t, instead of a, n, and d. State the formula in words.

5. How many numbers divisible by 8 are there between 50 and 500? Find their sum. 56; 15,456

Exercises

1. Find eight arithmetic means between $^-9$ and 18. $^-6$, $^-3$, 0, 3, 6, 9, 12, 15

2. Find the arithmetic mean of $^-3$ and 6. $\frac{3}{2}$

Each sum below is the beginning of an arithmetic series. Find the nth term of each series for the specified value of n.

3. $\frac{1}{2} + \frac{3}{4} + 1 + \cdots, \quad n = 15$ 4

4. $1 - \frac{1}{2} - 2 - \cdots, \quad n = 9$ $^-11$

5. $20 + 11 + 2 + \cdots, \quad n = 11$ $^-70$

6. $9 + 15 + 21 + \cdots, \quad n = 20$ 123

7. $3 + 10 + 17 + \cdots, \quad n = k$ $7k - 4$

8. $8 - 2 - 12 - \cdots, \quad n = k$ $18 - 10k$

In Exercises 9–14, find the sum of each arithmetic series.

9. $9 + 15 + 21 + \cdots + 93$ 765

10. $a = {^-10}, d = 5, n = 20$ 750

11. $a = \frac{1}{2}, d = {^-\frac{1}{4}}, n = 20$ $\frac{^-75}{2}$

12. $a = 1, d = {^-2}, n = 14$ $^-168$

13. $1 + \cdots + 2, n = 10$ 15

14. $a + \cdots + b$, n terms $\frac{n}{2}(a+b)$

15. Find the sum of all the positive integral multiples of 7 that do not exceed 600. 25,585

16. The sum of an arithmetic series with 13 terms and difference 3 is 286. Determine the first and the thirteenth term. 4; 40

△

17. If the third term of an arithmetic series is 15, and the seventeenth term is $^-27$, what must the sixth term be? 6

18. The fifth term of an arithmetic series is $^-18$ and the ninth term is 4. Find the sum of the first twenty terms. 245

19. Find the number of terms in an arithmetic series with $a = 5$, $d = 2$, and nth term 25. Find A_n. 11; 165

Exercise for Discussion 4 contains a formula which should be memorized.

Answer to Exercise for Discussion 4

4. $A_n = \frac{n}{2}(a + t)$; the sum of an arithmetic series equals half the number of terms multiplied by the sum of the first term and the last term.

Exercises

Exercises 17 through 24 may be postponed for use after the chapter has been completed.

Quiz

Each sum below is the beginning of an arithmetic series. Find the nth term of each series for the specified value of n.

1. $4 - 1 - 6 - \ldots, n = 10$ (ans: $^-41$)
2. $\frac{1}{2} + 1 + \frac{3}{2} + \ldots, n = 15$ (ans: $\frac{15}{2}$)

Find the sum of each of the following arithmetic series.

3. $5 + 8 + 11 + \cdots + 80$ (ans: 1105)
4. $a = 9, d = 6, n = 20$ (ans: 1320)

20. Find the number of terms in an arithmetic series with $a = 25$, $d = 6$, and $A_n = 441$. 9

21. If $a + b + c + d + e + f + g + h$ is an arithmetic series, which of the following is also an arithmetic series?

(a) $b + d + f + h$

(b) $a^2 + b^2 + c^2 + d^2$

(c) $\frac{1}{a} + \frac{1}{b} + \frac{1}{c} + \frac{1}{d} + \frac{1}{e}$

(d) $ka + kb + kc + kd + ke + kf$

22. (a) Find a value of x such that

$$(9x + 7) + (7x + 1) + (3x - 4)$$

will be an arithmetic series of three terms. $x = \frac{1}{2}$

(b) Find another value of x such that the three terms of the series in part (a), arranged in different order, continue to form an arithmetic series. $x = \frac{-8}{5}$ or $x = \frac{17}{8}$

23. Find the value of x such that $2x - 7$, $6x - 2$, and $8x + 4$ are the first three terms of an arithmetic series. $x = \frac{1}{2}$

24. If a clock strikes the number of hours on the hour, how many times will it strike in 1 week? 1092

13-5 GEOMETRIC SERIES

If we deposit \$200 in a savings bank that pays 4% interest compounded semiannually, then at the end of one-half year we shall be credited with .02 × 200, or \$4, interest. Our account will then total \$204. We shall receive .02 × 204, or \$4.08, interest the second half of the year, and our account will total \$208.08 at the end of 1 year. If we do not draw any money out of our account, how much will it total after 2 years? after 3 years? after 10 years? These questions lead us to the following problem.

Problem 1. If we deposit p dollars in a savings bank paying interest at the rate r for each interest period, and if we leave the principal and accumulated interest in the bank, how much will our account total after n interest periods?

Solution. It is understood that r is the actual interest, in dollars, paid by the bank for each dollar in our account at the end of each interest period. Thus, at the end of the first interest period, we shall be credited with rp dollars interest and the total amount in our account will be

$$p + rp, \quad \text{or } p(1 + r).$$

13-5 GEOMETRIC SERIES

As in arithmetic series, the important thing in geometric series is the definition. The following examples may be considered:

$$\tfrac{1}{2} + \tfrac{1}{4} + \tfrac{1}{8} + \tfrac{1}{16} + \tfrac{1}{32} + \cdots$$
$$2 - 6 + 18 - 54 + 162 - \cdots$$

The students should observe that each term is related to the neighboring two terms, so that:

$$\tfrac{1}{4} = \sqrt{\tfrac{1}{2} \cdot \tfrac{1}{8}},$$
$$\tfrac{1}{8} = \sqrt{\tfrac{1}{4} \cdot \tfrac{1}{16}},$$
$$6 = \sqrt{2 \cdot 18},$$
$$18 = \sqrt{6 \cdot 54}.$$

In the general pattern

$$a + aq + aq^2 + \cdots, \quad aq = \sqrt{a \cdot aq^2}.$$

Any two terms determine the series completely since the general pattern only contains two variables.

At the end of the second interest period, the total amount will be

$$[p(1 + r)] + r[p(1 + r)] = [p(1 + r)](1 + r) \\ = p(1 + r)^2.$$

At the end of three interest periods, the total amount will be

$$[p(1 + r)^2] + r[p(1 + r)^2] = [p(1 + r)^2](1 + r) \\ = p(1 + r)^3.$$

This suggests that our account will amount to $p(1 + r)^n$ dollars after n interest periods.

Using B_n to denote the actual amount of our account in the bank after n interest periods, we wish to prove that the equation

$$B_n = p(1 + r)^n$$

is true for every positive integer n. From our work above, we know that each of the following equations is true.

$$B_1 = p(1 + r)^1, \quad B_2 = p(1 + r)^2, \quad B_3 = p(1 + r)^3$$

We shall use mathematical induction to try to prove that the given equation is true for every positive integer n. We let

$$S = \{n \mid B_n = p(1 + r)^n \text{ is true}\}.$$

We know that 1, 2, and 3 are in set S, and we let k be any integer in S. Thus, the equation

$$B_k = p(1 + r)^k$$

is true; that is, we shall have $p(1 + r)^k$ dollars in our account at the end of k interest periods. At the end of the next interest period, we shall be credited with $r[p(1 + r)^k]$ dollars interest, and our account, B_{k+1}, will then total

$$[p(1 + r)^k] + r[p(1 + r)^k] = [p(1 + r)^k](1 + r) \\ = p(1 + r)^{k+1}.$$

Hence, the equation

$$B_{k+1} = p(1 + r)^{k+1}$$

is also true. This proves that $k + 1$ is in set S. Since 1 is in set S, and since, whenever k is in S, $k + 1$ is also in S, we have proved by mathematical induction that S is the set of *all* positive integers. Therefore, the formula $B_n = p(1 + r)^n$ is true for every positive integer n.

Thus, if the third term is 32 while the sixth term is 2048, then

$$\begin{cases} 32 = aq^2, \\ 2048 = aq^5, \end{cases}$$

and we can easily find a and q.

Problem 1 makes a good classroom approach to geometric series through a very practical exercise which should be of interest to everyone.

TWISTER

In a certain club, the membership consists of golfers, who always lie, lawyers, who never lie, and politicians, who alternately lie and tell the truth. If you met a member of this club, how, by asking only two questions, could you tell to which group he belongs?

Solution: The simplest method is to ask the same question twice, "Are you a politician?" Two yes answers would indicate a golfer, two no's a lawyer, and a no and a yes would indicate you had met a politician.

We may apply this formula to the example at the beginning of this section by letting $p = 200$ and the interest rate $r = .02$. Then after 2 years, or four interest periods, we shall have

$$200(1 + .02)^4$$

dollars in our account. After 3 years, or 6 interest periods, we shall have

$$200(1 + .02)^6$$

dollars; and after 10 years, we shall have

$$200(1 + .02)^{20}$$

dollars in our account.

We may approximate this latter number by using logarithms. Thus, if

$$B_{20} = 200 \times 1.02^{20},$$

then

$$\begin{aligned} \log B_{20} &= \log 200 + 20 \log 1.02 \\ &\doteq 2.3010 + (20 \times .0086) \\ &\doteq 2.4730. \end{aligned}$$

Hence,

$$B_{20} \doteq 297.10,$$

and we shall have approximately \$297.10 in our account after 10 years.

If we deposit \$200 in the bank at the beginning of each interest period for 10 years, how much money will we have in our account after 10 years? The first \$200 will collect interest for 20 periods and will be worth

$$200(1 + .02)^{20}$$

dollars at the end of 10 years. The next \$200, deposited at the start of the second interest period, will be worth

$$200(1 + .02)^{19}$$

dollars after 10 years. The next \$200, deposited at the start of the third interest period, will be worth

$$200(1 + .02)^{18}$$

dollars after 10 years, and so on, down to the last \$200 which draws interest for only one period and will be worth

$$200(1 + .02)$$

dollars at the end of the specified period. Therefore, the number of dollars in our account after 10 years is

$$200(1 + .02) + 200(1 + .02)^2 + \cdots + 200(1 + .02)^{19} + 200(1 + .02)^{20}.$$

This example illustrates the question to be discussed in our second problem.

Problem 2. A savings bank pays interest at the rate r for each interest period. If we deposit p dollars in the bank at the start of each of n successive interest periods, how much money will be in our account at the end of the nth interest period?

Solution. Reasoning as we did above, we see that the amount C_n which will be in our account at the end of the nth interest period is given by

$$C_n = p(1 + r) + p(1 + r)^2 + \cdots + p(1 + r)^{n-1} + p(1 + r)^n.$$

The series C_n is not an arithmetic series, since the first term is multiplied by $1 + r$ to obtain the second term, the second term is multiplied by $1 + r$ to yield the third term, and so on. This is an example of a geometric series, as defined below.

GEOMETRIC SERIES

An algebraic expression of the form

$$a + aq + aq^2 + \cdots + aq^{n-1}$$

is called a geometric series with n terms. The number a is called the first term, and the number q is called the ratio of this series.

We note that the *quotient* of any term divided by its predecessor is the ratio q. Some examples of geometric series are given below.

$$1 + 3 + 9 + 27 + 81 + 243; \quad a = 1, \quad q = 3, \quad n = 6$$

$$10 + 10^3 + 10^5 + 10^7 + 10^9; \quad a = 10, \quad q = 100, \quad n = 5$$

$$\tfrac{1}{4} + \tfrac{1}{8} + \tfrac{1}{16} + \tfrac{1}{32} + \tfrac{1}{64} + \tfrac{1}{128} + \tfrac{1}{256}; \quad a = \tfrac{1}{4}, \quad q = \tfrac{1}{2}, \quad n = 7$$

We shall now try to find a summation formula for a geometric series. Let G_n designate the geometric series with n terms defined above:

$$G_n = a + aq + aq^2 + \cdots + aq^{n-1}.$$

TWISTER

A blacksmith agrees to shoe a horse on the condition that he receive one penny for the first nail, two for the second, four for the third, and so on. If there are 24 nails in all, what was his total payment?

Solution: This is a geometric progression, where $a = 1$, $q = 2$, and $n = 24$. The sum is $2^{24} - 1$, which equals \$167,772.15.

If $q = 1$, then G_n is only na. This case will not be considered any further.

If $q \neq 1$, then a summation formula for G_n may be found in the following way. Multiplying G_n by q and using the distributive law, we obtain

$$G_n \cdot q = aq + aq^2 + aq^3 + \cdots + aq^{n-1} + aq^n.$$

If you look closely at the geometric series above, you will notice that its terms are very nearly the terms of G_n. In fact,

$$\begin{aligned} a + (G_n \cdot q) &= a + (aq + aq^2 + aq^3 + \cdots + aq^{n-1} + aq^n) \\ &= (a + aq + aq^2 + aq^3 + \cdots + aq^{n-1}) + aq^n \end{aligned}$$

and therefore,

$$a + (G_n \cdot q) = G_n + aq^n.$$

We may easily solve this latter equation for G_n:

$$\begin{aligned} (G_n \cdot q) - G_n &= aq^n - a, \\ G_n(q - 1) &= a(q^n - 1), \\ G_n &= \frac{a(q^n - 1)}{q - 1}. \end{aligned}$$

This proves the *summation formula for the geometric series:*

$$a + aq + aq^2 + \cdots + aq^{n-2} + aq^{n-1} = \frac{a(q^n - 1)}{q - 1}, \quad q \neq 1.$$

For example,

$$1 + 3 + 9 + 27 + 81 + 243 = \frac{1 \cdot (3^6 - 1)}{3 - 1}, \quad \text{or } 364,$$

$$10 + 10^3 + 10^5 + 10^7 + 10^9 = \frac{10(100^5 - 1)}{100 - 1}, \quad \text{or } 1{,}010{,}101{,}010,$$

$$\frac{1}{4} + \frac{1}{8} + \frac{1}{16} + \cdots + \frac{1}{256} = \frac{\frac{1}{4}[(\frac{1}{2})^7 - 1]}{\frac{1}{2} - 1}, \quad \text{or } \frac{127}{256}.$$

Let us find the sum of the series C_n appearing in Problem 2. Since this is a geometric series with first term $p(1 + r)$ and ratio $1 + r$,

$$C_n = \frac{p(1 + r)[(1 + r)^n - 1]}{(1 + r) - 1} = \frac{p(1 + r)}{r}[(1 + r)^n - 1].$$

For example, if $p = 200$, $r = .02$, and $n = 20$ as in an earlier example, then

$$200(1.02) + 200(1.02)^2 + \cdots + 200(1.02)^{20}$$
$$= \frac{200 \times 1.02}{.02}[(1.02)^{20} - 1].$$

Using our previous calculations showing that

$$200(1.02)^{20} \doteq 297.10,$$

we have

$$\frac{1.02}{.02}[200(1.02)^{20} - 200] \doteq 51 \times 97.10, \quad \text{or } 4952.$$

Thus, our total accumulated savings after 10 years will be approximately \$4952. More accurate computations would show it to be \$4954.63.

Exercises for Discussion

1. Determine a and q for each of the following geometric series. Continue each series through six terms, and find the specific term mentioned.
   (a) $8 + 4 + 2 \cdots$, fifteenth term
   (b) $b^2 - b + 1 - \cdots$, twentieth term
2. Find the sum of each of the following geometric series.
   (a) $3^2 + 3^3 + 3^4 + 3^5$ 360
   (b) $1 - \frac{1}{2} + \frac{1}{4} - \frac{1}{8} + \frac{1}{16} - \frac{1}{32}$ $\frac{21}{32}$
   (c) $a = 100$, $q = 1.02$, $n = 30$ Approximately 4055
   (d) $a = 10$, $q = .1$, $n = 10$ 11.11111111
3. Find the second, third, and fifth terms of a geometric series having first term 8 and fourth term 27. 12, 18, $\frac{81}{2}$
4. The first term of a geometric series is a negative number, the second term is 2, and the fourth term is 4. Find the first and third terms. $^{-}\sqrt{2}$, $^{-}2\sqrt{2}$
5. The terms between any two terms of a geometric series are called *the geometric means* between these two terms.
   (a) Find three geometric means between 15 and $\frac{5}{27}$. Is there more than one way of doing this? 5, $\frac{5}{3}$, $\frac{5}{9}$; $^{-}5$, $\frac{5}{3}$, $\frac{^{-}5}{9}$; yes
   (b) Find one geometric mean between $\frac{4}{9}$ and $\frac{9}{4}$. This is called the *geometric mean* of the two numbers. Do two numbers have more than one geometric mean? 1 or $^{-}1$; yes

Exercises for Discussion

It is suggested that all of the Exercises for Discussion be covered in class before the Exercises on the next page are assigned.

Answers to Exercise for Discussion 1

1. (a) $8 + 4 + 2 + 1 + \frac{1}{2} + \frac{1}{4} + \ldots$; $a = 8$; $q = \frac{1}{2}$; $\frac{1}{2^{11}} = \frac{1}{2048}$
   (b) $b^2 - b + 1 - \frac{1}{b} + \frac{1}{b^2} - \frac{1}{b^3} + \ldots$; $a = b^2$; $q = \frac{-1}{b}$; $\frac{-1}{b^{17}}$

Exercises

It is recommended that Exercises 11 and 12 be assigned.

Exercises 12 through 16 can be used as review either at the end of the chapter or at the end of the semester.

Answer to Exercise 9

9. $a = \sqrt{3}$; $q = \sqrt{2}$; $2\sqrt{6}$, $4\sqrt{3}$, $4\sqrt{6}$; $32\sqrt{3}$

Quiz

In Exercises 1 and 2, find the sum of each of the geometric series.

1. $3 + 3^3 + 3^5$ (ans: 273)

2. $a = 1$, $q = \frac{1}{2}$, $n = 4$ (ans: $\frac{15}{8}$)

In Exercises 3 and 4, determine a and q for each geometric series. Continue each through six terms, and then find the specific term mentioned.

3. $2 + 1 + \frac{1}{2} + \ldots$, ninth term (ans: $a = 2$, $q = \frac{1}{2}$; $\frac{1}{4}, \frac{1}{8}, \frac{1}{16}$; $1/2^7$)

4. $\frac{1}{2} + 1 + 2 + \ldots$, tenth term (ans: $a = \frac{1}{2}$, $q = 2$; 4, 8, 16; 2^8)

Exercises

In Exercises 1–6, find the sum of each of the geometric series.

1. $2 + 2^3 + 2^5 + 2^7 + 2^9$ 682

2. $1 + \frac{1}{3} + \frac{1}{9} + \frac{1}{27} + \frac{1}{81} + \frac{1}{243}$ $\frac{364}{243}$

3. $a = {}^-3$, $q = \frac{1}{2}$, $n = 8$ $\frac{{}^-765}{128}$

4. $2^4 - 2^5 + 2^6 - 2^7 + 2^8 - 2^9$ $^-336$

5. $a = 1$, $q = 2$, $n = 6$ 63

6. $a = 1$, $q = {}^-2$, $n = 6$ $^-21$

In Exercises 7–10, determine a and q for each geometric series. Continue each through six terms, and then find the specific term mentioned.

7. $16 + {}^-4 + 1 + \cdots$, tenth term $a = 16$, $q = \frac{{}^-1}{4}$; $\frac{{}^-1}{4}, \frac{1}{16}, \frac{{}^-1}{64}$; $\frac{{}^-1}{4^7}$

8. $3 + 1.2 + .48 + \cdots$, ninth term $a = 3$, $q = .4$; .192, .0768, .03072; .00196608

9. $\sqrt{3} + \sqrt{6} + 2\sqrt{3} + \cdots$, eleventh term

10. $\frac{1}{625} - \frac{1}{125} + \frac{1}{25} - \cdots$, twelfth term $a = \frac{1}{625}$, $q = {}^-5$; $\frac{{}^-1}{5}, 1, {}^-5$; ${}^-5^7 = {}^-78125$

11. What are the conditions that have to be imposed on the real numbers x, y, and z for

(a) $x + y + z$ to be a geometric series? $y^2 = xz$

(b) $x + y + z$ to be an arithmetic series? $y = \frac{x+z}{2}$

(c) y to be both the arithmetic and geometric mean of x and z? $x = y = z$

△

12. If t designates the nth term of a geometric series, write a formula for G_n in terms of a, q, and t instead of a, q, and n. $G_n = \frac{a - qt}{1 - q}$

13. If $a + b + c + d + e + f$ represents a geometric series of six terms, which of the following is also a geometric series?

(a) $b + d + f$

(b) $ka + kb + kc + kd + ke + kf$, k any real number

(c) $(a + k) + (b + k) + (c + k) + (d + k)$, k any real number

(d) $\sqrt{a} + \sqrt{b} + \sqrt{c} + \sqrt{d} + \sqrt{e} + \sqrt{f}$

14. A newspaper recently reported that a savings account in a bank was now worth \$3738. There had been no deposit since the original deposit of \$26 made 116 years ago. If interest had been added to the account every 6 months, what average rate of interest had the bank paid over this period? 4.4%, approximately

15. Assuming that an automobile depreciates in value 12% every year, find the value, at the end of 4 years, of a car costing \$2500. \$1499, approx.

16. Find a formula for the sum of the first n positive integral powers of 4. $\frac{4}{3}(4^n - 1)$

*13-6 INFINITE GEOMETRIC SERIES

The rational number $\frac{1}{3}$ has repeating decimal

$$.3333\ldots$$

which we can consider to be an infinite sum:

$$\tfrac{1}{3} = .3 + .03 + .003 + .0003 + \cdots$$

This is an example of an *infinite geometric series* with ratio .1. Thus, $.03 = .3 \times .1$, $.003 = .03 \times .1$, $.0003 = .003 \times .1$, and so on. We define an infinite geometric series in the following way.

INFINITE GEOMETRIC SERIES

An infinite geometric series is an algebraic expression of the form

$$a + aq + aq^2 + \cdots + aq^{n-1} + \cdots$$

Associated with an infinite geometric series are its *partial sums*

$$\begin{aligned} G_1 &= a, \\ G_2 &= a + aq, \\ G_3 &= a + aq + aq^2, \end{aligned}$$

and, in general,

$$G_n = a + aq + aq^2 + \cdots + aq^{n-1}.$$

Thus, G_n is the sum of the first n terms of an infinite geometric series. By a previous formula,

$$G_n = \frac{a(1 - q^n)}{1 - q}, \quad q \neq 1, \quad \text{for every positive integer } n.$$

If $0 < q < 1$, then q^n is a small number when n is large. For example, if $q = \frac{1}{2}$ and $n = 10$, then

$$q^n = \frac{1}{2^{10}} = \frac{1}{1024} < .001.$$

Therefore,

$$G_n \doteq \frac{a}{1 - q}, \quad \text{if } 0 < q < 1 \text{ and } n \text{ is large.}$$

*13-6 INFINITE GEOMETRIC SERIES

Division has already been used to generate an infinite series in the process of finding the infinite decimal representation for a rational number. The following example may be considered:

$$\begin{array}{r} .1818 \\ 11\overline{)2.0000} \\ 1\,1 \\ \hline 90 \\ 88 \\ \hline 20 \\ 11 \\ \hline 90 \\ 88 \\ \hline 2 \end{array}$$

$$\begin{aligned} \tfrac{2}{11} &= .18181818\ldots \\ &= .18 + .0018 + .000018 + \ldots \\ &= 18(10^{-2} + 10^{-4} + 10^{-6} + \ldots). \end{aligned}$$

Thus, the decimal representation for $\frac{2}{11}$ is the infinite geometric series with $a = .18$ and $q = .01$ or 10^{-2}. You may wish to ask the students what long division indicates about the rational algebraic expression $1/(1 - x)$.

$$\begin{array}{r} 1 + x + x^2 \\ 1 - x\overline{)1} \\ 1 - x \\ \hline x \\ x - x^2 \\ \hline x^2 \\ x^2 - x^3 \\ \hline x^3 \end{array}$$

$$\frac{1}{1 - x} = 1 + x + x^2 + x^3 + \ldots$$

It appears that $1/(1 - x)$ is represented by an infinite geometric series with $q = x$. Since x is a variable, the statement may be tested for a few values of x. If $x = 2$,

$$\frac{1}{1 - 2} \stackrel{?}{=} 1 + 2 + 2^2 + 2^3 + \ldots$$

$$^{-}1 = 1 + 2 + 4 + 8 + \ldots,$$

which is false. If $x = 0$,

$$\frac{1}{1-0} \stackrel{?}{=} 1 + 0 + 0^2 + 0^3 + \ldots$$

$$1 = 1,$$

which is true. If $x = \frac{1}{2}$,

$$\frac{1}{1-\frac{1}{2}} \stackrel{?}{=} 1 + \tfrac{1}{2} + (\tfrac{1}{2})^2 + (\tfrac{1}{2})^3 + \ldots,$$

$$2 \stackrel{?}{=} 1 + \tfrac{1}{2} + \tfrac{1}{4} + \tfrac{1}{8} + \ldots,$$

$$2 \stackrel{?}{=} 1\tfrac{7}{8} + \tfrac{1}{16} + \tfrac{1}{32} + \tfrac{1}{64} + \ldots,$$

$$2 \stackrel{?}{=} 1\tfrac{63}{64} + \tfrac{1}{128} + \tfrac{1}{256} + \tfrac{1}{512} + \ldots,$$

$$2 \stackrel{?}{=} 1\tfrac{511}{512} + \tfrac{1}{1024} + \tfrac{1}{2048} + \ldots,$$

which is probably true. That is,

$$\lim_{x \to \frac{1}{2}} f(x) = \frac{1}{1-x} = 2.$$

The infinite geometric series

$$1 + x + x^2 + x^3 + \ldots$$

is said to have a sum in the last two cases, and not in the first case. What are the most obvious differences between the cases? In the first case the terms increase. In the other two, the terms following the first are either zero, or approaching zero. It becomes apparent that a necessary condition for an infinite geometric series to have a sum is for q to satisfy the condition $|q| < 1$. Thus,

$$1 + x + x^2 + x^3 + \ldots$$

represents $1/(1-x)$ for all x,

$$|x| < 1.$$

The difference between an infinite geometric series which has a sum and one that doesn't may be made vivid with a graph.
You could consider

$$S = 1 + 2 + 2^2 + \ldots + 2^{n-1} + \ldots,$$

which is an example of an infinite geometric series not having a sum.

In fact, G_n gets closer and closer to $a/(1-q)$ as n gets larger and larger. For this reason, we call

$$\frac{a}{1-q}$$

the *sum* of the infinite geometric series.

If $^-1 < q \leqq 0$, then it is still true that q^n is close to 0 and hence that G_n is close to $a/(1-q)$ when n is large. Thus, we call $a/(1-q)$ the sum of the infinite geometric series in this case also. We can unite these two cases into the following formula for the infinite geometric series.

$$a + aq + aq^2 + \cdots + aq^{n-1} + \cdots = \frac{a}{1-q}, \quad |q| < 1.$$

In the example given previously, $.3 + .03 + .003 + \cdots$, we have $a = .3$ and $q = .1$. Therefore, by the formula,

$$.3 + .03 + .003 + \cdots = \frac{.3}{1-.1}, \quad \text{or } \frac{1}{3}.$$

As another example,

$$1 + \frac{1}{2} + \frac{1}{4} + \cdots + \frac{1}{2^{n-1}} + \cdots = \frac{1}{1-\frac{1}{2}}, \quad \text{or } 2.$$

If $|q| \geqq 1$, then the infinite geometric series does not have a sum. For example,

$$1 + 2 + 2^2 + \cdots + 2^{n-1} + \cdots \qquad (1)$$

does not have a sum because the partial sum

$$G_n = \frac{1 \cdot (1 - 2^n)}{1 - 2} = 2^n - 1$$

gets very large when n gets large. In fact, there is no limit on how big G_n can get; hence, there is no number assignable as the sum of this infinite series. If we assume that (1) has a sum, we obtain curious results. For example, if

$$S = 1 + 2 + 2^2 + \cdots + 2^{n-1} + \cdots$$

and if the distributive law holds for such sums, then

$$\begin{aligned} 2S &= 2(1 + 2 + 2^2 + \cdots + 2^{n-1} + \cdots \\ &= 2 + 2^2 + 2^3 + \cdots + 2^n + \cdots \end{aligned}$$

and

$$1 + 2S = 1 + 2 + 2^2 + 2^3 + \cdots + 2^n + \cdots$$
$$= S.$$

Solving the equation $1 + 2S = S$ for S, we obtain

$$S = {}^{-}1.$$

Thus, an infinite sum of positive numbers is a negative number. This is nonsense!

Each repeating decimal is an infinite geometric series. Since $a/(1 - q)$ is a rational number if a and q are rational, it follows that each repeating decimal is a rational number. For example, the repeating decimal

$$.\underline{135} = .135\,135\,135\ldots$$

is the same as the infinite geometric series

$$.135 + .000\,135 + .000\,000\,135 + \cdots$$

for which

$$a = .135 \quad \text{and} \quad q = 10^{-3}.$$

Therefore,

$$.\underline{135} = \frac{.135}{1 - 10^{-3}}, \quad \text{or} \quad \frac{.135}{.999}, \quad \text{or} \quad \frac{15}{111}, \quad \text{or} \quad \frac{5}{37}.$$

Exercises

Find the sum of each of the following infinite geometric series.

1. $1 + \frac{1}{3} + \frac{1}{9} + \cdots$ $\frac{3}{2}$

2. $9 - 3 + 1 - \cdots$ $\frac{27}{4}$

3. $0.07 + 0.007 + 0.0007 + \cdots$ $\frac{7}{90}$

4. $1 - \frac{1}{2} + \frac{1}{4} \cdots$ $\frac{2}{3}$

5. $12 + (0.3 + 0.03 + 0.003 + \cdots)$ $12\frac{1}{3}$

6. $\frac{1}{2} + \frac{1}{6} + \frac{1}{18} + \cdots$ $\frac{3}{4}$

7. $9 + 3 + 1 + \frac{1}{3} + \cdots$ $\frac{27}{2}$

8. $x + 1 + \dfrac{1}{x} + \dfrac{1}{x^2} + \cdots, \quad x > 1$ $\frac{x^2}{x-1}, x > 1$

In Exercises 9–16, find a common fraction for each repeating decimal.

9. $0.5555\ldots$ $\frac{5}{9}$

10. $0.06262\ldots$ $\frac{31}{495}$

11. $3.297297\ldots$ $\frac{122}{37}$

12. $2.69999\ldots$ $\frac{27}{10}$

13. $12.2121\ldots$ $\frac{403}{33}$

14. $0.64545\ldots$ $\frac{71}{110}$

15. $1.25454\ldots$ $\frac{69}{55}$

16. $0.066363\ldots$ $\frac{73}{1100}$

n	1	2	3	4
S	1	3	7	15

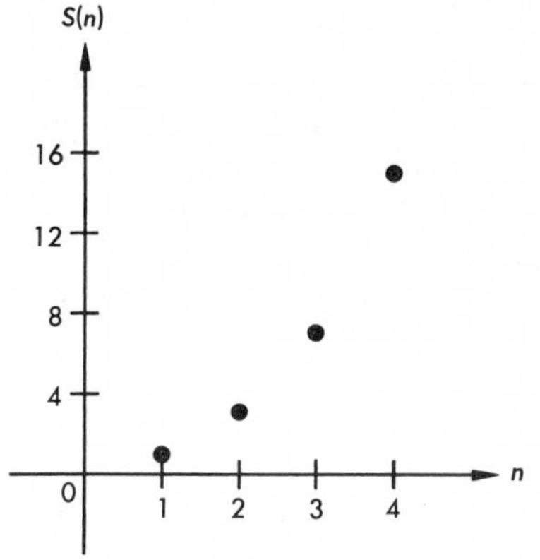

The graph rises infinitely high to the right. S is increasing and unbounded. On the other hand,

$$S = 1 + \tfrac{1}{2} + \tfrac{1}{4} + \tfrac{1}{8} + \ldots + \frac{1}{2^{n-1}} + \ldots$$

does have a sum.

n	1	2	3	4
S	1	$1\frac{1}{2}$	$1\frac{3}{4}$	$1\frac{7}{8}$

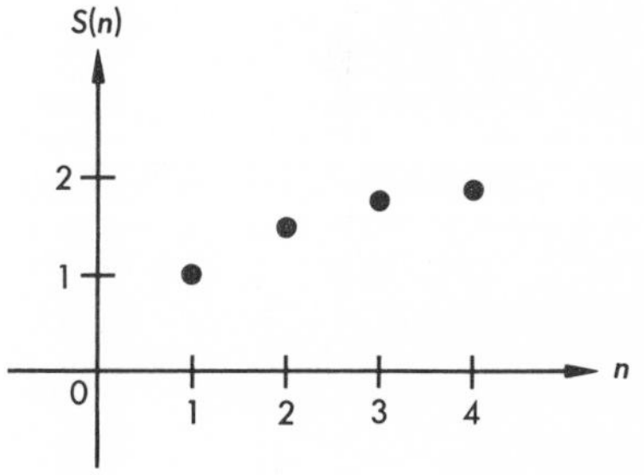

The graph rises, but stays under 2. S is increasing, but bounded.

Exercises

It is suggested that Exercise 8 be discussed. If Section 13-6 is omitted the first time you go through Chapter 13, it may be used as a filler sometime later in the semester because it is interesting, not difficult or tedious, and offers at least an introduction to the important topic of infinite series.

Quiz

Find the sum of each of the following infinite geometric series.

1. $2 + \frac{2}{3} + \frac{2}{9} + \ldots$ (ans: 3)
2. $1 - \frac{1}{4} + \frac{1}{16} - \ldots$ (ans: $\frac{4}{5}$)

In Exercises 3 and 4, find a common fraction for each repeating decimal.

3. 0.4141 . . . (ans: $\frac{41}{99}$)
4. .23636 . . . (ans: $\frac{13}{55}$)

17. What distance will a golf ball travel if it is dropped from a height of 72 inches and if, after each fall, it rebounds $\frac{9}{10}$ of the distance it fell? 1368 in.

18. A rubber ball falls from a height of 80 feet and on each rebound loses 25% of its previous height. What distance will it have traveled when it strikes the ground for the fifth time? How far will it travel before it comes to rest? $408\frac{1}{8}$ ft; 560 ft

19. In a square of side 12 inches, a second square is inscribed by joining the midpoints of the sides in order. In the second square, a third square is inscribed using the same method. If this process is continued indefinitely, what is the sum of the perimeters of all the squares? $48(2+\sqrt{2})$

KEY IDEAS AND KEY WORDS

The **induction property** is a fundamental property of the system of positive integers. It can be stated as follows:

> If a set S of positive integers contains 1, and if whenever S contains an integer k it also contains the integer $k + 1$, then the set S must be the set of all positive integers.

An algebraic expression of the form

$$a + (a + d) + (a + 2d) + \cdots + [a + (n - 1)d]$$

is called an **arithmetic series** with ***n*** **terms, first term** ***a***, and **difference** ***d***. The **sum** of the series above is given by

$$A_n = na + \frac{d}{2}(n^2 - n).$$

An algebraic expression of the form

$$a + aq + aq^2 + \cdots + aq^{n-1}$$

is called a **geometric series** with ***n*** **terms, first term** ***a***, and **ratio** ***q***. The **sum** of the series above is given by

$$G_n = \frac{a(q^n - 1)}{q - 1}, \quad q \neq 1.$$

Of course, $G_n = na$ if $q = 1$.

A geometric series with an infinite number of terms,

$$a + aq + aq^2 + \cdots + aq^{n-1} + \cdots,$$

is called an **infinite geometric series.** Its sum is given by

$$G = \frac{a}{1 - q}, \quad |q| < 1.$$

CHAPTER REVIEW

See Solution Manual for proofs.

1. Use mathematical induction to prove that each of the following formulas is correct for every positive integer n.

(a) $2 + 6 + 12 + \cdots + n(n + 1) = \dfrac{n(n + 1)(n + 2)}{3}$

(b) $6 + 24 + 60 + \cdots + n(n + 1)(n + 2) = \dfrac{n(n + 1)(n + 2)(n + 3)}{4}$

2. Given that A_n is the sum of an arithmetic series and

$$A_n = 3 + 8 + 13 + \cdots + [3 + (n - 1) \cdot 5],$$

$a = 3$, $d = 5$; $\frac{n}{2}(5n+1)$

state what a and d are, and find a formula for A_n.

3. Find five arithmetic means between 86 and 14. 74, 62, 50, 38, 26

4. How many numbers between 50 and 150 are exactly divisible by 7? Find their sum. 14; 1421

5. The sum of the first 15 terms of an arithmetic series is $^-165$. Find the first term and the difference, given that the fifteenth term is $^-32$. $a = 10$, $d = {}^-3$

6. If the fifth term of an arithmetic series is 27 and the eleventh term is 48, what is the first term? 13

7. If the fourth term of a geometric series is 3, and the ninth term is 729, what are the first three terms? $\frac{1}{9}$, $\frac{1}{3}$, 1

8. Insert five geometric means between $\frac{3}{4}$ and $\frac{16}{243}$.

9. The fifth term of a geometric series is 162, and the ratio is $^-3$. Find the first term and the sum of the first eight terms. $a = 2$, $G_n = {}^-3280$

10. (a) For the geometric series

$$\tfrac{2}{3} + \tfrac{1}{3} + \tfrac{1}{6} + \tfrac{1}{12} + \cdots,$$

find G_5, G_{10}, and G_{20}. $G_5 = \frac{31}{24}$; $G_{10} = \frac{341}{256}$; $G_{20} = \frac{2^{20}-1}{3 \times 2^{18}}$

(b) Find the sum of the infinite geometric series

$$\tfrac{2}{3} + \tfrac{1}{3} + \tfrac{1}{6} + \tfrac{1}{12} + \cdots$$ $\frac{4}{3}$

11. Find an equivalent common fraction for each repeating decimal.

(a) .2727 . . . $\frac{3}{11}$ (b) .134134 . . . $\frac{134}{999}$

12. Prove by mathematical induction that the formula

$$G_n = \frac{a(q^n - 1)}{q - 1}, \quad q \neq 1,$$

for the sum of a geometric series is true for every positive integer n.

Answer to Chapter Review Problem 8

8. $\frac{1}{2}, \frac{1}{3}, \frac{2}{9}, \frac{4}{27}, \frac{8}{81}$, or $^-\frac{1}{2}, \frac{1}{3}, {}^-\frac{2}{9}, \frac{4}{27}, {}^-\frac{8}{81}$

Continue each of the following series for two more terms. State whether the series is arithmetic or geometric.

13. $4 + 3 + \frac{9}{4} + \cdots$ $\frac{27}{16}$, $\frac{81}{64}$; geometric

14. $^-1 + 4 + 9 + \cdots$ 14, 19; arithmetic

15. $(a - 2) + a + (a + 2) + \cdots$ $(a+4)$, $(a+6)$; arithmetic

16. $a^3 + a(a^2 + a) + a(a^2 + 2a) + \cdots$ $a(a^2+3a)$, $a(a^2+4a)$; arithmetic

17. $1 + 1.1 + 1.21 + \cdots$ 1.331, 1.4641; geometric

In each exercise of Exercises 18–29, use the formula given for the nth term to write the first five terms of a series. Tell which series are arithmetic, which are geometric, and which are neither.

18. $3n$ $3+6+9+12+15$; arithmetic

19. $\frac{1}{3n}$ $\frac{1}{3}+\frac{1}{6}+\frac{1}{9}+\frac{1}{12}+\frac{1}{15}$; neither

20. $\left(\frac{1}{5}\right)^{n-2}$ $5+1+\frac{1}{5}+\frac{1}{25}+\frac{1}{125}$; geometric

21. 3^n $3+9+27+81+243$; geometric

22. $\frac{n - 1}{n + 1}$ $0+\frac{1}{3}+\frac{1}{2}+\frac{3}{5}+\frac{2}{3}$; neither

23. $2(10)^{n-1}$ $2+20+200+2000+20{,}000$; geometric

24. $4 - n$ $3+2+1+0-1$; arithmetic

25. $n(n + 1)$ $2+6+12+20+30$; neither

26. $(3)^{\frac{-n}{2}}$ $\frac{1}{\sqrt{3}}+\frac{1}{3}+\frac{1}{3\sqrt{3}}+\frac{1}{9}+\frac{1}{9\sqrt{3}}$; geometric

27. n^2 $1+4+9+16+25$; neither

28. $3n - 1$ $2+5+8+11+14$; arithmetic

29. $(^-1)^{n-1}\sqrt[3]{2^{2n}}$ $\sqrt[3]{4}-2\sqrt[3]{2}+4-4\sqrt[3]{4}+8\sqrt[3]{2}$; geometric

30. Show that if $x + y + z$ is a geometric series, then $\log x + \log y + \log z$ is an arithmetic series. See Solution Manual.

CHAPTER TEST

1. Find a formula for the sum A_n, given that

$$A_n = 20 + 16 + 12 + \cdots + (24 - 4n).$$ $22n - 2n^2$

2. Find the sum of all the positive integers less than 300 that are divisible by 8. 5624

3. Write a formula for the sum $6 + 6^2 + 6^3 + \cdots + 6^7$. $\frac{6}{5}(6^7 - 1)$

4. Find the sum of the infinite geometric series

$$4 - 2 + 1 - \tfrac{1}{2} + \tfrac{1}{4} - \tfrac{1}{8} + \cdots$$ $\frac{8}{3}$

5. Find a common fraction equivalent to the repeating decimal 1.24545. . . $\frac{137}{110}$

CHAPTER TEST

The material included in the chapter test was covered in the following sections:

Problems 1 and 2—Section 13-4
Problem 3—Section 13-5
Problems 4 and 5—Section 13-6
Problems 6 and 7(a)—Section 13-4
Problem 7(b)—Section 13-5
Problem 8—Sections 13-2, 13-3

6. The third term of an arithmetic series is $4 + \sqrt{3}$ and the tenth term is $11 + 8\sqrt{3}$. Find the first two terms. $2-\sqrt{3}$, 3

7. Use the given formula for each nth term to write the first five terms of a series. In each case, find the sum of the first ten terms, and name the type of series.

   (a) $5 + 2n$ 7+9+11+13+15; 160; arithmetic (b) 2^n 2+4+8+16+32; 2046; geometric

8. Give that $n \geqq 1$, prove that the sum of the first n powers of 3 is equal to

$$\frac{3(3^n - 1)}{2}.$$

In other words, prove that

$$3 + 3^2 + 3^3 + \cdots + 3^n = \frac{3(3^n - 1)}{2}.$$

Answer to Chapter Test Problem 8

8. P_1 is true: $3 = \frac{3(3^1 - 1)}{2} = 3$

Assume P_k is true:

$$G_k = 3 + 3^2 + 3^3 + \ldots + 3^k = \frac{3(3^k - 1)}{2}$$

To prove P_{k+1} is true:

$$G_{k+1} = 3 + 3^2 + 3^3 + \ldots + 3^k + 3^{k+1} = \frac{3(3^{k+1} - 1)}{2}$$

Proof:

$$\begin{aligned} G_{k+1} &= G_k + 3^{k+1} \\ &= \frac{3(3^k - 1)}{2} + 3^{k+1} \\ &= \frac{3^{k+1} - 3}{2} + 3^{k+1} \\ &= \tfrac{1}{2}(3^{k+1} - 3 + 2 \cdot 3^{k+1}) \\ &= \tfrac{1}{2}[(1 + 2)3^{k+1} - 3] \\ &= \tfrac{1}{2}[3 \cdot 3^{k+1} - 3] \\ &= \frac{3(3^{k+1} - 1)}{2} \end{aligned}$$

Since the statement P_n:

$$3 + 3^2 + 3^3 + \ldots + 3^n = \frac{3(3^n - 1)}{2}$$

is true when $n = 1$, and is true for $n = k + 1$ when it is true for $n = k$, then P_n is true for all positive integral values of n.

CHAPTER 14

Vector Algebras

This course began with the algebra of real numbers, proceeded to the algebra of complex numbers, and thence to the algebra of polynomials. The purpose of this chapter is to lay the groundwork for more extensive work in vectors, through a study of the algebra of vectors. Thus, many ideas from geometry and algebra may be tied together while at the same time a very important topic in physics is being introduced in a simple way. The role of definition and proposition in any logical study is also re-emphasized.

The following are some of the topics covered in Chapter 14:

- *Definition of a vector*
- *Equal vectors*
- *The zero vector*
- *Parallelogram law*
- *Addition of vectors*
- *Commutative and associative law for addition of vectors*
- *Identity and inverse elements for addition of vectors*
- *Cancellation law of vectors*
- *Definition of subtraction of vectors*
- *Scalar multiplication of vectors*
- *Properties of scalar multiplication*
- *Vector bases*
- *Position vectors*
- *Vector components*
- *Inner product of vectors*

It should not be necessary to spend more than one day on each section in Chapter 14, except for Section 14–2, where an extra day may be needed. Section 14–5

CHAPTER 14

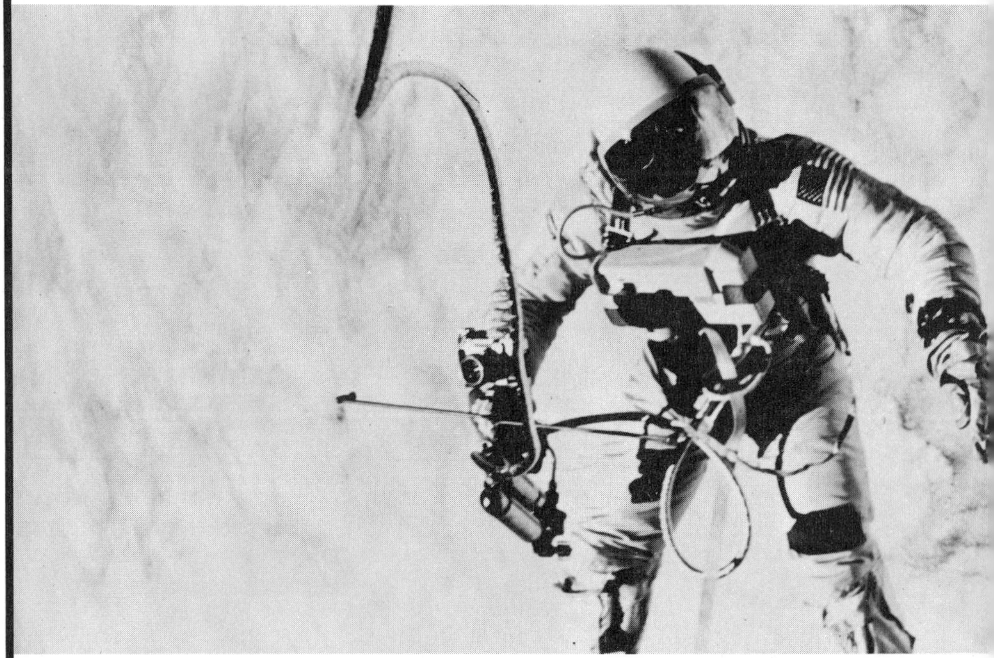

Vectors can be used to represent the forces acting on a man walking in space, such as the force exerted by a hand-held propellant gun. (Courtesy of the National Aeronautics and Space Administration)

VECTOR ALGEBRAS

At a given instant, we can partially describe the motion of an airplane by stating its speed and direction of motion. It is common practice to give such information by means of a directed line segment, called a *vector*. The length of the vector, measured in relation to a given scale, indicates the speed of the plane, and the direction of the vector shows the direction in which the plane is moving. For example, we could use a vector to indicate that a plane is traveling in a northeasterly direction at 600 miles per hour.

An algebra of vectors was developed because vectors are useful in describing not only the motion of an object but many other physical phenomena as well. This algebra is the topic of the present chapter.

should be assigned on an individual basis to bright students or to those who are taking or have taken physics.

14–1 VECTORS

Students should read this material carefully. Details of language and notation should be examined in class. At this stage, some precision may be expected of the students.

14–1 VECTORS

The study of geometry usually begins with a list of axioms which relate points, lines, and planes. In such a study, lines and planes are customarily considered to be sets of points. Thus, when we say that point A lies on line L, we mean that point A is an element of the set of points which is L; and when we say that line L lies in plane p, we mean that every point in set L is also in the set p. One of the axioms of euclidean geometry states that there is a unique line L containing any two distinct points A and B. Another axiom states that the points A and B on L separate L into three subsets, indicated by H, K, and $\overline{AB}$ in Fig. 14–1. Sets H and K are called rays, and $\overline{AB}$ is called a *segment* of line L. Segment $\overline{AB}$ consists of points A, B, and all points C on L between A and B. Instead of listing all the axioms, we shall assume that you are familiar with the elementary aspects of plane euclidean geometry. All the points and lines under discussion lie in some given plane.

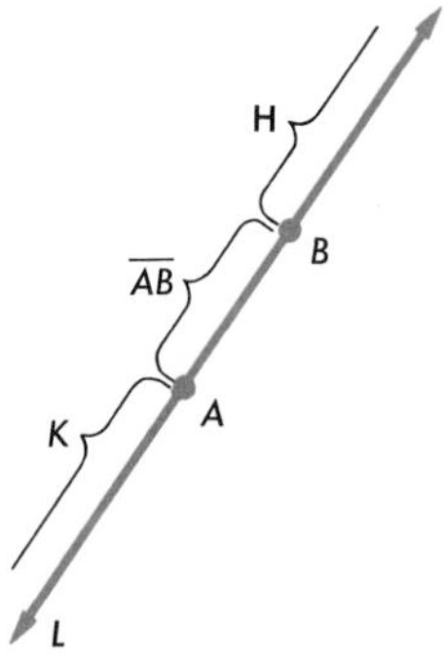

FIGURE 14–1

If our plane has a coordinate system on it, then according to the distance formula, each segment $\overline{AB}$ has a length, which we shall designate by AB. We shall write $AB = CD$ to indicate that the line segments $\overline{AB}$ and $\overline{CD}$ are equal in length, or congruent. It is important to remember that segment $\overline{AB}$ is a part of a line and that AB is a number. If $\overline{AB}$ and $\overline{CD}$ are two segments, then $\overline{AB} \cong \overline{CD}$ if, and only if, $AB = CD$.

A direction can be assigned to each segment by arbitrarily calling one of its endpoints the *initial point* and the other the *terminal point*. The *direction* assigned to the segment begins at the initial point and ends at the terminal point. Such a directed line segment is called a *vector*. If a vector has initial point A and terminal point B, then the vector is designated by

$$\overrightarrow{AB}.$$

Note that if $A \neq B$, then the vector $\overrightarrow{AB}$ is different from the vector $\overrightarrow{BA}$ since the initial point of each vector is the terminal point of the other. Thus, the direction of vector $\overrightarrow{BA}$ is opposite to that of $\overrightarrow{AB}$.

The vectors $\overrightarrow{AB}$ and $\overrightarrow{CD}$ are said to be equal if, and only if, $AB = CD$ and the vectors $\overrightarrow{AB}$ and $\overrightarrow{CD}$ have the same direction.

If vectors $\overrightarrow{AB}$ and $\overrightarrow{CD}$ do not lie on the same line, then we can decide whether or not $\overrightarrow{AB}$ and $\overrightarrow{CD}$ are equal by looking at the quadrilateral $ABDC$ in Fig. 14–2. Thus, $\overrightarrow{AB} = \overrightarrow{CD}$ if, and only if, $ABDC$ is a parallelogram. If $\overrightarrow{AB}$ and $\overrightarrow{CD}$ lie on the same line L, then $\overrightarrow{AB} = \overrightarrow{CD}$ if, and only if, $AB = CD$ and the direction from A to B is the same as the direction from C to D on the line L.

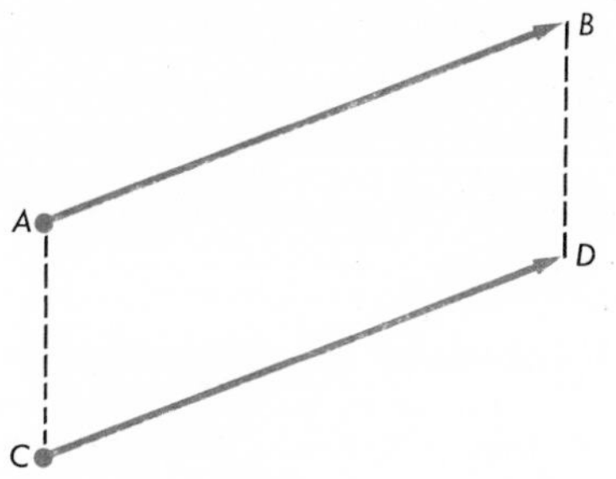

FIGURE 14–2

Several vectors are drawn in Fig. 14–3. Of these vectors, $\overrightarrow{AB} = \overrightarrow{CD}$ since $AB = CD$, each having length $\sqrt{8}$; $\overrightarrow{AB}$ is parallel to $\overrightarrow{CD}$, each having slope 1; and $\overrightarrow{AB}$ has the same direction as $\overrightarrow{CD}$, each being directed upward to the right. On the other hand, $\overrightarrow{AB} \neq \overrightarrow{JK}$ although $\overline{AB}$ is parallel and congruent to $\overline{JK}$. The reason that $\overrightarrow{AB}$ is not equal to $\overrightarrow{JK}$ is that the direction of one vector is opposite to the direction of the other. You may check to see that $\overrightarrow{EF} = \overrightarrow{GH}$ and that $\overrightarrow{AB} \neq \overrightarrow{MN}$.

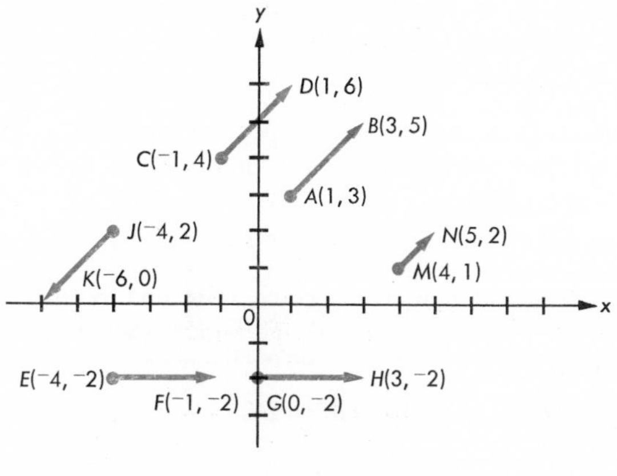

FIGURE 14–3

A vector such as $\overrightarrow{AA}$, which has the same initial point and terminal point, is called a *zero vector.* The vector $\overrightarrow{AA}$ consists of a single point. We shall consider every zero vector to have no direction and to be equal to all other zero vectors. For convenience, the symbol **0**† will be used to denote a zero vector.

If we are given a vector $\overrightarrow{AB}$ and a point C, then there exists a *unique* point D such that $\overrightarrow{AB} = \overrightarrow{CD}$. If point C is not on the same line as $\overrightarrow{AB}$, then D is a unique point such that $ABDC$ is a parallelogram. If C is on the same line L as $\overrightarrow{AB}$, then D is selected on L such that $AB = CD$, and the direction from A to B is the same as that from C to D.

Exercises for Discussion

1. List all nonzero vectors determined by three distinct points A, B, and C.
2. Given that $A_1, A_2, \ldots, A_n$ are n distinct points, how many nonzero vectors do they determine? ${}_nP_2 = n(n-1)$ vectors
3. Given points A, B, and C with respective coordinates (3, 1), (3, 5), and $(^-1, 1)$, find the coordinates of the points D, E, and F such that each of the following is true.
   (a) $\overrightarrow{AB} = \overrightarrow{CD}$ (b) $\overrightarrow{AC} = \overrightarrow{BE}$ (c) $\overrightarrow{BA} = \overrightarrow{AF}$
4. Given that vectors $\overrightarrow{AB}$ and $\overrightarrow{CD}$ are not collinear, what conditions on the quadrilateral containing these points will make the vectors $\overrightarrow{AB}$ and $\overrightarrow{CD}$ of equal length but of opposite direction? Quadrilateral must be a parallelogram.

Exercises

1. Given that A, B, C, and D are four points, no three of which are collinear, list all nonzero vectors determined by these points. Are any two of these vectors ever equal? $\overrightarrow{AB}$, $\overrightarrow{BA}$, $\overrightarrow{AC}$, $\overrightarrow{CA}$, $\overrightarrow{AD}$, $\overrightarrow{DA}$, $\overrightarrow{BC}$, $\overrightarrow{CB}$, $\overrightarrow{BD}$, $\overrightarrow{DB}$, $\overrightarrow{CD}$, $\overrightarrow{DC}$; yes
2. Given points A, B, and C with respective coordinates (0, 0), (2, 2), and $(^-3, 3)$, find the coordinates of the points D, E, and F such that each of the following is true.
   (a) $\overrightarrow{AC} = \overrightarrow{BD}$ $(^-1, 5)$ (b) $\overrightarrow{BA} = \overrightarrow{CE}$ $(^-5, 1)$ (c) $\overrightarrow{BC} = \overrightarrow{AF}$ $(^-5, 1)$
3. Given points A and B with respective coordinates (0, 0) and (4, 4), find the coordinates of the points D, E, and F such that each of the following is true.
   (a) $\overrightarrow{AD} = \overrightarrow{DB}$ (2, 2) (b) $\overrightarrow{AB} = \overrightarrow{BE}$ (8, 8) (c) $\overrightarrow{BA} = \overrightarrow{AF}$ $(^-4, ^-4)$

† It is common practice to use boldface roman type to denote vectors expressed by a single symbol (letter or number).

Exercises for Discussion and Exercises

It is suggested that all the Exercises for Discussion and Exercises be done.

Answers to Exercises for Discussion 1, 3

1. $\overrightarrow{AB}$, $\overrightarrow{BA}$, $\overrightarrow{AC}$, $\overrightarrow{CA}$, $\overrightarrow{BC}$, $\overrightarrow{CB}$. Note that there are ${}_3P_2 = (3)(2) = 6$ different vectors.
3. (a) Since $\overrightarrow{AB}$ is vertical, $\overrightarrow{CD}$ is also vertical; hence, the x-coordinate of D is $^-1$. Since $|\overrightarrow{AB}| = 4$, and $|\overrightarrow{CD}| = |\overrightarrow{AB}|$, it is concluded that $|\overrightarrow{CD}| = 4$. Hence, the y-coordinate of D is 5. Therefore, $D = (^-1, 5)$.
   (b) Since $\overrightarrow{BE} = \overrightarrow{AC}$, quadrilateral $ABEC$ is a parallelogram. But in part (a), a point D was found for which quadrilateral $ABDC$ is a parallelogram. Since there is only one point to serve as the fourth vertex of a parallelogram when three vertices are given, the conclusion is that $E = D$; hence, the coordinates of E are $(^-1, 5)$.
   (c) The coordinates of F are $(3, 1 - 4) = (3, ^-3)$.

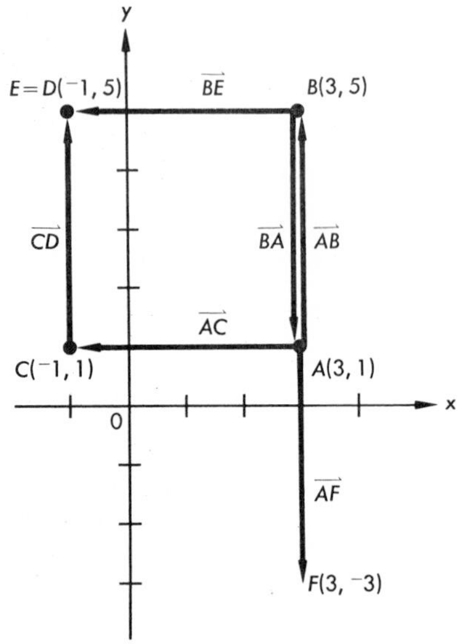

4. Given points A, B, and C with respective coordinates $(4, 1)$, $(^-2, 7)$, and $(3, ^-1)$, find the coordinates of the points D, E, and F such that each of the following is true.

(a) $\overrightarrow{AB} = \overrightarrow{CD}$ $(^-3, 5)$

(b) $\overrightarrow{AB}$ and $\overrightarrow{CE}$ have equal length and opposite direction $(9, ^-7)$

(c) $\overrightarrow{AB}$ and $\overrightarrow{CF}$ have the same direction and $CF = AB$ $(^-3, 5)$

5. Given points A, B, and C with respective coordinates $(0, 0)$, $(^-5, 1)$, and $(6, ^-2)$, find the coordinates of the points D, E, and F such that each of the following is true.

(a) $\overrightarrow{AC} = \overrightarrow{BE}$ $(1, ^-1)$

(b) $AB = 2CD$, and $\overrightarrow{AB}$ and $\overrightarrow{CD}$ have opposite direction $\left(\frac{17}{2}, \frac{^-5}{2}\right)$

(c) $2FC = 3AB$, and $\overrightarrow{FC}$ and $\overrightarrow{AB}$ have the same direction $\left(\frac{27}{2}, \frac{^-7}{2}\right)$

6. Given points A, B, C, and D with respective coordinates $(^-1, 2)$, $(5, 6)$, $(2, ^-2)$, and $(8, 2)$, determine whether $\overrightarrow{AB} = \overrightarrow{CD}$. Yes

14–2 ADDITION AND SUBTRACTION

Several centuries ago, physicists discovered that a force could conveniently be represented by a vector, with the direction of the vector indicating the direction of application of the force and the length of the vector indicating the size of the force. They also discovered that if two forces were applied to an object, then the resultant force could be found by the *parallelogram law.* Thus, if vectors $\overrightarrow{AB}$ and $\overrightarrow{AC}$ represent two forces applied to an object at A, the resultant force is represented by the diagonal vector $\overrightarrow{AE}$ of the parallelogram $ABEC$ in Fig. 14–4. The resultant force represented by $\overrightarrow{AE}$ has precisely the same effect on the object at A as the two forces represented by $\overrightarrow{AB}$ and $\overrightarrow{AC}$.

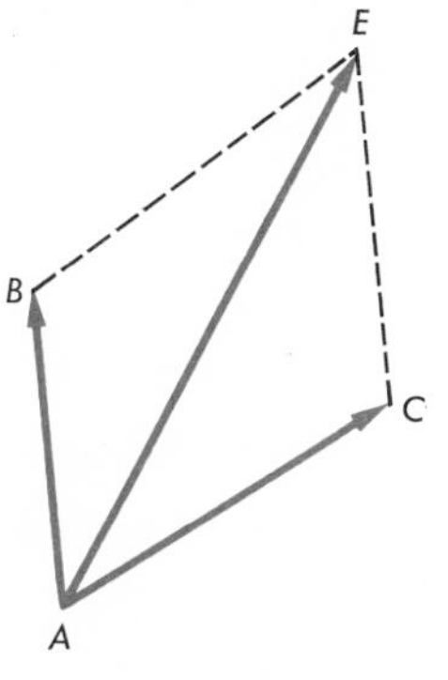

FIGURE 14–4

We shall define the sum of two vectors in essentially the same way in which the resultant was defined in Fig. 14–4. Thus, the sum of vectors $\overrightarrow{AB}$ and $\overrightarrow{CD}$ is defined in the following manner. (See Fig. 14–5.)

Quiz

Given points A, B, and C with respective coordinates $(2, 2)$, $(2, 6)$ and $(^-3, 0)$, find the coordinates of the points D, E, and F such that each of the following is true.

1. $\overrightarrow{AB} = \overrightarrow{CD}$ (ans: $(^-3, 4)$)
2. $\overrightarrow{EA} = \overrightarrow{AB}$ (ans: $(2, ^-2)$)
3. $\overrightarrow{AB}$ and $\overrightarrow{BF}$ have equal length and opposite direction. (ans: $(2, 2)$)

14–2 ADDITION AND SUBTRACTION

You may wish to refer to the development of the complex number system where first the number $a + bi$ was defined and then the sum of two such numbers was defined. Here a vector is defined and now we must also define the sum of two such entities. In each case, the definitions are such that the sum of two objects corresponds to another object of the same kind; thus, the sum of two complex numbers is a complex number and the sum of two vectors is a vector. That is, the system is set up for closure under addition.

DEFINITION OF ADDITION

$$\overrightarrow{AB} + \overrightarrow{CD} = \overrightarrow{AE},$$

where point E is chosen such that $\overrightarrow{BE} = \overrightarrow{CD}$

If vectors $\overrightarrow{AB}$ and $\overrightarrow{CD}$ lie on the same line L, then $\overrightarrow{AE}$, the sum of $\overrightarrow{AB}$ and $\overrightarrow{CD}$, is obtained in the way shown in Fig. 14–6. Perhaps the easiest way to remember the definition of addition is to consider the sum of $\overrightarrow{AB}$ and $\overrightarrow{BC}$, as shown in Fig. 14–7. Then by definition,

$$\overrightarrow{AB} + \overrightarrow{BC} = \overrightarrow{AC}.$$

Thus, in triangle ABC, the sum of the sides $\overrightarrow{AB}$ and $\overrightarrow{BC}$ is the side $\overrightarrow{AC}$.

The following is another property of vector addition.

UNIQUENESS OF ADDITION

If $\overrightarrow{AB} = \overrightarrow{A'B'}$ *and* $\overrightarrow{CD} = \overrightarrow{C'D'}$, *then* $\overrightarrow{AB} + \overrightarrow{CD} = \overrightarrow{A'B'} + \overrightarrow{C'D'}$.

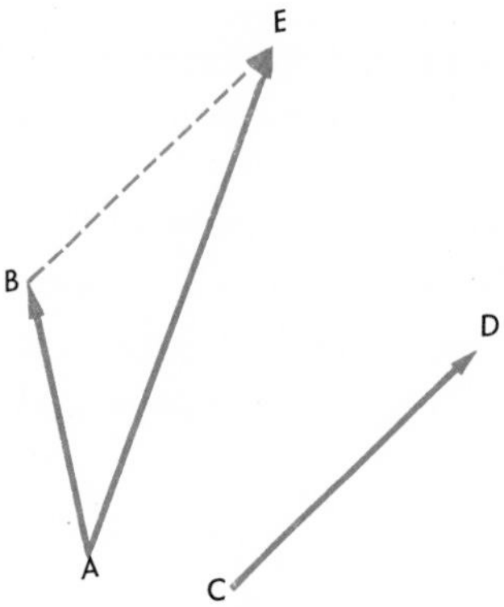

FIGURE 14–5

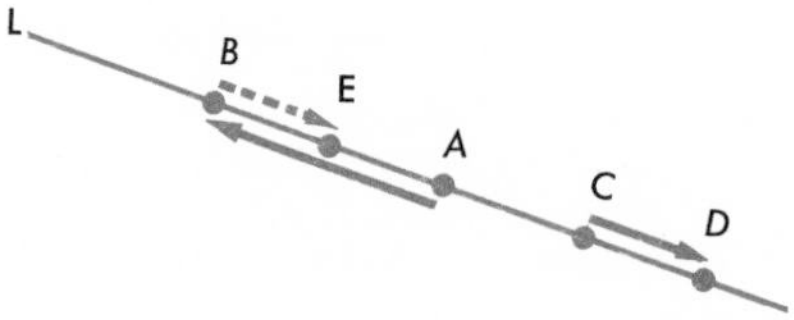

FIGURE 14–6

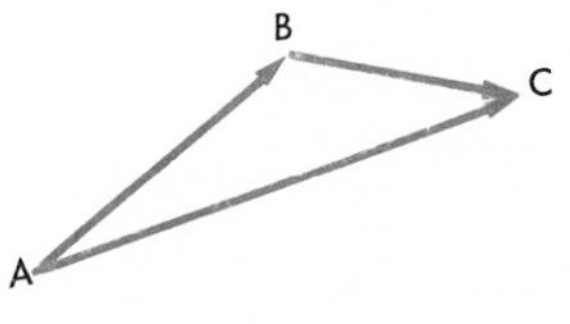

FIGURE 14–7

TWISTER

When Mark couldn't find anyone to play on the seesaw with him, he discovered he could play by himself by tying bricks to one end to balance his weight at the other end. He could do this by tying 16 bricks 7 feet from the pivot, if he sat 4 feet from the pivot. If the weight of a brick is equal to $\frac{3}{4}$ of the weight of a brick plus $\frac{3}{4}$ pound, how much does Mark weigh?

(A seesaw is balanced when the product of the weight and the distance from the pivot of one object is equal to the similar product of the other object.)

Solution: The brick is found to weigh 3 pounds. Thus,

$$16(3)(7) = 4x,$$
$$x = 84.$$

Mark weighs 84 pounds.

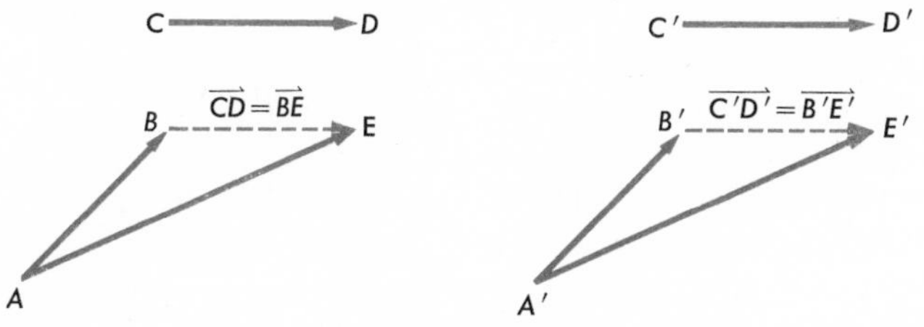

FIGURE 14-8

The validity of this property is demonstrated in Fig. 14-8. In this figure, $\overrightarrow{AB} + \overrightarrow{CD} = \overrightarrow{AE}$ and $\overrightarrow{A'B'} + \overrightarrow{C'D'} = \overrightarrow{A'E'}$. To show that $\overrightarrow{AE} = \overrightarrow{A'E'}$, we first observe the equations

$$\overrightarrow{CD} = \overrightarrow{C'D'}, \quad \overrightarrow{CD} = \overrightarrow{BE}, \quad \overrightarrow{C'D'} = \overrightarrow{B'E'}.$$

From these equations we may conclude that

$$\overrightarrow{BE} = \overrightarrow{B'E'}.$$

Triangles ABE and $A'B'E'$ are congruent because $\overrightarrow{AB} = \overrightarrow{A'B'}$, $\overrightarrow{BE} = \overrightarrow{B'E'}$, and the angle at B is equal to the angle at B'. Furthermore, since $\overline{AB}$ is parallel to $\overline{A'B'}$ and $\overline{BE}$ is parallel to $\overline{B'E'}$, it follows that $\overline{AE}$ is parallel and equal to $\overline{A'E'}$. Hence, $\overrightarrow{AE} = \overrightarrow{A'E'}$ so that $\overrightarrow{AB} + \overrightarrow{CD} = \overrightarrow{A'B'} + \overrightarrow{C'D'}$.

Vector addition has all the properties of addition of real numbers. We list these properties below.

It is recommended that these properties be illustrated with several drawings done on the board in colored chalks.

COMMUTATIVE LAW

$$\overrightarrow{AB} + \overrightarrow{CD} = \overrightarrow{CD} + \overrightarrow{AB} \quad \textit{for all vectors } \overrightarrow{AB}, \overrightarrow{CD}$$

ASSOCIATIVE LAW

$$\overrightarrow{AB} + (\overrightarrow{CD} + \overrightarrow{EF}) = (\overrightarrow{AB} + \overrightarrow{CD}) + \overrightarrow{EF}$$
$$\textit{for all vectors } \overrightarrow{AB}, \overrightarrow{CD}, \overrightarrow{EF}$$

IDENTITY ELEMENT

$$\overrightarrow{AB} + \mathbf{0} = \mathbf{0} + \overrightarrow{AB} = \overrightarrow{AB} \quad \textit{for each vector } \overrightarrow{AB}$$

The study of the properties of vectors provides an opportunity for continued comparison of the system of vectors with the real number system and the field of complex numbers.

Answers to Exercises for Discussion 1–3, 5–7, page 557

1: $\overrightarrow{AB} + \overrightarrow{BC} = \overrightarrow{AC}$, by definition of vector addition.

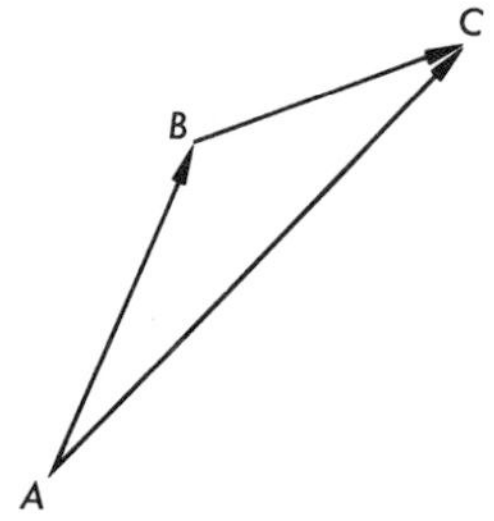

2. $\overrightarrow{AB} + (\overrightarrow{BC} + \overrightarrow{CD}) = \overrightarrow{AB} + \overrightarrow{BD} = \overrightarrow{AD}$

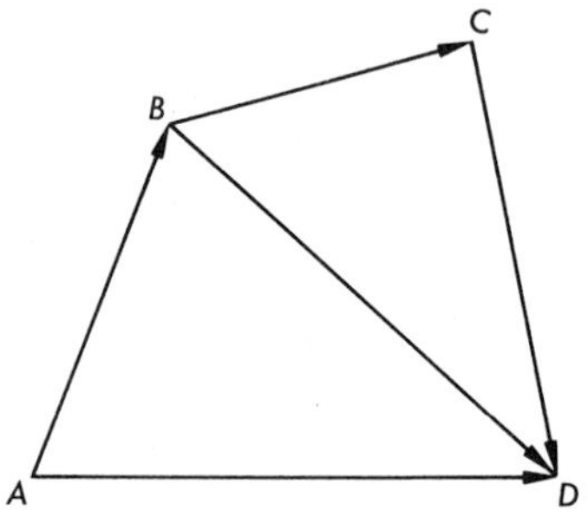

3. $(\overrightarrow{AB} + \overrightarrow{BC}) + \overrightarrow{CD} = \overrightarrow{AC} + \overrightarrow{CD} = \overrightarrow{AD}$

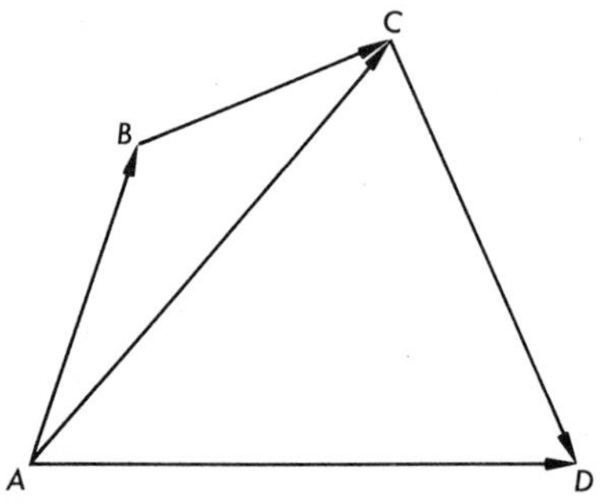

INVERSE ELEMENT

Each vector $\overrightarrow{AB}$ has an opposite, $^{-}\overrightarrow{AB}$, such that

$$\overrightarrow{AB} + {}^{-}\overrightarrow{AB} = {}^{-}\overrightarrow{AB} + \overrightarrow{AB} = \mathbf{0}.$$

The additive inverse, or opposite, of $\overrightarrow{AB}$ is $\overrightarrow{BA}$,

$$^{-}\overrightarrow{AB} = \overrightarrow{BA},$$

because by the definition of addition, $\overrightarrow{AB} + \overrightarrow{BA} = \overrightarrow{AA} = \mathbf{0}$ and $\overrightarrow{BA} + \overrightarrow{AB} = \overrightarrow{BB} = \mathbf{0}$.

We have constructed $\overrightarrow{AE} = \overrightarrow{AB} + \overrightarrow{CD}$ and $\overrightarrow{CF} = \overrightarrow{CD} + \overrightarrow{AB}$ in Fig. 14–9. It follows from geometry that $\overrightarrow{AE} = \overrightarrow{CF}$ and hence, that the commutative law holds. We shall leave the proof of the associative law as an exercise.

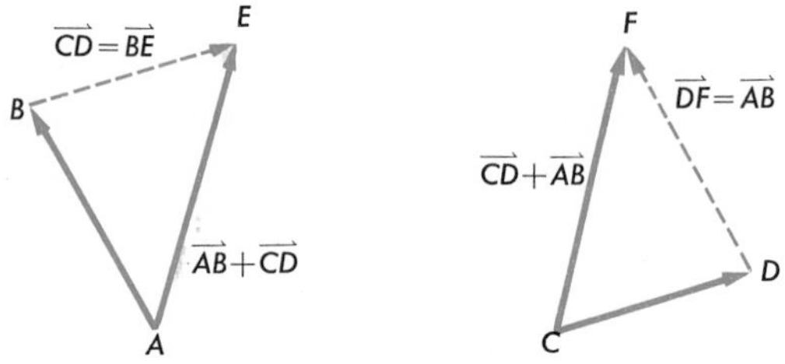

FIGURE 14–9

The following is another property of vector addition, whose proof is the same as that for the cancellation law of addition for numbers given on page 6.

CANCELLATION LAW

If $\overrightarrow{AB} + \overrightarrow{CD} = \overrightarrow{AB} + \overrightarrow{EF}$, then $\overrightarrow{CD} = \overrightarrow{EF}$.

Once we have defined the opposite of a vector, we can introduce the operation of subtraction of vectors.

DEFINITION OF SUBTRACTION

$$\overrightarrow{AB} - \overrightarrow{CD} = \overrightarrow{AB} + {}^{-}\overrightarrow{CD} \quad \textit{for all vectors } \overrightarrow{AB}, \overrightarrow{CD}$$

Problem. Prove that the diagonals of a parallelogram bisect each other.

Solution. Let $ABCD$ be a parallelogram, as shown in Fig. 14–10, and let E be the point of bisection of diagonal $\overline{AC}$. Since $\overrightarrow{AB} = \overrightarrow{DC}$ by assumption, and $\overrightarrow{AB} = \overrightarrow{AE} + \overrightarrow{EB}$ and $\overrightarrow{DC} = \overrightarrow{DE} + \overrightarrow{EC}$, we have

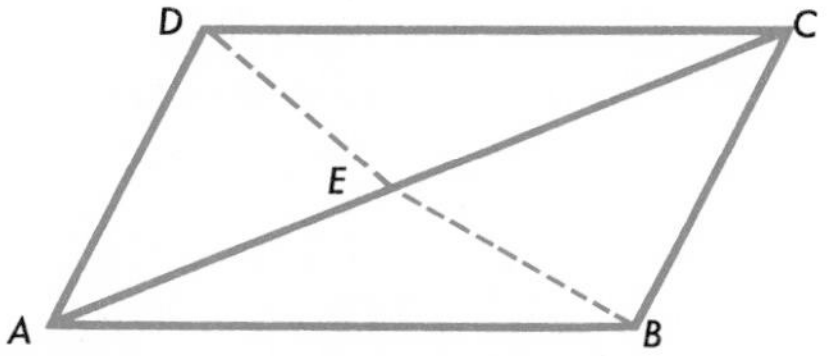

FIGURE 14–10

$$\overrightarrow{AE} + \overrightarrow{EB} = \overrightarrow{DE} + \overrightarrow{EC}.$$

Now $\overrightarrow{AE} = \overrightarrow{EC}$, and hence by the cancellation law, we have that

$$\overrightarrow{DE} = \overrightarrow{EB}.$$

Two nonzero vectors can be equal and have an endpoint in common if, and only if, they lie on the same line. Hence, E must lie on the diagonal $\overline{DB}$. Furthermore, it is the midpoint of $\overline{DB}$. This establishes the proof.

Exercises for Discussion

Each expression in Exercises 1–4 is equal to a vector having its endpoints among the four points A, B, C, and D. Find the indicated vector.

1. $\overrightarrow{AB} + \overrightarrow{BC} =$ __?__
2. $\overrightarrow{AB} + (\overrightarrow{BC} + \overrightarrow{CD}) =$ __?__
3. $(\overrightarrow{AB} + \overrightarrow{BC}) + \overrightarrow{CD} =$ __?__
4. $\overrightarrow{AB} - \overrightarrow{AC} =$ $\overrightarrow{CB}$__?__, since $\overrightarrow{AC} + \overrightarrow{CB} = \overrightarrow{AB}$
5. Given that $\overrightarrow{AB}$ and $\overrightarrow{AC}$ are not collinear, show that $\overrightarrow{AB} + \overrightarrow{AC}$ and $\overrightarrow{AB} - \overrightarrow{AC}$ are diagonals of the parallelogram having $\overline{AB}$ and $\overline{AC}$ as two of its adjacent sides.
6. Consider the points A, B, and C with respective coordinates $(0, 0)$, $(4, 0)$, and $(^{-}4, 0)$. What can you say about $\overrightarrow{AB} + \overrightarrow{AC}$?
7. Use the figure to show that vector addition is associative.

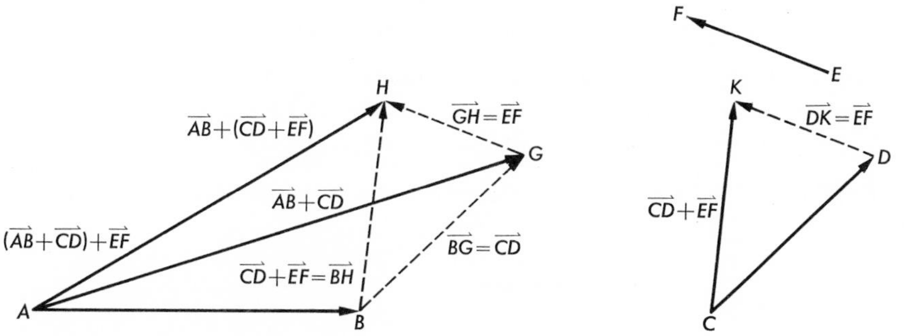

5. In the parallelogram $ABDC$,

$$\overrightarrow{AD} = \overrightarrow{AB} + \overrightarrow{BD} = \overrightarrow{AB} + \overrightarrow{AC},$$

and since

$$\overrightarrow{AC} + \overrightarrow{CB} = \overrightarrow{AB},$$

then

$$\overrightarrow{AB} - \overrightarrow{AC} = \overrightarrow{CB}.$$

Hence, the vectors $\overrightarrow{AB} + \overrightarrow{AC}$ and $\overrightarrow{AB} - \overrightarrow{AC}$ are the diagonals of the parallelogram having $\overrightarrow{AB}$ and $\overrightarrow{AC}$ as two of its sides.

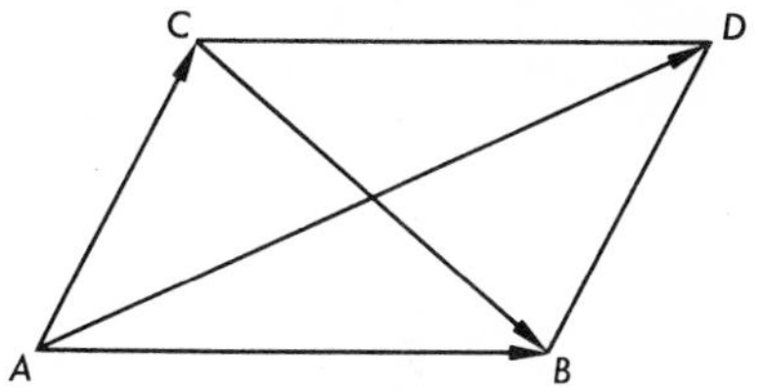

6. $\overrightarrow{AB} + \overrightarrow{AC} = \mathbf{0}$

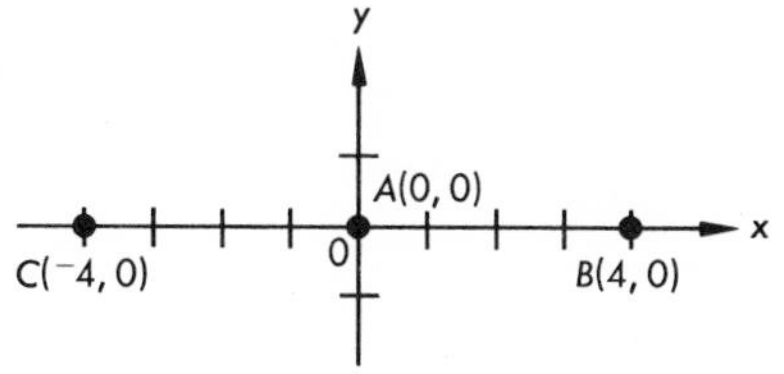

7.

$$\overrightarrow{CD} + \overrightarrow{EF} = \overrightarrow{BH}$$
$$\overrightarrow{AB} + \overrightarrow{BH} = \overrightarrow{AH}$$
$$\overrightarrow{AB} + \overrightarrow{CD} = \overrightarrow{AG}$$
$$\overrightarrow{AG} + \overrightarrow{EF} = \overrightarrow{AH}$$

Therefore,

$$\overrightarrow{AB} + \overrightarrow{BH} = \overrightarrow{AG} + \overrightarrow{EF}$$

and

$$\overrightarrow{AB} + (\overrightarrow{CD} + \overrightarrow{EF}) = (\overrightarrow{AB} + \overrightarrow{CD}) + \overrightarrow{EF}.$$

Quiz

Each expression in Exercises 1–5 is equal to a vector having its endpoints among the four points A, B, C, and D. For each expression, find the vector determined by these four points.

1. $\overrightarrow{CD} - \overrightarrow{AD}$ (ans: $\overrightarrow{CA}$)
2. $(\overrightarrow{AC} - \overrightarrow{DC}) + \overrightarrow{DB}$ (ans: $\overrightarrow{AB}$)
3. $(\overrightarrow{AD} + \overrightarrow{CB}) + \overrightarrow{DC}$ (ans: $\overrightarrow{AB}$)
4. $(\overrightarrow{BD} - \overrightarrow{AD}) + (\overrightarrow{AB} - \overrightarrow{CB})$ (ans: $\overrightarrow{BC}$)
5. $(\overrightarrow{AC} + \overrightarrow{BD}) + (\overrightarrow{CB} + \overrightarrow{DA})$ (ans: $\mathbf{0}$)

Exercises

Each expression in Exercises 1–6 is equal to a vector having its endpoints among the four points A, B, C, and D. For each expression, find the vector determined by these four points.

1. $\overrightarrow{AB} - \overrightarrow{AD} =$ __?__ $\overrightarrow{DB}$
2. $(\overrightarrow{AD} + \overrightarrow{AC}) - \overrightarrow{AD} =$ __?__ $\overrightarrow{AC}$
3. $\overrightarrow{AB} + (\overrightarrow{CD} - \overrightarrow{AD}) =$ __?__ $\overrightarrow{CB}$
4. $(\overrightarrow{AB} + \overrightarrow{CD}) + (\overrightarrow{BC} + \overrightarrow{DA}) =$ __?__ $\mathbf{0}$
5. $(\overrightarrow{AB} - \overrightarrow{CB}) + (\overrightarrow{CD} - \overrightarrow{AC}) =$ __?__ $\overrightarrow{CD}$
6. $(\overrightarrow{BD} - \overrightarrow{AC}) + (\overrightarrow{DB} - \overrightarrow{CA}) =$ __?__ $\mathbf{0}$

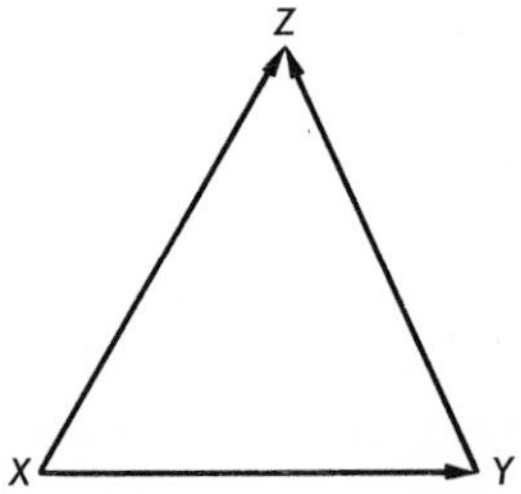

7. Which of the following statements are true for the figure at the right?
   - $\overrightarrow{XY} + \overrightarrow{YZ} = \overrightarrow{XZ}$ (circled)
   - $\overrightarrow{XY} - \overrightarrow{XZ} = \overrightarrow{YZ}$
   - $\overrightarrow{XZ} - \overrightarrow{YZ} = \overrightarrow{XY}$ (circled)
8. One vector has length 3; another vector has length 6 and a direction opposite to the first vector. What is the length of their sum? 3 What can you say about the direction of the sum of the vectors? Same as direction of longer vector

△

9. Show that if $\overrightarrow{AB} = \overrightarrow{CD}$, then $\overrightarrow{AC} = \overrightarrow{BD}$. See Solution Manual.
10. Given points A, B, and O with respective coordinates $(2, {}^-8)$, $({}^-5, 10)$, and $(0, 0)$, use the parallelogram law to find the coordinates of point C such that $\overrightarrow{OA} + \overrightarrow{OB} = \overrightarrow{OC}$. $({}^-3, 2)$
11. Given points Q, R, and O with respective coordinates $(11, 2)$, $(8, 5)$, and $(0, 0)$, use the parallelogram law to determine the coordinates of a point P such that $\overrightarrow{OQ} + \overrightarrow{OR} = \overrightarrow{OP}$. $(19, 7)$
12. If $\overrightarrow{AB} - \overrightarrow{CD} = \mathbf{0}$, is it necessarily true that $\overrightarrow{AB} = \overrightarrow{CD}$? Yes
13. Given points A, B, C, and D with respective coordinates $(0, 0)$, $(2, 2)$, $(0, 2)$, and $(2, 4)$, graph $\overrightarrow{AB}$ and $\overrightarrow{CD}$. Does $\overrightarrow{AB} = \overrightarrow{CD}$? Yes
14. In the figures, $\overrightarrow{BC}$ and $\overrightarrow{FE}$ are the differences of two vectors. Write the proper subtraction statement for each figure. $\overrightarrow{BC} = \overrightarrow{AC} - \overrightarrow{AB}$; $\overrightarrow{FE} = \overrightarrow{DE} - \overrightarrow{DF}$

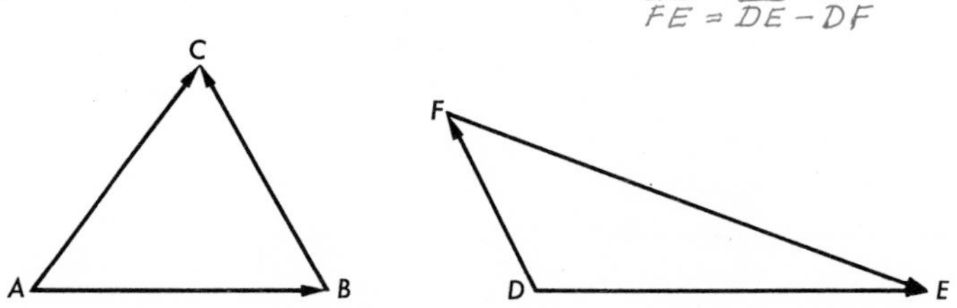

15. Given points A, B, and C in the figure, give an argument which shows that $(\overrightarrow{AB} + \overrightarrow{BC}) + \overrightarrow{CA} = 0$.

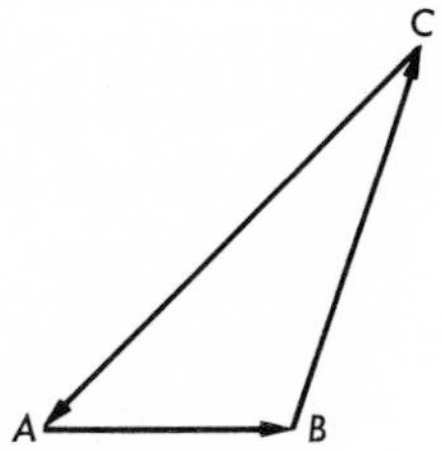

16. Show graphically that $^{-}(\overrightarrow{AB} - \overrightarrow{CD}) = {}^{-}\overrightarrow{AB} + \overrightarrow{CD}$.

17. Sketch a vector $\overrightarrow{AB}$ that has length 2 inches, is parallel to the lower edge of your paper, and has an arrow on its right-hand end. Sketch a second vector $\overrightarrow{CD}$ that has length 1.5 inches and makes an angle of 30° with $\overrightarrow{AB}$. Now sketch

$$2\overrightarrow{AB},\quad 3\overrightarrow{CD},\quad \overrightarrow{AB} + \overrightarrow{CD},\quad \overrightarrow{AB} - \overrightarrow{CD},\quad 2\overrightarrow{AB} - 3\overrightarrow{CD},\quad \frac{\overrightarrow{AB} + \overrightarrow{CD}}{2}.$$

14–3 SCALAR MULTIPLICATION

For a given vector $\overrightarrow{AB}$, let us define

$$\begin{aligned} 1\overrightarrow{AB} &= \overrightarrow{AB}, \\ 2\overrightarrow{AB} &= \overrightarrow{AB} + \overrightarrow{AB}, \\ 3\overrightarrow{AB} &= \overrightarrow{AB} + \overrightarrow{AB} + \overrightarrow{AB}, \end{aligned}$$

and so on. Whenever $k\overrightarrow{AB}$ has been defined, then we define

$$(k + 1)\overrightarrow{AB} = k\overrightarrow{AB} + \overrightarrow{AB}.$$

In this way, we may define $n\overrightarrow{AB}$ for every positive integer n. Intuitively,

$$n\overrightarrow{AB} = \underbrace{\overrightarrow{AB} + \overrightarrow{AB} + \cdots + \overrightarrow{AB}}_{n \text{ terms}}.$$

How could we define $n\overrightarrow{AB}$, given that n is a negative integer? We would define $(^{-}1)\overrightarrow{AB}$ to be $^{-}\overrightarrow{AB}$, the additive inverse of $\overrightarrow{AB}$. It should then seem natural to define $(^{-}2)\overrightarrow{AB}$ to be $^{-}(2\overrightarrow{AB})$, $(^{-}3)\overrightarrow{AB}$ to be $^{-}(3\overrightarrow{AB})$, and, in general,

$$(^{-}k)\overrightarrow{AB} = {}^{-}(k\overrightarrow{AB})$$

for every positive integer k. Finally, we define

$$0\overrightarrow{AB} = \mathbf{0}.$$

14–3 SCALAR MULTIPLICATION

Scalar multiplication for vectors may be compared with multiplication of an *i*-number by a real number.

With the definition above, $n\overrightarrow{AB}$ is defined for every vector $\overrightarrow{AB}$ and every integer n. Some examples are given in Fig. 14–11.

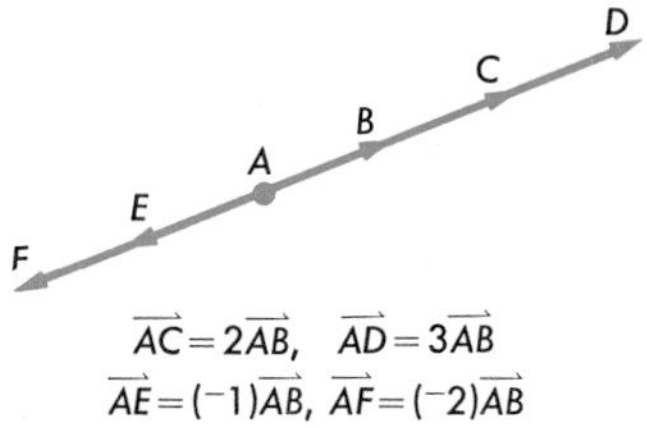

FIGURE 14–11

If the plane has a coordinate system on it, so that each vector $\overrightarrow{AB}$ has a length which we shall designate by $|\overrightarrow{AB}|$, then it follows from our definition of $n\overrightarrow{AB}$ that

$$|n\overrightarrow{AB}| = |n| \cdot |\overrightarrow{AB}|.$$

In other words, the length of vector $n\overrightarrow{AB}$ is $|n|$ times the length of $\overrightarrow{AB}$. With this in mind, let us define $r\overrightarrow{AB}$ for every real number r in the following way.

DEFINITION OF SCALAR MULTIPLICATION

The vector $r\overrightarrow{AB}$ has length $|r| \cdot |\overrightarrow{AB}|$ and the same direction as $\overrightarrow{AB}$ if $r > 0$, and a direction opposite to that of $\overrightarrow{AB}$ if $r < 0$.

(Def-SM)

In this way, we have defined a vector $r\overrightarrow{AB}$ for every vector $\overrightarrow{AB}$ and every real number r. Some examples are given in Fig. 14–12.

We now have defined a type of multiplication of a vector $\overrightarrow{AB}$ by a real number r, the product $r\overrightarrow{AB}$ being a vector. The multiplication of a vector by a number is called *scalar multiplication*. The real number r appearing in a product $r\overrightarrow{AB}$ is often called a *scalar*. Some properties of scalar multiplication are given below.

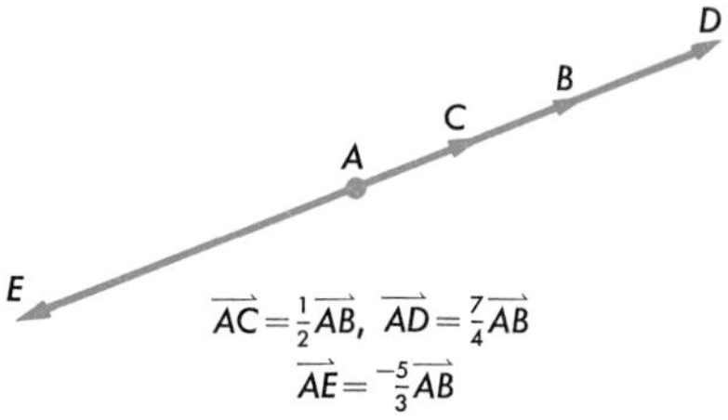

FIGURE 14–12

UNIQUENESS OF SCALAR MULTIPLICATION

If

$$\overrightarrow{AB} = \overrightarrow{CD},$$

then

$$r\overrightarrow{AB} = r\overrightarrow{CD} \textit{ for every real number } r. \qquad (SM\text{-}1)$$

You may wish to refer to the statements on page 168 about *i*-numbers and real numbers in order to see how they parallel the statements on this page about vectors and real numbers.

Proof. If $\overrightarrow{AB} = \overrightarrow{CD}$, then $|\overrightarrow{AB}| = |\overrightarrow{CD}|$ and $|r| \cdot |\overrightarrow{AB}| = |r| \cdot |\overrightarrow{CD}|$. Since $\overrightarrow{AB}$ and $\overrightarrow{CD}$ have the same direction, so do $r\overrightarrow{AB}$ and $r\overrightarrow{CD}$. Hence, vectors $r\overrightarrow{AB}$ and $r\overrightarrow{CD}$ are equal, since they have the same length and direction.

ASSOCIATIVE LAW OF SCALAR MULTIPLICATION

$$(rs)\overrightarrow{AB} = r(s\overrightarrow{AB}) \qquad (SM\text{-}2)$$

for every pair r, s of real numbers and every vector $\overrightarrow{AB}$

DISTRIBUTIVE LAWS OF SCALAR MULTIPLICATION

$$(r + s)\overrightarrow{AB} = r\overrightarrow{AB} + s\overrightarrow{AB}$$
$$r(\overrightarrow{AB} + \overrightarrow{CD}) = r\overrightarrow{AB} + r\overrightarrow{CD} \qquad (SM\text{-}3)$$

for every pair r, s of real numbers and every pair $\overrightarrow{AB}$, $\overrightarrow{CD}$ of vectors

Property (SM-2) is valid because the vectors $(rs)\overrightarrow{AB}$ and $r(s\overrightarrow{AB})$ have the same length, $|r| \cdot |s| \cdot |\overrightarrow{AB}|$, and the same direction, that of $\overrightarrow{AB}$ if $rs > 0$ and opposite to that of $\overrightarrow{AB}$ if $rs < 0$.

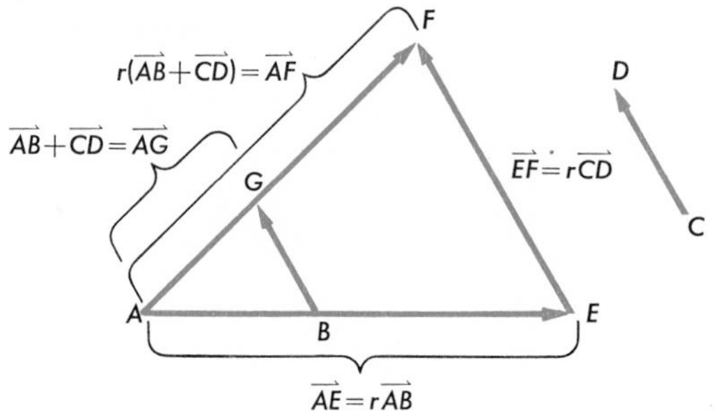

FIGURE 14-13

The second distributive law of (SM-3) is illustrated in Fig. 14-13 for $r > 0$. In this figure, triangles ABG and AEF are similar, with proportionality factor r. Hence, $\overrightarrow{AF} = r\overrightarrow{AG}$, or $r(\overrightarrow{AB} + \overrightarrow{CD})$. On the other hand, $\overrightarrow{AF} = \overrightarrow{AE} + \overrightarrow{EF}$, or $r\overrightarrow{AB} + r\overrightarrow{CD}$. Therefore,

$$r(\overrightarrow{AB} + \overrightarrow{CD}) = r\overrightarrow{AB} + r\overrightarrow{CD}.$$

Students should enjoy the proofs using vectors of the same theorems they once proved in geometry. You may wish to suggest that they look in their geometry texts for some theorems that could easily be proven by using vectors. They may find problems such as the one below.

A line joining the midpoints of two sides of a triangle is parallel to the third side and equal to one-half its length.

Proof. Use $\triangle ABC$ with E, F midpoints of sides AB and BC, respectively.

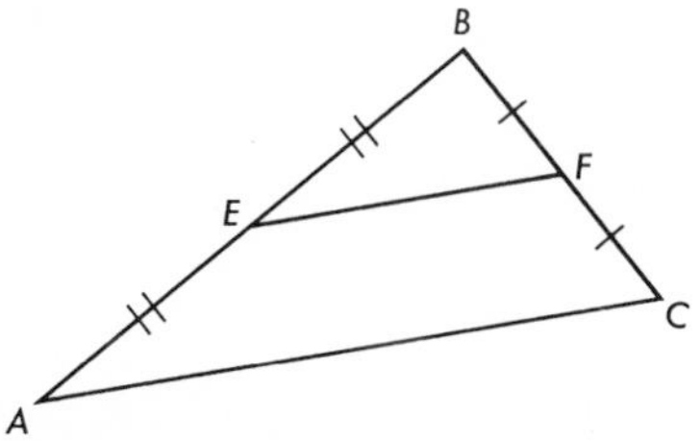

By the definition of vector addition,

$$\overrightarrow{AE} + \overrightarrow{EB} = \overrightarrow{AB}$$
$$\overrightarrow{BF} + \overrightarrow{FC} = \overrightarrow{BC},$$

and

$$\overrightarrow{AB} + \overrightarrow{BC} = \overrightarrow{AC}.$$

By assumption,

$$\overrightarrow{AE} = \overrightarrow{EB},$$
$$\overrightarrow{BF} = \overrightarrow{FC}.$$

Hence,

$$2\overrightarrow{EB} + 2\overrightarrow{BF} = \overrightarrow{AC},$$
$$\overrightarrow{EB} + \overrightarrow{BF} = \tfrac{1}{2}\overrightarrow{AC}.$$

But by the definition of vector addition,

$$\overrightarrow{EB} + \overrightarrow{BF} = \overrightarrow{EF},$$

so

$$\overrightarrow{EF} = \tfrac{1}{2}\overrightarrow{AC}.$$

Since $\overrightarrow{EF}$ is not on $\overrightarrow{AC}$, $\overrightarrow{EF} \parallel \overrightarrow{AC}$.

We shall leave the proof of the first distributive law of scalar multiplication as an exercise.

The set of all vectors in a plane is closed with respect to the operations of addition and scalar multiplication. The properties of these operations should not be hard to remember, since they are very similar to the properties of addition and multiplication of numbers. We shall henceforth speak of the *vector algebra*, or *algebra of vectors*, meaning the set of all vectors in a plane together with the operations of addition and scalar multiplication.

Some practice may be gained in using this vector algebra by proving well-known theorems of geometry. Consider, for instance, the following example.

Problem. Prove that the medians of a triangle meet at a point of trisection of each median.

Solution. Let $\overline{AD}$ be a median of triangle ABC, let E be the midpoint of side $\overline{AC}$, and let F be the point of trisection of $\overline{AD}$ nearer D (Fig. 14–14). In vector notation, $\overrightarrow{AE} = \overrightarrow{EC}$, $\overrightarrow{BD} = \overrightarrow{DC}$, and $\overrightarrow{AF} = 2\overrightarrow{FD}$. If we can prove that $\overrightarrow{BF} = 2\overrightarrow{FE}$, then we shall have proved that points B, F, and E are collinear (why?) and that F is a point of trisection of median $\overline{BE}$. With this in mind, we proceed as follows:

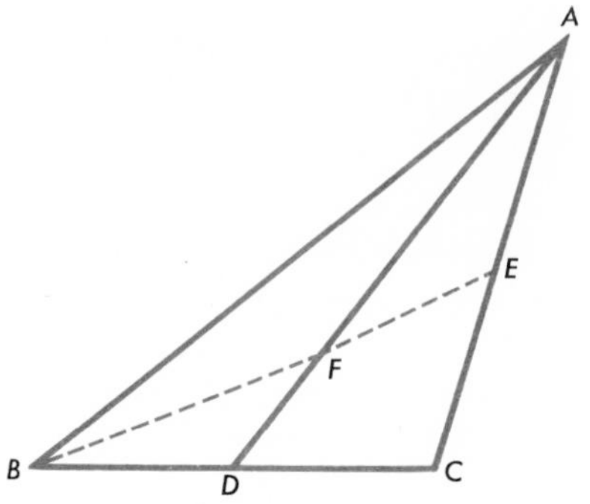

FIGURE 14–14

$$\overrightarrow{BF} + \overrightarrow{FD} = \overrightarrow{BD} \quad \text{and} \quad \overrightarrow{CF} + \overrightarrow{FD} = \overrightarrow{CD}.$$

Therefore,

$$\overrightarrow{BF} + \overrightarrow{FD} = {}^{-}(\overrightarrow{CF} + \overrightarrow{FD}) \quad \text{since} \quad \overrightarrow{BD} = {}^{-}\overrightarrow{CD}.$$

Similarly,

$$\overrightarrow{AF} + \overrightarrow{FE} = {}^{-}(\overrightarrow{CF} + \overrightarrow{FE}) \quad \text{since} \quad \overrightarrow{AE} = {}^{-}\overrightarrow{CE}.$$

Subtracting, we have

$$\overrightarrow{BF} + \overrightarrow{FD} - \overrightarrow{AF} - \overrightarrow{FE} = {}^{-}\overrightarrow{FD} + \overrightarrow{FE},$$

or

$$\overrightarrow{BF} = 2\overrightarrow{FE} + \overrightarrow{AF} - 2\overrightarrow{FD}.$$

Since $\overrightarrow{AF} = 2\overrightarrow{FD}$, we have

$$\overrightarrow{BF} = 2\overrightarrow{FE}.$$

We have proved that the point of trisection nearer D of median $\overline{AD}$ is also the point of trisection of any other median. This proves that the medians meet in a point of trisection of each median.

Exercises for Discussion

Given that $\overrightarrow{AC} = r\overrightarrow{AB}$, describe how point C is related to points A and B for each of the conditions in Exercises 1–3.

1. $r = \frac{1}{2}$ **2.** $r = {}^{-}\frac{1}{2}$ **3.** $0 < r < 1$

4. Points A, B, and C are on a number line, with points A and B having respective coordinates $^{-}1$ and 2. Find the coordinate of C, given that $\overrightarrow{AC} = r\overrightarrow{AB}$ and that r has each of the following values.

(a) $r = \frac{1}{3}$ 0 (b) $r = {}^{-}1$ $^{-}4$

5. Let $ABCD$ be a quadrilateral and E, F, G, and H be the respective midpoints of sides $\overline{AB}$, $\overline{BC}$, $\overline{CD}$, and $\overline{DA}$. Prove that $EFGH$ is a parallelogram.

Exercises

Given that $\overrightarrow{AC} = r\overrightarrow{AB}$, describe how point C is related to points A and B for each of the following conditions.

1. $r = \frac{2}{3}$ **2.** $^{-}1 < r < 0$ **3.** $\frac{1}{2} < r < \frac{2}{3}$

Points A, B, and C are on a number line, with points A and B having respective coordinates $^{-}2$ and 5. Find the coordinate of C, given that $\overrightarrow{AC} = r\overrightarrow{AB}$ and that r has each of the following values.

4. $r = {}^{-}\frac{1}{2}$ $\frac{^{-}11}{2}$ **5.** $r = 10$ 68 **6.** $r = {}^{-}100$ $^{-}702$

7. $r = \sqrt{3}$ $7\sqrt{3}-2$ **8.** $r = 1 + \sqrt{2}$ $5+7\sqrt{2}$

△

9. Given points O and P with respective coordinates $(0, 0)$ and $(2, 3)$, find the coordinates of the endpoint of each of the following vectors.

(a) $2\overrightarrow{OP}$ $(4, 6)$ (b) $^{-}5\overrightarrow{OP}$ $(^{-}10, ^{-}15)$ (c) $\frac{1}{2}\overrightarrow{OP}$ $(1, \frac{3}{2})$

10. Given points A and B with respective coordinates $(1, 1)$ and $(6, 1)$, find the coordinates of the endpoints of each of the following vectors.

(a) $3\overrightarrow{AB}$ $(16, 1)$ (b) $^{-}\frac{1}{2}\overrightarrow{AB}$ $(\frac{^{-}3}{2}, 1)$

Graph the vectors you found in parts (a) and (b). See Solution Manual.

Answers to Exercises for Discussion 1–3, 5

1. C is the midpoint of $\overline{AB}$.
2. C is on the line AB with A between C and B and

$$d(C, A) = \tfrac{1}{2}d(A, B).$$

3. C is any point on $\overline{AB}$ between A and B.
5. $\overrightarrow{EF} = \overrightarrow{EB} + \overrightarrow{BF} = \frac{1}{2}\overrightarrow{AB} + \frac{1}{2}\overrightarrow{BC}$
$= \frac{1}{2}(\overrightarrow{AB} + \overrightarrow{BC})$
$= \frac{1}{2}\overrightarrow{AC}$

Similarly, $\overrightarrow{HG} = \frac{1}{2}\overrightarrow{AC}$, and so $\overrightarrow{EF} = \overrightarrow{HG}$. In the same manner, we can show that $\overrightarrow{FG} = \overrightarrow{EH}$; this means that quadrilateral $EFGH$ is a parallelogram.

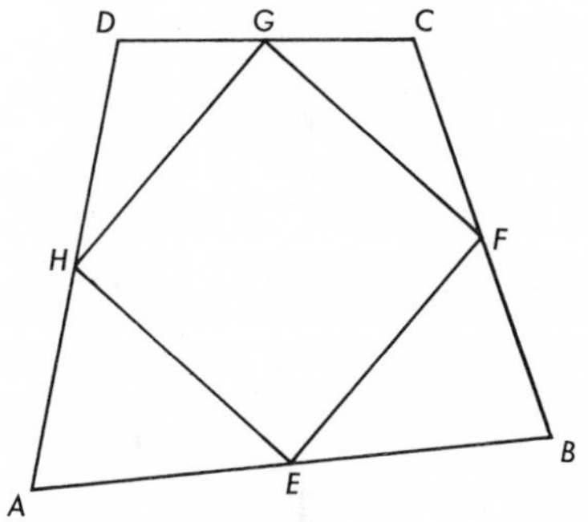

Answers to Exercises 1–3

1. C is point of trisection of $\overline{AB}$, and is nearer to B.
2. C is on line AB, with A between C and B, and C nearer to A than B is.
3. C is any point on $\overline{AB}$ between the midpoint of $\overline{AB}$ and the point of trisection of $\overline{AB}$ that is closer to B.

Quiz

Points A, B, and C are on a number line, with points A and B having respective coordinates $^{-}3$ and 1. Find the coordinate of C, given that $\overrightarrow{AC} = r\overrightarrow{AB}$ and that r has each of the following values.

1. $r = \frac{3}{4}$ (ans: 0)
2. $r = \frac{^{-}3}{4}$ (ans: $^{-}6$)
3. $r = 4$ (ans: 13)
4. $r = {}^{-}10$ (ans: $^{-}43$)

14–4 BASES

A thorough knowledge of this section will be of great benefit to the student who goes on to a more formal study of linear algebra.

Let points A, B, and C have respective coordinates (0, 0), (3, $^{-}2$), and (4, 3), and let $k = 3$ and $l = {}^{-}2$. Find the coordinates of the endpoint of each of the following vectors.

11. $\overrightarrow{AB} + \overrightarrow{AC}$ (7, 1) **12.** $k\overrightarrow{AB}$ (9, $^{-}6$)

13. $l\overrightarrow{AC}$ ($^{-}8$, $^{-}6$) **14.** $k\overrightarrow{AB} + l\overrightarrow{AC}$ (1, $^{-}12$)

15. $\overrightarrow{AB} - \overrightarrow{AC}$ ($^{-}1$, $^{-}5$) **16.** $k\overrightarrow{AB} - l\overrightarrow{AC}$ (17, 0)

▲

17. If $PQ = RS$, is it necessarily true that $\overrightarrow{PQ} = \overrightarrow{RS}$? No

18. If $\overrightarrow{PQ}$ is a scalar multiple of $\overrightarrow{RS}$, is $\overrightarrow{RS}$ necessarily a scalar multiple of $\overrightarrow{PQ}$? Yes

19. Given that $\overrightarrow{PQ}$ and $\overrightarrow{RS}$ have either the same or opposite direction, with $\overrightarrow{PQ} \neq \mathbf{0}$, explain why there is a unique real number k such that $k\overrightarrow{PQ} = \overrightarrow{RS}$.

20. Prove the first part of (SM-3). 19–20 See Solution Manual.

14–4 BASES

In the last section, we saw that for each vector $\overrightarrow{AB}$ and each real number r, the vector $r\overrightarrow{AB}$ lies on the line containing $\overrightarrow{AB}$. Conversely, it is true that for a given nonzero vector $\overrightarrow{AB}$ lying on a line L, every vector $\overrightarrow{CD}$ lying on L or on a line parallel to L is a scalar multiple of $\overrightarrow{AB}$. Thus, if we let

$$r = \frac{|\overrightarrow{CD}|}{|\overrightarrow{AB}|}, \quad \text{or } r = \frac{-|\overrightarrow{CD}|}{|\overrightarrow{AB}|},$$

according to whether $\overrightarrow{AB}$ and $\overrightarrow{CD}$ have the same or opposite direction, then $\overrightarrow{CD} = r\overrightarrow{AB}$.

If we are given two nonzero vectors that are not scalar multiples of each other, then every vector in the plane may be expressed as a combination of the two given vectors. To be more explicit, let the two given vectors $\overrightarrow{AB}$ and $\overrightarrow{AC}$ have the same initial point A, and let $\overrightarrow{AD}$ be any other vector having initial point A. Then $\overrightarrow{AD}$ is the diagonal of a parallelogram $AEDF$, two of whose sides lie along the lines containing $\overrightarrow{AB}$ and $\overrightarrow{AC}$. Two possible alternatives for the parallelogram $AEDF$ are shown in Fig. 14–15 and 14–16. In any case, $\overrightarrow{AE}$ is collinear with $\overrightarrow{AB}$ so that $\overrightarrow{AE} = r\overrightarrow{AB}$ for some real number r, and $\overrightarrow{AF}$ is collinear with $\overrightarrow{AC}$ so that $\overrightarrow{AF} = s\overrightarrow{AC}$ for some real number s. However, since $\overrightarrow{AD}$ is the diagonal of this parallelogram, $\overrightarrow{AD} = \overrightarrow{AE} + \overrightarrow{AF}$. Consequently,

$$\overrightarrow{AD} = r\overrightarrow{AB} + s\overrightarrow{AC}.$$

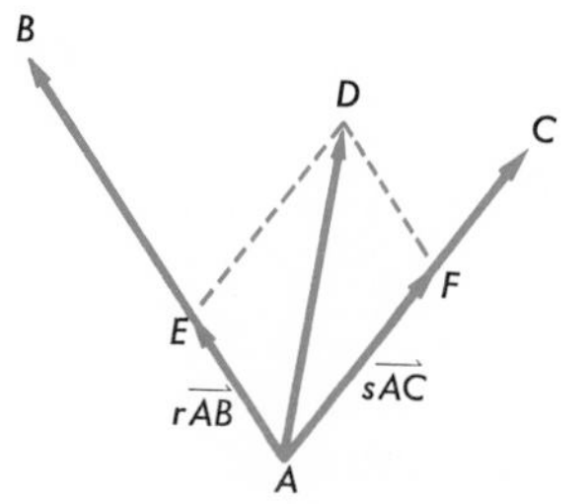

FIGURE 14–15

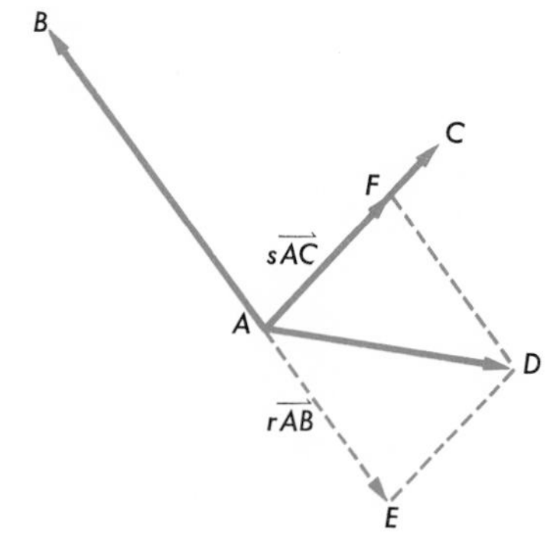

FIGURE 14–16

A set $\{\overrightarrow{AB}, \overrightarrow{CD}\}$ of two vectors is called a *basis* of our vector algebra if every vector $\overrightarrow{EF}$ may be uniquely expressed as a combination of $\overrightarrow{AB}$ and $\overrightarrow{CD}$ of the form

$$\overrightarrow{EF} = r\overrightarrow{AB} + s\overrightarrow{CD}, \quad r \text{ and } s \text{ scalars.}$$

According to these results, we can make the following statement.

Every set of two nonzero, nonparallel vectors is a basis.

Problem 1. Given vectors $\overrightarrow{AB}$, $\overrightarrow{AC}$, and $\overrightarrow{AD}$ as shown in Fig. 14–17, express $\overrightarrow{AD}$ as a combination of $\overrightarrow{AB}$ and $\overrightarrow{AC}$.

It is recommended that many exercises similar to Problem 1 be done at the board.

Solution. Clearly, $\overrightarrow{AB}$ and $\overrightarrow{AC}$ are nonzero and nonparallel vectors. Hence, $\{\overrightarrow{AB}, \overrightarrow{AC}\}$ is a basis of the vector algebra. To express $\overrightarrow{AD}$ as a combination of $\overrightarrow{AB}$ and $\overrightarrow{AC}$, we first find the coordinates of the vertices of the parallelogram $AEDF$ having $\overline{AD}$ as a diagonal. The equations of the lines on which the three given vectors lie are

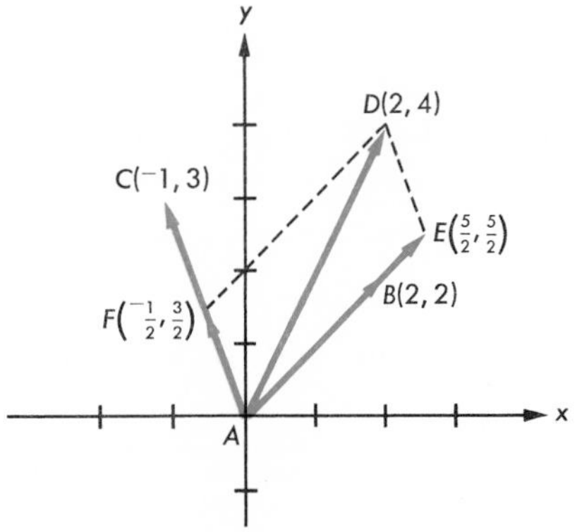

FIGURE 14–17

$$\overrightarrow{AB}: y = x,$$
$$\overrightarrow{AC}: y = {}^{-}3x,$$
$$\overrightarrow{AD}: y = 2x.$$

The line through point D and parallel to $\overrightarrow{AC}$ has equation

$$y - 4 = {}^{-}3(x - 2), \quad \text{or } y = {}^{-}3x + 10.$$

However, the line through point D parallel to $\overline{AB}$ has equation

$$y - 4 = 1(x - 2), \quad \text{or } y = x + 2.$$

Hence, the solution of the system of linear equations

$$\begin{cases} y = {}^{-}3x + 10, \\ y = x \end{cases}$$

yields the coordinates of E. We find that $x = \frac{5}{2}$ and $y = \frac{5}{2}$ is the solution of this system, so that E has coordinates $(\frac{5}{2}, \frac{5}{2})$. Similarly, the solution of the system of linear equations

$$\begin{cases} y = x + 2, \\ y = {}^{-}3x \end{cases}$$

yields the coordinates of F. This solution is given by $x = {}^{-}\frac{1}{2}$ and $y = \frac{3}{2}$, so that F has coordinates $({}^{-}\frac{1}{2}, \frac{3}{2})$. From the figure on page 565,

$$\overrightarrow{AD} = \overrightarrow{AE} + \overrightarrow{AF}.$$

To express $\overrightarrow{AE}$ as a scalar multiple of $\overrightarrow{AB}$, and $\overrightarrow{AF}$ as a scalar multiple of $\overrightarrow{AC}$, we need to find the lengths of these four vectors. By the distance formula,

$$\begin{aligned} |\overrightarrow{AB}| &= \sqrt{2^2 + 2^2}, \quad \text{or } 2\sqrt{2}, \\ |\overrightarrow{AE}| &= \sqrt{(\tfrac{5}{2})^2 + (\tfrac{5}{2})^2}, \quad \text{or } \tfrac{5}{2}\sqrt{2}, \\ |\overrightarrow{AC}| &= \sqrt{({}^{-}1)^2 + 3^2}, \quad \text{or } \sqrt{10}, \\ |\overrightarrow{AF}| &= \sqrt{({}^{-}\tfrac{1}{2})^2 + (\tfrac{3}{2})^2}, \quad \text{or } \tfrac{1}{2}\sqrt{10}. \end{aligned}$$

Now $\overrightarrow{AB}$ and $\overrightarrow{AE}$ have the same direction, and therefore,

$$\overrightarrow{AE} = r\overrightarrow{AB}, \quad \text{where } r = \frac{|\overrightarrow{AE}|}{|\overrightarrow{AB}|}, \quad \text{or } \frac{5}{4}.$$

Similarly, $\overrightarrow{AC}$ and $\overrightarrow{AF}$ have the same direction, so that

$$\overrightarrow{AF} = s\overrightarrow{AC}, \quad \text{where } s = \frac{|\overrightarrow{AF}|}{|\overrightarrow{AC}|}, \quad \text{or } \frac{1}{2}.$$

Hence,

$$\overrightarrow{AD} = \tfrac{5}{4}\overrightarrow{AB} + \tfrac{1}{2}\overrightarrow{AC}.$$

This is the solution of Problem 1.

You may wish to put several problems on the board, similar to the one illustrated by Fig. 14–18, which show how to find the coordinates of P given the coordinates of A and B.

Vectors, such as $\overrightarrow{AB}$, $\overrightarrow{AC}$, and $\overrightarrow{AD}$ in Fig. 14–17, whose initial points are at the origin are called *position vectors.* Every vector in the plane is equal to a unique position vector. Given a vector $\overrightarrow{AB}$, we must find the coordinates of the terminal point of the position vector $\overrightarrow{OP}$ for which $\overrightarrow{AB} = \overrightarrow{OP}$. In other words, if A has coordinates (x_1, y_1) and B has coordinates (x_2, y_2), what are the coordinates of P?

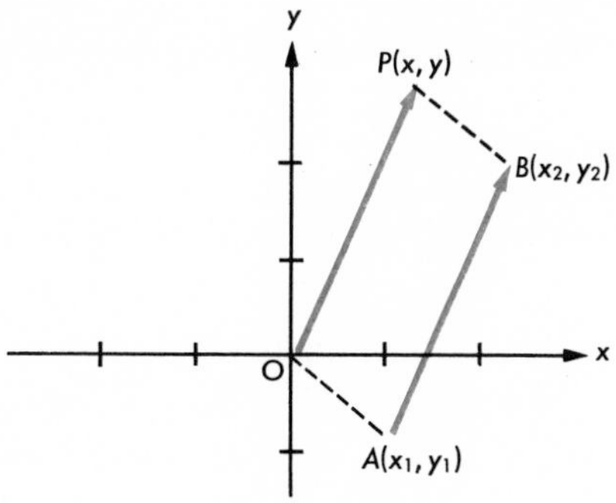

FIGURE 14–18

If $\overrightarrow{AB} = \overrightarrow{OP}$ and the segments $\overline{AB}$ and $\overline{OP}$ are not collinear, then $OABP$ is a parallelogram, as shown in Fig. 14–18. Hence, the slopes of the opposite sides of $OABP$ must be equal. Thus, if (x, y) are the coordinates of P, we must have

$$\frac{y}{x} = \frac{y_2 - y_1}{x_2 - x_1}.$$

We can make the following conclusion.

If A has coordinates (x_1, y_1), B has coordinates (x_2, y_2), and $AB = OP$, then P has coordinates

$$(x_2 - x_1, y_2 - y_1).$$

A particularly useful basis of our vector algebra consists of the set $\{\mathbf{i}, \mathbf{j}\}$, where $\mathbf{i}$ and $\mathbf{j}$ designate the position vectors having terminal points (1, 0) and (0, 1), respectively, as shown in Fig. 14–19. The vectors $\mathbf{i}$ and $\mathbf{j}$ are unit vectors in the sense that each has length 1. If A is the point $(x, 0)$ on the x-axis, then the position vector $\overrightarrow{OA}$ has length $|x|$ and its direction is that of $\mathbf{i}$ if $x > 0$, and is opposite to that of $\mathbf{i}$ if $x < 0$. Thus, $\overrightarrow{OA} = x\mathbf{i}$. Similarly, if B is

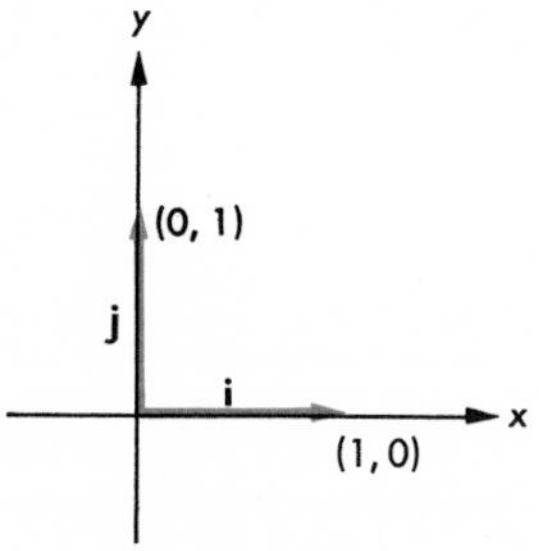

FIGURE 14–19

the point $(0, y)$, then $\overrightarrow{OB} = y\mathbf{j}$. Consequently, if P has coordinates (x, y), then

$$\overrightarrow{OP} = x\mathbf{i} + y\mathbf{j},$$

as shown in Fig. 14-20.

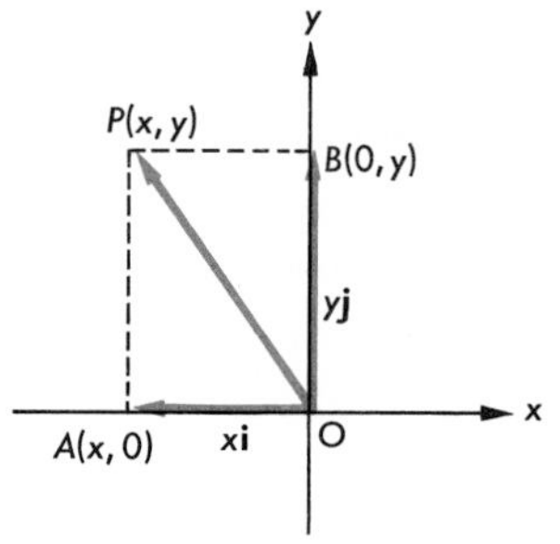

FIGURE 14-20

We saw that if A has coordinates (x_1, y_1) and B has coordinates (x_2, y_2), then $\overrightarrow{AB}$ is equal to the position vector $\overrightarrow{OP}$, where P has coordinates $(x_2 - x_1, y_2 - y_1)$. Hence,

$$\overrightarrow{AB} = (x_2 - x_1)\mathbf{i} + (y_2 - y_1)\mathbf{j}.$$

Problem 2. Express the vectors $\overrightarrow{AB}$ and $\overrightarrow{CD}$ in Fig. 14-21 in terms of **i** and **j**. Also express $\overrightarrow{AB} + \overrightarrow{CD}$ and $\overrightarrow{AB} - \overrightarrow{CD}$ in terms of **i** and **j**.

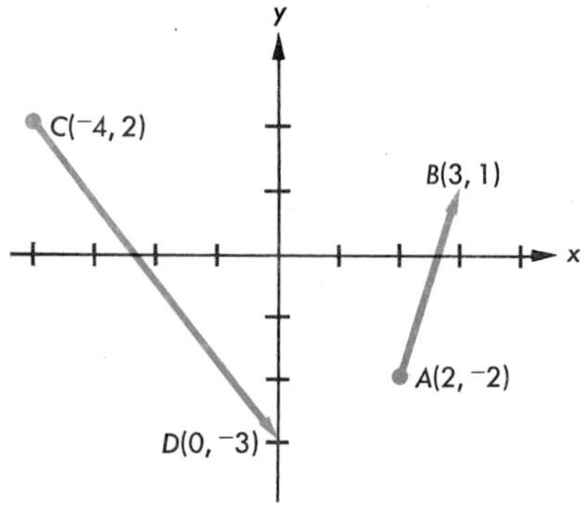

FIGURE 14-21

Solution. In view of the statement above,

$$\overrightarrow{AB} = (3 - 2)\mathbf{i} + (1 + 2)\mathbf{j}, \quad \text{or } \overrightarrow{AB} = \mathbf{i} + 3\mathbf{j},$$

$$\overrightarrow{CD} = (0 + 4)\mathbf{i} + ({}^{-}3 - 2)\mathbf{j}, \quad \text{or } \overrightarrow{CD} = 4\mathbf{i} - 5\mathbf{j}.$$

Hence,

$$\overrightarrow{AB} + \overrightarrow{CD} = 5\mathbf{i} - 2\mathbf{j}, \quad \overrightarrow{AB} - \overrightarrow{CD} = {}^{-}3\mathbf{i} + 8\mathbf{j}.$$

Exercises for Discussion

Let points A, B, and C have respective coordinates $(0, 0)$, $(2, 0)$, and $(0, {}^-1)$. Express vector $\overrightarrow{AD}$ as a combination of vectors $\overrightarrow{AB}$ and $\overrightarrow{AC}$, given that D has the following coordinates.

1. $({}^-3, {}^-5)$ ${}^-\frac{3}{5}\overrightarrow{AB} + 5\overrightarrow{AC}$ **2.** $(1, 0)$ $\frac{1}{2}\overrightarrow{AB} + 0\overrightarrow{AC}$

Express each of the following vectors in terms of **i** and **j**.

3. $\overrightarrow{AB}$, where $A(0, 0)$ and $B(7, {}^-3)$ $\overrightarrow{AB} = 7\mathbf{i} + 3\mathbf{j}$

4. $4\overrightarrow{AB}$, where $A({}^-1, 1)$ and $B(2, 5)$ $4\overrightarrow{AB} = 12\mathbf{i} + 16\mathbf{j}$

5. Solve the equation $x = {}^-3,\ y = {}^-2$

$$x\mathbf{i} + y\mathbf{j} = \overrightarrow{AC}, \quad \text{where } A(2, {}^-3) \text{ and } C({}^-1, {}^-5)$$

Exercises

Let points A, B, and C have respective coordinates $(0, 1)$, $(2, 0)$, and $(0, {}^-1)$. Express $\overrightarrow{AD}$ as a combination of $\overrightarrow{AB}$ and $\overrightarrow{AC}$, given that D has the following coordinates.

1. $(1, 0)$ $\frac{1}{2}\overrightarrow{AB} + \frac{1}{4}\overrightarrow{AC}$ **2.** $(0, 2)$ $0\overrightarrow{AB} - \frac{1}{2}\overrightarrow{AC}$ **3.** $(2, 3)$ $\overrightarrow{AB} - \frac{3}{2}\overrightarrow{AC}$ **4.** $({}^-1, 1)$ ${}^-\frac{1}{2}\overrightarrow{AB} + \frac{1}{4}\overrightarrow{AC}$

Let points A, B, and C have respective coordinates $(0, 0)$, $(1, {}^-1)$, and $({}^-1, {}^-1)$. Express vector $\overrightarrow{AD}$ as a combination of vectors $\overrightarrow{AB}$ and $\overrightarrow{AC}$, given that D has the following coordinates.

5. $(0, 0)$ $0\overrightarrow{AB} + 0\overrightarrow{AC}$ **6.** $(1, 1)$ $0\overrightarrow{AB} - \overrightarrow{AC}$ **7.** $(1, 0)$ $\frac{1}{2}\overrightarrow{AB} - \frac{1}{2}\overrightarrow{AC}$

8. $(0, 2)$ ${}^-\overrightarrow{AB} - \overrightarrow{AC}$ **9.** $({}^-2, 2)$ ${}^-2\overrightarrow{AB} + 0\overrightarrow{AC}$ **10.** $(1, 3)$ ${}^-\overrightarrow{AB} - 2\overrightarrow{AC}$

Express each of the following vectors in terms of **i** and **j**.

11. $\overrightarrow{AB}$, where $A(2, 0)$ and $B(0, 3)$ ${}^-2\mathbf{i} + 3\mathbf{j}$

12. $2\overrightarrow{AB}$, where $A(1, 1)$ and $B({}^-2, 2)$ ${}^-6\mathbf{i} + 2\mathbf{j}$

13. $5\overrightarrow{AB}$, where $A(1, 1)$ and $B({}^-2, 2)$ ${}^-15\mathbf{i} + 5\mathbf{j}$

△

14. Find the length of each of the following vectors.

(a) $\mathbf{i} + \mathbf{j}$ $\sqrt{2}$ (b) $4\mathbf{i} + \mathbf{j}$ $\sqrt{17}$ (c) ${}^-6\mathbf{i}$ 6 (d) $2\mathbf{i} - 3\mathbf{j}$ $\sqrt{13}$

15. Express the vectors $\overrightarrow{AB}$, $\overrightarrow{CD}$, $\overrightarrow{OE}$ in terms of **i** and **j**, given coordinate

$$A(1, {}^-1), \quad B(3, 2), \quad C({}^-7, 2), \quad D(0, {}^-4), \quad O(0, 0), \quad E(1, 3).$$

$\overrightarrow{AB} = 2\mathbf{i} + 3\mathbf{j}$; $\overrightarrow{CD} = 7\mathbf{i} - 6\mathbf{j}$; $\overrightarrow{OE} = \mathbf{i} + 3\mathbf{j}$

▲

16. What conclusions can you draw about the values of x, y, a, and b from each of the following statements?

(a) $x\mathbf{i} + y\mathbf{j} = \mathbf{0}$ $x = 0,\ y = 0$ (b) $x\mathbf{i} + y\mathbf{j} = a\mathbf{i} + b\mathbf{j}$ $x = a,\ y = b$

Exercises for Discussion and Exercises

It is suggested that all of the Exercises for Discussion and Exercises be covered, either in class, or as homework.

Quiz

Let points A, B, and C have respective coordinates $({}^-1, 0)$, $(2, 0)$, and $(0, {}^-1)$. Express $\overrightarrow{AD}$ as a combination of $\overrightarrow{AB}$ and $\overrightarrow{AC}$, given that D has the following coordinates:

1. $(1, {}^-1)$ (ans: $\frac{1}{3}\overrightarrow{AB} + \overrightarrow{AC}$)

2. $(0, \frac{1}{2})$ (ans: $\frac{1}{2}\overrightarrow{AB} - \frac{1}{2}\overrightarrow{AC}$)

Express the following vector in terms of **i** and **j**.

3. $3\overrightarrow{AB}$, where $A(1, 0)$ and $B(2, 2)$ (ans: $3\mathbf{i} + 6\mathbf{j}$)

*14-5 VECTORS IN PHYSICS

This section may be omitted if none of the students are studying, or have studied, physics.

The general formula for finding the magnitude of each force acting on an object, as shown in the figure, is

$$r(\mathbf{i}\cos\alpha + \mathbf{j}\sin\alpha) + s(^{-}\mathbf{i}\cos\beta + \mathbf{j}\sin\beta) - x\mathbf{j} = \mathbf{0}.$$

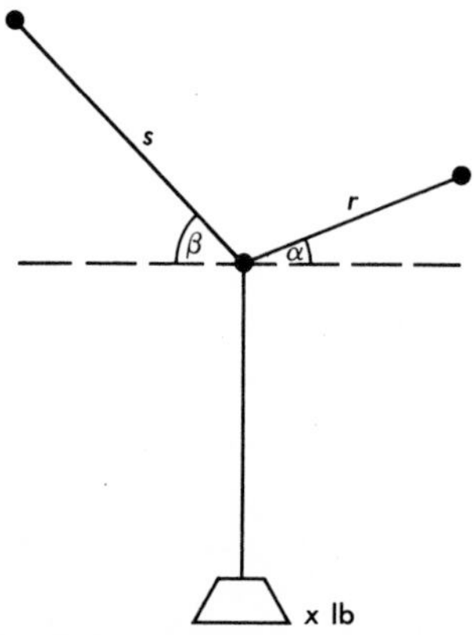

*14-5 VECTORS IN PHYSICS

Vectors are commonly used in physics to represent forces. The direction of application of the force is indicated by the direction of the vector, and the magnitude of the force is indicated by the length of the vector. For example, vector $\overrightarrow{AB}$ in Fig. 14-22 represents a force of 30 pounds acting in a northeasterly direction.

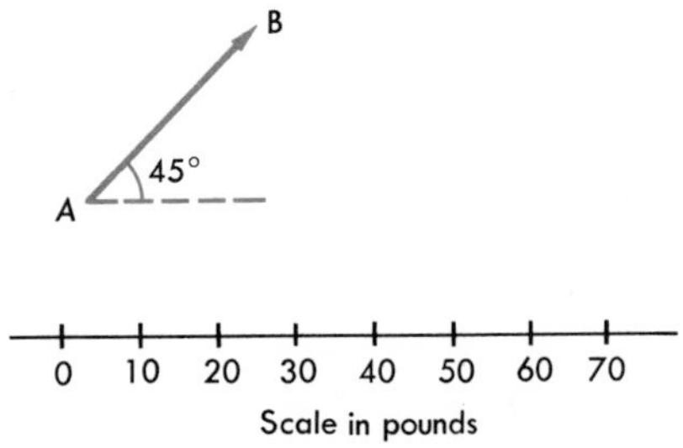

FIGURE 14-22

If two or more forces are acting on an object, then the effect of these forces on the object can be attained by a single force, called the *resultant.* When the forces acting on the object are represented by vectors, their resultant is represented by the sum of these vectors. If the object remains at rest under the actions of two or more forces, then it is said to be in *equilibrium.* If an object is in equilibrium, the sum of the vectors representing the forces must be the zero vector. In Fig. 14-23, for example, a 50-pound object suspended in midair by a rope has two forces acting on it. One, a force of 50 pounds which is due to gravity, is represented by vector $\overrightarrow{AB}$, and the other, a force of 50 pounds holding the object up, is represented by vector $\overrightarrow{CD}$. Clearly,

$$\overrightarrow{AB} + \overrightarrow{CD} = \mathbf{0}.$$

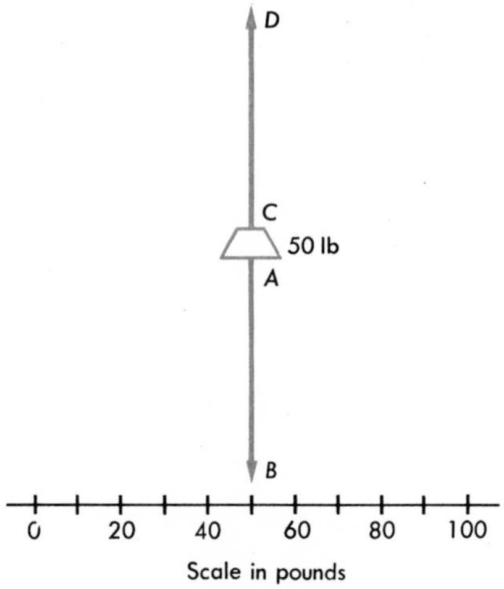

FIGURE 14-23

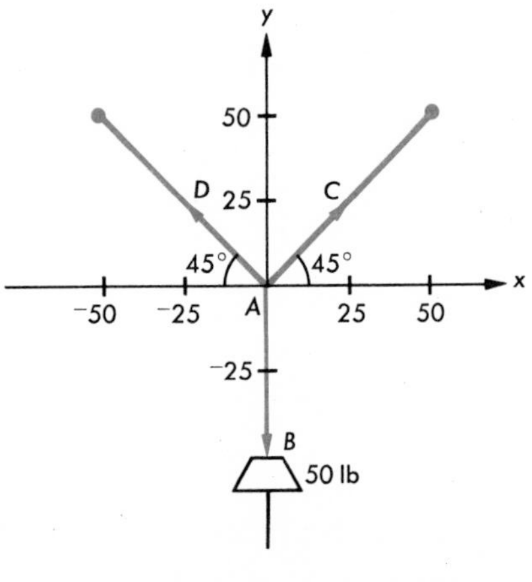

FIGURE 14-24

If the object is suspended by two ropes, as shown in Fig. 14–24, then we can compute the tension in each rope (that is, the magnitude of the force holding the object up in the direction of each rope). Let vectors $\overrightarrow{AC}$ and $\overrightarrow{AD}$ represent the forces acting in the direction of each rope. If a coordinate system is set up as in Fig. 14–24, then

$$\overrightarrow{AC} = r(\mathbf{i} + \mathbf{j}), \quad \overrightarrow{AD} = s(^{-}\mathbf{i} + \mathbf{j}), \quad \overrightarrow{AB} = {}^{-}50\mathbf{j},$$

where r and s are positive numbers to be determined. Since the object is in equilibrium,

$$r(\mathbf{i} + \mathbf{j}) + s(^{-}\mathbf{i} + \mathbf{j}) - 50\mathbf{j} = \mathbf{0}$$

and

$$(r - s)\mathbf{i} + (r + s - 50)\mathbf{j} = \mathbf{0}.$$

Hence, $r - s = 0$ and $r + s - 50 = 0$, so that $r = 25$ and $s = 25$. Thus, $\overrightarrow{AC} = 25(\mathbf{i} + \mathbf{j})$ and $\overrightarrow{AD} = 25(^{-}\mathbf{i} + \mathbf{j})$. Now $|\overrightarrow{AC}|$, or $25\sqrt{2}$, and $|\overrightarrow{AD}|$, or $25\sqrt{2}$, are the magnitudes of the forces acting along the two ropes. Therefore, the tension in each rope is $25\sqrt{2}$ pounds, or approximately 35.3 pounds.

Exercises

Each of the figures in Exercises 1–6 shows an object in equilibrium. Give the direction and magnitude of each force acting on the object.

50 lb, 50 lb

1.

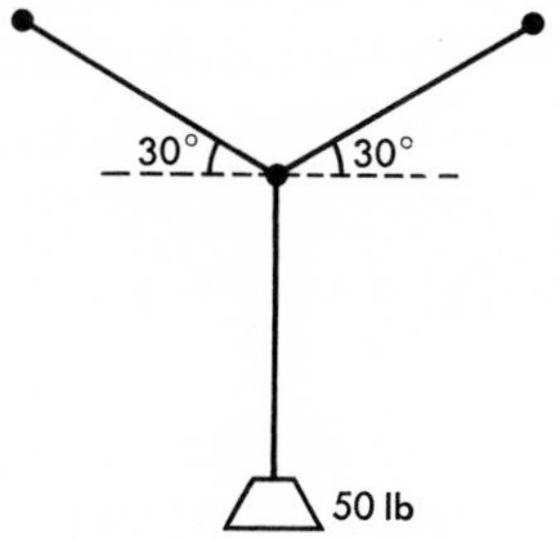

90 lb, 73 lb

2.

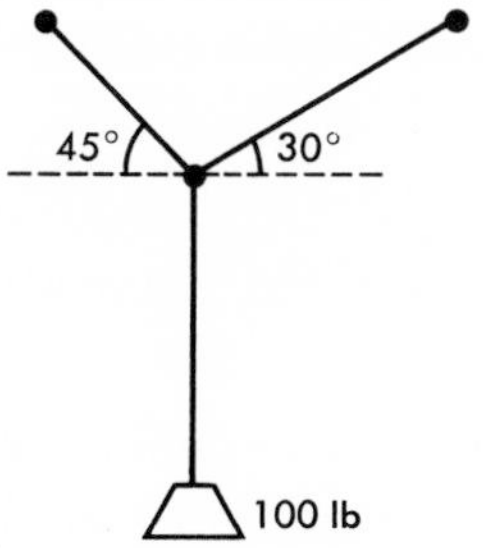

283 lb, 200 lb

3.

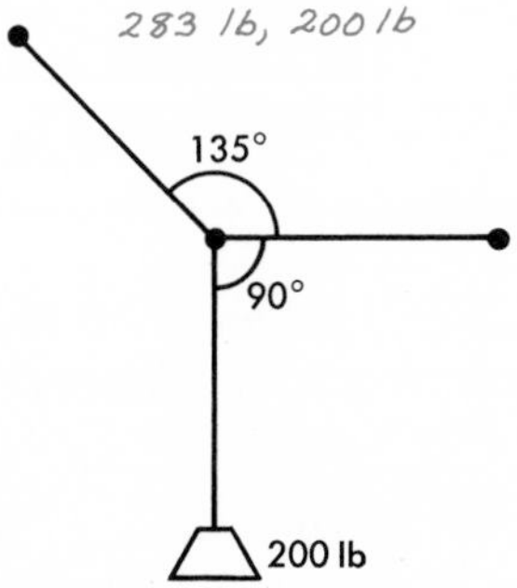

17.1°, 1078 lb

4.

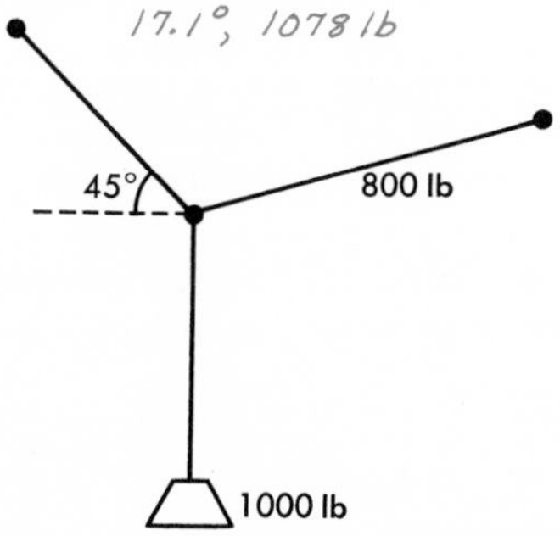

For example, in the problem illustrated by Fig. 14–24, we would have

$$r(\mathbf{i}\cos 45° + \mathbf{j}\sin 45°) + s(^{-}\mathbf{i}\cos 45° + \mathbf{j}\sin 45°) - 50\mathbf{j} = \mathbf{0}$$

$$\left(\frac{r}{\sqrt{2}} - \frac{s}{\sqrt{2}}\right)\mathbf{i} + \left(\frac{r}{\sqrt{2}} + \frac{s}{\sqrt{2}} - 50\right)\mathbf{j} = \mathbf{0}.$$

Since the object is in equilibrium, we have

$$\frac{r}{\sqrt{2}} - \frac{s}{\sqrt{2}} = 0$$

and

$$\frac{r}{\sqrt{2}} + \frac{s}{\sqrt{2}} - 50 = 0$$

so that $r = 25\sqrt{2}$ and $s = 25\sqrt{2}$. Thus,

$$\overrightarrow{AC} = 25\sqrt{2}\left(\mathbf{i}\cdot\frac{1}{\sqrt{2}} + \mathbf{j}\cdot\frac{1}{\sqrt{2}}\right) = 25(\mathbf{i} + \mathbf{j}),$$

$$\overrightarrow{AD} = 25(^{-}\mathbf{i} + \mathbf{j})$$

and

$$|\overrightarrow{AC}| = \sqrt{25^2 + 25^2} = 25\sqrt{2},$$

$$|\overrightarrow{AD}| = 25\sqrt{2}.$$

Quiz

The figure shows an object in equilibrium. Give the magnitude of each force acting on the object. (ans: 50 lb, $50\sqrt{3}$ lb)

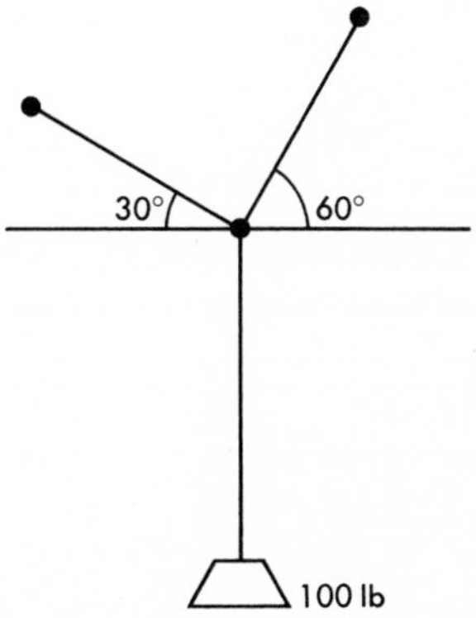

5. 37°, 53°

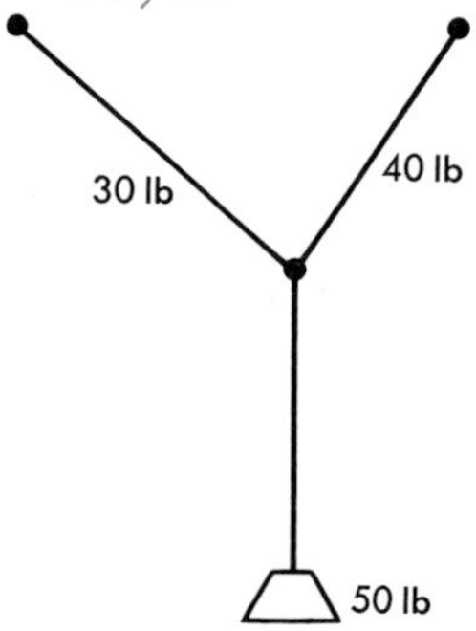

6. 35 lb, 68 lb

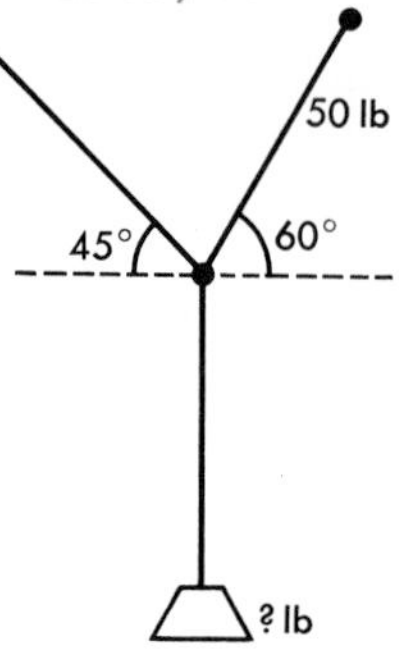

14–6 VECTOR COMPONENTS

In Section 14–4, we saw that each vector $\overrightarrow{AB}$ is equal to a unique vector of the form $x\mathbf{i} + y\mathbf{j}$. The numbers x and y are called the *components* of the vector $\overrightarrow{AB}$. In Fig. 14–22, for example, vector $\overrightarrow{AB}$ has components 1 and 3 and vector $\overrightarrow{CD}$ has components 4 and $^-5$.

The notation $[x, y]$ will be used to designate the components of a vector. For example, the vector $2\mathbf{i} + 7\mathbf{j}$ has components $[2, 7]$. If vector $\overrightarrow{AB}$ has components $[x_1, y_1]$ and $\overrightarrow{CD}$ has components $[x_2, y_2]$, then $\overrightarrow{AB} + \overrightarrow{CD}$ has components $[x_1 + x_2, y_1 + y_2]$. This is true because

$$(x_1\mathbf{i} + y_1\mathbf{j}) + (x_2\mathbf{i} + y_2\mathbf{j}) = (x_1 + x_2)\mathbf{i} + (y_1 + y_2)\mathbf{j}.$$

If vector $\overrightarrow{AB}$ has components $[x, y]$, then vector $r\overrightarrow{AB}$ has components $[rx, ry]$. This is so because

$$\overrightarrow{AB} = x\mathbf{i} + y\mathbf{j} \quad \text{and} \quad r\overrightarrow{AB} = r(x\mathbf{i} + y\mathbf{j}) = rx\mathbf{i} + ry\mathbf{j}.$$

The length of the vector with components $[x, y]$ is $\sqrt{x^2 + y^2}$.

Problem 1. Given points A and B with respective coordinates (x_1, y_1) and (x_2, y_2), and r a real number, find the coordinates of the point C on the line containing A and B such that $\overrightarrow{AC} = r\overrightarrow{AB}$.

Solution. We know that in terms of the basis $\{\mathbf{i}, \mathbf{j}\}$,

$$\overrightarrow{AB} = (x_2 - x_1)\mathbf{i} + (y_2 - y_1)\mathbf{j}.$$

Therefore, $\overrightarrow{AB}$ has components $[x_2 - y_1, y_2 - y_1]$ and $r\overrightarrow{AB}$ has components $[r(x_2 - x_1), r(y_2 - y_1)]$. If point C has coordinates (x, y), then

$$\overrightarrow{AC} = (x - x_1)\mathbf{i} + (y - y_1)\mathbf{j}$$

14–6 VECTOR COMPONENTS

It is suggested that you present some specific cases before taking up the general situation in Problem 1. For example, given $A(3, 6)$ and $B(^-1, ^-4)$ find C so that

$\overrightarrow{AC} = \frac{1}{2}\overrightarrow{AB}$ (ans: (1, 1));
$\overrightarrow{AC} = \frac{1}{3}\overrightarrow{AB}$ (ans: $(\frac{5}{3}, \frac{8}{3})$);
$\overrightarrow{AC} = \frac{1}{4}\overrightarrow{AB}$ (ans: $(2, \frac{7}{2})$);
$\overrightarrow{AC} = \frac{2}{3}\overrightarrow{AB}$ (ans: $(\frac{1}{3}, \frac{2}{3})$).

In these examples, C lies between A and B on $\overleftrightarrow{AB}$. You may wish to do some where C lies on $\overline{AB}$ extended by asking for C so that $\overrightarrow{AC} = \frac{3}{2}\overrightarrow{AB}$ (ans: $(^-3, ^-9)$), or $\overrightarrow{AC} = \frac{5}{4}\overrightarrow{AB}$ (ans: $(^-2, ^-\frac{13}{2})$).

and $\overrightarrow{AC}$ has components $[x - x_1, y - y_1]$. The vectors $\overrightarrow{AC}$ and $r\overrightarrow{AB}$ are equal if, and only if, they have the same components. Hence,

$$\overrightarrow{AC} = r\overrightarrow{AB}$$

if, and only if,

$$x - x_1 = r(x_2 - x_1) \quad \text{and} \quad y - y_1 = r(y_2 - y_1).$$

Thus, $x = x_1 + r(x_2 - x_1)$, $y = y_1 + r(y_2 - y_1)$, and point C has coordinates

$$\big(x_1 + r(x_2 - x_1), y_1 + r(y_2 - y_1)\big).$$

For example, if $r = 0$, then C and A are the same point, and if $r = 1$, C and B are the same point. If $r = \frac{1}{2}$ so that C is the midpoint of $\overline{AB}$, then the x-coordinate of C is

$$x_1 + \tfrac{1}{2}(x_2 - x_1), \quad \text{or } x_1 + \tfrac{1}{2}x_2 - \tfrac{1}{2}x_1, \quad \text{or } \tfrac{1}{2}x_1 + \tfrac{1}{2}x_2.$$

Similarly, $\frac{1}{2}y_1 + \frac{1}{2}y_2$ may be shown to be the y-coordinate of C when C is the midpoint of $\overline{AB}$. Thus, the segment with endpoints (x_1, y_1) and (x_2, y_2) has midpoint

$$\left(\frac{x_1 + x_2}{2}, \frac{y_1 + y_2}{2}\right)$$

Problem 2. Given the nonzero vectors $\overrightarrow{AB}$ and $\overrightarrow{CD}$ with respective components $[x_1, y_1]$ and $[x_2, y_2]$, prove that $\overrightarrow{AB}$ and $\overrightarrow{CD}$ are parallel or collinear if, and only if, $x_1y_2 = x_2y_1$.

Solution. We know that $\overrightarrow{AB}$ and $\overrightarrow{CD}$ are parallel or collinear if, and only if,

$$\overrightarrow{CD} = r\overrightarrow{AB}$$

for some nonzero real number r. Thus, we must prove that

$$\overrightarrow{CD} = r\overrightarrow{AB} \text{ for some } r \quad \text{if, and only if,} \quad x_1y_2 = x_2y_1.$$

Let us first assume that $\overrightarrow{CD} = r\overrightarrow{AB}$ for some number r. Then $\overrightarrow{CD}$ must have components $[rx_1, ry_1]$, that is,

$$x_2 = rx_1, \quad y_2 = ry_1.$$

Hence,

$$x_2y_1 = rx_1y_1, \quad x_1y_2 = rx_1y_1, \quad x_2y_1 = x_1y_2.$$

This proves that if $\overrightarrow{CD} = r\overrightarrow{AB}$, then $x_2y_1 = x_1y_2$.

In Problem 2, it is suggested that you consider several pairs of parallel or collinear vectors. For example,

$$\begin{cases} 2\mathbf{i} + 3\mathbf{j} \\ 4\mathbf{i} + 6\mathbf{j}, \end{cases} \quad \begin{cases} {}^{-}5\mathbf{i} + 4\mathbf{j} \\ 5\mathbf{i} - 4\mathbf{j}, \end{cases} \quad \begin{cases} 6\mathbf{i} - 5\mathbf{j} \\ {}^{-}3\mathbf{i} + \frac{5}{2}\mathbf{j}, \end{cases}$$

$$\begin{cases} \overrightarrow{AB}, \text{ with } A({}^{-}2, 3), B(0, 6) \\ \overrightarrow{CD}, \text{ with } C(0, 0), D(2, 3). \end{cases}$$

A check should be made to see that $x_1y_2 = x_2y_1$ in each case before considering the proof in general.

Answers to Exercises for Discussion 3–5

3. The sum $= 6\mathbf{i} + 5\mathbf{j}$.

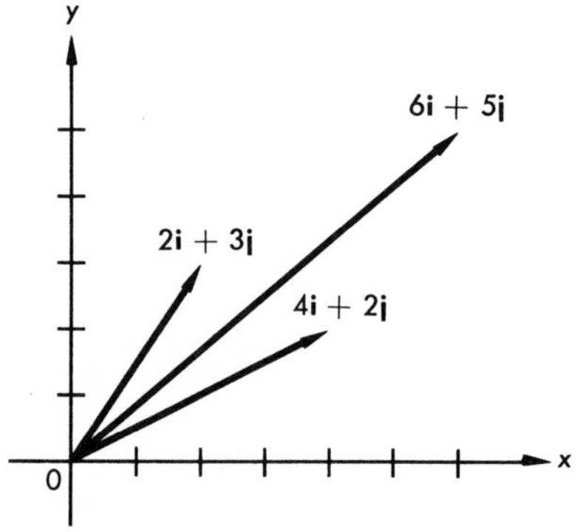

4. P moves along a straight line from $I(2, 3)$ to $T(12, {}^{-}27)$. It crosses the x-axis at $t = 1$.

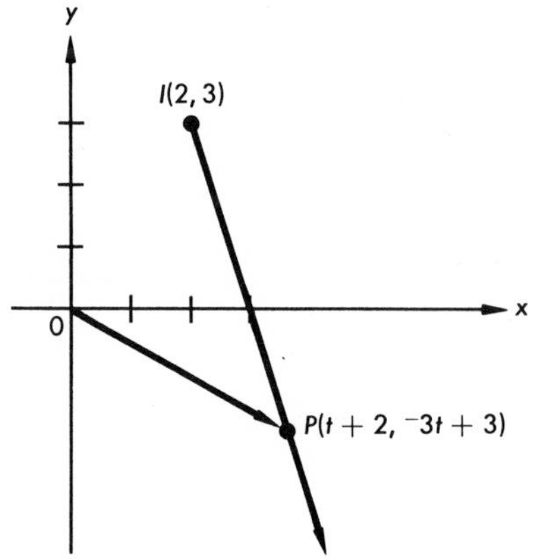

5. P moves along the parabola $y = \frac{1}{4}x^2$ in the first quadrant, starting from the origin. When P crosses the line

$$y = 3x - 8,$$

then

$$\tfrac{1}{4}x^2 = 3x - 8,$$

and so

$$x^2 - 12x + 32 = 0,$$
$$(x - 8)(x - 4) = 0,$$
$$x = 4 \text{ or } x = 8.$$

To prove the converse, let us assume that $x_1y_2 = x_2y_1$. Since the vector $\overrightarrow{AB}$ is not $\mathbf{0}$, either $x_1 \neq 0$ or $y_1 \neq 0$. If $x_1 \neq 0$, then we may solve the equation $x_1y_2 = x_2y_1$ for y_2, obtaining $y_2 = (x_2y_1)/x_1$. Hence,

$$y_2 = \left(\frac{x_2}{x_1}\right) y_1$$

and since it immediately follows that

$$x_2 = \left(\frac{y_2}{y_1}\right) x_1,$$

we have that $\overrightarrow{CD} = r\overrightarrow{AB}$, where the real number $r = x_2/x_1$. If $x_1 = 0$, we may let $r = y_2/y_1$ to obtain the same result. This proves that if $x_1y_2 = x_2y_1$, then $\overrightarrow{CD} = r\overrightarrow{AB}$ for some real number r, which concludes the proof of Problem 2.

For example, the vectors $\overrightarrow{AB}$ and $\overrightarrow{CD}$ with components $[{}^{-}1, 3]$ and $[2, {}^{-}6]$ are parallel or collinear, since ${}^{-}1 \times {}^{-}6 = 3 \times 2$. If vector $\overrightarrow{EF}$ has components $[{}^{-}3, 7]$, then $\overrightarrow{AB}$ and $\overrightarrow{EF}$ are not parallel since ${}^{-}1 \times 7 \neq {}^{-}3 \times 3$.

Exercises for Discussion

Given points A and B with respective coordinates $(3, {}^{-}1)$ and $({}^{-}3, 3)$, find the coordinates of point C on the line containing A and B such that $\overrightarrow{AC} = r\overrightarrow{AB}$ for each of the following values of r.

1. $r = {}^{-}1$ *If $r = {}^{-}1$, then $C = [3+({}^{-}1)({}^{-}3-3), {}^{-}1+({}^{-}1)(3-{}^{-}1)] = (9, {}^{-}5)$*
2. $r = \frac{1}{2}$ *If $r = \frac{1}{2}$, then $C = (0, 1)$*
3. Sketch the following pair of vectors and find their sum.

$$4\mathbf{i} + 2\mathbf{j}, \quad 2\mathbf{i} + 3\mathbf{j}$$ *Sum $= 6\mathbf{i} + 5\mathbf{j}$*

4. An object P is moving on a plane in such a way that t seconds after it starts, the position vector $\overrightarrow{OP}$ has components $[t + 2, {}^{-}3t + 3]$. Describe the path of the object between $t = 0$ and $t = 10$ seconds. At what time does the object cross the x-axis?
5. If the object P of Exercise 4 is moving so that t seconds after it starts, the position vector $\overrightarrow{OP}$ has components $[2\sqrt{t}, t]$, describe the path of the object. At what times does the object cross the line $y = 3x - 8$? When is the object 20 units away from its starting point?

Exercises

Given points A and B with respective coordinates $(3, {}^-1)$ and $({}^-3, 3)$, find the coordinates of point C on the line containing A and B such that $\overrightarrow{AC} = r\overrightarrow{AB}$ for each of the following values of r.

1. $r = 2$ $({}^-9, 7)$ **2.** $r = 10$ $({}^-57, 39)$ **3.** $r = {}^-3$ $(21, {}^-13)$ **4.** $r = 0$ $(3, {}^-1)$

5. Sketch the following pairs of vectors, and find their sum.
(a) $2\mathbf{i} + 3\mathbf{j}$, $\mathbf{i} + \mathbf{j}$ $3\mathbf{i} + 4\mathbf{j}$ (b) $2\mathbf{i} + 3\mathbf{j}$, ${}^-4\mathbf{i} + 2\mathbf{j}$ ${}^-2\mathbf{i} + 5\mathbf{j}$
(c) ${}^-\mathbf{i} - \mathbf{j}$, ${}^-\mathbf{i} + 3\mathbf{j}$ ${}^-2\mathbf{i} + 2\mathbf{j}$ See Solution Manual.

What are the components of each of the following vectors?

6. $\mathbf{r} = (x - 1)\mathbf{i} + (y + 2)\mathbf{j}$ $[x-1, y+2]$ **7.** $\mathbf{v} = x\mathbf{i} - y\mathbf{j} + 5\mathbf{i} + 3\mathbf{j}$ $[x+5, 3-y]$

8. $\frac{1}{2}(b\mathbf{i} - 4\mathbf{j})$ $[\frac{1}{2}b, {}^-2]$

△

9. Solve each of the following equations for x and y.
(a) $x\mathbf{i} + ({}^-4)\mathbf{j} = 7\mathbf{i} + y\mathbf{j}$ $x = 7, y = {}^-4$
(b) $5(\mathbf{i} + \mathbf{j}) - \mathbf{i} + y\mathbf{j} = x\mathbf{i} - 4\mathbf{j}$ $x = 4, y = {}^-9$

10. Determine the real numbers k and s such that
$s = 1, k = 2$
$$4\mathbf{i} + 3\mathbf{j} = k(\mathbf{i} - \mathbf{j}) + s(2\mathbf{i} + 5\mathbf{j}).$$

11. In the figure, $PQ = 6$ and $\theta = 30°$. Determine the components of $\overrightarrow{PQ}$.
$[3\sqrt{3}, 3]$

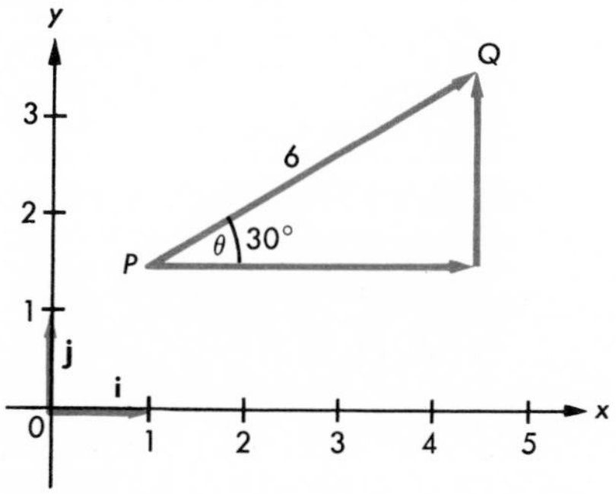

▲

See Solution Manual.

12. Given that points E and F are chosen on sides $\overline{AC}$ and $\overline{BC}$, respectively, of triangle ABC in such a way that $\overrightarrow{AE} = r\overrightarrow{AC}$ and $\overrightarrow{BF} = s\overrightarrow{BC}$, and that D is the point of intersection of lines containing $\overline{BE}$ and $\overline{AF}$, prove that
$$\overrightarrow{AD} = t\overrightarrow{AF} \quad \text{and} \quad \overrightarrow{BD} = u\overrightarrow{BE},$$
where $t = r/(r + s - rs)$ and $u = s/(r + s - rs)$. Use this result to prove that the three medians of a triangle meet at a point of trisection of each median.

P has an x-coordinate of 4 when $2\sqrt{t} = 4$; $\sqrt{t} = 2$; $t = 4$.
P has an x-coordinate of 8 when $2\sqrt{t} = 8$; $\sqrt{t} = 4$; $t = 16$. Also,
$$d(I, P) = \sqrt{(2\sqrt{t} - 0)^2 + (t - 0)^2} = \sqrt{4t + t^2};$$
$$d(I, P) = 20,$$
if and only if,
$$\sqrt{4t + t^2} = 20$$
$$t^2 + 4t - 400 = 0$$
$$t = \frac{{}^-4 + \sqrt{1616}}{2} = {}^-2 + 2\sqrt{101}.$$

Quiz

Given points A and B with respective coordinates $(2, 4)$ and $({}^-2, {}^-4)$, find the coordinates of point C on the line containing A and B such that $\overrightarrow{AC} = r\overrightarrow{AB}$ for each of the following values of r.

1. $r = \frac{1}{4}$ (ans: $(1, 2)$)
2. $r = 3$ (ans: $({}^-10, {}^-20)$)
3. $r = 0$ (ans: $(2, 4)$)

Sketch the following pair of vectors, and find their sum.

4. $\mathbf{i} + 2\mathbf{j}$, ${}^-\mathbf{i} + \mathbf{j}$ (ans: $3\mathbf{j}$)

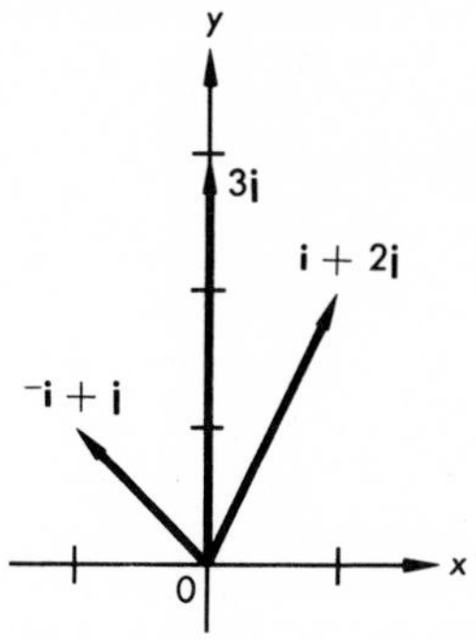

14–7 INNER PRODUCTS

The material in this chapter should be developed carefully. After defining the inner product, you could derive the formula at the bottom of the next page, and then use the inner product of two vectors to find the angle between them.

14–7 INNER PRODUCTS

Given two nonzero vectors $\overrightarrow{AB}$ and $\overrightarrow{AC}$ with the same initial point, the *angle between* $\overrightarrow{AB}$ *and* $\overrightarrow{AC}$ is defined to be the smallest angle θ having its vertex at A and containing sides $\overline{AB}$ and $\overline{AC}$. Several examples of θ are given in Fig. 14–25. We may define the angle between two nonzero vectors even if they do not have the same initial point. If $\overrightarrow{AB}$ and $\overrightarrow{CD}$ are the given vectors, then there exists a unique vector $\overrightarrow{AE}$ such that $\overrightarrow{CD} = \overrightarrow{AE}$. The angle θ between $\overrightarrow{AB}$ and $\overrightarrow{AE}$, as shown in Fig. 14–26, is defined to be the angle between $\overrightarrow{AB}$ and $\overrightarrow{CD}$. From its definition, the angle between two vectors always has measure between 0° and 180° inclusive.

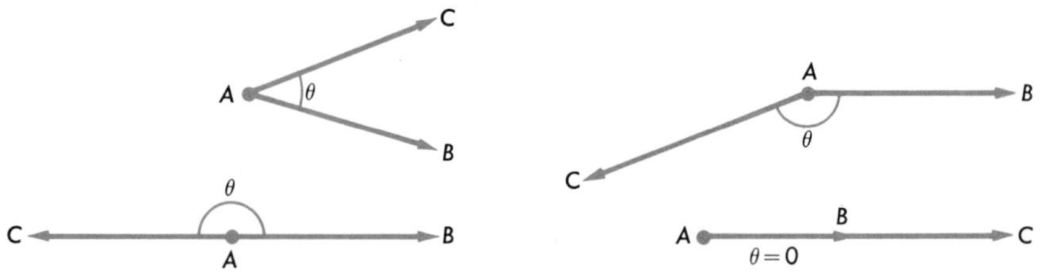

FIGURE 14–25

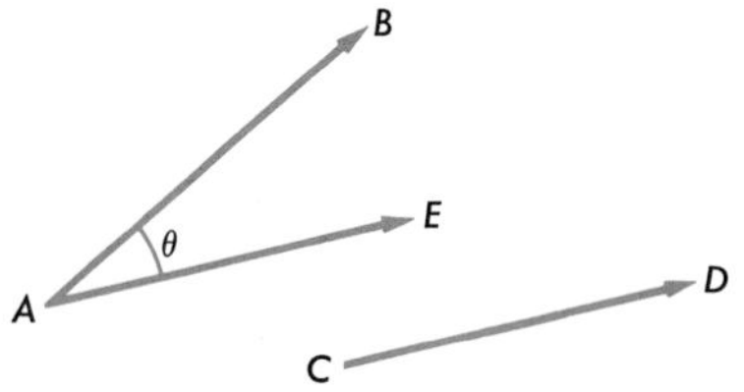

FIGURE 14–26

DEFINITION OF THE INNER PRODUCT OF TWO VECTORS

The inner product of two vectors is defined by

$$\overrightarrow{AB} \cdot \overrightarrow{CD} = |\overrightarrow{AB}|\,|\overrightarrow{CD}| \cos \theta,$$

where θ ***is the angle between*** $\overrightarrow{AB}$ ***and*** $\overrightarrow{CD}$***. If either*** $\overrightarrow{AB} = 0$ ***or*** $\overrightarrow{CD} = 0$***, then*** $\overrightarrow{AB} \cdot \overrightarrow{CD}$ ***is zero.***

Problem 1. If vectors $\overrightarrow{AB}$ and $\overrightarrow{AC}$ are as shown in Fig. 14–27, find $\overrightarrow{AB} \cdot \overrightarrow{AC}$.

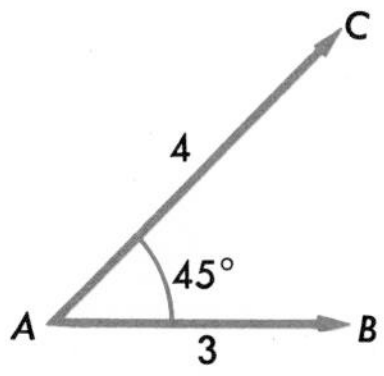

FIGURE 14–27

Solution. According to the definition,

$$\overrightarrow{AB} \cdot \overrightarrow{AC} = |\overrightarrow{AB}|\,|\overrightarrow{AC}| \cos 45^\circ$$

$$= 3 \cdot 4 \cdot \frac{\sqrt{2}}{2}, \quad \text{or } 6\sqrt{2}.$$

As this problem illustrates, the *inner product of two vectors is a number, not a vector.*

Two nonzero vectors are said to be perpendicular if the lines on which they lie are perpendicular. Evidently two nonzero vectors are perpendicular if, and only if, the angle between them is a right angle.

PERPENDICULARITY PROPERTY

The nonzero vectors $\overrightarrow{AB}$ and $\overrightarrow{CD}$ are perpendicular if, and only if, $\overrightarrow{AB} \cdot \overrightarrow{CD}$ is equal to zero.

If $\overrightarrow{AB}$ and $\overrightarrow{CD}$ are perpendicular, then the angle θ between them is a right angle, and therefore $\cos \theta = 0$. Hence,

$$\overrightarrow{AB} \cdot \overrightarrow{CD} = 0.$$

Conversely, if $\overrightarrow{AB} \cdot \overrightarrow{CD} = 0$, then $|\overrightarrow{AB}|\,|\overrightarrow{CD}| \cos \theta = 0$. Since $|\overrightarrow{AB}| \neq 0$ and $|\overrightarrow{CD}| \neq 0$ by assumption, we must have $\cos \theta = 0$. By definition, $0^\circ \leqq \theta \leqq 180^\circ$. Now there is precisely one angle between 0° and 180° whose cosine is zero: 90°. Hence, $\overrightarrow{AB}$ and $\overrightarrow{CD}$ are perpendicular.

The inner product of two vectors is easily computed if components of the vectors are known. For convenience, let us henceforth denote vectors by such symbols as **a**, **b**, **v**, and so on, when it is not important to know the endpoints of the vectors. The formula for the inner product of two vectors whose components are known is the following.

If vectors **a** *and* **b** *have components* $[x_1, y_1]$ *and* $[x_2, y_2]$*, respectively, then*

$$\mathbf{a} \cdot \mathbf{b} = x_1x_2 + y_1y_2.$$

TWISTER

When two dogs, Custer and Okuma, are hitched independently to a dogsled, they invariably run in directions differing by 60 degrees. The magnitude of Custer's pull is 26 pounds, while Okuma's is 17 pounds. What magnitude of pull would be required for a single dog to pull the dogsled in the same direction in which Custer and Okuma pull it together?

Solution:

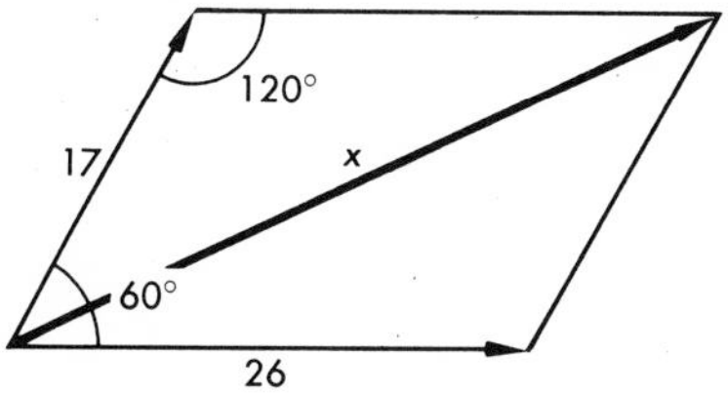

Since

$$x^2 = (26)^2 + (17)^2 - 2(26)(17)\cos 120^\circ$$
$$= 676 + 289 - 2(442)(-\tfrac{1}{2})$$
$$= 1407$$
$$x \doteq 37.5,$$

the magnitude of the single dog's pull would be approximately 37.5 pounds.

To prove this formula, let $\mathbf{a} = \overrightarrow{OA}$ and $\mathbf{b} = \overrightarrow{OB}$, as shown in Fig. 14–28. By what is given, we know that point A has coordinates (x_1, y_1) and B has coordinates (x_2, y_2). If θ is the angle between **a** and **b**, then by the law of cosines,

$$|\overrightarrow{AB}|^2 = |\mathbf{a}|^2 + |\mathbf{b}|^2 - 2|\mathbf{a}|\,|\mathbf{b}|\cos\theta.$$

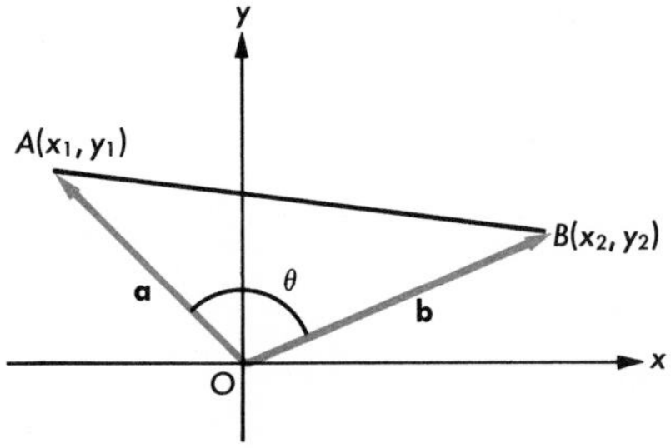

FIGURE 14–28

Using the distance formula as well as the known formula for the inner product and the formula for the length of a vector, we obtain the equivalent equation

$$(x_1 - x_2)^2 + (y_1 - y_2)^2 = (x_1^2 + y_1^2) + (x_2^2 + y_2^2) - 2\mathbf{a}\cdot\mathbf{b},$$

or

$$x_1^2 - 2x_1x_2 + x_2^2 + y_1^2 - 2y_1y_2 + y_2^2 = x_1^2 + y_1^2 + x_2^2 + y_2^2 - 2\mathbf{a}\cdot\mathbf{b}.$$

Hence,

$$^-2x_1x_2 - 2y_1y_2 = {}^-2\mathbf{a}\cdot\mathbf{b}$$

and

$$\mathbf{a}\cdot\mathbf{b} = x_1x_2 + y_1y_2.$$

This proves the formula.

Problem 2. Given that vectors **a**, **b**, and **c** are as shown in Fig. 14–29, find $\mathbf{a}\cdot\mathbf{b}$, $\mathbf{a}\cdot\mathbf{c}$, and $\mathbf{b}\cdot\mathbf{c}$.

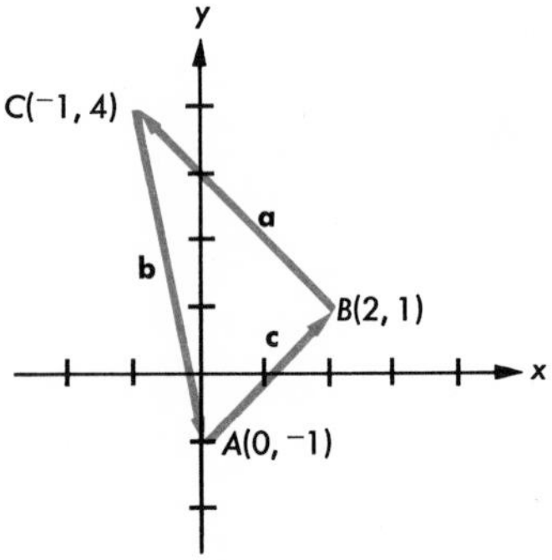

FIGURE 14–29

Solution. The components of **a** are $[^-1 - 2, 4 - 1]$, or $[^-3, 3]$; those of **b** are $[0 + 1, {}^-1 - 4]$, or $[1, {}^-5]$; and those of **c** are $[2 - 0, 1 + 1]$, or $[2, 2]$. Hence, by the formula above,

$$\mathbf{a}\cdot\mathbf{b} = (^-3\cdot 1) + (3\cdot{}^-5), \quad \text{or } ^-18,$$
$$\mathbf{a}\cdot\mathbf{c} = (^-3\cdot 2) + (3\cdot 2), \quad \text{or } 0,$$
$$\mathbf{b}\cdot\mathbf{c} = (1\cdot 2) + (^-5\cdot 2), \quad \text{or } ^-8.$$

Incidentally, we note that vectors **a** and **c** are perpendicular, since $\mathbf{a} \cdot \mathbf{c} = 0$. Thus, ABC is a right triangle with right angle at B.

The inner-product operation has some of the properties of multiplication of real numbers, as you can see by looking at the properties of the inner product listed below.

$$\mathbf{a} \cdot \mathbf{b} = \mathbf{b} \cdot \mathbf{a} \quad \textit{(commutative law)} \quad (IP\text{-}1)$$

$$(\mathbf{a} + \mathbf{b}) \cdot \mathbf{c} = (\mathbf{a} \cdot \mathbf{c}) + (\mathbf{b} \cdot \mathbf{c}) \quad \textit{(distributive law)} \quad (IP\text{-}2)$$

$$\left.\begin{aligned} (k\mathbf{a}) \cdot \mathbf{b} &= k(\mathbf{a} \cdot \mathbf{b}) \\ \mathbf{a} \cdot (k\mathbf{b}) &= k(\mathbf{a} \cdot \mathbf{b}) \end{aligned}\right\} \; k \textit{ a real number} \quad (IP\text{-}3)$$

$$\mathbf{a} \cdot \mathbf{a} = |\mathbf{a}|^2 \quad (IP\text{-}4)$$

The equations above are true for all vectors **a, b, c.**

Each of these properties may be proved by means of components. For example, to prove (IP-2), let **a, b,** and **c** have components $[x_1, y_1]$, $[x_2, y_2]$, and $[x_3, y_3]$, respectively. Then $\mathbf{a} + \mathbf{b}$ has components $[x_1 + x_2, y_1 + y_2]$ and

$$\begin{aligned} (\mathbf{a} + \mathbf{b}) \cdot \mathbf{c} &= (x_1 + x_2)x_3 + (y_1 + y_2)y_3 \\ &= x_1x_3 + x_2x_3 + y_1y_3 + y_2y_3 \end{aligned}$$

by our formula above. Next,

$$\mathbf{a} \cdot \mathbf{c} = x_1x_3 + y_1y_3, \quad \mathbf{b} \cdot \mathbf{c} = x_2x_3 + y_2y_3,$$

so that

$$(\mathbf{a} \cdot \mathbf{c}) + (\mathbf{b} \cdot \mathbf{c}) = x_1x_3 + y_1y_3 + x_2x_3 + y_2y_3.$$

Therefore,

$$(\mathbf{a} + \mathbf{b}) \cdot \mathbf{c} = (\mathbf{a} \cdot \mathbf{c}) + (\mathbf{b} \cdot \mathbf{c}).$$

We shall leave the proofs of (IP-1), (IP-3), and (IP-4) as exercises.

Problem 3. Are the diagonals of a parallelogram ever perpendicular?

Solution. If **a** and **b** designate nonparallel sides of a parallelogram, as shown in Fig. 14–30, then $\mathbf{a} - \mathbf{b}$ and $\mathbf{a} + \mathbf{b}$ are the two diagonals. Hence, the diagonals of the parallelogram are perpendicular if, and only if,

$$(\mathbf{a} - \mathbf{b}) \cdot (\mathbf{a} + \mathbf{b}) = 0.$$

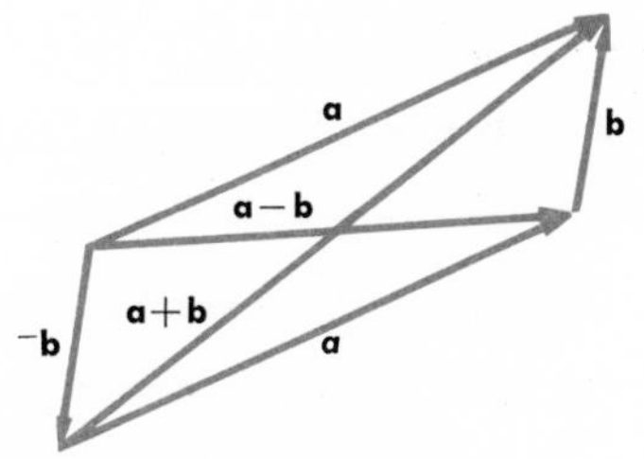

FIGURE 14–30

Have the class develop the proofs to (IP–1), (IP–3) and (IP–4) at the board. Problem 3 should be interesting to the students.

Using the properties (IP-1) through (IP-4), we have

$$\begin{aligned}(\mathbf{a} - \mathbf{b}) \cdot (\mathbf{a} + \mathbf{b}) &= (\mathbf{a} - \mathbf{b}) \cdot \mathbf{a} + (\mathbf{a} - \mathbf{b}) \cdot \mathbf{b} \\ &= (\mathbf{a} \cdot \mathbf{a}) + ({}^{-}\mathbf{b} \cdot \mathbf{a}) + (\mathbf{a} \cdot \mathbf{b}) + {}^{-}\mathbf{b} \cdot \mathbf{b} \\ &= (\mathbf{a} \cdot \mathbf{a}) - (\mathbf{b} \cdot \mathbf{a}) + (\mathbf{b} \cdot \mathbf{a}) - (\mathbf{b} \cdot \mathbf{b}) \\ &= |\mathbf{a}|^2 - |\mathbf{b}|^2.\end{aligned}$$

Therefore, the diagonals are perpendicular if, and only if, $|\mathbf{a}|^2 = |\mathbf{b}|^2$, or $|\mathbf{a}| = |\mathbf{b}|$. In words, the diagonals of a parallelogram are perpendicular if, and only if, the parallelogram is a rhombus or a square, that is, if it is equilateral.

Answer to Exercise for Discussion 1

1. Since the components of $\mathbf{a} = \mathbf{i}$ are [1, 0], and the components of $\mathbf{b} = \mathbf{j}$ are [0, 1],

$$\mathbf{a} \cdot \mathbf{b} = 1 \cdot 0 + 0 \cdot 1 = 0.$$

Exercises for Discussion

In Exercises 1–6, find $\mathbf{a} \cdot \mathbf{b}$.

1. $\mathbf{a} = \mathbf{i}, \quad \mathbf{b} = \mathbf{j}$
2. $\mathbf{a} = \mathbf{i}, \quad \mathbf{b} = \mathbf{i}$ $\mathbf{a} \cdot \mathbf{b} = 0 \cdot 0 + 1 \cdot 1 = 1$
3. $\mathbf{a} = \mathbf{j}, \quad \mathbf{b} = \mathbf{j}$ $\mathbf{a} \cdot \mathbf{b} = 1 \cdot 1 + 0 \cdot 0 = 1$
4. $\mathbf{a} = 2\mathbf{i} - \mathbf{j}, \quad \mathbf{b} = \mathbf{i} - 3\mathbf{j}$ $\mathbf{a} \cdot \mathbf{b} = 2 \cdot 1 + {}^{-}1 \cdot {}^{-}3 = 5$
5. $\mathbf{a} = \mathbf{i} + 3\mathbf{j}, \quad \mathbf{b} = \mathbf{j} - 3\mathbf{i}$ $\mathbf{a} \cdot \mathbf{b} = 1 \cdot {}^{-}3 + 3 \cdot 1 = 0$
6. $\mathbf{a} = 5\mathbf{i}, \quad \mathbf{b} = 2\mathbf{j} + 7\mathbf{i}$ $\mathbf{a} \cdot \mathbf{b} = 5 \cdot 7 + 0 \cdot 2 = 35$

Exercises

See Solution Manual for graphs and proofs.

In Exercises 1–5, tell whether the pairs of vectors are perpendicular. Graph the vectors.

1. $\mathbf{v} = 2\mathbf{i}, \ \mathbf{u} = 4\mathbf{j}$ Yes
2. $\mathbf{v} = {}^{-}3\mathbf{i}, \ \mathbf{u} = {}^{-}2\mathbf{j}$ Yes
3. $\mathbf{v} = \mathbf{i}, \ \mathbf{u} = {}^{-}\frac{1}{2}\mathbf{j}$ Yes
4. $\mathbf{v} = {}^{-}3\mathbf{i}, \ \mathbf{u} = \frac{2}{3}\mathbf{j}$ Yes
5. $\mathbf{v} = 2\mathbf{i}, \ \mathbf{u} = \mathbf{0}$ Not applicable

6. A triangle has vertices (⁻2, 0), (2, 0) and (0, 4). Find its area. 8 sq units

In each of the following exercises, vectors **a**, **b**, and **c** are sides of a triangle. Tell whether the triangle is right, isosceles, equilateral, or none of these.

7. $\mathbf{a} = \mathbf{i}, \ \mathbf{b} = \mathbf{j}, \quad \mathbf{c} = \mathbf{i} - \mathbf{j}$ Right and isosceles
8. $\mathbf{a} = \mathbf{i} + 3\mathbf{j}, \quad \mathbf{b} = \mathbf{j} - \mathbf{i}, \ \mathbf{c} = {}^{-}2(\mathbf{i} + \mathbf{j})$ Right
9. $\mathbf{a} = 3\mathbf{j}, \quad \mathbf{b} = \mathbf{i} + 2\mathbf{j}, \quad \mathbf{c} = \mathbf{i} + 5\mathbf{j}$ None
10. $\mathbf{a} = \mathbf{i} + \sqrt{3}\,\mathbf{j}, \quad \mathbf{b} = {}^{-}\mathbf{i} + \sqrt{3}\,\mathbf{j}, \quad \mathbf{c} = {}^{-}2\mathbf{i}$ Equilateral
11. $\mathbf{a} = 2\mathbf{i} + \mathbf{j}, \quad \mathbf{b} = 3\mathbf{j} - 2\mathbf{i}, \quad \mathbf{c} = 2\mathbf{j} - 4\mathbf{i}$ None

12. Find the inner product of each of the following pairs of vectors.

(a) $\mathbf{v} = x\mathbf{i} + y\mathbf{j}, \quad \mathbf{r} = 3\mathbf{i} - 2\mathbf{j}$ $3x - 2y$

(b) $\mathbf{v} = 2\mathbf{i}, \quad \mathbf{r} = 3\mathbf{j}$ 0

△

13. Prove (IP-1). **14.** Prove (IP-3). **15.** Prove (IP-4).

▲

16. Given that $\mathbf{a} = r[(\cos\theta)\mathbf{i} + (\sin\theta)\mathbf{j}]$ and $\mathbf{b} = s[(\cos\phi)\mathbf{i} + (\sin\phi)\mathbf{j}]$ are nonzero vectors, prove that **a** and **b** are perpendicular if, and only if, $\theta - \phi = n\pi/2$ for some odd integer n.

17. In triangle ABC, select point D on side $\overline{BC}$ and point E on side $\overline{AC}$ so that $\overline{AD}$ is perpendicular to $\overline{BC}$ and $\overline{BE}$ is perpendicular to $\overline{AC}$. If F is the point of intersection of $\overline{AD}$ and $\overline{BE}$, then show that the line through points C and F is perpendicular to side $\overline{AB}$. (Hint: Show that $\overrightarrow{CF} \cdot \overrightarrow{AB} = 0$ by letting $\overrightarrow{CF} = \overrightarrow{CA} + \overrightarrow{AF}$ and $\overrightarrow{AB} = \overrightarrow{AF} + \overrightarrow{FB}$.)

18. Prove that each of the following expressions is true for every pair **a**, **b** of vectors.

(a) $|\mathbf{a} + \mathbf{b}|^2 = |\mathbf{a}|^2 + |\mathbf{b}|^2 + 2\mathbf{a} \cdot \mathbf{b}$

(b) $|\mathbf{a} - \mathbf{b}|^2 = |\mathbf{a}|^2 + |\mathbf{b}|^2 - 2\mathbf{a} \cdot \mathbf{b}$

(c) $(\mathbf{a} \cdot \mathbf{b})^2 \leqq |\mathbf{a}|^2 \cdot |\mathbf{b}|^2$ When does the inequality sign hold?

KEY IDEAS AND KEY WORDS

A **vector** is a line segment having an **initial point** A, a **terminal point** B, and a **direction** from A to B. This vector is denoted by $\overrightarrow{AB}$, and its length is denoted by $|\overrightarrow{AB}|$. We call the vector $\overrightarrow{AA}$ of zero length the **zero vector, 0.** Vectors $\overrightarrow{AB}$ and $\overrightarrow{CD}$ are defined to be equal if, and only if, the quadrilateral $ABCD$ is a parallelogram.

The **sum of two vectors** is defined by

$$\overrightarrow{AB} + \overrightarrow{BC} = \overrightarrow{AC},$$

which is the resultant law of physics. Each vector has an **additive inverse,**

$$^{-}\overrightarrow{AB} = \overrightarrow{BA}.$$

Each vector $\overrightarrow{AB}$ may be multiplied by a **scalar** $\boldsymbol{r}$, which is a real number, thereby giving another vector $r\overrightarrow{AB}$, of length $|r|$ times the length of $\overrightarrow{AB}$.

The basic properties of addition and multiplication in the real number system are also valid in the **algebra of vectors.**

Quiz

In Exercises 1–4, find $\mathbf{a} \cdot \mathbf{b}$.

1. $\mathbf{a} = \mathbf{j}$, $\mathbf{b} = 2\mathbf{j}$ (ans: 2)

2. $\mathbf{a} = \mathbf{i} - 2\mathbf{j}$, $\mathbf{b} = 3\mathbf{j}$ (ans: $^{-}6$)

3. $\mathbf{a} = 2\mathbf{i} + \mathbf{j}$, $\mathbf{b} = {^{-}\mathbf{i}} - \mathbf{j}$ (ans: $^{-}3$)

4. $\mathbf{a} = 2\mathbf{i}$, $\mathbf{b} = \frac{1}{2}\mathbf{j}$ (ans: 0)

5. Which, if any, of the pairs of vectors in Exercises 1–4 are perpendicular? (ans: the vectors in Exercise 4)

The vectors **i** and **j** are defined in a **cartesian coordinate system** by

$$\mathbf{i} = \overrightarrow{OA} \quad \text{and} \quad \mathbf{j} = \overrightarrow{OB},$$

where O is the origin, A is the point (1, 0), and B is the point (0, 1). Each vector in the plane has the unique form

$$x\mathbf{i} + y\mathbf{j}$$

for some real numbers x and y; x and y are called the **components** of the vectors.

The **inner product** of vectors $\overrightarrow{AB}$ and $\overrightarrow{CD}$ is denoted by $\overrightarrow{AB} \cdot \overrightarrow{CD}$ and is defined by

$$\overrightarrow{AB} \cdot \overrightarrow{CD} = |\overrightarrow{AB}|\,|\overrightarrow{CD}| \cos\theta$$

where θ is the angle between $\overrightarrow{AB}$ and $\overrightarrow{CD}$. Two nonzero vectors, $\overrightarrow{AB}$ and $\overrightarrow{CD}$ are **perpendicular** if, and only if, $\overrightarrow{AB} \cdot \overrightarrow{CD} = 0$.

CHAPTER REVIEW

In Exercises 1–14, tell which of the statements are true and which are false. Correct the ones that you marked false.

1. If $A_1, A_2, \ldots, A_k$ are k distinct points, then they determine k nonzero vectors. *False; $k(k-1)$ nonzero vectors*
2. $\overrightarrow{AB} = \overrightarrow{CD}$ if, and only if, $|\overrightarrow{AB}| = |\overrightarrow{CD}|$ *False; $|\overrightarrow{AB}| = |\overrightarrow{CB}|$ and they have the same direction.*
3. $\overrightarrow{AB} - \overrightarrow{CD} = \overrightarrow{AB} + \overrightarrow{CD}$ *False; $= \overrightarrow{AB} + \overrightarrow{DC}$*
4. If A has coordinates (4, 9), B has coordinates (9, $^-4$), O has coordinates (0, 0), and $\overrightarrow{AB} = \overrightarrow{OP}$, then P has coordinates (13, 5). *False; (5, $^-13$)*
5. The product of a vector and a scalar is a scalar. *False; product is a vector.*
6. The nonparallel vectors $\overrightarrow{KL}$ and $\overrightarrow{MN}$ with lengths 2 and 10, respectively, form a basis. *True*
7. Subtraction of vectors is not commutative. *True*
8. In triangle ABC, $\overrightarrow{AB} + \overrightarrow{BC} = \overrightarrow{CA}$. *False; $= \overrightarrow{AC}$*
9. For any four points R, S, T, and U, $(\overrightarrow{RS} + \overrightarrow{TU}) - (\overrightarrow{TS} + \overrightarrow{RU}) = \mathbf{0}$. *True*
10. The vectors $\overrightarrow{AB}$ and $\overrightarrow{CD}$ with components [6, $^-3$] and [4, $^-8$] are parallel or collinear. *False; [8, $^-4$] or [$^-8$, 4]*
11. If $\overrightarrow{AB} \cdot \overrightarrow{AC} = 8$, where $|\overrightarrow{AB}| = 2$ and $|\overrightarrow{AC}| = 4$, then $\overrightarrow{AB}$ and $\overrightarrow{AC}$ are parallel or collinear. *True*
12. If vectors **a** and **b** have components [3, 1] and [$^-2$, 2], respectively, then $\mathbf{a} \cdot \mathbf{b} = 4$. *False; $= {}^-4$*
13. The inner product of two nonzero vectors is a vector. *False; inner product is a number.*
14. If $\mathbf{a} = \mathbf{i}$ and $\mathbf{b} = 2\mathbf{j}$, then $\mathbf{a} \cdot \mathbf{b} = 0$. *True*

15. Can every point be considered to be a zero vector? Explain your answer. Yes Can be considered as going from itself to itself.

16. Given that θ is the angle between $\overrightarrow{AB}$ and $\overrightarrow{CD}$ and that $|\overrightarrow{AB}| = 6$, $|\overrightarrow{CD}| = 3$, and $\overrightarrow{AB} \cdot \overrightarrow{CD}$ has each of the values below, find the measure of θ.

(a) 0 $\frac{\pi}{2}$ (b) 18 0 (c) 9 $\frac{\pi}{3}$

17. Find $\overrightarrow{AB} \cdot \overrightarrow{CD}$ given that $|\overrightarrow{AB}| = 5$, $|\overrightarrow{CD}| = 7$ and θ has each of the following values.

(a) 30° $\frac{35\sqrt{3}}{2}$ (b) 45° $\frac{35\sqrt{2}}{2}$

18. Given points M and N with respective coordinates (2, 11) and (3, 4), find the length of $\overrightarrow{MN}$. Graph $\overrightarrow{MN}$. $5\sqrt{2}$; See Solution Manual.

Find each of the vectors in Exercises 19 and 20 which has its endpoints among the four points A, B, C, and D.

19. $(\overrightarrow{BA} + \overrightarrow{CB}) + \overrightarrow{DC}$ $\overrightarrow{DA}$

20. $(\overrightarrow{CA} - \overrightarrow{BA}) - (\overrightarrow{DB} - \overrightarrow{DA})$ $\overrightarrow{CA}$

21. Given points S and T with respective coordinates (7, 3) and (1, 5), find the coordinates of point P such that $\overrightarrow{OS} + \overrightarrow{OP} = \overrightarrow{OT}$. $(^-6, 2)$

In Exercises 22 and 23, solve the equations for x and y.

22. $(3x)\mathbf{i} + (2y)\mathbf{j} = 6\overrightarrow{PQ}$ where $P(^-1, 2)$ and $Q(3, 4)$ $x = 8,\ y = 6$

23. $(2x + 3y)\mathbf{i} - (5y)\mathbf{j} = 6\mathbf{i} + 25\mathbf{j}$ $x = \frac{21}{2},\ y = {}^-5$

24. Given points A and B with respective coordinates (0, 11) and (4, 2), find the coordinates of point C on the line containing A and B such that $\overrightarrow{AC} = r\overrightarrow{AB}$ for each of the following values of r.

(a) $r = 6$ $(24, ^-43)$ (b) $r = 2$ $(8, ^-7)$

In each of the following exercises, vectors **a**, **b**, and **c** are sides of a triangle. Tell whether the triangle is right, isosceles, or equilateral.

25. $\mathbf{a} = 2\mathbf{i}$, $\mathbf{b} = 4\mathbf{j}$, $\mathbf{c} = 2(\mathbf{i} - 2\mathbf{j})$ Right

26. $\mathbf{a} = 2\mathbf{i}$, $\mathbf{b} = \mathbf{i} + \mathbf{j}$, $\mathbf{c} = \mathbf{i} - \mathbf{j}$ Right and isosceles

27. $\mathbf{a} = 2\mathbf{j}$, $\mathbf{b} = 2\mathbf{i} + \mathbf{j}$, $\mathbf{c} = 2\mathbf{i} - \mathbf{j}$ Isosceles

Find the sum of each of the following pairs of vectors.

28. $\mathbf{i} + \mathbf{j}$, $3\mathbf{i} + 2\mathbf{j}$ $4\mathbf{i} + 3\mathbf{j}$

29. $^-\mathbf{i} - \mathbf{j}$, $^-\mathbf{i} + 2\mathbf{j}$ $^-2\mathbf{i} + \mathbf{j}$

In Exercises 30–33, what are the components of each of the vectors?

30. $\mathbf{r} = x\cos\theta\mathbf{i} + y\sin\theta\mathbf{j}$ $[x\cos\theta, y\sin\theta]$

31. $\mathbf{s} = \mathbf{i} + \mathbf{j}$ $[1, 1]$

32. $\mathbf{v} = 2\mathbf{i}$ $[2, 0]$

33. $\mathbf{s} = {}^-x\mathbf{i} + 3\mathbf{i} + y\mathbf{j} - \mathbf{j}$ $[3 - x, y - 1]$

34. Find the length of the vector $3\mathbf{i} - 2\mathbf{j}$. $\sqrt{13}$

35. Find the length of the vector $\mathbf{i} + \mathbf{j}$. $\sqrt{2}$

CHAPTER TEST

The material included in the Chapter Test was covered in the following sections:

Problem 1—Sections 14-3, 14-4
Problems 2-4—Section 14-2
Problem 5—Section 14-6
Problem 6—Section 14-4
Problem 7—Section 14-6
Problems 8-11—Section 14-7

Answers to Chapter Test Problems 2, 3, 11

2.

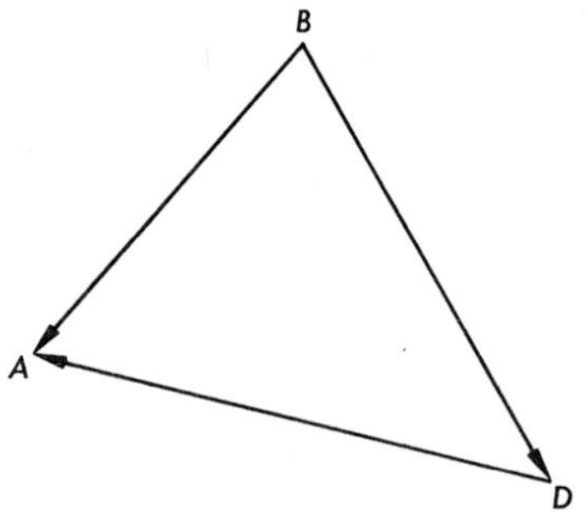

3.

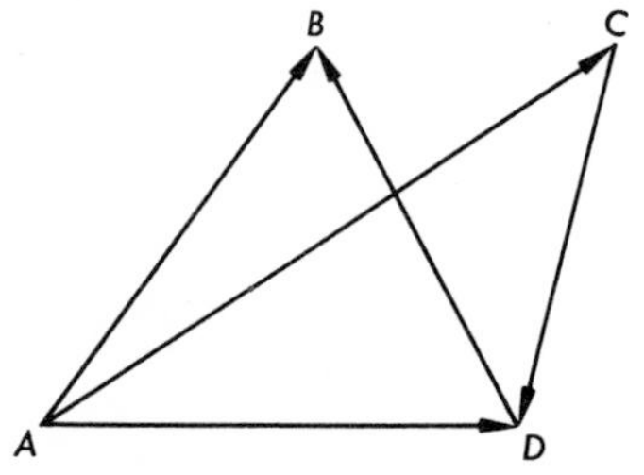

11. $\overrightarrow{OA} = 4\mathbf{i} + 4\mathbf{j}$

$\overrightarrow{OB} = {}^-4\mathbf{i} + 4\mathbf{j}$

$\overrightarrow{OA} \cdot \overrightarrow{OB} = (4) \cdot ({}^-4) + (4) \cdot (4) = 0$

Hence, $\overrightarrow{OA}$ and $\overrightarrow{OB}$ are perpendicular.

In Exercises 36–41, express each of the vectors in terms of **i** and **j**.

36. $\overrightarrow{AB}$, where $A(0, 0)$ and $B(14, {}^-6)$ $14\mathbf{i} - 6\mathbf{j}$

37. $2\overrightarrow{AB}$, where $A({}^-2, 2)$ and $B(4, 10)$ $12\mathbf{i} + 16\mathbf{j}$

38. $\overrightarrow{AB} + \overrightarrow{CD}$, where $A(4, 0)$, $B(0, 6)$, $C(0, 0)$, and $D({}^-8, {}^-2)$ ${}^-12\mathbf{i} + 4\mathbf{j}$

39. $\overrightarrow{AC} - \overrightarrow{BD}$, where $A(4, 0)$, $B(0, 6)$, $C(0, 0)$, and $D({}^-8, {}^-2)$ $4\mathbf{i} + 8\mathbf{j}$

40. $4\overrightarrow{AB} + 5\overrightarrow{CD}$, where $A(1, 1)$, $B({}^-1, 2)$, $C(1, {}^-2)$, and $D({}^-5, {}^-2)$ ${}^-38\mathbf{i} + 4\mathbf{j}$

41. Find the inner product of the two vectors $\overrightarrow{OA}$ and $\overrightarrow{OB}$, given that

$$O(0, 0), \quad A(2, 3), \quad B({}^-2, 3).$$ 5

CHAPTER TEST

1. Given points R and S with respective coordinates $(3, 1)$ and $(5, 3)$, determine the length of the vector $\overrightarrow{RS}$. $2\sqrt{2}$

Each of the vectors in Exercises 2 and 3 is equal to a vector having its endpoints among the four points A, B, C, and D. Find the indicated vector.

2. $\overrightarrow{BA} - \overrightarrow{DA}$ $\overrightarrow{BD}$

3. $(\overrightarrow{AC} + \overrightarrow{CD}) + \overrightarrow{DB}$ $\overrightarrow{AB}$

4. Given points A and B with respective coordinates $(3, 4)$ and $(6, 3)$, find the coordinates of point C such that $\overrightarrow{OA} + \overrightarrow{OB} = \overrightarrow{OC}$. $(9, 7)$

5. Given points A and B with respective coordinates $({}^-4, 2)$ and $(3, {}^-2)$, find the coordinates of the point C on the line containing A and B such that $\overrightarrow{AC} = r\overrightarrow{AB}$ for each of the following values of r.

(a) $r = \frac{1}{4}$ $\left(\frac{{}^-9}{4}, 1\right)$ (b) $r = {}^-5$ $({}^-39, 22)$

6. Express each of the following vectors in terms of **i** and **j**.

(a) $2\overrightarrow{AB}$, where $A({}^-3, 2)$ and $B(3, 3)$ $12\mathbf{i} + 2\mathbf{j}$

(b) $\overrightarrow{AC} - \overrightarrow{BD}$, where $A(3, 0)$, $B(0, 4)$, $C(0, 0)$, and $D(4, 7)$ ${}^-7\mathbf{i} - 3\mathbf{j}$

7. What are the components of each of the following vectors?

(a) $\mathbf{k} = x\mathbf{i}$ $[x, 0]$ (b) $\mathbf{m} = (3x)\mathbf{i} + 2\mathbf{j} - (2y)\mathbf{i}$ $[3x - 2y, 2]$

8. Given that $|\overrightarrow{AB}| = 2$, $|\overrightarrow{CD}| = 8$, and $\theta = 60°$, where θ is the angle between $\overrightarrow{AB}$ and $\overrightarrow{CD}$, find $\overrightarrow{AB} \cdot \overrightarrow{CD}$. 8

9. Given that $|\overrightarrow{AB}| = 2$, $|CD| = 8$, and $\overrightarrow{AB} \cdot \overrightarrow{CD} = 16$, find the measure of angle θ between $\overrightarrow{AB}$ and $\overrightarrow{CD}$. 0

10. Given that $\mathbf{a} = \mathbf{i} - \mathbf{j}$, $\mathbf{b} = \mathbf{i} + 2\mathbf{j}$, find $\mathbf{a} \cdot \mathbf{b}$. ${}^-1$

11. Given points O, A, and B with respective coordinates $(0, 0)$, $(4, 4)$, and $({}^-4, 4)$, prove that $\overrightarrow{OA}$ and $\overrightarrow{OB}$ are perpendicular.

Cumulative Review IV

See Solution Manual for graphs and proofs.

1. If a and b are real numbers, then $ab = 0$ if, and only if, either $a = 0$ or $b = 0$. Make use of this fact in drawing the graph of each of the following equations.
   (a) $(x + y - 1)(x - y + 1) = 0$
   (b) $(x^2 + y^2 - 4)(x + y - 2) = 0$
   (c) $(xy - 4)(xy + 4) = 0$
2. Graph each of the following.
   (a) $y = 2|x|$
   (b) $y > 2|x|$
   (c) $y = 2|x| + 1$
   (d) $y < 2|x| + 1$
3. Show that $1 - i$ is a zero of the polynomial See Solution Manual.

$$f(x) = x^4 - 6x^3 + 12x - 20,$$

and find the other zeros of $f(x)$. $1+i$, $2+\sqrt{14}$, $2-\sqrt{14}$

4. Prove that it is impossible to double a two-digit positive integer by reversing its digits.
5. Draw the graph of the equation

$$|x - 1| + |x + 1| + |y - 1| + |y + 1| = 4.$$

6. Draw the graph of the equation

$$|x - 1| + |x + 1| + |y - 1| + |y + 1| = 2\sqrt{2} + 4.$$

7. Describe the graph of the following equation, and sketch it.

$$x^2 - y^2 + 3x - y + 2 = 0$$

8. A closed rectangular box has a volume of 60 cubic feet and a surface area of 94 square feet. If the height of the box were doubled, the surface area would increase to 148 square feet. What are the dimensions of the box? Base: 4 ft by 5 ft; height: 3 ft
9. An ant can crawl around the base of a cubical room in 10 minutes. By taking a path of least length, how long does it take the ant to crawl from a corner of the floor to the diametrically opposite corner of the ceiling? $5\sqrt{5}/2$ min
10. In how many ways can the letters of the word *prom* be rearranged so that
    (a) the resulting rearrangement does not begin with the letter p? 18
    (b) no letter is in its original position? 9

11. In each of the following exercises, find a formula for A_n, and use mathematical induction to prove that your formula is true for every positive integer n.

(a) $A_n = 1 + 5 + 9 + \cdots + (4n - 3)$ $n(2n-1)$

(b) $A_n = 14 + 19 + 24 + \cdots + (9 + 5n)$ $\frac{n}{2}(5n+23)$

12. Let $S_n = \dfrac{1}{1 \cdot 2} + \dfrac{1}{2 \cdot 3} + \cdots + \dfrac{1}{n(n + 1)}$.

(a) Find S_1, S_2, S_3, and S_4. $\frac{1}{2}, \frac{2}{3}, \frac{3}{4}, \frac{4}{5}$

(b) Guess a formula for S_n. $\frac{n}{n+1}$

(c) Prove by mathematical induction that your formula in part (b) is true for every positive integer n.

13. In the following way, P_n is defined as a product for every positive integer $n \geq 2$.

$$P_n = \left(1 - \frac{1}{4}\right)\left(1 - \frac{1}{9}\right)\left(1 - \frac{1}{16}\right) \cdot \ldots \cdot \left(1 - \frac{1}{n^2}\right)$$

(a) Find P_2, P_3, P_4, P_5, and P_6. $\frac{3}{4}, \frac{2}{3}, \frac{5}{8}, \frac{3}{5}, \frac{7}{12}$

(b) Give a formula for P_n. $\frac{1}{2} \cdot \frac{n+1}{n}$

(c) Prove by mathematical induction that your formula in part (b) is correct for every positive integer $n \geq 2$.

14. The geometric series $a + aq + aq^2 + \cdots + aq^{n-1}$ has sum

$$G_n = \frac{a(1 - q^n)}{1 - q}$$

  $\frac{9}{2}, \frac{93}{16}, \frac{189}{32}, \frac{3069}{512}$

when $q \neq 1$. Given that $a = 3$ and $q = \frac{1}{2}$, find G_2, G_5, G_6, and G_{10}.

15. Find the sum of the infinite geometric series 2

$$1 + \frac{1}{2} + \frac{1}{4} + \cdots + \frac{1}{2^{n-1}} \cdots$$

16. Find the sum of the infinite geometric series

$$3 - .3 + .03 - \cdots + 3(^-.1)^{n-1} + \cdots \quad \frac{30}{11}$$

17. Let A_n denote the sum of the first n terms of the arithmetic series that starts out $a + (a + d) + (a + 2d) + \cdots$ Prove that

$$3A_{2n} = 3A_n + A_{3n}.$$

18. Two cyclists started out at the same time, one going from town P to town Q and the other from town Q to town P. Each cyclist traveled at a constant speed and, on arriving at his destination, immediately turned around and returned. They met for the first time 6 miles from P and 48 minutes later, they met for the second time 2 miles from P. Find the speed of each cyclist and the distance between the towns P and Q.

19. Prove by mathematical induction that the equation

$$\frac{1}{2} + \frac{2}{2^2} + \frac{3}{2^3} + \cdots + \frac{n}{2^n} = 2 - \frac{n+2}{2^n}$$

is true for every positive integer n.

20. (a) Given the formula

$$1^2 + 2^2 + 3^2 + \cdots + n^2 = \frac{n(n+1)(2n+1)}{6},$$

find a summation formula for $\frac{2}{3}n(n+1)(2n+1)$

$$2^2 + 4^2 + 6^2 + \cdots + (2n)^2 = S(n),$$

and prove your result by mathematical induction.

(b) Using the formulas of part (a), find a summation formula for

$$1^2 + 3^2 + 5^2 + \cdots + (2n-1)^2 = T(n),$$

and prove your result by mathematical induction. $\frac{n}{3}(4n^2-1)$

21. In a geometric series, the second term is 4 more than the first term, and the sum of the second and third terms is 24. Find the sum of the first six terms of the series (two solutions). 728 or 252

22. Find all possible values of x and y such that 3, x, and y will form the first three terms of an arithmetic series, and x, y, and 8 will form the first three terms of a geometric series. $x = \frac{9}{2}, y = 6; x = \frac{1}{2}, y = {}^-2$

23. Find a summation formula for

$$1 \cdot 3 + 2 \cdot 4 + 3 \cdot 5 + \cdots + n(n+2), \quad \frac{n(n+1)(2n+7)}{6}$$

and prove your result by mathematical induction.

24. Find each of the following sums.

(a) ${}^-2 - 5 - 8 - 11 - 14 - \cdots - 62$ ${}^-672$
(b) $1 + 2 + 2^2 + 2^3 + \cdots + 2^9$ 1023
(c) $1 - 3 + 3^2 - 3^3 + 3^4 - 3^5$ ${}^-182$

In each of the following exercises, find the sum and the inner product of the pairs of vectors.

25. $3\mathbf{i} + 7\mathbf{j}$, ${}^-2\mathbf{i} + 5\mathbf{j}$ $\mathbf{i} + 12\mathbf{j}$; 29

26. ${}^-10\mathbf{i} - 8\mathbf{j}$, ${}^-4\mathbf{i} - 3\mathbf{j}$ ${}^-14\mathbf{i} - 11\mathbf{j}$; 64

In each of the following exercises, find the sum and the inner product of vectors $\overrightarrow{AB}$ and $\overrightarrow{CD}$.

27. $A({}^-3, 5)$, $B(2, 8)$, $C(1, 3)$, and $D(4, 7)$ [8, 7]; 27

28. $A({}^-7, {}^-1)$, $B(2, {}^-8)$, $C({}^-2, 5)$, and $D(1, {}^-6)$ [12, ⁻18]; 104

In each of the following exercises, vectors **a**, **b**, and **c** are sides of a triangle. Tell whether the triangle is right, isosceles, or equilateral.

29. $\mathbf{a} = 2\mathbf{i}$, $\mathbf{b} = 2\mathbf{j}$, $\mathbf{c} = 2(\mathbf{i} + \mathbf{j})$ Right and isosceles

30. $\mathbf{a} = {}^-2\mathbf{i}$, $\mathbf{b} = {}^-2\mathbf{j}$, $\mathbf{c} = {}^-2\mathbf{i} - 2\mathbf{j}$ Right and isosceles

CHAPTER 15

Logic

Chapter 15 provides an opportunity for study of symbolic logic. Some students may have had a previous slight introduction to it in other mathematics courses. The concepts of this chapter are not only very useful in mathematics but are important in their own right also. Many students will study logic again later in more advanced mathematics courses. Some others may enter occupations requiring little formal training in mathematics, but this chapter, with its emphasis on precision in the use of words, may be for those students the most significant part of this course.

The following are some of the topics covered in Chapter 15:

- *Statement*
- *If/then connective*
- *Conjunction*
- *Disjunction*
- *Negation*
- *Truth table*
- *Logically equivalent statements*
- *Logically true and logically false statements*
- *Inverse*
- *Converse*
- *Contrapositive*
- *Valid argument*
- *Indirect argument*

It is recommended that two days be spent on Sections 15-2 and 15-4, and one day on Sections 15-1, 15-3, and 15-5.

CHAPTER 15

Logic circuit boards in the modules of computers are designed with the aid of symbolic logic. (Courtesy of Friden, Inc.)

LOGIC

Although the content of mathematics is both important and useful, the essence of mathematics is its structure and logical development. In this chapter, we shall study *symbolic logic* in order to examine some of the common forms of argument used in mathematics.

Logic, as a study of the "laws of thought," dates back to the time of Aristotle. However, mathematical logic was developed as recently as the 1850's and emerged as an important branch of mathematics in the twentieth century.

589

15–1 STATEMENTS AND CONNECTIVES

The reading and the exercises of Section 15–1 should be assigned before the material presented is discussed in class. Students generally have little or no difficulty with it and rather enjoy the idea of translating statements into symbolic form and vice versa.

15–1 STATEMENTS AND CONNECTIVES

The material in this chapter is not in the main sequence of algebraic topics. Therefore, this chapter may be studied at any time during this course.

A sentence that is either true or false, but not both, is called a *statement*. For example, the following two statements can be made about any given quadrilateral $ABCD$.

Quadrilateral $ABCD$ is a square.
Quadrilateral $ABCD$ is a parallelogram.

In the same way that we use symbols to denote numbers, sets, and other objects, we shall use symbols, such as p and q, to denote statements. For example, in the statements above, we might let p denote the first statement and q denote the second statement.

p: Quadrilateral $ABCD$ is a square.
q: Quadrilateral $ABCD$ is a parallelogram.

We shall combine simple statements, such as q and p, to form *compound statements*, such as the following.

Quadrilateral $ABCD$ is a parallelogram and quadrilateral $ABCD$ is a square.

To make compound statements from simple ones, we shall use certain words called *connectives*. The common connectives are *and*, which is denoted by $\wedge$; *or*, which is denoted by $\vee$; and *not*, which is denoted by $\sim$. The table below shows the ways in which these connectives are used with statements.

Statement	Symbolic form	Name
p and q	$p \wedge q$	conjunction of
p or q	$p \vee q$	disjunction of
not p	$\sim p$	negation

For example, if p and q are the two given statements about the quadrilateral $ABCD$, then $p \wedge q$, $p \vee q$, and $\sim p$ are the following statements.

$p \wedge q$: Quadrilateral $ABCD$ is a square and a parallelogram.
$p \vee q$: Quadrilateral $ABCD$ is a square or a parallelogram.
$\sim p$: Quadrilateral $ABCD$ is not a square.

We can combine the statements shown at the bottom of the preceding page to make more complicated statements. For example, the statement $q \wedge \sim p$ denotes the following.

$q \wedge \sim p$: Quadrilateral *ABCD* is a parallelogram and not a square.

The operations of *conjunction* and *disjunction* of statements in logic are analogous to the operations of *intersection* and *union* in set theory. The operation of *negation* can be compared to finding the *complement* of a set. In fact, logic and set theory are closely related subjects.

Let us now make another compound statement which relates p and q. If quadrilateral *ABCD* is a square, then it is a parallelogram. This is a *conditional statement*, rather than an assertion. The symbol is used for the *if–then* connective.

Statement	Symbolic form	Name
if p, then q	$p \rightarrow q$	conditional statement

In the following problem, we give further illustrations of the use of these four connectives.

Problem. Assign letters to the simple statements in each of the following compound statements, and then express the compound statement in symbolic form.

(a) The grass is wet and it has rained.

(b) If the grass is wet, it has rained.

(c) The grass is wet but it has not rained.

(d) It has not rained and the grass is not wet.

(e) The statement that it has rained and the grass is not wet is false.

Solution. Let p denote the statement "The grass is wet" and q the statement "It has rained." Then (a) becomes $p \wedge q$ and (b) becomes $p \rightarrow q$, although the word *then* in the *if–then* statement has been omitted as it frequently is in ordinary discourse. In (c), the word *but* has the same logical meaning as *and*, although it has more descriptive force. Thus, (c) becomes $p \wedge \sim q$. The statement in (d) that it has *not* rained *and* the grass is *not* wet becomes $\sim q \wedge \sim p$. In (e), the *negation* of "It has rained and the grass is not wet" is $\sim(q \wedge \sim p)$. Notice the use of parentheses to enclose the statement that is being negated.

Answers to Exercises 2, 3

2. (a) If I eat pie, I don't eat cake.
   (b) I eat pie, but not cake.
   (c) The statement that I eat pie and cake is false.
   (d) I do not eat pie or cake.
   (e) I eat pie and not cake or cake and not pie.
3. Use p for "A person has a car"; q for "He buys gasoline"; and r for "He has a power mower".

Quiz

1. Use p for "He has fair hair" and q for "He has blue eyes". Write each of the following in symbolic form.
   (a) He does not have fair hair but he has blue eyes. (ans: $\sim p \wedge q$)
   (b) If he has fair hair, he has blue eyes. (ans: $p \rightarrow q$)
2. Let p denote the statement "The dog chases the cat", and q the statement "The cat climbs a tree". Give verbal translations of each of the following.
   (a) $p \rightarrow q$ (ans: If the dog chases the cat, the cat climbs a tree.)
   (b) $\sim p \wedge q$ (ans: The dog does not chase the cat, and (or but) the cat climbs a tree.)

15-2 TRUTH TABLES AND EQUIVALENT STATEMENTS

If this is the students' first introduction to truth tables, you may wish to take time to explain that the columns on the left of the double line represent the possibilities of the four cases, and the column on the right, in color, represents the truth value of the conjunction taken

Exercises

1. Use p for "It is snowing" and q for "It is cold outside." Write each of the following in symbolic form.
   (a) It is snowing and it is cold outside. $p \wedge q$
   (b) It is snowing but it is not cold outside. $p \wedge \sim q$
   (c) If it is snowing, it is cold outside. $p \rightarrow q$
   (d) It is snowing or it is cold outside. $p \vee q$
   (e) It is not snowing and it is not cold outside. $\sim p \wedge \sim q$
   (f) The statement that it is snowing and it is cold outside is false. $\sim(p \wedge q)$
2. Use p for "I eat pie" and q for "I eat cake." Give verbal translations of each of the following.
   (a) $p \rightarrow \sim q$ (b) $p \wedge \sim q$ (c) $\sim(p \wedge q)$
   (d) $\sim p \vee \sim q$ (e) $(p \wedge \sim q) \vee (\sim p \wedge q)$
3. Assign letters to the three simple statements which are common to the following group of statements. Write each statement in symbolic form.
   (a) If a person has a car, he buys gasoline. $p \rightarrow q$
   (b) A person has a car and a power lawn mower. $p \wedge r$
   (c) If a person buys gasoline, then he has a car or a power mower. $q \rightarrow (p \vee r)$
   (d) A person buys gasoline or he does not have a car. $q \vee \sim p$
   (e) A person does not have a car, but if he owns a power mower, he buys gasoline. $\sim p \wedge (r \rightarrow q)$
   (f) The statement that a person does not have a car and does not own a power mower and buys gasoline is false. $\sim(\sim p \wedge \sim r \wedge q)$

15-2 TRUTH TABLES AND EQUIVALENT STATEMENTS

In this section, we shall develop methods for testing the truth or falsity of *compound* statements for all possible cases of the truth or falsity of their simple components. To do this, we shall give a *truth table* for each of the connectives.

Suppose that we make a statement p which is either true or false, but not both. If p is a true statement, then $\sim p$ is false; if p is false, then $\sim p$ must be true. This gives us the *truth table* for negation.

p	$\sim p$
T	F
F	T

Truth Table for Negation

Construction of the truth table for conjunction requires that we first list all possible combinations for the truth and falsity of two statements p and q. This is an elementary counting problem. Since we have the two possibilities T and F for p, and the two possibilities T and F for q, we have $2 \cdot 2$, or 4 cases, as listed in the truth table below.

p	q	$p \wedge q$
T	T	T
T	F	F
F	T	F
F	F	F

Truth Table for Conjunction

According to this table, *p and q* is a true statement if both p and q are true. Otherwise, the statement *p and q* is false.

Before constructing the truth table for the connective *or*, we must face the problem of the ambiguity of the use of the word *or* in ordinary discourse. Probably it is used most frequently in the sense of *one or the other but not both.* For example, the sentence

I shall have ice cream or sherbet for dessert

illustrates this use of the *exclusive or.*

Another usage of *or* is illustrated by the following property of the system of real numbers.

If $ab = 0$, then $a = 0$ or $b = 0$. (F-0)

Stated in words, it says that if the product of two numbers is zero, then *at least* one of the numbers is zero. This use of the connective *or* to mean *one or the other or possibly both* is called the *inclusive or.* The *inclusive or* is sometimes indicated in business documents by *and/or.*

In logic, we agree to use the *inclusive or* for disjunction. Consequently, the following is the truth table for disjunction.

p	q	$p \vee q$
T	T	T
T	F	T
F	T	T
F	F	F

Truth Table for Disjunction

According to this table, $p \vee q$ is true in all cases except the one in which both p and q are false. As we shall presently see, the exclusive *or* can be given in terms of the three connectives $\vee$, $\wedge$, and $\sim$.

as a whole. Students should understand that the truth value of the conjunction as a whole, depends upon the truth value of each of its individual parts, since, in normal usage, the conjunction is true only when both of its parts are true. Students will probably have little trouble accepting the truth table for the conjunction.

You may wish to use verbal statements to illustrate the truth tables. For example, the statement "I am going to the store and will buy ice cream", may be considered as an example of the conjunctive case. In order to make this conjunction true as a whole, a person would have to go to the store and would have to buy ice cream. However, if he does not go to the store, or if he does not buy ice cream, or if he does not do either, then the conjunction is false.

Students may have a more difficult time accepting the truth table for the disjunction because of the use of the inclusive or. However, very few students will wish to call the disjunction false when both of its parts are true. As an example of the disjunction, the statement, "I am going to buy a dog or a cat" may be considered. If the person buys a dog, the statement is true. If the person buys a cat, the statement is true. However, if the person buys neither a dog nor a cat, but buys a canary instead, the original statement is false. On the other hand, if the person buys both a dog and a cat, the truth value of the original disjunction is true, because the person has purchased at least one of them.

The truth table for the conditional statement usually presents the greatest problem to students. The two cases of most concern, those when the hypothesis, or p, is true, are usually easily seen. The other two cases, however, are not as obvious. It may work out best, rather than to justify these two cases, to ask your students to accept them on faith. The statement "If it rains, then I won't go shopping" may be used as an illustration for the conditional. If it does rain and the person does not go shopping, then the conditional statement is obviously true. However, if it does rain and the person decides to go shopping anyway, then the conditional statement is false. On the other hand if it doesn't rain, the person can either go shopping or not without hurting the truth value of the original conditional statement, since the truth value is dependent upon the fact that it first must rain. The person did not say what he would do if it did not rain. Under these conditions, the original statement can not be false, therefore it must be true.

If students have difficulty understanding the truth table for Problem 1, it is suggested that you write the table in Problem 1 on the board with the four column headings p, q, $q \vee \sim p$, $p \rightarrow q$, and with the truth values listed just for columns p and q. Then fill in truth values in the columns numbered 1 and finally those in the columns numbered 2. For another statement logically equivalent to $p \rightarrow q$, see Exercise 13 at the end of this section.

Finally, the following truth table represents the conditional statement *if p, then q*.

p	q	$p \rightarrow q$
T	T	T
T	F	F
F	T	T
F	F	T

Truth Table for the Conditional

Stated in words, this means that $p \rightarrow q$ is always true *unless* p is true and q is false.

You will probably agree with the first two rows of the truth table above. Our reason for labelling the last two cases true is somewhat similar to our reason for defining zero and negative exponents as we do. In other words, the set of labels for the two last cases in this table produces useful results. We shall return to this point later after we have illustrated the use of truth tables in analyzing more complicated statements.

Problem 1. Compare the truth table for $q \vee \sim p$ with that for $p \rightarrow q$.

Solution.

p	q	q	$\vee$	$\sim p$	p	$\rightarrow$	q
T	T	T	T	F	T	T	T
T	F	F	F	F	T	F	F
F	T	T	T	T	F	T	T
F	F	F	T	T	F	T	F
		1	2	1	1	2	1

The numbers below the columns indicate the order of events, and the final results are in color.

From our work above, we see that the truth tables of the statements $p \rightarrow q$ and $q \vee \sim p$ are the same. Statements which have the same truth tables are called *logically equivalent statements.* Thus, the statement *if p, then q* is logically equivalent to *either q or not p*. Both statements are true except when p is true and q is false. We could have defined *if p, then q* to be the same as q or *not p*. Then we would have obtained the truth table for $p \rightarrow q$ from that of $q \vee \sim p$.

Problem 2. Find truth tables for $p \vee \sim p$ and $p \wedge \sim p$.

Solution. Since each of these statements involves only one statement, the tables need just two rows.

p	p	$\vee$	$\sim p$
T	T	T	F
F	F	T	T
	1	2	1

p	p	$\wedge$	$\sim p$
T	T	F	F
F	F	F	T
	1	2	1

Thus, the statement $p \vee \sim p$ is true for every value of p and the statement $p \wedge \sim p$ is false for every value of p. These two statements are examples of *logically true* and *logically false* statements, respectively. In other words, they are examples of statements whose truth tables have a T in every row or an F in every row of the final column.

Problem 3. Find the truth table for the statement

$$(p \wedge \sim q) \vee (q \wedge \sim p).$$

Solution. This statement can be expressed in the following way:

p and not q or q and not p.

We proceed as shown in Tables 1, 2, and 3. Notice that the column headings represent p, q, and the substatements within the given statement.

p	q	(p	$\wedge$	$\sim q$)	$\vee$	(q	$\wedge$	$\sim p$)
T	T	T		F		T		F
T	F	T		T		F		F
F	T	F		F		T		T
F	F	F		T		F		T
		1		1		1		1

Table 1

In Table 1, we have listed the four possible cases for statements p and q. We have copied these cases in the columns under the symbols p and q in the compound statements. We have also used the truth table for negation to write values in color under the columns for $\sim q$ and $\sim p$.

If students have difficulty in understanding the truth tables for complicated statements and cannot see that the truth tables for such statements are built upon the truth or falsity of their simple components, it is suggested that you present the tables for Problem 3 on the board in such a way that students can see how the columns are developed in order to arrive at a final table such as that presented on the next page.

TWISTER

A college trustee, a professor, an instructor, and a janitor are named, Mr. Lewis, Mr. James, Mr. Peters, and Mr. Edwards, but not necessarily in the order given. Four students with the same names will be referred to here as Lew, Jim, Pete, and Ed. The father of one of the students is not absentminded, but always confuses Jim and Pete in class. Mr. James' daughter-in-law lives in San Francisco. The student with the same name as the professor belongs to Ed's fraternity. Mr. Peters is the instructor's father-in-law and has no grandchildren. The trustee's oldest son is 9 years old. The janitor's wife has never seen Mr. Edwards. What are the names of the trustee, professor, instructor, and janitor?

Solution: Mr. Peters is the trustee, Mr. Lewis the professor, Mr. Edwards the instructor, and Mr. James the janitor.

p	q	$p \wedge \sim q$			$\vee$	$q \wedge \sim p$		
T	T	T	F	F		T	F	F
T	F	T	T	T		F	F	F
F	T	F	F	F		T	T	T
F	F	F	F	T		F	F	T
		1	2	1		1	2	1

Table 2

In Table 2, the first column in color shows the values found by forming the conjunction of the values of p and $\sim q$. The second column in color shows the values found by forming the conjunction of the values of q and $\sim p$.

p	q	$p \wedge \sim q$			$\vee$	$q \wedge \sim p$		
T	T	T	F	F	F	T	F	F
T	F	T	T	T	T	F	F	F
F	T	F	F	F	T	T	T	T
F	F	F	F	T	F	F	F	T
		1	2	1	3	1	2	1

Table 3

In Table 3, the column in color shows the values found by forming the disjunction of the values of the two columns in color in Table 2.

In practice, we usually show this sequence of three steps in one table, as shown below.

p	q	$(p \wedge \sim q) \vee (q \wedge \sim p)$						
T	T	T	F	F	F	T	F	F
T	F	T	T	T	T	F	F	F
F	T	F	F	F	T	T	T	T
F	F	F	F	T	F	F	F	T
		1	2	1	3	1	2	1

Table 4

Now let us consider the verbal interpretation of the *exclusive or: p or q but not both p and q*. The truth table for the compound sentence $(p \wedge \sim q) \vee (q \wedge \sim p)$ has a T in the two cases in which one statement is true and the other false, and an F in the cases in which both statements are true and both are false. This is the set of truth values we would assign to the verbal statement of the exclusive *or*. We could invent a new symbol for the exclusive *or* (the symbol $\underline{\vee}$ is used by some logicians), and assign values F, T, T, F to the truth table of this new symbol. We shall not do this because we can express statements involving the exclusive *or* in terms of the connectives $\wedge$, $\vee$, and $\sim$ as we have just shown in Problem 3.

Exercises

Construct a truth table for each of the statements in Exercise 1–5.

1. $p \to \sim q$ **2.** $p \wedge \sim q$ **3.** $\sim(p \wedge q)$

4. $\sim p \vee \sim q$ **5.** $(p \wedge \sim q) \vee (\sim p \wedge q)$

1–5 See Solution Manual.

6. Are there any pairs of statements in Exercises 1–5 which are logically equivalent? Yes; 1, 3, 4

7. Show that $\sim(p \wedge \sim p)$ is a logically true statement and that $\sim(p \vee \sim p)$ is logically false. See Solution Manual.

8. (a) Show that $p \vee q$ is logically equivalent to $q \vee p$.
(b) Show that $p \wedge q$ is logically equivalent to $q \wedge p$. } See Solution Manual.
(c) Consider disjunction and conjunction as *operations* on pairs of statements, and tell which of the five fundamental properties of numbers can be used to describe the logical equivalences in parts (a) and (b). Commutative

9. Are $p \to q$ and $q \to p$ logically equivalent statements? No

10. Use truth tables to prove the following equivalences, which are called De Morgan's laws. See Solution Manual.
(a) $\sim(p \wedge q)$ is logically equivalent to $\sim p \vee \sim q$
(b) $\sim(p \vee q)$ is logically equivalent to $\sim p \wedge \sim q$
(c) Make up examples of statements for p and q to illustrate these laws.

11. Suppose that a is a real number and let p be the following statement.

p: a is positive.

Give a verbal statement of each of the following.
(a) $\sim p$ — a is not positive (b) $p \wedge \sim p$ — a is positive and a is not positive (c) $p \vee \sim p$ — a is positive or a is not positive

12. (a) Construct a truth table for $\sim(\sim p)$. This is usually written as $\sim\sim p$ and is called the *double negative* of p. See Solution Manual.
(b) Find a simpler statement which is logically equivalent to $\sim\sim p$. p
(c) Let p be the following statement.

p: It is snowing.

Form the double negative of p. It is not true that it is not snowing.

13. Show that the statement $p \to q$ is logically equivalent to the statement $\sim(p \wedge \sim q)$. Stated in words, this equivalence means that the verbal statement *if p, then q* is the same as the statement, See Solution Manual.

It is false that we have p and not q.

Quiz

1. Construct a truth table for each of the following statements.
(a) $\sim(p \wedge q)$ (b) $\sim p \wedge \sim q$

ans:

p	q	$\sim(p \wedge q)$	$\sim p \wedge \sim q$
T	T	F	F
T	F	T	F
F	T	T	F
F	F	T	T

2. Are the two statements in Exercise 1 logically equivalent? (ans: no)

3. Let p and q be the statements, p: I take Latin; q: I take French.
(a) Give verbal statements for each of the statements in Exercise 1. (ans: It is false that I take both Latin and French; I take neither Latin nor French.)
(b) Give the symbolic statement for: If I take Latin I take French and if I take French I take Latin.
(ans: $(p \to q) \wedge (q \to p)$)

14. Let p and q be the following statements.

$$p\text{:}\quad a = 0 \qquad \text{and} \qquad q\text{:}\quad b = 0.$$

Find a verbal statement that is logically equivalent to each of the following statements.

(a) $\sim(p \vee q)$ *It is not true that $a = 0$ or $b = 0$.* (b) $\sim(\sim p \wedge \sim q)$. *It is not true that $a \neq 0$ and $b \neq 0$.*

15. (a) Construct a truth table for $(p \vee q) \wedge [\sim(p \wedge q)]$, and compare this truth table with that in Problem 3 on page 595.

(b) Give a verbal statement of this symbolic statement in which you take specific examples of statements p and q.
See Solution Manual.

15-3 VARIATIONS OF THE CONDITIONAL

Certainly mathematics abounds with statements of the form *if . . . then* and *if and only if*. This section introduces the important notion of contrapositive and provides the basis for various forms of indirect argument discussed in Section 15-5.

15-3 VARIATIONS OF THE CONDITIONAL

Many theorems and related statements in mathematics have the *if-then* form. Therefore, it is worthwhile for us to study the conditional connective in some detail. For convenience, let us call p the *hypothesis* and q the *conclusion* in the conditional statement $p \rightarrow q$.

First, let us consider the truth tables of the four related statements below.

Statement	Converse	Inverse	Contrapositive
$p \rightarrow q$	$q \rightarrow p$	$\sim p \rightarrow \sim q$	$\sim q \rightarrow \sim p$

We see from the truth table below that the following statements are equivalent.

$$p \rightarrow q \quad \text{and} \quad \sim q \rightarrow \sim p$$

$$q \rightarrow p \quad \text{and} \quad \sim p \rightarrow \sim q$$

The statement $q \rightarrow p$ is called the *converse* of the statement $p \rightarrow q$. According to the table, a conditional statement and its converse are *not logically equivalent*. You probably know from experience that the truth of a statement does not insure the truth of its converse.

p	q	$p \rightarrow q$	$q \rightarrow p$	$\sim p \rightarrow \sim q$	$\sim q \rightarrow \sim p$
T	T	T T T	T T T	F T F	F T F
T	F	T F F	F T T	F T T	T F F
F	T	F T T	T F F	T F F	F T T
F	F	F T F	F T F	T T T	T T T

For example, the general statement

If a quadrilateral is a square, then it is a parallelogram,

is true, but its converse,

If a quadrilateral is a parallelogram, then it is a square,

is false.

The statement $\sim q \rightarrow \sim p$ is called the *contrapositive* of the statement $p \rightarrow q$. To form the contrapositive of an *if–then* statement, we negate the hypothesis and conclusion, and then form the converse statement. Since an *if–then* statement and its contrapositive are logically equivalent, the assertion of the truth or falsity of a particular statement $p \rightarrow q$ is equivalent to the assertion of the truth or falsity of its contrapositive statement, $\sim q \rightarrow \sim p$. In a later section, we shall see that this is a basis for a particular form of mathematical proof.

Sometimes we wish to combine an *if–then* statement with its converse by using the connective *and* to form the statement $p \rightarrow q$ *and* $q \rightarrow p$. A shorter way of writing this statement is

$$p \leftrightarrow q,$$

which is read *p if, and only if, q*. Let us determine the truth table for $p \leftrightarrow q$. Since $p \leftrightarrow q$ is defined as $(p \rightarrow q) \wedge (q \rightarrow p)$, we obtain the following truth table.

p	q	(p	$\rightarrow$	q)	$\wedge$	(q	$\rightarrow$	p)
T	T	T	T	T	T	T	T	T
T	F	T	F	F	F	F	T	T
F	T	F	T	T	F	T	F	F
F	F	F	T	F	T	F	T	F
		1	2	1	3	1	2	1

Thus, the statement *p if, and only if, q* is true unless *p* and *q* have different truth values, that is, unless one is true and the other false.

A closer look at the words in the statement *p, if and only if, q* suggests a slightly different interpretation from that used in the definition of $p \leftrightarrow q$. Thus, the statement seems to contain the compound statements *p if q* and *p only if q*. The first statement gives us $q \rightarrow p$ but the second statement, literally translated, suggests $\sim q \rightarrow \sim p$. However, since $\sim q \rightarrow \sim p$ is the contrapositive of $p \rightarrow q$, we see that our definition of *if and only if* as $(p \rightarrow q) \wedge (q \rightarrow p)$ is consistent with the ordinary usage of words.

The statement $p \leftrightarrow q$ is also called a *biconditional* statement.

The use of *p only if q* (see Exercise 17, page 604, and Exercises 8 and 13, on page 608) should not be confused with *p if, and only if, q*; *p only if q* is logically equivalent to *if not q, then not p*, which, in turn, is the contrapositive of (and hence the equivalent to) *if p, then q*.

Some students may have heard of still a third form, p *is necessary and sufficient for* q, which, interpreted literally, is

$$(\sim p \to \sim q) \wedge (p \to q).$$

Again, this is logically equivalent to the biconditional $p \leftrightarrow q$.

Answer to Exercise 2

2. If the plane is late, the weather is bad ($q \to p$). If the plane is not late, the weather is not bad ($\sim q \to \sim p$). If the weather is not bad, the plane is not late ($\sim p \to \sim q$).

Quiz

1. Write each of the following in symbolic form. Let p denote the statement "It is cold" and q the statement "He wears a scarf".
   (a) He wears a scarf if it is cold. (ans: $p \to q$)
   (b) He wears a scarf only if it is cold. (ans: $\sim p \to \sim q$)
   (c) He wears a scarf if, and only if, it is cold. (ans: $p \leftrightarrow q$)
2. If *ABCD* is a square, then *ABCD* is a rectangle. For this statement give the verbal statement of:
   (a) The contrapositive (ans: If *ABCD* is not a rectangle, it is not a square)
   (b) The converse (ans: If *ABCD* is a rectangle, it is a square)
   (c) The inverse (ans: If *ABCD* is not a square, it is not a rectangle.)

Which of the four statements are true? (ans: The original statement and its contrapositive are true.)

Still another logically equivalent form of $p \leftrightarrow q$ is the type of statement seen frequently in geometry, *if* p, *then* q, *and conversely*. In fact, this last form is probably most suggestive of the double arrow in $p \leftrightarrow q$.

We shall not be concerned about these different verbal statements for $p \leftrightarrow q$ because they are all logically equivalent to the compound statement

$$(p \to q) \wedge (q \to p).$$

You probably remember that the proof of a geometric or algebraic theorem of the form $p \leftrightarrow q$ requires the proof of two statements, one of the form $p \to q$ and the other its converse, $q \to p$.

Exercises

1. Let p denote "The weather is bad" and q denote "The plane is late." Write each of the following in symbolic form.
   (a) If the weather is bad, the plane is late. $p \to q$
   (b) The plane is late if, and only if, the weather is bad. $q \leftrightarrow p$
   (c) The weather is bad if the plane is late. $q \to p$
   (d) The plane is late only if the weather is bad. $q \to p$
2. Form the converse, contrapositive, and inverse of the statement in part (a) of Exercise 1, and express each in symbolic form.
3. Form the contrapositive of the contrapositive of $p \to q$. To what statement is your resulting statement logically equivalent? $\sim(\sim p) \to \sim(\sim q)$; $p \to q$
4. Why is $\sim p \leftrightarrow \sim q$ logically equivalent to $p \leftrightarrow q$? Give your answer without using truth tables. See Solution Manual.
5. Using the results of Exercise 4, find a statement which is logically equivalent to $p \leftrightarrow (q \vee r)$ and involves only the connectives $\sim$ and $\wedge$ used with $\leftrightarrow$. (You will need to use De Morgan's laws of Exercise 10 on page 597.) $\sim p \leftrightarrow (\sim q \wedge \sim r)$
6. Using Exercises 4 and 5, give a verbal statement which is logically equivalent to the statement The product of two numbers is not zero if, and only if,
$$ab = 0 \text{ if, and only if, } a = 0 \text{ or } b = 0.$$
both factors are different from zero.
7. Give a verbal statement concerning odd integers which is logically equivalent to the statement. The product of two integers is even if, and only if, at least one of the integers is even. The product of two integers is odd if, and only if, both the integers are odd.
8. Construct the truth table for $\sim(p \to q)$. Find an equivalent statement which uses only the connectives $\sim$ and $\wedge$. Is $\sim(p \to q)$ equivalent to $\sim p \to \sim q$? See Solution Manual; $p \wedge \sim q$; no

15-4 LOGICAL IMPLICATION AND VALID ARGUMENT

In the truth table for the conditional $p \to q$, where statements p and q are assigned all four possible pairs of truth values, there is an F in the second row for the case where p is true and q is false and a T in all other rows. Thus, the conditional statement $p \to q$ is not logically true. In Problem 1, we consider a more complex conditional statement.

Problem 1. Construct the truth table for the statement

$$[(p \to q) \wedge p] \to q.$$

Solution.

p	q	$[(p$	$\to$	$q)$	$\wedge$	$p]$	$\to$	q
T	T	T	T	T	T	T	T	T
T	F	T	F	F	F	T	T	F
F	T	F	T	T	F	F	T	T
F	F	F	T	F	F	F	T	F
		1	1	1	2	1	3	1

Thus, the conditional statement with hypothesis $(p \to q) \wedge p$ and conclusion q is a *logically true statement.*

When a conditional statement is logically true, we say that the hypothesis logically *implies* the conclusion, or that the conclusion *follows from* the hypothesis. For example, in any true mathematical theorem, the hypothesis *implies* the conclusion. The truth table in Problem 1 shows that $(p \to q) \wedge p$ logically *implies* the statement q.

Since the truth table for any conditional has T's in the rows where the hypothesis is *false*, we need look only at cases in which the hypothesis is *true* to test a conditional statement for implication. Thus, we could say the following.

Statement p implies q if, whenever p is true, q is also true.

It is this notion that most people have in mind when they make a conditional, or *if–then*, statement. This accounts for their initial shock when they see the last two rows of the truth table for $p \to q$. For example, a person asserting, "If you drink coffee, you won't sleep" really means to assert that drinking coffee implies lack of sleep and, of course, sees no point in saying this to a person who does *not* drink coffee (the case of false hypothesis).

15-4 LOGICAL IMPLICATION AND VALID ARGUMENT

By definition of logical implication, statement p implies statement q if, and only if, the truth table of $p \to q$ has only T's in the final column. You may wish to have the students use this test for implication on several examples before attempting the shortcut suggested in the next paragraph.

In particular, if p is never true (is logically false) then p implies q, whatever the statement q. (See Exercise 14 on page 604.)

The hypothesis and conclusion of a logically true conditional statement are related. They cannot take on all four pairs of truth values, since it is impossible to have a *true* hypothesis and *false* conclusion. This relationship is called a *logical implication.*

To *prove* a mathematical theorem, we must show that the hypothesis of the theorem logically *implies* the conclusion. In constructing a mathematical proof or in making a verbal argument, we usually form a chain of statements, prefacing the last of these with the word *therefore*. The statements in the chain are not all independent, and we rely strongly on notions of implication. We illustrate this with a simple example.

Problem 2. Symbolize the following argument.

If it is raining, I will take an umbrella.
It is raining. *Therefore*, I will take an umbrella.

Solution. Let p be the statement, "It is raining" and q the statement "I will take an umbrella." We write this argument in the form

$$\begin{array}{l} p \to q \\ p \\ \hline q \end{array}$$

Using the notation of the mathematician David Hilbert, who made outstanding contributions to the field of mathematical logic in the early twentieth century, we have drawn a horizontal line under the first two statements to denote the word *therefore*. Each statement which lies above such a horizontal line is called a premise, and each statement below the line is called a conclusion of the argument.

An argument is said to be valid according to the following definition.

If an argument has, for example, premises p_1, p_2, p_3 followed by conclusion q, it is a valid argument if the conditional statement

$$(p_1 \wedge p_2 \wedge p_3) \to q$$

is logically true.

DEFINITION OF A VALID ARGUMENT

An argument is valid if, and only if, the conjunction of (all) the premises implies the conclusion.

Now return to the truth table used in Problem 1. Note that it contains the two premises and the conclusion of the argument in Problem 2 and, furthermore, that it shows that the conjunction of these true premises implies the conclusion. In other words, this truth table establishes the validity of the argument of Problem 2.

You may have learned from experience that the argument in the next problem is *invalid*!

Problem 3. Test the following argument for validity.

> If John studies hard, he will pass the course. John passes the course. Therefore, he studied hard.

Solution.

p: John studies hard.

q: John passes the course.

The symbolized argument and its truth table are given below.

$p \rightarrow q$
q
———
p

p	q	$[(p$	$\rightarrow$	$q)$	$\wedge$	$q]$	$\rightarrow$	p
T	T	T	T	T	T	T	T	T
T	F	T	F	F	F	F	T	T
F	T	F	T	T	T	T	F	F
F	F	F	T	F	F	F	T	F
		1	2	1	3	1	4	1

The colored column shows that the argument is *invalid* since the conjunction of the premises does *not* imply the conclusion (we do not have all T's in column 4). Note that the case in which both premises are true and yet the conclusion is false is that of John not studying hard and passing the course. This case destroys the validity of the argument.

Exercises

1–6 See Solution Manual.

In Exercises 1–5, show that the first statement in each pair *implies* the second.

1. $p \wedge q$, p (Hint: Use a truth table to show that $(p \wedge q) \rightarrow p$ is logically true.)
2. $p \wedge q$, q
3. $p \leftrightarrow q$, $p \rightarrow q$
4. $p \leftrightarrow q$, $q \rightarrow p$
5. $p \wedge q$, $p \rightarrow q$
6. In Exercises 1–5, show that the second member of each pair does *not* imply the first.

7–13 See Solution Manual.

In Exercises 7–13, test each argument for validity.

7. Valid
$p \vee q$
$\sim p$
———
q

8. Invalid
$p \vee q$
p
———
$\sim q$

9. Valid
$p \rightarrow q$
$\sim q$
———
$\sim p$

10. Invalid
$p \rightarrow q$
$\sim p$
———
$\sim q$

11. $p \wedge q$
$\sim p \rightarrow q$
———
$\sim q$ Invalid

12. $p \leftrightarrow q$
$\sim p$
———
$\sim q$ Valid

13. $(p \vee q) \rightarrow r$
$q \rightarrow \sim r$
———
p Invalid

Some students may see that not all entries in this table need be completed, in line with the italicized statement in red on page 601. Thus, they may show their work as follows.

p	q	$[(p \rightarrow q)$	$\wedge q]$	$\rightarrow p$
T	T	T	T	T
T	F			
F	T	(T	T	F)
F	F	T		

Here, cases of either one or both premises $p \rightarrow q$, q false, have been omitted and the case destroying the validity of the argument is circled.

Answer to Exercise 18, page 604

18. $p \rightarrow q$
$r \vee \sim q$
$\sim r$
———
$\sim p$ valid

Quiz

1. Test the following arguments for validity.

(a) $\sim p \rightarrow q$

$\underline{\sim q}$

p (ans: valid)

(b) $\sim p \rightarrow q$

$\underline{p}$

$\sim q$ (ans: invalid)

2. Symbolize the following argument and test for validity. The mystery guest is either a young person or has a cold. The guest has a cold. Therefore, the mystery guest is not a young person. Let p denote the statement "Mystery guest is a young person" and q the statement "Mystery guest has a cold".

(ans: $p \vee q$

$\underline{q}$

$\sim p$ invalid)

15–5 PROOF SCHEMA AND INDIRECT ARGUMENT

Whenever the conditional $p \rightarrow q$ and the hypothesis p of this conditional are both true, one may detach the conclusion q and claim it is true. This is, of course, the heart of mathematical arguments which cite a true *if-then* statement as a theorem, have the hypothesis of this theorem satisfied in a given situation, and then arrive at the statement that the conclusion of the theorem holds. For example, "If a triangle is isosceles, the angles opposite the congruent sides are congruent. $\triangle ABC$ has $\overline{AB} \cong \overline{AC}$. Therefore, angle $B \cong$ angle C".

You could ask students whether the schema

$$\begin{array}{l} p \rightarrow q \\ \underline{q} \\ p \end{array}$$

in which the hypothesis is detached, is valid. (See Problem 3 on the previous page.)

14–19 See Solution Manual.

14. Show that $p \wedge \sim p$ implies any statement q. (Hint: Remember that $p \wedge \sim p$ is logically false.)

Write each of the following arguments in symbolic language. Then test each argument for validity.

15. If a candidate does not win the party's nomination, he will not be elected. A candidate wins the party's nomination. Therefore, he is elected. $\sim p \rightarrow \sim q$, $\underline{p}$, q Invalid

16. If the sky is not cloudy, it will not rain. It is raining. Therefore, the sky is cloudy. $q \rightarrow p$, $\underline{q}$, p Valid

17. Only the brave deserve the fair. You deserve the fair. Therefore, you are brave. $q \rightarrow p$, $\underline{q}$, p Valid

18. If I work diligently, I finish by noon. Either the clock is fast or I do not finish by noon. But the clock is not fast. Therefore, I do not work diligently.

19. If a person is sane, he can do logic. An insane person is not fit to serve on a jury. Jones cannot do logic. Therefore, Jones is not fit to serve on a jury. $p \rightarrow q$, $\sim p \rightarrow \sim r$, $\underline{\sim q}$, $\sim r$ Valid

15–5 PROOF SCHEMA AND INDIRECT ARGUMENT

In the previous section, we have tested the validity of *particular* arguments. However, the configuration of each of these arguments, called by Hilbert a *proof schema*, can be applied to all arguments of that form. Consider, for example, the proof schema displayed below. It is shown in the valid argument in Problem 2 on page 602, and is called the rule of detachment (*modus ponens*).

$$\begin{array}{l} p \rightarrow q \\ \underline{p} \\ q \end{array}$$

The rule of detachment is one of the patterns of reasoning used repeatedly in constructing proofs of mathematical theorems.

Another useful proof schema, called the *transitivity property of the conditional* (*transitivity of* $\rightarrow$), is given below.

$$\begin{array}{l} p \rightarrow q \\ \underline{q \rightarrow r} \\ p \rightarrow r \end{array}$$

The following truth table establishes the validity of this argument.

p	q	r	$[(p \to q)$	$\wedge$	$(q \to r)]$	$\to$	$(p \to r)$
T	T	T	T	T	T	T	T
T	T	F	T	F	F	T	F
T	F	T	F	F	T	T	T
T	F	F	F	F	T	T	F
F	T	T	T	T	T	T	T
F	T	F	T	F	F	T	T
F	F	T	T	T	T	T	T
F	F	F	T	T	T	T	T
			1	2	1	3	1

The use of the transivity property of the conditional is illustrated in the following problem.

You may wish to enliven this problem by taking examples of verbal statements for p, q, r, s. See Exercise 9, page 608.

Problem 1. Show that the following is a valid argument.

$$\begin{array}{l} p \to q \\ q \to r \\ r \to s \\ \underline{p \qquad} \\ s \end{array}$$

Solution.

$$\begin{array}{ll} p \to q & \text{(given) (premise)} \\ \underline{q \to r} & \text{(given)} \\ p \to r & \text{(transitivity of } \to) \\ \underline{r \to s} & \text{(given)} \\ p \to s & \text{(transitivity of } \to) \\ \underline{p \qquad} & \text{(given)} \\ s & \text{(rule of detachment)} \end{array}$$

The proofs of many mathematical theorems follow this pattern. However, in the *statement* of the theorem, the hypothesis may not contain all of the premises used in the proof. Some premises are introduced as the proof develops. Then the reason cited is an axiom or a previously proved theorem which asserts the truth of the premise. The theorem proved, then, actually has these axioms or previously proved theorems as additional premises.

It should be clear that if we replace a statement or any component of a statement by a logically equivalent statement, the original statement is *logically true* if, and only if, the statement containing the replacement is *logically true*. The reason for this is that logically equivalent statements have the same truth table.

In Section 15–3, we showed that the statement $p \to q$ is logically equivalent to its contrapositive, $\sim q \to \sim p$. Hence, *a proof of the contrapositive of a theorem constitutes (automatically) a proof of the theorem itself.* This principle is the basis of one of the proof forms called *proof by indirect reasoning*, which we illustrate in Problem 2.

Problem 2. Suppose that the property of multiplication by zero has been established: If $a = 0$ or $b = 0$, then $ab = 0$. Prove the following theorem.

$$\text{If } ab \neq 0, \text{ then } a \neq 0 \text{ and } b \neq 0.$$

Solution. To prove this theorem we first denote the statements $a = 0$, $b = 0$, and $ab = 0$ by p, q, and r, respectively. We are to prove that the following is logically true.

$$\sim r \to (\sim p \wedge \sim q)$$

The contrapositive of this statement is

$$\sim(\sim p \wedge \sim q) \to \sim(\sim r).$$

By applying one of De Morgan's laws (see Exercise 10 on page 597) and the double negative (see Exercise 12 on page 597), we determine that $\sim(\sim p \wedge \sim q)$ is equivalent to $p \vee q$ and that $\sim\sim r$ is equivalent to r. Thus, the contrapositive becomes

$$(p \vee q) \to r.$$

Stated in words, this says that if $a = 0$ or $b = 0$, then $ab = 0$. This is the statement of the theorem previously established, and hence, our original theorem is true.

The proof of this theorem as it is given in mathematics texts usually proceeds in the following way.

1. Given $ab \neq 0$.
2. Suppose it is false that $a \neq 0$ and $b \neq 0$.
3. Then at least one of a, b is 0.
4. But then $ab = 0$ by the zero multiplication property.
5. This contradicts the hypothesis that $ab \neq 0$ and hence, our *supposition* is false.

Therefore, if $ab \neq 0$, then $a \neq 0$ and $b \neq 0$.

We can facilitate the interpretation of the supposition in step 2 by noticing that it is logically equivalent to the statement in step 3, since $\sim(\sim p \wedge \sim q)$ is equivalent to $p \vee q$.

Once one correctly forms the contrapositive of the statement which is to be proved, arriving at

$$(p \vee q) \to r,$$

one recognizes this contrapositive as a (true) theorem, so that the statement under consideration is also true.

The use of logical symbolism may help one avoid the logical error of thinking that the negation of the statement "$a \neq 0$ and $b \neq 0$" is equivalent to "$a = 0$ and $b = 0$" (since $\sim(\sim p \wedge \sim q)$ is equivalent to $p \vee q$ by one of the De Morgan laws).

Another form of proof is called *reductio ad absurdum,* or proof by contradiction, which you encountered in your study of geometry. The following is an example.

Problem 3. Prove that if two different lines intersect, their intersection contains only one point.

Solution. Suppose that the two lines intersect in two different points, P and Q. Then two different lines contain points P and Q. However, this contradicts the *line postulate:* For every two different points, there is exactly one line that contains both points. Therefore, the theorem stated in the problem is true.

The above argument for p implies q has the form $(p \wedge \sim q)$ which implies $(r \wedge \sim r)$, as we now show. Let p, q be the following statements.

p: The two intersecting lines are different.

q: The two intersecting lines meet in only one point.

Let r be the line postulate. We show that whenever both premises p and $\sim q$ are true, the conclusion $r \wedge \sim r$ is true. Of course r is true by assumption. Therefore, we have to show only that whenever both p and $\sim q$ are true, $\sim r$ is true. This is done in the above verbal argument.

We shall let you verify that the two statements

$$p \rightarrow q \quad \text{and} \quad (p \wedge \sim q) \rightarrow (r \wedge \sim r)$$

are logically equivalent for any statements p, q, and r. This verification establishes the validity of the *reductio ad absurdum* reasoning.

Since $r \wedge (\sim r)$ is a logically false or contradictory statement, to say $(p \wedge \sim q) \rightarrow (r \wedge \sim r)$ is to say "if $p \wedge \sim q$, then there is a contradiction".

Exercises

1-4 See Solution Manual.

Use truth tables to test the following arguments for validity.

1. If he has subversive ideas, he will vote against the bill. He will vote against the bill. Therefore, he has subversive ideas. Invalid
2. The murderer either fled through the skylight or disguised himself as a visiting policeman. He did not flee through the skylight. Therefore, he disguised himself as a visiting policeman. Valid
3. Potatoes will make a heavy crop, if and only if, they are planted at the full moon. If the potato crop is light, wheat prices are high. Therefore, if potatoes are planted at the full moon, wheat prices will be high. Invalid
4. If the speaker is well-known, his lecture is worth attending. His lecture is short or it is not worth attending. But his lecture is not short. Therefore, the speaker is not well-known. Valid

Quiz

1. Using the fact that a statement and its contrapositive are logically equivalent and using the transitivity property of the conditional, show without truth tables that the following is a valid argument.

$$\begin{array}{c} p \rightarrow q \\ \underline{\sim r \rightarrow \sim q} \\ p \rightarrow r \end{array}$$

(ans: $\sim r \rightarrow \sim q$ is equivalent to $q \rightarrow r$. Hence,

$$\begin{array}{c} p \rightarrow q \\ \underline{q \rightarrow r} \\ p \rightarrow r \end{array}$$

by the transitivity of the conditional)

2. (a) If a, b, c, d are real numbers, the following is a true inequality statement.

If $a > b$ and $c > d$, then $a + c > b + d$. Give the contrapositive of this statement, using the symbol $\ngtr$ for "is not greater than". Is the contrapositive statement true? (ans: If $a + c \ngtr b + d$ then $a \ngtr b$ or $c \ngtr d$; yes.)

(b) Give the converse and inverse statements of the given statement. Are either or both of these false? Illustrate with specific examples. (ans:
Converse: If $a + c > b + d$ then $a > b$ and $c > d$.
Inverse: If $a \ngtr b$ or $c \ngtr d$, then $a + c \ngtr b + d$. For example, $4 + 3 > 5 + 1$, but $4 \ngtr 5$ (although $3 > 1$); $4 \ngtr 5$, yet $4 + 3 > 5 + 1$.

(Note: the statement "If $a \ngtr b$ and $c \ngtr d$, then $a + c \ngtr b + d$" is a true statement (that is, if $a \leqq b$ and $c \leqq d$ then

$$a + c \leqq b + d),$$

but is not the contrapositive, converse, or inverse statement of the statement of this exercise.)

See Solution Manual.

5. (a) Show that $p \vee q$ is logically equivalent to $\sim p \rightarrow q$.
(b) Use part (a) to show that the valid argument of Exercise 2 has the proof schema of the law of detachment, or *modus ponens*.

6. In the sequence of proof schemas given below, we reduce the original proof schema for the valid argument in Exercise 4 to a simpler one in successive steps. Supply the missing rules of logic used in this process. (The symbol $\Rightarrow$ is used here to mean *logically implies*.)

$$\begin{array}{c} p \rightarrow q \\ r \vee \sim q \\ \underline{\sim r} \\ \sim p \end{array} \quad \xRightarrow{\text{Exercise 5(a)}} \quad \begin{array}{c} p \rightarrow q \\ \sim r \rightarrow \sim q \\ \underline{\sim r} \\ \sim p \end{array} \quad \overset{?}{\Rightarrow} \quad \begin{array}{c} \left.\begin{array}{c} p \rightarrow q \\ q \rightarrow r \end{array}\right\} \\ \underline{\sim r} \\ \sim p \end{array} \overset{?}{\Rightarrow} \quad \begin{array}{c} p \rightarrow r \\ \underline{\sim r} \\ \sim p \end{array}$$

Contra-positive Transitivity of the conditional

$$\overset{?}{\Rightarrow} \quad \begin{array}{c} \sim r \rightarrow \sim p \\ \underline{\sim r} \\ \sim p \end{array}$$

Contra-positive

7-13 See Solution Manual.

Exercises 7–9 are adapted from problems posed by Lewis Carroll. Find a chain of conditional statements for each of these arguments, and supply the missing conclusion.

7. If fruit is unripe, it is unwholesome. If fruit is grown in the shade, it is unripe. This fruit is wholesome. Therefore, __?__.

8. If one hogs the conversation, one appears conceited. One is well-informed only if one is good company. If one appears conceited, one is not good company, Therefore, __?__.

9. If a kitten loves fish, he is teachable. A kitten with no tail will not play with a gorilla. If a kitten has whiskers, he loves fish. If a kitten has green eyes, he is unteachable. If a kitten has no whiskers, he has no tail. Therefore, __?__.

10. Show that $p \rightarrow q$ is logically equivalent to $(p \wedge \sim q) \rightarrow (r \wedge \sim r)$.

11. (a) An even integer is a number of the form $2n$, with n an integer. Show that a product of two integers x and y, with x even, is an even integer.
(b) Use indirect argument and the theorem of part (a) to prove that if the product of two integers is odd, then both integers are odd.

12. Suppose that a group of 367 people are in a room. Use indirect argument to prove that at least two of these people have the same birthday.

13. Test for validity of the arguments in parts (a) and (b), each of which uses the following premise:

A person will live to be 80 only if he has a sensible diet.

(a) Mr. Smith dies before he is 80. *Therefore*, Mr. Smith did not have a sensible diet. Invalid
(b) Mr. Jones has a sensible diet. *Therefore*, Mr. Jones will live to be 80 or over. Invalid

KEY IDEAS AND KEY WORDS

In logic, a **statement** is a sentence which is either true or false, but is not both true and false.

If p and q are statements, we use the **connectives** described below.

negation	$\sim p$	not p
conjunction	$p \wedge q$	p and q
disjunction	$p \vee q$	p or q
conditional	$p \rightarrow q$	if p, then q

The following are truth tables for these connectives.

p	$\sim p$
T	F
F	T

p	q	$p \wedge q$	$p \vee q$	$p \rightarrow q$
T	T	T	T	T
T	F	F	T	F
F	T	F	T	T
F	F	F	F	T

A statement is **logically true** or **logically false** if there is a T or an F, respectively, in every row of the final column of its truth table.

Two statements are **logically equivalent** if they have the same final column in their truth tables. Examples of logically equivalent pairs of statements are the following.

$\sim\sim p$ (double negative) and p

$\sim(p \wedge q)$ and $\sim p \vee \sim q$ } De Morgan's Laws

$\sim(p \vee q)$ and $\sim p \wedge \sim q$ }

The **statement** $p \rightarrow q$ has three related statements.

converse	$q \rightarrow p$
inverse	$\sim p \rightarrow \sim q$
contrapositive	$\sim q \rightarrow \sim p$

A statement and its contrapositive form a **logically equivalent pair.** In other words,

$p \rightarrow q$ **is logically equivalent to** $\sim q \rightarrow \sim p$.

If a conditional statement $p \rightarrow q$ is logically true, we say that the hypothesis p **implies** the conclusion q.

TWISTER

When the day after tomorrow is yesterday, today will be as far from Tuesday as today was from Tuesday when the day before yesterday was tomorrow. What day of the week is it?

Solution: The day of the week is Tuesday. For when the day after tomorrow (Thursday) is "yesterday", "today" will be Friday; and when the day before yesterday (Sunday) was "tomorrow", "today" was Saturday. There are two days between Tuesday and Friday and between Saturday and Tuesday.

An argument is written in symbolic form by listing vertically the various premises and by separating the conclusion from the premises by a horizontal line.

$$\begin{array}{l} p \rightarrow q \\ \underline{p \qquad} \\ q \end{array} \qquad (1)$$

$$\begin{array}{l} p \rightarrow q \\ \underline{q \qquad} \\ p \end{array} \qquad (2)$$

The argument is **valid** if the conjunction of all the premises **implies** the conclusion. Argument (1) above is valid, whereas argument (2) is invalid.

The symbolic form of a valid argument is called a **proof schema.** The proof schema in argument (1) is known as the **law of detachment,** or ***modus ponens.*** Another proof schema, called the **transitivity of the conditional,** is

$$\begin{array}{l} p \rightarrow q \\ \underline{q \rightarrow r} \\ p \rightarrow r. \end{array}$$

One form of proof by **indirect argument** is based on the logical equivalence of a statement and its contrapositive. Thus, the proof of a theorem of the form $\sim q \rightarrow \sim p$ automatically gives a proof of the theorem $p \rightarrow q$.

Another form of indirect argument is called ***reductio ad absurdum.*** To prove the theorem $p \rightarrow q$, one shows that $p \wedge \sim q$ implies a contradiction or a logically false conclusion, $r \wedge \sim r$.

CHAPTER REVIEW

Make a truth table for each of the statements in Exercises 1–4. See Solution Manual.

1. $\sim(p \wedge \sim q)$
2. $[(p \rightarrow q) \wedge q] \rightarrow p$
3. $(p \wedge q) \vee r$
4. $[(p \wedge q) \vee (p \wedge r)] \rightarrow [p \wedge (r \vee q)]$.
5. Which of the following statements are logically equivalent to the statement, "It is false that at least one of the two dice is loaded."
   (a) Neither of the dice is loaded.
   (b) At least one die is fair.
   (c) Both dice are fair.
   (d) Neither of the dice is fair.
   (e) Both dice are loaded.
6. For any three statements p, q, and r, use truth tables to show that $p \rightarrow q$ and $q \rightarrow r$ cannot both be false at the same time. See Solution Manual.

7. Let p denote the statement, "A person is musically inclined"; q, the statement, "A person can do mathematics"; and r, the statement, "A person is good at debate." By using truth tables or the application of various logical principles (for example, transitivity of the conditional), show that the following is a valid argument. See Solution Manual.

   If a person can do mathematics, he is musically inclined. If a person cannot do mathematics, he is not good at debate. Tom is not musically inclined. *Therefore*, Tom is not good at debate.

8. Form a chain of conditional statements for the argument given below, and supply the missing conclusion.

   If the game is cancelled, the tie will not be broken. If it rains, the game will be cancelled. The tie is broken. *Therefore*, __?__.

9. (a) Using the definition of an even integer as an integer which can be written in the form $2n$ for some integer n, show that the square of an even integer is even.
   (b) Prove by indirect argument that if the square of an integer is odd, then that integer is odd.

10. Suppose that each individual in a town of 17,577 inhabitants has exactly three initials in his name. Prove that at least two individuals must have the same set of initials.

9–10 See Solution Manual.

CHAPTER TEST

1. Using a truth table, determine whether the following statement is logically true, logically false, or neither logically true nor logically false.

$$(p \vee q) \vee (\sim p)$$ Logically true

2. Let p denote "Mary passed the course" and q denote "John passed the course." Which of the following are logically equivalent to the statement,

   "It is not the case that Mary and John both failed the course"?

   (a) $\sim(\sim p \vee \sim q)$ (b) $\sim(\sim p \wedge \sim q)$ (c) $(\sim p) \wedge (\sim q)$
   (d) $p \vee q$ (e) $p \wedge q$.

3. Using a truth table, test the following argument for validity.

$$\begin{array}{l} p \vee q \\ q \to p \\ \hline q \end{array}$$ Invalid

4. Find a chain of conditional statements for the following argument, and supply the missing conclusion.

   A person is successful in playing the organ only if he has studied piano. If one is unwilling to practice an hour a day, one cannot study piano. Susie plays the organ successfully. *Therefore*, __?__.

Answer to Chapter Review Problem 8

8. $$\left.\begin{array}{l} p \to \sim q \\ r \to p \end{array}\right\} \Rightarrow r \to \sim q \Rightarrow q \to \sim r$$
$$\begin{array}{l} q \\ \hline \end{array} \qquad \begin{array}{l} q \\ \hline \end{array} \qquad \begin{array}{l} q \\ \hline \sim r \end{array}$$

It does not rain.

Chapter Test

The material included in the Chapter Test was covered in the following sections:

Problems 1 and 2—Section 15–2
Problem 3—Section 15–4
Problem 4—Section 15–5

Answer to Chapter Test Problem 4

4. Use p for "Plays organ successfully"; q for "Studied the piano"; and r for "Willing to practice an hour a day."

$$\begin{array}{l} p \to q \\ \sim r \to \sim q \end{array} \Rightarrow \left.\begin{array}{l} p \to q \\ q \to r \end{array}\right\} \Rightarrow p \to r$$
$$\begin{array}{l} p \\ \hline \end{array} \qquad \begin{array}{l} p \\ \hline \end{array} \qquad \begin{array}{l} p \\ \hline r \end{array}$$

Susie is willing to practice an hour a day.

APPENDIX

Table of Squares and Square Roots

N	N^2	$\sqrt{N}$	N	N^2	$\sqrt{N}$
1	1	1	51	2,601	7.141
2	4	1.414	52	2,704	7.211
3	9	1.732	53	2,809	7.280
4	16	2	54	2,916	7.348
5	25	2.236	55	3,025	7.416
6	36	2.449	56	3,136	7.483
7	49	2.646	57	3,249	7.550
8	64	2.828	58	3,364	7.616
9	81	3	59	3,481	7.681
10	100	3.162	60	3,600	7.746
11	121	3.317	61	3,721	7.810
12	144	3.464	62	3,844	7.874
13	169	3.606	63	3,969	7.937
14	196	3.742	64	4,096	8
15	225	3.873	65	4,225	8.062
16	256	4	66	4,356	8.124
17	289	4.123	67	4,489	8.185
18	324	4.243	68	4,624	8.246
19	361	4.359	69	4,761	8.307
20	400	4.472	70	4,900	8.367
21	441	4.583	71	5,041	8.426
22	484	4.690	72	5,184	8.485
23	529	4.796	73	5,329	8.544
24	576	4.899	74	5,476	8.602
25	625	5	75	5,625	8.660
26	676	5.099	76	5,776	8.718
27	729	5.196	77	5,929	8.775
28	784	5.292	78	6,084	8.832
29	841	5.385	79	6,241	8.888
30	900	5.477	80	6,400	8.944
31	961	5.568	81	6,561	9
32	1,024	5.657	82	6,724	9.055
33	1,089	5.745	83	6,889	9.110
34	1,156	5.831	84	7,056	9.165
35	1,225	5.916	85	7,225	9.220
36	1,296	6	86	7,396	9.274
37	1,369	6.083	87	7,569	9.327
38	1,444	6.164	88	7,744	9.381
39	1,521	6.245	89	7,921	9.434
40	1,600	6.325	90	8,100	9.487
41	1,681	6.403	91	8,281	9.539
42	1,764	6.481	92	8,464	9.592
43	1,849	6.557	93	8,649	9.644
44	1,936	6.633	94	8,836	9.695
45	2,025	6.708	95	9,025	9.747
46	2,116	6.782	96	9,216	9.798
47	2,209	6.856	97	9,409	9.849
48	2,304	6.928	98	9,604	9.899
49	2,401	7	99	9,801	9.950
50	2,500	7.071	100	10,000	10

Table of Values of Trigonometric Functions

deg	rad	sin	cos	tan	deg	rad	sin	cos	tan
0	.000	.000	1.000	.000					
1	.017	.017	1.000	.017	46	.803	.719	.695	1.036
2	.035	.035	.999	.035	47	.820	.731	.682	1.072
3	.052	.052	.999	.052	48	.838	.743	.669	1.111
4	.070	.070	.998	.070	49	.855	.755	.656	1.150
5	.087	.087	.996	.087	50	.873	.766	.643	1.192
6	.105	.105	.995	.105	51	.890	.777	.629	1.235
7	.122	.122	.993	.123	52	.908	.788	.616	1.280
8	.140	.139	.990	.141	53	.925	.799	.602	1.327
9	.157	.156	.988	.158	54	.942	.809	.588	1.376
10	.175	.174	.985	.176	55	.960	.819	.574	1.428
11	.192	.191	.982	.194	56	.977	.829	.559	1.483
12	.209	.208	.978	.213	57	.995	.839	.545	1.540
13	.227	.225	.974	.231	58	1.012	.848	.530	1.600
14	.244	.242	.970	.249	59	1.030	.857	.515	1.664
15	.262	.259	.966	.268	60	1.047	.866	.500	1.732
16	.279	.276	.961	.287	61	1.065	.875	.485	1.804
17	.297	.292	.956	.306	62	1.082	.883	.470	1.881
18	.314	.309	.951	.325	63	1.100	.891	.454	1.963
19	.332	.326	.946	.344	64	1.117	.899	.438	2.050
20	.349	.342	.940	.364	65	1.134	.906	.423	2.145
21	.367	.358	.934	.384	66	1.152	.914	.407	2.246
22	.384	.375	.927	.404	67	1.169	.921	.391	2.356
23	.401	.391	.921	.424	68	1.187	.927	.375	2.475
24	.419	.407	.914	.445	69	1.204	.934	.358	2.605
25	.436	.423	.906	.466	70	1.222	.940	.342	2.747
26	.454	.438	.899	.488	71	1.239	.946	.326	2.904
27	.471	.454	.891	.510	72	1.257	.951	.309	3.078
28	.489	.470	.883	.532	73	1.274	.956	.292	3.271
29	.506	.485	.875	.554	74	1.292	.961	.276	3.487
30	.524	.500	.866	.577	75	1.309	.966	.259	3.732
31	.541	.515	.857	.601	76	1.326	.970	.242	4.011
32	.559	.530	.848	.625	77	1.344	.974	.225	4.331
33	.576	.545	.839	.649	78	1.361	.978	.208	4.705
34	.593	.559	.829	.675	79	1.379	.982	.191	5.145
35	.611	.574	.819	.700	80	1.396	.985	.174	5.671
36	.628	.588	.809	.727	81	1.414	.988	.156	6.314
37	.646	.602	.799	.754	82	1.431	.990	.139	7.115
38	.663	.616	.788	.781	83	1.449	.993	.122	8.144
39	.681	.629	.777	.810	84	1.466	.995	.105	9.514
40	.698	.643	.766	.839	85	1.484	.996	.087	11.430
41	.716	.656	.755	.869	86	1.501	.998	.070	14.301
42	.733	.669	.743	.900	87	1.518	.999	.052	19.081
43	.751	.682	.731	.933	88	1.536	.999	.035	28.636
44	.768	.695	.719	.966	89	1.553	1.000	.017	57.290
45	.785	.707	.707	1.000	90	1.571	1.000	.000	—

Table of Common Logarithms

N	0	1	2	3	4	5	6	7	8	9
10	.0000	.0043	.0086	.0128	.0170	.0212	.0253	.0294	.0334	.0374
11	.0414	.0453	.0492	.0531	.0569	.0607	.0645	.0682	.0719	.0755
12	.0792	.0828	.0864	.0899	.0934	.0969	.1004	.1038	.1072	.1106
13	.1139	.1173	.1206	.1239	.1271	.1303	.1335	.1367	.1399	.1430
14	.1461	.1492	.1523	.1553	.1584	.1614	.1644	.1673	.1703	.1732
15	.1761	.1790	.1818	.1847	.1875	.1903	.1931	.1959	.1987	.2014
16	.2041	.2068	.2095	.2122	.2148	.2175	.2201	.2227	.2253	.2279
17	.2304	.2330	.2355	.2380	.2405	.2430	.2455	.2480	.2504	.2529
18	.2553	.2577	.2601	.2625	.2648	.2672	.2695	.2718	.2742	.2765
19	.2788	.2810	.2833	.2856	.2878	.2900	.2923	.2945	.2967	.2989
20	.3010	.3032	.3054	.3075	.3096	.3118	.3139	.3160	.3181	.3201
21	.3222	.3243	.3263	.3284	.3304	.3324	.3345	.3365	.3385	.3404
22	.3424	.3444	.3464	.3483	.3502	.3522	.3541	.3560	.3579	.3598
23	.3617	.3636	.3655	.3674	.3692	.3711	.3729	.3747	.3766	.3784
24	.3802	.3820	.3838	.3856	.3874	.3892	.3909	.3927	.3945	.3962
25	.3979	.3997	.4014	.4031	.4048	.4065	.4082	.4099	.4116	.4133
26	.4150	.4166	.4183	.4200	.4216	.4232	.4249	.4265	.4281	.4298
27	.4314	.4330	.4346	.4362	.4378	.4393	.4409	.4425	.4440	.4456
28	.4472	.4487	.4502	.4518	.4533	.4548	.4564	.4579	.4594	.4609
29	.4624	.4639	.4654	.4669	.4683	.4698	.4713	.4728	.4742	.4757
30	.4771	.4786	.4800	.4814	.4829	.4843	.4857	.4871	.4886	.4900
31	.4914	.4928	.4942	.4955	.4969	.4983	.4997	.5011	.5024	.5038
32	.5051	.5065	.5079	.5092	.5105	.5119	.5132	.5145	.5159	.5172
33	.5185	.5198	.5211	.5224	.5237	.5250	.5263	.5276	.5289	.5302
34	.5315	.5328	.5340	.5353	.5366	.5378	.5391	.5403	.5416	.5428
35	.5441	.5453	.5465	.5478	.5490	.5502	.5514	.5527	.5539	.5551
36	.5563	.5575	.5587	.5599	.5611	.5623	.5635	.5647	.5658	.5670
37	.5682	.5694	.5705	.5717	.5729	.5740	.5752	.5763	.5775	.5786
38	.5798	.5809	.5821	.5832	.5843	.5855	.5866	.5877	.5888	.5899
39	.5911	.5922	.5933	.5944	.5955	.5966	.5977	.5988	.5999	.6010
40	.6021	.6031	.6042	.6053	.6064	.6075	.6085	.6096	.6107	.6117
41	.6128	.6138	.6149	.6160	.6170	.6180	.6191	.6201	.6212	.6222
42	.6232	.6243	.6253	.6263	.6274	.6284	.6294	.6304	.6314	.6325
43	.6335	.6345	.6355	.6365	.6375	.6385	.6395	.6405	.6415	.6425
44	.6435	.6444	.6454	.6464	.6474	.6484	.6493	.6503	.6513	.6522
45	.6532	.6542	.6551	.6561	.6571	.6580	.6590	.6599	.6609	.6618
46	.6628	.6637	.6646	.6656	.6665	.6675	.6684	.6693	.6702	.6712
47	.6721	.6730	.6739	.6749	.6758	.6767	.6776	.6785	.6794	.6803
48	.6812	.6821	.6830	.6839	.6848	.6857	.6866	.6875	.6884	.6893
49	.6902	.6911	.6920	.6928	.6937	.6946	.6955	.6964	.6972	.6981
50	.6990	.6998	.7007	.7016	.7024	.7033	.7042	.7050	.7059	.7067
51	.7076	.7084	.7093	.7101	.7110	.7118	.7126	.7135	.7143	.7152
52	.7160	.7168	.7177	.7185	.7193	.7202	.7210	.7218	.7226	.7235
53	.7243	.7251	.7259	.7267	.7275	.7284	.7292	.7300	.7308	.7316
54	.7324	.7332	.7340	.7348	.7356	.7364	.7372	.7380	.7388	.7396

Table of Common Logarithms (*Continued*)

N	0	1	2	3	4	5	6	7	8	9
55	.7404	.7412	.7419	.7427	.7435	.7443	.7451	.7459	.7466	.7474
56	.7482	.7490	.7497	.7505	.7513	.7520	.7528	.7536	.7543	.7551
57	.7559	.7566	.7574	.7582	.7589	.7597	.7604	.7612	.7619	.7627
58	.7634	.7642	.7649	.7657	.7664	.7672	.7679	.7686	.7694	.7701
59	.7709	.7716	.7723	.7731	.7738	.7745	.7752	.7760	.7767	.7774
60	.7782	.7789	.7796	.7803	.7810	.7818	.7825	.7832	.7839	.7846
61	.7853	.7860	.7868	.7875	.7882	.7889	.7896	.7903	.7910	.7917
62	.7924	.7931	.7938	.7945	.7952	.7959	.7966	.7973	.7980	.7987
63	.7993	.8000	.8007	.8014	.8021	.8028	.8035	.8041	.8048	.8055
64	.8062	.8069	.8075	.8082	.8089	.8096	.8102	.8109	.8116	.8122
65	.8129	.8136	.8142	.8149	.8156	.8162	.8169	.8176	.8182	.8189
66	.8195	.8202	.8209	.8215	.8222	.8228	.8235	.8241	.8248	.8254
67	.8261	.8267	.8274	.8280	.8287	.8293	.8299	.8306	.8312	.8319
68	.8325	.8331	.8338	.8344	.8351	.8357	.8363	.8370	.8376	.8382
69	.8388	.8395	.8401	.8407	.8414	.8420	.8426	.8432	.8439	.8445
70	.8451	.8457	.8463	.8470	.8476	.8482	.8488	.8494	.8500	.8506
71	.8513	.8519	.8525	.8531	.8537	.8543	.8549	.8555	.8561	.8567
72	.8573	.8579	.8585	.8591	.8597	.8603	.8609	.8615	.8621	.8627
73	.8633	.8639	.8645	.8651	.8657	.8663	.8669	.8675	.8681	.8686
74	.8692	.8698	.8704	.8710	.8716	.8722	.8727	.8733	.8739	.8745
75	.8751	.8756	.8762	.8768	.8774	.8779	.8785	.8791	.8797	.8802
76	.8808	.8814	.8820	.8825	.8831	.8837	.8842	.8848	.8854	.8859
77	.8865	.8871	.8876	.8882	.8887	.8893	.8899	.8904	.8910	.8915
78	.8921	.8927	.8932	.8938	.8943	.8949	.8954	.8960	.8965	.8971
79	.8976	.8982	.8987	.8993	.8998	.9004	.9009	.9015	.9020	.9025
80	.9031	.9036	.9042	.9047	.9053	.9058	.9063	.9069	.9074	.9079
81	.9085	.9090	.9096	.9101	.9106	.9112	.9117	.9122	.9128	.9133
82	.9138	.9143	.9149	.9154	.9159	.9165	.9170	.9175	.9180	.9186
83	.9191	.9196	.9201	.9206	.9212	.9217	.9222	.9227	.9232	.9238
84	.9243	.9248	.9253	.9258	.9263	.9269	.9274	.9279	.9284	.9289
85	.9294	.9299	.9304	.9309	.9315	.9320	.9325	.9330	.9335	.9340
86	.9345	.9350	.9355	.9360	.9365	.9370	.9375	.9380	.9385	.9390
87	.9395	.9400	.9405	.9410	.9415	.9420	.9425	.9430	.9435	.9440
88	.9445	.9450	.9455	.9460	.9465	.9469	.9474	.9479	.9484	.9489
89	.9494	.9499	.9504	.9509	.9513	.9518	.9523	.9528	.9533	.9538
90	.9542	.9547	.9552	.9557	.9562	.9566	.9571	.9576	.9581	.9586
91	.9590	.9595	.9600	.9605	.9609	.9614	.9619	.9624	.9628	.9633
92	.9638	.9643	.9647	.9652	.9657	.9661	.9666	.9671	.9675	.9680
93	.9685	.9689	.9694	.9699	.9703	.9708	.9713	.9717	.9722	.9727
94	.9731	.9736	.9741	.9745	.9750	.9754	.9759	.9763	.9768	.9773
95	.9777	.9782	.9786	.9791	.9795	.9800	.9805	.9809	.9814	.9818
96	.9823	.9827	.9832	.9836	.9841	.9845	.9850	.9854	.9859	.9863
97	.9868	.9872	.9877	.9881	.9886	.9890	.9894	.9899	.9903	.9908
98	.9912	.9917	.9921	.9926	.9930	.9934	.9939	.9943	.9948	.9952
99	.9956	.9961	.9965	.9969	.9974	.9978	.9983	.9987	.9991	.9996

LIST OF ABBREVIATIONS AND SYMBOLS

ABBREVIATIONS

(A>), (A<) Addition to each side
(A-1) First addition formula
(A-2) Second addition formula
(A-3) Third addition formula
(A-4) Fourth addition formula
(A-A) Associative law of addition
(A-M) Associative law of multiplication
(C-A) Commutative law of addition
(C-M) Commutative law of multiplication
(Can-A) Cancellation law of addition
(Can-M) Cancellation law of multiplication
(Clos-A) Closure of *P* under addition
(Clos-M) Closure of *P* under multiplication
(D) Distributive law
(D-1) First double-angle formula
(D-2) Second double-angle formula
(Def >) Definition of greater than
(Def <) Definition of less than
(Def ≧) Definition of greater than or equal to
(Def ≦) Definition of less than or equal to
(Def-Cu. Rt.) Definition of cube root
(Def-Div) Definition of division
(Def-Exp) Definition of exponents
(Def-Neg. Exp.) Definition of a negative exponent
(Def-*n*th Rt.) Definition of *n*th root
(Def-Rat. Exp.) Definition of rational exponents
(Def-SM) Definition of scalar multiplication
(Def-Sq. Rt.) Definition of square root
(Def-Sub) Definition of subtraction
(Def $|x|$) Definition of absolute value
(F-0) Factors of zero
(FI-1) First fundamental identity
(FI-2) Second fundamental identity
(FI-3) Third fundamental identity
(FI-4) Fourth fundamental identity
(FI-5) Fifth fundamental identity
(FI-6) Sixth fundamental identity
(FI-7) Seventh fundamental identity
(FI-8) Eighth fundamental identity
(FI-9) Ninth fundamental identity
(FI-10) Tenth fundamental identity
(FI-11) Eleventh fundamental identity
(FI-12) Twelfth fundamental identity
(FI-13) Thirteenth fundamental identity
(FI-14) Fourteenth fundamental identity
(FI-15) Fifteenth fundamental identity
(Fr-D) Division of fractions
(Fr-M) Multiplication of fractions
(H-1) First half-angle formula
(H-2) Second half-angle formula
(Id-A) Additive identity
(Id-M) Multiplicative identity
(Inv-A) Additive inverse property
(Inv-M) Multiplicative inverse property
(LE-1) First law of exponents
(LE-2) Second law of exponents
(LE-3) Third law of exponents
(LE-4) Fourth law of exponents
(LE-5) Fifth law of exponents
(LL-1) First law of logarithms
(LL-2) Second law of logarithms
(LL-3) Third law of logarithms
(LR-1) First law of radicals
(LR-2) Second law of radicals
($^+$M>), ($^+$M<) Multiplication of each side by a positive number
($^-$M>), ($^-$M<) Multiplication of each side by a negative number
(Neg-M) Negative multiplication
(Opp-Sum) Opposite of a sum

618

(Q) Quotient equals zero
(R-A) Rearrangement property of addition
(R-M) Rearrangement property of multiplication
(R-P) Rational power law
(Recip-Prod) Reciprocal of a product
(SM-1) Uniqueness of scalar multiplication
(SM-2) Associative law of scalar multiplication
(SM-3) Distributive laws of scalar multiplication
(T >) Transitive law for greater than
(T <) Transitive law for less than
(Tri) Trichotomy law
(U-A) Uniqueness of addition
(U-Div) Uniqueness of division
(U-M) Uniqueness of multiplication
(U-Pos. Rad.) Uniqueness of positive radicals
(U-S) Uniqueness of subtraction
(U-Q) Uniqueness of quotients
(Zero-M) Multiplication by zero

SYMBOLS

$=$	Equal to
$\neq$	Not equal to
$\doteq$	Approximately equal to
$[x]$	Greatest-integer function
$>$	Greater than
$<$	Less than
$\{\ \}$	Set
$\subset$	Subset
$\cap$	Intersection
$\cup$	Union
$\emptyset$	Empty Set
$\geqq$	Greater than or equal to
$\leqq$	Less than or equal to
$\ngtr$	Not greater than
$\nless$	Not less than
$\lvert x \rvert$	Absolute value
AB	Distance between the points A and B
$d(AB)$	Directed distance
$\overline{AB}$	Segment $\overline{AB}$
i	$i^2 = {}^-1$
r	Conjugate of the complex number r
$\overset{\frown}{AB}$	Arc $\overset{\frown}{AB}$
${}_nP_r$	Number of permutations of r objects from a set of n objects
${}_nC_r$, or $\binom{n}{r}$	Number of combinations of r objects from a set of n objects
$n!$	n factorial
$\overrightarrow{AB}$	Vector $\overrightarrow{AB}$
$\mathbf{a}$	Vector $\mathbf{a}$
$\mathbf{0}$	Zero vector
$\mathbf{i}, \mathbf{j}$	Unit vectors
$\wedge$	And (conjunction)
$\vee$	Or (disjunction)
$\sim$	Not (negation)
$\rightarrow$	If-then (conditional statement)
$\leftrightarrow$	If and only if

GLOSSARY

Absolute value. $|a| = a$ if $a \geqq 0$ and $|a| = {}^{-}a$ if $a < 0$.
Additive identity. The additive identity element is 0.
Additive inverse. Each real number x has a unique opposite, ${}^{-}x$.
Arithmetic series. An algebraic expression of the form

$$a + (a + d) + (a + 2d) + \cdots + [a + (n - 1)d].$$

Associative law of addition. $(a + b) + c = a + (b + c)$.
Associative law of multiplication. $(ab) \cdot c = a \cdot (bc)$.

Binomial distribution theorem. In a sequence of n Bernoulli trials with probability of success p, the probability of exactly k successes in the n trials is given by

$$\binom{n}{k} p^k (1 - p)^{n-k}$$

for $k = 0, 1, 2, \ldots, n$.

Binomial theorem. For every pair x, y of real numbers and every positive integer n,

$$(x + y)^n = \binom{n}{0}x^n + \binom{n}{1}x^{n-1}y + \cdots + \binom{n}{k}x^{n-k}y^k + \cdots + \binom{n}{n}y^n.$$

Cancellation law of addition. If $a + c = b + c$, then $a = b$.
Cancellation law of multiplication. If $ac = bc$ and $c \neq 0$, then $a = b$.
Closed interval. If P and Q are two points on a number line, the closed interval is the set consisting of P and Q and all points between P and Q.
Combination. Any arrangement of the elements or some of the elements of a given set.
Commutative law of addition. $a + b = b + a$.
Commutative law of multiplication. $ab = ba$.
Complex number. Every number of the form $a + bi$ where a and b are real numbers and $i = \sqrt{{}^{-}1}$.
Conjunction. The statement $p \wedge q$ meaning *p and q*.
Contrapositive. The related statement $\sim q \rightarrow \sim p$ of the statement $p \rightarrow q$.
Converse. The related statement $q \rightarrow p$ of the statement $p \rightarrow q$.

Determinant. The real number associated with each square matrix.
Direct variation. Two variables x and y vary directly if they are related by an equation of the form $y = kx$ for some nonzero number k.
Directly proportional ordered pairs. (x_1, y_1) and (x_2, y_2) are directly proportional if

$$\frac{x_1}{y_1} = \frac{x_2}{y_2}.$$

620

Discriminant of a quadratic equation. The discriminant is $b^2 - 4ac$ for the quadratic equation $ax^2 + bx + c = 0$.
Disjunction. The statement $p \vee q$ meaning *p or q*.
Distributive law. $a(b + c) = ab + ac$.
Domain of a function. *See* Function.

Ellipse. Given two points A and B in a plane and a positive number k greater than AB, the set consisting of all points P in a plane such that $AP + BP = k$.
Empty set. A set with no elements. It is denoted by $\emptyset$.
Extremes. In a proportion

$$\frac{a}{b} = \frac{c}{d},$$

a and d are the extremes.

Function. If to each value of a variable, there corresponds a unique value of a second variable, the correspondence between these two variables is called a function. If to each value of a variable x, there corresponds a unique value of a variable y, then we say that y is a function of x. The set of values of x is called the *domain of the function*, and the set of values of y is called the *range of the function*.

Geometric series. An algebraic expression of the form

$$a + aq + aq^2 + \cdots + aq^{n-1}.$$

Greater than. $x > y$ if, and only if, $x - y$ is positive.

Half-open interval. If P and Q are two points on a number line, the half-open interval is the set consisting of either P or Q and all points between P and Q.
Half-plane. Each of two pieces into which a line divides a plane.
Hyperbola. Given two points A and B in a plane and a positive number k less than AB, the set consisting of every point P in the plane such that either $AP - BP = k$ or $BP - AP = k$.

Induction property. If a set S of positive integers contains 1, and if whenever S contains the integer k, it also contains the integer $k + 1$, then the set S must be the set of all positive integers.
Infinite geometric series. A geometric series with an infinite number of terms, $a + aq + aq^2 + \cdots + aq^{n-1} + \cdots$
Inner product. $\overrightarrow{AB} \cdot \overrightarrow{CD} = |\overrightarrow{AB}|\,|\overrightarrow{CD}| \cos\theta$ where θ is the angle between $\overrightarrow{AB}$ and $\overrightarrow{CD}$.
Intersection of A and B. All elements common to both A and B, denoted by $A \cap B$.
Inverse. The related statement $\sim p \to \sim q$ of the statement $p \to q$.

Inverse trigonometric functions.

$$\arcsin x = s, \text{ where } \sin s = x \text{ and } \frac{-\pi}{2} \leqq s \leqq \frac{\pi}{2}$$

$$\arccos x = s, \text{ where } \cos s = x \text{ and } 0 \leqq s \leqq \pi$$

$$\arctan x = s, \text{ where } \tan s = x \text{ and } \frac{-\pi}{2} < s < \frac{\pi}{2}$$

Inverse variation. Two variables x and y vary inversely if they are related by an equation of the form

$$y = \frac{k}{x}$$

for some nonzero number k.

Inversely proportional ordered pairs. $(x_1 y_1)$ and (x_2, y_2) are inversely proportional if

$$\frac{x_1}{y_1} = \frac{y_2}{x_2}.$$

Less than. $x < y$ if, and only if, $y - x$ is positive.

Logarithm functions. The logarithm function to the base b, $\log_b$, is given by $\log_b s = r$, where $b^r = s$ (assuming $b > 0$ and $b \neq 1$).

Matrix. A rectangular array of numbers.

Mean proportional. If the means of a proportion are equal, their common value is called a mean proportional between the extremes.

Means. In a proportion

$$\frac{a}{b} = \frac{c}{d},$$

b and c are called the means.

Multiplicative identity. The multiplicative identity element is 1.

Multiplicative inverse. If the product of two numbers is 1, each number is a multiplicative inverse, or reciprocal, of the other.

Mutually exclusive events. If $A \cap B = \emptyset$, A and B are said to be mutually exclusive events.

Negation. The statement $\sim p$ meaning *not p*.

Open interval. If P and Q are two points on a line, the open interval is the set of all points on the line between P and Q.

Open ray. A ray without its endpoint.

Opposites. Each real number has an additive inverse, called its opposite.

Order properties. The set P of positive numbers is closed under addition and under multiplication. The trichotomy law holds.

Parabola. If F is a point and L is a line not containing F, a parabola is the set of all points P in the plane containing F and L such that $PF = PQ$, where Q is at the foot of the perpendicular drawn from P to L.

Permutation. An arrangement of symbols, in which repetitions of symbols is not allowed.
Prime number. An integer greater than 1 which has 1 and itself as its only positive divisors.
Pythagorean theorem. If a and b are the lengths of the legs and c is the length of the hypotenuse of a right triangle, then $a^2 + b^2 = c^2$.

Quadratic equation. A second-degree polynomial equation.
Quadratic formula. If $ax^2 + bx + c = 0$, then

$$x = \frac{{}^{-}b \pm \sqrt{b^2 - 4ac}}{2a}.$$

Range of a function. *See* Function.
Rational exponents.

$$x^{\frac{m}{n}} = \sqrt[n]{x^m} = (\sqrt[n]{x})^m.$$

Ray. Each of the two pieces into which a point P divides a line. The ray includes P.
Rearrangement property of addition. The addends of a sum may be rearranged in any order.
Rearrangement property of multiplication. The multiplicands of a product may be rearranged in any order.
Reciprocal. *See* Multiplicative inverse.

Solution set. The set of all solutions.
Subset. If every element of set A is contained in set B, then A is called a subset of B. It is denoted by $A \subset B$.

Transitive law. If $x > y$ and $y > z$, then $x > z$.
Trichotomy law. Every real number is either a positive number, a negative number, or 0.
Trigonometric functions. If α is an acute angle of the right triangle ABC, a is the side opposite α, b the side adjacent to α, and c the hypotenuse, then

$$\sin \alpha = \frac{a}{c}, \quad \cos \alpha = \frac{b}{c}, \quad \tan \alpha = \frac{a}{b}.$$

Union. The union of sets A and B consists of all the elements in either set A or set B. It is denoted by $A \cup B$.

Vector. A line segment having an initial point A, a terminal point B, and a direction from A to B. This vector is denoted by $\overrightarrow{AB}$.

INDEX